# enVisionmath 2.0

SCOTT FORESMAN · ADDISON WESLEY

**Volume 1** Topics 1–8


## Authors

**Randall I. Charles**
Professor Emeritus
Department of Mathematics
San Jose State University
San Jose, California

**Jennifer Bay-Williams**
Professor of Mathematics Education
College of Education and Human Development
University of Louisville
Louisville, Kentucky

**Robert Q. Berry, III**
Associate Professor of Mathematics Education
Department of Curriculum, Instruction and Special Education
University of Virginia
Charlottesville, Virginia

**Janet H. Caldwell**
Professor of Mathematics
Rowan University
Glassboro, New Jersey

**Zachary Champagne**
Assistant in Research
Florida Center for Research in Science, Technology, Engineering, and Mathematics (FCR-STEM)
Jacksonville, Florida

**Juanita Copley**
Professor Emerita, College of Education
University of Houston
Houston, Texas

**Warren Crown**
Professor Emeritus of Mathematics Education
Graduate School of Education
Rutgers University
New Brunswick, New Jersey

**Francis (Skip) Fennell**
L. Stanley Bowlsbey Professor of Education and Graduate and Professional Studies
McDaniel College
Westminster, Maryland

**Karen Karp**
Professor of Mathematics Education
Department of Early Childhood and Human Development
University of Louisville
Louisville, Kentucky

**Stuart J. Murphy**
Visual Learning Specialist
Boston, Massachusetts

**Jane F. Schielack**
Professor of Mathematics
Associate Dean for Assessment and Pre K-12 Education, College of Science
Texas A&M University
College Station, Texas

**Jennifer M. Suh**
Associate Professor for Mathematics Education
George Mason University
Fairfax, Virginia

**Jonathan A. Wray**
Mathematics Instructional Facilitator
Howard County Public Schools
Ellicott City, Maryland



PEARSON

Glenview, Illinois    Boston, Massachusetts    Chandler, Arizona    Hoboken, New Jersey

## Mathematicians

**Roger Howe**
Professor of Mathematics
Yale University
New Haven, Connecticut

**Gary Lippman**
Professor of Mathematics and Computer Science
California State University, East Bay
Hayward, California

## ELL Consultants

**Janice R. Corona**
Independent Education Consultant
Dallas, Texas

**Jim Cummins**
Professor
The University of Toronto
Toronto, Canada

## Common Core State Standards Reviewers

**Debbie Crisco**
Math Coach
Beebe Public Schools
Beebe, Arkansas

**Kathleen A. Cuff**
Teacher
Kings Park Central School District
Kings Park, New York

**Erika Doyle**
Math and Science Coordinator
Richland School District
Richland, Washington

**Susan Jarvis**
Math and Science Curriculum Coordinator
Ocean Springs Schools
Ocean Springs, Mississippi

**Velvet M. Simington**
K-12 Mathematics Director
Winston-Salem/Forsyth County Schools
Winston-Salem, North Carolina



ISBN-13: 978-0-328-82783-1
ISBN-10: 0-328-82783-5

PEARSON

8 16

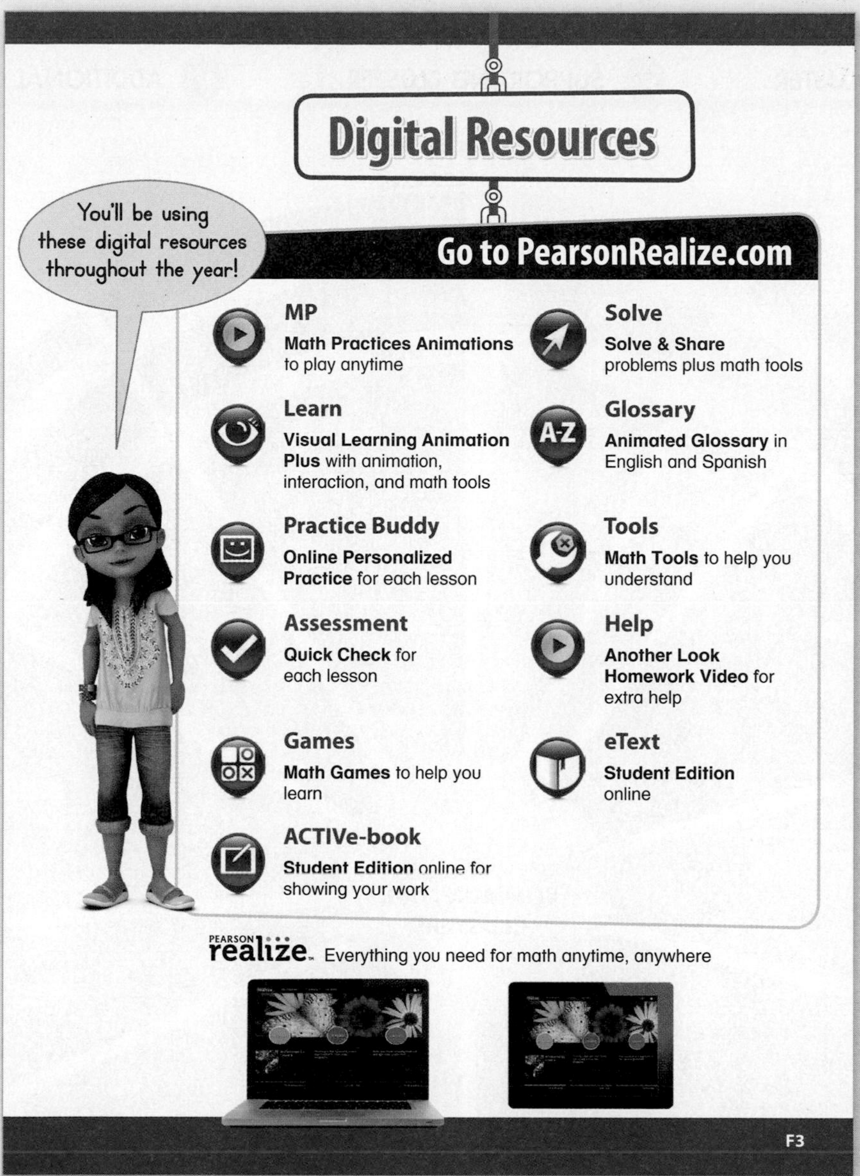


## Additional Digital Resources

### eText

**Teacher's Edition eText** includes all pages from the Teacher's Edition plus access to printable resources and the animated glossary.

### PD

**Professional Development Videos** include a **Topic Overview Video** that is presented by the authors and provides important information about the topic. A **Listen and Look For Lesson Video** at the start of each lesson provides helpful information for teaching the lesson.

### Think

**Today's Challenge** for each topic is a set of 5 problems on separate screens that use the same data. They can be projected in class or assigned electronically to individuals. A Teacher's Guide with a page for each problem is available in print and online.

### Assessment

**Online assessments** are auto scored and include: Placement Test, lesson Quick Check, Topic Assessments, Cumulative/Benchmark Assessments, End-of-Year Assessment, and Fluency Assessments.

All print resources are also available online as eText pages or PDF files at PearsonRealize.com.

# GRADE 6 CONTENT OVERVIEW

MAJOR CLUSTER
SUPPORTING CLUSTER
ADDITIONAL CLUSTER

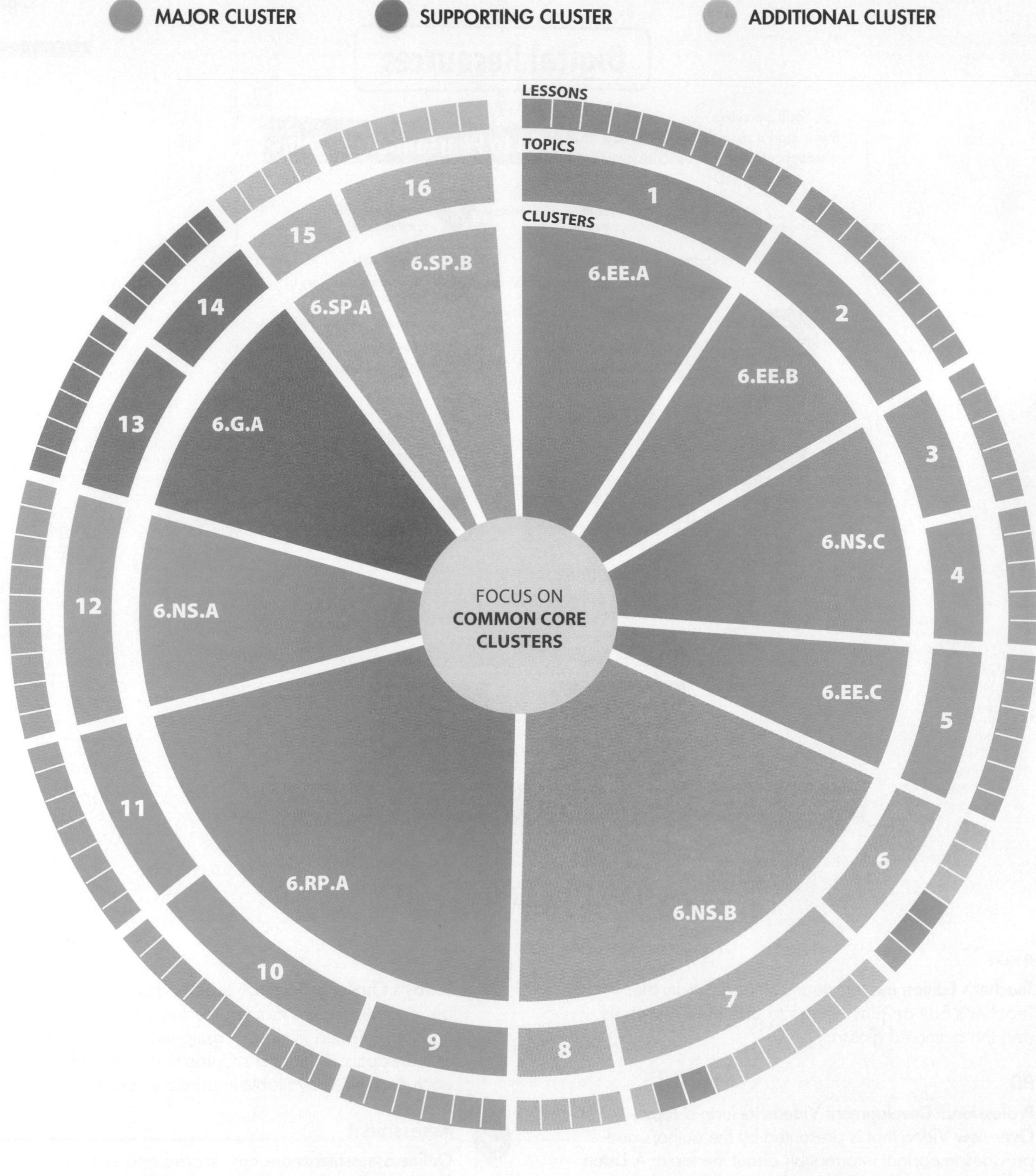


## COMMON CORE DOMAINS

| | | | |
|---|---|---|---|
| **6.RP** | RATIOS & PROPORTIONAL RELATIONSHIPS | **6.G** | GEOMETRY |
| **6.NS** | THE NUMBER SYSTEM | **6.SP** | STATISTICS & PROBABILITY |
| **6.EE** | EXPRESSIONS & EQUATIONS | | |

| FOCUS ON | TOPICS |
|---|---|
| MAJOR CLUSTER **6.EE.A**<br>Apply and extend previous understandings of arithmetic to algebraic expressions. | **1** Algebra: Understand Numerical and Algebraic Expressions |
| MAJOR CLUSTER **6.EE.B**<br>Reason about and solve one-variable equations and inequalities. | **2** Algebra: Solve Equations and Inequalities |
| MAJOR CLUSTER **6.NS.C**<br>Apply and extend previous understandings of numbers to the system of rational numbers. | **3** Rational Numbers<br>**4** Algebra: Coordinate Geometry |
| MAJOR CLUSTER **6.EE.C**<br>Represent and analyze quantitative relationships between dependent and independent variables. | **5** Algebra: Patterns and Equations |
| ADDITIONAL CLUSTER **6.NS.B**<br>Compute fluently with multi-digit numbers and find common factors and multiples. | **6** Fluently Divide Whole Numbers<br>**7** Fluently Add, Subtract, Multiply, and Divide Decimals<br>**8** Common Factors and Multiples |
| MAJOR CLUSTER **6.RP.A**<br>Understand ratio concepts and use ratio reasoning to solve problems. | **9** Ratio Concepts and Reasoning<br>**10** Ratio Concepts: Rates<br>**11** Ratio Concepts: Percent |
| MAJOR CLUSTER **6.NS.A**<br>Apply and extend previous understandings of multiplication and division to divide fractions by fractions. | **12** Divide Fractions by Fractions |
| SUPPORTING CLUSTER **6.G.A**<br>Solve real-world and mathematical problems involving area, surface area, and volume. | **13** Solve Area Problems<br>**14** Solve Surface Area and Volume Problems |
| ADDITIONAL CLUSTER **6.SP.A**<br>Develop understanding of statistical variability. | **15** Measures of Center and Variability |
| ADDITIONAL CLUSTER **6.SP.B**<br>Summarize and describe distributions. | **16** Display and Summarize Data |

IN TOPIC 1, FOCUS ON

**MAJOR CLUSTER 6.EE.A**

Apply and extend previous understandings of arithmetic to algebraic expressions.

**TOPIC 1 CLUSTER OVERVIEW**



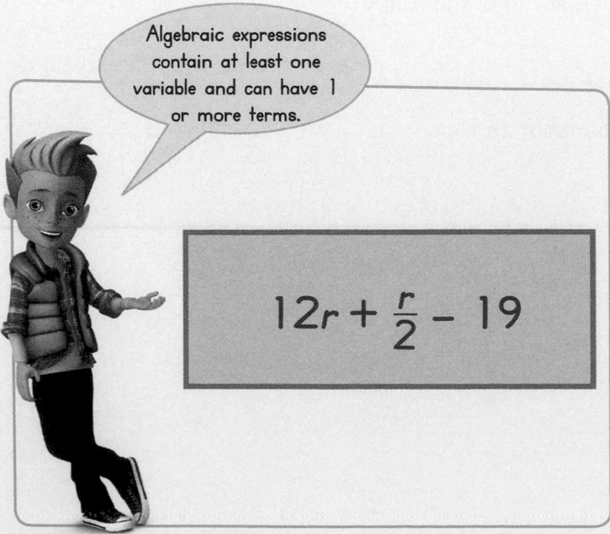

Algebraic expressions contain at least one variable and can have 1 or more terms.

$$12r + \frac{r}{2} - 19$$

# TOPIC 1

## Algebra: Understand Numerical and Algebraic Expressions

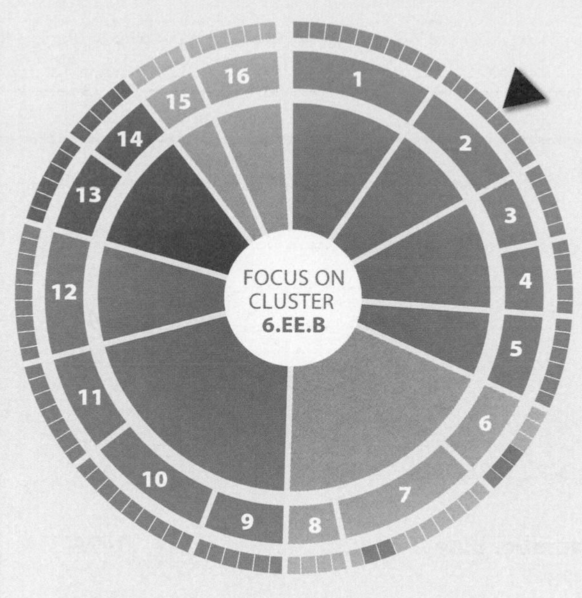


IN TOPIC 2, FOCUS ON

**MAJOR CLUSTER 6.EE.B**

Reason about and solve one-variable equations and inequalities.

**TOPIC 2 CLUSTER OVERVIEW**



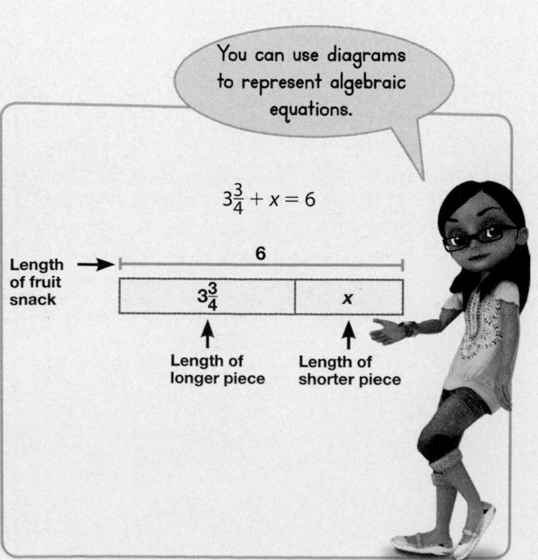


# TOPIC 2

## Algebra: Solve Equations and Inequalities

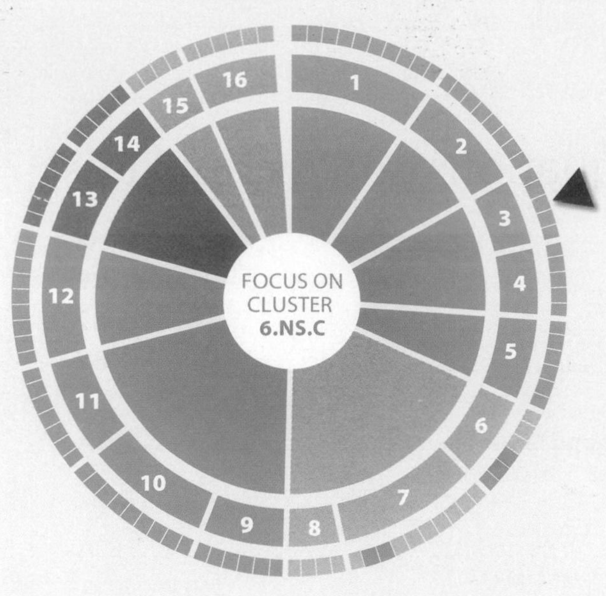


IN TOPICS 3 AND 4, FOCUS ON

**MAJOR CLUSTER 6.NS.C**

Apply and extend previous understandings of numbers to the system of rational numbers.

**TOPICS 3 AND 4 CLUSTER OVERVIEW**

# TOPIC 3
## Rational Numbers

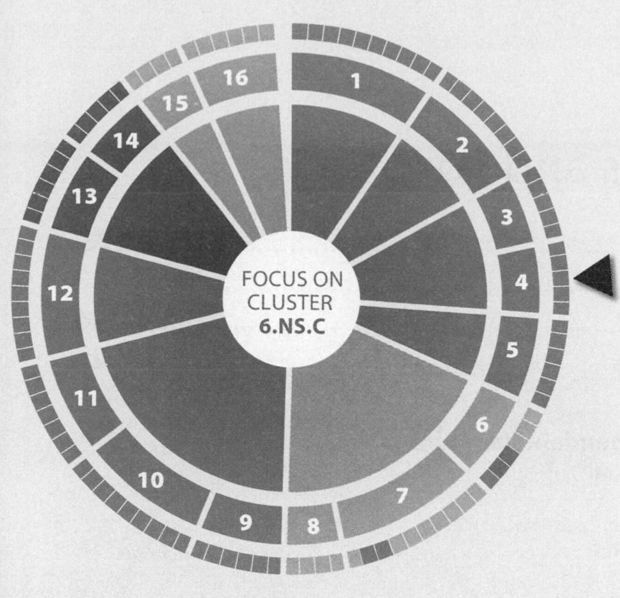


IN TOPICS 3 AND 4, FOCUS ON

**MAJOR CLUSTER 6.NS.C**

Apply and extend previous understandings of numbers to the system of rational numbers.

**TOPICS 3 AND 4 CLUSTER OVERVIEW**



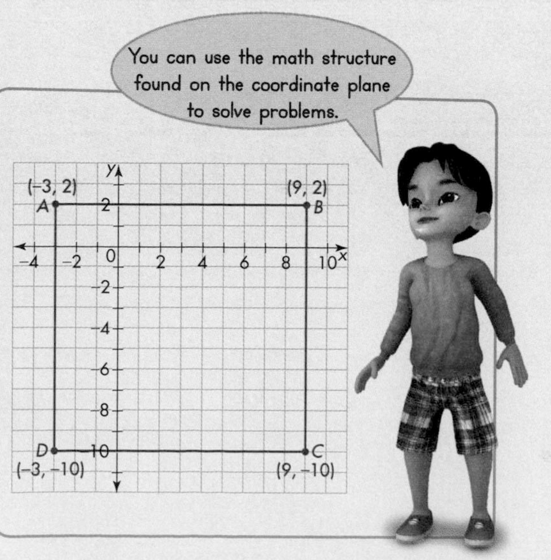


# TOPIC 4

## Algebra: Coordinate Geometry

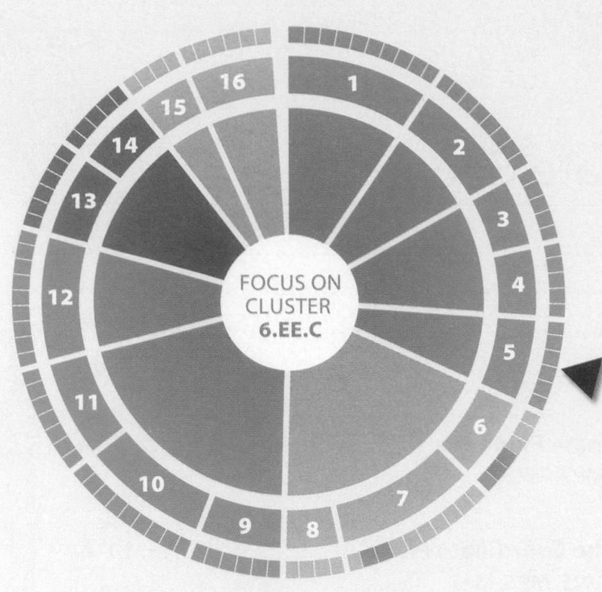


IN TOPIC 5, FOCUS ON

**MAJOR CLUSTER 6.EE.C**

Represent and analyze quantitative relationships between dependent and independent variables.

**TOPIC 5 CLUSTER OVERVIEW**



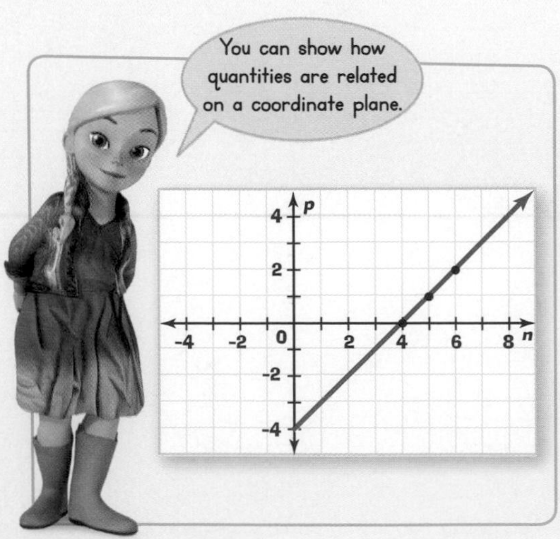

You can show how quantities are related on a coordinate plane.
p
n

# TOPIC 5
## Algebra: Patterns and Equations

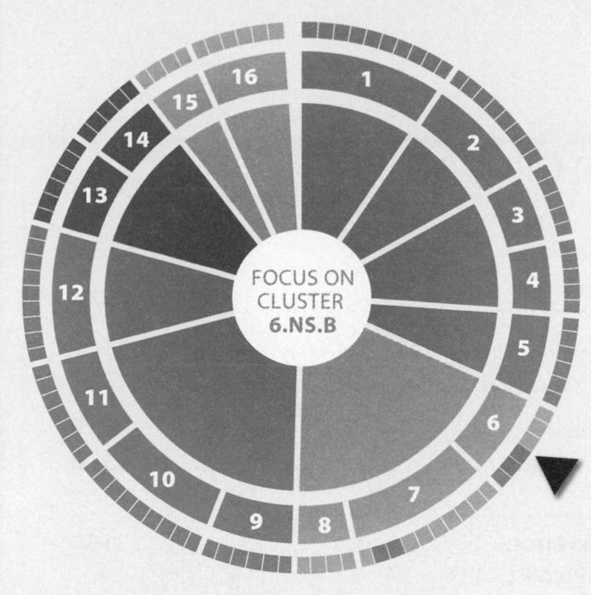


IN TOPICS 6–8, FOCUS ON

**ADDITIONAL CLUSTER 6.NS.B**

Compute fluently with multi-digit numbers and find common factors and multiples.

**TOPICS 6–8 CLUSTER OVERVIEW**

# TOPIC 6
## Fluently Divide Whole Numbers

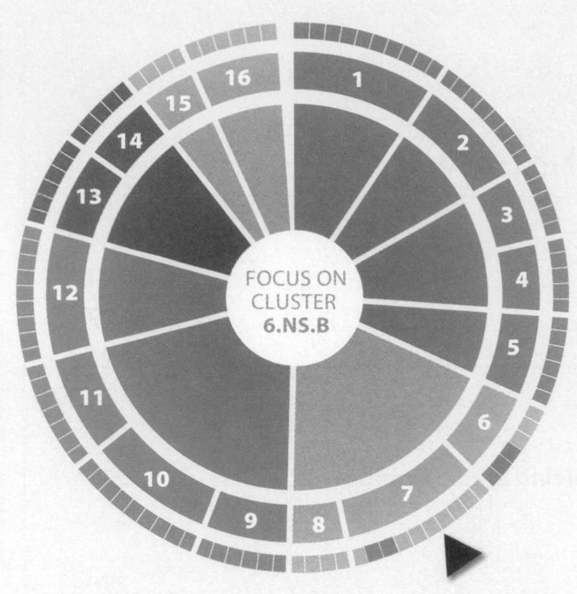


IN TOPICS 6–8, FOCUS ON

**ADDITIONAL CLUSTER 6.NS.B**

Compute fluently with multi-digit numbers and find common factors and multiples.

**TOPICS 6–8 CLUSTER OVERVIEW**



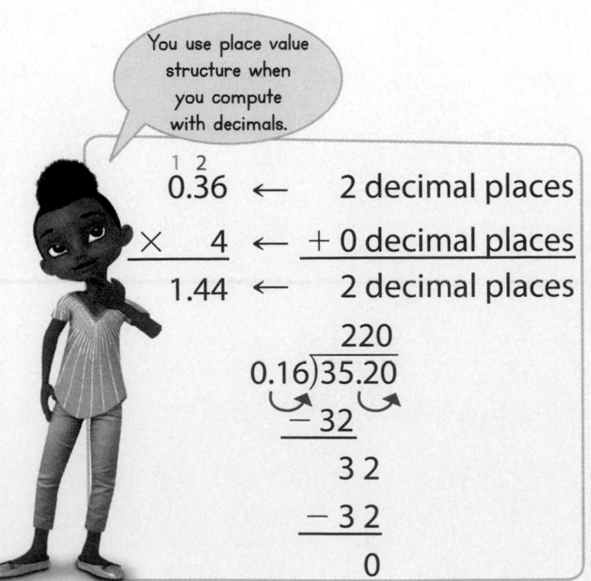


# TOPIC 7

## Fluently Add, Subtract, Multiply, and Divide Decimals

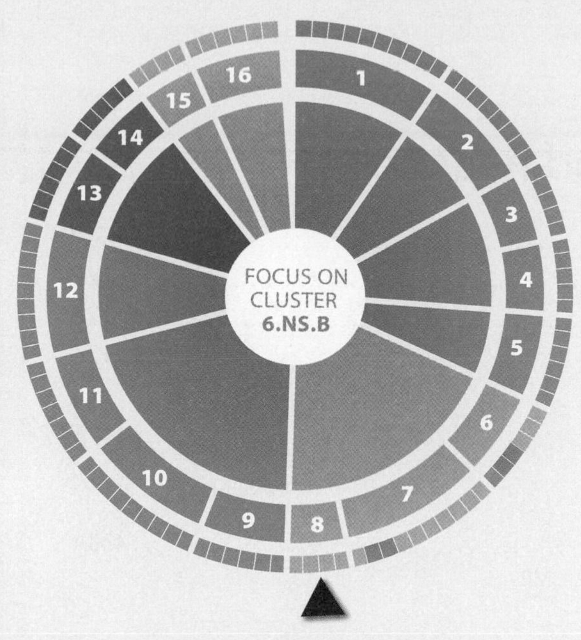


IN TOPICS 6–8, FOCUS ON

**ADDITIONAL CLUSTER 6.NS.B**

Compute fluently with multi-digit numbers and find common factors and multiples.

**TOPICS 6–8 CLUSTER OVERVIEW**



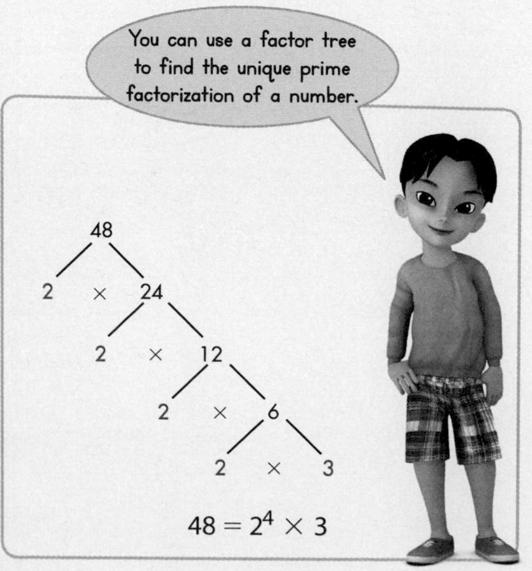


# TOPIC 8
## Common Factors and Multiples

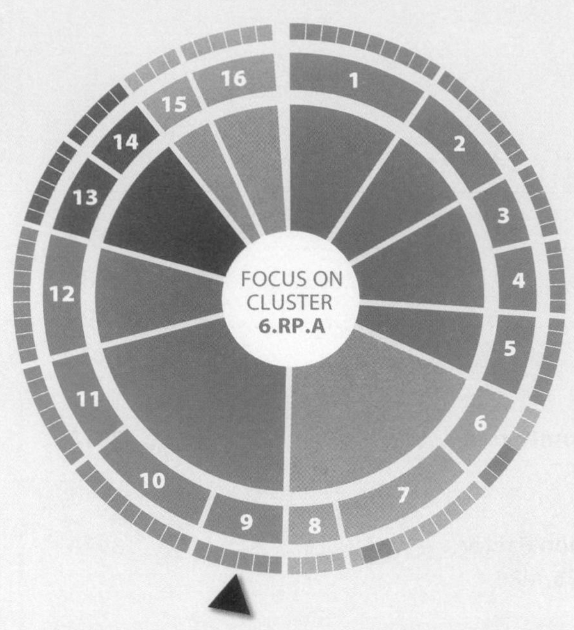


IN TOPICS 9–11, FOCUS ON

**MAJOR CLUSTER 6.RP.A**

Understand ratio concepts and use ratio reasoning to solve problems.

**TOPICS 9–11 CLUSTER OVERVIEW**



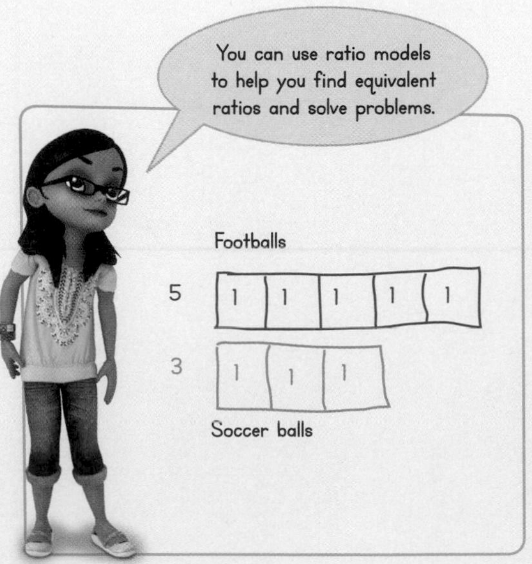


# TOPIC 9
## Ratio Concepts and Reasoning

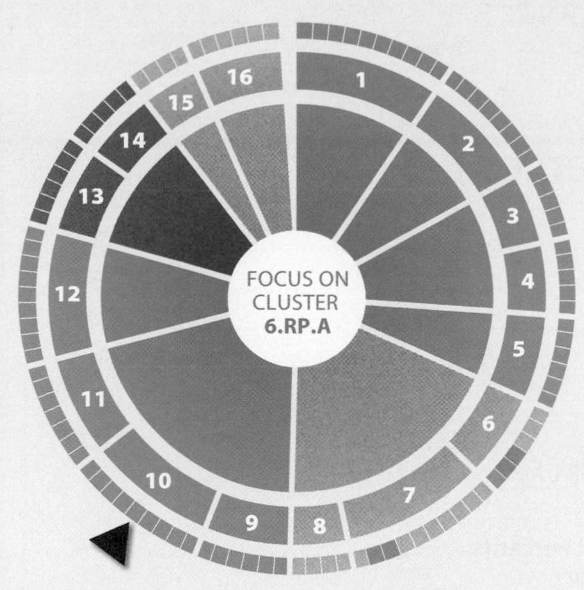


IN TOPICS 9–11, FOCUS ON

**MAJOR CLUSTER 6.RP.A**

Understand ratio concepts and use ratio reasoning to solve problems.

**TOPICS 9–11 CLUSTER OVERVIEW**

Rates compare quantities that have different units, like kilometers per minute.

| Distance (km) | Time (min) |
|---|---|
| 5 | $1\frac{1}{2}$ |
| 10 | 3 |
| 15 | $4\frac{1}{2}$ |
| 20 | 6 |
| 25 | $7\frac{1}{2}$ |

# TOPIC 10
## Ratio Concepts: Rates

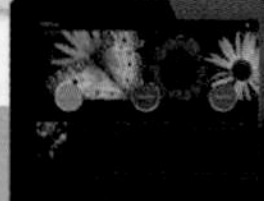

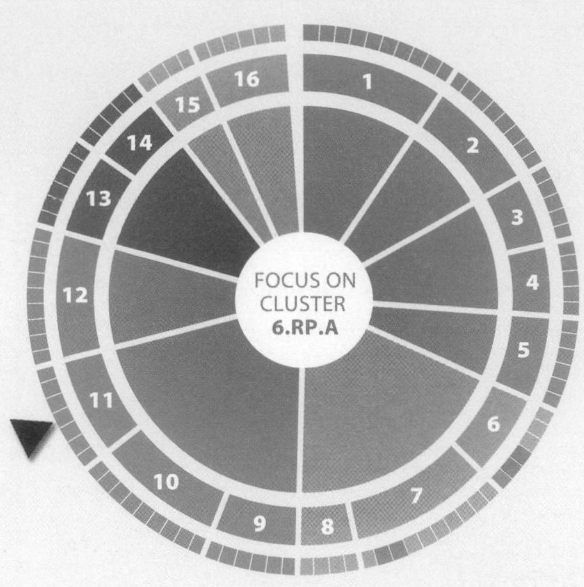


IN TOPICS 9–11, FOCUS ON

**MAJOR CLUSTER 6.RP.A**

Understand ratio concepts and use ratio reasoning to solve problems.

**TOPICS 9–11 CLUSTER OVERVIEW**



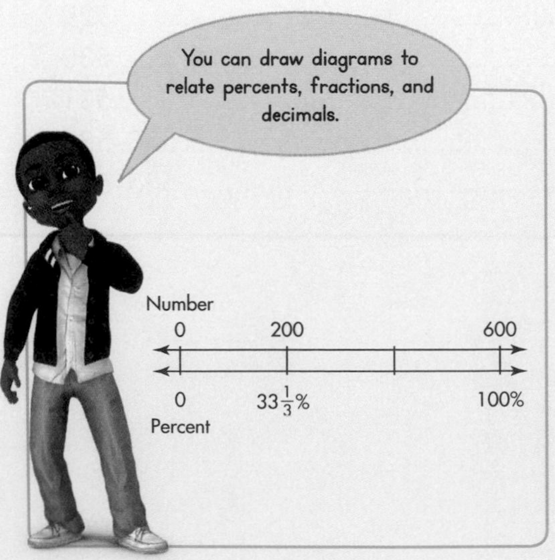


# TOPIC 11

## Ratio Concepts: Percent

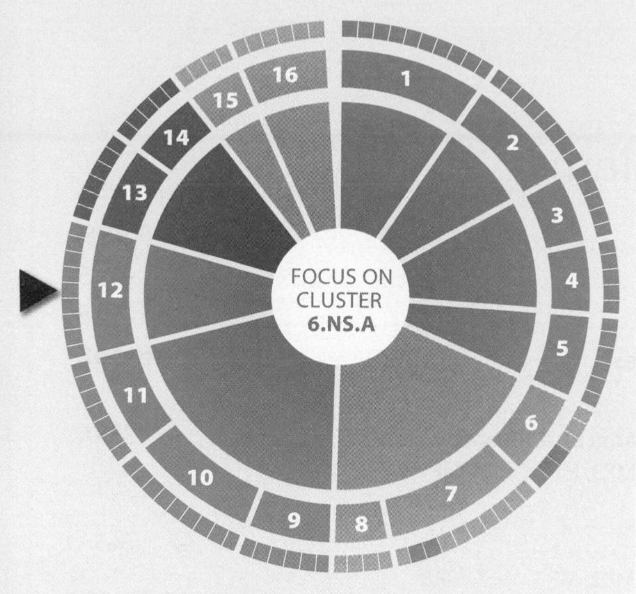


IN TOPIC 12, FOCUS ON

**MAJOR CLUSTER 6.NS.A**

Apply and extend previous understandings of multiplication and division to divide fractions by fractions.

**TOPIC 12 CLUSTER OVERVIEW**



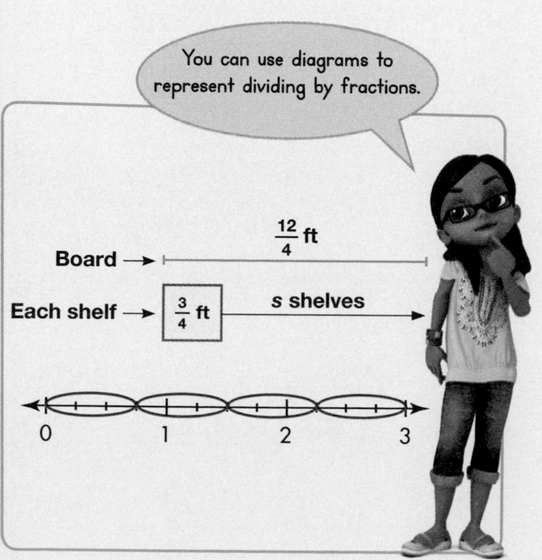


# TOPIC 12
## Divide Fractions by Fractions

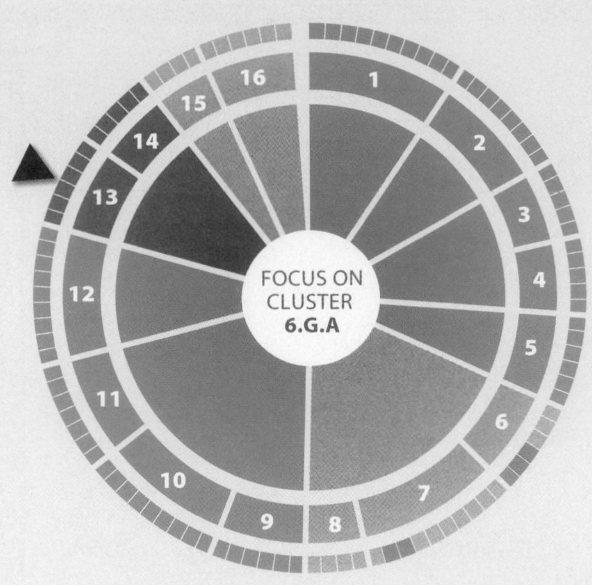


IN TOPICS 13 AND 14, FOCUS ON

**SUPPORTING CLUSTER 6.G.A**

Solve real-world and mathematical problems involving area, surface area, and volume.

*Supporting Cluster 6.G.A supports Major Cluster 6.EE.A. The Topics 13 and 14 problems that involve formulas apply the work with writing and evaluating expressions in Topic 1.*

**TOPICS 13 AND 14 CLUSTER OVERVIEW**



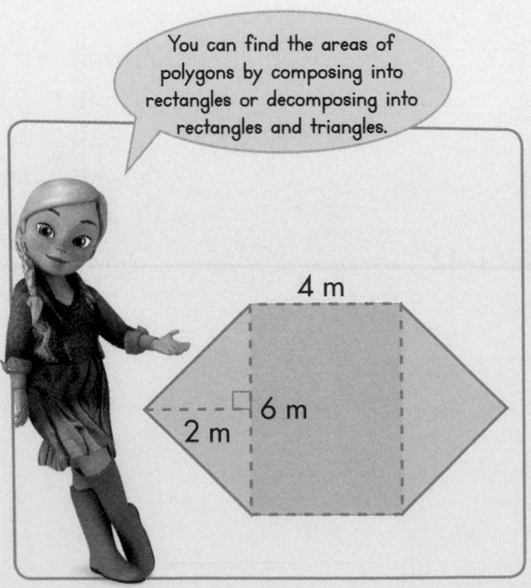

You can find the areas of polygons by composing into rectangles or decomposing into rectangles and triangles.
4 m
6 m
2 m

# TOPIC 13

## Solve Area Problems

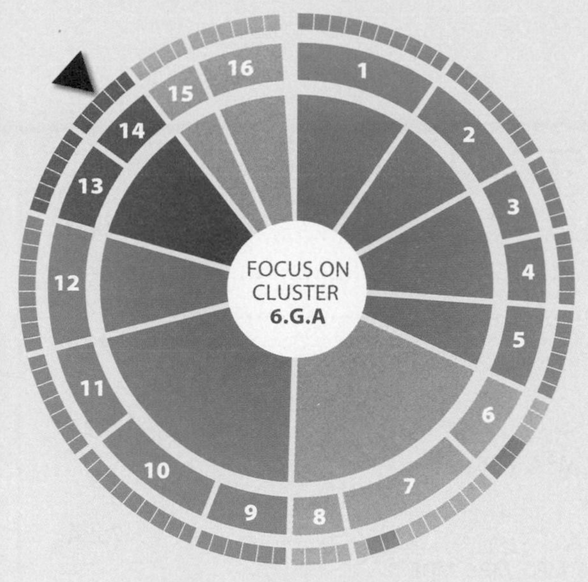


IN TOPICS 13 AND 14, FOCUS ON

**SUPPORTING CLUSTER 6.G.A**

Solve real-world and mathematical problems involving area, surface area, and volume.

*Supporting Cluster 6.G.A supports Major Cluster 6.EE.A. The Topics 13 and 14 problems that involve formulas apply the work with writing and evaluating expressions in Topic 1.*

**TOPICS 13 AND 14 CLUSTER OVERVIEW**



You can use a net to represent a three-dimensional figure, and use the net to find the surface area of the figure.

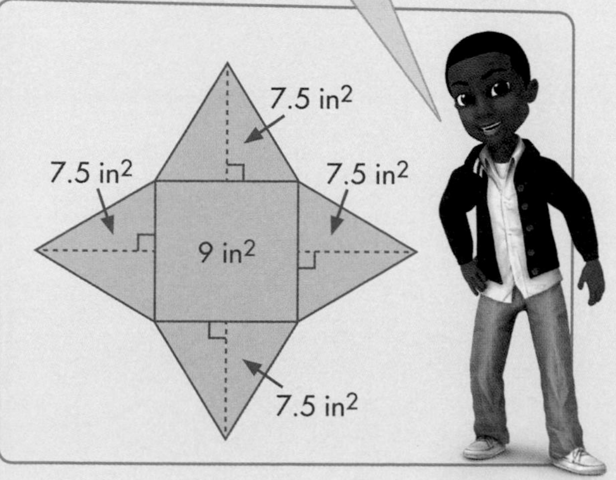


# TOPIC 14
## Solve Surface Area and Volume Problems

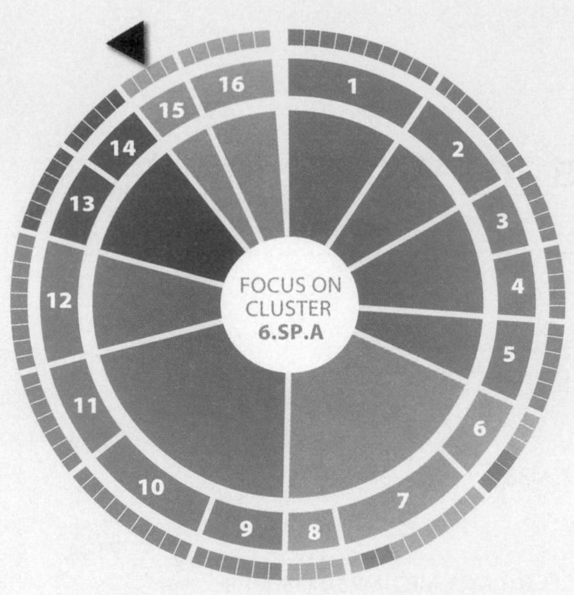


IN TOPIC 15, FOCUS ON

**ADDITIONAL CLUSTER 6.SP.A**

Develop understanding of statistical variability.

**TOPIC 15 CLUSTER OVERVIEW**



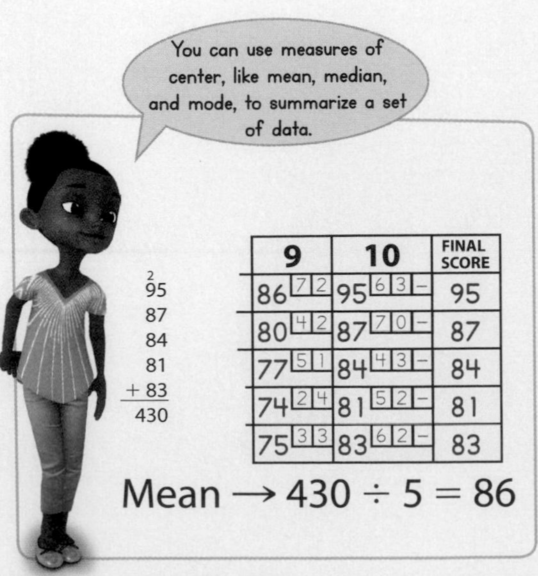


# TOPIC 15
## Measures of Center and Variability

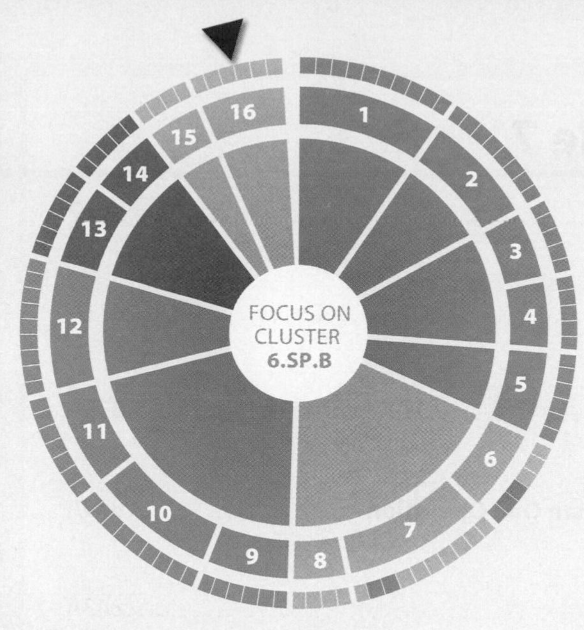
FOCUS ON
CLUSTER
6.SP.B

IN TOPIC 16, FOCUS ON

**ADDITIONAL CLUSTER 6.SP.B**

Summarize and describe distributions.

**TOPIC 16 CLUSTER OVERVIEW**

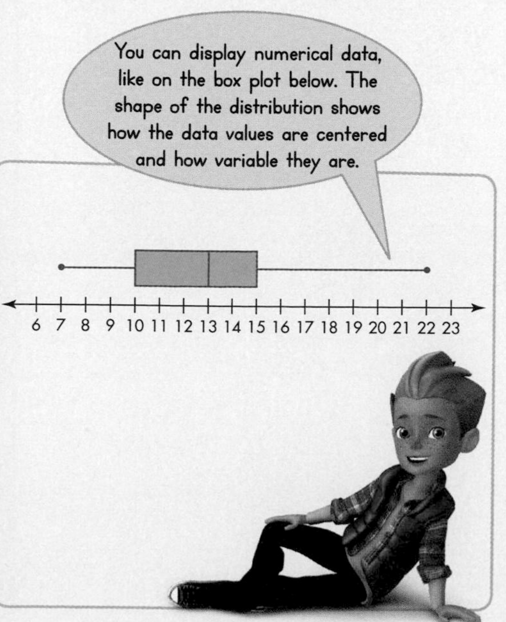
You can display numerical data, like on the box plot below. The shape of the distribution shows how the data values are centered and how variable they are.
6 7 8 9 10 11 12 13 14 15 16 17 18 19 20 21 22 23

# TOPIC 16
## Display and Summarize Data

## STEP UP to Grade 7

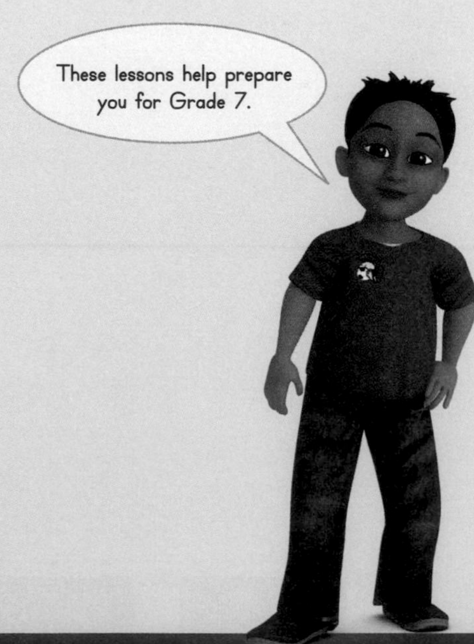
These lessons help prepare you for Grade 7.

# GRADE 6 COMMON CORE STANDARDS

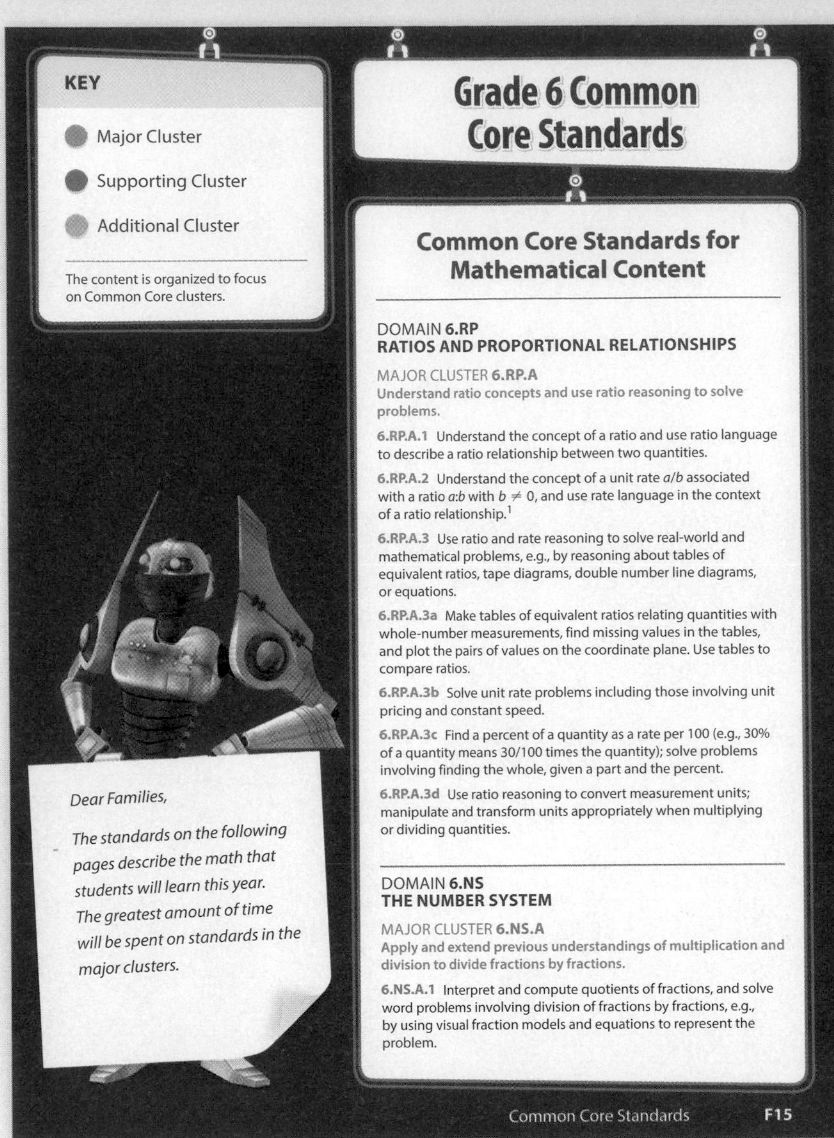

**KEY**

- Major Cluster
- Supporting Cluster
- Additional Cluster

The content is organized to focus on Common Core clusters.

## Grade 6 Common Core Standards

### Common Core Standards for Mathematical Content

DOMAIN **6.RP**
**RATIOS AND PROPORTIONAL RELATIONSHIPS**

MAJOR CLUSTER **6.RP.A**
**Understand ratio concepts and use ratio reasoning to solve problems.**

**6.RP.A.1** Understand the concept of a ratio and use ratio language to describe a ratio relationship between two quantities.

**6.RP.A.2** Understand the concept of a unit rate $a/b$ associated with a ratio $a{:}b$ with $b \neq 0$, and use rate language in the context of a ratio relationship.[1]

**6.RP.A.3** Use ratio and rate reasoning to solve real-world and mathematical problems, e.g., by reasoning about tables of equivalent ratios, tape diagrams, double number line diagrams, or equations.

**6.RP.A.3a** Make tables of equivalent ratios relating quantities with whole-number measurements, find missing values in the tables, and plot the pairs of values on the coordinate plane. Use tables to compare ratios.

**6.RP.A.3b** Solve unit rate problems including those involving unit pricing and constant speed.

**6.RP.A.3c** Find a percent of a quantity as a rate per 100 (e.g., 30% of a quantity means 30/100 times the quantity); solve problems involving finding the whole, given a part and the percent.

**6.RP.A.3d** Use ratio reasoning to convert measurement units; manipulate and transform units appropriately when multiplying or dividing quantities.

DOMAIN **6.NS**
**THE NUMBER SYSTEM**

MAJOR CLUSTER **6.NS.A**
**Apply and extend previous understandings of multiplication and division to divide fractions by fractions.**

**6.NS.A.1** Interpret and compute quotients of fractions, and solve word problems involving division of fractions by fractions, e.g., by using visual fraction models and equations to represent the problem.

*Dear Families,*

*The standards on the following pages describe the math that students will learn this year. The greatest amount of time will be spent on standards in the major clusters.*



- Major Cluster
- Supporting Cluster
- Additional Cluster

### Common Core Standards for Mathematical Content

ADDITIONAL CLUSTER **6.NS.B**
**Compute fluently with multi-digit numbers and find common factors and multiples.**

**6.NS.B.2** Fluently divide multi-digit numbers using the standard algorithm.

**6.NS.B.3** Fluently add, subtract, multiply, and divide multi-digit decimals using the standard algorithm for each operation.

**6.NS.B.4** Find the greatest common factor of two whole numbers less than or equal to 100 and the least common multiple of two whole numbers less than or equal to 12. Use the distributive property to express a sum of two whole numbers 1–100 with a common factor as a multiple of a sum of two whole numbers with no common factor.

MAJOR CLUSTER **6.NS.C**
**Apply and extend previous understandings of numbers to the system of rational numbers.**

**6.NS.C.5** Understand that positive and negative numbers are used together to describe quantities having opposite directions or values (e.g., temperature above/below zero, elevation above/below sea level, credits/debits, positive/negative electric charge); use positive and negative numbers to represent quantities in real-world contexts, explaining the meaning of 0 in each situation.

**6.NS.C.6** Understand a rational number as a point on the number line. Extend number line diagrams and coordinate axes familiar from previous grades to represent points on the line and in the plane with negative number coordinates.

**6.NS.C.6a** Recognize opposite signs of numbers as indicating locations on opposite sides of 0 on the number line; recognize that the opposite of the opposite of a number is the number itself, e.g., $-(-3) = 3$, and that 0 is its own opposite.

**6.NS.C.6b** Understand signs of numbers in ordered pairs as indicating locations in quadrants of the coordinate plane; recognize that when two ordered pairs differ only by signs, the locations of the points are related by reflections across one or both axes.

**6.NS.C.6c** Find and position integers and other rational numbers on a horizontal or vertical number line diagram; find and position pairs of integers and other rational numbers on a coordinate plane.

**6.NS.C.7** Understand ordering and absolute value of rational numbers.

**6.NS.C.7a** Interpret statements of inequality as statements about the relative position of two numbers on a number line diagram.

**6.NS.C.7b** Write, interpret, and explain statements of order for rational numbers in real-world contexts.

**6.NS.C.7c** Understand the absolute value of a rational number as its distance from 0 on the number line; interpret absolute value as magnitude for a positive or negative quantity in a real-world situation.

**6.NS.C.7d** Distinguish comparisons of absolute value from statements about order.

**6.NS.C.8** Solve real-world and mathematical problems by graphing points in all four quadrants of the coordinate plane. Include use of coordinates and absolute value to find distances between points with the same first coordinate or the same second coordinate.

DOMAIN **6.EE**
**EXPRESSIONS AND EQUATIONS**

MAJOR CLUSTER **6.EE.A**
**Apply and extend previous understandings of arithmetic to algebraic expressions.**

**6.EE.A.1** Write and evaluate numerical expressions involving whole-number exponents.

**6.EE.A.2** Write, read, and evaluate expressions in which letters stand for numbers.

**6.EE.A.2a** Write expressions that record operations with numbers and with letters standing for numbers.

**6.EE.A.2b** Identify parts of an expression using mathematical terms (sum, term, product, factor, quotient, coefficient); view one or more parts of an expression as a single entity.




You may wish to have students take home these six pages of Common Core Standards and share them with their families. Students can create a booklet of these pages by putting the three sheets in order and then stapling the left side of the sheets at the top, the middle, and the bottom.

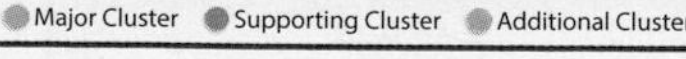


## Common Core Standards for Mathematical Content

6.EE.A.2c Evaluate expressions at specific values of their variables. Include expressions that arise from formulas used in real-world problems. Perform arithmetic operations, including those involving whole-number exponents, in the conventional order when there are no parentheses to specify a particular order (Order of Operations).

6.EE.A.3 Apply the properties of operations to generate equivalent expressions.

6.EE.A.4 Identify when two expressions are equivalent (i.e., when the two expressions name the same number regardless of which value is substituted into them).

MAJOR CLUSTER **6.EE.B**
**Reason about and solve one-variable equations and inequalities.**

6.EE.B.5 Understand solving an equation or inequality as a process of answering a question: which values from a specified set, if any, make the equation or inequality true? Use substitution to determine whether a given number in a specified set makes an equation or inequality true.

6.EE.B.6 Use variables to represent numbers and write expressions when solving a real-world or mathematical problem; understand that a variable can represent an unknown number, or, depending on the purpose at hand, any number in a specified set.

6.EE.B.7 Solve real-world and mathematical problems by writing and solving equations of the form $x + p = q$ and $px = q$ for cases in which $p$, $q$ and $x$ are all nonnegative rational numbers.

6.EE.B.8 Write an inequality of the form $x > c$ or $x < c$ to represent a constraint or condition in a real-world or mathematical problem. Recognize that inequalities of the form $x > c$ or $x < c$ have infinitely many solutions; represent solutions of such inequalities on number line diagrams.

MAJOR CLUSTER **6.EE.C**
**Represent and analyze quantitative relationships between dependent and independent variables.**

6.EE.C.9 Use variables to represent two quantities in a real-world problem that change in relationship to one another; write an equation to express one quantity, thought of as the dependent variable, in terms of the other quantity, thought of as the independent variable. Analyze the relationship between the dependent and independent variables using graphs and tables, and relate these to the equation.

### DOMAIN 6.G
### GEOMETRY

SUPPORTING CLUSTER **6.G.A**
**Solve real-world and mathematical problems involving area, surface area, and volume.**

6.G.A.1 Find the area of right triangles, other triangles, special quadrilaterals, and polygons by composing into rectangles or decomposing into triangles and other shapes; apply these techniques in the context of solving real-world and mathematical problems.

6.G.A.2 Find the volume of a right rectangular prism with fractional edge lengths by packing it with unit cubes of the appropriate unit fraction edge lengths, and show that the volume is the same as would be found by multiplying the edge lengths of the prism. Apply the formulas $V = \ell w h$ and $V = b h$ to find volumes of right rectangular prisms with fractional edge lengths in the context of solving real-world and mathematical problems.

6.G.A.3 Draw polygons in the coordinate plane given coordinates for the vertices; use coordinates to find the length of a side joining points with the same first coordinate or the same second coordinate. Apply these techniques in the context of solving real-world and mathematical problems.

6.G.A.4 Represent three-dimensional figures using nets made up of rectangles and triangles, and use the nets to find the surface area of these figures. Apply these techniques in the context of solving real-world and mathematical problems.



Major Cluster Supporting Cluster Additional Cluster

## Common Core Standards for Mathematical Content

### DOMAIN 6.SP
### STATISTICS AND PROBABILITY

ADDITIONAL CLUSTER **6.SP.A**
**Develop understanding of statistical variability.**

6.SP.A.1 Recognize a statistical question as one that anticipates variability in the data related to the question and accounts for it in the answers.

6.SP.A.2 Understand that a set of data collected to answer a statistical question has a distribution which can be described by its center, spread, and overall shape.

6.SP.A.3 Recognize that a measure of center for a numerical data set summarizes all of its values with a single number, while a measure of variation describes how its values vary with a single number.

ADDITIONAL CLUSTER **6.SP.B**
**Summarize and describe distributions.**

6.SP.B.4 Display numerical data in plots on a number line, including dot plots, histograms, and box plots.

6.SP.B.5 Summarize numerical data sets in relation to their context, such as by:

6.SP.B.5a Reporting the number of observations.

6.SP.B.5b Describing the nature of the attribute under investigation, including how it was measured and its units of measurement.

6.SP.B.5c Giving quantitative measures of center (median and/or mean) and variability (interquartile range and/or mean absolute deviation), as well as describing any overall pattern and any striking deviations from the overall pattern with reference to the context in which the data were gathered.

6.SP.B.5d Relating the choice of measures of center and variability to the shape of the data distribution and the context in which the data were gathered.

[1]Expectations for unit rates in this grade are limited to non-complex fractions.

## Common Core Standards for Mathematical Practice

### MP.1 MAKE SENSE OF PROBLEMS AND PERSEVERE IN SOLVING THEM.

Mathematically proficient students start by explaining to themselves the meaning of a problem and looking for entry points to its solution. They analyze givens, constraints, relationships, and goals. They make conjectures about the form and meaning of the solution and plan a solution pathway rather than simply jumping into a solution attempt. They consider analogous problems, and try special cases and simpler forms of the original problem in order to gain insight into its solution. They monitor and evaluate their progress and change course if necessary. Older students might, depending on the context of the problem, transform algebraic expressions or change the viewing window on their graphing calculator to get the information they need. Mathematically proficient students can explain correspondences between equations, verbal descriptions, tables, and graphs or draw diagrams of important features and relationships, graph data, and search for regularity or trends. Younger students might rely on using concrete objects or pictures to help conceptualize and solve a problem. Mathematically proficient students check their answers to problems using a different method, and they continually ask themselves, "Does this make sense?" They can understand the approaches of others to solving complex problems and identify correspondences between different approaches.

### MP.2 REASON ABSTRACTLY AND QUANTITATIVELY.

Mathematically proficient students make sense of quantities and their relationships in problem situations. They bring two complementary abilities to bear on problems involving quantitative relationships: the ability to *decontextualize*—to abstract a given situation and represent it symbolically and manipulate the representing symbols as if they have a life of their own, without necessarily attending to their referents—and the ability to *contextualize*, to pause as needed during the manipulation process in order to probe into the referents for the symbols involved. Quantitative reasoning entails habits of creating a coherent representation of the problem at hand; considering the units involved; attending to the meaning of quantities, not just how to compute them; and knowing and flexibly using different properties of operations and objects.

### MP.3 CONSTRUCT VIABLE ARGUMENTS AND CRITIQUE THE REASONING OF OTHERS.

Mathematically proficient students understand and use stated assumptions, definitions, and previously established results in constructing arguments. They make conjectures and build a logical progression of statements to explore the truth of their conjectures. They are able to analyze situations by breaking them into cases, and can recognize and use counterexamples. They justify their conclusions, communicate them to others, and respond to the arguments of others. They reason inductively about data, making plausible arguments that take into account the context from which the data arose. Mathematically proficient students are also able to compare the effectiveness of two plausible arguments, distinguish correct logic or reasoning from that which is flawed, and—if there is a flaw in an argument—explain what it is. Elementary students can construct arguments using concrete referents such as objects, drawings, diagrams, and actions. Such arguments can make sense and be correct, even though they are not generalized or made formal until later grades. Later, students learn to determine domains to which an argument applies. Students at all grades can listen or read the arguments of others, decide whether they make sense, and ask useful questions to clarify or improve the arguments.

### MP.4 MODEL WITH MATHEMATICS.

Mathematically proficient students can apply the mathematics they know to solve problems arising in everyday life, society, and the workplace. In early grades, this might be as simple as writing an addition equation to describe a situation. In middle grades, a student might apply proportional reasoning to plan a school event or analyze a problem in the community. By high school, a student might use geometry to solve a design problem or use a function to describe how one quantity of interest depends on another. Mathematically proficient students who can apply what they know are comfortable making assumptions and approximations to simplify a complicated situation, realizing that these may need revision later. They are able to identify important quantities in a practical situation and map their relationships using such tools as diagrams, two-way tables, graphs, flowcharts and formulas. They can analyze those relationships mathematically to draw conclusions. They routinely interpret their mathematical



## Common Core Standards for Mathematical Practice

results in the context of the situation and reflect on whether the results make sense, possibly improving the model if it has not served its purpose.

### MP.5 USE APPROPRIATE TOOLS STRATEGICALLY.

Mathematically proficient students consider the available tools when solving a mathematical problem. These tools might include pencil and paper, concrete models, a ruler, a protractor, a calculator, a spreadsheet, a computer algebra system, a statistical package, or dynamic geometry software. Proficient students are sufficiently familiar with tools appropriate for their grade or course to make sound decisions about when each of these tools might be helpful, recognizing both the insight to be gained and their limitations. For example, mathematically proficient high school students analyze graphs of functions and solutions generated using a graphing calculator. They detect possible errors by strategically using estimation and other mathematical knowledge. When making mathematical models, they know that technology can enable them to visualize the results of varying assumptions, explore consequences, and compare predictions with data. Mathematically proficient students at various grade levels are able to identify relevant external mathematical resources, such as digital content located on a website, and use them to pose or solve problems. They are able to use technological tools to explore and deepen their understanding of concepts.

### MP.6 ATTEND TO PRECISION.

Mathematically proficient students try to communicate precisely to others. They try to use clear definitions in discussion with others and in their own reasoning. They state the meaning of the symbols they choose, including using the equal sign consistently and appropriately. They are careful about specifying units of measure, and labeling axes to clarify the correspondence with quantities in a problem. They calculate accurately and efficiently, express numerical answers with a degree of precision appropriate for the problem context. In the elementary grades, students give carefully formulated explanations to each other. By the time they reach high school they have learned to examine claims and make explicit use of definitions.

### MP.7 LOOK FOR AND MAKE USE OF STRUCTURE.

Mathematically proficient students look closely to discern a pattern or structure. Young students, for example, might notice that three and seven more is the same amount as seven and three more, or they may sort a collection of shapes according to how many sides the shapes have. Later, students will see $7 \times 8$ equals the well remembered $7 \times 5 + 7 \times 3$, in preparation for learning about the distributive property. In the expression $x^2 + 9x + 14$, older students can see the 14 as $2 \times 7$ and the 9 as $2 + 7$. They recognize the significance of an existing line in a geometric figure and can use the strategy of drawing an auxiliary line for solving problems. They also can step back for an overview and shift perspective. They can see complicated things, such as some algebraic expressions, as single objects or as being composed of several objects. For example, they can see $5 - 3(x - y)^2$ as 5 minus a positive number times a square and use that to realize that its value cannot be more than 5 for any real numbers $x$ and $y$.

### MP.8 LOOK FOR AND EXPRESS REGULARITY IN REPEATED REASONING.

Mathematically proficient students notice if calculations are repeated, and look both for general methods and for shortcuts. Upper elementary students might notice when dividing 25 by 11 that they are repeating the same calculations over and over again, and conclude they have a repeating decimal. By paying attention to the calculation of slope as they repeatedly check whether points are on the line through (1, 2) with slope 3, middle school students might abstract the equation $(y - 2)/(x - 1) = 3$. Noticing the regularity in the way terms cancel when expanding $(x - 1)(x + 1)$, $(x - 1)(x^2 + x + 1)$, and $(x - 1)(x^3 + x^2 + x + 1)$ might lead them to the general formula for the sum of a geometric series. As they work to solve a problem, mathematically proficient students maintain oversight of the process, while attending to the details. They continually evaluate the reasonableness of their intermediate results.

# INTRODUCTION

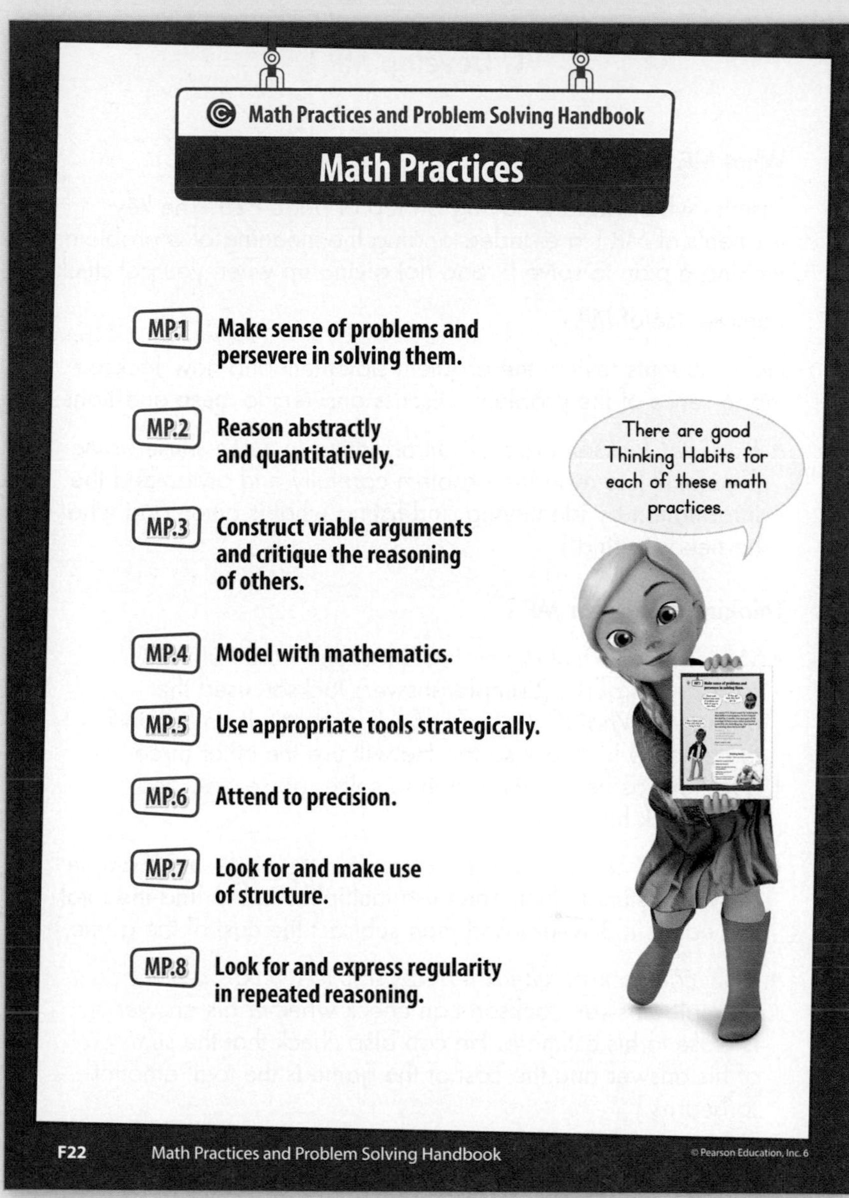


## INTRODUCING THE HANDBOOK

This handbook can be used at the beginning of the year and at any teachable moment. Explain to students that the handbook will help them become good math thinkers and good math problem solvers.

| | |
|---|---|
| **F22–F30** | Math Practices |
| **F31** | Problem Solving Guide |
| **F32** | Problem Solving Recording Sheet |
| **F33–F38** | Bar Diagrams |

## INTRODUCING THE MATH PRACTICES

Use pages F22–F30 to introduce students to the Mathematical Practices. Math Practices are the habits of mind, processes, and dispositions that enable a learner to understand mathematics and to use or do mathematics with understanding. Encourage students to refer back to these pages any time during the year, either in the Student's Edition or the eText.

The Thinking Habits, shown in the clouds on pages F23–F30, help students to engage the various math practices. These Thinking Habits are also shown in the Math Practices and Problem Solving lessons within the topics.

# MP.1 MAKE SENSE OF PROBLEMS AND PERSEVERE IN SOLVING THEM

## 1. Develop MP.1

### What MP.1 Means

Discuss what Marta is saying on top of page F23. The key elements of MP.1 are understanding the meaning of a problem, making a plan to solve it, and not giving up when you get stuck.

### Sample Use of MP.1

Have students review the problem statement and how Jackson made sense of the problem. Discuss answers to these questions.

- *How did Jackson organize information to make sense of the problem?* [He read the problem carefully and organized the information by identifying and listing what is given and what he needs to find.]

### Thinking Habits for MP.1

- *Which of the Thinking Habits questions were helpful to Jackson? Explain.* [Sample answer: Jackson used the questions *What do I need to find?* and *What do I know?* to complete his work so far. He will use the other three questions as he makes a plan to solve, persevere, and then check his answer.]
- *What plan could Jackson use to solve the problem?* [Sample answer: Estimate first. Then use multiplication to find the total Jon earns in 3 weeks and then subtract the cost of the game.]
- *How can Jackson check that his solution makes sense?* [Sample answer: Jackson can check whether his answer is close to his estimate. He can also check that the sum of his answer and the cost of the game is the total amount Jon earns.]

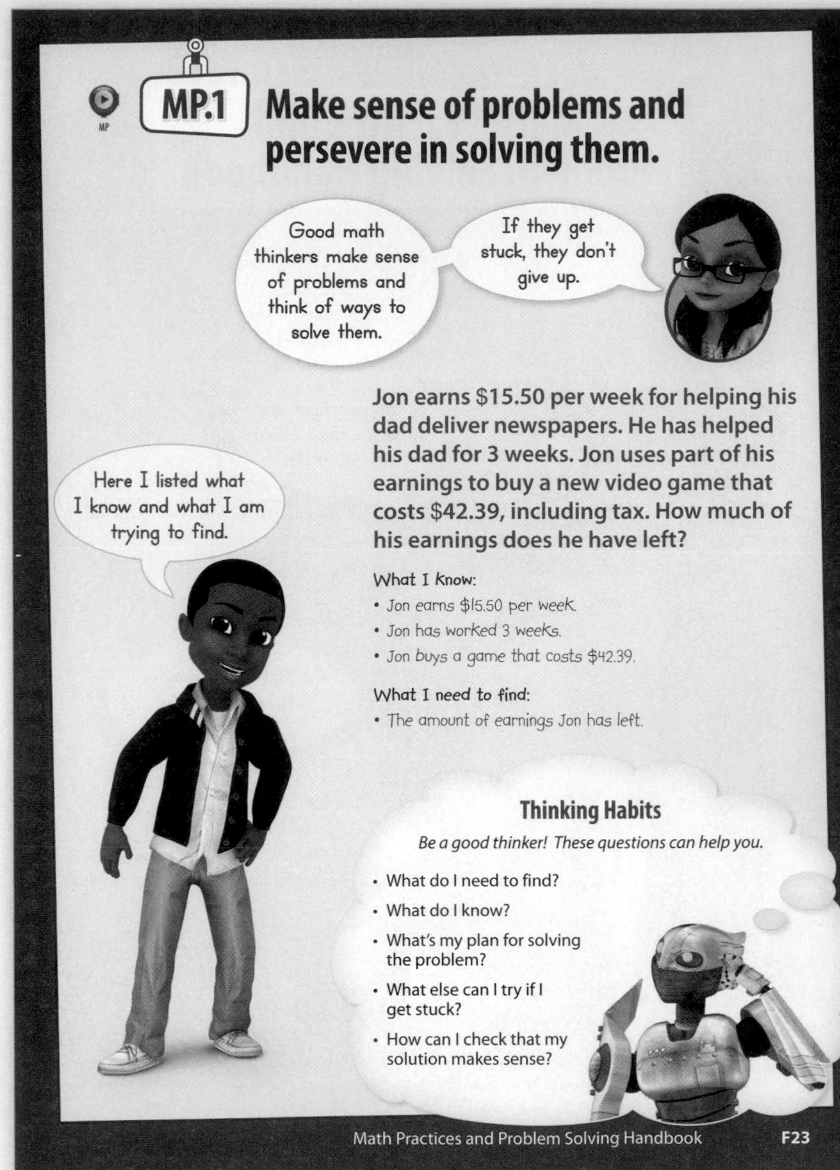


**Other Resources for Developing MP.1** include the following:

- MP **Math Practices Animations** An animation for each math practice is available at PearsonRealize.com. You might want to play the MP.1 animation as you use page F23 and at other times throughout the year as needed.
- **Math Practices Posters** A poster for each math practice is available to display in your classroom. You might want to display the MP.1 poster after playing the MP.1 animation.
- **Math Practices and Problem Solving Lessons** Lessons 2-8, 9-6, and 15-4 focus on MP.1.

realize.
PearsonRealize.com

MP

## 2. Connect MP.1

### Connect MP.1 to Content

To see the many places MP.1 is connected to content standards within lessons, look for "MP.1" in red type.

Also see "Connecting Math Practices to Content Standards" in the Teacher's Edition, pages 1F, 79F, 139F, 223F, 271F, 423F, 591F, 655F, 745F, and 781F.

Below is a problem from Topic 2 in which students apply MP.1 by using a bar diagram to make sense of a problem and think of ways to solve it.

> Bo kept track of how far he walked in May and June with his pedometer. He walked 3 times as far in June as he did in May. He walked 152 miles during the two months. How far did Bo walk in May and in June?

### Connect MP.1 to Other Math Practices

Deep understanding of mathematics, as well as success with problem solving, calls for engaging a combination of math practices. MP.1 is an overarching practice that strongly connects to all other mathematical practices. The following examples illustrate connections between MP.1 and other math practices.

- **MP.2 Reason Abstractly and Quantitatively** When students make sense of problems and persevere in solving them, they reason about how quantities are related and use math symbols to represent the problem situation.
- **MP.6 Attend to Precision** As students make sense of problems and carry out their plans to solve them, they need to be precise in their work. Do they understand definitions of math words and symbols? Are they using definitions correctly in their answers?

## 3. Assess MP.1

### MP.1 Behaviors

Listen and look for the following behaviors to monitor students' ongoing development of proficiency with MP.1.

- ✓ Gives a good explanation of the problem.
- ✓ Thinks about a plan before jumping into the solution.
- ✓ Thinks of similar problems, tries special cases, or uses a simpler form of the problem.
- ✓ Organizes data or uses representations to help make sense of the problem, if needed.
- ✓ Identifies likely strategies for solving the problem.
- ✓ Pauses when solving problems to make sure that the work being done makes sense.
- ✓ Makes sure the answer makes sense before stopping work.
- ✓ Does not give up when stuck.
- ✓ Looks for ways to get past being stuck.
- ✓ Tries alternative ways to solve the problem when stuck.

Use the list of MP.1 behaviors above and the following rubric to evaluate a student's overall proficiency with MP.1.

| Math Practices Proficiency Rubric | |
|---|---|
| 4 | **Exemplary** The student exhibits all of the behaviors. |
| 3 | **Proficient** The student exhibits most of the behaviors. |
| 2 | **Emerging** The student exhibits about half of the behaviors. |
| 1 | **Needs Improvement** The student exhibits less than half of the behaviors. |

# MP.2 REASON ABSTRACTLY AND QUANTITATIVELY

## 1. Develop MP.2

**What MP.2 Means**

Discuss what Jada is saying on top of page F24. The key element of MP.2 is reasoning about quantities and using math to represent how the quantities are related.

**Sample Use of MP.2**

Have students review the problem statement and how Zeke used math to show how the quantities in the problem are related. Discuss answers to these questions.

- *How does the bar diagram represent the quantities in the problem?* [It shows the total cost of the juice drinks divided equally among the 6 drinks.]
- *How do you know that a division equation can be used to represent the relationships shown by the bar diagram?* [A quantity is divided into equal amounts, so you can use division.]

**Thinking Habits for MP.2**

- *Which of the Thinking Habits questions were helpful to Zeke? Explain.* [Sample answer: All three questions were helpful to Zeke because he used numbers, symbols, a diagram, and an equation to reason about the quantities in the problem and to represent how they are related.]

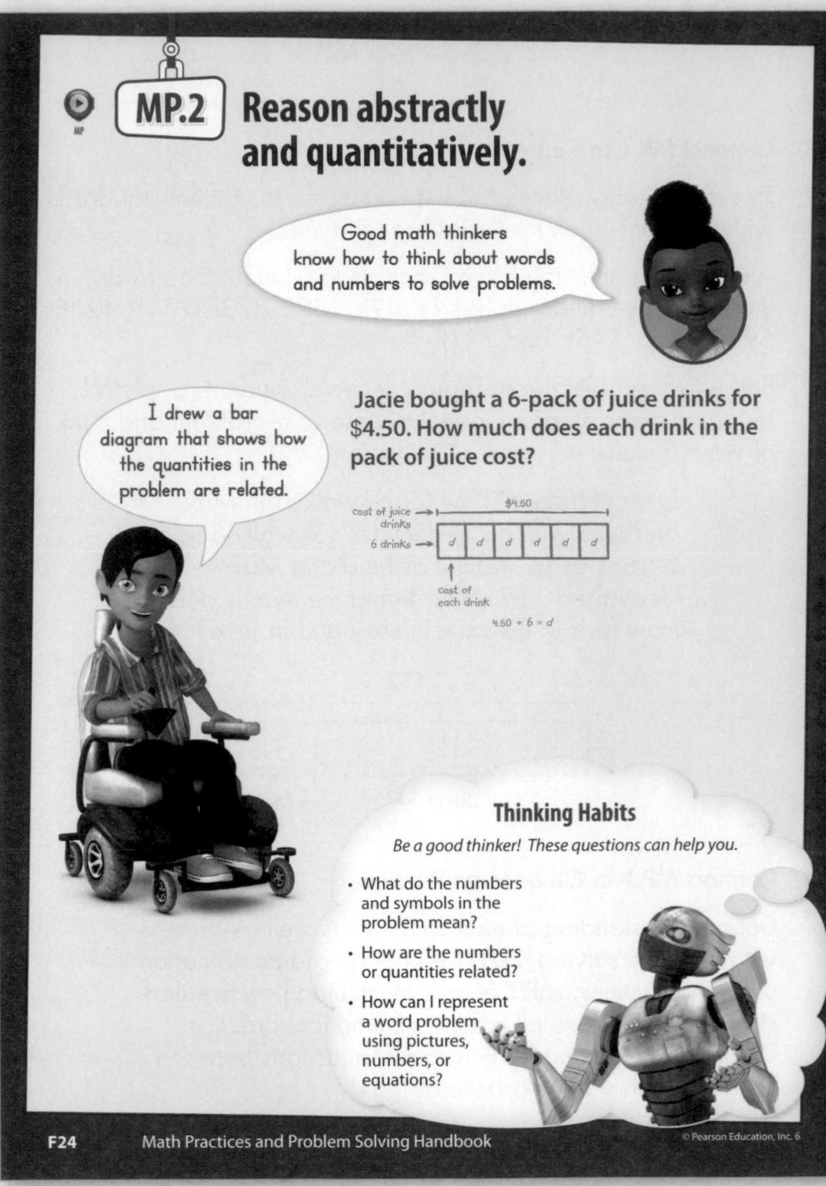


**Other Resources for Developing MP.2** include the following:

- **Math Practices Animations** An animation for each math practice is available at PearsonRealize.com. You might want to play the MP.2 animation as you use page F24 and at other times throughout the year as needed.
- **Math Practices Posters** A poster for each math practice is available to display in your classroom. You might want to display the MP.2 poster after playing the MP.2 animation.
- **Math Practices and Problem Solving Lessons** Lessons 3-5 and 14-5 focus on MP.2.

## 2. Connect MP.2

### Connect MP.2 to Content

To see the many places MP.2 is connected to content standards within lessons, look for "MP.2" in red type.

Also see "Connecting Math Practices to Content Standards" in the Teacher's Edition, pages 1F, 79F, 139F, 223F, 271F, 423F, 591F, 655F, 745F, and 781F.

Below is a problem in Topic 14 where students translate a real-world context into a pictorial representation and then use the net to calculate areas in order to recommend a bid amount.

John is a building contractor. He is asked to supply an estimate, or bid, to shingle the roof of this new gazebo.

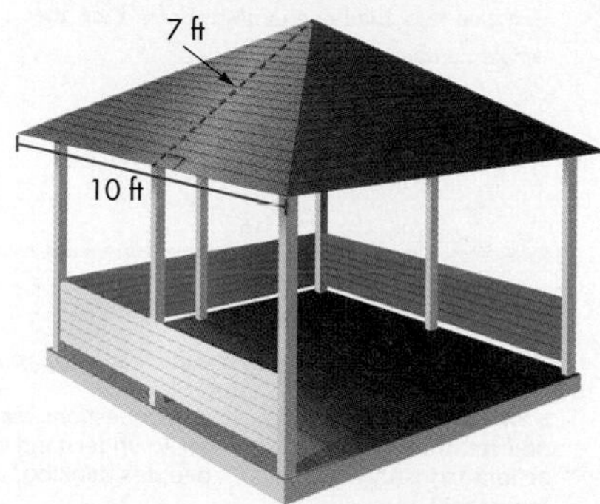



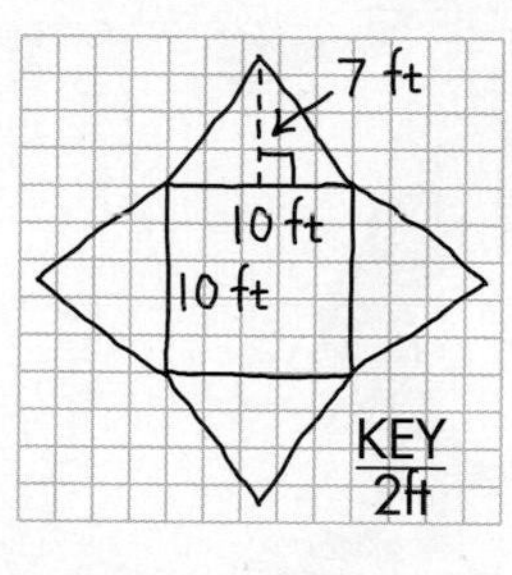



### Connect MP.2 to Other Math Practices

Deep understanding of mathematics, as well as success with problem solving, calls for engaging a combination of math practices. The following examples illustrate connections between MP.2 and other math practices.

- **MP.3 Construct Viable Arguments and Critique the Reasoning of Others** When students reason about quantities, they apply the math they know to represent the situation mathematically. Students may use objects, drawings, equations, or other methods to represent how quantities relate in order to solve a problem.
- **MP.4 Model with Mathematics** When students reason about quantities, they apply the math they know to represent the situation mathematically. Students use symbols to represent and to solve a problem.

## 3. Assess MP.2

### MP.2 Behaviors

Listen and look for the following behaviors to monitor students' ongoing development of proficiency with MP.2.

✓ Identifies and understands the quantities in the problem.

✓ Shows and explains how quantities are related (e.g., bar diagram).

✓ Translates real-world contexts correctly to numbers, expressions, equations, or concrete or pictorial representations.

✓ Connects numbers, expressions, equations, or concrete or pictorial representations back to real-world contexts.

Use the list of MP.2 behaviors above and the following rubric to evaluate a student's overall proficiency with MP.2.

| Math Practices Proficiency Rubric | |
|---|---|
| 4 | **Exemplary** The student exhibits all of the behaviors. |
| 3 | **Proficient** The student exhibits most of the behaviors. |
| 2 | **Emerging** The student exhibits about half of the behaviors. |
| 1 | **Needs Improvement** The student exhibits less than half of the behaviors. |

# MP.3 CONSTRUCT VIABLE ARGUMENTS AND CRITIQUE THE REASONING OF OTHERS

## 1. Develop MP.3

**What MP.3 Means**

Discuss what Daniel is saying on top of page F25. The key elements of MP.3 are to critically analyze the mathematics of others and to develop clear and accurate mathematical arguments to explain and justify your thinking and solutions.

**Sample Use of MP.3**

Have students review the problem statement and Marta's explanation. Discuss answers to these questions.

- *How does Marta use a drawing to justify her argument?* [She uses a fraction strip diagram to show that $\frac{5}{6} \times 2$ is less than 2.]
- *Is Marta's explanation clear and complete? Explain.* [Sample answer: Yes, she uses words, numbers, and symbols to explain her reasoning and to provide an example.]

**Thinking Habits for MP.3**

- *What questions could Marta ask Jo in order to better understand Jo's thinking?* [Sample answer: Marta could ask Jo to show an example and explain why she thinks her statement is always true.]
- *Could Marta have used a counterexample in her explanation? Explain.* [No, a counterexample is an example that shows a statement is false. Jo's statement is true.]
- *Which of the Thinking Habits questions were helpful to Marta? Explain.* [Sample answer: All three questions about constructing arguments were helpful. Marta gave a clear and complete explanation and used a diagram with correct numbers and symbols to justify her argument.]

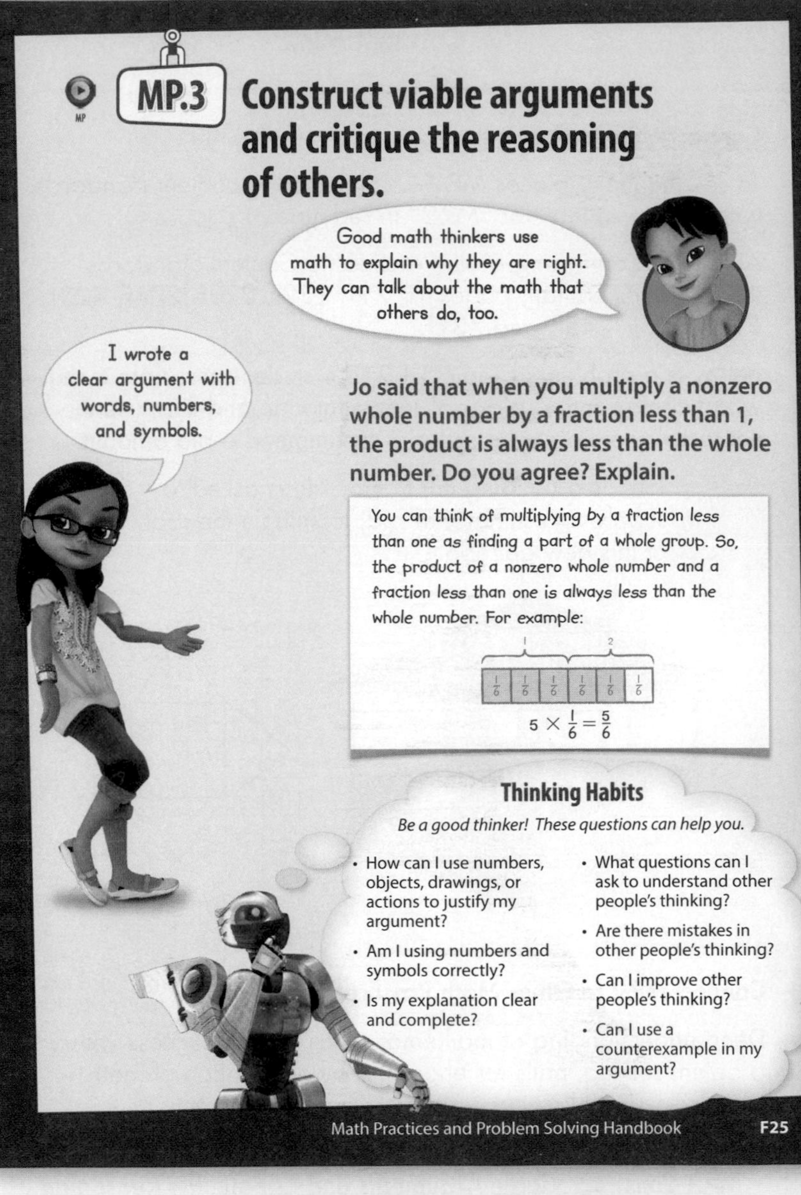


**Other Resources for Developing MP.3** include the following:

- **Math Practices Animations** An animation for each math practice is available at PearsonRealize.com. You might want to play the MP.3 animation as you use page F25 and at other times throughout the year as needed.
- **Math Practices Posters** A poster for each math practice is available to display in your classroom. You might want to display the MP.3 poster after playing the MP.3 animation.
- **Math Practices and Problem Solving Lessons** Lessons 4-5, 8-4, and 16-6 focus on MP.3.

## 2. Connect MP.3

### Connect MP.3 to Content

To see the many places MP.3 is connected to content standards within lessons, look for "MP.3" in red type.

Also see "Connecting Math Practices to Content Standards" in the Teacher's Edition, pages 1F, 79F, 139F, 223F, 271F, 423F, 591F, 655F, 745F, and 781F.

Below is a problem from Topic 4 in which students critique the reasoning of others and construct an argument using graphs and math to justify the claim.

> Sophia drew a floor plan of her classroom on a coordinate plane. She placed the corners of a closet floor at *A* (−4, 4), *B* (2, 4), *C* (2, 1), and *D* (−4, 1). Sophia says that the closet floor is a rectangle with an area of 18 square feet. Each unit on the grid represents 1 foot. Do you agree with Sophia's claims? Construct an argument to justify your answer.

### Connect MP.3 to Other Math Practices

Deep understanding of mathematics, as well as success with problem solving, calls for engaging a combination of math practices. The following examples illustrate connections between MP.3 and other math practices.

- **MP.2 Reason Abstractly and Quantitatively** Students make sense of how quantities are related in order to construct viable arguments or analyze a mathematical statement for accuracy. They use logical reasoning and identify reasoning that is flawed.
- **MP.6 Attend to Precision** Students use clear and precise mathematical language when constructing arguments to justify their reasoning or the reasoning of others. They use numbers and symbols correctly and calculate accurately.

## 3. Assess MP.3

### MP.3 Behaviors

Listen and look for the following behaviors to monitor students' ongoing development of proficiency with MP.3.

- ✓ Provides complete and clear explanations of one's thinking and work.
- ✓ Decides if other students' explanations make sense; clarifies or improves other students' arguments.
- ✓ Uses counterexamples when appropriate.
- ✓ Asks questions to understand other people's thinking.
- ✓ Identifies mistakes in other people's thinking.
- ✓ Provides suggestions for improving other people's thinking.

Use the list of MP.3 behaviors above and the following rubric to evaluate a student's overall proficiency with MP.3.

| Math Practices Proficiency Rubric | |
|---|---|
| 4 | **Exemplary** The student exhibits all of the behaviors. |
| 3 | **Proficient** The student exhibits most of the behaviors. |
| 2 | **Emerging** The student exhibits about half of the behaviors. |
| 1 | **Needs Improvement** The student exhibits less than half of the behaviors. |

# MP.4 MODEL WITH MATHEMATICS

## 1. Develop MP.4

### What MP.4 Means

Discuss what Marta is saying on top of page F26. The key elements of MP.4 are identifying and applying previously learned concepts and procedures to solve a problem.

### Sample Use of MP.4

Have students review the problem statement, Alex's plan, and Alex's work. Discuss answers to these questions.

- *How does Alex's drawing represent the problem?* [It shows the total length of the wall divided by 6 shelves that are all the same width.]
- *How does the equation represent the problem?* [The division equation shows the total length of the wall, 32.5 feet, divided by 6 equal-sized shelves to find the width of each shelf, *w*.]

### Thinking Habits for MP.4

- *Which of the Thinking Habits questions were helpful to Alex? Explain.* [Sample answer: All of the questions were helpful. Alex used his knowledge of division, as well as a picture, an equation, numbers, and symbols to represent the problem.]

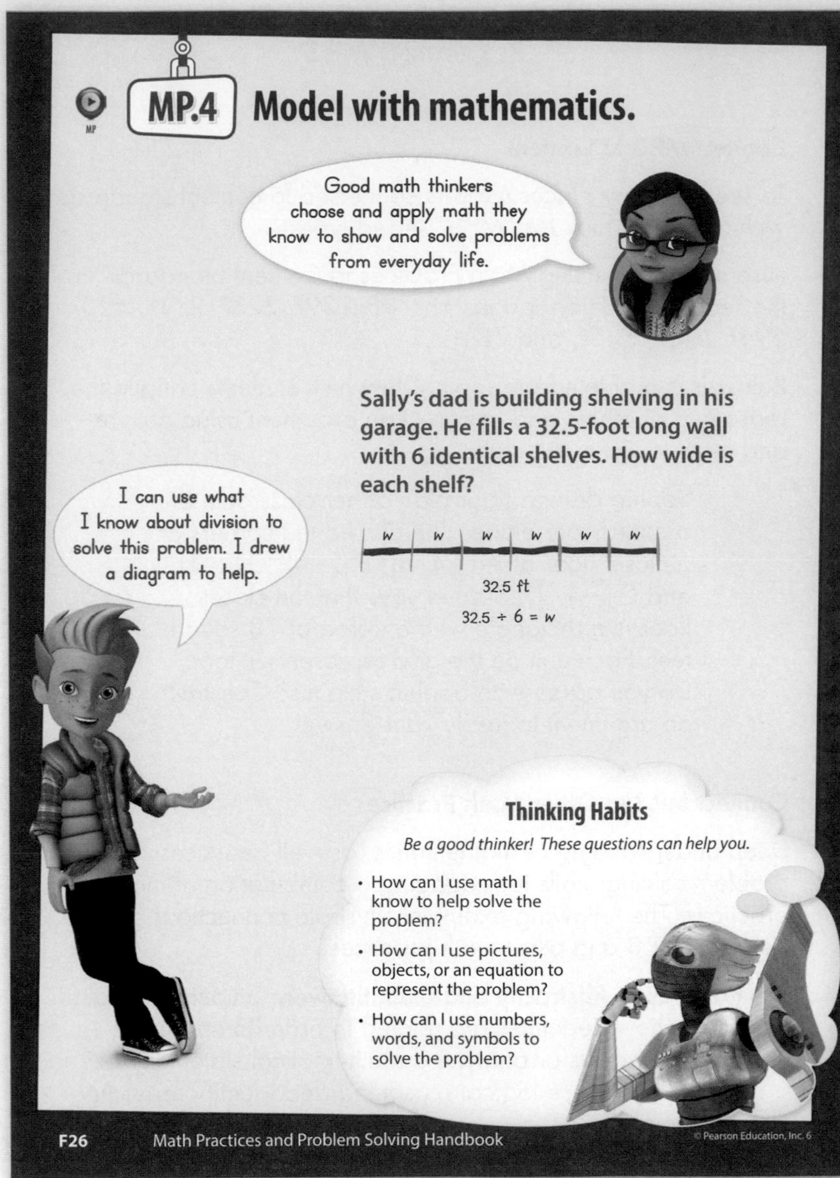
MP
MP.4 Model with mathematics.
Good math thinkers choose and apply math they know to show and solve problems from everyday life.
Sally's dad is building shelving in his garage. He fills a 32.5-foot long wall with 6 identical shelves. How wide is each shelf?
I can use what I know about division to solve this problem. I drew a diagram to help.
w w w w w w
32.5 ft
32.5 ÷ 6 = w
Thinking Habits
Be a good thinker! These questions can help you.
• How can I use math I know to help solve the problem?
• How can I use pictures, objects, or an equation to represent the problem?
• How can I use numbers, words, and symbols to solve the problem?
F26 Math Practices and Problem Solving Handbook

**Other Resources for Developing MP.4** include the following:

- **Math Practices Animations** An animation for each math practice is available at PearsonRealize.com. You might want to play the MP.4 animation as you use page F26 and at other times throughout the year as needed.
- **Math Practices Posters** A poster for each math practice is available to display in your classroom. You might want to display the MP.4 poster after playing the MP.4 animation.
- **Math Practices and Problem Solving Lessons** Lesson 5-6 focuses on MP.4.

## 2. Connect MP.4

**Connect MP.4 to Content**

To see the many places MP.4 is connected to content standards within lessons, look for "MP.4" in red type.

Also see "Connecting Math Practices to Content Standards" in the Teacher's Edition, pages 1F, 79F, 139F, 223F, 271F, 423F, 591F, 655F, 745F, and 781F.

Below is a problem from Topic 5 in which students will employ MP.4 by using a table and writing an equation to represent the relationship between quantities in a problem.

> Helen's cookie recipe calls for 1.5 packages of chocolate chips for each batch of cookies. She has 1 package of chocolate chips. How many more packages will she need to buy to have enough for 16 batches?

**Connect MP.4 to Other Math Practices**

Deep understanding of mathematics, as well as success with problem solving, calls for engaging a combination of math practices. The following examples illustrate connections between MP.4 and other math practices.

- **MP.2 Reason Abstractly and Quantitatively** When students model with math, they apply the math they have learned to a new problem. Students reason abstractly and quantitatively in order to represent quantities in a problem situation with familiar math models, such as a diagram or an equation.
- **MP.5 Use Appropriate Tools Strategically** When students model with math, various tools help them represent the math they know to solve a problem. Students can use tools such as paper and pencil and technology tools to make a mathematical representation or model.

## 3. Assess MP.4

**MP.4 Behaviors**

Listen and look for the following behaviors to monitor students' ongoing development of proficiency with MP.4.

✓ Identifies the correct prior knowledge that needs to be applied to solve a problem.

✓ Identifies the hidden question(s) in multiple-step problems.

✓ Uses numbers, symbols, and words to solve problems.

✓ Identifies the operation(s) needed to solve a problem.

✓ Uses estimation as appropriate.

Use the list of MP.4 behaviors above and the following rubric to evaluate a student's overall proficiency with MP.4.

| Math Practices Proficiency Rubric | |
|---|---|
| 4 | **Exemplary** The student exhibits all of the behaviors. |
| 3 | **Proficient** The student exhibits most of the behaviors. |
| 2 | **Emerging** The student exhibits about half of the behaviors. |
| 1 | **Needs Improvement** The student exhibits less than half of the behaviors. |

# MP.5 USE APPROPRIATE TOOLS STRATEGICALLY

## 1. Develop MP.5

### What MP.5 Means

Discuss what Zeke is saying on top of page F27. The key elements of MP.5 are choosing the right tool to solve a problem and using it strategically.

### Sample Use of MP.5

Have students review the problem statement and Jada's plan to find the volume of the pencil box. Discuss answers to these questions.

- *How does using unit cubes to fill the box help Jada solve the problem?* [Sample answer: Jada can count the number of unit cubes it takes to fill the box to find its volume.]
- *Did Jada choose and use the unit cubes appropriately? Explain.* [Yes, Jada chose unit cubes, which have a volume of 1 cubic inch, and used them to fill the box and to find its volume.]
- *Is there a different tool that Jada could use to find the volume of the box?* [Sample answer: Yes, she could use pencil and paper and calculate the volume of the box using the formula $V = \ell wh$.]

### Thinking Habits for MP.5

- *Which of the Thinking Habits questions were helpful to Jada? Explain.* [Sample answer: All of the questions were helpful. Jada chose to use unit cubes as a tool to help her find the volume of the pencil box.]

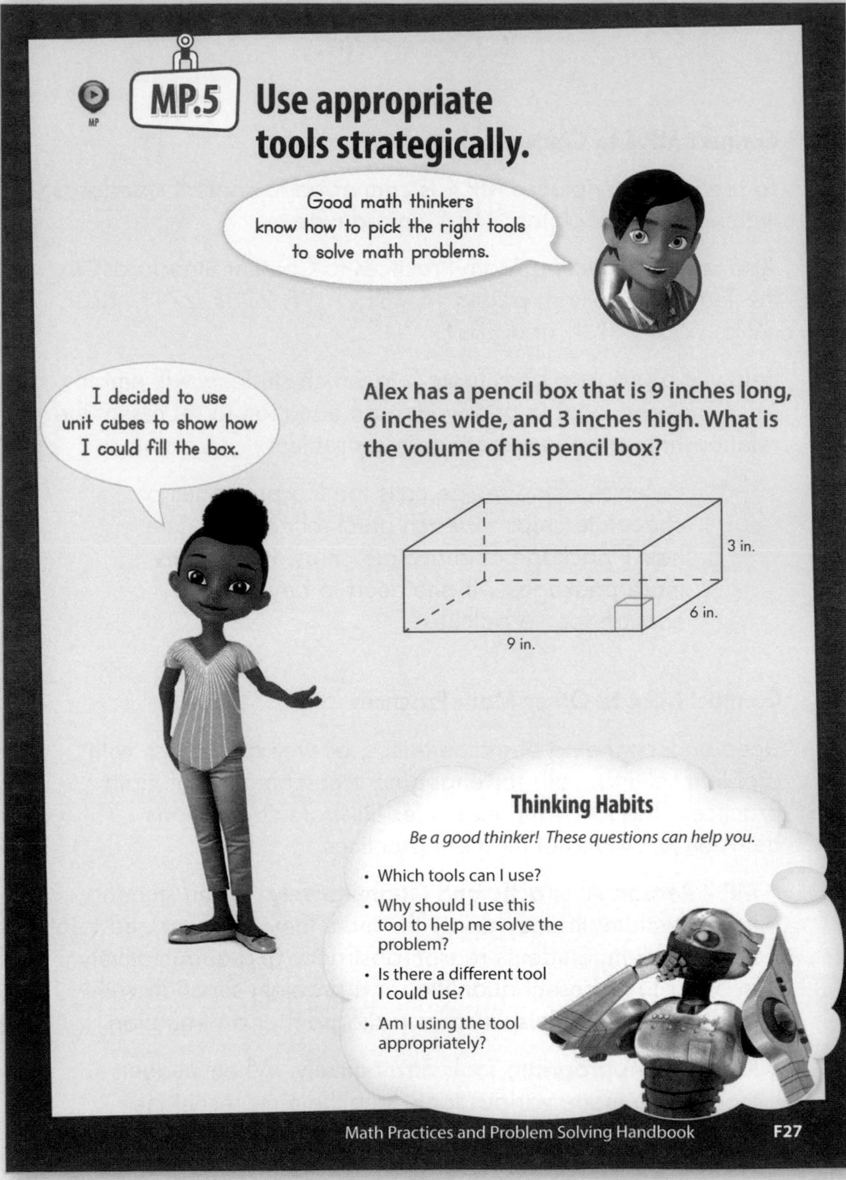


**Other Resources for Developing MP.5** include the following:

- MP **Math Practices Animations** An animation for each math practice is available at PearsonRealize.com. You might want to play the MP.5 animation as you use page F27 and at other times throughout the year as needed.
- **Math Practices Posters** A poster for each math practice is available to display in your classroom. You might want to display the MP.5 poster after playing the MP.5 animation.
- **Math Practices and Problem Solving Lessons** Lesson 7-10 focuses on MP.5.

PEARSON realize.
PearsonRealize.com

## 2. Connect MP.5

**Connect MP.5 to Content**

To see the many places MP.5 is connected to content standards within lessons, look for "MP.5" in red type.

Also see "Connecting Math Practices to Content Standards" in the Teacher's Edition, pages 1F, 79F, 139F, 223F, 271F, 423F, 591F, 655F, 745F, and 781F.

Below is a problem from Topic 7 in which students will choose a tool and use it appropriately to solve a problem.

Zack found this table on the Internet. He has a stack of quarters and dimes that is 12 millimeters tall. Three of the coins are quarters, and the rest are dimes. What is the value of his stack of coins? What is the mass of his coins?

| | Penny | Nickel | Dime | Quarter | Half Dollar |
|---|---|---|---|---|---|
| Mass | 2.500 g | 5.000 g | 2.268 g | 5.670 g | 11.340 g |
| Thickness | 1.52 mm | 1.95 mm | 1.35 mm | 1.75 mm | 2.15 mm |

**Connect MP.5 to Other Math Practices**

Deep understanding of mathematics, as well as success with problem solving, calls for engaging a combination of math practices. The following examples illustrate connections between MP.5 and other math practices.

- **MP.4 Model with Mathematics** As students choose appropriate tools, they make sense of problems and analyze the relationships between the quantities. Students decide which tools can best be used to represent the problem situation and solution.
- **MP.6 Attend to Precision** As students use appropriate tools strategically, they attend to the precision of the tool. They recognize the degree of precision of the tool and recognize its limitations as they assess its usefulness in solving a problem.

## 3. Assess MP.5

**MP.5 Behaviors**

Listen and look for the following behaviors to monitor students' ongoing development of proficiency with MP.5.

✓ Identifies available tools.

✓ Thinks about correct tools to use without prompting.

✓ Uses tools correctly and accurately.

✓ Knows when to use a particular tool.

✓ Decides if the results obtained using a tool make sense.

Use the list of MP.5 behaviors above and the following rubric to evaluate a student's overall proficiency with MP.5.

| Math Practices Proficiency Rubric | |
|---|---|
| 4 | **Exemplary** The student exhibits all of the behaviors. |
| 3 | **Proficient** The student exhibits most of the behaviors. |
| 2 | **Emerging** The student exhibits about half of the behaviors. |
| 1 | **Needs Improvement** The student exhibits less than half of the behaviors. |

# MP.6 ATTEND TO PRECISION

## 1. Develop MP.6

### What MP.6 Means

Discuss what Jada is saying on top of page F28. The key elements of MP.6 are calculating fluently and accurately and communicating with clear and precise mathematical language.

### Sample Use of MP.6

Have students review the problem statement and how Carlos attended to precision in his work to solve the problem. Discuss answers to these questions.

- *How does Carlos use numbers and symbols correctly?* [Sample answer: Carlos uses numbers and the multiplication symbol to show how the quantities in the problem are related and to show how he computes the answer.]
- *How does Carlos write his answer clearly?* [Sample answer: Carlos uses a complete sentence that includes units to describe the solution.]
- *How can Carlos check whether he calculated accurately?* [Sample answer: He can double check his work, and check that $5\frac{1}{3} \div \frac{2}{3} = 8$.]

### Thinking Habits for MP.6

- *Which of the Thinking Habits questions were helpful to Carlos? Explain.* [Sample answer: All of the questions were helpful. Carlos used the appropriate numbers, units, and symbols to represent the problem, calculate accurately, and present his answer clearly.]

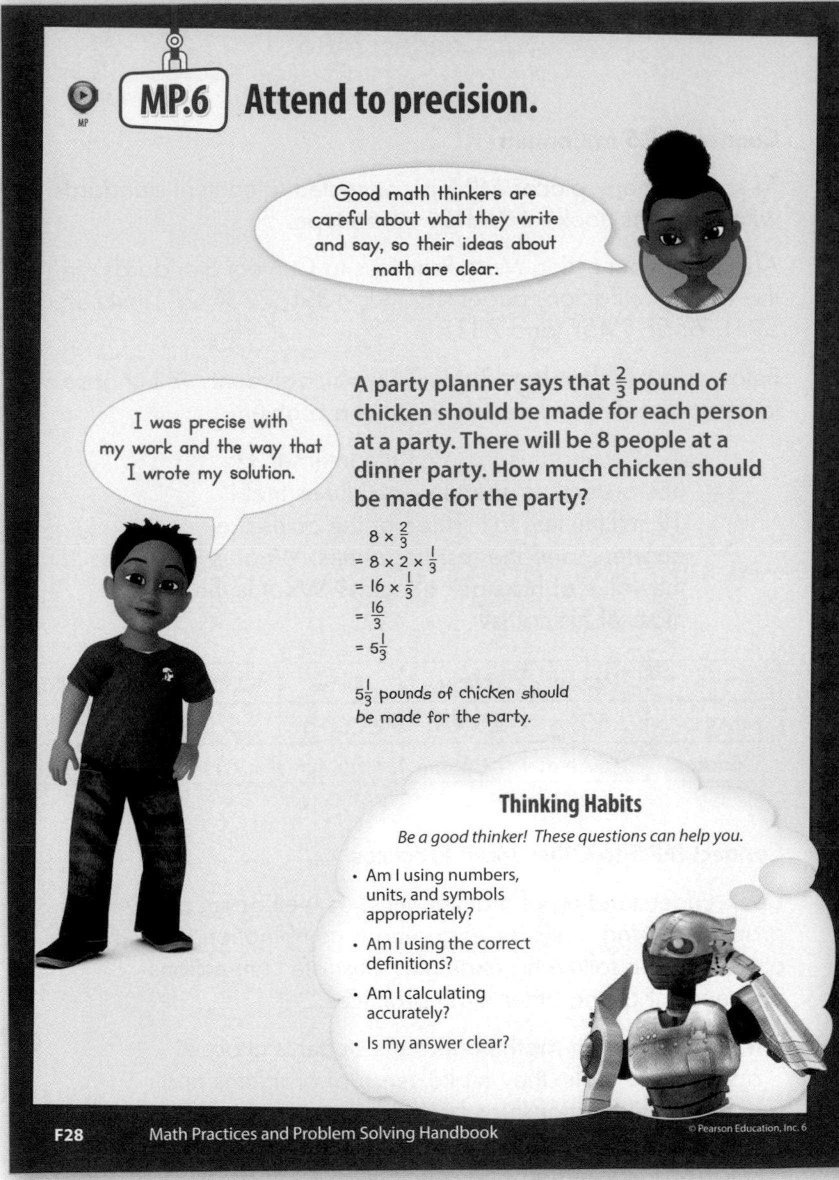

MP
MP.6 Attend to precision.
Good math thinkers are careful about what they write and say, so their ideas about math are clear.
A party planner says that $\frac{2}{3}$ pound of chicken should be made for each person at a party. There will be 8 people at a dinner party. How much chicken should be made for the party?
I was precise with my work and the way that I wrote my solution.
$8 \times \frac{2}{3}$
$= 8 \times 2 \times \frac{1}{3}$
$= 16 \times \frac{1}{3}$
$= \frac{16}{3}$
$= 5\frac{1}{3}$
$5\frac{1}{3}$ pounds of chicken should be made for the party.
Thinking Habits
Be a good thinker! These questions can help you.
Am I using numbers, units, and symbols appropriately?
Am I using the correct definitions?
Am I calculating accurately?
Is my answer clear?
F28 Math Practices and Problem Solving Handbook
© Pearson Education, Inc. 6


**Other Resources for Developing MP.6** include the following:

- **Math Practices Animations** An animation for each math practice is available at PearsonRealize.com. You might want to play the MP.6 animation as you use page F28 and at other times throughout the year as needed.
- **Math Practices Posters** A poster for each math practice is available to display in your classroom. You might want to display the MP.6 poster after playing the MP.6 animation.
- **Math Practices and Problem Solving Lessons** Lessons 6-6, 10-9, and 12-9 focus on MP.6.

MP

## 2. Connect MP.6

**Connect MP.6 to Content**

To see the many places MP.6 is connected to content standards within lessons, look for "MP.6" in red type.

Also see "Connecting Math Practices to Content Standards" in the Teacher's Edition, pages 1F, 79F, 139F, 223F, 271F, 423F, 591F, 655F, 745F, and 781F.

Below is a problem from Topic 10 in which students will attend to precision as they calculate accurately and present their answers clearly with appropriate numbers, units, and symbols.

Kevin and Valeria have just completed a keyboarding class. Their test results are shown in the table. They each have a 9,000-word report to type. Who will finish first? Explain your answer.

| Student | Minutes | Words Typed | Errors/ 100 words |
|---|---|---|---|
| Kevin | 7 | 441 | 2 |
| Valeria | 5 | 360 | 3 |

**Connect MP.6 to Other Math Practices**

Deep understanding of mathematics, as well as success with problem solving, calls for engaging a combination of math practices. The following examples illustrate connections between MP.6 and other math practices.

- **MP.1 Make Sense of Problems and Persevere in Solving Them** Students attend to precision as they make sense of a problem and plan a solution pathway, and as they continually assess the accuracy of their work.
- **MP.3 Construct Viable Arguments and Critique the Reasoning of Others** Students use correct mathematical language, symbols, and precise calculations when they construct arguments to explain and justify their mathematics and the mathematics of others.

## 3. Assess MP.6

**MP.6 Behaviors**

Listen and look for the following behaviors to monitor students' ongoing development of proficiency with MP.6.

✓ Computes accurately.

✓ Uses symbols and definitions appropriately.

✓ Uses problem-solving strategies accurately.

✓ Specifies and uses units of measure appropriately.

✓ Decides whether an exact answer or estimate is needed.

✓ Calculates efficiently, accurately, and fluently.

✓ Communicates clearly.

Use the list of MP.6 behaviors above and the following rubric to evaluate a student's overall proficiency with MP.6.

| Math Practices Proficiency Rubric | |
|---|---|
| 4 | **Exemplary** The student exhibits all of the behaviors. |
| 3 | **Proficient** The student exhibits most of the behaviors. |
| 2 | **Emerging** The student exhibits about half of the behaviors. |
| 1 | **Needs Improvement** The student exhibits less than half of the behaviors. |

# MP.7 LOOK FOR AND MAKE USE OF STRUCTURE

## 1. Develop MP.7

**What MP.7 Means**

Discuss what Jackson is saying on top of page F29. The key element of MP.7 is looking for and using patterns in math to solve problems.

**Sample Use of MP.7**

Have students review the problem statement, Emily's plan, and Emily's work. Discuss answers to these questions.

- *What pattern does Emily use to solve the problem?* [Sample answer: Emily uses the pattern in metric measures to write that 1 m = 100 cm.]
- *How did Emily use place-value structure to multiply?* [Sample answer: Emily used place-value structure to multiply a decimal by the power of ten $10^2$, or 100, by moving the decimal point two places to the right.]
- *Which equivalent expressions does Emily use to write 0.25 meter as centimeters?* [Sample answer: $0.25 \times 10^2$; $0.25 \times 100$; 25]

**Thinking Habits for MP.7**

- *Which of the Thinking Habits questions were helpful to Emily? Explain.* [Sample answer: All of the questions were helpful. Emily sees and uses patterns and writes expressions in different and equivalent ways to solve the problem.]

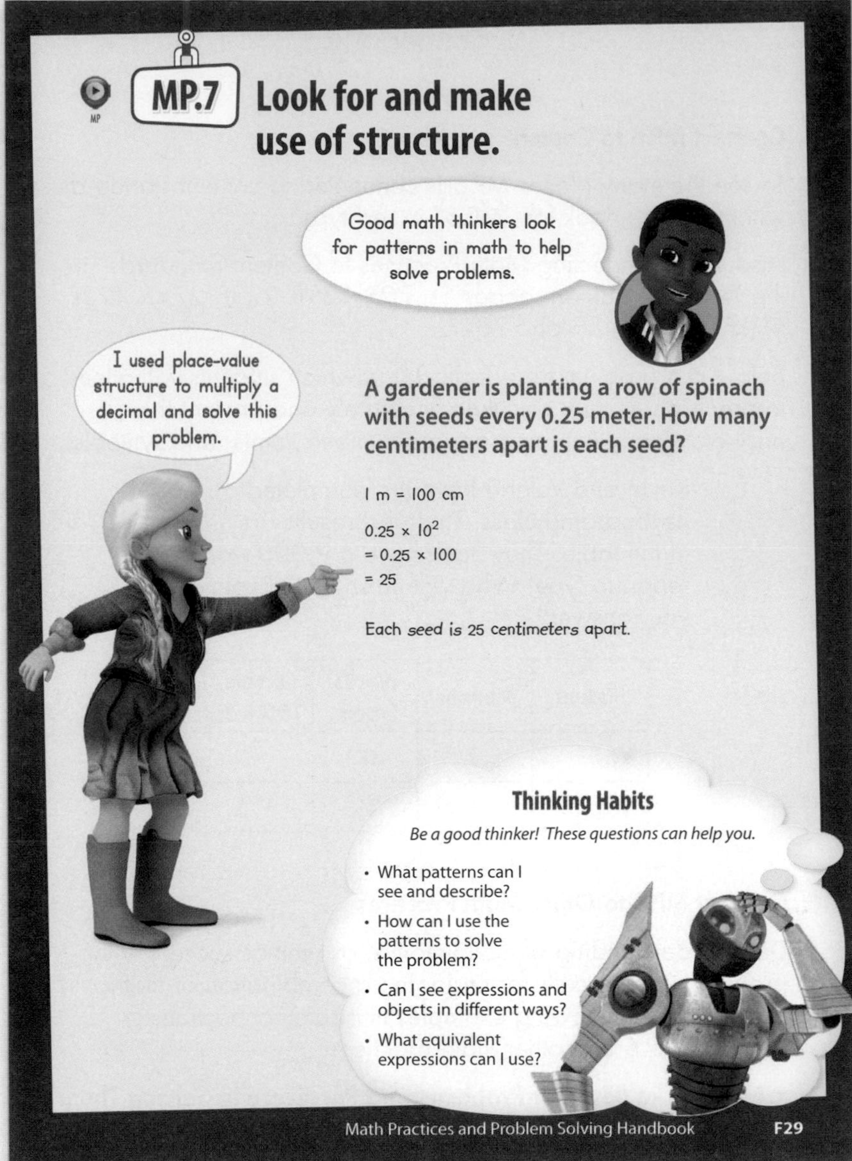

MP
MP.7 Look for and make use of structure.
Good math thinkers look for patterns in math to help solve problems.
I used place-value structure to multiply a decimal and solve this problem.
A gardener is planting a row of spinach with seeds every 0.25 meter. How many centimeters apart is each seed?
1 m = 100 cm
0.25 × 10²
= 0.25 × 100
= 25
Each seed is 25 centimeters apart.
Thinking Habits
Be a good thinker! These questions can help you.
• What patterns can I see and describe?
• How can I use the patterns to solve the problem?
• Can I see expressions and objects in different ways?
• What equivalent expressions can I use?
Math Practices and Problem Solving Handbook F29


**Other Resources for Developing MP.7** include the following:

- **Math Practices Animations** An animation for each math practice is available at PearsonRealize.com. You might want to play the MP.7 animation as you use page F29 and at other times throughout the year as needed.
- **Math Practices Posters** A poster for each math practice is available to display in your classroom. You might want to display the MP.7 poster after playing the MP.7 animation.
- **Math Practices and Problem Solving Lessons** Lessons 1-10 and 13-6 focus on MP.7.

## 2. Connect MP.7

**Connect MP.7 to Content**

To see the many places MP.7 is connected to content standards within lessons, look for "MP.7" in red type.

Also see "Connecting Math Practices to Content Standards" in the Teacher's Edition, pages 1F, 79F, 139F, 223F, 271F, 423F, 591F, 655F, 745F, and 781F.

Below is a problem from Topic 13 in which students could look for and make use of patterns and structure in the coordinate plane and the relationships between the areas of a rectangle and triangle to solve a problem.

Use the rectangle shown to make an isosceles triangle that has an area of 12 square units.

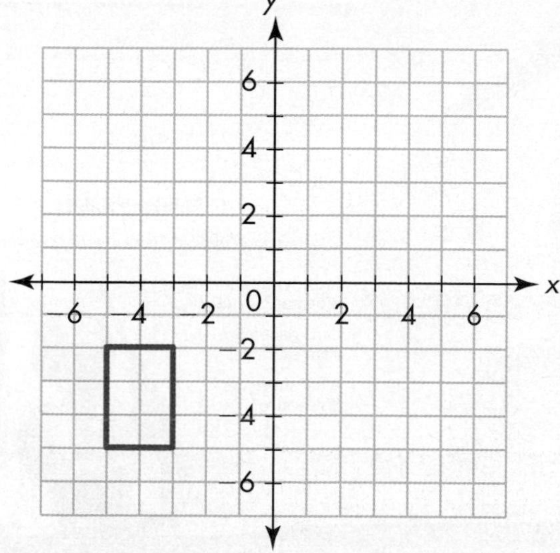


**Connect MP.7 to Other Math Practices**

Deep understanding of mathematics, as well as success with problem solving, calls for engaging a combination of math practices. The following examples illustrate connections between MP.7 and other math practices.

- **MP.2 Reason Abstractly and Quantitatively** As students look for and identify patterns or mathematical structure, they make sense of quantities and recognize relationships between quantities. Students use reasoning as they apply the patterns they found to solve problems in the same context.
- **MP.8 Look For and Express Regularity in Repeated Reasoning** As students look for and make use of structure, they identify patterns that can be generalized and may be used as a shortcut to solve problems.

## 3. Assess MP.7

**MP.7 Behaviors**

Listen and look for the following behaviors to monitor students' ongoing development of proficiency with MP.7.

✓ Analyzes and describes patterns in numbers.

✓ Analyzes and describes common attributes and patterns in shapes and solids.

✓ Analyzes expressions, equations, procedures, and objects to represent, describe, and work with them in different ways.

Use the list of MP.7 behaviors above and the following rubric to evaluate a student's overall proficiency with MP.7.

| Math Practices Proficiency Rubric | |
|---|---|
| 4 | **Exemplary** The student exhibits all of the behaviors. |
| 3 | **Proficient** The student exhibits most of the behaviors. |
| 2 | **Emerging** The student exhibits about half of the behaviors. |
| 1 | **Needs Improvement** The student exhibits less than half of the behaviors. |

# MP.8 LOOK FOR AND EXPRESS REGULARITY IN REPEATED REASONING

## 1. Develop MP.8

**What MP.8 Means**

Discuss what Emily is saying on top of page F30. The key elements of MP.8 are looking for procedures or calculations that repeat and making generalizations.

**Sample Use of MP.8**

Have students review the problem statement, Daniel's plan, and Daniel's work. Discuss answers to these questions.

- *Are there repeated quantities or calculations in the problem? Explain.* [Yes; both expressions use the quantities 534 and 10; a pattern of moving the decimal places in numbers to the right or left can be used when multiplying and dividing by 10.]
- *What generalization does Daniel use to solve the problem?* [Sample answer: Daniel generalized that multiplying a quantity by 10 results in a greater quantity than dividing the same quantity by 10.]
- *Did Daniel notice a shortcut? Explain.* [Sample answer: Yes, Daniel reasoned about the quantities rather than doing the actual calculations and then comparing the results.]

**Thinking Habits for MP.8**

- *Which of the Thinking Habits questions were helpful to Daniel? Explain.* [Sample answer: Daniel used the questions *Can I generalize from examples?* and *What shortcuts do I notice?* Though there weren't any repeated calculations, Daniel noticed repeated quantities, which allowed him to generalize to solve the problem.]

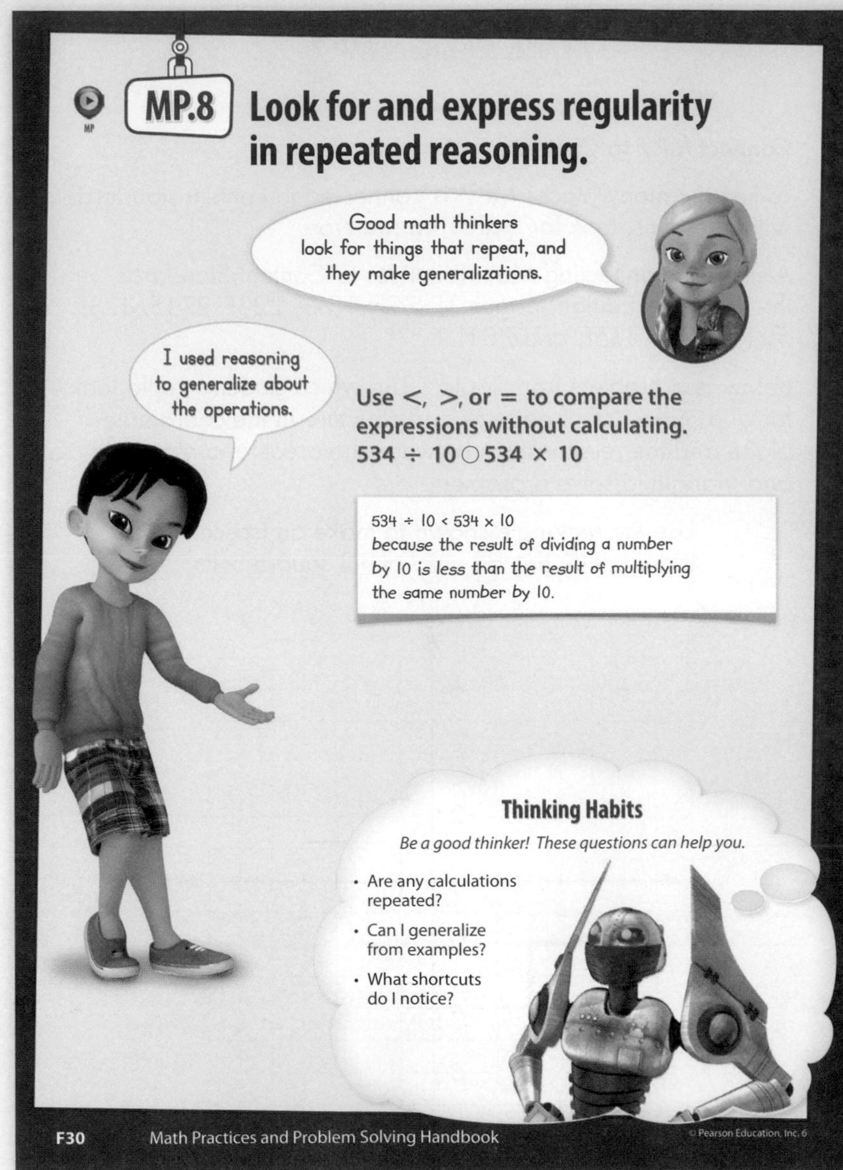
MP
MP.8 Look for and express regularity in repeated reasoning.
Good math thinkers look for things that repeat, and they make generalizations.
I used reasoning to generalize about the operations.
Use <, >, or = to compare the expressions without calculating.
534 ÷ 10 ○ 534 × 10
534 ÷ 10 < 534 × 10 because the result of dividing a number by 10 is less than the result of multiplying the same number by 10.
Thinking Habits
Be a good thinker! These questions can help you.
Are any calculations repeated?
Can I generalize from examples?
What shortcuts do I notice?
F30 Math Practices and Problem Solving Handbook
© Pearson Education, Inc. 6

**Other Resources for Developing MP.8** include the following:

- MP **Math Practices Animations** An animation for each math practice is available at PearsonRealize.com. You might want to play the MP.8 animation as you use page F30 and at other times throughout the year as needed.
- **Math Practices Posters** A poster for each math practice is available to display in your classroom. You might want to display the MP.8 poster after playing the MP.8 animation.
- **Math Practices and Problem Solving Lessons** Lesson 11-7 focuses on MP.8.

PEARSON realize.
PearsonRealize.com

MP

## 2. Connect MP.8

### Connect MP.8 to Content

To see the many places MP.8 is connected to content standards within lessons, look for "MP.8" in red type.

Also see "Connecting Math Practices to Content Standards" in the Teacher's Edition, pages 1F, 79F, 139F, 223F, 271F, 423F, 591F, 655F, 745F, and 781F.

Below is a problem from Topic 11 in which students will look for patterns and repeated reasoning and generalize to solve a problem.

> Tillman's Sporting Goods is offering a storewide 30%-off sale. Jesse has a 20%-off coupon he can use on the sale price. Is 20% off of 30% the same as 50% off? Explain.

### Connect MP.8 to Other Math Practices

Deep understanding of mathematics, as well as success with problem solving, calls for engaging a combination of math practices. The following examples illustrate connections between MP.8 and other math practices.

- **MP.6 Attend to Precision** Students attend to the details of the problem as they look for repeated calculations, quantities, or reasoning. Throughout the problem-solving process, they continually evaluate whether their results are reasonable.
- **MP.7 Look For and Make Use of Structure** As students look for and make use of structure and identify mathematical patterns, they recognize repeated calculations and regularity in results, and they generalize methods and shortcuts based on these observations.

## 3. Assess MP.8

### MP.8 Behaviors

Listen and look for the following behaviors to monitor students' ongoing development of proficiency with MP.8.

✓ Notices and describes when certain calculations or steps in a procedure are repeated.

✓ Generalizes from examples or repeated observations.

✓ Recognizes and understands appropriate shortcuts.

✓ Evaluates the reasonableness of intermediate results.

Use the list of MP.8 behaviors above and the following rubric to evaluate a student's overall proficiency with MP.8.

| Math Practices Proficiency Rubric | |
|---|---|
| 4 | **Exemplary** The student exhibits all of the behaviors. |
| 3 | **Proficient** The student exhibits most of the behaviors. |
| 2 | **Emerging** The student exhibits about half of the behaviors. |
| 1 | **Needs Improvement** The student exhibits less than half of the behaviors. |

# PROBLEM SOLVING GUIDE

## PROBLEM SOLVING GUIDE

### Background from the Authors

Mathematical Practices are involved in all aspects of mathematics learning. Because the **enVision**math**2.0** authors believe that mathematical practices have a particularly strong link to the phases of problem solving, we developed the Problem Solving Guide to help teachers infuse the phases of problem solving with the relevant mathematical practices. All eight of the mathematical practices are built into the Problem Solving Guide.

- **MP.1 Make sense of problems and persevere in solving them.** Students need to make sense of problems as well as their work and answers throughout the entire problem-solving process. MP.1 is particularly relevant when beginning to solve a problem and when checking one's work and solution.
- **MP.2 Reason abstractly and quantitatively.** MP.2 comes into play when first making sense of a problem. Students need to identify the quantities in the problem and understand how they are related.
- **MP.3 Construct viable arguments and critique the reasoning of others.** MP.3 is particularly important when sharing one's work solving a problem and when reviewing the work of others.
- **MP.4 Model with mathematics.** MP.4 is at the heart of problem solving. Students must identify previously learned concepts and procedures that they can bring to bear to find solutions.
- **MP.5 Use appropriate tools strategically.** MP.5 is part of every problem-solving experience. Students need to decide which tools are best for helping to understand and solve problems. They then need to apply the chosen tool or tools strategically to find solutions.
- **MP.6 Attend to precision.** MP.6 is involved in all phases of problem solving. Students need to be precise in understanding the conditions of a problem. They need to be precise in their work finding a solution, and they need to be precise in communicating their work and answer to others.
- **MP.7 Look for and make use of structure.** MP.7 is helpful in identifying a possible solution strategy for a problem. MP.7 helps students identify math they have used before that might be helpful in solving a given problem.
- **MP.8 Look for and express regularity in repeated reasoning.** MP.8 should be part of every problem-solving experience, as students should identify generalizations about the process used to solve a problem or the mathematical content developed.

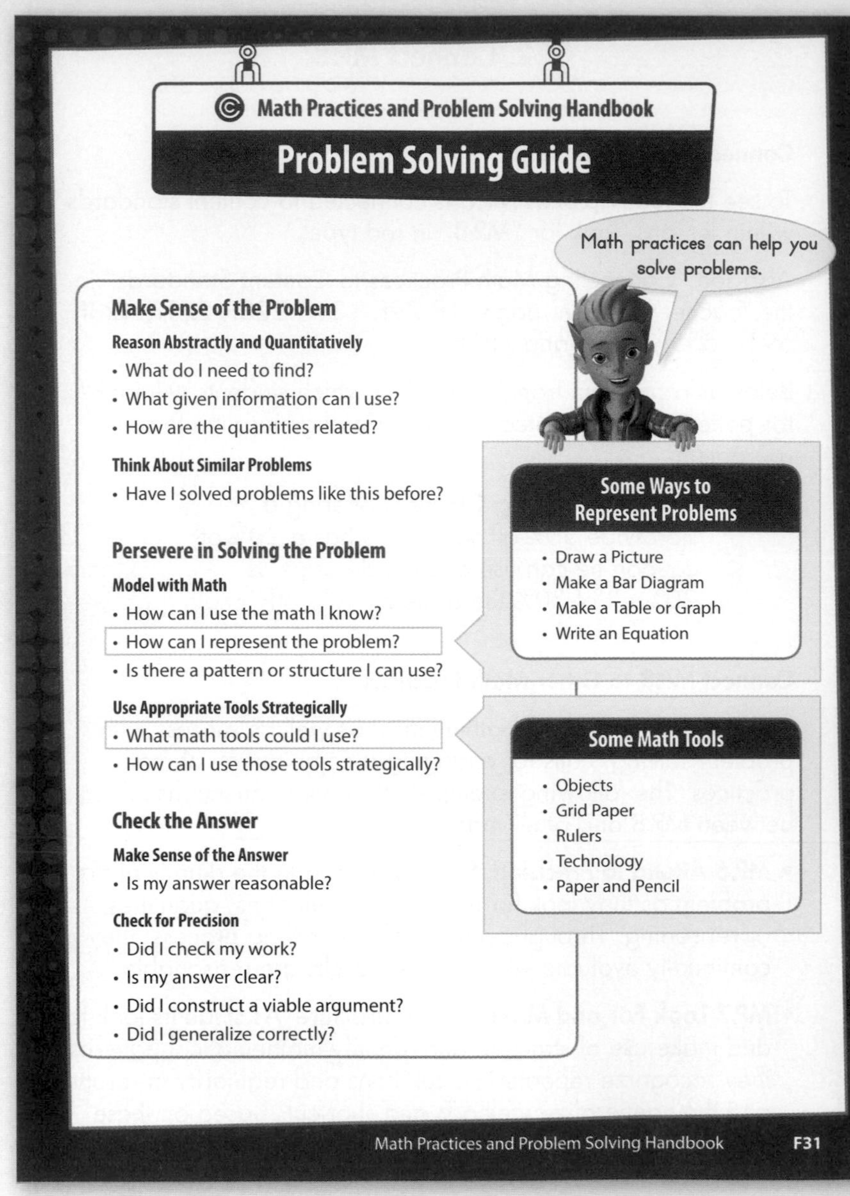


### Some Suggestions for Using the Problem Solving Guide

- For students who often struggle, use the guide to walk through solutions to problems. Doing this models the thinking students can do when they tackle problems on their own.
- For students who are stuck solving a given problem, use questions from the guide to help assess why they are stuck and help them get past being stuck.
- Reference the guide to remind students of ways they might represent problems or tools they might consider for solving a problem.
- Use the Problem Solving Guide together with the Problem Solving Recording Sheet to facilitate classroom conversations.

# PROBLEM SOLVING RECORDING SHEET

## PROBLEM SOLVING RECORDING SHEET

### Background from the Authors

The three main phases in the Problem Solving Recording Sheet correspond to the three main phases in the Problem Solving Guide shown on the facing page. Here is some more information about these phases.

Research in mathematics education has made clear that there are certain thinking phases in the problem-solving process that students move through when solving a problem. Some people have described three phases, others four, and others more. Also, many different words have been used over the years to capture the essence of a phase. The Problem Solving Recording Sheet shown here shows three phases of problem solving. Here are those phases together with common words used over the years that you may have encountered.

- Make Sense of the Problem (Understand the Problem)
- Persevere in Solving the Problem (Plan and Solve the Problem)
- Check the Answer (Answer the Problem and Look Back)

We have learned some things about phases of problem solving.

- They are almost never followed in a linear fashion.
- They are not independent of one another.
- They do not reflect an algorithm for solving problems; following them does not guarantee correct solutions.
- They help many students approach solving problems systematically increasing their chances of success.

### Some Suggestions for Using the Problem Solving Recording Sheet

- If some of your students have anxiety and negative beliefs about their abilities as problem solvers, use the Problem Solving Recording Sheet as a tool for helping them to solve problems.
- Use the Problem Solving Recording Sheet in class when modeling and discussing problem solutions like those in the Math Practices and Problem Solving section of the lesson.
- Have students use the Problem Solving Recording Sheet when working on problems in groups or independently.

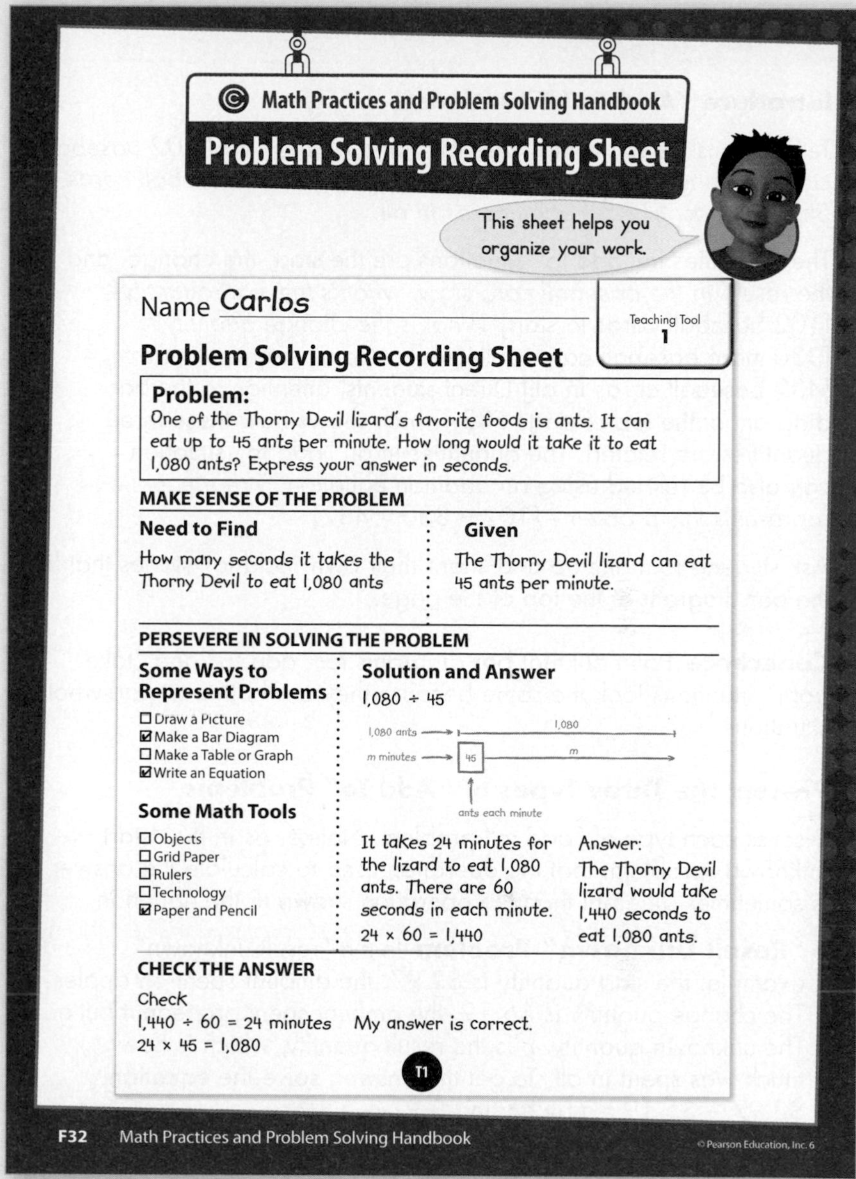


### A Caution

Be careful to not use the Problem Solving Guide or the Problem Solving Recording Sheet to lower the cognitive level of thinking and reasoning students are doing when solving a problem. If students are actively applying a strategy for solving a problem, whether correct or incorrect, do not interrupt their thinking. Allow errors to unfold and be resolved. Also, do not direct students to use a particular tool that is mentioned. Allow students to choose tools they feel are helpful. And finally, do not treat the questions like a series of closed questions which, if answered correctly by students, will guarantee the correct solution is found.

# BAR DIAGRAMS

## ADD TO

### Introduce "Add To" Situations

Tell students the following "add to" story. *Mallory had 102 baseball cards. During the summer, she collected 330 more baseball cards. She now has 432 baseball cards in all.*

The quantities in "add to" situations are the start, the change, and the result. *In the baseball card story, what is the start quantity?* [102 baseball cards to start] *What is the change quantity?* [330 more baseball cards collected] *What is the result quantity?* [432 baseball cards in all] Direct students' attention to the bar diagram at the top of page F33, which shows how these three quantities are related. The quantities in an "add to" situation can also be related using an addition equation. *What equation represents this problem?* [$102 + 330 = 432$]

Ask students to make up and share their own "add to" stories that fit the bar diagram at the top of the page.

**Coherence** Point out that bar diagrams for "add to" and "take from" situations look the same because they are both part-part-whole situations.

### Present the Three Types of "Add To" Problems

Discuss each type of "add to" problem. Notice, as in the "start unknown" problem, that the operation used to calculate the answer is sometimes different than the operation shown in the equation.

- **"Result Unknown" Problem** In the "result unknown" example, the start quantity is \$3.97, the amount spent on apples. The change quantity is \$5.19, the amount spent on peanut butter. The unknown quantity, *t*, is the result quantity, which is how much was spent in all. To get the answer, solve the equation $\$3.97 + \$5.19 = t$ by finding $3.97 + 5.19$.
- **"Start Unknown" Problem** In the "start unknown" example, the change quantity is the $1\frac{1}{8}$ miles that Kari ran. The result quantity is the $3\frac{7}{8}$ miles that Kari traveled in all. The unknown quantity, *w*, is the start quantity, which is how many miles Kari walked. To get the answer, solve the equation $w + 1\frac{3}{8} = 3\frac{7}{8}$ by finding $3\frac{7}{8} - 1\frac{3}{8}$.
- **"Change Unknown" Problem** Present the "change unknown" problem shown at the right. The start quantity is 205,221 views on Saturday. The result quantity is the 618,901 total views over the weekend. The unknown quantity, *s*, is the change quantity, which is how many views the website got on Sunday. To get the answer, solve the equation $205{,}221 + s = 618{,}901$ by finding $618{,}901 - 205{,}221$.

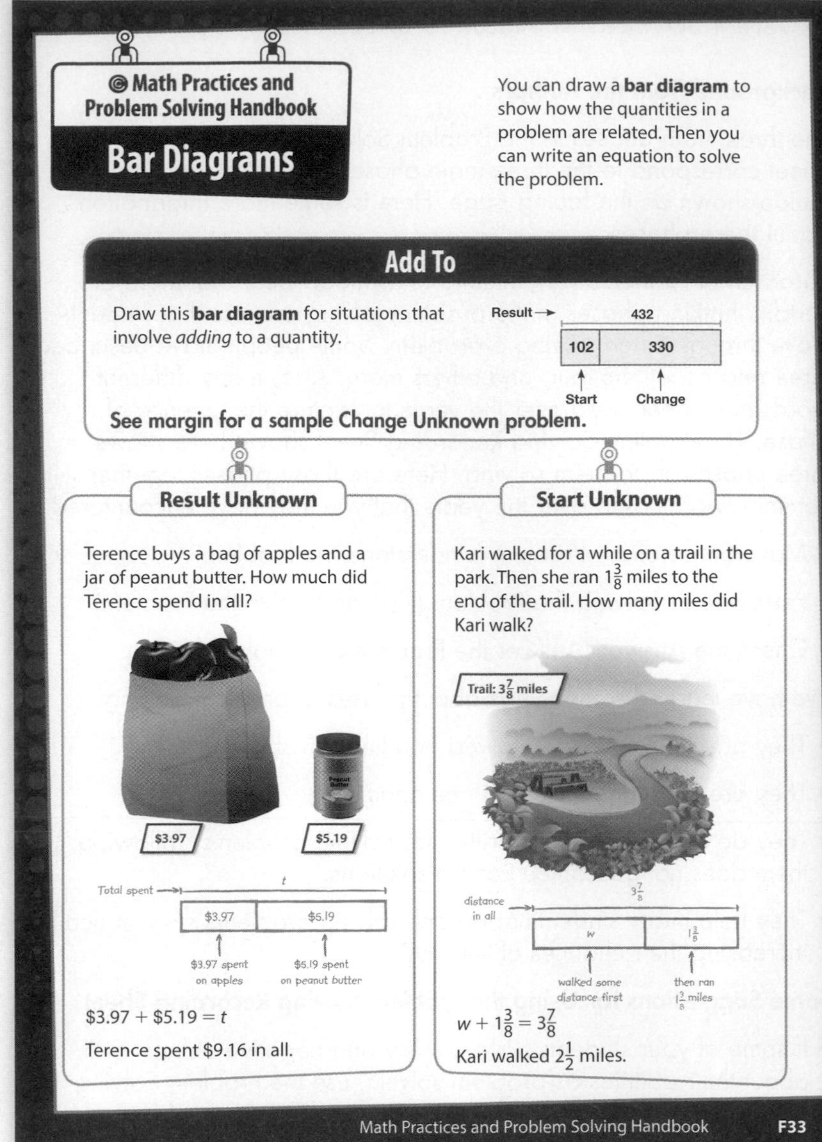


**Sample "Change Unknown" Problem** A news website got 205,221 views on Saturday and even more views on Sunday. The website had 618,901 total views over the weekend. How many views did the website get on Sunday?

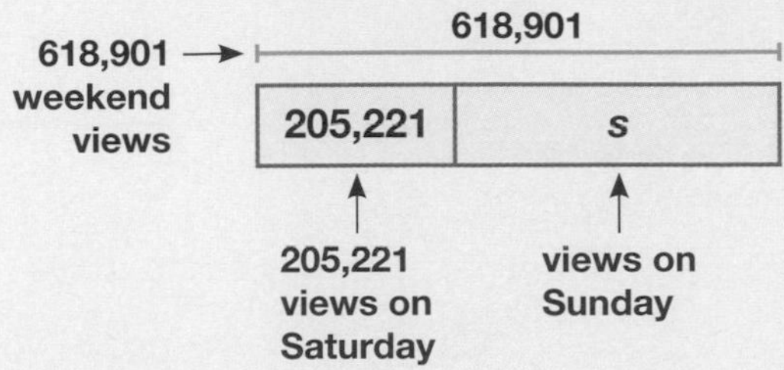


$205{,}221 + s = 618{,}901$

The website got 413,680 views on Sunday.

## TAKE FROM

### Introduce "Take From" Situations

Tell students the following "take from" story. *An international festival was held in a large convention center. On Saturday morning, 18,600 people arrived. By late afternoon, 12,000 people had left. There were 6,600 people still at the festival.*

The quantities in "take from" situations are the start, the change, and the result. *In the international festival story, what is the start quantity?* [18,600 people to start] *What is the change quantity?* [12,000 people left] *What is the result quantity?* [6,600 people still at the festival] Direct students' attention to the bar diagram at the top of page F34, which shows how these three quantities are related. The quantities in a "take from" situation can also be related using a subtraction equation. *What equation represents this problem?* [$18{,}600 - 12{,}000 = 6{,}600$]

Ask students to make up and share their own "take from" stories that fit the bar diagram at the top of the page.

**Coherence** Point out that bar diagrams for "add to" and "take from" situations look the same because they are both part-part-whole situations.

### Present the Three Types of "Take From" Problems

Discuss each type of "take from" problem. Notice, as in the "start unknown" problem, that the operation used to calculate the answer is sometimes different than the operation shown in the equation.

- **"Result Unknown" Problem** In the "result unknown" example, the start quantity is $15\frac{1}{4}$ cups of flour. The change quantity is the $3\frac{1}{3}$ cups of flour used. The unknown quantity, $f$, is the result quantity, which is how many cups of flour are left. To get the answer, solve the equation $15\frac{1}{4} - 3\frac{1}{3} = f$ by finding $15\frac{1}{4} - 3\frac{1}{3}$.
- **"Start Unknown" Problem** In the "start unknown" example, the change quantity is the 2.4 gallons of gas used. The result quantity is the 6.73 gallons of gas left. The unknown quantity, $g$, is the start quantity, which is how many gallons of gas Mr. Adkins started with. To get the answer, solve the equation $g - 2.4 = 6.73$ by finding $6.73 + 2.4$.
- **"Change Unknown" Problem** Present the "change unknown" problem shown at the right. The start quantity is 2.6 pounds of chestnuts. The result quantity is the 1.9 pounds of chestnuts left. The unknown quantity, $c$, is the change quantity, which is how many pounds of chestnuts were removed. To get the answer, solve the equation $2.6 - c = 1.9$ or $c + 1.9 = 2.6$ by finding $2.6 - 1.9$.

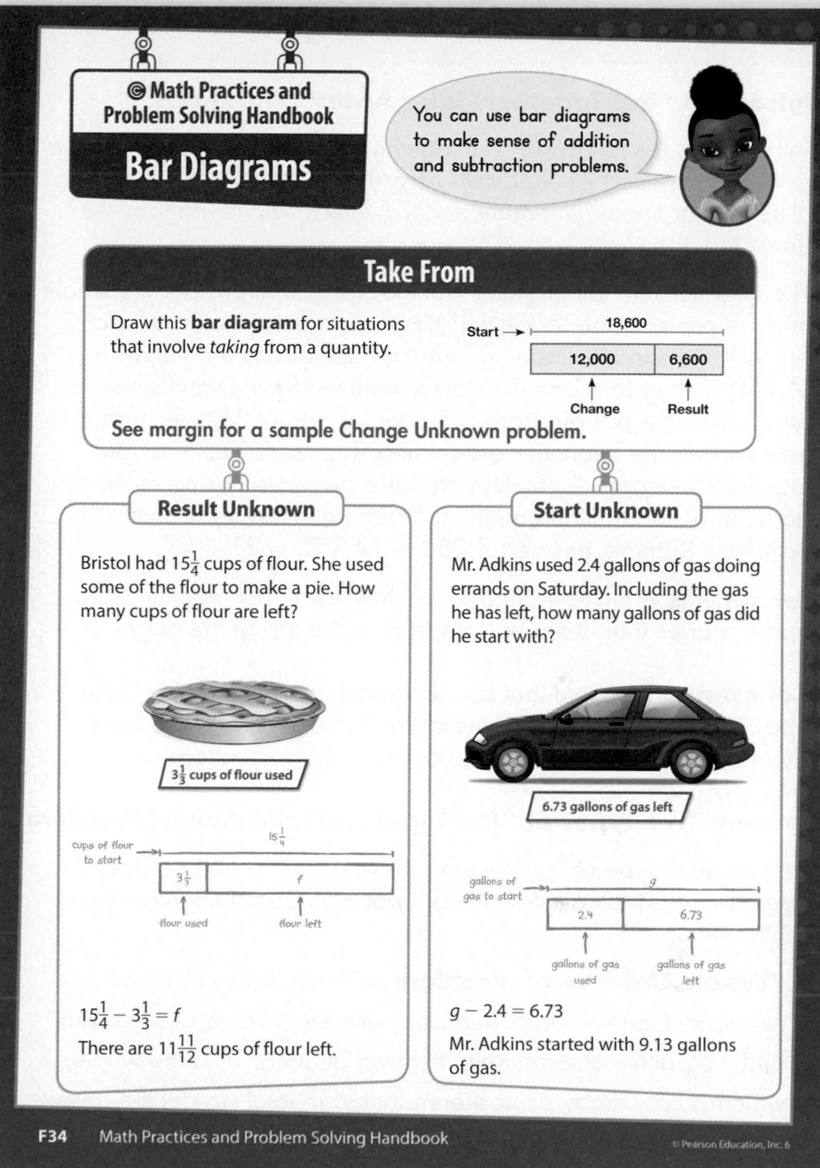

Math Practices and Problem Solving Handbook

**Bar Diagrams**



**Take From**

Draw this **bar diagram** for situations that involve *taking* from a quantity.



**See margin for a sample Change Unknown problem.**

**Result Unknown**

Bristol had $15\frac{1}{4}$ cups of flour. She used some of the flour to make a pie. How many cups of flour are left?



$15\frac{1}{4} - 3\frac{1}{3} = f$

There are $11\frac{11}{12}$ cups of flour left.

**Start Unknown**

Mr. Adkins used 2.4 gallons of gas doing errands on Saturday. Including the gas he has left, how many gallons of gas did he start with?



$g - 2.4 = 6.73$

Mr. Adkins started with 9.13 gallons of gas.

F34 Math Practices and Problem Solving Handbook



**Sample "Change Unknown" Problem** Roland scooped 2.6 pounds of roasted chestnuts into a bag. After he gave some of the chestnuts to his friend, Roland had 1.9 pounds of chestnuts left. How many pounds of chestnuts did Roland give his friend?

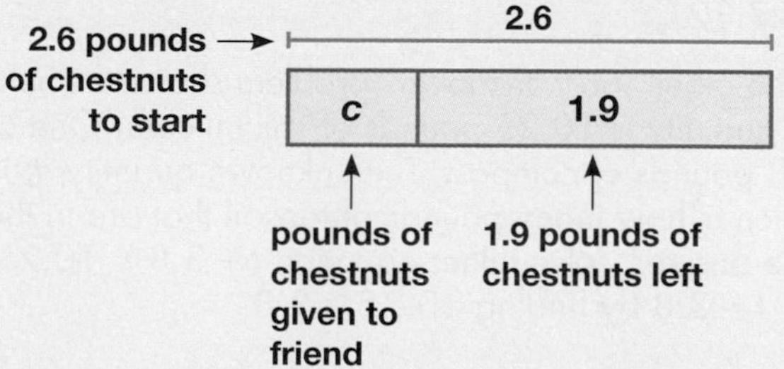


$2.6 - c = 1.9$ or $c + 1.9 = 2.6$

Roland gave 0.7 pound of chestnuts to his friend.

# BAR DIAGRAMS

## PUT TOGETHER/TAKE APART

### Introduce "Put Together/Take Apart" Situations

Tell students the following "put together/take apart" story. *A soccer stadium was filled with 21,400 fans. There were 7,250 fans cheering for the visiting team and 14,150 fans cheering for the home team.*

The quantities in "put together/take apart" situations are the whole and the parts. *In the soccer fan story, what quantity is the whole?* [21,400 fans in the stadium] *What quantities are the parts?* [7,250 visiting fans and 14,150 hometown fans] Direct students' attention to the bar diagram at the top of page F35, which shows how these three quantities are related. The quantities in a "put together/take apart" situation can also be related using either an addition or subtraction equation. *What equation represents this problem?* [Sample answer: 7,250 + 14,150 = 21,400]

Ask students to make up and share their own "put together/take apart" stories that fit the bar diagram at the top of the page.

**Coherence** Point out that bar diagrams for "put together/take apart" situations look the same as for "add to" and "take from" situations because they are all part-part-whole situations.

### Present Two Types of "Put Together/Take Apart" Problems

Discuss each type of "put together/take apart" problem. The operation used to calculate the answer may be addition or subtraction.

- **"Whole Unknown" Problem** In the "whole unknown" example, the two "part" quantities are $19\frac{3}{10}$ acres of soybeans and $16\frac{3}{8}$ acres of corn. The unknown quantity, $a$, is the whole, which is how many acres were planted in total. To get the answer, solve the equation $19\frac{3}{10} + 16\frac{3}{8} = a$ by finding $19\frac{3}{10} + 16\frac{3}{8}$.
- **"Part Unknown" Problem** In the "part unknown" example, the "whole" quantity is 64.9 pounds of honey. One of the parts is the 27.32 pounds of honey that the first hive produced. The unknown quantity, $h$, is the other part, which is how many pounds of honey that the second hive produced. To get the answer, solve either equation $27.32 + h = 64.9$ or $64.9 - 27.32 = h$ by finding $64.9 - 27.32$.

  Present the other "part unknown" problem shown at the right. The "whole" quantity is 10.25 pounds of soil mixture. One of the parts is the 3.8 pounds of compost. The unknown quantity, $t$, is the other part, which is how many pounds of topsoil that are in the planter. To get the answer, solve either equation $t + 3.8 = 10.25$ or $10.25 - t = 3.8$ by finding $10.25 - 3.8$.

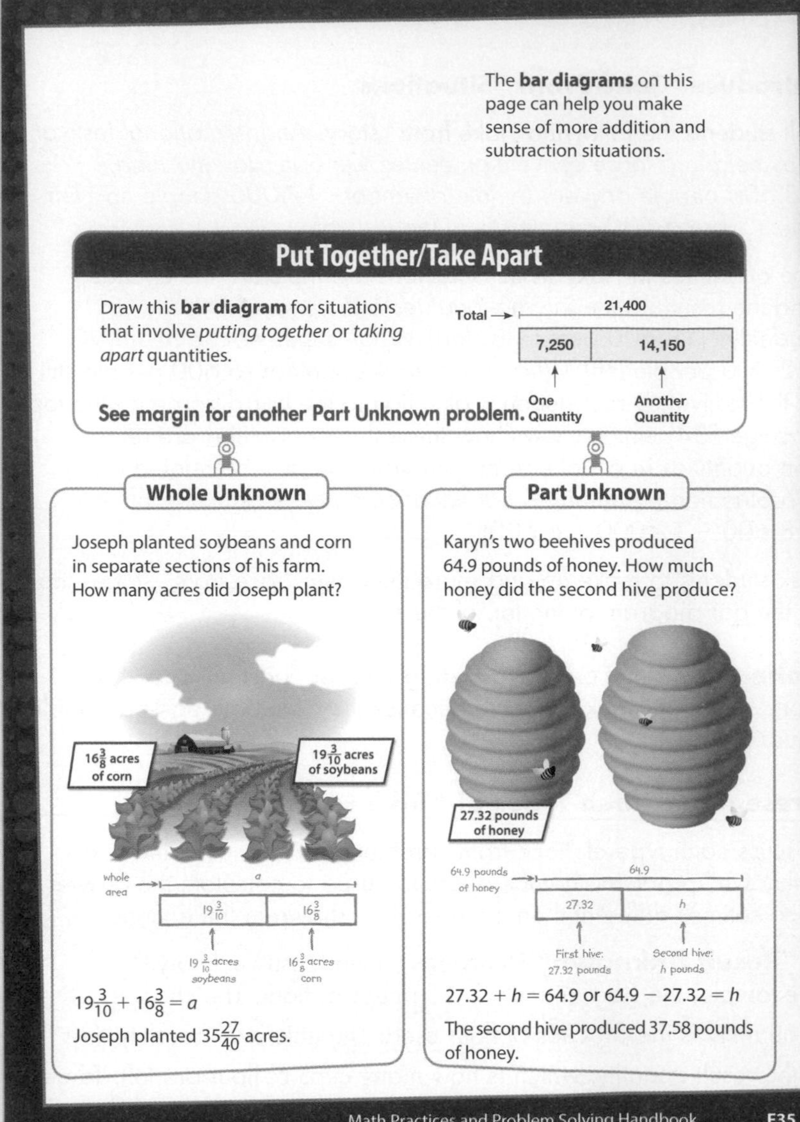


**Another Sample "Part Unknown" Problem** Drew mixed topsoil and compost to create a soil mixture for growing vegetables. One planter contains 10.25 pounds of the soil mixture, which includes 3.8 pounds of compost. How much topsoil is in the planter?

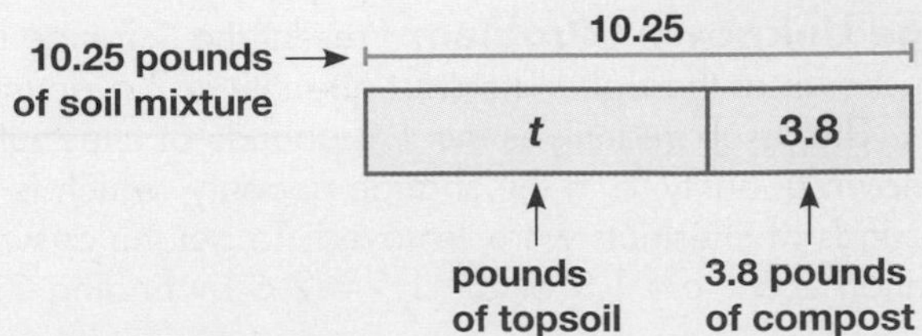


$t + 3.8 = 10.25$ or $10.25 - t = 3.8$

There are 6.45 pounds of topsoil in the planter.

## COMPARE: ADDITION AND SUBTRACTION

### Introduce "Compare: Addition and Subtraction" Situations

Tell students the following "compare" story. *In a science experiment, Trina studied how the size of an ant colony can vary based on its food source. One ant colony in her experiment had 1,890 ants. Another colony had 1,170 ants, which is 720 fewer ants than the first colony.*

The quantities in "compare: addition and subtraction" situations are the bigger quantity, the smaller quantity, and the difference. *In the ant colony story, what is the bigger quantity?* [1,890 ants in the first colony] *What is the smaller quantity?* [1,170 ants in the other colony] *What is the difference?* [720 ants] Direct students' attention to the bar diagram at the top of page F36, which shows how these three quantities are related. The quantities in this type of "compare" situation can also be related using either an addition or subtraction equation. *What equation represents this problem?* [Sample answer: $1{,}890 - 720 = 1{,}170$]

Ask students to make up and share their own "compare" stories that fit the bar diagram at the top of the page.

**Coherence** Point out that bar diagrams for "compare" situations are similar to those for "add to" and "take from" situations because they all show how quantities in a problem situation are related.

### Present the Three Types of "Compare: Addition and Subtraction" Problems

Discuss each type of "compare" problem. Notice that the difference between two quantities can be labeled as "more" or "fewer" depending on the comparison, but the difference quantity itself is the same.

- **"Difference Unknown" Problem** In the "difference unknown" example, the bigger quantity is 2.1168 square inches of the desktop screen. The smaller quantity is 118.75 square inches of the laptop screen. The unknown quantity, $s$, is the difference, which is how many more square inches the desktop screen has than the laptop screen. To get the answer, solve either equation $118.75 + s = 211.68$ or $211.68 - 118.75 = s$ by finding $211.68 - 118.75$.
- **"Smaller Unknown" Problem** In the "smaller unknown" example, the bigger quantity is the $8\frac{4}{5}$ pounds of the male iguana. The difference is $4\frac{1}{10}$ pounds. The unknown quantity, $p$, is the smaller quantity, which is how many pounds the female iguana weighs. To get the answer, solve either equation $8\frac{4}{5} - p = 4\frac{1}{10}$ or $p + 4\frac{1}{10} = 8\frac{4}{5}$ by finding $8\frac{4}{5} - 4\frac{1}{10}$.
- **"Bigger Unknown" Problem** Present the "bigger unknown" problem shown at the right. The smaller quantity is Ellis's time of 9.82 seconds. The difference is 0.4 second. The unknown quantity, $c$, is the bigger quantity, which is how many seconds it took Cameron to finish the race. To get the answer, solve either equation $c - 9.82 = 0.4$ or $9.82 + 0.4 = c$ by finding $9.82 + 0.4$.

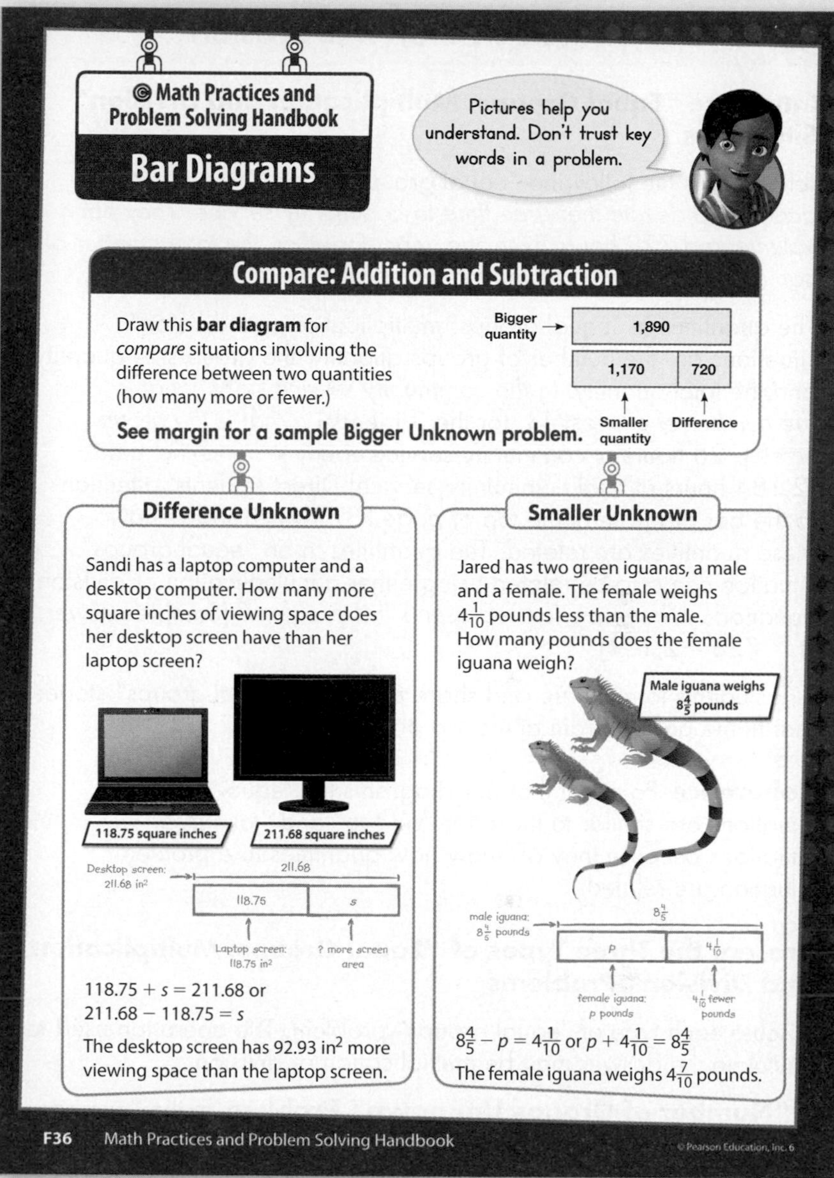

Math Practices and Problem Solving Handbook

**Bar Diagrams**

Pictures help you understand. Don't trust key words in a problem.

**Compare: Addition and Subtraction**

Draw this **bar diagram** for *compare* situations involving the difference between two quantities (how many more or fewer.)

**See margin for a sample Bigger Unknown problem.**



**Difference Unknown**

Sandi has a laptop computer and a desktop computer. How many more square inches of viewing space does her desktop screen have than her laptop screen?



$118.75 + s = 211.68$ or
$211.68 - 118.75 = s$

The desktop screen has 92.93 in² more viewing space than the laptop screen.

**Smaller Unknown**

Jared has two green iguanas, a male and a female. The female weighs $4\frac{1}{10}$ pounds less than the male. How many pounds does the female iguana weigh?



$8\frac{4}{5} - p = 4\frac{1}{10}$ or $p + 4\frac{1}{10} = 8\frac{4}{5}$

The female iguana weighs $4\frac{7}{10}$ pounds.

F36 Math Practices and Problem Solving Handbook © Pearson Education, Inc. 6

**Sample "Bigger Unknown" Problem** During a track meet, Ellis won the 50-meter dash with a time of 9.82 seconds. Cameron came in second just 0.4 second after Ellis. What was Cameron's finish time?

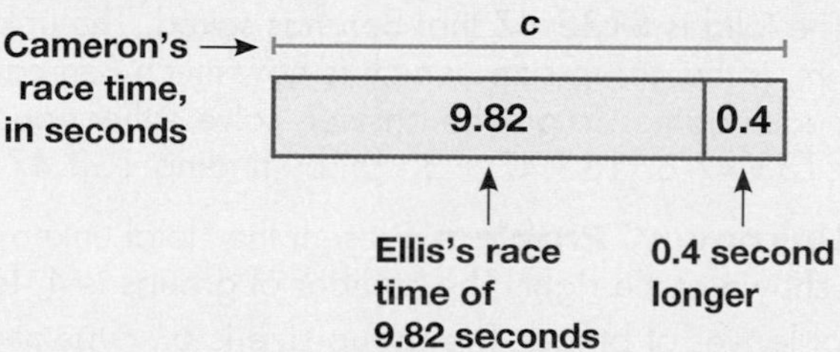


$c - 9.82 = 0.4$ or $9.82 + 0.4 = c$

Cameron finished the race in 10.22 seconds.

# BAR DIAGRAMS

## EQUAL GROUPS: MULTIPLICATION AND DIVISION

### Introduce "Equal Groups: Multiplication and Division" Situations

Tell students the following "equal groups" story. *Three friends decided to devote their free time to community service. They each volunteered 728 hours over one year. Together, the total number of community service hours they volunteered was 2,184 hours.*

The quantities in "equal groups: multiplication and division" situations are the number of groups quantity, the group size quantity, and the total quantity. *In the community service story, what is the number of groups?* [3, for the 3 friends] *What is the group size?* [728 hours of community service each] *What is the total?* [2,184 hours of total community service] Direct students' attention to the bar diagram at the top of page F37, which shows how these quantities are related. The quantities in an "equal groups" situation can also be related using either a multiplication or division equation. *What equation represents this problem?* [Sample answer: $3 \times 728 = 2{,}184$]

Ask students to make up and share their own "equal groups" stories that fit the bar diagram at the top of the page.

**Coherence** Point out that bar diagrams for "equal groups" situations are similar to those for "add to" and "take from" situations because they all show how quantities in a problem situation are related.

### Present the Three Types of "Equal Groups: Multiplication and Division" Problems

Discuss each type of "equal groups" problem. The operation used to calculate the answer may be multiplication or division.

- **"Number of Groups Unknown" Problem** In the "number of groups unknown" example, the group size is \$65 for each pass. The total is \$390 that Sierra's parents spent. The unknown quantity, $p$, is the number of groups, which is how many passes were purchased. To get the answer, solve either equation $p \times 65 = 390$ or $390 \div 65 = p$ by finding $390 \div 65$.
- **"Group Size Unknown" Problem** In the "group size unknown" example, the number of groups is 3, for the number of games. The total is \$133.47 that Ben has saved. The unknown quantity, $m$, is the group size, which is how much Ben can spend at each game. To get the answer, solve either equation $3 \times m = 133.47$ or $133.47 \div 3 = m$ by finding $133.47 \div 3$.
- **"Total Unknown" Problem** Present the "total unknown" problem shown at the right. The number of groups is 4, for the number of loaves of bread. The group size is $6\frac{1}{2}$ cups of flour for each loaf. The unknown quantity, $c$, is the total, which is how many cups of flour Trevor used. To get the answer, solve either equation $4 \times 6\frac{1}{2} = c$ or $c \div 4 = 6\frac{1}{2}$ by finding $4 \times 6\frac{1}{2}$.

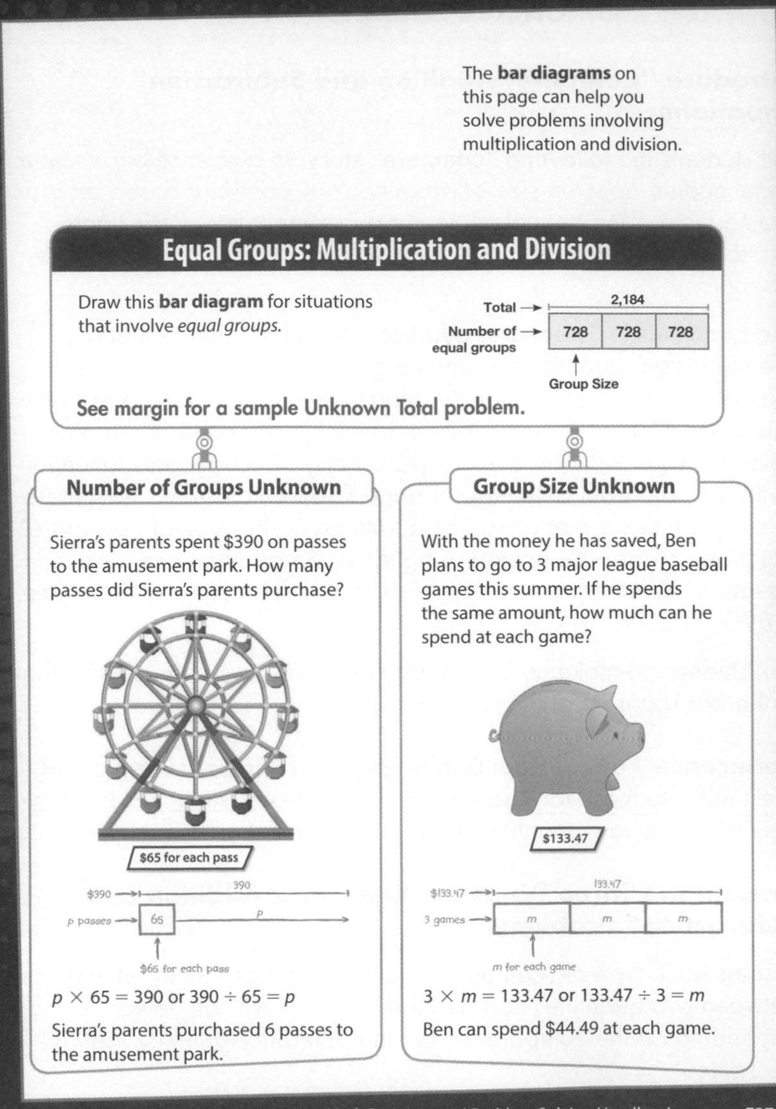
The **bar diagrams** on this page can help you solve problems involving multiplication and division.

**Equal Groups: Multiplication and Division**

Draw this **bar diagram** for situations that involve *equal groups*.



See margin for a sample Unknown Total problem.

**Number of Groups Unknown**

Sierra's parents spent \$390 on passes to the amusement park. How many passes did Sierra's parents purchase?



$p \times 65 = 390$ or $390 \div 65 = p$

Sierra's parents purchased 6 passes to the amusement park.

**Group Size Unknown**

With the money he has saved, Ben plans to go to 3 major league baseball games this summer. If he spends the same amount, how much can he spend at each game?



$3 \times m = 133.47$ or $133.47 \div 3 = m$

Ben can spend \$44.49 at each game.

Math Practices and Problem Solving Handbook F37

**Sample "Total Unknown" Problem** Trevor baked 4 loaves of homemade bread for a bake sale. The recipe for 1 loaf of bread calls for $6\frac{1}{2}$ cups of flour. How many cups of flour did Trevor use in all?

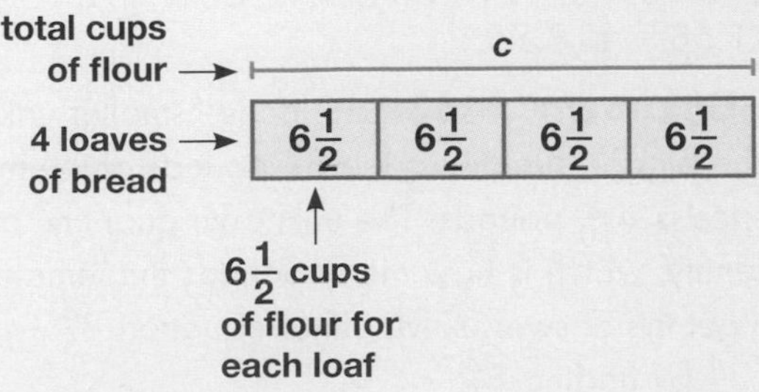


$4 \times 6\frac{1}{2} = c$ or $c \div 4 = 6\frac{1}{2}$

Trevor used 26 cups of flour in all.

## COMPARE: MULTIPLICATION AND DIVISION

### Introduce "Compare: Multiplication and Division" Situations

Tell students the following "compare" story. *A flower shop sold 3 times as many bouquets of roses in February as it sold in January. The shop sold 550 bouquets of roses in January, and it sold 1,650 bouquets of roses in February.*

The quantities in "compare: multiplication and division" situations are the bigger quantity, the smaller quantity, and the multiplier. *In the flower shop story, what is the bigger quantity?* [1,650 bouquets in February] *What is the smaller quantity?* [550 bouquets in January] *What is the multiplier?* [3 times as many] Direct students' attention to the bar diagram at the top of page F38, which shows how these three quantities are related. The quantities in this type of "compare" situation can also be related using either a multiplication or division equation. *What equation represents this problem?* [Sample answer: $550 \times 3 = 1{,}650$]

Ask students to make up and share their own "compare" stories that fit the bar diagram at the top of the page.

**Coherence** Students have already used bar diagrams for "compare: addition and subtraction" situations. Bar diagrams for "compare: multiplication and division" situations are similar because they show how the quantities in a problem situation are related.

### Present the Three Types of "Compare: Multiplication and Division" Problems

Discuss each type of "compare" problem. The operation used to calculate the answer may be multiplication or division.

- **"Bigger Unknown" Problem** In the "bigger unknown" example, the smaller quantity is the $2\frac{1}{4}$ bales of hay that Marci's horse eats. The multiplier is 3 times as much. The unknown quantity, $b$, is the bigger quantity, which is how many bales of hay Craig's horses eat. To get the answer, solve either equation $2\frac{1}{4} \times 3 = b$ or $b \div 2\frac{1}{4} = 3$ by finding $2\frac{1}{4} \times 3$.
- **"Multiplier Unknown" Problem** In the "multiplier unknown" example, the bigger quantity is \$6.32 for the new book. The smaller quantity is \$0.79 for the used book. The unknown quantity, $n$, is the multiplier, which is how many times as much as the new book cost than the used book. To get the answer, solve either equation $0.79 \times n = 6.32$ or $6.32 \div 0.79 = n$ by finding $6.32 \div 0.79$.
- **"Smaller Unknown" Problem** Present the "smaller unknown" problem shown at the right. The bigger quantity is 380 legs on the millipede. The multiplier is 10 times as many. The unknown quantity, $c$, is the smaller quantity, which is how many legs the centipede has. To get the answer, solve either equation $c \times 10 = 380$ or $380 \div 10 = c$ by finding $380 \div 10$.

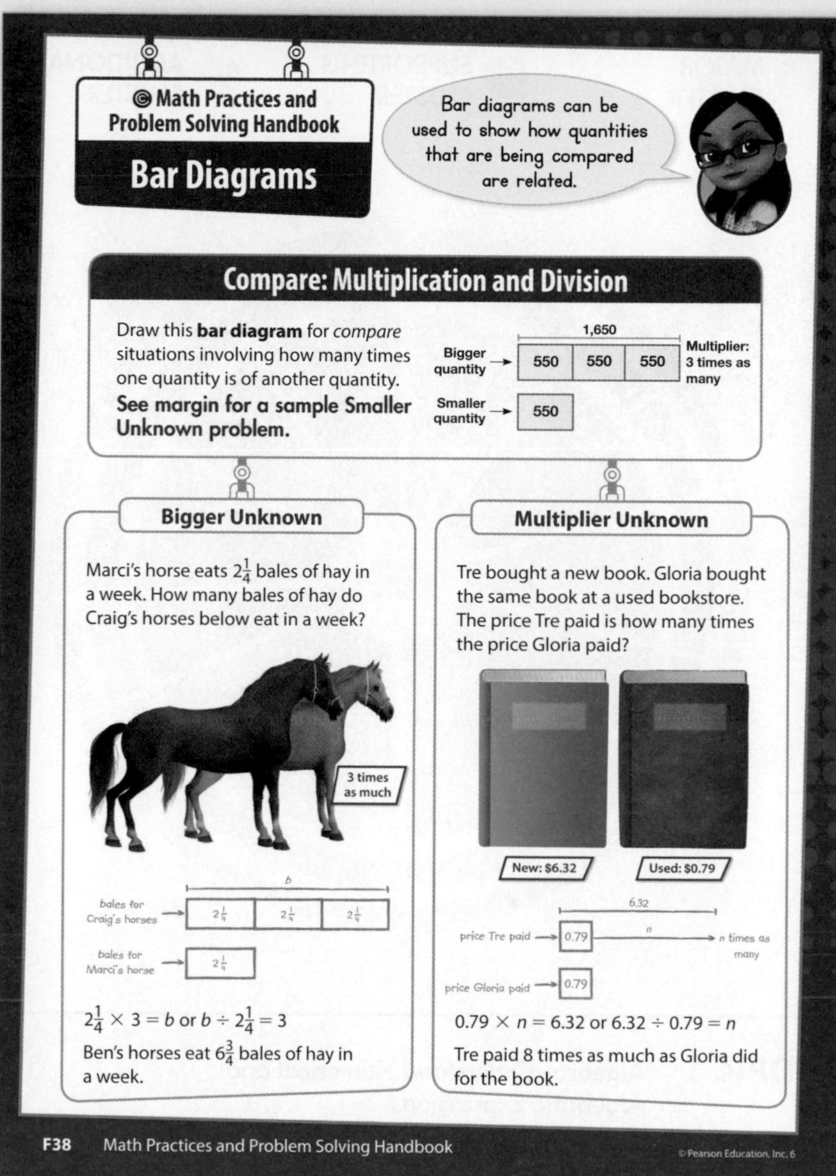

Math Practices and Problem Solving Handbook

**Bar Diagrams**

Bar diagrams can be used to show how quantities that are being compared are related.

**Compare: Multiplication and Division**

Draw this **bar diagram** for *compare* situations involving how many times one quantity is of another quantity. **See margin for a sample Smaller Unknown problem.**

Bigger quantity → 550 | 550 | 550 (total 1,650) Multiplier: 3 times as many
Smaller quantity → 550

**Bigger Unknown**

Marci's horse eats $2\frac{1}{4}$ bales of hay in a week. How many bales of hay do Craig's horses below eat in a week?

3 times as much

bales for Craig's horses → $2\frac{1}{4}$ | $2\frac{1}{4}$ | $2\frac{1}{4}$ (total $b$)
bales for Marci's horse → $2\frac{1}{4}$

$2\frac{1}{4} \times 3 = b$ or $b \div 2\frac{1}{4} = 3$

Ben's horses eat $6\frac{3}{4}$ bales of hay in a week.

**Multiplier Unknown**

Tre bought a new book. Gloria bought the same book at a used bookstore. The price Tre paid is how many times the price Gloria paid?

New: \$6.32 Used: \$0.79

price Tre paid → 0.79 ... (total 6.32) → $n$ times as many
price Gloria paid → 0.79

$0.79 \times n = 6.32$ or $6.32 \div 0.79 = n$

Tre paid 8 times as much as Gloria did for the book.

F38 Math Practices and Problem Solving Handbook © Pearson Education, Inc. 6

**Sample "Smaller Unknown" Problem** The number of legs that one millipede has is 10 times as many as the number of legs that one centipede has. If the millipede has 380 legs, how many legs does the centipede have?

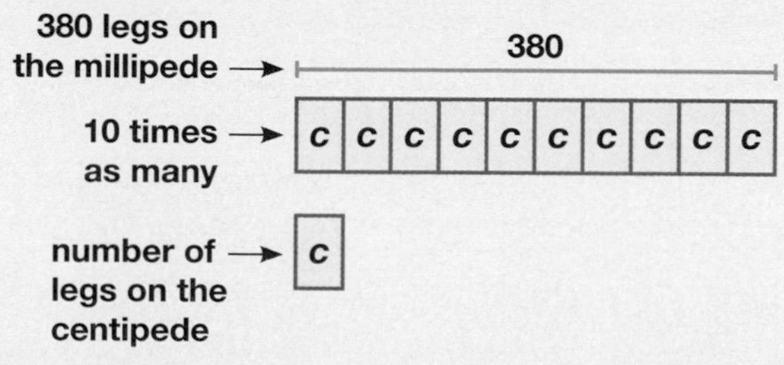


$c \times 10 = 380$ or $380 \div 10 = c$

The centipede has 38 legs.

# MAJOR CLUSTER 6.EE.A

## MATH BACKGROUND: FOCUS

FCR FOCUS | COHERENCE | RIGOR

 MAJOR CLUSTER

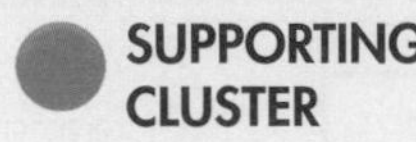 SUPPORTING CLUSTER

 ADDITIONAL CLUSTER

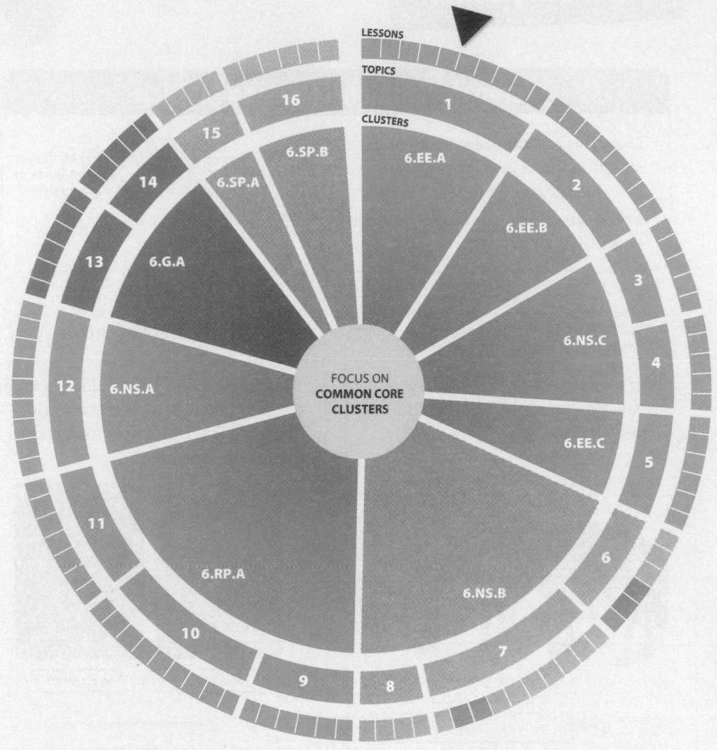


**TOPIC 1** Algebra: Understand Numerical and Algebraic Expressions

TOPIC 1 FOCUSES ON

**MAJOR CLUSTER 6.EE.A**

Apply and extend previous understandings of arithmetic to algebraic expressions.

### Content Focus in enVisionmath2.0

Topic 1 applies and extends previous understandings of arithmetic and numerical expressions to algebraic expressions. Grade 6 students interpret, evaluate, and write algebraic expressions, including ones with exponents, related to both mathematical and real-world contexts.

## NUMERICAL EXPRESSIONS

- **Write and Evaluate Numbers with Exponents** In Lesson 1-1, students learn how to write and evaluate numbers with whole-number exponents. For example, $2^3$ represents multiplying three factors of 2.

  $$2^3 = 2 \times 2 \times 2 = 8$$

  Any non-zero base raised to an exponent of 0 always equals 1. (6.EE.A.1)

- **Evaluate Numerical Expressions** Lesson 1-2 builds on the use of order of operations students learned in earlier grades. Students evaluate numerical expressions which now include exponents, fractions, and decimals. Step 2, in the list below, is new to this grade. (6.EE.A.1)

### Order of Operations

1. Evaluate parentheses and brackets from inside out.
2. Evaluate powers.
3. Multiply and divide from left to right.
4. Add and subtract from left to right.

| | |
|---|---|
| $[7(3.8 + 5.6) - 42.9] + 4^2 - 3$ | Inner parentheses, add |
| $[7(9.4) - 42.9] + 4^2 - 3$ | Brackets, multiply first |
| $[65.8 - 42.9] + 4^2 - 3$ | Brackets, subtract |
| $[22.9] + 4^2 - 3$ | Evaluate powers |
| $22.9 + 16 - 3$ | Add and subtract |
| $35.9$ | |

PD

Content Focus in enVisionmath2.0 (continued)

## ALGEBRAIC EXPRESSIONS

- **Write Algebraic Expressions** An algebraic expression is a type of math expression that has at least one variable and at least one operation. Variables allow the generalization of arithmetic patterns and a more efficient approach to solving problems. Lesson 1-3 provides students with opportunities to make sense of real-world problems and write algebraic expressions that describe them. (6.EE.A.2a, 6.EE.B.6)

- **Identify Parts of an Expression** In Lesson 1-4, students use coefficients and terms in algebraic expressions. They also apply vocabulary they have used for years such as sum, product, and quotient. Appropriate vocabulary helps students understand expressions and work with them. (6.EE.A.2b)

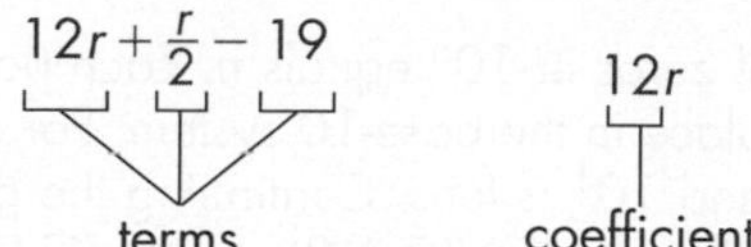


- **Evaluate Algebraic Expressions and Formulas** In Lesson 1-5, students use substitution to evaluate algebraic expressions for a given value of one or more variables. After substituting, they have a numerical expression to evaluate using the order of operations, as they did earlier in the topic.

What is the value of $3a - 6b \div c + d^2$, when $a = 9$, $b = 8$, $c = 4$, and $d = 3$?

| | |
|---|---|
| $3a - 6b \div c + d^2 = 3(9) - 6(8) \div 4 + 3^2$ | Use substitution to replace each variable with its value. |
| $= 27 - 48 \div 4 + 9$<br>$= 27 - 12 + 9$<br>$= 24$ | Use order of operations to evaluate the numerical expression. |

In Lesson 1-9, students use what they have learned about evaluating algebraic expressions to solve problems by evaluating formulas. (6.EE.A.2c, 6.EE.B.6)

## EQUIVALENT EXPRESSIONS

- **Generate and Identify Equivalent Expressions** Lessons 1-6, 1-7, and 1-8 provide students with opportunities to use the Commutative, Associative, and Distributive Properties to write, simplify, and identify equivalent expressions containing variables. (6.EE.A.3, 6.EE.A.4)

Equivalent expressions have the same value regardless of the value that is substituted for the variable in the expressions. Students can use substitution or properties of operations to test whether or not expressions are equivalent. They can find an expression equivalent to a given expression by applying the properties of operations.

$3(4x - 1) = 3(4x) - 3(1)$ ← Distributive Property

$= (3 \cdot 4)x - 3$ ← Associative Property of Multiplication

$= 12x - 3$

$3(4x - 1)$ and $12x - 3$ are equivalent expressions.

Students can simplify an algebraic expression by using properties to combine like terms. For example, the Commutative Property of Addition and the Distributive Property can be used to combine the coefficients of $3x + 7 + 2x + 2$.

| | |
|---|---|
| $3x + 7 + 2x + 2$ | |
| $= 3x + 2x + 7 + 2$ | Commutative Property of Addition |
| $= (3 + 2)x + 7 + 2$ | Distributive Property |
| $= 5x + 9$ | |

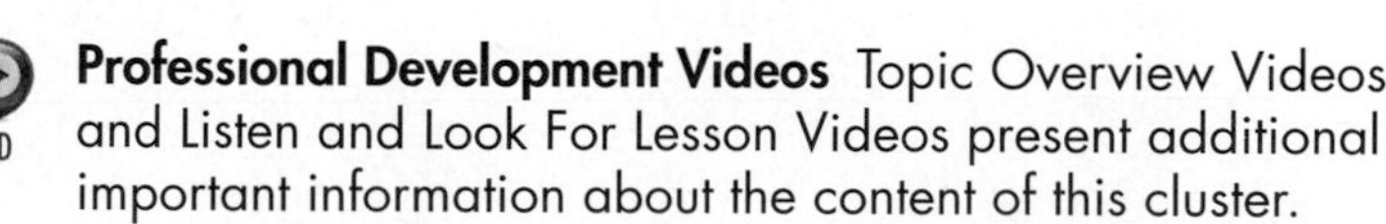

**Professional Development Videos** Topic Overview Videos and Listen and Look For Lesson Videos present additional important information about the content of this cluster.

# MAJOR CLUSTER 6.EE.A

## MATH BACKGROUND: COHERENCE

FOCUS | FCR COHERENCE | RIGOR

### Content Coherence in enVisionmath2.0

Students learn best when ideas are connected in a coherent curriculum. This coherence is achieved through various types of connections including connections within clusters, across clusters, across domains, and across grades.

#### BIG IDEAS IN GRADES K–6

Big Ideas are the conceptual underpinnings of **enVision**math**2.0** and provide conceptual cohesion of the content. Big Ideas connect Essential Understandings throughout the program.

A Big Idea that connects most of the work in this cluster is that variables can be used to stand for a number. Some mathematical and real-world situations can be represented using variables, operations, and numbers in expressions and equations. Properties of operations are equally true for algebraic expressions as for numerical expressions. For example:

Yuri walked $p$ poodles and $b$ bulldogs on Monday. He walked the same number of poodles and bulldogs each day Tuesday through Friday. Write an algebraic expression to represent how many total dogs were walked in this 5-day period.

$$5p + 5b$$

The problem can also be represented by an equivalent expression which can be found using the Distributive Property.

$$5p + 5b = 5(p + b)$$

For a complete list of Big Ideas, see pages 110–111 in the *Teacher's Edition Program Overview.*

#### LOOK BACK

*How does Topic 1 connect to what students learned earlier?*

#### GRADE 5

- **Patterns with Exponents and Powers of 10** Students first encountered exponents in Topic 1. Students used whole-number exponents to express powers of 10.

factors, exponent

$$1{,}000 = 10 \times 10 \times 10 = 10^3$$

base

The number of zeros in $10^n$ equals $n$. Each power of 10 represents a place in the base-10 system. For example, $10^2$ is hundreds, and $10^1$ is tens. Continuing the pattern to $n = 0$ implies that $10^0 = 1$. (5.NBT.A.2)

- **Use Formulas** In Topic 10, students used formulas containing variables to solve problems involving volume. (5.MD.C.5b)

Volume of a Rectangular Prism

Volume = length × width × height

$$V = \ell \times w \times h$$

- **Evaluate, Write, and Interpret Numerical Expressions** In Topic 13, students used the order of operations to simplify numerical expressions that contain parentheses. This laid a firm foundation for the work in Grade 6, which includes expressions with exponents. (5.OA.A.1)

Also in Topic 13, students wrote numerical expressions to represent real-world contexts. (5.OA.A.2)

Ronnie's Rentals charges $25 plus $15 per hour to rent a chain saw. David rented a chain saw for 5 hours. Write an expression to show how you could calculate the total amount David paid.

$$25 + (5 \times 15)$$

## TOPIC 1

*How is content connected within Topic 1?*

- **Exponents and Expressions** In Lesson 1-2, students use what they learned in Lesson 1-1 about evaluating numbers with exponents to evaluate numerical expressions which include exponents. (6.EE.A.1) In Lessons 1-5 and 1-9, students use what they learned in Lesson 1-2 about evaluating numerical expressions to evaluate algebraic expressions for specific values of the variable and to solve problems by using formulas. (6.EE.A.2c, 6.EE.B.6)

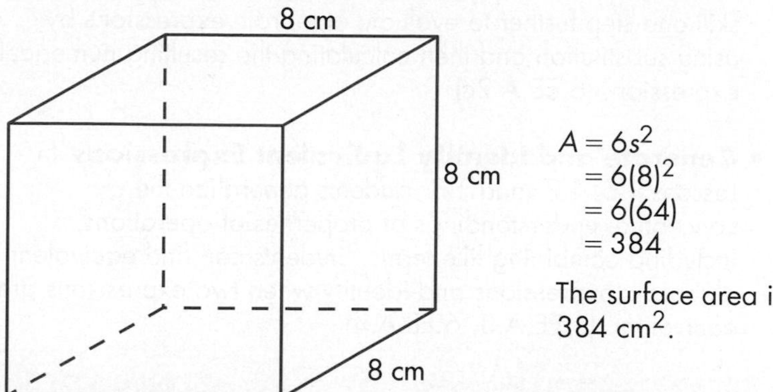


$A = 6s^2$
$= 6(8)^2$
$= 6(64)$
$= 384$

The surface area is 384 $cm^2$.

- **Equivalent Expressions** Students extend their understanding of using properties to write equivalent expressions from Lesson 1-6 to simplify algebraic expressions in Lesson 1-7. In Lesson 1-8, students use what they learned in Lessons 1-2 and 1-5 about evaluating numerical and algebraic expressions as well as their understanding of properties to test whether or not two expressions are equivalent. (6.EE.A.3, 6.EE.A.4)

- **Represent Using Variables** Topic 1 also develops content from Major Cluster 6.EE.B on using variables to represent numbers and write expressions. (6.EE.B.6)

## LOOK AHEAD

*How does Topic 1 connect to what students will learn later?*

### LATER IN GRADE 6

- **Solve Equations** In Topic 2, students will use their understanding of simplifying numerical and algebraic expressions to solve one-variable equations. (6.EE.A.2c, 6.EE.A.3, 6.EE.A.4)

$$3\tfrac{3}{4} + x = 6$$
$$3\tfrac{3}{4} + x - 3\tfrac{3}{4} = 6 - 3\tfrac{3}{4}$$
$$x = 5\tfrac{4}{4} - 3\tfrac{3}{4}$$
$$x = 2\tfrac{1}{4}$$

After using a property of equality, students simplify each side of the equation as if each were an expression.

- **Expressions** As students gain proficiency with more difficult computations, they will evaluate expressions involving these computations. These include division of whole numbers in Lesson 6-4, operations with decimals in Lesson 7-8, and operations with fractions and mixed numbers in Lesson 12-7. They will also write algebraic expressions with decimals in Lesson 7-8. (6.EE.A.2a, 6.EE.A.2c)

- **Formulas** In Topics 13 and 14, students will use what they learned about evaluating formulas to solve problems involving areas of triangles and parallelograms, and involving volumes of solids with fractional edge lengths. (6.EE.A.2c, 6.EE.B.6, 6.G.A.1, 6.G.A.2)

# MATH BACKGROUND: RIGOR



**Content Rigor in enVisionmath2.0**

A rigorous curriculum emphasizes conceptual understanding, procedural skill and fluency, and applications.

## CONCEPTUAL UNDERSTANDING

- **Understand Exponents** In Lesson 1-1, students learn that exponents provide a convenient notation for writing repeating factors. Students also understand the meaning of when the exponent is zero. An understanding of the notational aspects of exponents will help students throughout their mathematics education. (6.EE.A.1)

- **Understand Variables and the Relationship Between Numerical and Algebraic Expressions** A variable is a letter which represents an unknown number. Use of a variable allows a problem situation to be generalized and easily solved for more than one possible value. In Lesson 1-5, students substitute values for the variables in an algebraic expression, in order to generate numerical expressions. (6.EE.A.2)

  $20 + 3n$ represents the number of miniature cars Erik has, where $n$ is the number of cars in each of Erik's smaller cases. It is relatively easy to evaluate the expression to find how many total cars Erik has if each small case holds 12, 14, or another number of cars.

  Substitute 12 for $n$.
  $20 + 3n$
  $= 20 + 3(12)$
  $= 20 + 36$
  $= 56$

  If each smaller case holds 12 cars, Erik has 56 cars.

  Substitute 14 for $n$.
  $20 + 3n$
  $= 20 + 3(14)$
  $= 20 + 42$
  $= 62$

  If each smaller case holds 14 cars, Erik has 62 cars.

- **Make Sense of Equivalency in Relationship to Algebraic Expressions** In Lesson 1-8, students work with equivalent expressions. Students realize that anything they can do with numbers, they can do with variables because a variable represents a number—even if the number is unknown. Thus the Commutative, Associative, and Distributive Properties can be applied to algebraic expressions to get equivalent expressions. (6.EE.A.3, 6.EE.A.4)

## PROCEDURAL SKILL AND FLUENCY

There are no standards in this cluster that call for fluency.

- **Evaluate Expressions with Exponents** In Lesson 1-2, students combine the conceptual understanding of exponents developed in Lesson 1-1 with what they know about the order of operations in order to evaluate numerical expressions that contain exponents. (6.EE.A.1) In Lesson 1-5, they extend this skill one step further to evaluate algebraic expressions by using substitution and then calculating the resulting numerical expression. (6.EE.A.2c)

- **Generate and Identify Equivalent Expressions** In Lessons 1-6, 1-7, and 1-8, students generalize the conceptual understandings of properties of operations, including combining like terms. Students can find equivalent algebraic expressions and identify when two expressions are equivalent. (6.EE.A.3, 6.EE.A.4)

## APPLICATIONS

- **Expressions** Throughout Topic 1, students write numerical or algebraic expressions to show relationships in real-world contexts. It is important to specify which unknown number or quantity represents which variable within the context of a problem. (6.EE.A.1, 6.EE.A.2a)

- **Formulas** In Lesson 1-9, students evaluate formulas to solve problems. (6.EE.A.2c)

  **11. Math and Science** The density, $d$, of an object can be found by using the formula $d = \frac{m}{v}$, where $m$ is the mass of the object and $v$ is its volume. What is the density of an object that has a mass of 65 grams and a volume of 8 cubic meters?

# MATH PRACTICES

**Connecting Math Practices and Content Standards in enVisionmath2.0**

Math practices and content standards are connected within all lessons including the lessons that focus on math practices.

## MATH PRACTICES WITHIN LESSONS

- **MP.1 Make sense of problems and persevere in solving them.**
  Students make sense of problems and persevere in order to get a correct answer. A representation, such as an algebraic expression, can be used to solve real-world problems. (e.g., p. 24, Item 13)
- **MP.2 Reason abstractly and quantitatively.**
  Students understand exponents, variables, and expressions to help make sense of how numbers, variables, and expressions are used to solve problems. (e.g., p. 19, Look Back!)
- **MP.3 Construct viable arguments and critique the reasoning of others.**
  Students critique the reasoning of others by considering how an expression was generated to solve a problem. (e.g., p. 18, Item 13)
- **MP.4 Model with mathematics.**
  Students model by using algebraic expressions to describe calculations involved in various situations. (e.g., p. 24, Item 12)
- **MP.5 Use appropriate tools strategically.**
  Students can use measuring tools to determine distance, length, weight, and temperature when working with expressions written as formulas. (e.g., p. 55, Solve and Share)
- **MP.6 Attend to precision.**
  Students are precise in the way they write and carry out the calculations involved in simplifying numerical expressions and evaluating algebraic expressions. (e.g., p. 30, Item 10)
- **MP.7 Look for and make use of structure.**
  Students analyze the structure of algebraic expressions. They look for patterns and use properties of operations to write equivalent expressions. (e.g., p. 62, Convince Me!)
- **MP.8 Look for and express regularity in repeated reasoning.**
  Students use formulas and symbols to generalize relationships between two or more quantities. (e.g., p. 31, Look Back!)

## LESSON THAT FOCUSES ON MATH PRACTICES

- **Lesson 1-10** This lesson focuses on MP.7. Students analyze the structure of algebraic expressions that represent situations in real-world contexts. They simplify algebraic expressions by combining like terms. They find and describe patterns, and use properties of operations to solve the problem.

### Thinking Habits

*Be a good thinker! These questions can help you.*

- What patterns can I see and describe?
- How can I use the patterns to solve the problem?
- Can I see expressions and objects in different ways?
- What equivalent expressions can I use?

Revisit the information about MP.7 in these other resources:

- **Math Practices and Problem Solving Handbook** before Topic 1; includes Math Practices Proficiency Rubrics.
- **Math Practices Posters** to display in your classroom.
- **Math Practices Animations,** one for each math practice, available at PearsonRealize.com.

# MAJOR CLUSTER 6.EE.A

## DIFFERENTIATED INSTRUCTION

 Intervention  On-Level  Advanced

PearsonRealize.com

 Learn  Practice Buddy Tools  Assessment Games

### Ongoing Intervention

**During the core lesson,** monitor progress, reteach as needed, and extend students' thinking.

**Guiding Questions**

- **In the Teacher's Edition** Guiding questions are used to monitor understanding during instruction.

**Online Guiding Questions** Guiding questions are also in the online Visual Learning Animation Plus.

**Prevent Misconceptions**
This feature in the Teacher's Edition is embedded in the guiding questions.

**Error Intervention: If... then...**
This feature in the Teacher's Edition is provided during Guided Practice. It spotlights common errors and gives suggestions for addressing them.

**Reteaching**
Reteaching sets are at the end of the topic in the Student's Edition. They provide additional examples, reminders, and practice. Use these sets as needed before students do the Independent Practice.

**Higher Order Thinking**
These problems require students to think more deeply about the rich, conceptual knowledge developed in the lesson.

**Practice Buddy Online**

Online auto-scored practice is provided for each lesson. On-screen learning aids include Help Me Solve This and View an Example.

### Strategic Intervention

**At the end of the lesson,** assess to identify students' strengths and needs and then provide appropriate support.

**Quick Check**

**In the Student's Edition** Assess the lesson using 3 items checked in the Teacher's Edition.

**Online Quick Check** You can also assess the lesson using 5 online, machine-scored items.

**Intervention Activity** 
Teachers work with struggling students.

**Reteach to Build Understanding** I
This is a page of guided reteaching.

**Technology Center** I O A

**Digital Math Tools Activities** reinforce the lesson content or previously taught content using a suite of digital math tools.

**Online Games** provide practice on the lesson content or previously taught content.

**Homework and Practice** 
Use the leveled assignment to provide differentiated homework and practice.

*Additional resources to support differentiated instruction for on-level and advanced students include:*

**On-Level and Advanced Activity Centers** O A

- **Center Games** are provided in on-level and advanced versions.
- **Math and Science Activity** is related to the topic science theme introduced at the start of the topic.
- **Problem-Solving Reading Mat** is used with a lesson-specific activity.

### Intensive Intervention

**As needed,** provide more instruction that is on or below grade level for students who are struggling.

**Math Diagnosis and Intervention System 2.0**

- **Diagnosis** Use the diagnostic tests in the system. Also, use the item analysis charts given with program assessments at the start of a grade or topic, or at the end of a topic, group of topics, or the year.
- **Intervention Lessons** These two-page lessons include guided instruction followed by practice. The system includes lessons below, on, and above grade level.
- **Teacher Support** Teacher Notes provide the support needed to conduct a short lesson. The lesson focuses on vocabulary, concept development, and practice. The Teacher's Guide contains individual and class record forms and correlations to Student's Edition lessons.

**Resources for Fluency Success**

- A variety of print and digital resources are provided to ensure success on Common Core fluency standards. See Steps to Fluency Success on pages 271K–271N and 317E–317H.

# THE LANGUAGE OF MATH

PEARSON
realize.
PearsonRealize.com

Glossary

Games

## English Language Learners

**Provide ELL support** through visual learning throughout the program, ELL instruction in every lesson, and additional ideas in an ELL Toolkit.

**Visual Learning**
The visual learning that is infused in **enVision**math**2.0** provides support for English language learners. This support includes a Visual Learning Animation Plus and a Visual Learning Bridge for each lesson.

**English Language Learners Instruction** 
Lessons provide instruction for English language learners at Beginning, Intermediate, and Advanced levels of English proficiency.

**English Language Learners Toolkit**
This resource provides professional development and resources for supporting English language learners.

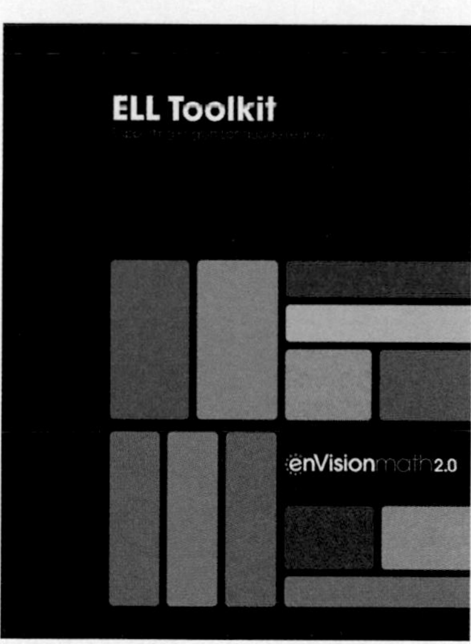
ELL Toolkit
enVisionmath2.0

## Math Vocabulary

**Build math vocabulary** using the vocabulary cards, vocabulary activities, vocabulary review, and glossary plus the online glossary and vocabulary game.

**My Word Cards**
Vocabulary cards for a topic are provided in the Student's Edition. Students use the example on the front of the card to complete the definition on the back.

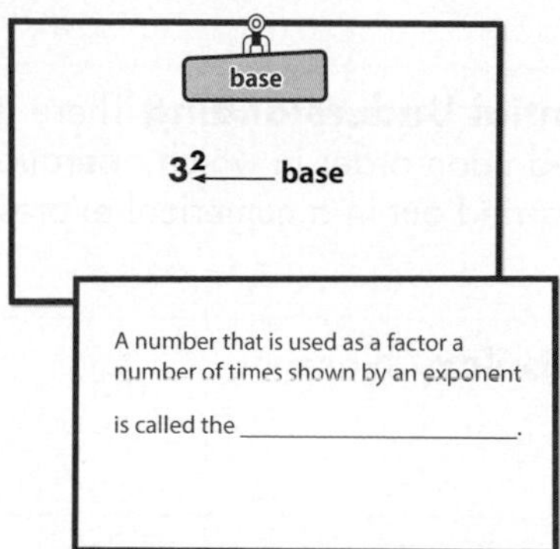
base
3² base
A number that is used as a factor a number of times shown by an exponent
is called the ______.

**Vocabulary Activities**
The Teacher's Edition provides vocabulary activities at the start of topics. These include activities for vocabulary in My Word Cards and/or activities for vocabulary in Review What You Know.

**Vocabulary Review**
A page of vocabulary review is provided at the end of each topic. It reviews vocabulary used in the topic.

**Glossary**
A glossary is provided at the back of the Student's Edition.

**Animated Glossary**

Glossary
An online, bilingual, animated glossary uses motion and sound to build understanding of math vocabulary.

**Online Vocabulary Game**

Games
An online vocabulary game is available in the Game Center.

## Math and Reading

**Connect reading and math** using a data-filled reading mat for the topic with accompanying activity masters and guide.

**Problem-Solving Reading Mats**
There is a large, beautiful mat for each topic. At the start of the topic, help students become familiar with the mat and the vocabulary used by reading the mat aloud as students follow along. Use the Problem-Solving Reading Activity Guide for suggestions about how to use the mat.

**Problem-Solving Reading Activity**
At the end of some lessons, a Problem-Solving Reading Activity provides a page of math problems to solve by using the data on the mat.

# TOPIC PLANNER

## ALGEBRA: UNDERSTAND NUMERICAL AND ALGEBRAIC EXPRESSIONS

### Lesson 1-1

**EXPONENTS** pp. 7–12

**Content Standard 6.EE.A.1**
**Mathematical Practices MP.2, MP.3, MP.4, MP.7, MP.8**

**Objective** Write and evaluate numbers with whole-number exponents.

**Essential Understanding** A whole-number exponent can be used to represent repeated multiplication of a number.

**Vocabulary** Base, Exponent, Power, Evaluate

**ELL Listening:** Learn academic vocabulary heard during instruction.

**Materials** Calculators (optional), index cards

**On-Level and Advanced Activity Centers**
- Center Games

### Lesson 1-2

**EVALUATE NUMERICAL EXPRESSIONS** pp. 13–18

**Content Standards 6.EE.A.1, 6.EE.A.3**
**Mathematical Practices MP.1, MP.3, MP.4, MP.6, MP.7**

**Objective** Use the order of operations to evaluate numerical expressions.

**Essential Understanding** There is an agreed upon order in which operations are carried out in a numerical expression.

**Vocabulary** None

**ELL Reading:** Use visual support to enhance/confirm understanding.

**Materials** Calculators (optional)

**On-Level and Advanced Activity Centers**
- Center Games

### Lesson 1-3

**USE VARIABLES TO WRITE EXPRESSIONS** pp. 19–24

**Content Standards 6.EE.A.2a, 6.EE.B.6**
**Mathematical Practices MP.1, MP.2, MP.4, MP.6, MP.7, MP.8**

**Objective** Use variables to write algebraic expressions.

**Essential Understanding** Algebraic expressions use variables to describe situations in which all of the information is not known.

**Vocabulary** Variable, Algebraic expression

**ELL Speaking:** Speak using content-area vocabulary in context.

**Materials** None

**On-Level and Advanced Activity Centers**
- Center Games

## LESSON RESOURCES

Digital

Print

- Student's Edition
- Daily Common Core Review
- Reteach to Build Understanding
- Center Games
- Math and Science Activity
- Problem-Solving Reading Mat
- Problem-Solving Reading Activity

Digital

- Listen and Look For PD Lesson Video
- Student's Edition eText
- Today's Challenge
- Solve & Share
- Visual Learning Animation Plus
- Animated Glossary
- Math Tools
- Practice Buddy Online Practice
- Quick Check
- Another Look Homework Video
- Math Games

Digital

## Lesson 1-4

**IDENTIFY PARTS OF AN EXPRESSION**
pp. 25–30

Content Standard **6.EE.A.2b**
Mathematical Practices **MP.1, MP.3, MP.4, MP.6**

**Objective** Identify parts of an expression.

**Essential Understanding** Parts of expressions can be described using words such as *term*, *coefficient*, *product*, and *factor*.

**Vocabulary** Term, Coefficient

**ELL Learning Strategies:** Use prior knowledge to understand meanings.

**Materials** Strips of paper, scissors

**On-Level and Advanced Activity Centers**

- Math and Science Activity

## Lesson 1-5

**EVALUATE ALGEBRAIC EXPRESSIONS**
pp. 31–36

Content Standards **6.EE.A.2c, 6.EE.B.6**
Mathematical Practices **MP.2, MP.3, MP.4, MP.7, MP.8**

**Objective** Evaluate algebraic expressions using substitution.

**Essential Understanding** The value of an algebraic expression can be found by replacing the variables with given numbers and doing the calculation that results.

**Vocabulary** Substitution

**ELL Speaking:** Share information in cooperative learning interactions.

**Materials** Index cards

**On-Level and Advanced Activity Centers**

- Center Games

## Lesson 1-6

**WRITE EQUIVALENT EXPRESSIONS**
pp. 37–42

Content Standards **6.EE.A.3, 6.EE.A.4**
Mathematical Practices **MP.3, MP.4, MP.7, MP.8**

**Objective** Write equivalent expressions.

**Essential Understanding** The Distributive Property and other properties of operations are used to write equivalent expressions.

**Vocabulary** Equivalent expressions

**ELL Listening:** Seek clarification of spoken language.

**Materials** None

**On-Level and Advanced Activity Centers**

- Problem-Solving Reading Mat

## TOPIC RESOURCES

Digital

Print

**Start of Topic**

- Math and Science Project
- Home-School Connection
- Review What You Know
- My Word Cards

**End of Topic**

- Fluency Practice Activity
- Vocabulary Review
- Reteaching
- Topic Assessment
- Topic Performance Assessment
- Placement Test
- Basic-Facts Timed Tests

Digital

**Start of Topic**

- Topic Overview PD Video

**End of Topic**

- Math Practices Animations
- Online Topic Assessment
- ExamView® Test Generator
- Practice Buddy Fluency Practice/Assessment

PearsonRealize.com

TOPIC 1

# TOPIC PLANNER

## ALGEBRA: UNDERSTAND NUMERICAL AND ALGEBRAIC EXPRESSIONS

### Lesson 1-7

SIMPLIFY ALGEBRAIC EXPRESSIONS pp. 43–48

Content Standards **6.EE.A.3, 6.EE.A.4**
Mathematical Practices **MP.1, MP.3, MP.4, MP.6, MP.7**

**Objective** Simplify algebraic expressions by combining like terms.

**Essential Understanding** Algebraic expressions can be simplified using the properties of operations to combine like terms and generate equivalent expressions.

**Vocabulary** Like terms, Simplify

**ELL Reading:** Demonstrate comprehension by retelling information.

**Materials** None

**On-Level and Advanced Activity Centers**
- Center Games

### Lesson 1-8

EQUIVALENT EXPRESSIONS pp. 49–54

Content Standards **6.EE.A.3, 6.EE.A.4**
Mathematical Practices **MP.1, MP.3, MP.7, MP.8**

**Objective** Identify equivalent algebraic expressions.

**Essential Understanding** Equivalent expressions have the same value regardless of the number substituted for the variable. Properties of operations can be used to verify that expressions are equivalent.

**Vocabulary** None

**ELL Reading:** Use reading supports: graphic organizers.

**Materials** Index cards

**On-Level and Advanced Activity Centers**
- Problem-Solving Reading Mat

### Lesson 1-9

FORMULAS pp. 55–60

Content Standard **6.EE.A.2c**
Mathematical Practices **MP.3, M.4, M.5, MP.6, MP.8**

**Objective** Use formulas to solve problems.

**Essential Understanding** A formula is a rule that uses symbols to relate two or more quantities. Formulas are used to solve problems in areas such as geometry, finance, and science.

**Vocabulary** Formula

**ELL Reading:** Use support from peers/teachers to develop vocabulary.

**Materials** Index cards

**On-Level and Advanced Activity Centers**
- Math and Science Activity

Notes

Digital

## Lesson 1-10

**MATH PRACTICES AND PROBLEM SOLVING: LOOK FOR AND MAKE USE OF STRUCTURE** pp. 61–66

Mathematical Practices **MP.7 Also MP.2, MP.3, MP.6**

Content Standards **6.EE.A.3, 6.EE.A.2c**

**Objective** Solve problems by using structure to analyze algebraic expressions.

**Essential Understanding** Good math thinkers look for relationships in math to help solve problems.

**Vocabulary** None

**ELL** Speaking: Express ideas.

**Materials** None

**On-Level and Advanced Activity Centers**
- Center Games

# TOPIC OPENER

# ALGEBRA: UNDERSTAND NUMERICAL AND ALGEBRAIC EXPRESSIONS

## TOPIC ESSENTIAL QUESTION

**What are expressions and how can they be written and evaluated?**

Revisit the Topic Essential Question throughout the topic, and see a note about answering the question in the Teacher's Edition for the Topic Assessment.

## MATH AND SCIENCE PROJECT STEM

**Science Theme** The science theme for this project is **Energy and Food Chains**. This theme will be revisited in the Math and Science Activities in Lessons 1-4 and 1-9 and in some lesson exercises.

Point out that a food chain is just one path of energy in an interconnected food web. Plants are "producers" since they convert energy from the sun. "Consumers" get energy by eating organisms from the next lower level in a food chain. In their research, students will find that about 10% of energy is transferred from one level of the food chain to the next. You may need to tell students that 10% is equivalent to one-tenth.

Have students identify the consumers and producers in the example of energy flow from the sun to an owl. Point out the connection between predator and prey.

*Sun/energy → grass/producer → grasshopper/primary consumer → mouse/secondary consumer → owl/tertiary consumer.*

**Project-Based Learning** Have students work on the **Math and Science Project** over the course of several days.

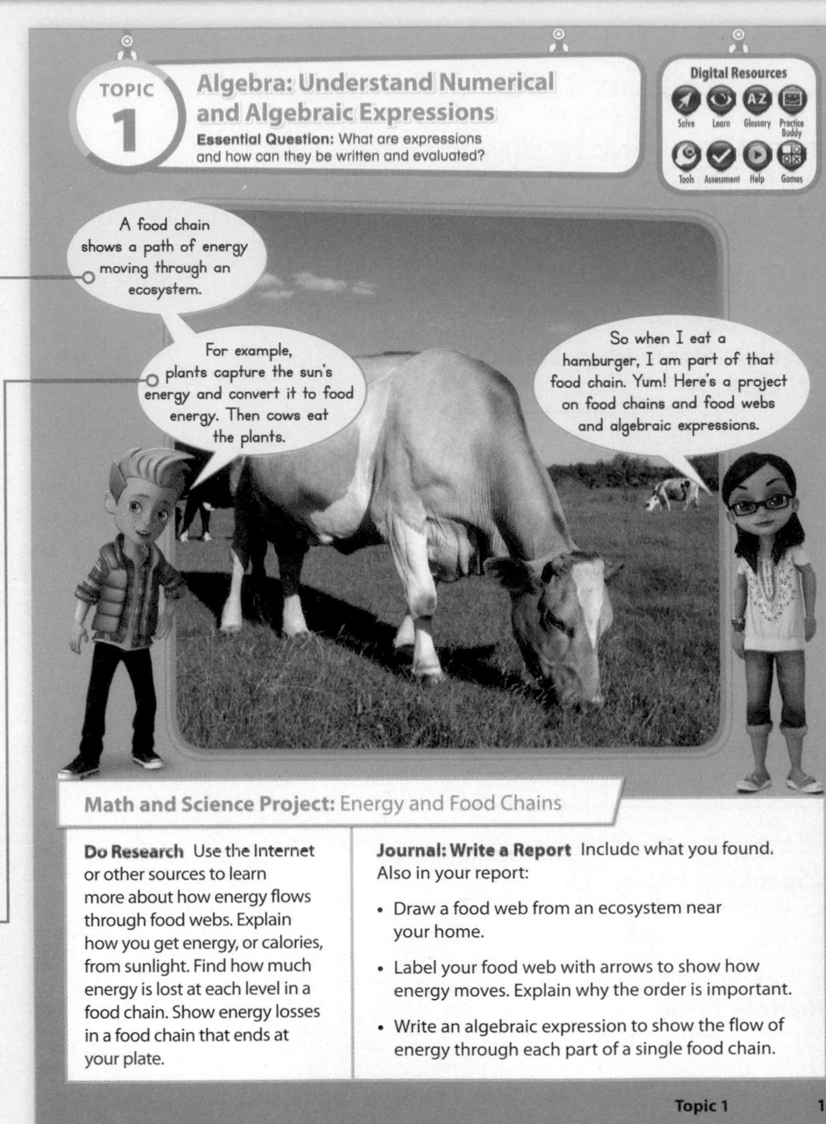

TOPIC 1 Algebra: Understand Numerical and Algebraic Expressions

**Essential Question:** What are expressions and how can they be written and evaluated?

Digital Resources: Solve, Learn, Glossary, Practice Buddy, Tools, Assessment, Help, Games

A food chain shows a path of energy moving through an ecosystem.

For example, plants capture the sun's energy and convert it to food energy. Then cows eat the plants.

So when I eat a hamburger, I am part of that food chain. Yum! Here's a project on food chains and food webs and algebraic expressions.

**Math and Science Project:** Energy and Food Chains

**Do Research** Use the Internet or other sources to learn more about how energy flows through food webs. Explain how you get energy, or calories, from sunlight. Find how much energy is lost at each level in a food chain. Show energy losses in a food chain that ends at your plate.

**Journal: Write a Report** Include what you found. Also in your report:

- Draw a food web from an ecosystem near your home.
- Label your food web with arrows to show how energy moves. Explain why the order is important.
- Write an algebraic expression to show the flow of energy through each part of a single food chain.

Topic 1 1

## EXTENSION

A food web is more complex than a food chain because it shows how energy paths in an ecosystem overlap to interconnect all the plants and animals. Have students collaborate on building a food web. Each small team can choose a different ecosystem.

### Sample Student Work for Math and Science Project

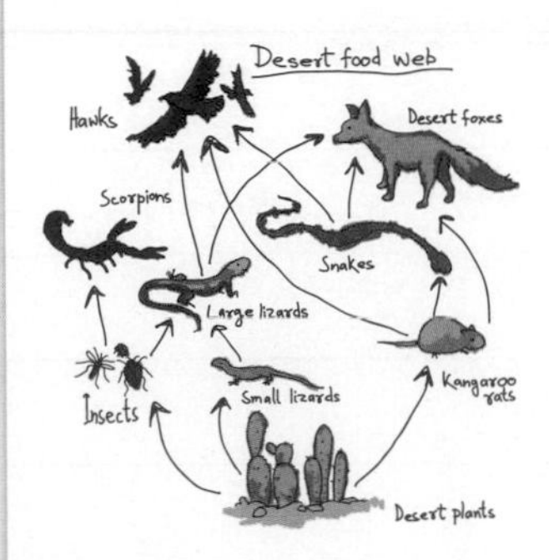


Let E equal the amount of energy an organism has. When a consumer at the next level of the food chain eats this organism, only 10% of the energy gets transferred.

The expression for the energy transfer is $0.1 \times E$.

## Home-School Connection

Name ____________________

Home-School Connection Topic 1

**Algebra: Understand Numerical and Algebraic Expressions**

**Topic 1 Standards**

6.EE.A.1, 6.EE.A.2a, 6.EE.A.2b, 6.EE.A.2c, 6.EE.A.3, 6.EE.A.4, 6.EE.B.6

*See the front of the Student's Edition for complete standards.*

Dear Family,

Your child is learning how to read, write, and evaluate expressions that represent situations and patterns, and how to use order of operations and properties when evaluating expressions. He or she will use variables to represent numbers and write expressions to solve real-world and mathematical problems.

Suppose your son or daughter has grown 2 inches since the last time he or she was measured. To represent your child's current height, you could use the variable $h$ to represent the previous height and add 2. So, the expression $h + 2$ would represent your child's current height. To evaluate the expression, you would substitute your child's previous height for $h$.

Here is an activity you can try to help your child learn how to write and evaluate expressions.

**Household Expressions**

One way to help your child develop skills in writing and evaluating expressions is to write expressions for everyday situations, and then evaluate the expressions for different numbers. Here are some typical situations you might use.

Food Preparation: What expression can you use to show dividing some pancakes among 4 family members? ($p \div 4$, where $p$ is the number of pancakes)

Chores: What expression can you use to show the total amount of time it takes to do chores, if it takes 20 minutes to do each chore? ($20c$ or $20 \times c$, where $c$ is the number of chores)

**Observe Your Child**

**Focus on Mathematical Practice 4**

Model with mathematics.

Help your child become proficient with Mathematical Practice 4. When working with expressions with your child, make sure that he or she names and defines the variable before writing the expression. Stress that once a variable has been chosen, it represents the same measure throughout the situation.



Send this page home at the start of Topic 1 to give families an overview of the content in the topic.

Name ______________________

# Review What You Know

## Vocabulary

Choose the best term from the box. Write it on the blank.

- formula
- order of operations
- numerical expression
- variable

1. A(n) **formula** is a rule that uses symbols to relate two or more quantities.
2. A(n) **numerical expression** is a mathematical phrase that includes numbers and at least one operation.
3. A quantity that is unknown may be represented by a(n) **variable**.

## Numerical Expressions

Evaluate each numerical expression.

4. $56 - 27 + (16 \div 4)$ **33**
5. $94 - (5 \times 6) \div 6 \times 11$ **39**
6. $[21 \div 3] + (18 \div 6)$ **10**
7. $2 \times 36 - (12 + 7)$ **53**
8. $12 \div (2 + 1) \times 15 \div 3$ **20**
9. $15 - (2 \times 3) \times 2 + 9$ **12**

## Perimeter and Area

Use the formulas $P = 2\ell + 2w$ and $A = \ell w$, where $\ell$ is the length and $w$ is the width, to find the perimeter, $P$, and the area, $A$, of each figure.

10. 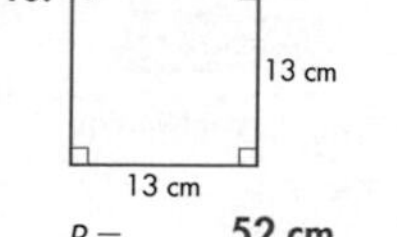


$P =$ **52 cm**
$A =$ **169 square cm**

11. 21 in. by 5 in.

$P =$ **52 in.**
$A =$ **105 square in.**

12. 15 m by 9 m

$P =$ **48 m**
$A =$ **135 square m**

## Operations and Expressions

13. How are the terms difference, sum, quotient, and product alike?
**Sample answer: Each term indicates that an operation has been performed.**
14. What does it mean to evaluate an expression?
**Sample answer: It means to find the value of the expression.**





## Vocabulary Review Activity

Have students use Teaching Tool 8 (Word Map) to display information about each vocabulary review word. For example, remind students that a numerical expression is a mathematical phrase that includes numbers and at least one operation. Then have students complete the word map by giving examples of numerical expressions, listing words that are related to a numerical expression, and writing a description of a numerical expression.

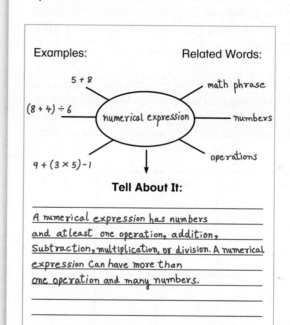

Examples: Related Words:

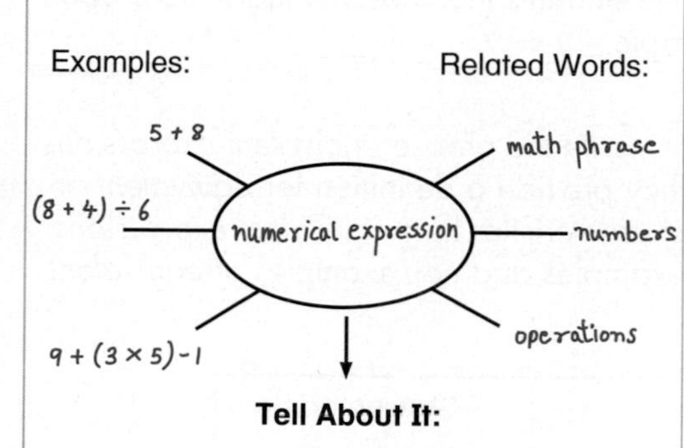


**Tell About It:**

A numerical expression has numbers and atleast one operation, addition, Subtraction, multiplication, or division. A numerical expression Can have more than one operation and many numbers.

## RtI Item Analysis for Diagnosis and Intervention

| Item | Standard | MDIS |
|---|---|---|
| 1–3 | 5.OA.A.2 | F44, F47 |
| 4–9 | 5.OA.A.1 | F41 |
| 10–12 | 3.MD.C.7b, 3.MD.D.8 | F47 |
| 13 | 5.OA.A.2 | G2, G35 |
| 14 | 5.OA.A.1 | F41 |

# TOPIC OPENER

## ALGEBRA: UNDERSTAND NUMERICAL AND ALGEBRAIC EXPRESSIONS

### Topic 1 Vocabulary Words Activity

**Understand the Meaning**

Use Teaching Tool 5 (Frayer Model) as a graphic organizer to help students look at words in different ways in order to fully understand their meanings. Have students write one of the vocabulary words in the center oval. Then have them write the definition and characteristics of the word, and provide examples and non-examples. Students can use words, numbers, symbols, and pictures to complete the model. You may wish to have students work in groups to complete models for different vocabulary words. Tell students that they will learn more about these words in this topic.

For example, students write the phrase *equivalent expressions* in the center oval. They provide a definition for *equivalent expressions*, name characteristics that *equivalent expressions* have, and provide examples and non-examples of *equivalent expressions*.

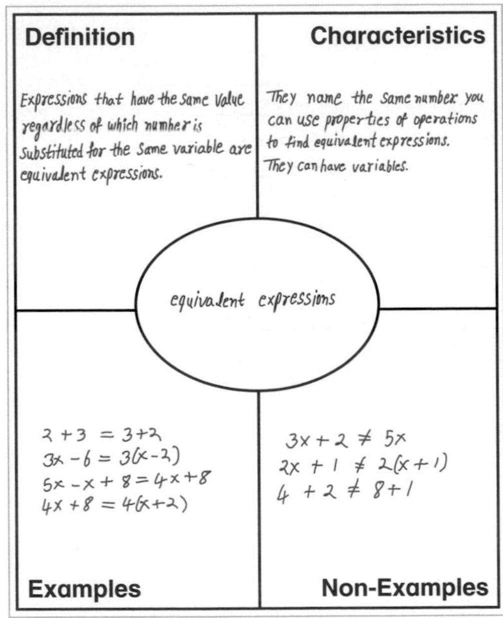


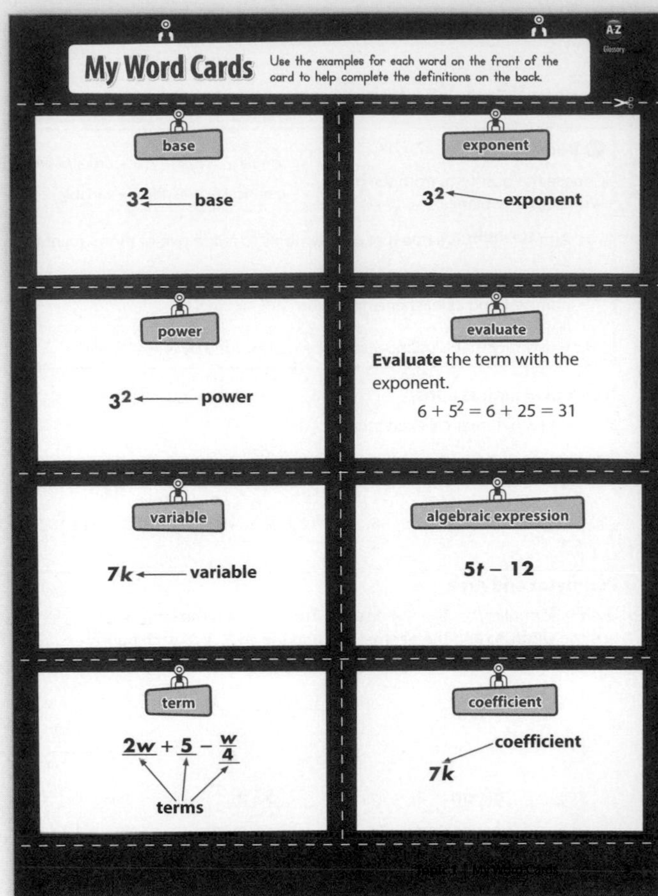


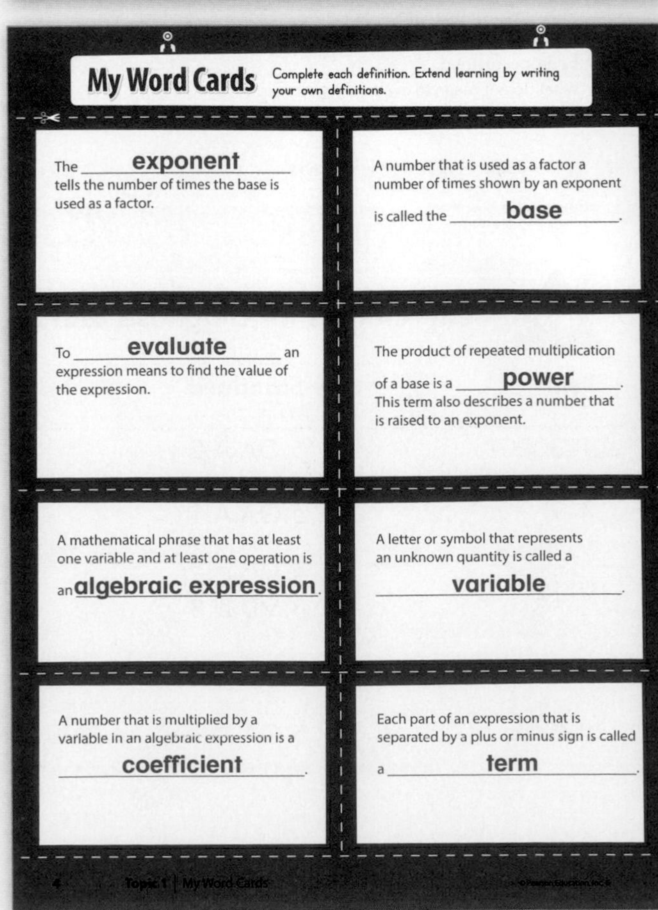

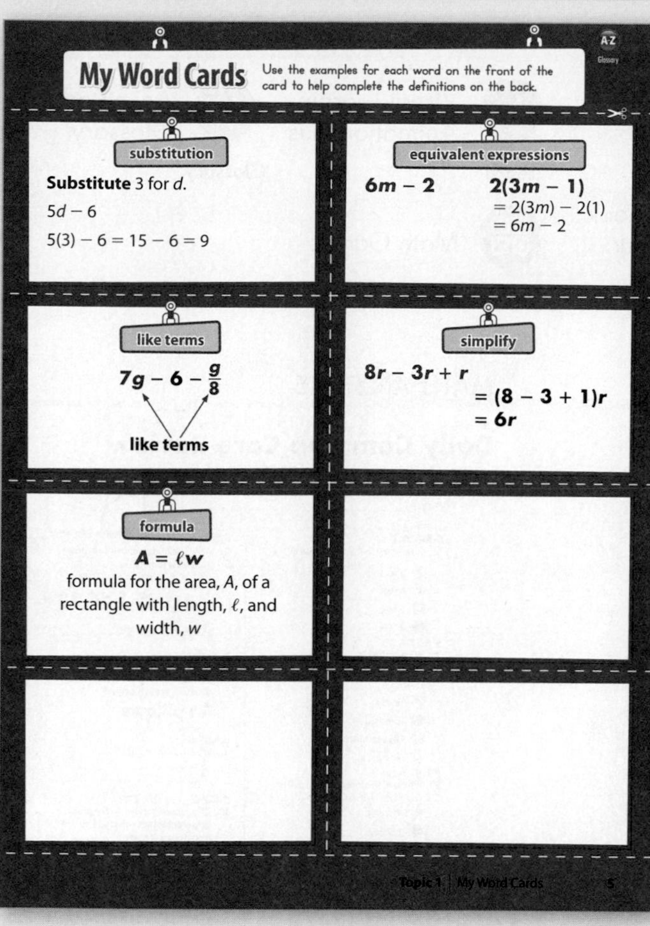

## My Word Cards

Use the examples for each word on the front of the card to help complete the definitions on the back.

**substitution**

**Substitute** 3 for $d$.

$5d - 6$

$5(3) - 6 = 15 - 6 = 9$

**equivalent expressions**

$\mathbf{6m - 2}$ $\quad$ $\mathbf{2(3m - 1)}$

$= 2(3m) - 2(1)$

$= 6m - 2$

**like terms**

$7g - 6 - \frac{g}{8}$

like terms

**simplify**

$8r - 3r + r$

$= (8 - 3 + 1)r$

$= 6r$

**formula**

$A = \ell w$

formula for the area, $A$, of a rectangle with length, $\ell$, and width, $w$

Topic 1 | My Word Cards 5

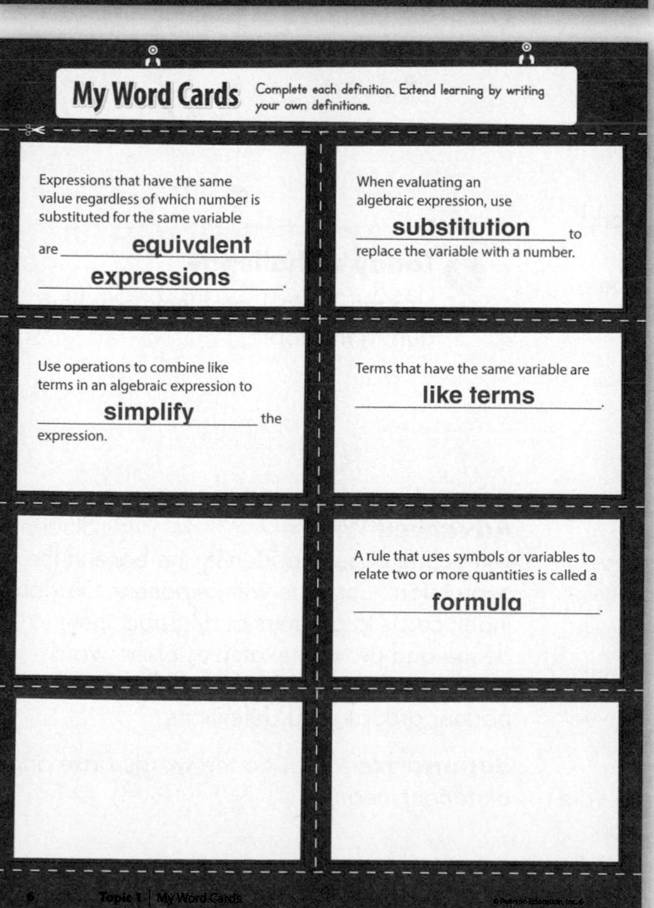

## My Word Cards

Complete each definition. Extend learning by writing your own definitions.

Expressions that have the same value regardless of which number is substituted for the same variable are **equivalent expressions**.

When evaluating an algebraic expression, use **substitution** to replace the variable with a number.

Use operations to combine like terms in an algebraic expression to **simplify** the expression.

Terms that have the same variable are **like terms**.

A rule that uses symbols or variables to relate two or more quantities is called a **formula**.

6 Topic 1 | My Word Cards © Pearson Education, Inc. 6

# LESSON 1-1

# EXPONENTS

## DIGITAL RESOURCES PearsonRealize.com

eText — Student and Teacher eTexts

PD — Listen and Look For Lesson Video

Think — Today's Challenge

Solve — Solve and Share

Learn — Visual Learning Animation Plus

Glossary — Animated Glossary

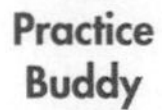
Practice Buddy — Online Personalized Practice

Tools — Math Tools

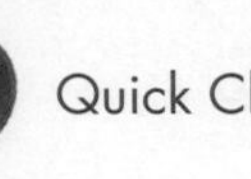
Assessment — Quick Check

Help — Another Look Homework Video

Games — Math Games

## LESSON OVERVIEW FCR FOCUS • COHERENCE • RIGOR

### FOCUS

**Domain 6.EE** Expressions and Equations

**Cluster 6.EE.A** Apply and extend previous understandings of arithmetic to algebraic expressions.

**Content Standard 6.EE.A.1** Write and evaluate numerical expressions involving whole-number exponents.

**Mathematical Practices MP.2, MP.3, MP.4, MP.7, MP.8**

**Objective** Write and evaluate numbers with whole-number exponents.

**Essential Understanding** A whole-number exponent can be used to represent repeated multiplication of a number.

**Vocabulary** Base, Exponent, Power, Evaluate

**Materials** Calculators (optional)

### COHERENCE

In Grade 5, students learned how to use exponents to denote powers of 10. For example, $10^4 = 10 \times 10 \times 10 \times 10 = 10{,}000$. This lesson focuses on extending students' understanding of exponents to include other bases. For example, $3^4 = 3 \times 3 \times 3 \times 3 = 81$. Students learn how to write and evaluate numbers with whole-number exponents. In Lessons 1-2 and 1-5, students will write and evaluate both numerical expressions and algebraic expressions that contain exponents.

### RIGOR

This lesson emphasizes a blend of **conceptual understanding** with **procedural skill**. Students interpret and generate numbers that have whole-number exponents. They solve problems involving exponents in both mathematical and real-world contexts. By looking for patterns, students come to understand that any non-zero number raised to a power of 0 has a value of 1.

PD Watch the Listen and Look For Lesson Video.

## MATH ANYTIME

### Daily Common Core Review

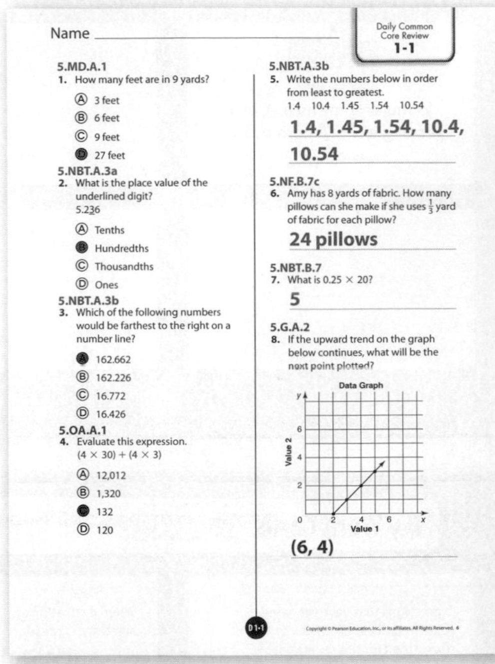
Name ______

Daily Common Core Review 1-1

5.MD.A.1
1. How many feet are in 9 yards?
Ⓐ 3 feet
Ⓑ 6 feet
Ⓒ 9 feet
● 27 feet

5.NBT.A.3a
2. What is the place value of the underlined digit?
5.236
Ⓐ Tenths
● Hundredths
Ⓒ Thousandths
Ⓓ Ones

5.NBT.A.3b
3. Which of the following numbers would be farthest to the right on a number line?
● 162.662
Ⓑ 162.226
Ⓒ 16.772
Ⓓ 16.426

5.OA.A.1
4. Evaluate this expression.
$(4 \times 30) + (4 \times 3)$
Ⓐ 12,012
Ⓑ 1,320
● 132
Ⓓ 120

5.NBT.A.3b
5. Write the numbers below in order from least to greatest.
1.4 10.4 1.45 1.54 10.54
**1.4, 1.45, 1.54, 10.4, 10.54**

5.NF.B.7c
6. Amy has 8 yards of fabric. How many pillows can she make if she uses $\frac{1}{3}$ yard of fabric for each pillow?
**24 pillows**

5.NBT.B.7
7. What is $0.25 \times 20$?
**5**

5.G.A.2
8. If the upward trend on the graph below continues, what will be the next point plotted?

**(6, 4)**

D1-1



### Today's Challenge

Think Use the Topic 1 problems any time during this topic.

## ENGLISH LANGUAGE LEARNERS 

**Listening** Learn academic vocabulary heard during instruction.

*Use with the Visual Learning Bridge on Student's Edition p. 8.*

Read Box B as students listen. Write $2 \times 2 \times 2 = 2^3$. Point to the base. *The base is the number multiplied repeatedly.* Point to the exponent. *The exponent is the number of times the base is multiplied.*

**Beginning** Ask students to write *base* and *exponent* on separate index cards and listen as the words are read. Write $4 \times 4 \times 4 = 4^3$. Point to the base. *Is 4 the base or the exponent?* Students hold up the correct card. Repeat for the exponent.

**Intermediate** Write $4 \times 4 \times 4 = 4^3$. Point to the base. *The base is the number that is multiplied repeatedly.* Point to the exponent. *The exponent is the number of times the base is used as a factor.* Instruct students to write *base* and *exponent* on index cards and work with partners to define the words. Students will listen as partners read the definitions.

**Advanced** Write $4 \times 4 \times 4 = 4^3$. Students will define *base* and identify the base in the expression. Continue with *exponent*. Distribute index cards to partners and instruct them to define and provide examples of the words *base* and *exponent*. Partners will listen to other partner groups read definitions.

**Summarize** What do the words *base* and *exponent* mean?

# DEVELOP: PROBLEM-BASED LEARNING

PearsonRealize.com

**COHERENCE: Engage learners by connecting prior knowledge to new ideas.**
Students extend their understanding of exponents by modeling, recording, and describing patterns of repeated multiplication.

10–15 min

Solve

## BEFORE

1. **Pose the Solve-and-Share Problem**
**MP.7 Look for Relationships** Listen and look for students who recognize that the relationship between the number of folds and the number of sections relates to repeated multiplication.

2. **Build Understanding**
*How many times will you fold the paper in half?* [5] *How many sections do you think will be made?* [Sample answer: 32]

## DURING

3. **Ask Guiding Questions As Needed**
*What do you notice about the number of folds and the corresponding number of 2s?* [Sample answer: The number of folds is equal to the number of 2s.] *How can you use the relationship between the number of folds and the number of 2s to find the number of sections without folding and counting?* [Sample answer: You know that the number of folds and the number of 2s are the same, so you can write a repeated multiplication using the correct number of 2s and then multiply to find the number of sections.]

## AFTER

4. **Share and Discuss Solutions**
Start with students' solutions. If needed, project Gabrielle's work to discuss how to describe the pattern in the table.

5. **Transition to the Visual Learning Bridge**
*An expression in which the same number is repeatedly multiplied can be written using an exponent.*

6. **Extension for Early Finishers**
*If a sheet of paper is folded in half 20 times, how many 2s do you need to multiply to find the number of sections?* [20]

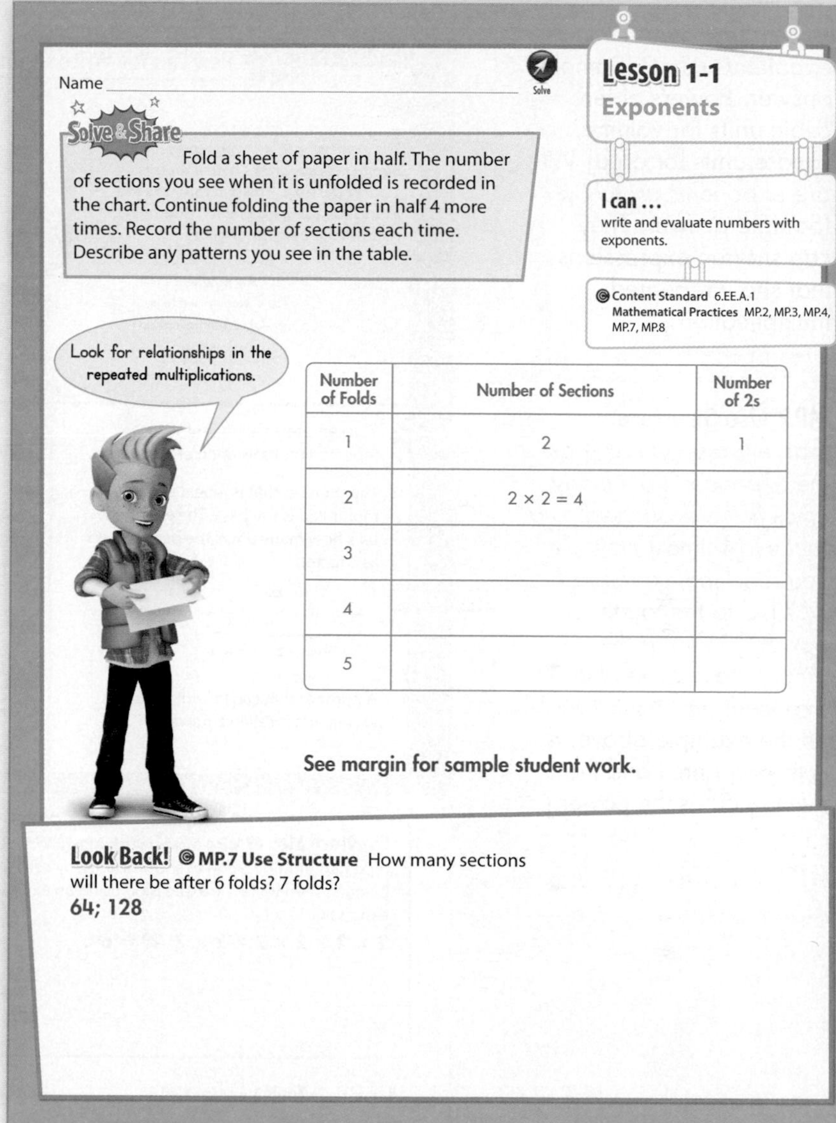

Name

Lesson 1-1
Exponents

Solve & Share

Fold a sheet of paper in half. The number of sections you see when it is unfolded is recorded in the chart. Continue folding the paper in half 4 more times. Record the number of sections each time. Describe any patterns you see in the table.

I can … write and evaluate numbers with exponents.

Content Standard 6.EE.A.1
Mathematical Practices MP.2, MP.3, MP.4, MP.7, MP.8

Look for relationships in the repeated multiplications.

| Number of Folds | Number of Sections | Number of 2s |
|---|---|---|
| 1 | 2 | 1 |
| 2 | 2 × 2 = 4 | |
| 3 | | |
| 4 | | |
| 5 | | |

See margin for sample student work.

**Look Back!** **MP.7 Use Structure** How many sections will there be after 6 folds? 7 folds?
64; 128

Digital Resources at PearsonRealize.com    Topic 1 | Lesson 1-1    7

## Analyze Student Work

Gabrielle's Work

| Number of Folds | Number of Sections | Number of 2s |
|---|---|---|
| 1 | 2 | 1 |
| 2 | 2 × 2 = 4 | 2 |
| 3 | 2 × 2 × 2 = 8 | 3 |
| 4 | 2 × 2 × 2 × 2 = 16 | 4 |
| 5 | 2 × 2 × 2 × 2 × 2 = 32 | 5 |

Each fold multiplies the number of sections from the previous fold by 2. So each fold is equal to the number of 2s in the equation.

Gabrielle completes the table and clearly describes the pattern.

Connor's Work

| Number of Folds | Number of Sections | Number of 2s |
|---|---|---|
| 1 | 2 | 1 |
| 2 | 2 × 2 = 4 | 2 |
| 3 | 2 × 2 × 2 = 8 | 3 |
| 4 | 2 × 2 × 2 × 2 = 16 | 4 |
| 5 | 2 × 2 × 2 × 2 × 2 = 32 | 5 |

Connor correctly completes the table, but does not describe a pattern.

## STEP 2 DEVELOP: VISUAL LEARNING

The *Visual Learning Bridge* connects students' thinking in Solve & Share to important math ideas in the lesson. Use the *Visual Learning Bridge* to make these ideas explicit. Also available as a *Visual Learning Animation Plus* at PearsonRealize.com

PEARSON realize. PearsonRealize.com

Learn Glossary

*When have you seen exponents used?* [Sample answer: Powers of ten, cubic units for volume, square units for area] *Why are exponents useful?* [Sample answer: They can shorten expressions that show repeated multiplication.]

**MP.7 Use Structure**
*If an expression has 4 as the exponent, how many times is the base used as a factor?* [4 times] *How do you read the expression $5^4$?* ["5 to the fourth power"] *What is the difference between the exponent and the power?* [In the example above, 4 is the exponent and the number $5^4$ is the power.]

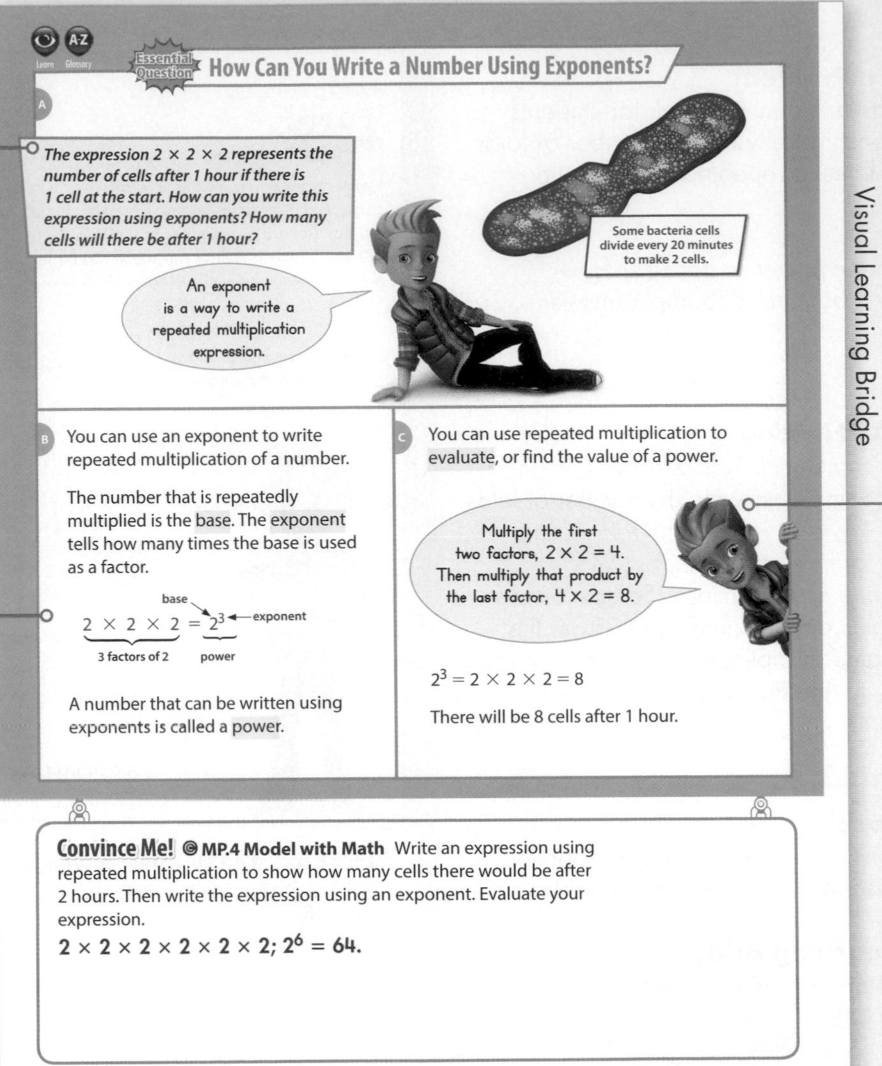

Visual Learning Bridge

Learn Glossary

Essential Question **How Can You Write a Number Using Exponents?**

A

*The expression 2 × 2 × 2 represents the number of cells after 1 hour if there is 1 cell at the start. How can you write this expression using exponents? How many cells will there be after 1 hour?*

Some bacteria cells divide every 20 minutes to make 2 cells.
An exponent is a way to write a repeated multiplication expression.



B

You can use an exponent to write repeated multiplication of a number.

The number that is repeatedly multiplied is the base. The exponent tells how many times the base is used as a factor.

$\underbrace{2 \times 2 \times 2}_{\text{3 factors of 2}} = \underbrace{2^3}_{\text{power}}$ (base: 2; exponent: 3)

A number that can be written using exponents is called a power.

C

You can use repeated multiplication to evaluate, or find the value of a power.

Multiply the first two factors, 2 × 2 = 4. Then multiply that product by the last factor, 4 × 2 = 8.



$2^3 = 2 \times 2 \times 2 = 8$

There will be 8 cells after 1 hour.

**Convince Me!** **MP.4 Model with Math** Write an expression using repeated multiplication to show how many cells there would be after 2 hours. Then write the expression using an exponent. Evaluate your expression.

**$2 \times 2 \times 2 \times 2 \times 2 \times 2$; $2^6 = 64$.**

8 **Topic 1** | Lesson 1-1 © Pearson Education, Inc. 6

*Using an exponent, what would be the expression for "3 to the fifth power"?* [$3^5$] *How do you expand the expression $3^5$ to show the repeated multiplication?* [Write down the base, 3, the number of times indicated by the exponent, 5. Then place multiplication signs between the repeated numbers.] *How can you evaluate $3^5$?* [First, find the product of 3 × 3. Then multiply that product by 3. Continue multiplying until you have used five factors of 3. So, 3 × 3 = 9; 9 × 3 = 27; 27 × 3 = 81; 81 × 3 = 243.]

**Prevent Misconceptions**

When evaluating an expression with an exponent, some students might count the number of times they multiply instead of the number of times they use the base as a factor. Remind them that $2^3$ means 3 factors of 2, not 3 rounds of multiplication.

**Convince Me!** **MP.4 Model with Math** Situations requiring multiplication can be represented in more than one way. Repeated multiplication can be written as a number raised to an exponent. Exponential expressions are usually shorter than the equivalent, or expanded, expression written as repeated multiplication.

**Coherence** In Grade 5, students used whole-number exponents to denote powers of 10. They now use exponents to represent repeated factors of the same number other than ten.

Revisit the Essential Question. Exponents can be used to represent repeated multiplication. The base indicates the number that is repeatedly multiplied, and the exponent indicates how many times the base is used as a factor. So, 2 × 2 × 2 can be written as $2^3$ since there are three 2s being multiplied.

## QUICK CHECK

Check mark indicates items for prescribing differentiation on the next page.
Items 5 and 17 are worth 1 point. Item 16 is worth up to 3 points.

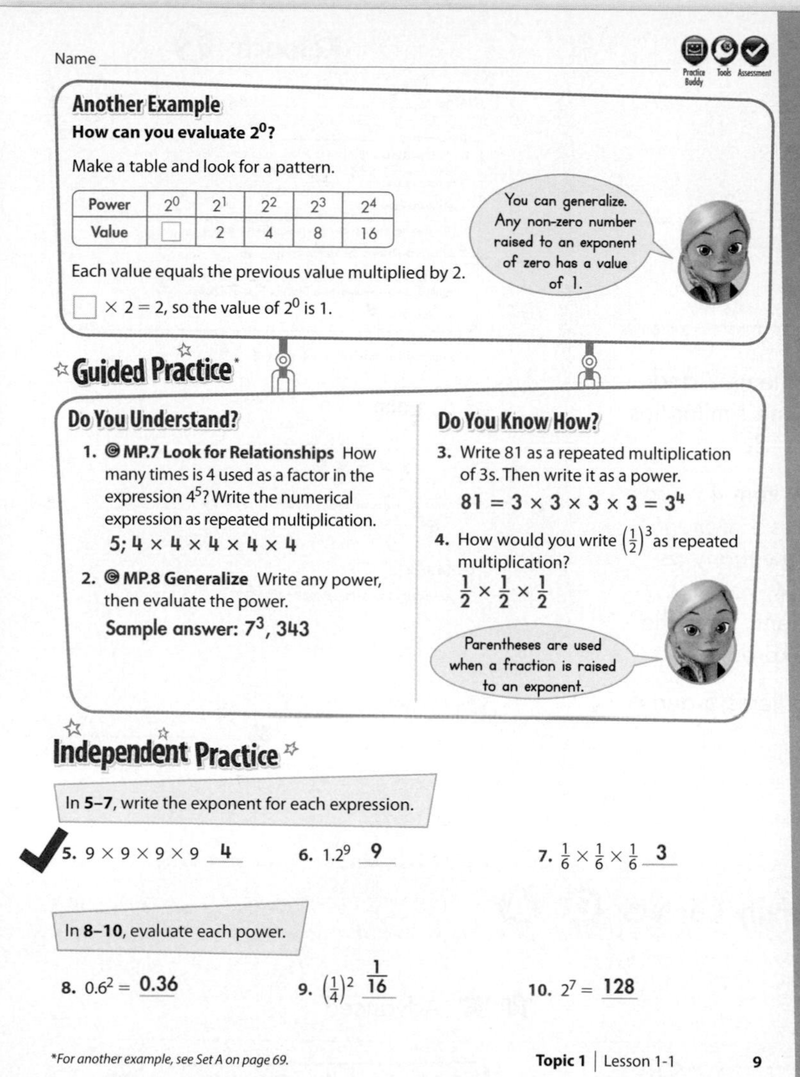

Name ______

### Another Example

**How can you evaluate $2^0$?**

Make a table and look for a pattern.

| Power | $2^0$ | $2^1$ | $2^2$ | $2^3$ | $2^4$ |
|---|---|---|---|---|---|
| Value | ☐ | 2 | 4 | 8 | 16 |

Each value equals the previous value multiplied by 2.

☐ × 2 = 2, so the value of $2^0$ is 1.

You can generalize. Any non-zero number raised to an exponent of zero has a value of 1.

### Guided Practice*

**Do You Understand?**

1. **MP.7 Look for Relationships** How many times is 4 used as a factor in the expression $4^5$? Write the numerical expression as repeated multiplication.
   **5; 4 × 4 × 4 × 4 × 4**
2. **MP.8 Generalize** Write any power, then evaluate the power.
   **Sample answer: $7^3$, 343**

**Do You Know How?**

3. Write 81 as a repeated multiplication of 3s. Then write it as a power.
   **$81 = 3 \times 3 \times 3 \times 3 = 3^4$**
4. How would you write $\left(\frac{1}{2}\right)^3$ as repeated multiplication?
   **$\frac{1}{2} \times \frac{1}{2} \times \frac{1}{2}$**

Parentheses are used when a fraction is raised to an exponent.

### Independent Practice*

In **5–7**, write the exponent for each expression.

5. $9 \times 9 \times 9 \times 9$ **4**
6. $1.2^9$ **9**
7. $\frac{1}{6} \times \frac{1}{6} \times \frac{1}{6}$ **3**

In **8–10**, evaluate each power.

8. $0.6^2 =$ **0.36**
9. $\left(\frac{1}{4}\right)^2$ **$\frac{1}{16}$**
10. $2^7 =$ **128**

*For another example, see Set A on page 69.

Topic 1 | Lesson 1-1 9

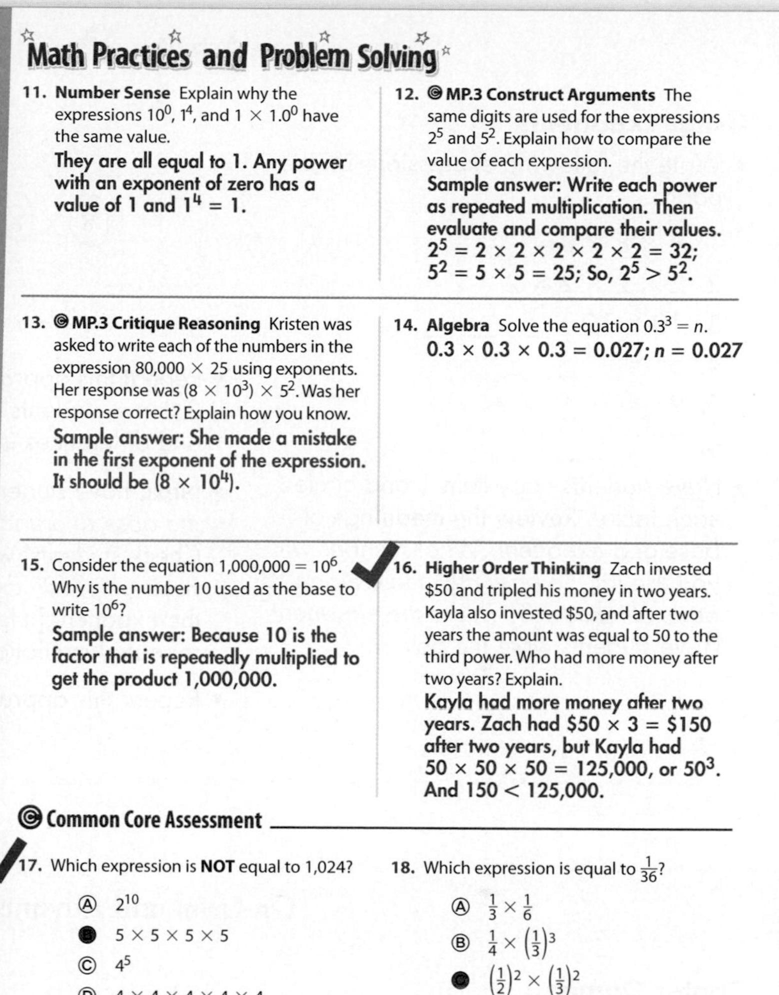

### Math Practices and Problem Solving*

11. **Number Sense** Explain why the expressions $10^0$, $1^4$, and $1 \times 1.0^0$ have the same value.
    **They are all equal to 1. Any power with an exponent of zero has a value of 1 and $1^4 = 1$.**
12. **MP.3 Construct Arguments** The same digits are used for the expressions $2^5$ and $5^2$. Explain how to compare the value of each expression.
    **Sample answer: Write each power as repeated multiplication. Then evaluate and compare their values. $2^5 = 2 \times 2 \times 2 \times 2 \times 2 = 32$; $5^2 = 5 \times 5 = 25$; So, $2^5 > 5^2$.**
13. **MP.3 Critique Reasoning** Kristen was asked to write each of the numbers in the expression 80,000 × 25 using exponents. Her response was $(8 \times 10^3) \times 5^2$. Was her response correct? Explain how you know.
    **Sample answer: She made a mistake in the first exponent of the expression. It should be $(8 \times 10^4)$.**
14. **Algebra** Solve the equation $0.3^3 = n$.
    **$0.3 \times 0.3 \times 0.3 = 0.027$; $n = 0.027$**
15. Consider the equation $1{,}000{,}000 = 10^6$. Why is the number 10 used as the base to write $10^6$?
    **Sample answer: Because 10 is the factor that is repeatedly multiplied to get the product 1,000,000.**
16. **Higher Order Thinking** Zach invested \$50 and tripled his money in two years. Kayla also invested \$50, and after two years the amount was equal to 50 to the third power. Who had more money after two years? Explain.
    **Kayla had more money after two years. Zach had \$50 × 3 = \$150 after two years, but Kayla had 50 × 50 × 50 = 125,000, or $50^3$. And 150 < 125,000.**

**Common Core Assessment**

17. Which expression is **NOT** equal to 1,024?
    Ⓐ $2^{10}$
    ● $5 \times 5 \times 5 \times 5 \times 5$
    Ⓒ $4^5$
    Ⓓ $4 \times 4 \times 4 \times 4 \times 4$
18. Which expression is equal to $\frac{1}{36}$?
    Ⓐ $\frac{1}{3} \times \frac{1}{6}$
    Ⓑ $\frac{1}{4} \times \left(\frac{1}{3}\right)^3$
    ● $\left(\frac{1}{2}\right)^2 \times \left(\frac{1}{3}\right)^2$
    Ⓓ $\frac{1}{2} \times \frac{1}{3} \times \frac{1}{3} \times \frac{1}{3}$

10 Topic 1 | Lesson 1-1 © Pearson Education, Inc. 6

**Another Example** *Repeat this example with a base of 3, 4, or 100. What number completes the table?* [1] *How is the base of the power related to the pattern in the table?* [Each value is increased by a factor equal to the base.] Point out to students that any non-zero number raised to an exponent of zero must equal 1 and that the same number raised to an exponent of one is itself.

**Error Intervention: Item 3**

**If** students have difficulty writing the repeated multiplication,
**then ask:** *What is 3 × 3?* [9] *What do you get if you multiply the product by another 3?* [27] *What do you get if you multiply by another 3?* [81] *How many 3s did you multiply to get 81?* [4] *How do you show that as a repeated multiplication?* [3 × 3 × 3 × 3 = 81] *How do you show that as a power?* [$3^4 = 81$]

**Reteaching** Assign Reteaching Set A on p. 69.

**Item 13 MP.3 Critique Reasoning** Some students might evaluate each expression and check whether the two values are equal. Other students might find it more efficient to check whether Kristen used exponents correctly to represent each factor, 80,000 and 25. Students must remember that if a number ends in 4 zeros, then it has a factor of $10^4$.

**Item 15 Coherence** In Grade 5, students used exponents to represent powers of 10. You may want to remind students about the connection between the exponent and the number of zeros in a power of 10.

**Item 17** This item illustrates that some numbers can be written using exponents in more than one way. In this case, both $2^{10}$ and $4^5$ are equal to 1,024.

**Multi-Step Problems** *Page 10 Item 16; Page 12 Items 18–20*

# ASSESS AND DIFFERENTIATE

Use the **QUICK CHECK** on the previous page to prescribe differentiated instruction.

**I Intervention** 0–3 points on the Quick Check

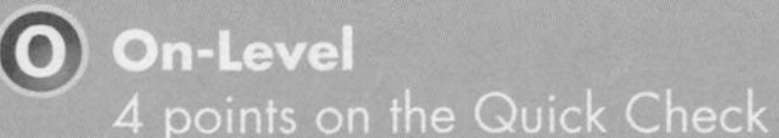

**O On-Level** 4 points on the Quick Check

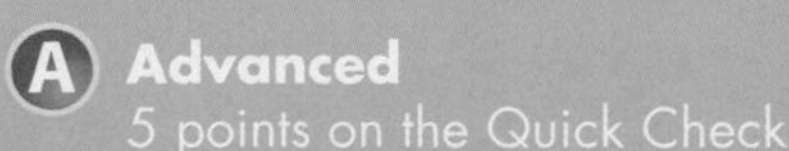

**A Advanced** 5 points on the Quick Check

## Intervention Activity 

### Using Exponents

- Write the following expressions on the board.

**1.** $8 \times 8 \times 8 =$ ____

**2.** $2 \times 2 \times 2 \times 2 \times 2 =$ ____

**3.** $10 \times 10 =$ ____

**4.** $5^4 =$ ____

**5.** $9^5 =$ ____

**6.** $7^1 =$ ____

- Have students copy Item 1 and circle each factor. Review the meanings of *base* and *exponent*. *What number will you use for the base?* [8] *How many 8s are multiplied?* [3] *This is the exponent.* Have students write the power.

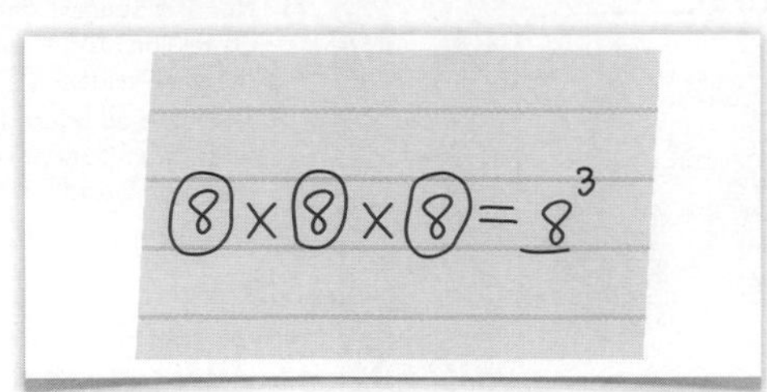



- Repeat this approach for Items 2 and 3. Have students discuss the similarities and differences in Items 1–3.
- Next, have students copy Item 4. *Circle the base and underline the exponent.* Check students' work. *How many 5s are multiplied? Explain.* [4; Four is the exponent.] Have students write the repeated multiplication expression.
- Repeat this approach for Items 5 and 6.

## Reteach I

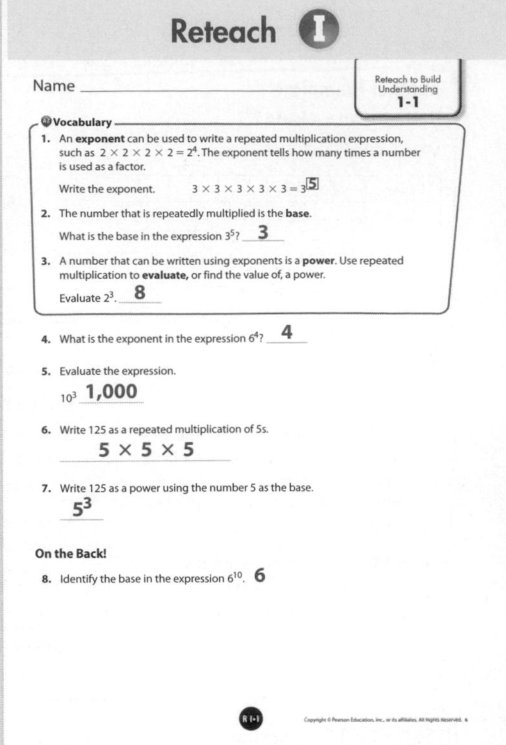

Name

Reteach to Build Understanding 1-1

**Vocabulary**

**1.** An **exponent** can be used to write a repeated multiplication expression, such as $2 \times 2 \times 2 \times 2 = 2^4$. The exponent tells how many times a number is used as a factor.

Write the exponent. $3 \times 3 \times 3 \times 3 \times 3 = 3^{5}$

**2.** The number that is repeatedly multiplied is the **base**.

What is the base in the expression $3^5$? 3

**3.** A number that can be written using exponents is a **power**. Use repeated multiplication to **evaluate**, or find the value of, a power.

Evaluate $2^3$. 8

**4.** What is the exponent in the expression $6^4$? 4

**5.** Evaluate the expression.

$10^3$ 1,000

**6.** Write 125 as a repeated multiplication of 5s.

$5 \times 5 \times 5$

**7.** Write 125 as a power using the number 5 as the base.

$5^3$

**On the Back!**

**8.** Identify the base in the expression $6^{10}$. 6

R 1-1



## On-Level and Advanced Activity Centers O A

### Center Games

Students work individually or in pairs to answer questions about numbers written in exponential form or expanded form. Have students explain their thinking as they play the game.

 On-Level

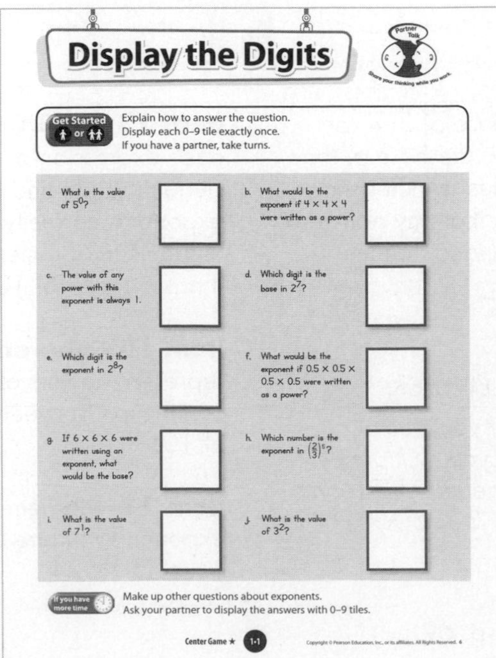

**Display the Digits**

Get Started: Explain how to answer the question. Display each 0–9 tile exactly once. If you have a partner, take turns.

a. What is the value of $5^0$?

b. What would be the exponent if $4 \times 4 \times 4$ were written as a power?

c. The value of any power with this exponent is always 1.

d. Which digit is the base in $2^7$?

e. Which digit is the exponent in $2^8$?

f. What would be the exponent if $0.5 \times 0.5 \times 0.5 \times 0.5$ were written as a power?

g. If $6 \times 6 \times 6$ were written using an exponent, what would be the base?

h. Which number is the exponent in $\left(\frac{2}{3}\right)^1$?

i. What is the value of $7^1$?

j. What is the value of $3^2$?

If you have more time: Make up other questions about exponents. Ask your partner to display the answers with 0–9 tiles.

Center Game ★ 1-1

 Advanced

**Display the Digits**

Get Started: Explain how to answer the question. Display each 0–9 tile exactly once. If you have a partner, take turns.

a. What is the value of the missing exponent that would make this statement true? $256^? = 256$

b. Which number is the exponent in $23^6$?

c. Which digit is the base in $7^6$?

d. What would be the exponent if $3 \times 3 \times 3 \times 3 \times 3$ were written as a power?

e. What is the value of $8 \times 7^0$?

f. What would be the exponent if $\frac{1}{2} \times \frac{1}{2} \times \frac{1}{2} \times \frac{1}{2}$ were written as a power?

g. What is the value of $3 \times (0.3)^0$?

h. What is the value of the missing exponent that would make this statement true? $3^0 = 5^?$

i. If $9 \times 9 \times 9 \times 9$ were written using an exponent, what would be the base?

j. A base number is raised to an exponent of 4 and the result is 16. What is the value of the base number?

If you have more time: Make up other questions about exponents. Ask your partner to display the answers with 0–9 tiles.

Center Game ★★ 1-1

**TIMING**

The time allocated to Step 3 will depend on the teacher's instructional decisions and differentiation routines.

15–30 min

PEARSON realize
PearsonRealize.com

Help

Practice Buddy

Tools

Games

## Technology Center    

Tools

Games

### Math Tools and Math Games

A link to a specific math tools activity or math game to use with this lesson is provided at PearsonRealize.com.

## Leveled Assignment  Items 1–8, 11–14, 19, 20 O Items 2–13, 17, 19, 20  Items 3, 6, 9–13, 15–20

Name ______

Help Practice Buddy Tools Games

**Homework & Practice 1-1**
**Exponents**

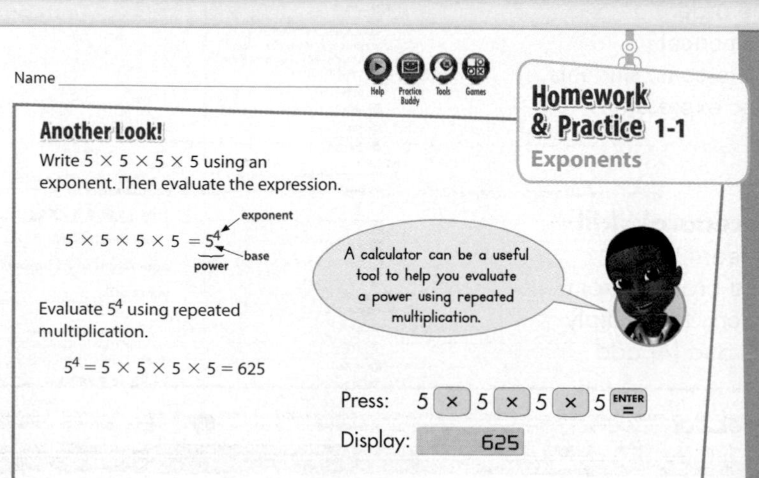


In **1–3**, write the base number for each expression.

**1.** $5^{12}$ 5
**2.** $1.2^2$ 1.2
**3.** $\left(\frac{1}{3}\right)^4$ $\frac{1}{3}$

In **4–6**, write the exponent for each expression.

**4.** 7 × 7 × 7 × 7 4
**5.** $\left(\frac{2}{3}\right)^8$ 8
**6.** 0.5 × 0.5 × 0.5 3

In **7–12**, evaluate each expression.

**7.** $9^3 =$ 729
**8.** $\left(\frac{1}{4}\right)^3 =$ $\frac{1}{64}$
**9.** $3^5 =$ 243
**10.** $\left(\frac{1}{8}\right)^3$ $\frac{1}{512}$
**11.** $99^0 =$ 1
**12.** $1.5^2 =$ 2.25

You use structure when you evaluate expressions with exponents.

**13.** **MP.3 Construct Arguments** Is $0.3^4$ equal to $0.9^2$? Explain.
**No; Sample answer: When I evaluate both expressions, $0.3^4$ is equal to 0.0081 and $0.9^2$ is equal to 0.81.**

**14. Number Sense** What are two ways you can represent the number 27 using the number 3?
**$3^3$ and 3 × 3 × 3**

**15.** **MP.2 Reasoning** What is the value of $1^{102}$? What is the value of any power of 1? Justify your answer.
**1; Any power of 1 equals 1 because 1 times 1, no matter how many times it is repeated, will always equal 1.**

**16.** Humans can distinguish up to 18,400,000 individual dots called pixels on a typical computer display. Can a human distinguish pixels on a same-sized HDTV with $2 \times 10^6$ pixels? Explain.
**Yes; Sample answer: $2 \times 10^6 = 2{,}000{,}000$, and $2{,}000{,}000 < 18{,}400{,}000$.**

**17. Higher Order Thinking** In case of an emergency, the school has a calling list so everyone is called in the least amount of time. Each of the first 3 people on the list calls another 3 people on the list. Then, each of the people in the second group calls another 3 people on the list, and so on. The 5th group of people will make 243 calls. Is this statement accurate? Explain.
**Yes; The 1st group is $3^1 = 3$, the 2nd group is $3^2 = 9$, and so on. The 5th group is $3^5$ which does equal 243.**

**18.** **MP.7 Use Structure** An investment of $1 is put in an account. Every 8 years, the money doubles. No additional money was added to the account. Would the expression 1 × 2 × 2 × 2 × 2 × 2 × 2 correctly represent how much was in the investment account after 48 years? Explain.
**Yes; Sample answer: Since 48 ÷ 8 = 6, the account doubled 6 times. The product doubles six times in the expression.**

### Common Core Assessment

**19.** Which expression is equal to 343?

Ⓐ $8^3$
Ⓑ 6 × 6 × 6
● $7^3$
Ⓓ 7 × 7 × 7 × 7

**20.** Which expression is **NOT** equal to 0.125?

Ⓐ $0.5^3$
● 0.5 × 3
Ⓒ 0.5 × 0.5 × 0.5
Ⓓ $0.5 \times 0.5^2$

# LESSON 1-2

# EVALUATE NUMERICAL EXPRESSIONS

## DIGITAL RESOURCES PearsonRealize.com

eText — Student and Teacher eTexts

PD — Listen and Look For Lesson Video

Think — Today's Challenge

Solve — Solve and Share

Learn — Visual Learning Animation Plus

Glossary — Animated Glossary

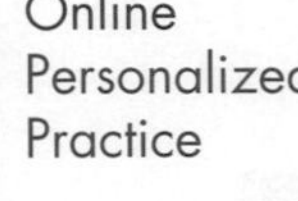
Practice Buddy — Online Personalized Practice

Tools — Math Tools

Assessment — Quick Check

Help — Another Look Homework Video

Games — Math Games

## LESSON OVERVIEW — FCR FOCUS • COHERENCE • RIGOR

### FOCUS

**Domain 6.EE** Expressions and Equations

**Cluster 6.EE.A** Apply and extend previous understandings of arithmetic to algebraic expressions.

**Content Standard 6.EE.A.1** Write and evaluate numerical expressions involving whole-number exponents. Also **6.EE.A.3**.

**Mathematical Practices MP.1, MP.3, MP.4, MP.6, MP.7**

**Objective** Use the order of operations to evaluate numerical expressions.

**Essential Understanding** There is an agreed upon order in which operations are carried out in a numerical expression.

**Materials** Calculators (optional)

### COHERENCE

In Grade 5, students learned how to evaluate numerical expressions that contain parentheses or brackets. Lesson 1-2 focuses on extending this work to expressions containing fractions, decimals, and exponents, as well as parentheses within brackets. Students follow the order of operations to evaluate numerical expressions. In later Topic 1 lessons, students extend this work to algebraic expressions and formulas.

### RIGOR

This lesson emphasizes **procedural skill**. In any expression, students learn to (1) evaluate parentheses and brackets from inside out, (2) evaluate powers, (3) multiply and divide from left to right, and (4) add and subtract from left to right.

PD Watch the Listen and Look For Lesson Video.

## MATH ANYTIME

### Daily Common Core Review

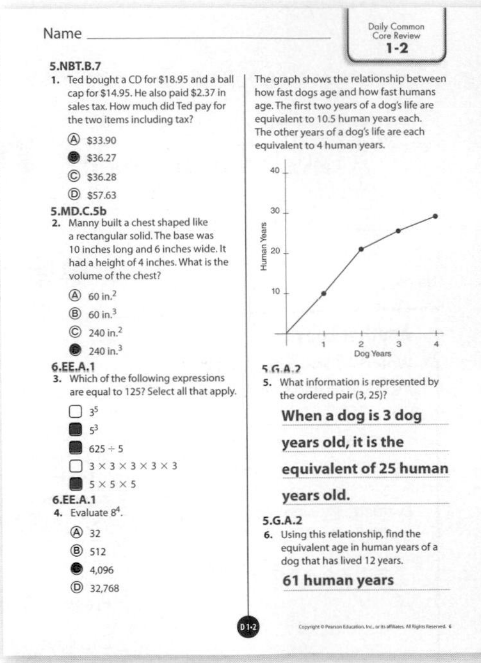
Name ____________

Daily Common Core Review 1-2

5.NBT.B.7

1. Ted bought a CD for \$18.95 and a ball cap for \$14.95. He also paid \$2.37 in sales tax. How much did Ted pay for the two items including tax?

Ⓐ \$33.90
● \$36.27
Ⓒ \$36.28
Ⓓ \$57.63

5.MD.C.5b

2. Manny built a chest shaped like a rectangular solid. The base was 10 inches long and 6 inches wide. It had a height of 4 inches. What is the volume of the chest?

Ⓐ 60 in.$^2$
Ⓑ 60 in.$^3$
Ⓒ 240 in.$^2$
● 240 in.$^3$

6.EE.A.1

3. Which of the following expressions are equal to 125? Select all that apply.

☐ $3^5$
■ $5^3$
■ $625 \div 5$
☐ $3 \times 3 \times 3 \times 3 \times 3$
■ $5 \times 5 \times 5$

6.EE.A.1

4. Evaluate $8^4$.

Ⓐ 32
Ⓑ 512
● 4,096
Ⓓ 32,768

The graph shows the relationship between how fast dogs age and how fast humans age. The first two years of a dog's life are equivalent to 10.5 human years each. The other years of a dog's life are each equivalent to 4 human years.



5.G.A.2

5. What information is represented by the ordered pair (3, 25)?

**When a dog is 3 dog years old, it is the equivalent of 25 human years old.**

5.G.A.2

6. Using this relationship, find the equivalent age in human years of a dog that has lived 12 years.

**61 human years**

D1•2



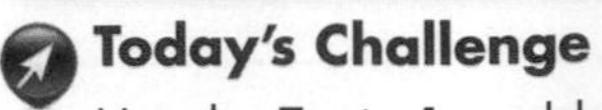

Think Use the Topic 1 problems any time during this topic.

## ENGLISH LANGUAGE LEARNERS 

**Reading** Use visual support to enhance/confirm understanding.

*Use with the Visual Learning Bridge on Student's Edition p. 14.*

Read the *Order of Operations*, Box A. Draw a visual reminder by each operation (e.g., ( ) and [ ] by the first operation). Write $\frac{1}{2} \times 4^2 - [2 + (3.6 \div 0.9)]$. *According to the Order of Operations, which operation is first?* Draw a line under $(3.6 \div 0.9)$. Perform the operation and continue evaluating the expression.

**Beginning** Review the *Order of Operations* with students. Write $\frac{1}{4} \times 2^4 + [5 + (48 \div 6)]$. Ask students to point to, then underline, the first operation. *What visual helped you remember?* Perform the operation and continue evaluating the expression.

**Intermediate** Review the *Order of Operations* with students. Write $\frac{1}{4} \times 2^4 + [5 + (48 \div 6)]$. Instruct student partners to divide a sheet of paper into four parts. In the first space, ask them to record the first operations, evaluating parentheses and brackets from inside out. *Tell your partner the visual that helped you remember.* Continue evaluating each step in a different part of the paper.

**Advanced** Students will review the *Order of Operations* with partners. Write $\frac{1}{4} \times 2^4 + [5 + (48 \div 6)]$. Instruct students to write and perform each operation on a separate line. Then have them write the visual symbol next to each step.

**Summarize** What are the steps of the *Order of Operations*?

# DEVELOP: PROBLEM-BASED LEARNING

**COHERENCE: Engage learners by connecting prior knowledge to new ideas.**
Students extend their understanding of the order of operations by writing and evaluating an expression that represents a real-world situation.

10–15 min

Solve

## BEFORE

1. **Pose the Solve-and-Share Problem**
**MP.7 Look for Relationships** Listen and look for students who relate numerical expressions to the problem situation and use the correct order of operations to evaluate.

2. **Build Understanding**
*What are you asked to do?* [Write and evaluate an expression to find the total amount in fees collected.] *What information will you use?* [50 bags were overweight at a fee of $49 bag. 6 bags were oversized at a fee of $75 per bag.]

## DURING

3. **Ask Guiding Questions As Needed**
*What expression represents fees collected for the overweight bags?* [50 × 49] *The oversized bags?* [6 × 75] *How would you use these expressions to find the total fees?* [Add them.] *Are parentheses necessary in this expression?* [No; multiplication is done before addition.]

## AFTER

4. **Share and Discuss Solutions**
Solve Start with students' solutions. If needed, project Jack's work to discuss how to evaluate the expression.

5. **Transition to the Visual Learning Bridge**
*When evaluating an expression with more than one operation, follow the correct order of operations.*

6. **Extension for Early Finishers**
*Write an expression with parentheses that has a different value if you remove the parentheses.* [Sample answer: 20 × (4 + 3) and 20 × 4 + 3]

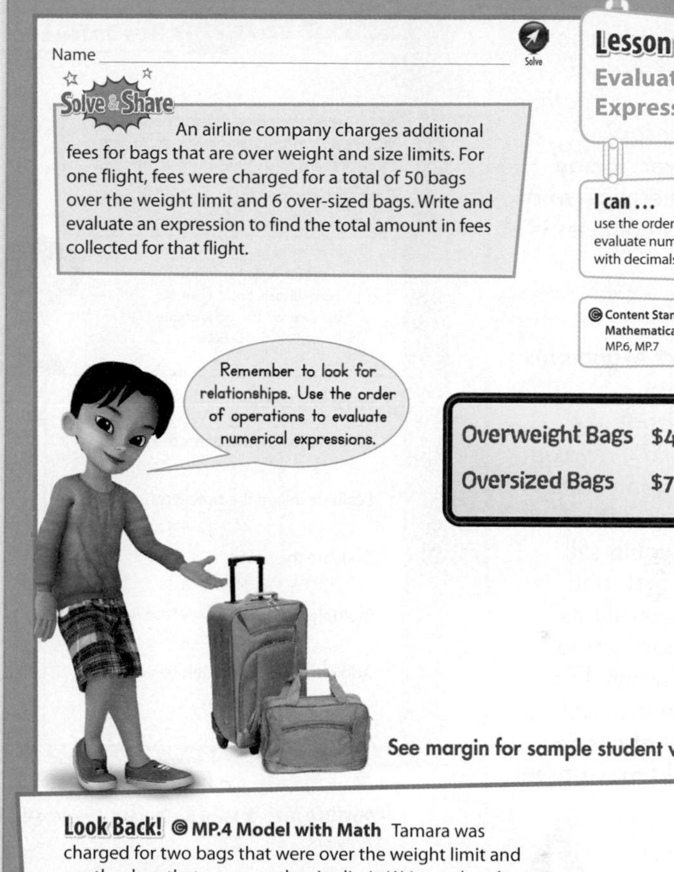

Name
Solve & Share
Lesson 1-2
Evaluate Numerical Expressions
An airline company charges additional fees for bags that are over weight and size limits. For one flight, fees were charged for a total of 50 bags over the weight limit and 6 over-sized bags. Write and evaluate an expression to find the total amount in fees collected for that flight.
I can ...
use the order of operations to evaluate numerical expressions with decimals and fractions.
Content Standards 6.EE.A.1, 6.EE.A.3
Mathematical Practices MP.1, MP.3, MP.4, MP.6, MP.7
Remember to look for relationships. Use the order of operations to evaluate numerical expressions.
Overweight Bags $49 per bag
Oversized Bags $75 per bag
See margin for sample student work.
Look Back! MP.4 Model with Math Tamara was charged for two bags that were over the weight limit and another bag that was over the size limit. Write and evaluate a numerical expression to find how much Tamara was charged for her bags.
Sample answer: (2 × 49) + 75 = 173; Tamara was charged $173 in fees for her bags.
Digital Resources at PearsonRealize.com
Topic 1 | Lesson 1-2
13


## Analyze Student Work

**Jack's Work**

(50 × 49) + (6 × 75)
2,450 + 450
2,900
The total amount of fees was $2,900.

Jack's expression is correct, and he evaluates it using the correct order of operations.

**Taylor's Work**

50 × 49 + 6 × 75
2,450 + 6 × 75
2,456 × 75
$184,200 total fees.

Taylor's expression is also correct, but she does not follow the order of operations when she evaluates it.

# STEP 2 DEVELOP: VISUAL LEARNING

PEARSON realize. PearsonRealize.com

Learn Glossary

The *Visual Learning Bridge* connects students' thinking in Solve & Share to important math ideas in the lesson. Use the *Visual Learning Bridge* to make these ideas explicit. Also available as a *Visual Learning Animation Plus* at PearsonRealize.com

*Why do you think brackets are used rather than having one set of parentheses inside another set of parentheses?* [Sample answer: It may be hard to determine what each set of parentheses is enclosing.]

**MP.3 Construct Arguments** *If there were no parentheses inside the brackets, would the value of this expression change? Why or why not?* [No; the brackets would still be evaluated first, and the order of operations calls for division before addition.] Point out that if a step in the order of operations is not needed, students should move onto the next step.

**Prevent Misconceptions** (1 RtI)

When finding the value of one part of an expression, students might forget to rewrite the rest of the expression. Encourage them to "bring down" all parts of the expression.

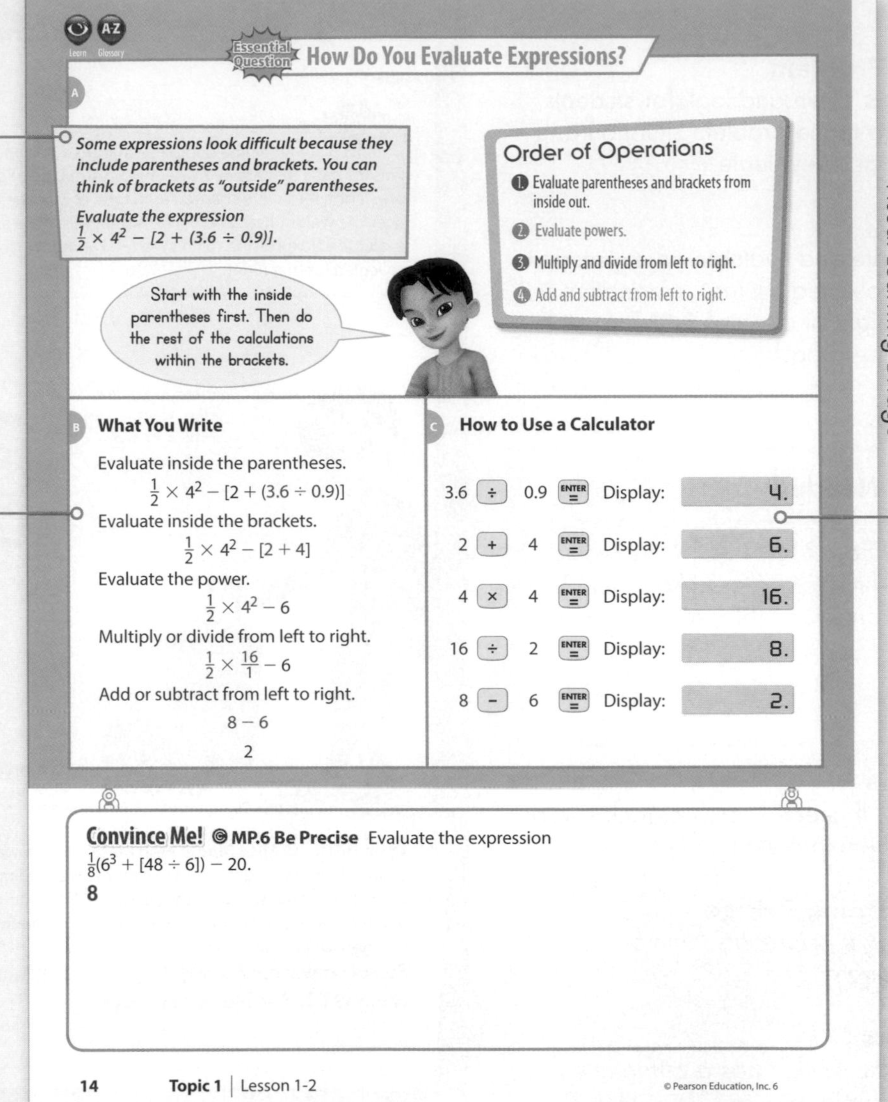

Visual Learning Bridge

Learn Glossary

Essential Question **How Do You Evaluate Expressions?**

A

*Some expressions look difficult because they include parentheses and brackets. You can think of brackets as "outside" parentheses.*

*Evaluate the expression* $\frac{1}{2} \times 4^2 - [2 + (3.6 \div 0.9)]$.

Start with the inside parentheses first. Then do the rest of the calculations within the brackets.

**Order of Operations**

1. Evaluate parentheses and brackets from inside out.
2. Evaluate powers.
3. Multiply and divide from left to right.
4. Add and subtract from left to right.

B **What You Write**

Evaluate inside the parentheses.

$\frac{1}{2} \times 4^2 - [2 + (3.6 \div 0.9)]$

Evaluate inside the brackets.

$\frac{1}{2} \times 4^2 - [2 + 4]$

Evaluate the power.

$\frac{1}{2} \times 4^2 - 6$

Multiply or divide from left to right.

$\frac{1}{2} \times \frac{16}{1} - 6$

Add or subtract from left to right.

$8 - 6$

$2$

C **How to Use a Calculator**

| Keys | Display |
|---|---|
| 3.6 ÷ 0.9 ENTER | 4. |
| 2 + 4 ENTER | 6. |
| 4 × 4 ENTER | 16. |
| 16 ÷ 2 ENTER | 8. |
| 8 − 6 ENTER | 2. |

**Convince Me!** **MP.6 Be Precise** Evaluate the expression $\frac{1}{8}(6^3 + [48 \div 6]) - 20$.

8

14 Topic 1 | Lesson 1-2 © Pearson Education, Inc. 6

*How do you evaluate this expression using a calculator that has parentheses and brackets keys?* [Type the complete expression as shown. The calculator uses the order of operations.] Students may use the calculator as a tool, but they need to know how to use it correctly. A simple test is to enter $1 + 2 \cdot 3$. If the result is 7, the calculator uses the order of operations. If the result is 9, students will need to follow the example in Box C. *What keys on a calculator can be used to evaluate powers?* [A caret key (^) or an exponent key ($y^x$) can be used between the base and exponent.]

**Convince Me! MP.6 Be Precise** *In this problem, what are the inside grouping symbols?* [Brackets] *After you evaluate the brackets, what do you do next?* [Evaluate inside the parentheses.] *Can you subtract 20 next? Explain.* [No; you need to multiply the sum inside the parentheses by $\frac{1}{8}$.]

**Coherence** In Grade 5, students evaluated simple numerical expressions without powers and multiple grouping symbols. Now, they learn the order in which to perform operations when an expression includes exponents and more than one grouping symbol. This develops the proficiency students will need for evaluating algebraic expressions later in Topic 1 and throughout the program.

Revisit the Essential Question. A specific order must be followed when evaluating expressions with more than one operation. By following the order of operations, expressions can be evaluated correctly and consistently.

PEARSON realize.
PearsonRealize.com

## ☑ QUICK CHECK

Check mark indicates items for prescribing differentiation on the next page.
Item 12 is worth 1 point. Items 16 and 17 are worth up to 2 points.

20–30 min

Practice Buddy

Tools

Assessment

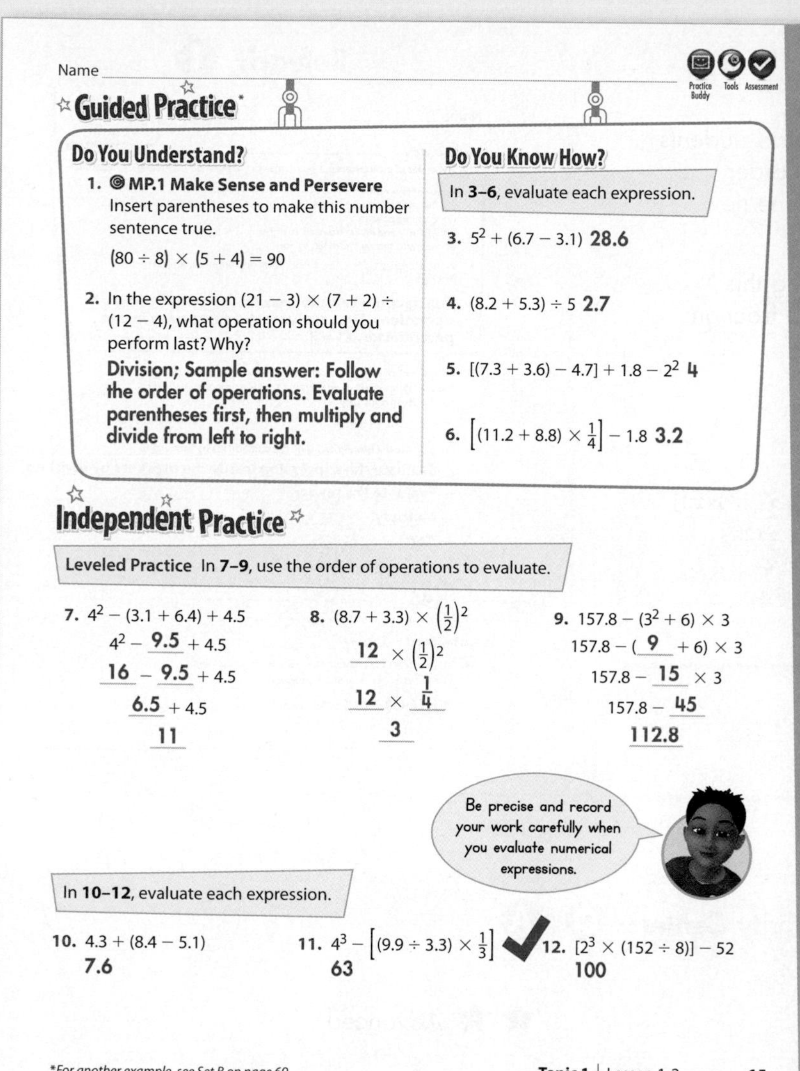

Name ______

### Guided Practice*

**Do You Understand?**

1. **MP.1 Make Sense and Persevere** Insert parentheses to make this number sentence true.
$(80 \div 8) \times (5 + 4) = 90$

2. In the expression $(21 - 3) \times (7 + 2) \div (12 - 4)$, what operation should you perform last? Why?
**Division; Sample answer: Follow the order of operations. Evaluate parentheses first, then multiply and divide from left to right.**

**Do You Know How?**

In **3–6**, evaluate each expression.

3. $5^2 + (6.7 - 3.1)$ **28.6**

4. $(8.2 + 5.3) \div 5$ **2.7**

5. $[(7.3 + 3.6) - 4.7] + 1.8 - 2^2$ **4**

6. $\left[(11.2 + 8.8) \times \frac{1}{4}\right] - 1.8$ **3.2**

### Independent Practice*

Leveled Practice In **7–9**, use the order of operations to evaluate.

7. $4^2 - (3.1 + 6.4) + 4.5$
$4^2 - \underline{9.5} + 4.5$
$\underline{16} - \underline{9.5} + 4.5$
$\underline{6.5} + 4.5$
$\underline{11}$

8. $(8.7 + 3.3) \times \left(\frac{1}{2}\right)^2$
$\underline{12} \times \left(\frac{1}{2}\right)^2$
$\underline{12} \times \underline{\frac{1}{4}}$
$\underline{3}$

9. $157.8 - (3^2 + 6) \times 3$
$157.8 - (\underline{9} + 6) \times 3$
$157.8 - \underline{15} \times 3$
$157.8 - \underline{45}$
$\underline{112.8}$

Be precise and record your work carefully when you evaluate numerical expressions.



In **10–12**, evaluate each expression.

10. $4.3 + (8.4 - 5.1)$
**7.6**

11. $4^3 - \left[(9.9 \div 3.3) \times \frac{1}{3}\right]$
**63**

✓ 12. $[2^3 \times (152 \div 8)] - 52$
**100**

*For another example, see Set B on page 69.



### Math Practices and Problem Solving*

13. **MP.7 Use Structure** How do you know which part of the numerical expression to evaluate first? Explain.
$(26 + 2.5) - [(8.3 \times 3) + (1^3 - 0.25)]$
**Sample answer: Use the order of operations. Compute inside parentheses, then inside the brackets, then multiply or divide from left to right. Finally add or subtract from left to right.**

14. **Math and Science** In an ecosystem, some animals get energy by eating plants. An elk can eat 20 pounds of plants each day. Write and evaluate an expression to find how many pounds of plants a herd of 18 elk can eat in one week. **2,520 lbs; Sample answer: $18(20 \times 7) = 2{,}520$**

15. **MP.4 Model with Math** Lillian bought four hairbrushes at \$3.99 each. She had a coupon for \$1 off. Her mom paid for half of the remaining cost. Write and evaluate a numerical expression to find how much Lillian paid toward the purchase of the hairbrushes.
**$[(4 \times 3.99) - 1] \div 2 = (15.96 - 1) \div 2 = 7.48$; Lillian paid \$7.48.**

✓ 16. **Higher Order Thinking** Frederick evaluates the numerical expression $[(53.7 + 37.2) - (3^3 + 3.8)] - 8.6$. He records the answer as 51.5. Lana evaluates the numerical expression $53.7 + 37.2 - 3^3 + 3.8 - 8.6$. She records the answer as 59.1. The expressions have the same numbers and operations. Explain how Frederick and Lana can both be correct.
**Sample answer: They both followed the order of operations but the grouping symbols require Frederick to calculate the numbers in a different order than Lana.**

#### Common Core Assessment

✓ 17. Draw lines to match each number on the right to the equivalent numerical expression on the left.

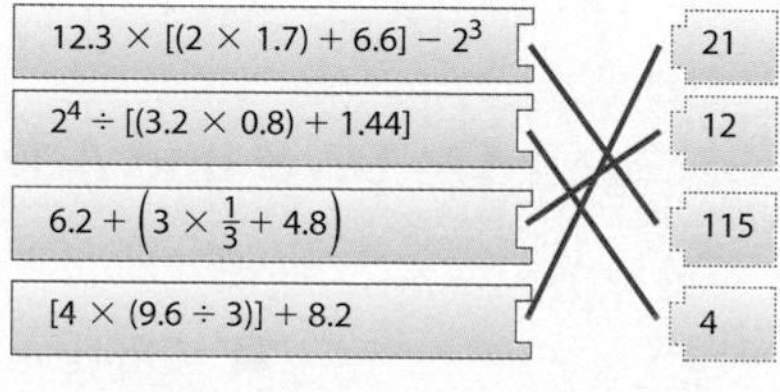

12.3 × [(2 × 1.7) + 6.6] − 2³
2⁴ ÷ [(3.2 × 0.8) + 1.44]
6.2 + (3 × 1/3 + 4.8)
[4 × (9.6 ÷ 3)] + 8.2
21
12
115
4






**Error Intervention: Items 5 and 6**

**If** students have difficulty deciding which operation to do first, **then** have them read Step 1 in the order of operations. *Does the expression have parentheses or brackets?* [Yes; it has both.] *Are the parentheses inside the brackets, or are the brackets inside the parentheses?* [The parentheses are inside the brackets.] *So, start with the parentheses and then move out to the brackets.*

**Item 15 MP.4 Model with Math** Remind students that sometimes there is more than one way to write an expression. Since the order of operations indicates that multiplication is done before subtraction, some students would be correct in writing $(4 \times 3.99 - 1) \div 2$. Others might use parentheses or show multiplication by $\frac{1}{2}$ instead of division by 2: $[(4 \times 3.99) - 1] \times \frac{1}{2}$.

**Reteaching** Assign Reteaching Set B on p. 69.

**Items 10–17 Coherence** In Grade 5, students learned to use parentheses and brackets in numerical expressions (5.OA.A.1). Students apply their previous understanding, plus what they learned in Lesson 1-1 about exponents, in order to evaluate numerical expressions with fractions and decimals as well. As they continue their work in Topic 1, students will use this understanding to write and evaluate algebraic expressions.

**Item 16 Higher Order Thinking** This item illustrates that the value of an expression can depend on whether the expression has parentheses and brackets, and on how the numbers and operations are grouped in the expression.

**Multi-Step Problems** *Page 16 Items 14 and 15; Page 18 Items 15 and 16*

# ASSESS AND DIFFERENTIATE

Use the **QUICK CHECK** on the previous page to prescribe differentiated instruction.

**I Intervention** 0–3 points on the Quick Check

**O On-Level** 4 points on the Quick Check

**A Advanced** 5 points on the Quick Check

## Intervention Activity I

### The Order of Operations

- Write the expression $6^2 - [(2 + 5) \times 3]$ on the board. Ask students to copy the expression, then read and follow each step of the order of operations to evaluate the expression. [15]
- Write the following expression next to the first one: $4^2 - [(4.2 + 1.8) \times 2.1]$ *This expression is similar to the first expression, except it contains decimals. Look at your papers. What was the first operation you performed in the first expression?* [I added 2 + 5 in the parentheses.] *So, what should you do first in the new expression?* [Add 4.2 + 1.8 in the parentheses.] Continue drawing comparisons to the first expression as you guide students to follow each step of the order of operations to evaluate the new expression. [3.4]
- Repeat this approach using this expression that contains a fraction: $3^2 - \left[(4 + 8) \times \frac{1}{3}\right]$ [5]

| | |
|---|---|
| $6^2-[(2+5)\times3]$ | $4^2-[(4.2+1.8)\times2.1]$ |
| $6^2-[7\times3]$ | $4^2-[6.0\times2.1]$ |
| $6^2-21$ | $4^2-12.6$ |
| $36-21$ | $16-12.6$ |
| $15$ | $3.4$ |

## Reteach I

Name ______________________

Reteach to Build Understanding 1-2

**Vocabulary**

1. The **order of operations** is a set of rules to follow when evaluating expressions.

**Order of Operations**
(1) Evaluate expressions in parentheses and brackets from the inside out.
(2) Evaluate powers.
(3) Multiply and divide from left to right.
(4) Add and subtract from left to right.

In the expression $(21 - 3) \div 6 + 9^2$, what operation should you perform first? Why?

**Subtraction; Sample answer: Follow the order of operations. First evaluate the expression inside parentheses, 21 − 3.**

2. Fill in the blanks to explain the order in which you would perform the operations when evaluating the following expression. The first one has been done for you.

$6^2 + [(59 - 4) \div 11] \times 2$

(1) Evaluate the expression inside the parentheses by subtracting.
(2) **Evaluate the expression inside the brackets by dividing.**
(3) **Evaluate the power.**
(4) **Multiply.**
(5) **Add.**

3. Evaluate the expression $6^2 + [(59 - 4) \div 11] \times 2$ by following the steps you wrote.

**46**

**On the Back!**

4. Use the order of operations to evaluate the expression $(11^2 - 21) \times \left(\frac{1}{2}\right)^2 + 5$. Show your work.

**30; Check students' work.**

R 1-2



## On-Level and Advanced Activity Centers O A

### Center Games

Students work in pairs or small groups to evaluate numerical expressions using the order of operations. Have students record their work and explain their thinking as they play the game.

★ On-Level

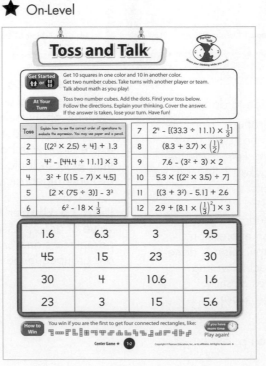

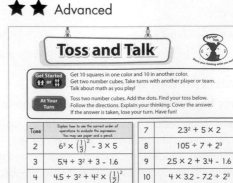

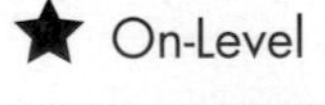

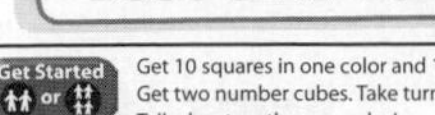

**Get Started** Get 10 squares in one color and 10 in another color. Get two number cubes. Take turns with another player or team. Talk about math as you play!

**At Your Turn** Toss two number cubes. Add the dots. Find your toss below. Follow the directions. Explain your thinking. Cover the answer. If the answer is taken, lose your turn. Have fun!

| Toss | Explain how to use the correct order of operations to evaluate the expression. You may use paper and a pencil. |
|---|---|
| 2 | $[(2^3 \times 2.5) \div 4] + 1.3$ |
| 3 | $4^2 - [44.4 \div 11.1] \times 3$ |
| 4 | $3^2 + [(15 - 7) \times 4.5]$ |
| 5 | $[2 \times (75 \div 3)] - 3^3$ |
| 6 | $6^2 - 18 \times \frac{1}{3}$ |
| 7 | $2^4 - [(33.3 \div 11.1) \times \frac{1}{3}]$ |
| 8 | $(8.3 + 3.7) \times \left(\frac{1}{2}\right)^2$ |
| 9 | $7.6 - (3^2 \div 3) \times 2$ |
| 10 | $5.3 \times [(2^2 \times 3.5) \div 7]$ |
| 11 | $[(3 + 3^2) - 5.1] + 2.6$ |
| 12 | $2.9 + [8.1 \times \left(\frac{1}{3}\right)^2] \times 3$ |

| | | | |
|---|---|---|---|
| 1.6 | 6.3 | 3 | 9.5 |
| 45 | 15 | 23 | 30 |
| 30 | 4 | 10.6 | 1.6 |
| 23 | 3 | 15 | 5.6 |

**How to Win** You win if you are the first to get four connected rectangles, like:

**If you have more time** Play again!

Center Game ★ 1-2



★★ Advanced

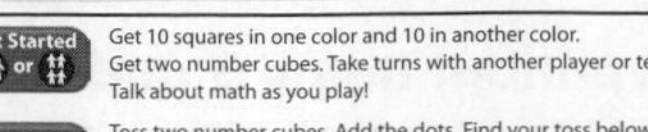



**Get Started** Get 10 squares in one color and 10 in another color. Get two number cubes. Take turns with another player or team. Talk about math as you play!

**At Your Turn** Toss two number cubes. Add the dots. Find your toss below. Follow the directions. Explain your thinking. Cover the answer. If the answer is taken, lose your turn. Have fun!

| Toss | Explain how to use the correct order of operations to evaluate the expression. You may use paper and a pencil. |
|---|---|
| 2 | $6^3 \times \left(\frac{1}{3}\right)^2 - 3 \times 5$ |
| 3 | $5.4 \div 3^2 + 3 - 1.6$ |
| 4 | $4.5 \div 3^2 + 4^2 \times \left(\frac{1}{2}\right)^2$ |
| 5 | $5 - 0.2^2 \times 20 + 1$ |
| 6 | $32 - 45 \times \left(\frac{1}{3}\right)^2$ |
| 7 | $2.3^2 + 5 \times 2$ |
| 8 | $105 \div 7 + 2^3$ |
| 9 | $2.5 \times 2 + 3.4 - 1.6$ |
| 10 | $4 \times 3.2 - 7.2 \div 2^3$ |
| 11 | $24 \div 2^2 + 2.6 \times \frac{1}{2}$ |
| 12 | $2^2 \times 5 - 12 \times \left(\frac{1}{2}\right)^2$ |

| | | | |
|---|---|---|---|
| 4.5 | 23 | 17 | 27 |
| 7.3 | 15.29 | 5.2 | 9 |
| 9 | 7.3 | 27 | 6.8 |
| 5.2 | 2 | 15.29 | 11.9 |

**How to Win** You win if you are the first to get four connected rectangles, like:

**If you have more time** Play again!

Center Game ★★ 1-2

**TIMING**

The time allocated to Step 3 will depend on the teacher's instructional decisions and differentiation routines.

15–30 min

PEARSON realize. PearsonRealize.com

Help

Practice Buddy

Tools

Games

## Technology Center    

 Tools  Games

### Math Tools and Math Games

A link to a specific math tools activity or math game to use with this lesson is provided at PearsonRealize.com.

## Leveled Assignment  Items 1–8, 13, 16, 17  Items 4–9, 13–17  Items 6–12, 13–15, 17

Name ______________________

## Homework & Practice 1-2

### Evaluate Numerical Expressions

**Another Look!**

Use the order of operations to evaluate the expression $2.3^2 + [(9 \times 4) + 9] \times \left(\frac{1}{3}\right)^2$.

| First, evaluate inside the parentheses. | Then, evaluate any powers. | Next, multiply or divide from left to right. | Finally, add or subtract from left to right. |
|---|---|---|---|
| $2.3^2 + [(9 \times 4) + 9] \times \left(\frac{1}{3}\right)^2$<br>Evaluate inside any other grouping symbols, such as brackets.<br>$2.3^2 + [36 + 9] \times \left(\frac{1}{3}\right)^2$ | $2.3^2 + 45 \times \left(\frac{1}{3}\right)^2$ | $5.29 + 45 \times \frac{1}{9}$ | $5.29 + 5$<br>The value of the numerical expression is 10.29. |

In **1–3**, use the order of operations to evaluate.

**1.** $0.2^2 \div [7.9 - (4.1 + 1.8)]$

$0.2^2 \div [7.9 - \underline{\mathbf{5.9}}]$

$0.2^2 \div \underline{\mathbf{2}}$

$\underline{\mathbf{0.04}} \div \underline{\mathbf{2}}$

$\underline{\mathbf{0.02}}$

**2.** $(14.7 + 9.3) \times \left(\frac{1}{2}\right)^2$

$\underline{\mathbf{24}} \times \left(\frac{1}{2}\right)^2$

$\underline{\mathbf{24}} \times \underline{\mathbf{\frac{1}{4}}}$

$\underline{\mathbf{6}}$

**3.** $12.3 + (6^2 - 11.8) - 1$

$12.3 + (\underline{\mathbf{36}} - 11.8) - 1$

$12.3 + \underline{\mathbf{24.2}} - 1$

$\underline{\mathbf{36.5}} - 1$

$\underline{\mathbf{35.5}}$

When expressions do not have grouping symbols, what is the first operation you evaluate?

In **4–12**, evaluate each expression.

**4.** $5^2 - 9 \div 3$
**22**

**5.** $8 + 6 - 2 \times 2 - 3^2$
**1**

**6.** $4^2 \div [(3.2 \times 2) + 1.6]$
**2**

**7.** $8 + (6 - 2) \times 2 - 3^2$
**7**

**8.** $[(12 \times 2^2) - (18.4 + 0.6)] + 3^2$
**38**

**9.** $\left[(19 + 1^5) \div \frac{1}{2}\right] + 5$
**45**

**10.** $4 \times (5 + 5) \div 20 + 6^2$
**38**

**11.** $5^2 - [(0.2 \times 8) + 0.4] \times \frac{1}{2}$
**24**

**12.** $36 \div 9 + 4 \times 5 - 3$
**21**



**13.** **MP.3 Critique Reasoning** Ivy's basketball team scored 38 points in the first game of the season. The next two games they scored a total of 77 points. For every point scored, \$0.50 is put in a jar to use for a party after the season. Ivy says you can use the expression $38 + 77 \times 0.5$ to find how much money is in the jar after the third game. Is she correct? Explain.

**No; Sample answer: She forgot to place parentheses around 38 + 77. The value of her expression is \$76.50. The correct value is \$57.50.**

**14.** **Higher Order Thinking** A printing error in a math book removed the brackets and parentheses from a numerical expression. Rewrite the expression $3^2 + 7 \times 4 + 5$ with parentheses so that it is equivalent to 69.

$\mathbf{(3^2 + 7) \times 4 + 5}$

**15.** Jessica bought a new computer for \$800. She put \$120 down and got a student discount of \$50. Her mother gave her $\frac{1}{2}$ of the balance for her birthday. Use the numerical expression to find the amount Jessica still owes for the computer.

$[800 - (120 + 50)] \div 2$

**Jessica owes \$315 for the computer.**

**16.** Luke needs a new fence around his garden, but the gate across the narrow end of the garden will not be replaced. Write and evaluate a numerical expression to find how many feet of fencing Luke needs.

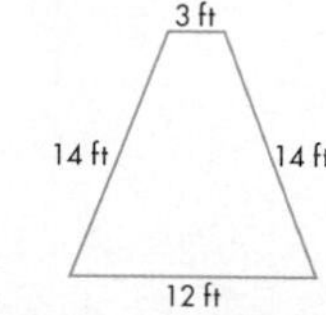


$\mathbf{12 + (2 \times 14) = 40}$ **feet**

### Common Core Assessment

**17.** Draw lines to match each number on the right to the equivalent expression on the left.

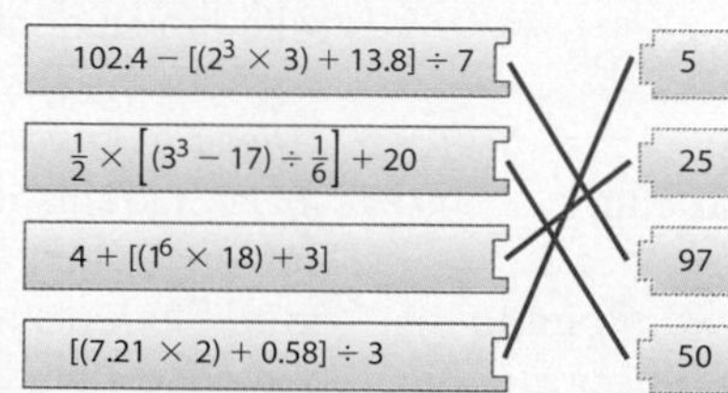

102.4 − [(2³ × 3) + 13.8] ÷ 7
½ × [(3³ − 17) ÷ ⅙] + 20
4 + [(1⁶ × 18) + 3]
[(7.21 × 2) + 0.58] ÷ 3
5
25
97
50

# LESSON 1-3

# USE VARIABLES TO WRITE EXPRESSIONS

## DIGITAL RESOURCES PearsonRealize.com

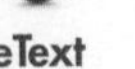
eText — Student and Teacher eTexts

PD — Listen and Look For Lesson Video

Think — Today's Challenge

Solve — Solve and Share

Learn — Visual Learning Animation Plus

Glossary — Animated Glossary

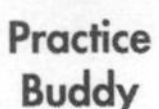
Practice Buddy — Online Personalized Practice

Tools — Math Tools

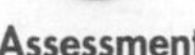
Assessment — Quick Check

Help — Another Look Homework Video

Games — Math Games

## LESSON OVERVIEW FCR FOCUS • COHERENCE • RIGOR

### FOCUS

**Domain 6.EE** Expressions and Equations

**Cluster 6.EE.A** Apply and extend previous understandings of arithmetic to algebraic expressions.

**Content Standard 6.EE.A.2a** Write expressions that record operations with numbers and with letters standing for numbers. *For example, express the calculation "Subtract y from 5" as 5 – y.* Also **6.EE.B.6**.

**Mathematical Practices MP.1, MP.2, MP.4, MP.6, MP.7, MP.8**

**Objective** Use variables to write algebraic expressions.

**Essential Understanding** Algebraic expressions use variables to describe situations in which all of the information is not known.

**Vocabulary** Variable, Algebraic expression

### COHERENCE

In Lesson 1-2, students evaluated numerical expressions. In Grade 5, they worked with volume formulas containing letter variables. In this lesson, they learn to write algebraic expressions, including those that model real-world problems. Students consider word phrases and operations that can be written as algebraic expressions involving variables. Encourage students to choose variables that make sense and are easy to remember. Later in Topic 1, students build on this understanding to analyze, simplify, and evaluate algebraic expressions.

### RIGOR

This lesson emphasizes a blend of **conceptual understanding** and **procedural skill**. Students represent relationships between known and unknown quantities by using numbers, variables, and symbols. They apply this understanding to write algebraic expressions for both mathematical and real-world situations.

PD Watch the Listen and Look For Lesson Video.

## MATH ANYTIME

### Daily Common Core Review

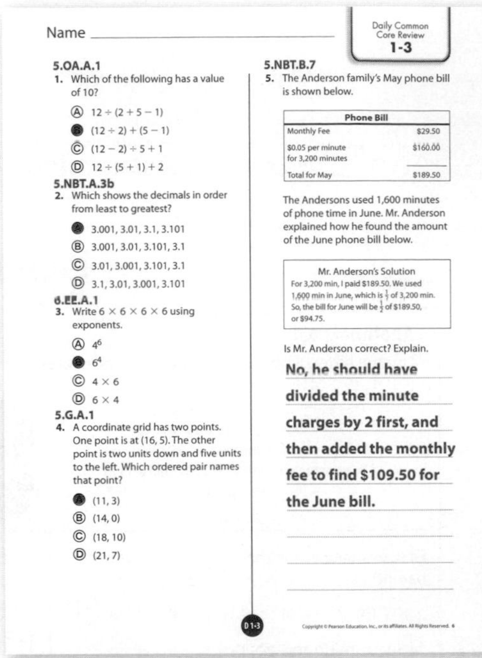

Name ________________

Daily Common Core Review **1-3**

**5.OA.A.1**

1. Which of the following has a value of 10?
   - Ⓐ $12 \div (2 + 5 - 1)$
   - ● $(12 \div 2) + (5 - 1)$
   - Ⓒ $(12 - 2) \div 5 + 1$
   - Ⓓ $12 \div (5 + 1) + 2$

**5.NBT.A.3b**

2. Which shows the decimals in order from least to greatest?
   - ● 3.001, 3.01, 3.1, 3.101
   - Ⓑ 3.001, 3.01, 3.101, 3.1
   - Ⓒ 3.01, 3.001, 3.101, 3.1
   - Ⓓ 3.1, 3.01, 3.001, 3.101

**6.EE.A.1**

3. Write $6 \times 6 \times 6 \times 6$ using exponents.
   - Ⓐ $4^6$
   - ● $6^4$
   - Ⓒ $4 \times 6$
   - Ⓓ $6 \times 4$

**5.G.A.1**

4. A coordinate grid has two points. One point is at (16, 5). The other point is two units down and five units to the left. Which ordered pair names that point?
   - ● (11, 3)
   - Ⓑ (14, 0)
   - Ⓒ (18, 10)
   - Ⓓ (21, 7)

**5.NBT.B.7**

5. The Anderson family's May phone bill is shown below.

| Phone Bill | |
|---|---|
| Monthly Fee | $29.50 |
| $0.05 per minute for 3,200 minutes | $160.00 |
| Total for May | $189.50 |

The Andersons used 1,600 minutes of phone time in June. Mr. Anderson explained how he found the amount of the June phone bill below.

Mr. Anderson's Solution
For 3,200 min, I paid $189.50. We used 1,600 min in June, which is $\frac{1}{2}$ of 3,200 min. So, the bill for June will be $\frac{1}{2}$ of $189.50, or $94.75.

Is Mr. Anderson correct? Explain.

**No, he should have divided the minute charges by 2 first, and then added the monthly fee to find $109.50 for the June bill.**

D 1-3

### Today's Challenge

Think Use the Topic 1 problems any time during this topic.

## ENGLISH LANGUAGE LEARNERS ELL

**Speaking** Speak using content-area vocabulary in context.

*Use with the Visual Learning Bridge on Student's Edition p. 20.*

Read Box B. Point to the *n* on the chart. *The letter n is a variable. A variable is used when a number is not known.* Point to $4 \times n$. Explain that $4 \times n$ is an algebraic expression. *Algebraic expressions have at least one variable and at least one operation.*

**Beginning** Write *algebraic expression* and *variable.* Read the words and their definitions with the students. Write $4 \times n$. *This is an algebraic expression.* Point to the *n*. *The letter n is a variable.* Write $n \div 5$. *What is this?* Students respond using the following sentence stem: $n \div 5$ is an ________. Point to *n*. Students respond using the following sentence stem: *n* is a ________.

**Intermediate** Write *algebraic expression* and *variable.* Instruct students to read the words and their definitions to partners. Write $4 \times n$. *This is an algebraic expression.* Point to *n*. *This is a variable.* Write $n \div 5$. *What is this?* Point to *n*. *What is this?* Students will respond using complete sentences.

**Advanced** Write *algebraic expression* and *variable.* Ask students to define the words to partners and identify the algebraic expressions and variables in the following: $4 \times n$ and $n \div 5$. Instruct students to use full sentences when they share with their partners.

**Summarize** What are *algebraic expressions* and *variables?*

# DEVELOP: PROBLEM-BASED LEARNING

**COHERENCE: Engage learners by connecting prior knowledge to new ideas.**
Students extend their understanding of patterns to find a mathematical relationship that can be represented using a variable in an algebraic expression.

10–15 min

Solve

## BEFORE

**1. Pose the Solve-and-Share Problem**
**MP.8 Generalize** Listen and look for students who recognize the pattern in the table and are able to generalize the mathematical relationship.

**2. Build Understanding**
*What is the benefit of organizing information in a table or chart?* [You can analyze the information quickly to see how quantities are related.] *What information does the table show?* [The number of games won by the Hornets and the number of games won by the Lynx] *Why might the letter n be used to represent any number of games?* [Sample answer: The word *number* starts with *n*.]

## DURING

**3. Ask Guiding Questions As Needed**
*What patterns or relationships are shown in the table?* [Sample answer: The Lynx always win 2 more games than the Hornets.] *What mathematical rule could you write to describe this relationship?* [Sample answer: Plus 2] *How can you apply this rule to represent the number of games won by the Lynx?* [$n + 2$]

## AFTER

**4. Share and Discuss Solutions**
Solve Start with students' solutions. If needed, project Olivia's work to discuss how to write an algebraic expression.

**5. Transition to the Visual Learning Bridge**
*You can use letters to represent unknown values in algebraic expressions.*

**6. Extension for Early Finishers**
*Let n represent a number. Write an expression to represent five less than the number.* [$n - 5$] *Five more than the number.* [$n + 5$, $5 + n$] *The product of the number and 5.* [$5n$, $5 \times n$, $5(n)$]

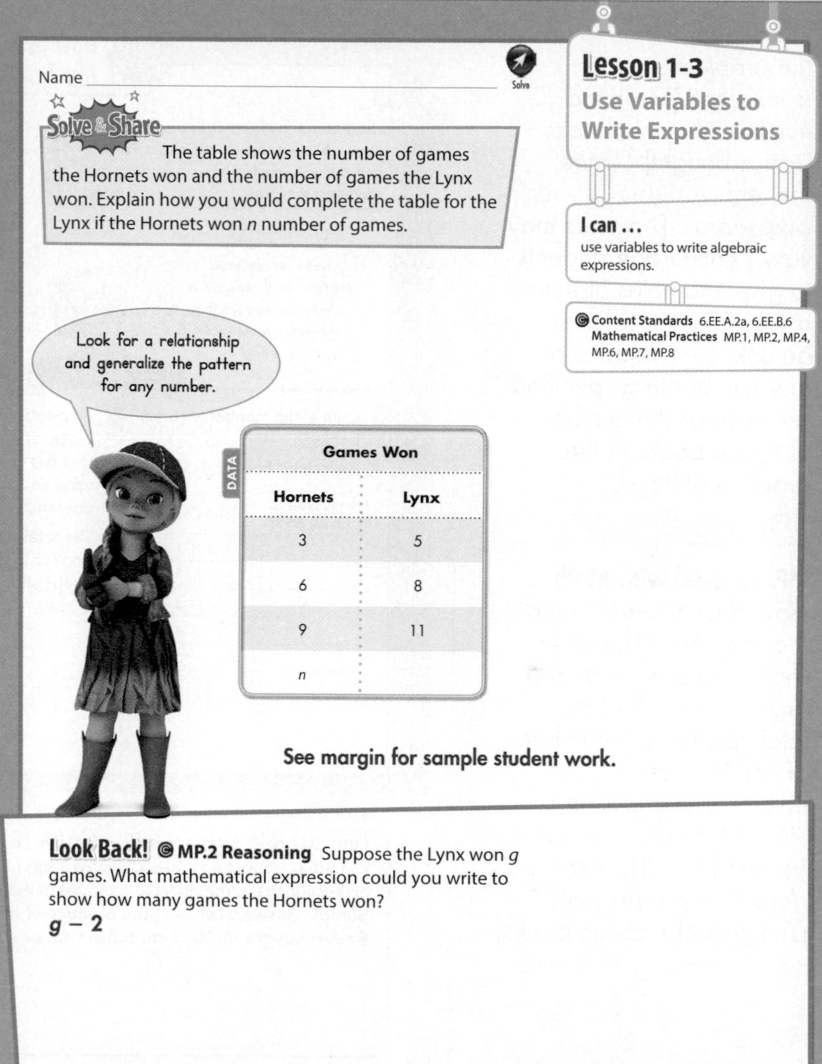

Name

Solve & Share

The table shows the number of games the Hornets won and the number of games the Lynx won. Explain how you would complete the table for the Lynx if the Hornets won *n* number of games.

**Lesson 1-3**
**Use Variables to Write Expressions**

**I can ...**
use variables to write algebraic expressions.

Content Standards 6.EE.A.2a, 6.EE.B.6
Mathematical Practices MP.1, MP.2, MP.4, MP.6, MP.7, MP.8

Look for a relationship and generalize the pattern for any number.



DATA

| Games Won | |
|---|---|
| Hornets | Lynx |
| 3 | 5 |
| 6 | 8 |
| 9 | 11 |
| *n* | |

**See margin for sample student work.**

**Look Back!** **MP.2 Reasoning** Suppose the Lynx won *g* games. What mathematical expression could you write to show how many games the Hornets won?
**$g - 2$**

Digital Resources at PearsonRealize.com **Topic 1** | Lesson 1-3 **19**

## Analyze Student Work

Olivia's Work

DATA

| Games Won | | |
|---|---|---|
| Hornets | | Lynx |
| 3 + 2 | = | 5 |
| 6 + 2 | = | 8 |
| 9 + 2 | = | 11 |
| *n* | | n + 2 |

The Lynx always win 2 more games than the Hornets. I added 2 to n.

Olivia correctly finds the mathematical relationship between games won and applies it to the unknown number, *n*.

Grace's Work

DATA

| Games Won | |
|---|---|
| Hornets | Lynx |
| 3 | 5 |
| 6 | 8 |
| 9 | 11 |
| *n* | 14 |

The pattern is add 3. The missing number is 14.

Grace finds a pattern in the table but does not relate the Hornets' wins to Lynx's wins.

# DEVELOP: VISUAL LEARNING

The *Visual Learning Bridge* connects students' thinking in Solve & Share to important math ideas in the lesson. Use the *Visual Learning Bridge* to make these ideas explicit. Also available as a *Visual Learning Animation Plus* at PearsonRealize.com

ELL Visual Learning

PEARSON realize. PearsonRealize.com

Learn Glossary

*What information in the problem situation is missing?* [The exact number of comic books Darius bought] *Define the term variable in your own words.* [Answers may vary.] Encourage students to give examples of how a variable can refer to an unknown value or to any number in a specified set, such as the number of comic books in the problem at hand.

**MP.4 Model with Math**
*How does the table model the problem?* [The table shows the operation and factor used to find the total cost for any number of comic books.] *What numerical expression shows the cost of 3 comic books?* [4 × 3] *What does 4 × n represent?* [The cost of *n* comic books]

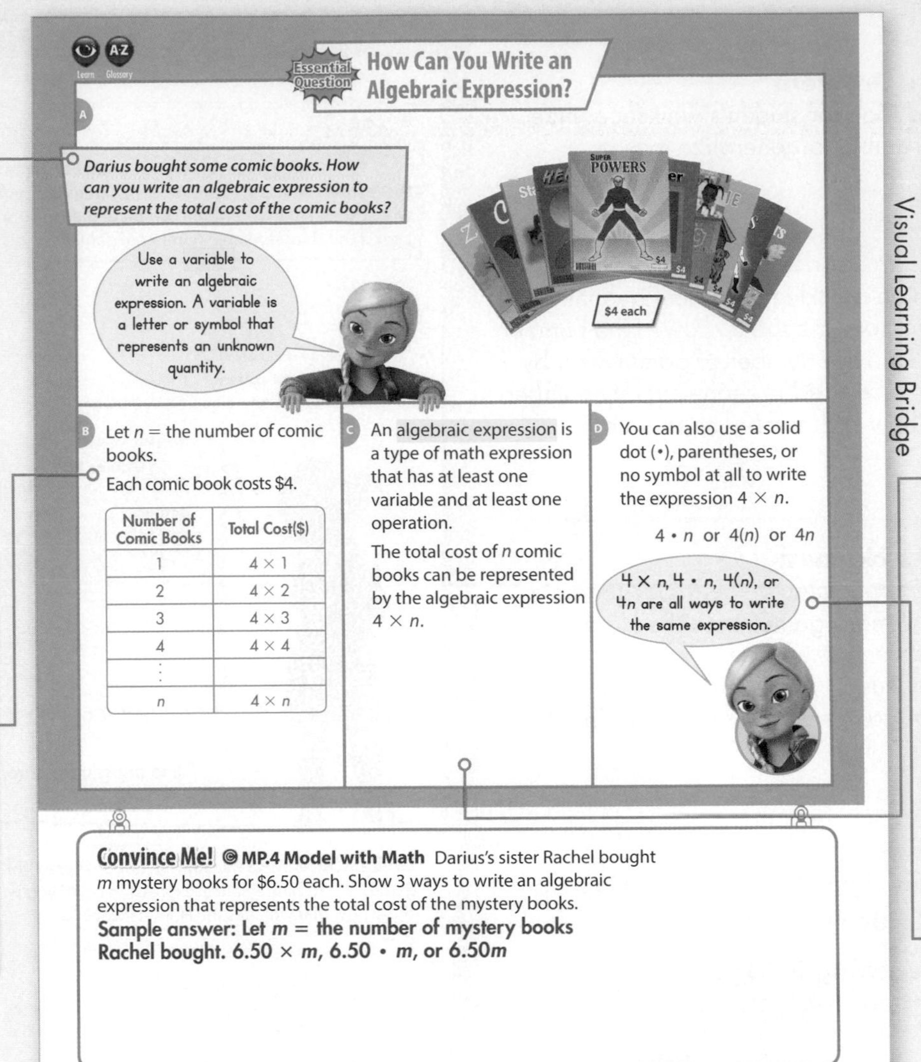

How Can You Write an Algebraic Expression?
Darius bought some comic books. How can you write an algebraic expression to represent the total cost of the comic books?
Use a variable to write an algebraic expression. A variable is a letter or symbol that represents an unknown quantity.
$4 each
Let n = the number of comic books.
Each comic book costs $4.
Number of Comic Books | Total Cost($)
1 | 4 × 1
2 | 4 × 2
3 | 4 × 3
4 | 4 × 4
n | 4 × n
An algebraic expression is a type of math expression that has at least one variable and at least one operation.
The total cost of n comic books can be represented by the algebraic expression 4 × n.
You can also use a solid dot (•), parentheses, or no symbol at all to write the expression 4 × n.
4 • n or 4(n) or 4n
4 × n, 4 • n, 4(n), or 4n are all ways to write the same expression.
Convince Me! MP.4 Model with Math Darius's sister Rachel bought m mystery books for $6.50 each. Show 3 ways to write an algebraic expression that represents the total cost of the mystery books.
Sample answer: Let m = the number of mystery books Rachel bought. 6.50 × m, 6.50 • m, or 6.50m
20 Topic 1 | Lesson 1-3
Visual Learning Bridge


**MP.6 Be Precise**
*How is an algebraic expression like a numerical expression? How is it different?* [Numerical expressions and algebraic expressions both have quantities connected by math operations. Algebraic expressions use variables to represent unknown quantities. Numerical expressions do not have variables; all the information is known.]

**Prevent Misconceptions**

Some students may not understand why a operation symbol is not needed to express the product of a number and a variable. Explain that a multiplication sign, ×, can be mistaken for the variable *x*. Using a dot or no symbol helps avoid confusion.

**Convince Me! MP.4 Model with Math** Mathematically proficient students can apply definitions and concepts to new problems. *What operation will you use to find the total cost of m books?* [Multiplication] *What are three ways to represent multiplication in an expression?* [A solid dot, parentheses, or no symbol between the number and the variable]

**Coherence** In Grade 5, students analyzed numerical patterns and represented the relationships with numerical expressions. In the canoe problem, students learn how to write algebraic expressions involving variables to represent relationships in which one of the quantities is unknown. Students will draw on this understanding as they continue to work with algebraic expressions in Topic 1.

Revisit the Essential Question. A variable can be used to represent an unknown quantity in real-world and mathematical problems. An algebraic expression represents the relationship between the unknown quantity and other quantities in the problem. Students should define all variables.

## QUICK CHECK

Check mark indicates items for prescribing differentiation on the next page.
Item 10 is worth 1 point. Items 15 and 17 are worth up to 2 points.

20–30 min

Practice Buddy

Tools

Assessment

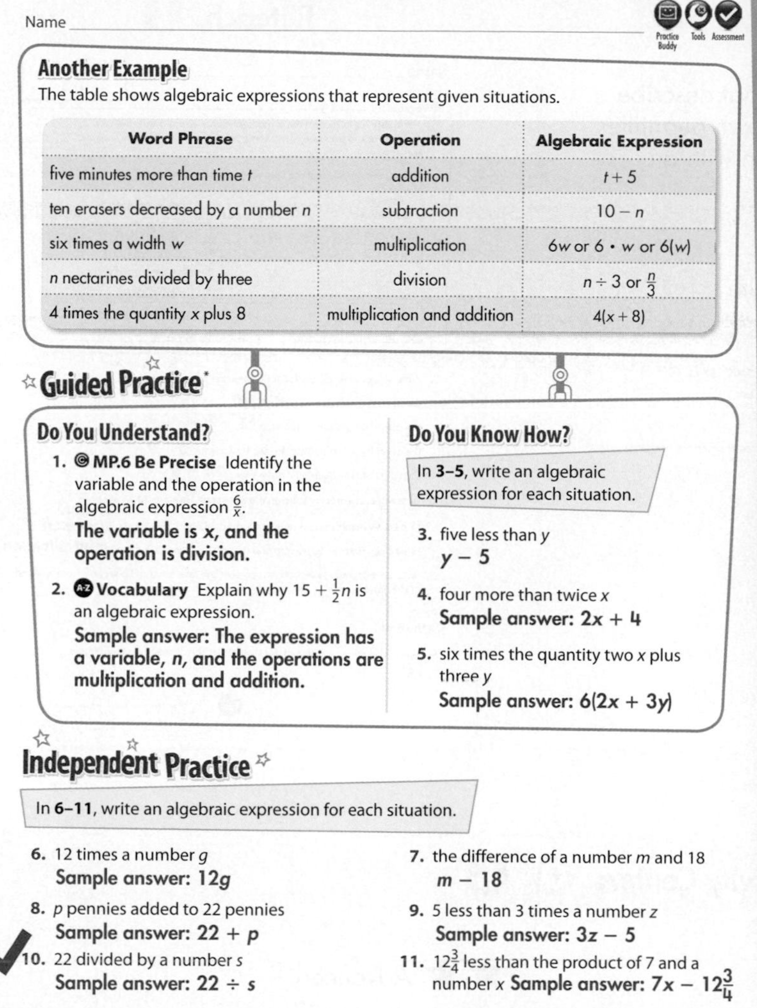

Name ______________________

### Another Example

The table shows algebraic expressions that represent given situations.

| Word Phrase | Operation | Algebraic Expression |
|---|---|---|
| five minutes more than time $t$ | addition | $t + 5$ |
| ten erasers decreased by a number $n$ | subtraction | $10 - n$ |
| six times a width $w$ | multiplication | $6w$ or $6 \cdot w$ or $6(w)$ |
| $n$ nectarines divided by three | division | $n \div 3$ or $\frac{n}{3}$ |
| 4 times the quantity $x$ plus 8 | multiplication and addition | $4(x + 8)$ |

### Guided Practice*

**Do You Understand?**

1. **MP.6 Be Precise** Identify the variable and the operation in the algebraic expression $\frac{6}{x}$.
   **The variable is $x$, and the operation is division.**
2. **Vocabulary** Explain why $15 + \frac{1}{2}n$ is an algebraic expression.
   **Sample answer: The expression has a variable, $n$, and the operations are multiplication and addition.**

**Do You Know How?**

In **3–5**, write an algebraic expression for each situation.

3. five less than $y$
   **$y - 5$**
4. four more than twice $x$
   **Sample answer: $2x + 4$**
5. six times the quantity two $x$ plus three $y$
   **Sample answer: $6(2x + 3y)$**

### Independent Practice

In **6–11**, write an algebraic expression for each situation.

6. 12 times a number $g$
   **Sample answer: $12g$**
7. the difference of a number $m$ and 18
   **$m - 18$**
8. $p$ pennies added to 22 pennies
   **Sample answer: $22 + p$**
9. 5 less than 3 times a number $z$
   **Sample answer: $3z - 5$**
10. ✓ 22 divided by a number $s$
   **Sample answer: $22 \div s$**
11. $12\frac{3}{4}$ less than the product of 7 and a number $x$ **Sample answer: $7x - 12\frac{3}{4}$**

*For another example, see Set C on page 69.



### Math Practices and Problem Solving

12. A float in the Tournament of Roses parade may use as many flowers as a florist sells in 6 years. If $f$ is the number of flowers a florist sells in 1 year, write an algebraic expression to represent the number of flowers a float in the parade may use.
    **Sample answer: $6f$**
13. **MP.1 Make Sense and Persevere** A group of cows produced the same number of gallons, $g$, of milk each day for a week. Sara collected the milk for six days. Write an expression to show the number of gallons Sara did **NOT** collect.
    **Sample answer: $7g - 6g$**
14. Yuri walked $p$ poodles and $b$ bulldogs on Monday. He walked the same number of poodles and bulldogs each day Tuesday through Friday as he did on Monday. Write an algebraic expression to represent how many total dogs were walked in this 5-day period.
    **Sample answer: $5p + 5b$**
15. ✓ **Higher Order Thinking** Some students equally share 2 baskets of apples. Each basket has 12 apples. Write an algebraic expression to represent this situation. Then explain how you chose which variable and operations to use.
    **Sample answer: $(2 \times 12) \div s$; I let $s$ = the number of students. The words 'share' and 'equally' told me to use division. I also need to multiply to find the total number of apples shared.**
16. **MP.4 Model with Math** The figure is a regular octagon with side length $s$. Write two algebraic expressions that use different operations to represent the perimeter of the figure.
    **Sample answer: $8s$; $s + s + s + s + s + s + s + s$**

#### Common Core Assessment

17. ✓ Which algebraic expression could **NOT** represent the phrase below?

    Four more than the product 3 times the number of $c$ cats

    Ⓐ $4 + 3c$
    ● $(4 + 3)c$
    Ⓒ $3 \cdot c + 4$
    Ⓓ $(3 \times c) + 4$

18. Which phrase could be best represented by the algebraic expression $\frac{w}{4} - 4$?

    Ⓐ the quotient of four and a number $w$
    Ⓑ the difference between a number $w$ and 4
    ● four less than the quotient of $w$ divided by 4
    Ⓓ four less than a number $w$





**Another Example** Be sure students understand what each variable represents. *What does the letter "t" represent in the first row?* [Time] *What does the letter "w" represent in the third row?* [Width] To help students to use the word clues in each row, have them say each word phrase another way. For example, instead of *ten erasers decreased by a number* n, *they could say ten erasers take away a number* n.

**Error Intervention: Item 3**

**If** students incorrectly write $5 - y$,

**then** point out that $y - 5$ and $5 - y$ are not equivalent. Unlike addition, subtraction is not commutative. *Suppose I ask you to find the number that is 5 less than 8. How would you figure that out?* [Subtract 5 from 8] *How do you write the expression?* [$8 - 5$] *So, how would you represent 5 less than y?* [$y - 5$]

**Reteaching** Assign Reteaching Set C on p. 69.

**Item 14** Ask students why this algebraic expression has two different variables. They should reason that Yuri might not have walked the same number of poodles as bulldogs. The same variable can be repeated in an expression only when the variable represents the same amount each time, as in Items 13 and 16.

**Item 16 MP.4 Model with Math** *Your classmate says that* s *has to have the same value everywhere it appears. Do you agree? Explain.* [Yes; because the variable $s$ represents the side length of the octagon, it has the same value everywhere it appears in the same problem.]

**Item 17** This item illustrates that there may be more than one correct way to write an algebraic expression.

**Multi-Step Problems** *Page 22 Items 15 and 16; Page 24 Items 13 and 14*

# ASSESS AND DIFFERENTIATE

Use the **QUICK CHECK** on the previous page to prescribe differentiated instruction.

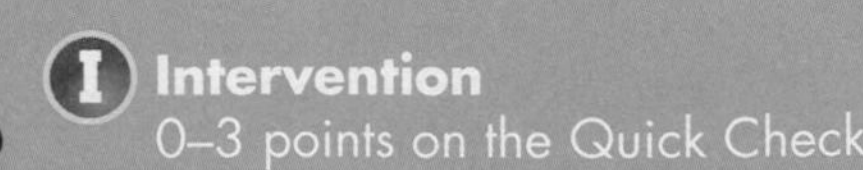
**Intervention**
0–3 points on the Quick Check

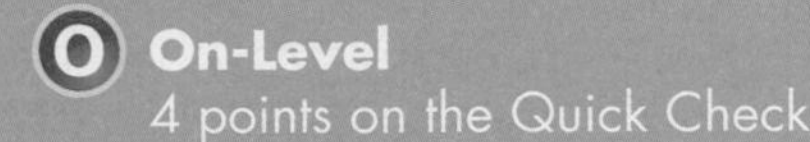
**On-Level**
4 points on the Quick Check

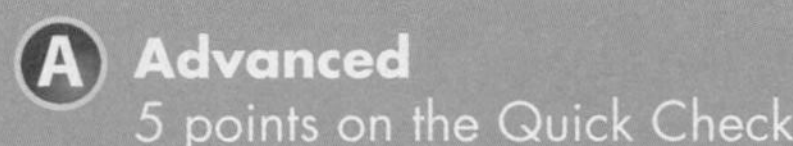
**Advanced**
5 points on the Quick Check

## Intervention Activity (I)

### Using Variables to Write Algebraic Expressions

- *Suppose I have a bag of apples and I want to divide them evenly among 3 people. If there are 15 apples in the bag, what numerical expression shows how to figure out how many apples each person gets?* [15 ÷ 3]
- *What if I haven't counted how many apples are in the bag. Let's say the letter a represents the number of apples. Write an algebraic expression that represents how many apples each person gets.* [$a \div 3$]
- Ask additional questions that describe a simple situation with known quantities and then a similar situation with an unknown quantity.

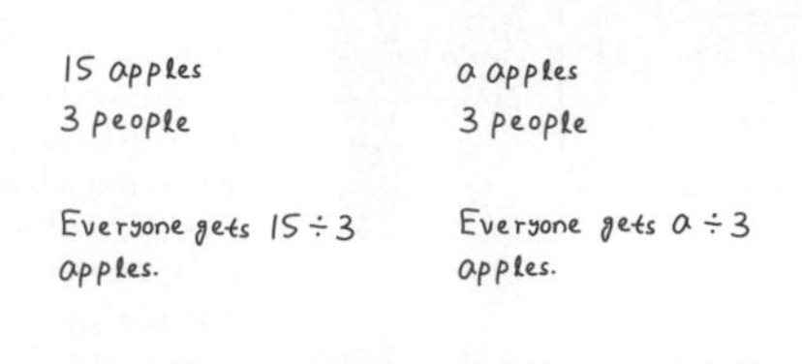

15 apples
3 people
a apples
3 people
Everyone gets 15 ÷ 3 apples.
Everyone gets a ÷ 3 apples.

## Reteach (I)

Name ____________

Reteach to Build Understanding 1-3

**Vocabulary**

1. A **variable** is a letter or symbol that represents an unknown quantity. An **algebraic expression** is an expression that has one or more variables and at least one operation.

   Identify the variable and the operation(s) in each algebraic expression.

| Algebraic Expression | Variable | Operation(s) |
|---|---|---|
| $7 + m$ | **m** | **addition** |
| $p - 12$ | **p** | **subtraction** |
| $15w$ | **w** | **multiplication** |
| $\frac{c}{8}$ | **c** | **division** |
| $2(h + 15)$ | **h** | **multiplication and addition** |

2. Write an algebraic expression for each situation.

   twenty less than a number $n$ **$n - 20$**

   the sum of fifteen and a number $b$ **$15 + b$**

   the quotient of twenty-four divided by a number $g$ **$\frac{24}{g}$**

   six more than the quantity $d$ times two **$2d + 6$**

3. Luca works at a grocery store on the weekends. He earns $8.50 per hour.

   Choose a variable to represent the number of hours Luca works. **Sample answer: $h$**

   What operation can be used to find the total amount Luca earns? **multiplication**

   Write an algebraic expression to represent the total amount Luca earns from working at the grocery store. **$8.50h$**

**On the Back!**

4. Write an algebraic expression for three times the quantity $q$ minus eleven.

   **$3(q - 11)$**

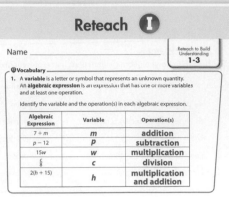

## On-Level and Advanced Activity Centers (O) (A)

### Center Games

Students work in pairs or small groups to match algebraic expressions and word phrases. Have students explain how the parts of the algebraic expression match the parts of the word phrase as they play.

★ On-Level

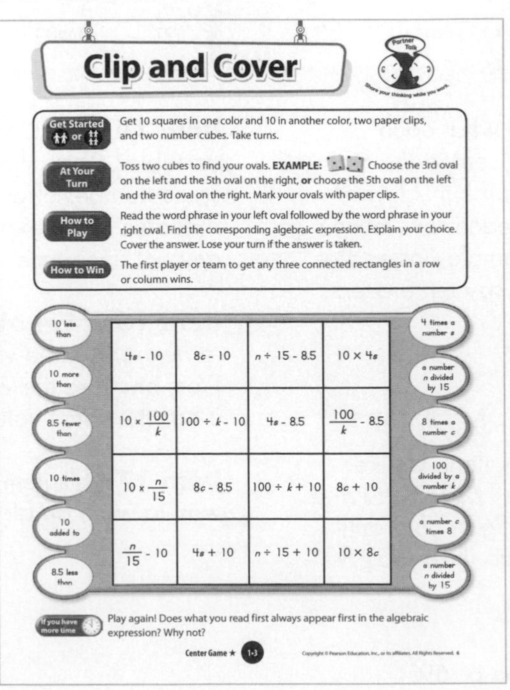

**Clip and Cover**

Partner Talk — Share your thinking while you work.

**Get Started** (2 or 4 players): Get 10 squares in one color and 10 in another color, two paper clips, and two number cubes. Take turns.

**At Your Turn**: Toss two cubes to find your ovals. **EXAMPLE:** [3] [5] Choose the 3rd oval on the left and the 5th oval on the right, **or** choose the 5th oval on the left and the 3rd oval on the right. Mark your ovals with paper clips.

**How to Play**: Read the word phrase in your left oval followed by the word phrase in your right oval. Find the corresponding algebraic expression. Explain your choice. Cover the answer. Lose your turn if the answer is taken.

**How to Win**: The first player or team to get any three connected rectangles in a row or column wins.

Left ovals: 10 less than; 10 more than; 8.5 fewer than; 10 times; 10 added to; 8.5 less than

Right ovals: 4 times a number $s$; a number $n$ divided by 15; 8 times a number $c$; 100 divided by a number $k$; a number $c$ times 8; a number $n$ divided by 15

| | | | |
|---|---|---|---|
| $4s - 10$ | $8c - 10$ | $n \div 15 - 8.5$ | $10 \times 4s$ |
| $10 \times \frac{100}{k}$ | $100 \div k - 10$ | $4s - 8.5$ | $\frac{100}{k} - 8.5$ |
| $10 \times \frac{n}{15}$ | $8c - 8.5$ | $100 \div k + 10$ | $8c + 10$ |
| $\frac{n}{15} - 10$ | $4s + 10$ | $n \div 15 + 10$ | $10 \times 8c$ |

**If you have more time**: Play again! Does what you read first always appear first in the algebraic expression? Why not?

Center Game ★ 1-3

★★ Advanced

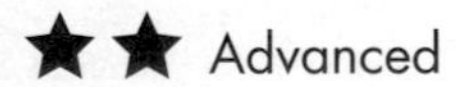

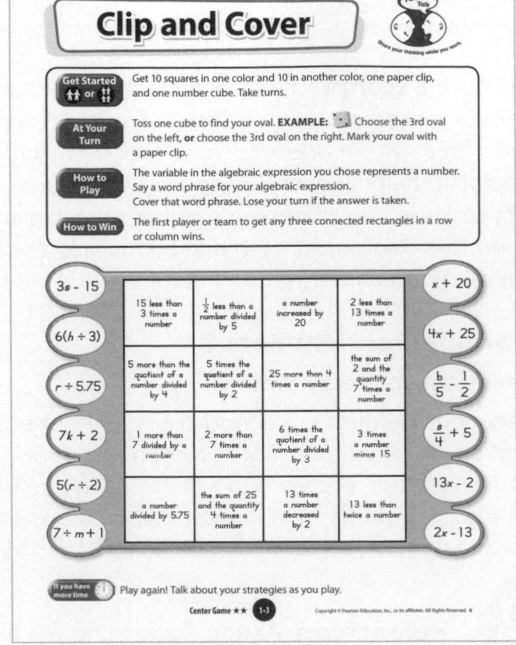

**Clip and Cover**

Partner Talk — Share your thinking while you work.

**Get Started** (2 or 4 players): Get 10 squares in one color and 10 in another color, one paper clip, and one number cube. Take turns.

**At Your Turn**: Toss one cube to find your oval. **EXAMPLE:** [3] Choose the 3rd oval on the left, **or** choose the 3rd oval on the right. Mark your oval with a paper clip.

**How to Play**: The variable in the algebraic expression you chose represents a number. Say a word phrase for your algebraic expression. Cover that word phrase. Lose your turn if the answer is taken.

**How to Win**: The first player or team to get any three connected rectangles in a row or column wins.

Left ovals: $3s - 15$; $6(h \div 3)$; $r \div 5.75$; $7k + 2$; $5(r \div 2)$; $7 \div m + 1$

Right ovals: $x + 20$; $4x + 25$; $\frac{b}{5} - \frac{1}{2}$; $\frac{s}{4} + 5$; $13x - 2$; $2x - 13$

| | | | |
|---|---|---|---|
| 15 less than 3 times a number | $\frac{1}{2}$ less than a number divided by 5 | a number increased by 20 | 2 less than 13 times a number |
| 5 more than the quotient of a number divided by 4 | 5 times the quotient of a number divided by 2 | 25 more than 4 times a number | the sum of 2 and the quantity 7 times a number |
| 1 more than 7 divided by a number | 2 more than 7 times a number | 6 times the quotient of a number divided by 3 | 3 times a number minus 15 |
| a number divided by 5.75 | the sum of 25 and the quantity 4 times a number | 13 times a number decreased by 2 | 13 less than twice a number |

**If you have more time**: Play again! Talk about your strategies as you play.

Center Game ★★ 1-3

**TIMING**

The time allocated to Step 3 will depend on the teacher's instructional decisions and differentiation routines.

15–30 min

PEARSON realize. PearsonRealize.com

 Help  Practice Buddy  Tools  Games

## Technology Center   

 Tools  Games

### Math Tools and Math Games

A link to a specific math tools activity or math game to use with this lesson is provided at PearsonRealize.com.

## Leveled Assignment  Items 1–8, 11, 12, 16, 17  Items 3–8, 12–17  Items 5–10, 12–17

Name ______________________

### Homework & Practice 1-3

**Use Variables to Write Expressions**

**Another Look!**

A variable, written as a letter, represents a quantity that can change. You can use a variable to write an algebraic expression that has at least one operation.

Here are some word phrases and their corresponding algebraic expressions.

How can an algebraic expression represent a given situation?

| Word Phrase | Variable | Operation | Algebraic Expression |
|---|---|---|---|
| ten **more than** a number *b* | *b* | Addition | $b + 10$ |
| the **sum** of 8 and a number *c* | *c* | | $8 + c$ |
| five **less than** a number *d* | *d* | Subtraction | $d - 5$ |
| 15 **decreased by** a number *e* | *e* | | $15 - e$ |
| the **product** of 8 and a number *f* | *f* | Multiplication | $8f$ |
| 19 **times** a number *g* | *g* | | $19g$ |
| the quotient of a number *h* **divided by** 2 | *h* | Division | $\frac{h}{2}$ |
| 50 **divided by** a number *i* | *i* | | $50 \div i$ |

In **1–10**, write an algebraic expression for each situation.

Remember, an algebraic expression includes at least one variable and at least one operation.

1. 6 more than a number *c*
   **Sample answer: $6 + c$**
2. 2.5 less than a number *d*
   $d - 2.5$
3. 50 divided by a number *f*
   **Sample answer: $50 \div f$**
4. twice a number *n*
   **Sample answer: $2n$**
5. 12 fewer than *h* hats
   $h - 12$
6. 4 times the sum of *x* and $\frac{1}{2}$
   **Sample answer: $4\left(x + \frac{1}{2}\right)$**
7. 6 less than the quotient of *z* divided by 3
   **Sample answer: $\frac{z}{3} - 6$**
8. Twice a number *k* plus the quantity *s* minus 2
   **Sample answer: $2k + (s - 2)$**
9. 8 more than *s* stripes
   **Sample answer: $8 + s$**
10. 5 times the quantity *m* divided by 2
    **Sample answer: $5\left(\frac{m}{2}\right)$**



In **11–14**, use the chart at the right.

11. A pet store is having a pet fish sale. Lenny bought *p* platies and *l* loaches. Write an algebraic expression to represent the total cost of the fish.
    **Sample answer: $2p + 4l$**
12. **MP.4 Model with Math** Mr. Bolden bought *g* guppies and paid with a $20 bill. Write an algebraic expression to represent how much change Mr. Bolden got back.
    **Sample answer: $20 - 3g$**
13. **MP.1 Make Sense and Persevere** Ms. Wilson bought two bags of pet fish for her twin nieces. Each bag has *g* guppies and one tetra. She also bought one box of fish food that cost *d* dollars. Write an algebraic expression to represent how much she paid in all.
    **Sample answer: $2(3g + 5) + d$**
14. In 3 days the pet store sold 27 guppies. The store sold twice as many platies as guppies. Evaluate the expression below to find the dollar amount of sales of guppies and platies.
    $27 \cdot 3 + (2 \cdot 27) \cdot 2$
    **$189**
15. **Higher Order Thinking** Describe a situation that can be represented by the algebraic expression $6b + w$.
    **Sample answer: The cost of 6 brownies, *b*, and 1 waffle cone, *w*.**

Be sure to tell what quantities are represented by the variables, *b* and *w*.

### Common Core Assessment

16. Which algebraic expression could represent the phrase below?

    Six pencils less than *p* packs of pencils that have 5 pencils in each pack

    ● $5p - 6$
    Ⓑ $p - 6$
    Ⓒ $5 \cdot (p - 6)$
    Ⓓ $6 - 5p$
17. Which of the following is the variable in the algebraic expression $(6.5 + 2.2y) \div 3$?

    Ⓐ 6.5
    Ⓑ 2.2
    ● *y*
    Ⓓ 3

# LESSON 1-4

## IDENTIFY PARTS OF AN EXPRESSION

### DIGITAL RESOURCES PearsonRealize.com

 Student and Teacher eTexts
 eText

 Listen and Look For Lesson Video
 PD

 Today's Challenge
Think

 Solve and Share
Solve

 Visual Learning Animation Plus
Learn

 Animated Glossary
Glossary

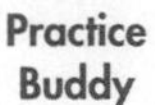 Online Personalized Practice
Practice Buddy

Math Tools
Tools

  Quick Check
Assessment

 Another Look Homework Video
Help

 Math Games
Games

### LESSON OVERVIEW FCR FOCUS • COHERENCE • RIGOR

**FOCUS**

**Domain 6.EE** Expressions and Equations

**Cluster 6.EE.A** Apply and extend previous understandings of arithmetic to algebraic expressions.

**Content Standard 6.EE.A.2b** Identify parts of an expression using mathematical terms (sum, term, product, factor, quotient, coefficient); view one or more parts of an expression as a single entity. *For example, describe the expression 2(8 + 7) as a product of two factors; view (8 + 7) as both a single entity and a sum of two terms.*

**Mathematical Practices MP.1, MP.3, MP.4, MP.6**

**Objective** Identify parts of an expression.

**Essential Understanding** Parts of expressions can be described using words such as *term, coefficient, product,* and *factor.*

**Vocabulary** Term, Coefficient

**COHERENCE**

In the first three lessons of Topic 1, students wrote and evaluated numerical expressions and wrote algebraic expressions. This lesson focuses on using precise math terminology to identify parts of an expression. A *term* is part of an expression separated by a plus or minus sign. For example, the expression $1 + a - 2 + 3bc$ has four terms: 1, $a$, 2, and $3bc$. A term may contain one or more variables. The term $3bc$ contains two variables, $b$ and $c$; the number being multiplied by the variables, 3, is called a *coefficient.* Students will apply this understanding in Lessons 1-5 through 1-8 as they evaluate, write, and simplify algebraic expressions.

**RIGOR**

This lesson emphasizes **procedural skill**. Students use both previously learned vocabulary and new vocabulary to identify parts of an expression. Remind students that an expression does *not* contain an equal sign. If a mathematical statement contains an equal sign, it is called an *equation.*

PD Watch the Listen and Look For Lesson Video.

### MATH ANYTIME

**Daily Common Core Review**

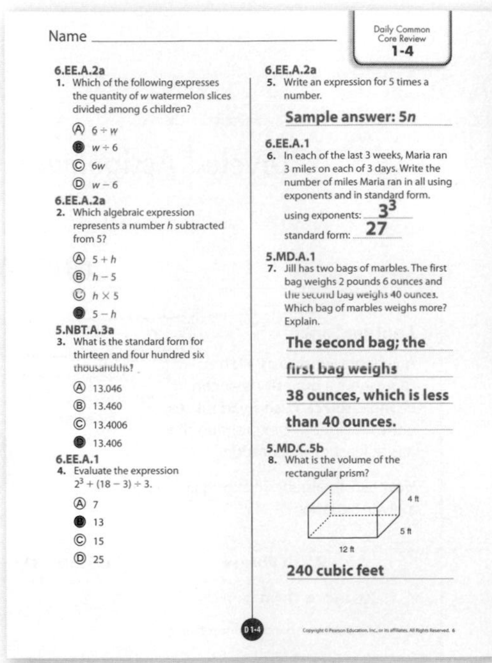

Name ______

Daily Common Core Review 1-4

6.EE.A.2a
1. Which of the following expresses the quantity of $w$ watermelon slices divided among 6 children?
Ⓐ $6 \div w$
● $w \div 6$
Ⓒ $6w$
Ⓓ $w - 6$

6.EE.A.2a
2. Which algebraic expression represents a number $h$ subtracted from 5?
Ⓐ $5 + h$
Ⓑ $h - 5$
Ⓒ $h \times 5$
● $5 - h$

5.NBT.A.3a
3. What is the standard form for thirteen and four hundred six thousandths?
Ⓐ 13.046
Ⓑ 13.460
Ⓒ 13.4006
● 13.406

6.EE.A.1
4. Evaluate the expression $2^3 + (18 - 3) \div 3$.
Ⓐ 7
● 13
Ⓒ 15
Ⓓ 25

6.EE.A.2a
5. Write an expression for 5 times a number.
**Sample answer: $5n$**

6.EE.A.1
6. In each of the last 3 weeks, Maria ran 3 miles on each of 3 days. Write the number of miles Maria ran in all using exponents and in standard form.
using exponents: $3^3$
standard form: 27

5.MD.A.1
7. Jill has two bags of marbles. The first bag weighs 2 pounds 6 ounces and the second bag weighs 40 ounces. Which bag of marbles weighs more? Explain.
**The second bag; the first bag weighs 38 ounces, which is less than 40 ounces.**

5.MD.C.5b
8. What is the volume of the rectangular prism?

**240 cubic feet**

D 1-4



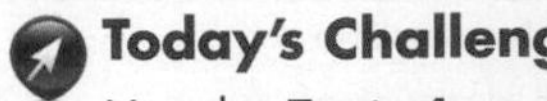 **Today's Challenge**

Think Use the Topic 1 problems any time during this topic.

### ENGLISH LANGUAGE LEARNERS 

**Learning Strategies** Use prior knowledge to understand meanings.

*Use with the Solve & Share on Student's Edition p. 25.*

Remind students of the meaning of the word *variable.* Ask them to identify the variable in $4t - 5 + (3 \div 2)$. Point to 4. Explain to students that 4 is a *coefficient.* A coefficient is a number that is multiplied by a variable.

**Beginning** Write $12r + \frac{r}{2} - 9$. Point to $r$. Ask students to remind their partners that $r$ is a variable using the following sentence frame: The letter $r$ is a ______. Point to 12. *The number 12 is the coefficient. A coefficient is multiplied by the variable.* Write $6n$. Ask students to identify the variable and coefficient.

**Intermediate** Write $12r + \frac{r}{2} - 9$. Ask students to remind their partners what a *variable* is and identify the variable in the mathematical expression. Point to 12. *The number 12 is the coefficient. A coefficient is multiplied by the variable.* Write $6n$. Ask students to identify the variable and coefficient using complete sentences.

**Advanced** Write $12r + \frac{r}{2} - 9$. Ask students to remind their partners what a *variable* is and identify the variable in the mathematical expression. Point to 12 and remind students that 12 is a coefficient. Ask students to explain to their partners the meaning of *coefficient.*

**Summarize** How are *variables* and *coefficients* related?

# DEVELOP: PROBLEM-BASED LEARNING

**COHERENCE: Engage learners by connecting prior knowledge to new ideas.**
Students extend their understanding of expressions by using specific math terminology to identify and describe parts of an expression.

10–15 min

Solve

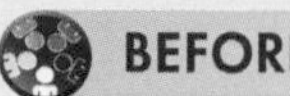

## BEFORE

1. **Pose the Solve-and-Share Problem**
**MP.6 Be Precise** Listen and look for students who use mathematical vocabulary to describe the given expression. Draw attention to these vocabulary words.

2. **Build Understanding**
*What types of mathematical expressions have you learned about?* [Numerical expressions, like $3 + 4$, and algebraic expressions, like $x \div 2$] *What is math language?* [Vocabulary words and phrases that explain mathematical ideas]

## DURING

3. **Ask Guiding Questions As Needed**
*How are expressions separated into different parts?* [Plus or minus signs] *What mathematical vocabulary terms could you use to name parts of any expression?* [Sample answers: variable, parentheses, addend, divisor, dividend, sum, difference, quotient, product]

## AFTER

4. **Share and Discuss Solutions**
Solve Start with students' solutions. If needed, project Marco's work to discuss ways to describe the expression.

5. **Transition to the Visual Learning Bridge**
*Mathematicians use specific math language to describe mathematical expressions and to identify parts of expressions.*

6. **Extension for Early Finishers**
*Write an algebraic expression that has a difference in its divisor.* [Sample answer: $\frac{x}{x-3}$]

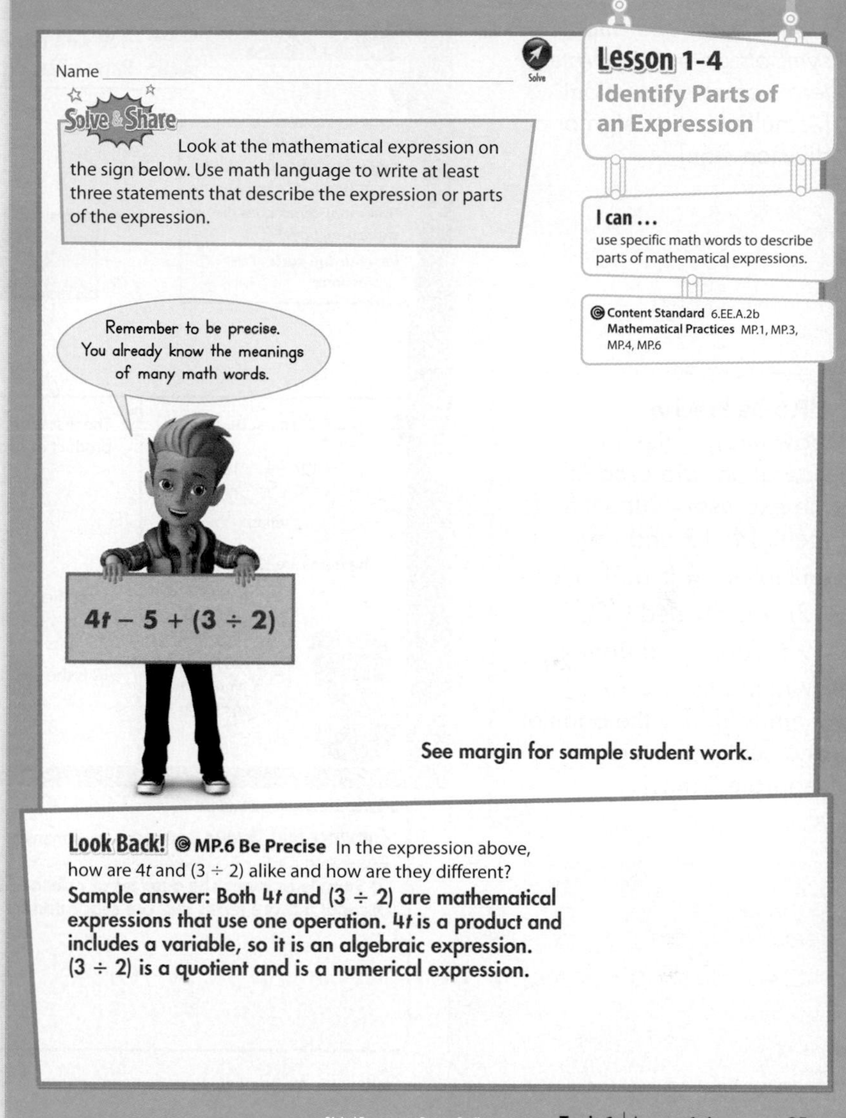

Name
Solve & Share
Look at the mathematical expression on the sign below. Use math language to write at least three statements that describe the expression or parts of the expression.
Lesson 1-4
Identify Parts of an Expression
I can ...
use specific math words to describe parts of mathematical expressions.
Content Standard 6.EE.A.2b
Mathematical Practices MP.1, MP.3, MP.4, MP.6
Remember to be precise. You already know the meanings of many math words.
4t − 5 + (3 ÷ 2)
See margin for sample student work.
Look Back! MP.6 Be Precise In the expression above, how are 4t and (3 ÷ 2) alike and how are they different?
Sample answer: Both 4t and (3 ÷ 2) are mathematical expressions that use one operation. 4t is a product and includes a variable, so it is an algebraic expression. (3 ÷ 2) is a quotient and is a numerical expression.
Digital Resources at PearsonRealize.com
Topic 1 | Lesson 1-4
25


## Analyze Student Work

**Marco's Work**

It's an algebraic expression. The t is a variable. 4 and t are factors. It uses all 4 operations.

Marco uses math language to write four complete sentences that describe the expression.

**Liana's Work**

Algebraic expression
Has a variable
Also has numbers and operations

Liana writes three phrases, using math language, that also describe the expression.

# STEP 2 DEVELOP: VISUAL LEARNING

The *Visual Learning Bridge* connects students' thinking in Solve & Share to important math ideas in the lesson. Use the *Visual Learning Bridge* to make these ideas explicit. Also available as a *Visual Learning Animation Plus* at PearsonRealize.com

Learn Glossary

*Which math operation symbols do not separate terms of an expression?* [A multiplication sign or a division sign]

**MP.6 Be Precise**
*How many different operations are used in the expression? Identify them.* [4; 12 and $r$ are multiplied; $\frac{r}{2}$ is added to $12r$; $r$ is divided by 2; 19 is subtracted from $\frac{r}{2}$.] *Why are there only 3 terms?* [Only the addition and subtraction signs separate terms.]

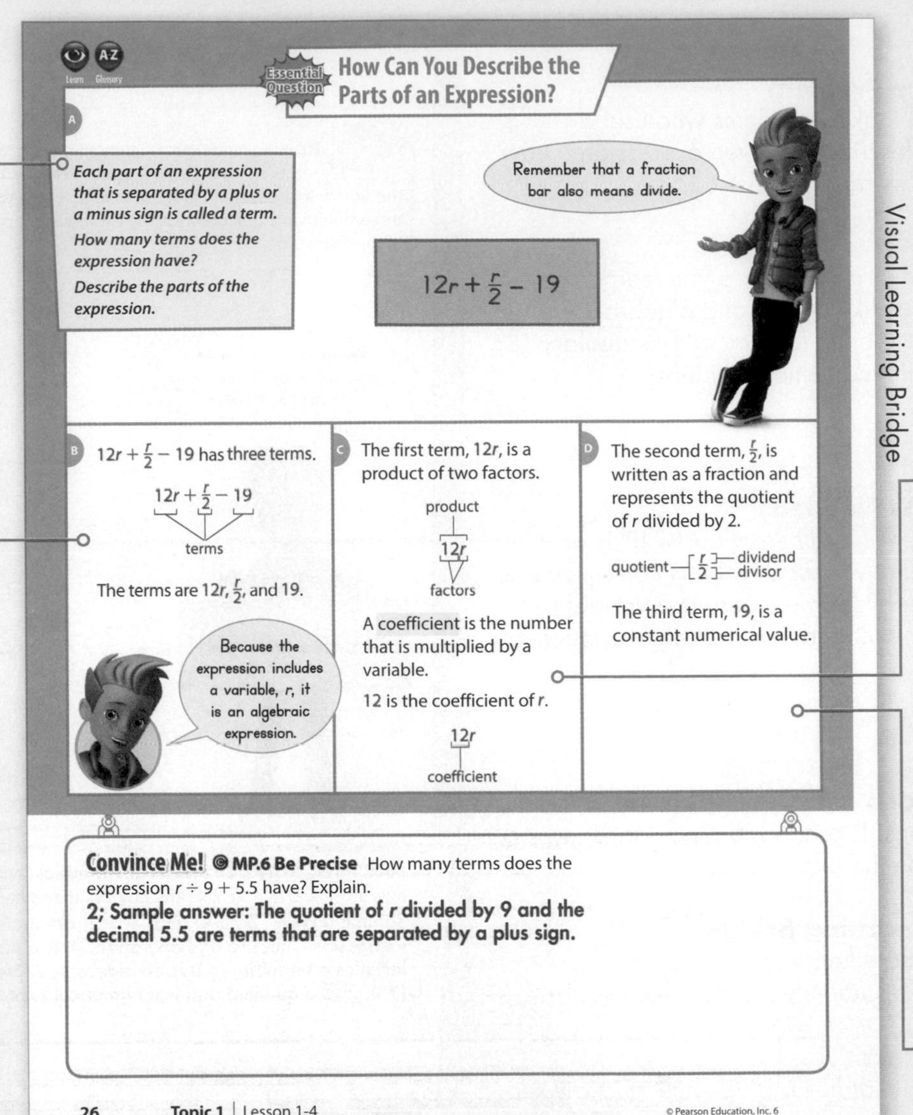

Visual Learning Bridge

Essential Question **How Can You Describe the Parts of an Expression?**

A

*Each part of an expression that is separated by a plus or a minus sign is called a term.*
*How many terms does the expression have?*
*Describe the parts of the expression.*

$12r + \frac{r}{2} - 19$

Remember that a fraction bar also means divide.

B

$12r + \frac{r}{2} - 19$ has three terms.

$12r + \frac{r}{2} - 19$ — terms

The terms are $12r$, $\frac{r}{2}$, and 19.

Because the expression includes a variable, $r$, it is an algebraic expression.

C

The first term, $12r$, is a product of two factors.

product — $12r$ — factors

A coefficient is the number that is multiplied by a variable.

12 is the coefficient of $r$.

$12r$ — coefficient

D

The second term, $\frac{r}{2}$, is written as a fraction and represents the quotient of $r$ divided by 2.

quotient — $\frac{r}{2}$ — dividend, divisor

The third term, 19, is a constant numerical value.

**Convince Me!** **MP.6 Be Precise** How many terms does the expression $r \div 9 + 5.5$ have? Explain.
**2; Sample answer: The quotient of $r$ divided by 9 and the decimal 5.5 are terms that are separated by a plus sign.**

26 Topic 1 | Lesson 1-4 © Pearson Education, Inc. 6

*How can you tell that 12r is a product?* [When there is no operation symbol written between a number (or coefficient) and a variable, the operation is multiplication.]

**Prevent Misconceptions** 

When considering the term $12r$, some students may confuse the vocabulary words *term* and *factor*. Remind students that factors are multiplied together to create a product. The term $12r$ has two factors.

**MP.3 Construct Arguments**
*Why is $\frac{r}{2}$ a quotient?* [A fraction bar means divide.] *Why is 19 considered a constant numerical value?* [Its value does not change.] *Why isn't $\frac{r}{2}$ considered a constant numerical value?* [Since the value of a variable can change, the value of $\frac{r}{2}$ can change. Therefore, it is not constant.]

**Convince Me!** **MP.6 Be Precise** Students need to understand the meaning of *term* to answer the question. You may want to rewrite the expression as $\frac{r}{9} + 5.5$ to provide students with another way of looking at the problem. Using mathematical language correctly allows clear and precise communication of mathematical ideas.

Revisit the Essential Question. Parts of an expression can be described in many different ways. Point out to students that the vocabulary words *term*, *coefficient*, *product*, *quotient*, and *factor* are just some of the mathematical terms that can be used.

## QUICK CHECK

Check mark indicates items for prescribing differentiation on the next page.
Item 7 is worth 1 point. Items 16 and 17 are worth up to 2 points.

20–30 min

Practice Buddy

Tools

Assessment

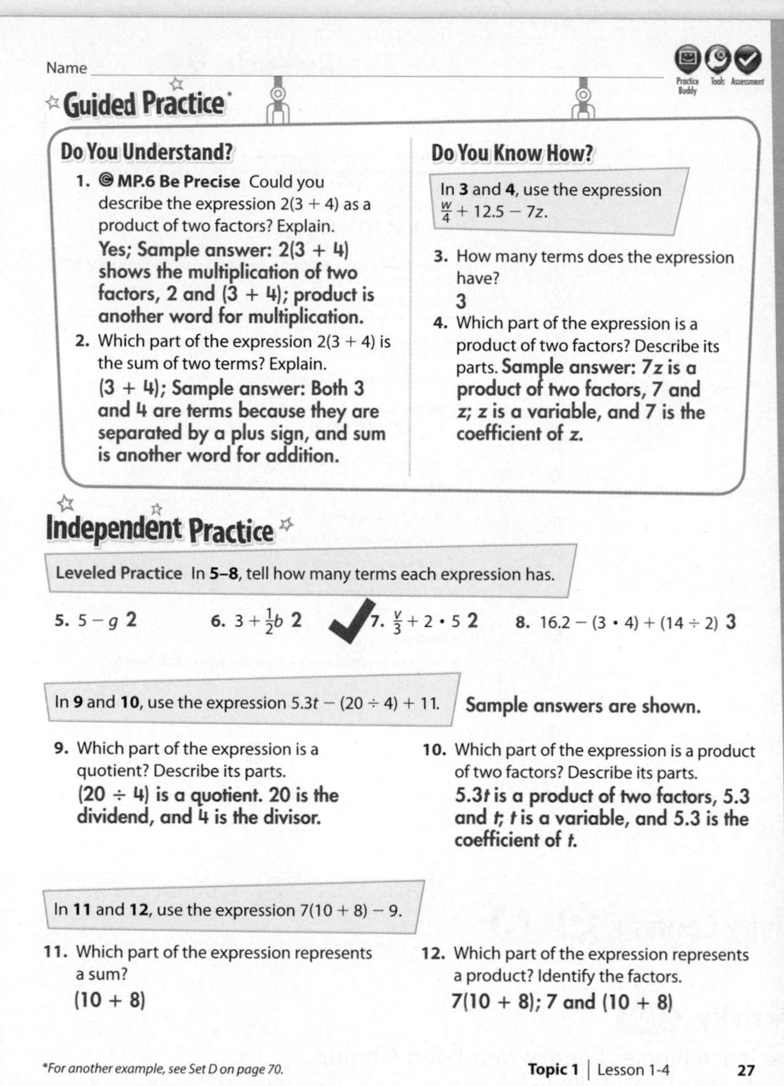

Name

### Guided Practice*

**Do You Understand?**

1. MP.6 Be Precise Could you describe the expression 2(3 + 4) as a product of two factors? Explain.
**Yes; Sample answer: 2(3 + 4) shows the multiplication of two factors, 2 and (3 + 4); product is another word for multiplication.**
2. Which part of the expression 2(3 + 4) is the sum of two terms? Explain.
**(3 + 4); Sample answer: Both 3 and 4 are terms because they are separated by a plus sign, and sum is another word for addition.**

**Do You Know How?**

In **3** and **4**, use the expression $\frac{w}{4} + 12.5 - 7z$.

3. How many terms does the expression have?
**3**
4. Which part of the expression is a product of two factors? Describe its parts. **Sample answer: 7z is a product of two factors, 7 and z; z is a variable, and 7 is the coefficient of z.**

### Independent Practice

Leveled Practice In **5–8**, tell how many terms each expression has.

5. $5 - g$ **2**
6. $3 + \frac{1}{2}b$ **2**
7. $\frac{y}{3} + 2 \cdot 5$ **2**
8. $16.2 - (3 \cdot 4) + (14 \div 2)$ **3**

In **9** and **10**, use the expression $5.3t - (20 \div 4) + 11$. **Sample answers are shown.**

9. Which part of the expression is a quotient? Describe its parts.
**(20 ÷ 4) is a quotient. 20 is the dividend, and 4 is the divisor.**
10. Which part of the expression is a product of two factors? Describe its parts.
**5.3t is a product of two factors, 5.3 and t; t is a variable, and 5.3 is the coefficient of t.**

In **11** and **12**, use the expression $7(10 + 8) - 9$.

11. Which part of the expression represents a sum?
**(10 + 8)**
12. Which part of the expression represents a product? Identify the factors.
**7(10 + 8); 7 and (10 + 8)**

*For another example, see Set D on page 70.



### Math Practices and Problem Solving

In **13** and **14**, use the table at the right.

13. MP.4 Model with Math Write an expression to show how much longer the round trip to San Diego is than the round trip to San Jose. How many terms does the expression have?
**1,012 − 236; 2 terms**
14. MP.1 Make Sense and Persevere Last month, a truck driver made 5 round trips to Los Angeles and some round trips to San Diego. Write an expression that shows how many round trips he made in all. Identify and describe the part of the expression that shows how many trips he made to San Diego.
**Sample answer: (5 · 770) + 1,012n; The product 1,012n shows the round trips to San Diego; n is a variable that represents the unknown number of trips, and 1,012 is the coefficient of n.**

DATA

| Sacramento to ... | Round trip Distance (miles) |
|---|---|
| San Jose | 236 |
| Los Angeles | 770 |
| San Diego | 1,012 |

15. MP.3 Critique Reasoning Anthony says that the expression abc has three terms because it uses three different variables. Critique Anthony's reasoning and explain whether he is correct.
**Sample answer: Anthony is not correct; abc has only one term since there is no addition or subtraction operation.**
16. Higher Order Thinking Write a numerical expression with a value of 45. The expression must include at least three terms, one power, and one set of parentheses.
**Sample answer: $3^2 + (84 \div 2) - 6$**

### Common Core Assessment

17. Use the expression below to complete the table. The first column lists parts of the expression. Identify the parts of the expression that correspond to the descriptions to complete the table.

$y \div 3(4 - 2) + 5.5$

| Description of Part | Part |
|---|---|
| Variable | **y** |
| Difference | **(4 − 2)** |
| Product | **3(4 − 2)** |
| Constant numerical value | **5.5** |





**Error Intervention: Item 1**

**If** students do not provide a good explanation,

**then** review the definition of *factor* with them. *Remember that factors are numbers or variables that are multiplied together. Are the numbers 3 and 4 factors? Explain.* [No; they are being added.] *What operation is indicated by the number 2 in front of the set of parentheses?* [Multiplication] *So, there are two factors, the number 2 and the set of parentheses, (3 + 4).*

**Item 7** Students might incorrectly answer 3 terms. Remind students that terms are separated by a plus sign or a minus sign. *What symbol is between the numbers 2 and 5?* [A multiplication sign] *So, are 2 and 5 separate terms?* [No] *How many parts are separated by the plus sign?* [2]

**Reteaching** Assign Reteaching Set D on p. 70.

**Item 14 MP.1 Make Sense and Persevere** Encourage students to write the expression one term at a time, as they read the problem again and refer to the table at the right. *What expression can you write to show the number of miles the truck traveled to and from Los Angeles?* [5 • 770] *To and from San Diego?* [1,012n]

**Item 15 MP.3 Critique Reasoning** Emphasize that terms are separated by plus and minus signs. If an expression has no plus or minus signs, it has only 1 term.

**Item 16 Higher Order Thinking** If students have difficulty writing an expression with a value of 45 with three terms, have them start with an expression with two terms with a value of 45. One strategy would be to write one of the two terms as a power. Then they can rewrite the other term as an expression with two terms, and add parentheses around it.

**Multi-Step Problems** *Page 28 Item 14; Page 30 Item 10*

# ASSESS AND DIFFERENTIATE

Use the **QUICK CHECK** on the previous page to prescribe differentiated instruction.

**I Intervention** 0–3 points on the Quick Check

**O On-Level** 4 points on the Quick Check

**A Advanced** 5 points on the Quick Check

## Intervention Activity 

### Parts of an Expression

**Materials**

Strips of paper, scissors

- Organize the class into pairs.
- Ask each student to write four expressions, each with at least three terms and no parentheses. Have them write each expression on a separate strip of paper.
- Have the partners trade strips of paper.
- For each expression, have each student state how many terms are in the expression and check the answer by cutting the strip of paper at each plus or minus sign.

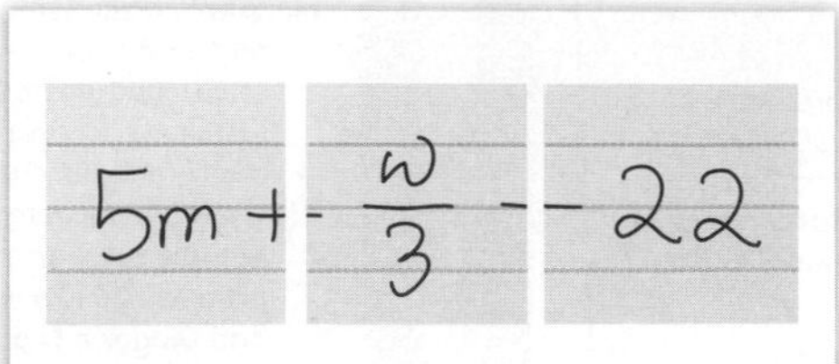


## Reteach I

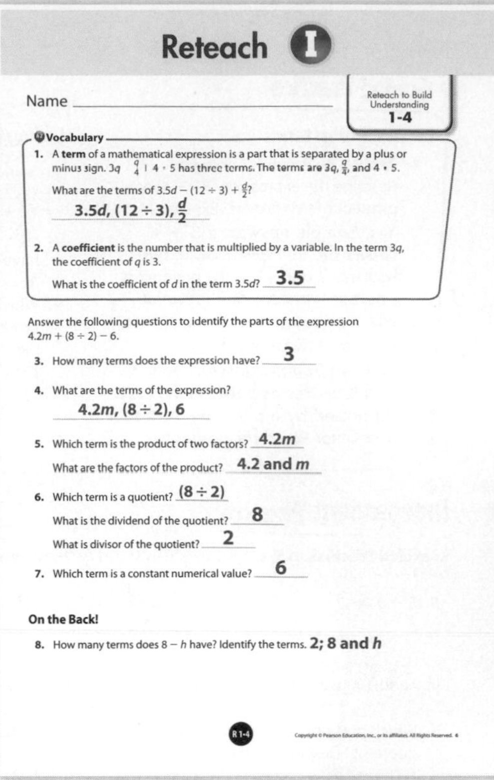

Name ____________________

Reteach to Build Understanding 1-4

**Vocabulary**

1. A **term** of a mathematical expression is a part that is separated by a plus or minus sign. $3q \; \frac{q}{4} \mid 4 \cdot 5$ has three terms. The terms are $3q$, $\frac{q}{4}$, and $4 \cdot 5$.

   What are the terms of $3.5d - (12 \div 3) + \frac{d}{2}$?

   **$3.5d, (12 \div 3), \frac{d}{2}$**

2. A **coefficient** is the number that is multiplied by a variable. In the term $3q$, the coefficient of $q$ is 3.

   What is the coefficient of $d$ in the term $3.5d$? **3.5**

Answer the following questions to identify the parts of the expression $4.2m + (8 \div 2) - 6$.

3. How many terms does the expression have? **3**
4. What are the terms of the expression?

   **$4.2m, (8 \div 2), 6$**
5. Which term is the product of two factors? **$4.2m$**

   What are the factors of the product? **4.2 and $m$**
6. Which term is a quotient? **$(8 \div 2)$**

   What is the dividend of the quotient? **8**

   What is divisor of the quotient? **2**
7. Which term is a constant numerical value? **6**

**On the Back!**

8. How many terms does $8 - h$ have? Identify the terms. **2; 8 and $h$**

R 1-4



## On-Level and Advanced Activity Centers O A

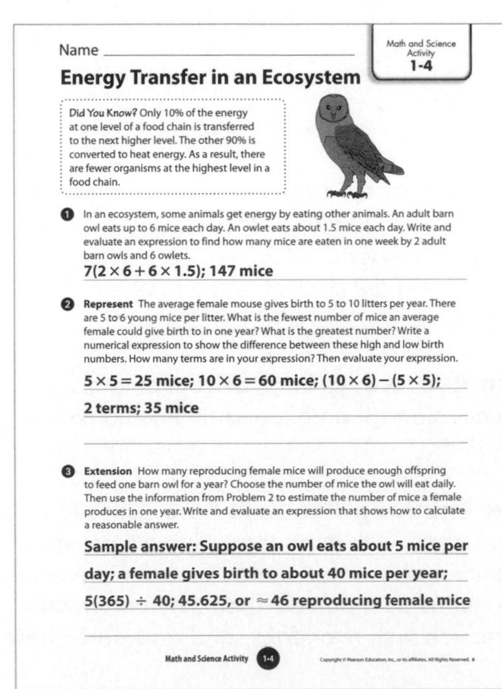

Name ____________________

Math and Science Activity 1-4

### Energy Transfer in an Ecosystem

*Did You Know?* Only 10% of the energy at one level of a food chain is transferred to the next higher level. The other 90% is converted to heat energy. As a result, there are fewer organisms at the highest level in a food chain.

1. In an ecosystem, some animals get energy by eating other animals. An adult barn owl eats up to 6 mice each day. An owlet eats about 1.5 mice each day. Write and evaluate an expression to find how many mice are eaten in one week by 2 adult barn owls and 6 owlets.

   **$7(2 \times 6 + 6 \times 1.5)$; 147 mice**

2. **Represent** The average female mouse gives birth to 5 to 10 litters per year. There are 5 to 6 young mice per litter. What is the fewest number of mice an average female could give birth to in one year? What is the greatest number? Write a numerical expression to show the difference between these high and low birth numbers. How many terms are in your expression? Then evaluate your expression.

   **$5 \times 5 = 25$ mice; $10 \times 6 = 60$ mice; $(10 \times 6) - (5 \times 5)$; 2 terms; 35 mice**

3. **Extension** How many reproducing female mice will produce enough offspring to feed one barn owl for a year? Choose the number of mice the owl will eat daily. Then use the information from Problem 2 to estimate the number of mice a female produces in one year. Write and evaluate an expression that shows how to calculate a reasonable answer.

   **Sample answer: Suppose an owl eats about 5 mice per day; a female gives birth to about 40 mice per year; $5(365) \div 40$; 45.625, or $\approx 46$ reproducing female mice**

Math and Science Activity 1-4



### Math and Science Activity STEM

This activity revisits the science theme, Energy and Food Chains, introduced on page 1 in the Student's Edition.

### Sample Student Work

1. one day → 2 owls eat 6 mice each + 6 owlets eat 1.5 mice each

one week is 7 days → $7[2(6) + 6(1.5)]$

$7[12 + 9]$

$7[21]$

147 mice

**TIMING**

The time allocated to Step 3 will depend on the teacher's instructional decisions and differentiation routines.

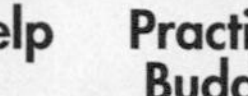

## Technology Center

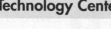

### Math Tools and Math Games

A link to a specific math tools activity or math game to use with this lesson is provided at PearsonRealize.com.

## Leveled Assignment

 Items 1–9, 11, 14  Items 3–8, 10–14  Items 3–5, 7, 8, 10–14

Name ____________________

Help Practice Buddy Tools Games

## Homework & Practice 1-4

### Identify Parts of an Expression

**Another Look!**

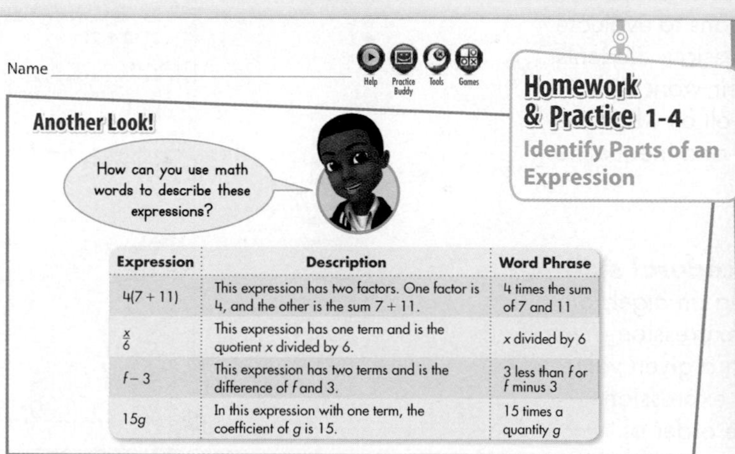


| Expression | Description | Word Phrase |
|---|---|---|
| $4(7 + 11)$ | This expression has two factors. One factor is 4, and the other is the sum $7 + 11$. | 4 times the sum of 7 and 11 |
| $\frac{x}{6}$ | This expression has one term and is the quotient $x$ divided by 6. | $x$ divided by 6 |
| $f - 3$ | This expression has two terms and is the difference of $f$ and 3. | 3 less than $f$ or $f$ minus 3 |
| $15g$ | In this expression with one term, the coefficient of $g$ is 15. | 15 times a quantity $g$ |

In **1–4**, tell how many terms each expression has.

**1.** $4c + 7\frac{1}{2}$
**2**

**2.** $80.6 - 3p - q$
**3**

**3.** $(7 \cdot 2) \div s$
**1**

**4.** $100 + (8 \cdot 6) - 50 + 2$
**4**

In **5** and **6**, use the expression $1 + \frac{z}{3} + 2w$.

**5.** Which part of the expression is a quotient? Describe its parts. **Sample answer: $\frac{z}{3}$ is a quotient. $z$ is the dividend, and 3 is the divisor.**

**6.** Which part of the expression is a product of two factors? Describe its parts. **Sample answer: $2w$ is a product of two factors, 2 and $w$; $w$ is a variable, and 2 is the coefficient of $w$.**

In **7** and **8**, use the expression $\frac{3}{4} + 3(14 - 7)$.

**7.** Which part of the expression represents a difference?
**$(14 - 7)$**

**8.** Which part of the expression represents a product? Identify the factors.
**$3(14 - 7)$; 3 and $(14 - 7)$**



In **9** and **10**, use the menu at the right.

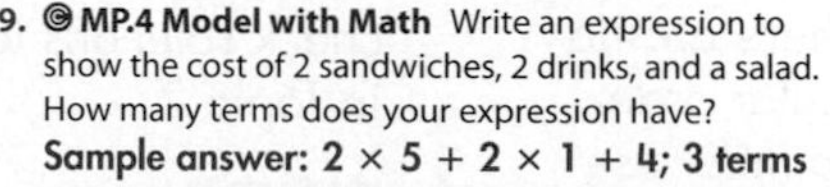
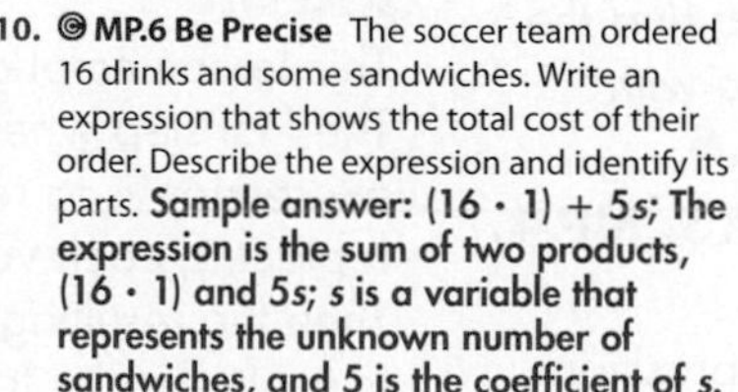
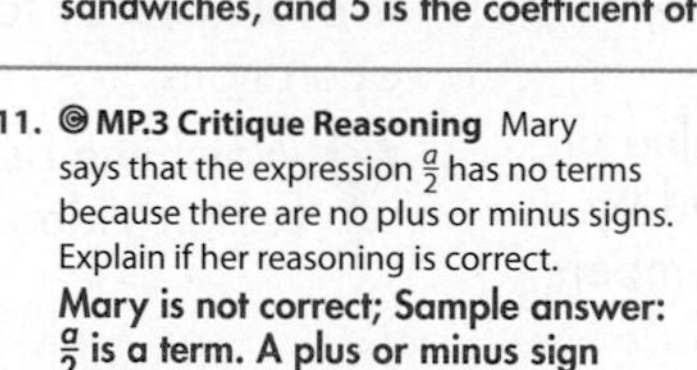
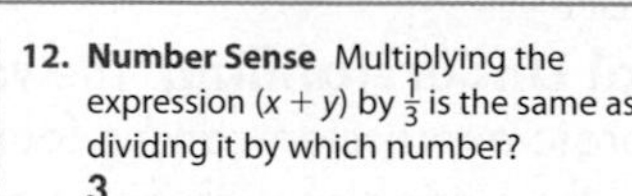

Lunch Menu
Sandwich . . . . . . $5
Soup . . . . . . . . . . $2
Salad . . . . . . . . . $4
Drink . . . . . . . . . $1


**9.** **MP.4 Model with Math** Write an expression to show the cost of 2 sandwiches, 2 drinks, and a salad. How many terms does your expression have?
**Sample answer: $2 \times 5 + 2 \times 1 + 4$; 3 terms**

**10.** **MP.6 Be Precise** The soccer team ordered 16 drinks and some sandwiches. Write an expression that shows the total cost of their order. Describe the expression and identify its parts. **Sample answer: $(16 \cdot 1) + 5s$; The expression is the sum of two products, $(16 \cdot 1)$ and $5s$; $s$ is a variable that represents the unknown number of sandwiches, and 5 is the coefficient of $s$.**

**11.** **MP.3 Critique Reasoning** Mary says that the expression $\frac{a}{2}$ has no terms because there are no plus or minus signs. Explain if her reasoning is correct.
**Mary is not correct; Sample answer: $\frac{a}{2}$ is a term. A plus or minus sign would indicate a second term.**

**12.** **Number Sense** Multiplying the expression $(x + y)$ by $\frac{1}{3}$ is the same as dividing it by which number?
**3**

**13.** **Higher Order Thinking** For $6 + 5(12 - 8)$, which word best describes the entire expression: sum, difference, product, or quotient? Explain your reasoning. **Sample answer: Sum; if you simplify the expression, the last operation will be addition.**

**Common Core Assessment**

**14.** Use the expression shown at the right to complete the table below. The first column lists parts of the expression. Complete the second column, identifying the parts of the expression that correspond to the descriptions.

$$3t - \frac{10}{(4 + 1)} - 2$$

| Description of Part | Part |
|---|---|
| Coefficient | **3** |
| Quotient | **$\frac{10}{(4 + 1)}$** |
| Sum | **$(4 + 1)$** |
| Product | **$3t$** |

# LESSON 1-5

# EVALUATE ALGEBRAIC EXPRESSIONS

## DIGITAL RESOURCES PearsonRealize.com

eText — Student and Teacher eTexts

PD — Listen and Look For Lesson Video

Think — Today's Challenge

Solve — Solve and Share

Learn — Visual Learning Animation Plus

Glossary — Animated Glossary

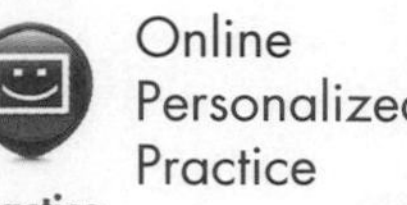
Practice Buddy — Online Personalized Practice

Tools — Math Tools

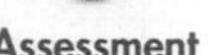
Assessment — Quick Check

Help — Another Look Homework Video

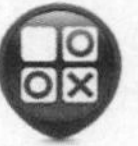
Games — Math Games

## LESSON OVERVIEW 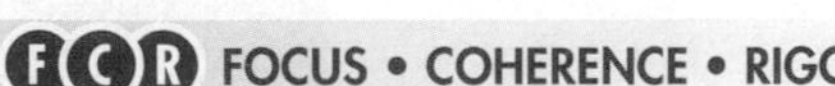 FOCUS • COHERENCE • RIGOR

### FOCUS

**Domain 6.EE** Expressions and Equations

**Cluster 6.EE.A** Apply and extend previous understandings of arithmetic to algebraic expressions.

**Content Standard 6.EE.A.2c** Evaluate expressions at specific values of their variables. Include expressions that arise from formulas used in real-world problems. Perform arithmetic operations, including those involving whole-number exponents, in the conventional order when there are no parentheses to specify a particular order (Order of Operations). *For example, use the formulas* $V = s^3$ *and* $A = 6s^2$ *to find the volume and surface area of a cube with sides of length* $s = \frac{1}{2}$. Also **6.EE.B.6**.

**Mathematical Practices MP.2, MP.3, MP.4, MP.7, MP.8**

**Objective** Evaluate algebraic expressions using substitution.

**Essential Understanding** The value of an algebraic expression can be found by replacing the variables with given numbers and doing the calculation that results.

**Vocabulary** Substitution

### COHERENCE

In Lesson 1-2, students used the order of operations to evaluate numerical expressions. In this lesson, students focus on evaluating algebraic expressions. They substitute given values for the variables and then use the order of operations to evaluate the resulting numerical expression. Students will use this procedure in their work with formulas in Lesson 1-9, as well as when they check solutions to equations and inequalities in Topic 2.

### RIGOR

This lesson emphasizes **procedural skill**. The first step when evaluating an algebraic expression is to rewrite the expression replacing each variable with a given value. Then the resulting numerical expression is evaluated by following the order of operations.

PD Watch the Listen and Look For Lesson Video.

## MATH ANYTIME

### Daily Common Core Review

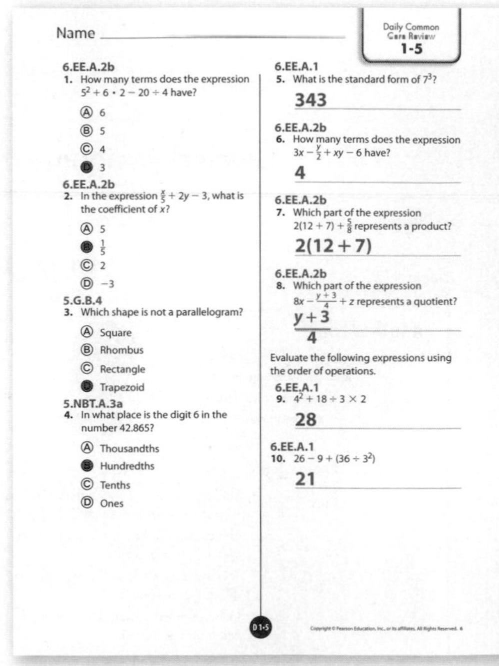
Name ______

Daily Common Core Review 1-5

6.EE.A.2b
1. How many terms does the expression $5^2 + 6 \cdot 2 - 20 \div 4$ have?
   - Ⓐ 6
   - Ⓑ 5
   - Ⓒ 4
   - ● 3

6.EE.A.2b
2. In the expression $\frac{x}{5} + 2y - 3$, what is the coefficient of $x$?
   - Ⓐ 5
   - ● $\frac{1}{5}$
   - Ⓒ 2
   - Ⓓ −3

5.G.B.4
3. Which shape is not a parallelogram?
   - Ⓐ Square
   - Ⓑ Rhombus
   - Ⓒ Rectangle
   - ● Trapezoid

5.NBT.A.3a
4. In what place is the digit 6 in the number 42.865?
   - Ⓐ Thousandths
   - ● Hundredths
   - Ⓒ Tenths
   - Ⓓ Ones

6.EE.A.1
5. What is the standard form of $7^3$? **343**

6.EE.A.2b
6. How many terms does the expression $3x - \frac{y}{2} + xy - 6$ have? **4**

6.EE.A.2b
7. Which part of the expression $2(12 + 7) + \frac{5}{8}$ represents a product? **$2(12 + 7)$**

6.EE.A.2b
8. Which part of the expression $8x - \frac{y+3}{4} + z$ represents a quotient? **$\frac{y+3}{4}$**

Evaluate the following expressions using the order of operations.

6.EE.A.1
9. $4^2 + 18 \div 3 \times 2$ **28**

6.EE.A.1
10. $26 - 9 + (36 \div 3^2)$ **21**

D1-5

### Today's Challenge

Think Use the Topic 1 problems any time during this topic.

## ENGLISH LANGUAGE LEARNERS 

**Speaking** Share information in cooperative learning interactions.

*Use with the Solve & Share on Student's Edition p. 31.*

Read the Solve & Share. *What is known?* [Jason has 20 cards; there are 12 cards in each pack.] *How do you determine the number of cards Jason will have if he buys 3 packs of cards?* Instruct students to write an algebraic expression for the number of cards Jason will have if he buys 3 packs.

**Beginning** *How many cards does Jason have?* Write + and *20* on separate index cards. *How many cards are in each pack?* Write *12* on an index card. *How many packs of cards will Jason buy?* Write *(3)* on an index card. Ask students to work together to use the cards to create an algebraic expression.

**Intermediate** Ask students to work as a group to identify the known and unknown information. Write +, *20*, *12*, and *(3)* on index cards. Ask students to work together to use the cards to create an algebraic expression.

**Advanced** Instruct students to discuss in their group the known and unknown information. *How would this information be written on index cards if we only write one piece of information on each card?* Ask students to work together to use the index cards to create an algebraic expression.

**Summarize** Why is known and unknown information important for creating algebraic expressions?

# DEVELOP: PROBLEM-BASED LEARNING

**COHERENCE: Engage learners by connecting prior knowledge to new ideas.**
Students extend their understanding of numerical and algebraic expressions to evaluate an algebraic expression for given values of the variable.

10–15 min

Solve

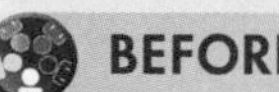

## BEFORE

1. **Pose the Solve-and-Share Problem**
**MP.7 Use Structure** Listen and look for students who begin with the algebraic expression and evaluate it for each given value of the variable.

2. **Build Understanding**
*What information are you given?* [Jason has 20 sports cards. Sports cards come in packs of 12.] *In the expression 20 + 12p, what does 20 represent?* [The 20 cards Jason has to start his collection] *What does 12p represent?* [The number of cards in $p$ packs that he will add to his collection]

## DURING

3. **Ask Guiding Questions As Needed**
*How can the algebraic expression help solve the problem?* [The same expression can be used for any value of $p$.] *How do you know which values for p you should use?* [If Jason buys 3 packs of cards, use $p = 3$. If Jason buys 8 packs of cards, use $p = 8$.]

## AFTER

4. **Share and Discuss Solutions**
Solve Start with students' solutions. If needed, project Thai's work to discuss how to use the algebraic expression to solve the problem.

5. **Transition to the Visual Learning Bridge**
*You can represent some real-world problems using an algebraic expression. Then evaluate the expression for given values of the variable.*

6. **Extension for Early Finishers**
On the board, write $5x + 4y + 3z$. *Evaluate this expression for $x = 6$, $y = 5$, and $z = 10$.* [80]

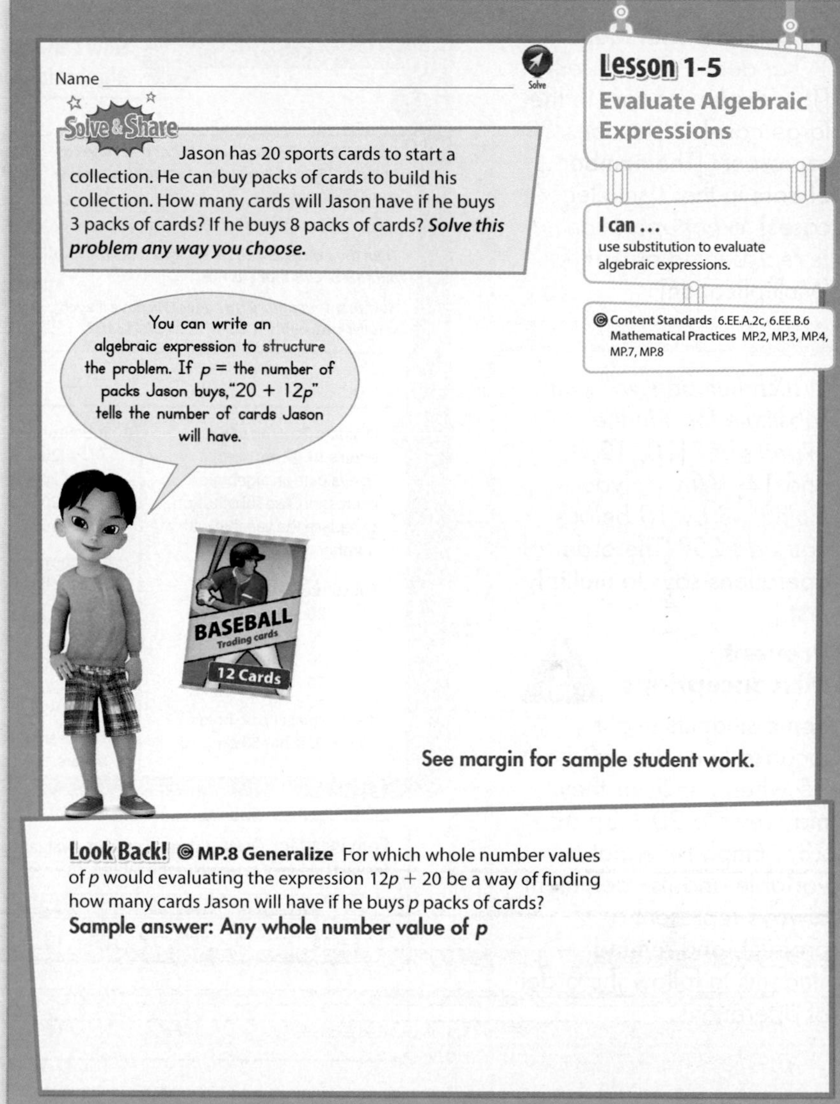

Name
Solve & Share
Jason has 20 sports cards to start a collection. He can buy packs of cards to build his collection. How many cards will Jason have if he buys 3 packs of cards? If he buys 8 packs of cards? Solve this problem any way you choose.
Lesson 1-5
Evaluate Algebraic Expressions
I can ...
use substitution to evaluate algebraic expressions.
Content Standards 6.EE.A.2c, 6.EE.B.6
Mathematical Practices MP.2, MP.3, MP.4, MP.7, MP.8
You can write an algebraic expression to structure the problem. If p = the number of packs Jason buys, "20 + 12p" tells the number of cards Jason will have.
BASEBALL
Trading cards
12 Cards
See margin for sample student work.
Look Back! MP.8 Generalize For which whole number values of p would evaluating the expression 12p + 20 be a way of finding how many cards Jason will have if he buys p packs of cards?
Sample answer: Any whole number value of p
Digital Resources at PearsonRealize.com
Topic 1 | Lesson 1-5
31


## Analyze Student Work

**Thai's Work**

20 + 12p
20 + 12 · 3 = 20 + 36 = 56 cards
20 + 12 · 8 = 20 + 96 = 116 cards
Jason will have 56 cards if he buys 3 packs and 116 cards if he buys 8 packs.

Thai writes the given algebraic expression that models the problem and then correctly evaluates the expression for 3 packs and 8 packs of sports cards.

**Marisa's Work**

12 · 3 = 36
+20
56 Cards

12 · 8 = 96
+20
116 Cards

If Jason buys 3 Packs, he'll have 56 Cards.
If he buys 8 packs, he'll have 116 Cards.

Marisa also solves the problem for both 3 packs and 8 packs, but does not relate the problem to the algebraic expression.

# DEVELOP: VISUAL LEARNING

The *Visual Learning Bridge* connects students' thinking in Solve & Share to important math ideas in the lesson. Use the *Visual Learning Bridge* to make these ideas explicit. Also available as a *Visual Learning Animation Plus* at PearsonRealize.com

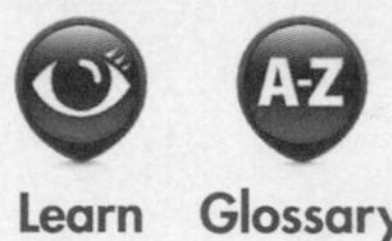


**MP.4 Model with Math** *What does 20 represent?* [The number of cars in the large case] *What does 3n represent?* [The number of cars in the 3 smaller cases] *What operation is represented by 3n?* [Multiplication]

*Which numbers will you substitute for n in the expression?* [10, 12, and 14] *Why do you multiply 3 by 10 before you add 20?* [The order of operations says to multiply first.]

**Prevent Misconceptions** 

Some students might incorrectly evaluate $3n$ as 35 when $n = 5$, or they may rewrite $20 + 3n$ as $23n$. Emphasize that a variable and its coefficient always represent a product, and remind students to follow the order of operations.

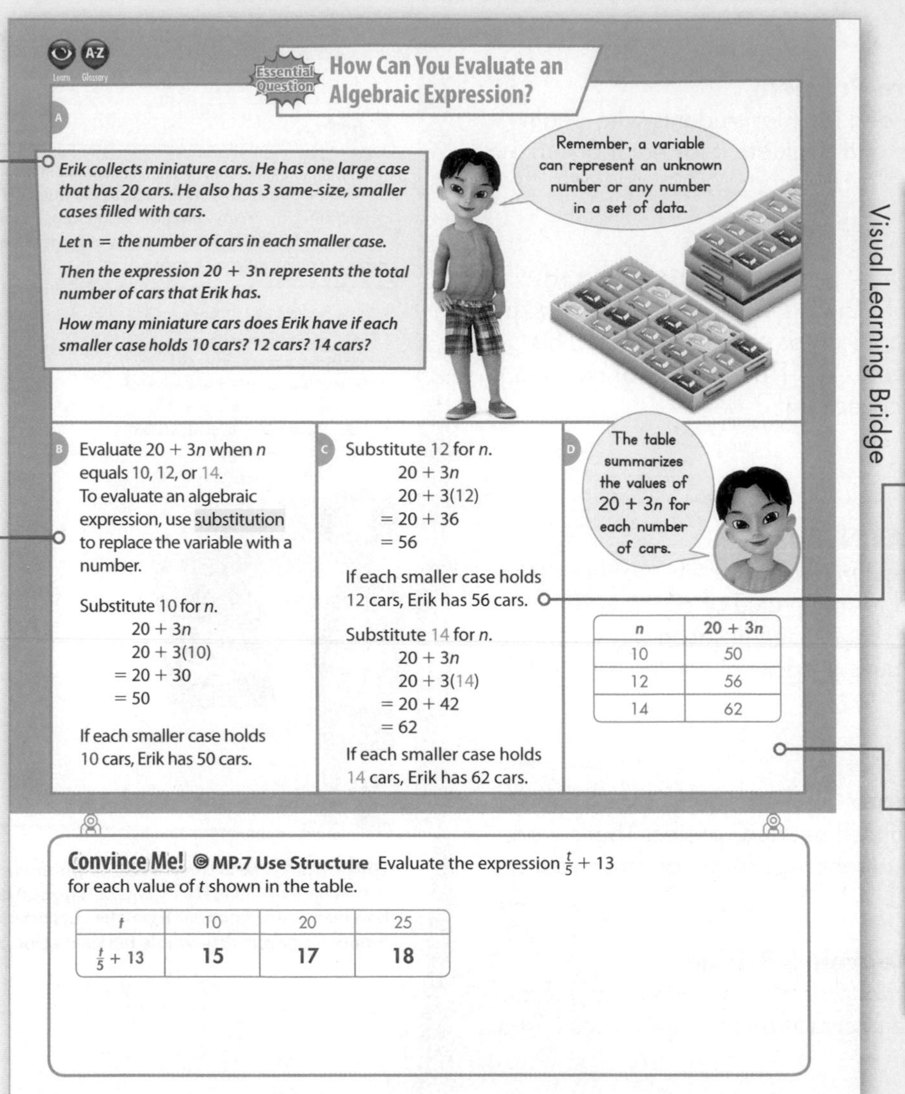


**MP.7 Use Structure** *How is each evaluation of the expression the same?* [3 is multiplied by a number, and then 20 is added to that product.] *How is each evaluation of the expression different?* [The value substituted for the variable changes, so 3 is multiplied by a different number each time.]

*What do the numbers in the second column represent?* [The total number of Erik's cars] *What do the numbers in the last row mean in the context of the problem?* [It shows that Erik would have 62 cars if there were 14 cars in each of the smaller cases.]

**Convince Me! MP.7 Use Structure** Students recognize the algebraic expression as a combination of parts (terms, constants, and operations). They use this same structure each time they evaluate the expression, simply substituting different values for the variable.

**Coherence** Students gained experience with substitution in Grade 5 when they used the volume formula. In Lesson 1-2, they learned the order of operations for numerical expressions. Now students use those understandings to evaluate algebraic expressions. They will continue to develop their skills evaluating algebraic expressions in their work with formulas in Lesson 1-9. These skills will also prepare them for their study of equations and inequalities in Topic 2.

Revisit the Essential Question. The value of an algebraic expression can be found by substituting the variables with given numbers and doing the calculation that results. Remind students to follow the order of operations.

realize. PearsonRealize.com

## QUICK CHECK

Check mark indicates items for prescribing differentiation on the next page. Item 10 is worth 1 point. Items 17 and 18 are worth up to 2 points.

20–30 min

Practice Buddy Tools Assessment

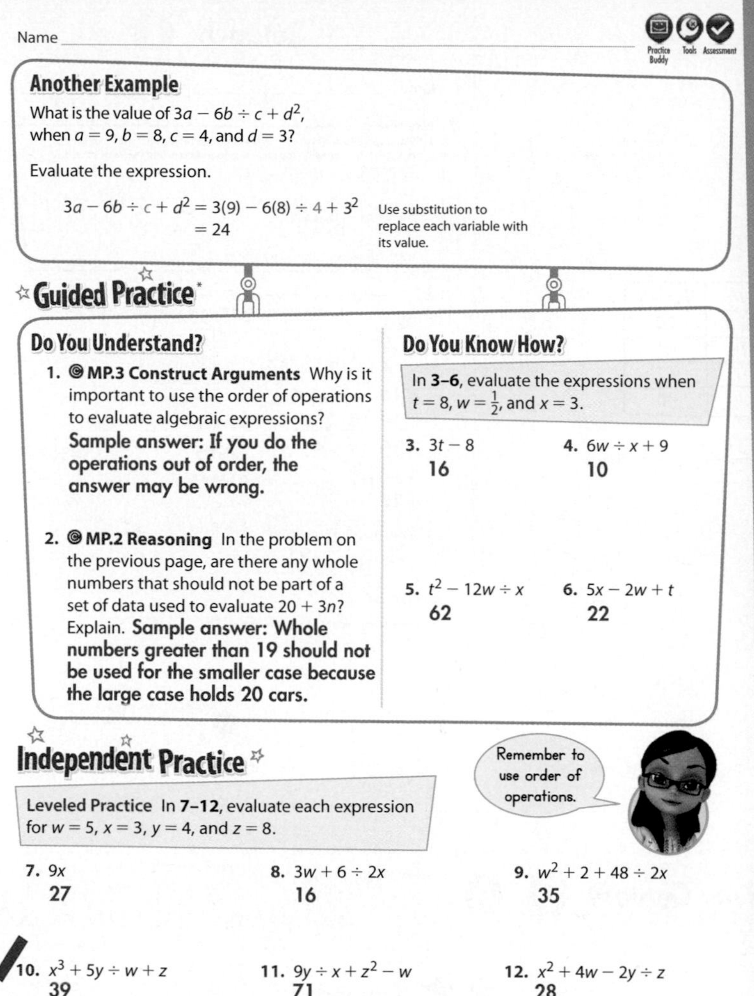

Name

**Another Example**

What is the value of $3a - 6b \div c + d^2$, when $a = 9$, $b = 8$, $c = 4$, and $d = 3$?

Evaluate the expression.

$3a - 6b \div c + d^2 = 3(9) - 6(8) \div 4 + 3^2$
$= 24$

Use substitution to replace each variable with its value.

**Guided Practice***

**Do You Understand?**

1. MP.3 Construct Arguments Why is it important to use the order of operations to evaluate algebraic expressions?
**Sample answer: If you do the operations out of order, the answer may be wrong.**

2. MP.2 Reasoning In the problem on the previous page, are there any whole numbers that should not be part of a set of data used to evaluate $20 + 3n$? Explain. **Sample answer: Whole numbers greater than 19 should not be used for the smaller case because the large case holds 20 cars.**

**Do You Know How?**

In 3–6, evaluate the expressions when $t = 8$, $w = \frac{1}{2}$, and $x = 3$.

3. $3t - 8$ **16**
4. $6w \div x + 9$ **10**
5. $t^2 - 12w \div x$ **62**
6. $5x - 2w + t$ **22**

**Independent Practice**

Remember to use order of operations.

Leveled Practice In 7–12, evaluate each expression for $w = 5$, $x = 3$, $y = 4$, and $z = 8$.

7. $9x$ **27**
8. $3w + 6 \div 2x$ **16**
9. $w^2 + 2 + 48 \div 2x$ **35**
10. $x^3 + 5y \div w + z$ **39**
11. $9y \div x + z^2 - w$ **71**
12. $x^2 + 4w - 2y \div z$ **28**

*For another example, see Set E on page 70.

Topic 1 | Lesson 1-5 33

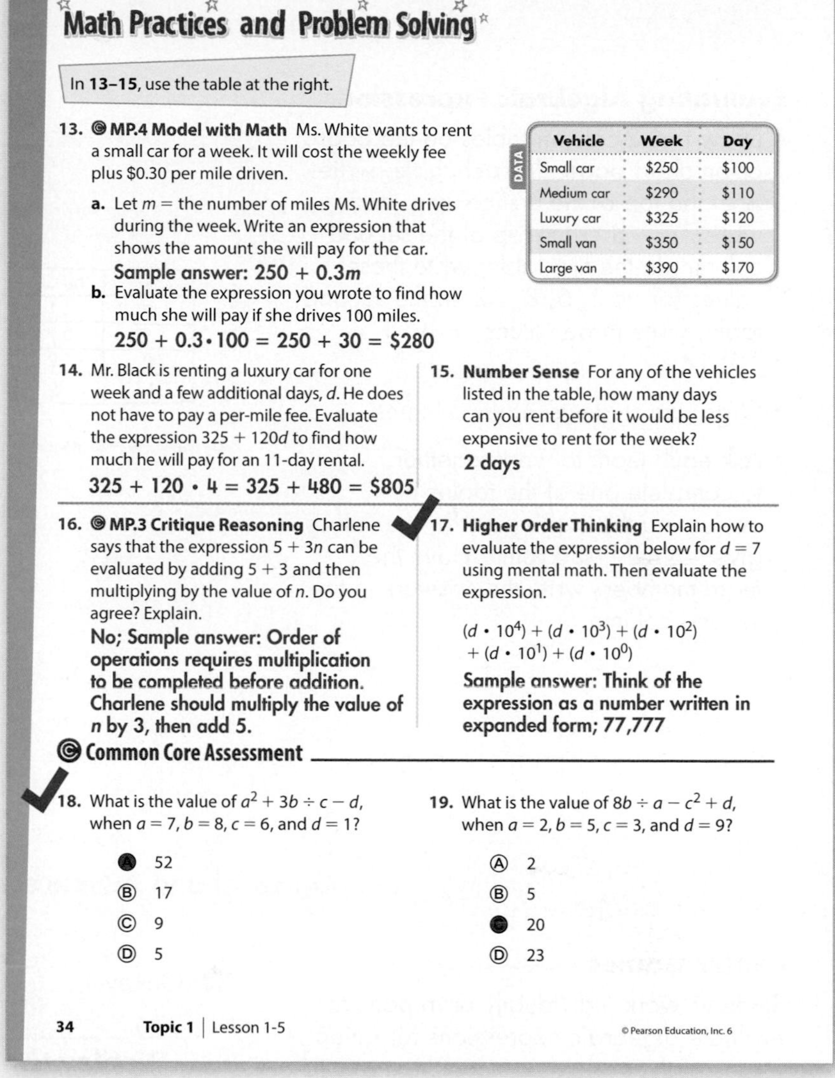

**Math Practices and Problem Solving**

In 13–15, use the table at the right.

13. MP.4 Model with Math Ms. White wants to rent a small car for a week. It will cost the weekly fee plus \$0.30 per mile driven.
a. Let $m$ = the number of miles Ms. White drives during the week. Write an expression that shows the amount she will pay for the car.
**Sample answer: $250 + 0.3m$**
b. Evaluate the expression you wrote to find how much she will pay if she drives 100 miles.
**$250 + 0.3 \cdot 100 = 250 + 30 = \$280$**

DATA

| Vehicle | Week | Day |
|---|---|---|
| Small car | \$250 | \$100 |
| Medium car | \$290 | \$110 |
| Luxury car | \$325 | \$120 |
| Small van | \$350 | \$150 |
| Large van | \$390 | \$170 |

14. Mr. Black is renting a luxury car for one week and a few additional days, $d$. He does not have to pay a per-mile fee. Evaluate the expression $325 + 120d$ to find how much he will pay for an 11-day rental.
**$325 + 120 \cdot 4 = 325 + 480 = \$805$**

15. Number Sense For any of the vehicles listed in the table, how many days can you rent before it would be less expensive to rent for the week?
**2 days**

16. MP.3 Critique Reasoning Charlene says that the expression $5 + 3n$ can be evaluated by adding $5 + 3$ and then multiplying by the value of $n$. Do you agree? Explain.
**No; Sample answer: Order of operations requires multiplication to be completed before addition. Charlene should multiply the value of $n$ by 3, then add 5.**

17. Higher Order Thinking Explain how to evaluate the expression below for $d = 7$ using mental math. Then evaluate the expression.
$(d \cdot 10^4) + (d \cdot 10^3) + (d \cdot 10^2) + (d \cdot 10^1) + (d \cdot 10^0)$
**Sample answer: Think of the expression as a number written in expanded form; 77,777**

**Common Core Assessment**

18. What is the value of $a^2 + 3b \div c - d$, when $a = 7$, $b = 8$, $c = 6$, and $d = 1$?
(A) 52
(B) 17
(C) 9
(D) 5

19. What is the value of $8b \div a - c^2 + d$, when $a = 2$, $b = 5$, $c = 3$, and $d = 9$?
(A) 2
(B) 5
(C) 20
(D) 23

34 Topic 1 | Lesson 1-5

© Pearson Education, Inc. 6

**Another Example** *How many variables does the algebraic expression have?* [4] *What steps will you take to evaluate the algebraic expression?* [First, substitute the values of the variables into the expression. Then follow the order of operations by evaluating the power $3^2$, multiplying and dividing through the expression, and then adding and subtracting through the expression.]

**Error Intervention: Items 3–6**

**If** students incorrectly evaluate the expression,

**then** discuss these three steps for checking their work: (1) Did you substitute the correct values for the variables? (2) Did you follow the order of operations? (3) Is each of your calculations correct?

**Reteaching** Assign Reteaching Set E on p. 70.

**Item 13 MP.4 Model with Math** Make sure students understand that they need to use 0.3 or 0.30 in the expression to represent \$0.30.

**Item 14** Check that students understand how the expression represents the situation. *How much does it cost to rent a luxury car for one week?* [\$325] *How would you represent the cost to rent a luxury car for d days? Explain.* [$120d$; Since the cost is \$120 per day, you need to multiply 120 by the number of days, $d$.]

**Item 15 Number Sense** Encourage students to use mental math to find the 2-day and 3-day costs for all or most of the vehicles listed in the table.

**Items 18–19** Each expression contains four different variables. Remind students to attend to precision (MP.6) as they substitute the correct value for each one.

**Multi-Step Problems** *Page 34 Items 13–15; Page 36 Items 11, 12, and 14*

# ASSESS AND DIFFERENTIATE

Use the **QUICK CHECK** on the previous page to prescribe differentiated instruction.

**I Intervention**
0–3 points on the Quick Check

**O On-Level**
4 points on the Quick Check

**A Advanced**
5 points on the Quick Check

## Intervention Activity 

### Evaluating Algebraic Expressions

- Draw two 2-column tables on the board or on chart paper. In each table, write $w$ at the top of the first column, and write $7w - 8$ at the top of the second column. In the first table, write these values for $w$: 3, 5, 8, 12. In the second table, write these values for $w$: 4, 7, 10, 14.
- Organize students into two teams.
- Ask each team to work together to complete one of the tables by evaluating the expression for the values given in the first column. Have the team members write the answers in the second column.

| w | 7w − 8 |
|---|---|
| 3 | 13 |
| 5 | 27 |
| 8 | 48 |
| 12 | 76 |

| w | 7w − 8 |
|---|---|
| 4 | 20 |
| 7 | 41 |
| 10 | 62 |
| 14 | 90 |

## Reteach I

Name ____________________

Reteach to Build Understanding
1-5

**Vocabulary**

1. When **substitution** is used to evaluate an algebraic expression, a variable is replaced with a number. You can use substitution to find the value of $3a + 4$ when $a = 2$.

$3a + 4$
$= 3(2) + 4$ ← Substitute 2 for $a$.
$= 6 + 4$ ← Multiply.
$= 10$ ← Add.

What is the value of $2x - 1$ when $x = 3$? **5**

2. Use substitution to find the value of $m^2 - 2n + \frac{2}{3}p$ when $m = 4$, $n = 2$, and $p = 6$. Use the order of operations to simplify. Fill in the blanks.

$m^2 - 2n + \frac{2}{3}p$
$= (\mathbf{4})^2 - 2(\mathbf{2}) + \frac{2}{3}(\mathbf{6})$ ← Substitute the values for each variable.
$= \mathbf{16} - 2(\mathbf{2}) + \frac{2}{3}(\mathbf{6})$ ← Evaluate powers.
$= \mathbf{16} - \mathbf{4} + \frac{2}{3}(\mathbf{6})$ ← Multiply.
$= \mathbf{16} - \mathbf{4} + \mathbf{4}$ ← Multiply.
$= \mathbf{12} + \mathbf{4}$ ← Subtract.
$= \mathbf{16}$ ← Add.

3. What is the value of the expression $158 - 8t - (u \div v)$ when $t = 7$, $u = 42$, and $v = 6$? **95**

**On the Back!**

4. What is the value of $15b - 2$ when $b = \frac{1}{5}$?
**1**

R 1•5 

## On-Level and Advanced Activity Centers O A

### Center Games

Students work individually or in pairs to evaluate algebraic expressions for given values of the variables. Have them record their work on paper before selecting the correct tile.

★ On-Level

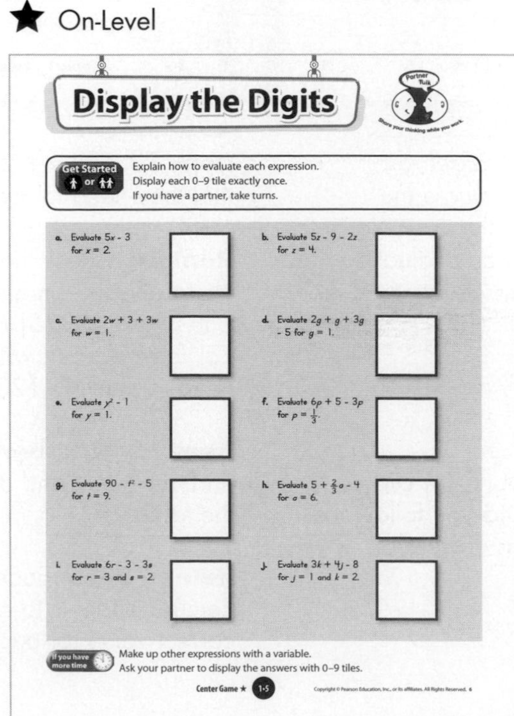

**Display the Digits**



Get Started (1 or 2 students): Explain how to evaluate each expression. Display each 0–9 tile exactly once. If you have a partner, take turns.

a. Evaluate $5x - 3$ for $x = 2$.
b. Evaluate $5z - 9 - 2z$ for $z = 4$.
c. Evaluate $2w + 3 + 3w$ for $w = 1$.
d. Evaluate $2g + g + 3g - 5$ for $g = 1$.
e. Evaluate $y^2 - 1$ for $y = 1$.
f. Evaluate $6p + 5 - 3p$ for $p = \frac{1}{3}$.
g. Evaluate $90 - f^2 - 5$ for $f = 9$.
h. Evaluate $5 + \frac{2}{3}a - 4$ for $a = 6$.
i. Evaluate $6r - 3 - 3s$ for $r = 3$ and $s = 2$.
j. Evaluate $3k + 4j - 8$ for $j = 1$ and $k = 2$.

If you have more time: Make up other expressions with a variable. Ask your partner to display the answers with 0–9 tiles.

Center Game ★ 1•5 

★★ Advanced

**Display the Digits**

Partner Talk
Share your thinking while you work.

Get Started (1 or 2 students): Explain how to evaluate each expression. Display each 0–9 tile exactly once. If you have a partner, take turns.

a. Evaluate $(3b + 5) \div (b - 1)$ for $b = 5$.
b. Evaluate $(\frac{1}{3}q^2 - 4) \div (p + 4)$ for $p = 4$ and $q = 6$.
c. Evaluate $(2 + 3c) \times (d - 7)$ for $c = 5$ and $d = 7$.
d. Evaluate $6r^2 + 5r - 1$ for $r = \frac{1}{2}$.
e. Evaluate $4x - (x - \frac{1}{5})$ for $x = \frac{3}{5}$.
f. Evaluate $\frac{1}{2}f + \frac{1}{4}g^2 + 3h$ for $f = 5$, $g = 3$, and $h = \frac{3}{4}$.
g. Evaluate $3t^2 - (8t - 12)$ for $t = 2$.
h. Evaluate $5a + [b - (3c - 4)]$ for $a = 1$, $b = 3$, and $c = 2$.
i. Evaluate $(v + w^2) - (w + 2v - 7)$ for $v = 9$ and $w = 3$.
j. Evaluate $[8x \div (4x - 6)] + (x^2 - 4)$ for $x = 3$.

If you have more time: Make up other expressions with variables. Ask your partner to display the answers with 0–9 tiles.

Center Game ★★ 1•5 

**TIMING**

The time allocated to Step 3 will depend on the teacher's instructional decisions and differentiation routines.

15–30 min

PEARSON realize. PearsonRealize.com

Help

Practice Buddy

Tools

Games

## Technology Center

Tools

Games

### Math Tools and Math Games

A link to a specific math tools activity or math game to use with this lesson is provided at PearsonRealize.com.

## Leveled Assignment

 Items 1–4, 9–13, 15, 16  Items 5–11, 13–16  Items 6–16

Name ________________

**Homework & Practice 1-5**

**Evaluate Algebraic Expressions**

**Another Look!**

Evaluate the expression $5a + 2b \div c - d^2$, when $a = 9, b = 6, c = 3$, and $d = 5$.

Use substitution to replace each variable with its value. Then use the order of operations to simplify.

$5a + 2b \div c - d^2 = 5(9) + 2(6) \div 3 + 5^2$

$= 74$

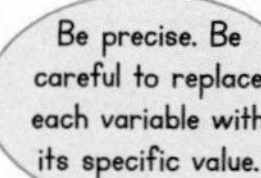

Be precise. Be careful to replace each variable with its specific value.

**Leveled Practice** In **1–8**, find the value of each expression when $a = \frac{1}{3}, b = 9, c = 5$, and $d = 10$.

**1.** $6a + 4$
**6**

**2.** $5a - \frac{2}{3}$
**1**

**3.** $5d \div c + 2$
**12**

**4.** $b^2 - 9a$
**78**

**5.** $12a + c - b$
**0**

**6.** $\frac{1}{2}d + c^2 - b$
**21**

**7.** $d^2 \div 2c - b + 3a$
**2**

**8.** $3c + b^2 \div 27a - d$
**14**

In **9** and **10**, evaluate each expression for the set of values given in each table.

**9.**

| $c$ | 1 | 2 | 3 |
|---|---|---|---|
| $28 - c^3 + 6$ | **33** | **26** | **7** |

**10.**

| $d$ | 28 | 49 | 63 |
|---|---|---|---|
| $\frac{d}{7} - 3 + 10$ | **11** | **14** | **16** |



In **11** and **12**, use the table at the right.

| Number of Pets | Per Day | Per Hour |
|---|---|---|
| One dog | $20 | $7 |
| Two dogs | $25 | $9 |
| One or two cats | $15 | $6 |

**11. MP.4 Model with Math** Tamera has a pet sitting business. The table shows how much she charges. Last week, she sat for one dog and for two cats.

**a.** Suppose she spent $h$ hours sitting the dog and 2 days sitting the cats. Write an expression that shows how much she earned.
**Sample answer: $7h + 2 \cdot 15$**

**b.** Evaluate the expression you wrote to find how much she earned if she sat 2 hours for the dog.
**$7 \cdot 2 + 2 \cdot 15 = 14 + 30 = \$44$**

**12. Number Sense** For any of the pet sitting services listed in the table, how many hours can you purchase before it would be cheaper to pay for one day?
**2 hours**

**13.** Conner is learning how to surf. He can pay $65 for a basic training course and then rent a surfboard for $6 per hour. He wrote the expression $65 + 6x$ to find out how much it would cost to go surfing. How much will it cost if he surfs for 4 hours?
**$65 + 6 \cdot 4 = 65 + 24 = \$89$**

**14. Higher Order Thinking** Rita and Janet signed up for two different dance classes. Rita's dance class charges $20 plus $8 per lesson. Janet's dance class charges $12 per lesson. How many lessons will it take for Janet's class to cost the same amount as Rita's class? Explain how you decided.
**5 lessons; Sample answer: I wrote expressions with a variable representing the number of lessons each person takes. Then I substituted different values for the number of lessons until both expressions had the same value; $20 + (8 \times 5) = 20 + 40 = 60$ and $12 \times 5 = 60$.**

**Common Core Assessment**

**15.** What is the value of $3g \div h^2 + k - n$, when $g = 12, h = 3, k = 10$, and $n = 1$?

Ⓐ 21
Ⓑ 16
Ⓒ 15
● 13

**16.** What is the value of $\frac{1}{2}x + y^2 - 4z \div t$, when $x = 10, y = 4, z = 5$, and $t = 2$?

Ⓐ 3
Ⓑ 4
● 11
Ⓓ 18

# LESSON 1-6

# WRITE EQUIVALENT EXPRESSIONS

## DIGITAL RESOURCES PearsonRealize.com

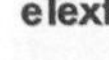
Student and Teacher eTexts

PD
Listen and Look For Lesson Video

Think
Today's Challenge

Solve
Solve and Share

Learn
Visual Learning Animation Plus

Glossary
Animated Glossary

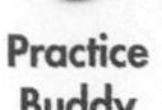
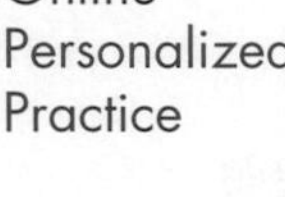
Practice Buddy
Online Personalized Practice

Tools
Math Tools

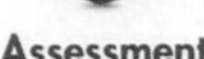
Assessment
Quick Check

Help
Another Look Homework Video

Games
Math Games

## LESSON OVERVIEW

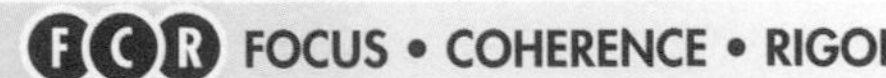


### FOCUS

**Domain 6.EE** Expressions and Equations

**Cluster 6.EE.A** Apply and extend previous understandings of arithmetic to algebraic expressions.

**Content Standard 6.EE.A.3** Apply the properties of operations to generate equivalent expressions. *For example, apply the distributive property to the expression $3(2 + x)$ to produce the equivalent expression $6 + 3x$; apply the distributive property to the expression $24x + 18y$ to produce the equivalent expression $6(4x + 3y)$; apply properties of operations to $y + y + y$ to produce the equivalent expression $3y$.* Also **6.EE.A.4**.

**Mathematical Practices MP.3, MP.4, MP.7, MP.8**

**Objective** Write equivalent expressions.

**Essential Understanding** The Distributive Property and other properties of operations are used to write equivalent expressions.

**Vocabulary** Equivalent expressions

### COHERENCE

In Lesson 1-6, students focus on generating equivalent expressions using the properties of operations in a formal way. Students have been using the Commutative and Associative Properties of addition since Grade 1, and of multiplication since Grade 3. They have also used the Distributive Property in different capacities, including area models in Grade 3, and multi-digit multiplication in Grade 4. Students who are accustomed to mentally calculating $3 \times 27$ as $3 \times (20 + 7) = 60 + 21$ can now see that $3(a + 7) = 3a + 21$ for all numbers $a$. Understanding equivalent expressions will be essential to solving equations and inequalities in Topic 2.

### RIGOR

This lesson emphasizes a blend of **conceptual understanding** and **procedural skill**. Students learn how to apply the Distributive Property to expressions like $5(4 + x)$ to produce the equivalent expression $20 + 5x$, and vice versa.

PD Watch the Listen and Look For Lesson Video.

## MATH ANYTIME

### Daily Common Core Review

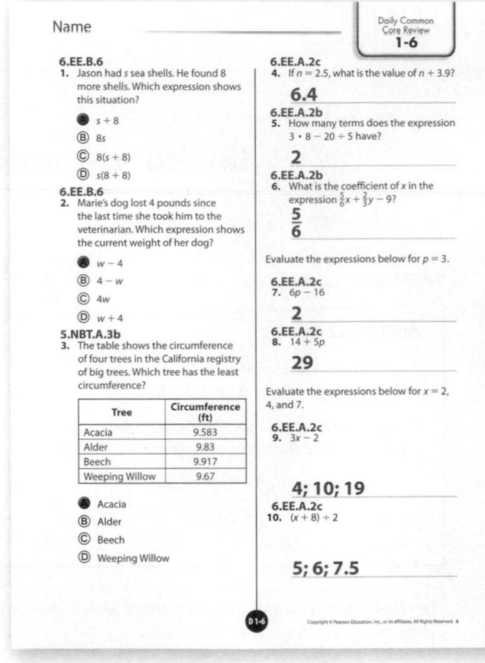
Name ______

Daily Common Core Review 1-6

6.EE.B.6
1. Jason had $s$ sea shells. He found 8 more shells. Which expression shows this situation?
   - Ⓐ $s + 8$ (filled)
   - Ⓑ $8s$
   - Ⓒ $8(s + 8)$
   - Ⓓ $s(8 + 8)$

6.EE.B.6
2. Marie's dog lost 4 pounds since the last time she took him to the veterinarian. Which expression shows the current weight of her dog?
   - Ⓐ $w - 4$ (filled)
   - Ⓑ $4 - w$
   - Ⓒ $4w$
   - Ⓓ $w + 4$

5.NBT.A.3b
3. The table shows the circumference of four trees in the California registry of big trees. Which tree has the least circumference?

| Tree | Circumference (ft) |
|---|---|
| Acacia | 9.583 |
| Alder | 9.83 |
| Beech | 9.917 |
| Weeping Willow | 9.67 |

   - Ⓐ Acacia (filled)
   - Ⓑ Alder
   - Ⓒ Beech
   - Ⓓ Weeping Willow

6.EE.A.2c
4. If $n = 2.5$, what is the value of $n + 3.9$?
   **6.4**

6.EE.A.2b
5. How many terms does the expression $3 \cdot 8 - 20 \div 5$ have?
   **2**

6.EE.A.2b
6. What is the coefficient of $x$ in the expression $\frac{5}{6}x + \frac{2}{3}y - 9$?
   $\frac{5}{6}$

Evaluate the expressions below for $p = 3$.

6.EE.A.2c
7. $6p - 16$
   **2**

6.EE.A.2c
8. $14 + 5p$
   **29**

Evaluate the expressions below for $x = 2$, 4, and 7.

6.EE.A.2c
9. $3x - 2$
   **4; 10; 19**

6.EE.A.2c
10. $(x + 8) \div 2$
   **5; 6; 7.5**

D 1-6

### Today's Challenge

Think Use the Topic 1 problems any time during this topic.

## ENGLISH LANGUAGE LEARNERS

**Listening** Seek clarification of spoken language.

*Use with the Visual Learning Bridge on Student's Edition p. 38.*

Read the information in Box A regarding *equivalent expressions*. Ask students to indicate if clarification is needed. *In other words, equivalent expressions are two mathematical expressions with equal value.* Write $3(4x - 1)$. Demonstrate how to write an equivalent expression using the Distributive and Associative Properties of Multiplication. Write $2x + 4 =$ ___.

**Beginning** Ask students if they understand the Distributive Property. Demonstrate rewriting the expression using the Distributive Property.

**Intermediate** Ask students if they understand the Distributive Property and provide clarification, as needed. Instruct students to work with partners to rewrite the expression using the Distributive Property.

**Advanced** Instruct students to ask their partners how to use the Distributive Property to rewrite the expression. Have them seek clarification as needed. Have students work with their partners to rewrite the expression.

**Summarize** How are different properties of operations used to generate equivalent expressions?

# DEVELOP: PROBLEM-BASED LEARNING

**COHERENCE: Engage learners by connecting prior knowledge to new ideas.**
Students extend their understanding of properties of operations to generate equivalent algebraic expressions and use precise language to explain why the two expressions have the same value.

10–15 min

Solve

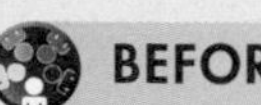

## BEFORE

1. **Pose the Solve-and-Share Problem**
**MP.3 Construct Arguments** Listen and look for students who generate equivalent expressions and explain their work using precise language, including the properties of operations.

2. **Build Understanding**
*How would you read aloud the given algebraic expression?* [Sample answer: 2 times the quantity 3 times $x$ plus 1] *What are you asked to do?* [Write an expression equivalent to $2(3x + 1)$ and explain why it's equivalent.]

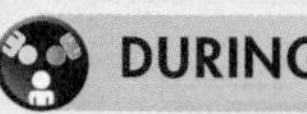

## DURING

3. **Ask Guiding Questions As Needed**
*What are some properties of operations?* [Commutative Property, Associative Property, Distributive Property] *How can you use one of the properties to write the expression in a different way?* [Sample answer: You can use the Commutative Property to write $2(3x + 1) = 2(1 + 3x)$.] *How can you check if the expressions are equivalent?* [Sample answer: Substitute the same number for the variable in both expressions and evaluate them to see if they are equal. Test another value or two to be sure.]

## AFTER

4. **Share and Discuss Solutions**
Solve Start with students' solutions. If needed, project Victor's work to discuss how to write an equivalent expression.

5. **Transition to the Visual Learning Bridge**
*Use properties of operations to write equivalent expressions.*

6. **Extension for Early Finishers**
*Use the Distributive Property to write an expression that is equivalent to $8x + 4$.* [Sample answers: $2(4x + 2)$ or $4(2x + 1)$]

Name

Solve & Share

Write an expression equivalent to $2(3x + 1)$. Explain why your expression is equivalent to $2(3x + 1)$. ***Solve this problem any way you choose.***

**Lesson 1-6**
**Write Equivalent Expressions**

**I can ...**
use the properties of operations to write equivalent expressions.

**Content Standards** 6.EE.A.3, 6.EE.A.4
**Mathematical Practices** MP.3, MP.4, MP.7, MP.8

You can use properties of operations to construct arguments about math. Which properties of operations do you know?



**See margin for sample student work.**

**Look Back!** **MP.7 Look for Relationships** Write an expression equivalent to $2(3x - 1)$. Explain what this expression has in common with the expression in the problem above.
**Sample answer: $2(3x - 1) = (2 \cdot 3x) - (2 \cdot 1) = 6x - 2$; The terms of $2(3x - 1)$ are the same as in $2(3x + 1)$, except you subtract instead of add.**

Digital Resources at PearsonRealize.com **Topic 1** | Lesson 1-6 **37**

## Analyze Student Work

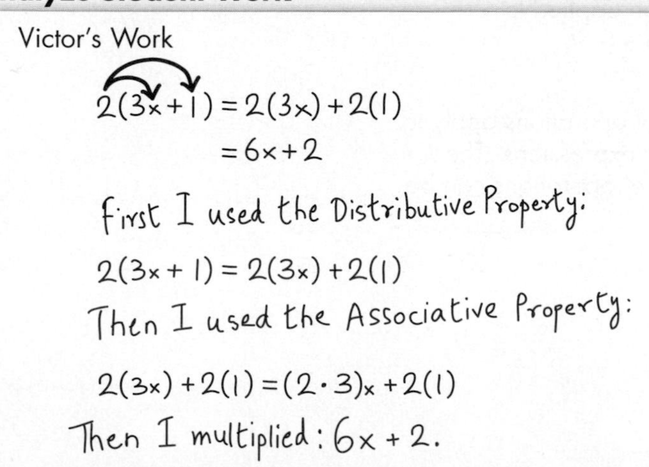

Victor's Work
2(3x+1) = 2(3x) + 2(1)
= 6x + 2
First I used the Distributive Property:
2(3x + 1) = 2(3x) + 2(1)
Then I used the Associative Property:
2(3x) + 2(1) = (2 · 3)x + 2(1)
Then I multiplied: 6x + 2.


Victor correctly applies the Distributive and Associative Properties to write an equivalent expression and includes an explanation for each step.

Ali's Work

$2(3x + 1) = 2(1 + 3x)$ Commutative Property of Addition

$= (1 + 3x)(2)$ Commutative Property of Multiplication

Ali correctly applies the Commutative Properties of Addition and Multiplication to generate different, but equivalent, expressions.

# DEVELOP: VISUAL LEARNING

Learn Glossary

The *Visual Learning Bridge* connects students' thinking in Solve & Share to important math ideas in the lesson. Use the *Visual Learning Bridge* to make these ideas explicit. Also available as a *Visual Learning Animation Plus* at PearsonRealize.com

*Explain in words how to apply the Commutative Properties.* [You can switch the order of addends or factors.] *Explain in words how to apply the Associative Properties.* [You can regroup addends or factors.] *Explain in words how to apply the Distributive Property.* [Multiply each term inside the parentheses by the number outside the parentheses.]

**MP.7 Use Structure**
*How do you know that $12x - 3$ is equivalent to $3(4x - 1)$?* [Sample answer: They would have the same value no matter what value you substitute for the variable in both expressions.]

**Prevent Misconceptions**

Some students might incorrectly write $3(4x - 1)$ as $12x - 1$. They did not distribute the 3 to the last term, 1. Remind students that when they use the Distributive Property, they must multiply the number outside the parentheses by each term inside the parentheses.

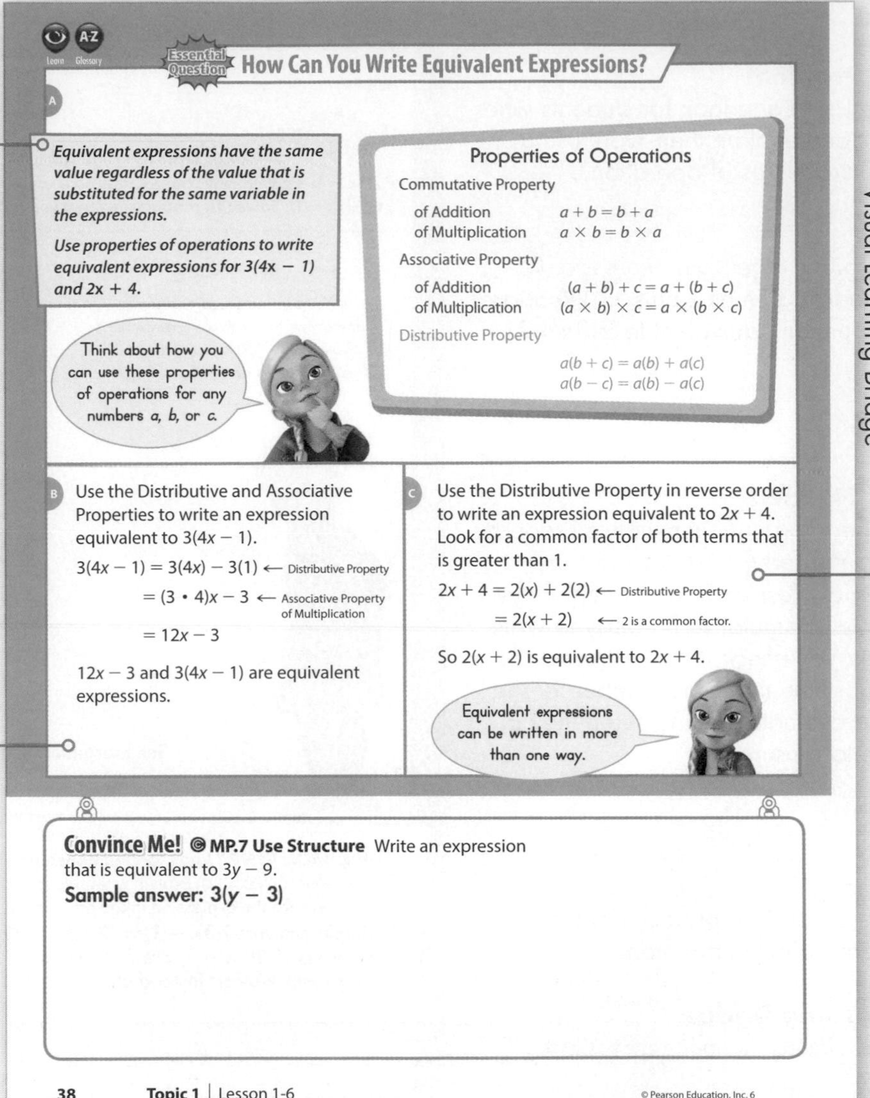

Learn Glossary

Essential Question **How Can You Write Equivalent Expressions?**

A

*Equivalent expressions have the same value regardless of the value that is substituted for the same variable in the expressions.*

*Use properties of operations to write equivalent expressions for $3(4x - 1)$ and $2x + 4$.*

Properties of Operations

Commutative Property
of Addition $a + b = b + a$
of Multiplication $a \times b = b \times a$

Associative Property
of Addition $(a + b) + c = a + (b + c)$
of Multiplication $(a \times b) \times c = a \times (b \times c)$

Distributive Property
$a(b + c) = a(b) + a(c)$
$a(b - c) = a(b) - a(c)$

Think about how you can use these properties of operations for any numbers *a*, *b*, or *c*.



B Use the Distributive and Associative Properties to write an expression equivalent to $3(4x - 1)$.

$3(4x - 1) = 3(4x) - 3(1)$ ← Distributive Property
$= (3 \cdot 4)x - 3$ ← Associative Property of Multiplication
$= 12x - 3$

$12x - 3$ and $3(4x - 1)$ are equivalent expressions.

C Use the Distributive Property in reverse order to write an expression equivalent to $2x + 4$. Look for a common factor of both terms that is greater than 1.

$2x + 4 = 2(x) + 2(2)$ ← Distributive Property
$= 2(x + 2)$ ← 2 is a common factor.

So $2(x + 2)$ is equivalent to $2x + 4$.

Equivalent expressions can be written in more than one way.



**Convince Me!** MP.7 Use Structure Write an expression that is equivalent to $3y - 9$.
**Sample answer: $3(y - 3)$**

38 **Topic 1** | Lesson 1-6 © Pearson Education, Inc. 6

Visual Learning Bridge

**MP.3 Construct Arguments**
*Why is 2 a common factor of both terms in the expression?* [The factors of 2 are 1 and 2; 2 is also a factor of 4.] *What does it mean to use the Distributive Property in reverse order?* [You start with two terms that have a common factor and rewrite them so that the common factor is used to multiply a sum or difference of two terms.]

**Convince Me!** **MP.7 Use Structure** The properties of operations provide a structure for generating equivalent expressions. The Distributive Property "of multiplication over addition" can also be applied to subtraction in this problem since $-9$ is equivalent to $+(-9)$.

Essential Question Revisit the Essential Question. Properties of operations apply to both numerical expressions and algebraic expressions. The Distributive Property and other properties of operations can be used to generate equivalent expressions.

## QUICK CHECK

Check mark indicates items for prescribing differentiation on the next page. Item 7 is worth 1 point. Items 23 and 24 are worth up to 2 points.

20–30 min

Practice Buddy | Tools | Assessment

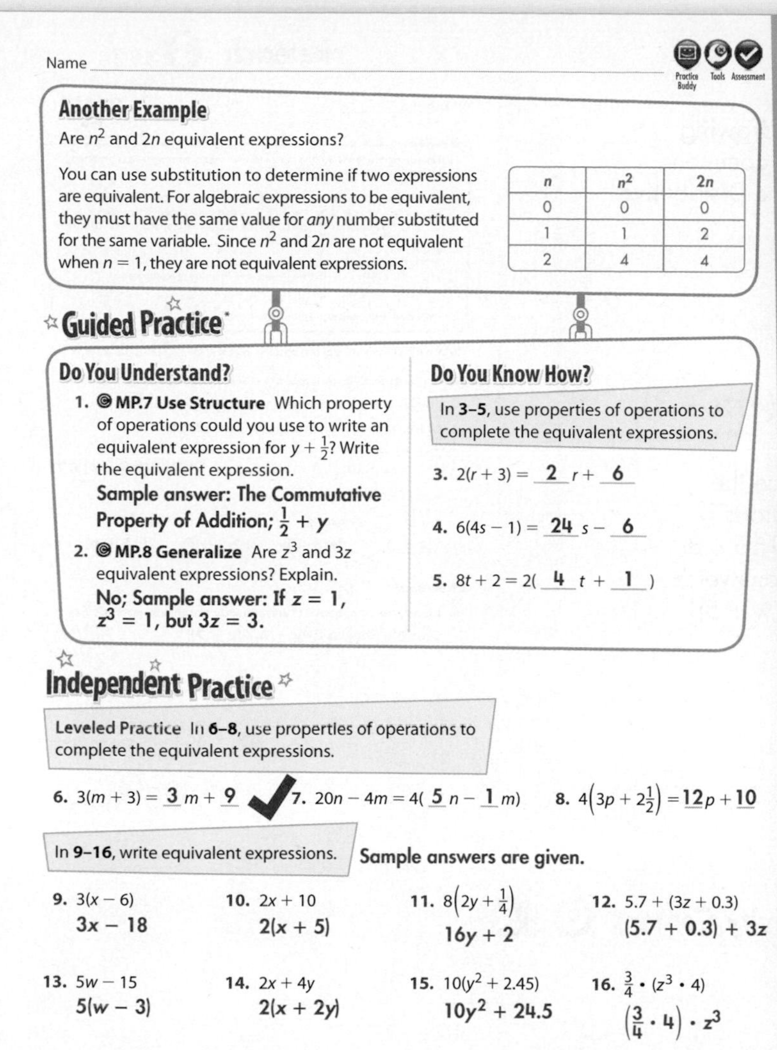

Name ______________

**Another Example**

Are $n^2$ and $2n$ equivalent expressions?

You can use substitution to determine if two expressions are equivalent. For algebraic expressions to be equivalent, they must have the same value for *any* number substituted for the same variable. Since $n^2$ and $2n$ are not equivalent when $n = 1$, they are not equivalent expressions.

| $n$ | $n^2$ | $2n$ |
|---|---|---|
| 0 | 0 | 0 |
| 1 | 1 | 2 |
| 2 | 4 | 4 |

**Guided Practice***

**Do You Understand?**

1. **MP.7 Use Structure** Which property of operations could you use to write an equivalent expression for $y + \frac{1}{2}$? Write the equivalent expression.
   **Sample answer: The Commutative Property of Addition; $\frac{1}{2} + y$**
2. **MP.8 Generalize** Are $z^3$ and $3z$ equivalent expressions? Explain.
   **No; Sample answer: If $z = 1$, $z^3 = 1$, but $3z = 3$.**

**Do You Know How?**

In **3–5**, use properties of operations to complete the equivalent expressions.

3. $2(r + 3) =$ **2** $r +$ **6**
4. $6(4s - 1) =$ **24** $s -$ **6**
5. $8t + 2 = 2($ **4** $t +$ **1** $)$

**Independent Practice***

Leveled Practice In **6–8**, use properties of operations to complete the equivalent expressions.

6. $3(m + 3) =$ **3** $m +$ **9**
7. $20n - 4m = 4($ **5** $n -$ **1** $m)$
8. $4\left(3p + 2\frac{1}{2}\right) =$ **12** $p +$ **10**

In **9–16**, write equivalent expressions. **Sample answers are given.**

9. $3(x - 6)$ **$3x - 18$**
10. $2x + 10$ **$2(x + 5)$**
11. $8\left(2y + \frac{1}{4}\right)$ **$16y + 2$**
12. $5.7 + (3z + 0.3)$ **$(5.7 + 0.3) + 3z$**
13. $5w - 15$ **$5(w - 3)$**
14. $2x + 4y$ **$2(x + 2y)$**
15. $10(y^2 + 2.45)$ **$10y^2 + 24.5$**
16. $\frac{3}{4} \cdot (z^3 \cdot 4)$ **$\left(\frac{3}{4} \cdot 4\right) \cdot z^3$**

*For another example, see Set F on page 70.

Topic 1 | Lesson 1-6 39

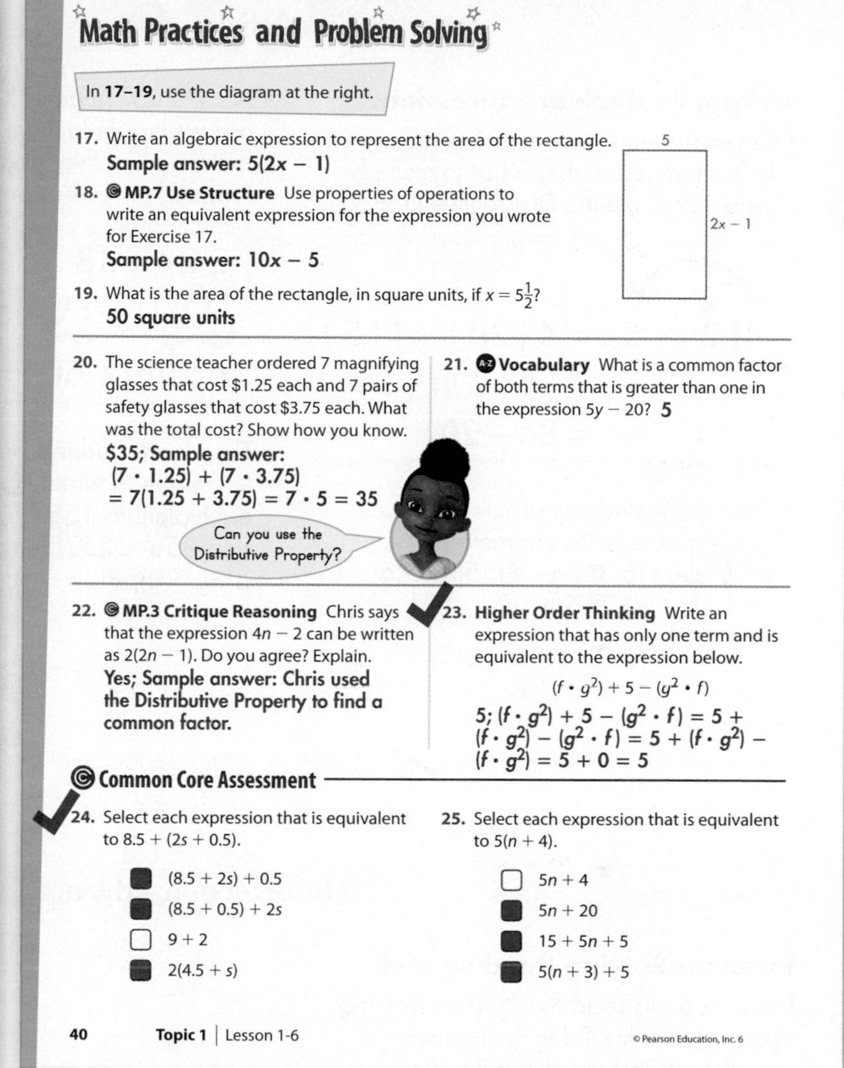

**Math Practices and Problem Solving***

In **17–19**, use the diagram at the right.



17. Write an algebraic expression to represent the area of the rectangle.
    **Sample answer: $5(2x - 1)$**
18. **MP.7 Use Structure** Use properties of operations to write an equivalent expression for the expression you wrote for Exercise 17.
    **Sample answer: $10x - 5$**
19. What is the area of the rectangle, in square units, if $x = 5\frac{1}{2}$?
    **50 square units**
20. The science teacher ordered 7 magnifying glasses that cost $1.25 each and 7 pairs of safety glasses that cost $3.75 each. What was the total cost? Show how you know.
    **$35; Sample answer: $(7 \cdot 1.25) + (7 \cdot 3.75) = 7(1.25 + 3.75) = 7 \cdot 5 = 35$**



21. **Vocabulary** What is a common factor of both terms that is greater than one in the expression $5y - 20$? **5**
22. **MP.3 Critique Reasoning** Chris says that the expression $4n - 2$ can be written as $2(2n - 1)$. Do you agree? Explain.
    **Yes; Sample answer: Chris used the Distributive Property to find a common factor.**
23. **Higher Order Thinking** Write an expression that has only one term and is equivalent to the expression below.
    $(f \cdot g^2) + 5 - (g^2 \cdot f)$
    **$5; (f \cdot g^2) + 5 - (g^2 \cdot f) = 5 + (f \cdot g^2) - (g^2 \cdot f) = 5 + (f \cdot g^2) - (f \cdot g^2) = 5 + 0 = 5$**

**Common Core Assessment**

24. Select each expression that is equivalent to $8.5 + (2s + 0.5)$.
    - ■ $(8.5 + 2s) + 0.5$
    - ■ $(8.5 + 0.5) + 2s$
    - □ $9 + 2$
    - ■ $2(4.5 + s)$
25. Select each expression that is equivalent to $5(n + 4)$.
    - □ $5n + 4$
    - ■ $5n + 20$
    - ■ $15 + 5n + 5$
    - ■ $5(n + 3) + 5$

40 Topic 1 | Lesson 1-6



**Another Example** *What is the value of* $n^2$ *when* $n = 2$? [4] *What is the value of 2n when n = 2?* [4] *So, are the expressions equivalent? Why or why not?* [No; Sample explanation: The expressions do not have the same value when $n = 1$; $n^2 = 1$ and $2n = 2$. Equivalent expressions must have the same value no matter what number is substituted for the variable.]

**Error Intervention: Item 5**

**If** students have trouble using the Distributive Property in reverse, **then** tell them to first find the common factors of $8t$ and 2. [1, 2] *A common factor is written in front of the parentheses. What number do you multiply 2 by to get 8t?* [4] *What number do you multiply 2 by to get 2?* [1]

**Reteaching** Assign Reteaching Set F on p. 70.

**Item 17** Encourage students to think about the operation used to find the area of a rectangle. *How do you find the area of a rectangle?* [Multiply length by width.] *What expression shows the length multiplied by the width of this rectangle?* [$5(2x - 1)$].

**Item 22 MP.3 Critique Reasoning** The Commutative, Associative, and Distributive Properties apply to both numerical expressions and algebraic expressions. *What property can you use to explain why you agree or disagree with Chris's statement?* [Distributive Property]

**Item 23 Higher Order Thinking** The Commutative Property of Addition can be applied to write the first two terms in a different order: $(f \cdot g^2) + 5 - (g^2 \cdot f) = 5 + (f \cdot g^2) - (g^2 \cdot f)$. Then the Commutative Property of Multiplication can be applied to switch the order of the factors in the last term: $5 + (f \cdot g^2) - (g^2 \cdot f) = 5 + (f \cdot g^2) - (f \cdot g^2)$. Since the last two terms are the same, their difference is 0: $5 + (f \cdot g^2) - (f \cdot g^2) = 5 + 0 = 5$.

**Multi-Step Problems** *Page 40 Items 20, 24, and 25; Page 42 Items 20, 24, and 25*

# ASSESS AND DIFFERENTIATE

Use the **QUICK CHECK** on the previous page to prescribe differentiated instruction.

**(I) Intervention** 0–3 points on the Quick Check

**(O) On-Level** 4 points on the Quick Check

**(A) Advanced** 5 points on the Quick Check

## Intervention Activity (I)

### Writing Equivalent Expressions

- Show students how drawing arrows can help them remember what to multiply when they use the Distributive Property.

$$4(2n-5) = 4(2n) - 4(5)$$
$$= (4 \cdot 2)n - 20$$
$$= 8n - 20$$

- Then have students practice the technique to write expressions equivalent to $3(5m+8)$; $5(7d-6)$; and $7(c+4)$. [$15m+24$; $35d-30$; $7c+28$]
- Next, show students how drawing arrows can help them use common factors when they apply the Distributive Property in reverse order.

$$24m + 18$$
$$6(4m) + 6(3) = 6(4m+3)$$

- Then have students practice the technique to write expressions equivalent to $15g+20$; $16p-8$; and $35w+25$. [Sample answers: $5(3g+4)$; $8(2p-1)$; $5(7w+5)$]

## Reteach 

Name ____________________

Reteach to Build Understanding
**1-6**

**Vocabulary**

**Equivalent expressions** have the same value no matter what value is substituted for the same variable in the expressions.

1. Properties of operations can be used to write equivalent expressions. For example, you can show that $2(3x+1)$ and $6x+2$ are equivalent expressions by using the Distributive Property and the Associative Property of Multiplication.

$2(3x+1)$
$= 2(3x) + 2(1)$ ← Use the Distributive Property.
$= (2 \cdot 3)x + 2(1)$ ← Use the Associative Property of Multiplication.
$= 6x + 2$ ← Multiply.

What is an equivalent expression for $4(3t-2)$? **$12t - 8$**

2. What is a common factor of both terms in $22m - 33$? **11**

3. Rewrite the term $22m$ as a product of 11 and another factor. **11(2m)**

Rewrite the term 33 as a product of 11 and another factor. **11(3)**

4. Fill in the blanks to write an equivalent expression for $22m - 33$.

$22m - 33 = 11(\mathbf{2m}) - 11(\mathbf{3})$ ← 11 is a common factor.
$= 11(\mathbf{2m} - \mathbf{3})$ ← Use the **Distributive Property**.

5. Write an equivalent expression for each expression below.

| $9z + 27$ | $4(w-5)$ | $6(12-3b)$ | $80 + 20n$ |
|---|---|---|---|
| **$9(z+3)$** | **$4w - 20$** | **$72 - 18b$** | **$20(4+n)$** |

**On the Back!**

6. Use properties of operations to write two equivalent expressions for $2(2y-4)$.

**Sample answers: $4y - 8$, $4(y - 2)$**

## On-Level and Advanced Activity Centers (O) (A)

### Problem-Solving Reading Mat

Have students read the Problem-Solving Reading Mat for Topic 1 and then complete Problem-Solving Reading Activity 1-6.

See the Problem-Solving Reading Activity Guide for other suggestions on how to use this mat.

## TIMING

The time allocated to Step 3 will depend on the teacher's instructional decisions and differentiation routines.

15–30 min

Help | Practice Buddy | Tools | Games

## Technology Center    

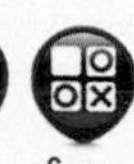
Tools Games

### Math Tools and Math Games

A link to a specific math tools activity or math game to use with this lesson is provided at PearsonRealize.com.

## Leveled Assignment  Items 1–12, 19–21, 24, 25  Items 1–3, 7–14, 19–25  Items 11–25

Name ____________

Help Practice Buddy Tools Games

### Homework & Practice 1-6
### Write Equivalent Expressions

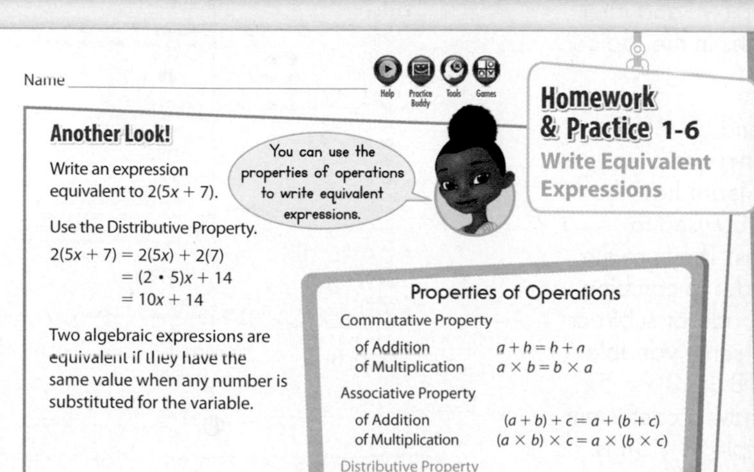

Another Look!
Write an expression equivalent to 2(5x + 7).
You can use the properties of operations to write equivalent expressions.
Use the Distributive Property.
2(5x + 7) = 2(5x) + 2(7)
= (2 • 5)x + 14
= 10x + 14
Two algebraic expressions are equivalent if they have the same value when any number is substituted for the variable.
Properties of Operations
Commutative Property
of Addition a + b = b + a
of Multiplication a × b = b × a
Associative Property
of Addition (a + b) + c = a + (b + c)
of Multiplication (a × b) × c = a × (b × c)
Distributive Property
across Addition a(b + c) = a(b) + a(c)
across Subtraction a(b − c) = a(b) − a(c)


In **1–6**, use properties of operations to complete the equivalent expressions.

1. $5(m-2) =$ **5** $m -$ **10**
2. $24x + 18y = 6($ **4** $x +$ **3** $y)$
3. $2\left(9p - \frac{1}{2}\right) =$ **18** $p -$ **1**
4. $8(2x-3)$ and **16** $x - 24$
5. $5(3x-9)$ and **15** $x -$ **45**
6. $6(2x+9)$ and **12** $x +$ **54**

In **7–18**, use properties of operations to write equivalent expressions. **Sample answers are given.**

7. $3(6x-7)$ **$18x - 21$**
8. $4(9x-2)$ **$36x - 8$**
9. $6(8x+1)$ **$48x + 6$**
10. $35x + 30$ **$5(7x + 6)$**
11. $4(x+7)$ **$4x + 28$**
12. $5x - 15y$ **$5(x - 3y)$**
13. $6\left(3y - \frac{1}{2}\right)$ **$18y - 3$**
14. $1.6 + (2z + 0.4)$ **$(1.6 + 0.4) + 2z$**
15. $8w - 16$ **$8(w - 2)$**
16. $2.2x + 2.2$ **$2.2(x + 1)$**
17. $100(z^2 - 5.38)$ **$100z^2 - 538$**
18. $8 \cdot \left(y^3 \cdot \frac{3}{4}\right)$ **$\left(8 \cdot \frac{3}{4}\right) \cdot y^3$**



In **19–21**, use the sign at the right.

| Pencil Pack | $1.50 |
|---|---|
| Notebook | $2 |
| Markers | $2.50 |

19. MP.4 **Model with Math** Ms. Thomas ordered 5 pencil packs, $n$ notebooks, and 5 sets of markers. Write an algebraic expression that represents the cost of Ms. Thomas's order.
**Sample answer:**
**$(5 \cdot 1.50) + (n \cdot 2) + (5 \cdot 2.50)$**

20. MP.7 **Use Structure** Use properties of operations to write an equivalent expression for the expression you wrote for Exercise 19.
**Sample answers: $5(1.50 + 2.50) + 2n$; $20 + 2n$; $2(10 + n)$**

21. What was the total cost of Ms. Thomas' order if she ordered 20 notebooks?
**$60; $2(10 + 20) = 20 \cdot 30 = 60$**

You can use properties of operations to write equivalent expressions in more than one way.

22. MP.4 **Model with Math** The formula for the perimeter of a rectangle is $2\ell + 2w$, where $\ell$ is the length and $w$ is the width. How can you use the Distributive Property to write an equivalent expression for $2\ell + 2w$?
**$2(\ell + w)$**

23. **Higher Order Thinking** Explain why the expression you wrote in Exercise 22 is easier to use than $2\ell + 2w$.
**Sample answer: $2\ell + 2w$ requires three calculations; $2(\ell + w)$ only requires two calculations.**

### Common Core Assessment

24. Select each expression that is equivalent to $4\frac{1}{2} + \left(3t + 1\frac{1}{2}\right)$.
- ■ $\left(4\frac{1}{2} + 3t\right) + 1\frac{1}{2}$
- ■ $\left(4\frac{1}{2} + 1\frac{1}{2}\right) + 3t$
- ■ $6 + 3t$
- ■ $3(2 + t)$

25. Select each expression that is equivalent to $8x - 24$.
- ■ $8(x-3)$
- ☐ $8(x-24)$
- ■ $9(x-3) - (x-3)$
- ■ $(5+3)x - 24$

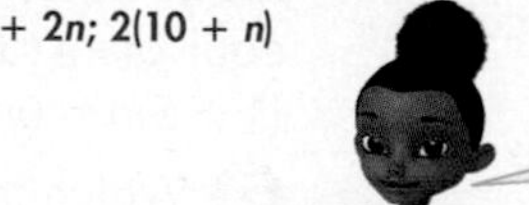

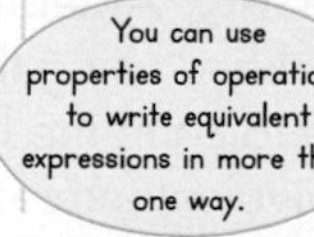

# LESSON 1-7

# SIMPLIFY ALGEBRAIC EXPRESSIONS

## DIGITAL RESOURCES PearsonRealize.com

eText — Student and Teacher eTexts

PD — Listen and Look For Lesson Video

Think — Today's Challenge

Solve — Solve and Share

Learn — Visual Learning Animation Plus

Glossary — Animated Glossary

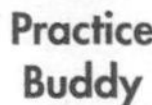
Practice Buddy — Online Personalized Practice

Tools — Math Tools

Assessment — Quick Check

Help — Another Look Homework Video

Games — Math Games

## LESSON OVERVIEW FCR FOCUS • COHERENCE • RIGOR

### FOCUS

**Domain 6.EE** Expressions and Equations

**Cluster 6.EE.A** Apply and extend previous understandings of arithmetic to algebraic expressions.

**Content Standard 6.EE.A.3** Apply the properties of operations to generate equivalent expressions. *For example, apply the distributive property to the expression 3(2 + x) to produce the equivalent expression 6 + 3x; apply the distributive property to the expression 24x + 18y to produce the equivalent expression 6(4x + 3y); apply properties of operations to y + y + y to produce the equivalent expression 3y*. Also **6.EE.A.4**.

**Mathematical Practices MP.1, MP.3, MP.4, MP.6, MP.7**

**Objective** Simplify algebraic expressions by combining like terms.

**Essential Understanding** Algebraic expressions can be simplified using the properties of operations to combine like terms and generate equivalent expressions.

**Vocabulary** Like terms, Simplify

### COHERENCE

In Lesson 1-6, students used properties of operations to write equivalent algebraic expressions. In this lesson, students write equivalent algebraic expressions by combining like terms to simplify expressions. Students will apply these concepts as they work with formulas in Lesson 1-9, and later with equations and inequalities in the Topic 2.

### RIGOR

This lesson emphasizes a blend of **conceptual understanding** and **procedural skill**. Students learn how the properties of operations can be used to simplify algebraic expressions. They use the properties to justify that in order to combine like terms with like variables, add or subtract the coefficients and keep the same variable. For example, $18x - 13x = (18 - 13)x = 5x$. If a variable term does not show a coefficient, the coefficient is 1. For example, $n + 5n$ is equivalent to $1n + 5n$, which simplifies to $(1 + 5)n = 6n$.

PD Watch the Listen and Look For Lesson Video.

## MATH ANTIME

### Daily Common Core Review

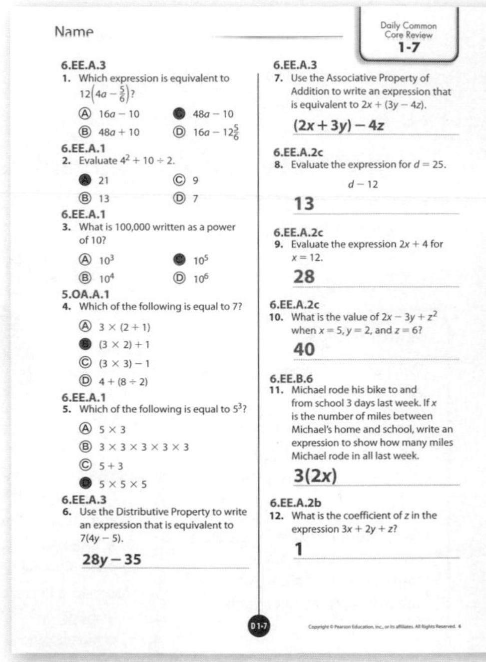
Name ____________

Daily Common Core Review 1-7

6.EE.A.3
1. Which expression is equivalent to $12\left(4a - \frac{5}{6}\right)$?
   (A) $16a - 10$
   (B) $48a + 10$
   ● $48a - 10$
   (D) $16a - 12\frac{5}{6}$

6.EE.A.1
2. Evaluate $4^2 + 10 \div 2$.
   ● 21
   (B) 13
   (C) 9
   (D) 7

6.EE.A.1
3. What is 100,000 written as a power of 10?
   (A) $10^3$
   (B) $10^4$
   ● $10^5$
   (D) $10^6$

5.OA.A.1
4. Which of the following is equal to 7?
   (A) $3 \times (2 + 1)$
   ● $(3 \times 2) + 1$
   (C) $(3 \times 3) - 1$
   (D) $4 + (8 \div 2)$

6.EE.A.1
5. Which of the following is equal to $5^3$?
   (A) $5 \times 3$
   (B) $3 \times 3 \times 3 \times 3 \times 3$
   (C) $5 + 3$
   ● $5 \times 5 \times 5$

6.EE.A.3
6. Use the Distributive Property to write an expression that is equivalent to $7(4y - 5)$.
   **$28y - 35$**

6.EE.A.3
7. Use the Associative Property of Addition to write an expression that is equivalent to $2x + (3y - 4z)$.
   **$(2x + 3y) - 4z$**

6.EE.A.2c
8. Evaluate the expression for $d = 25$.
   $d - 12$
   **13**

6.EE.A.2c
9. Evaluate the expression $2x + 4$ for $x = 12$.
   **28**

6.EE.A.2c
10. What is the value of $2x - 3y + z^2$ when $x = 5, y = 2$, and $z = 6$?
   **40**

6.EE.B.6
11. Michael rode his bike to and from school 3 days last week. If $x$ is the number of miles between Michael's home and school, write an expression to show how many miles Michael rode in all last week.
   **$3(2x)$**

6.EE.A.2b
12. What is the coefficient of $z$ in the expression $3x + 2y + z$?
   **1**

D 1-7

### Today's Challenge

Think Use the Topic 1 problems any time during this topic.

## ENGLISH LANGUAGE LEARNERS ELL

**Reading** Demonstrate comprehension by retelling information.

*Use with Convince Me! on Student's Edition p. 44.*

Read Convince Me! Write $4z + 7 - z - 4$ on the board. *To simplify the algebraic expression, find terms with the same variable part.* Students will identify the like terms and determine that: $4z - z = 3z$. *What is the next step to simplify the algebraic expression?* Students will identify the numerical terms and simplify. $7 - 4 = 3$. Write the simplified algebraic expression on the board: $4z + 7 - z - 4 = 3z + 3$.

**Beginning** Read Convince Me! wtih students. Write the following on index cards: $4z + 7 - z - 4$; $=$; $4z - z = 3z$; $7 - 4 = 3$; $3z + 3$. Ask students to retell information by putting the index cards in the correct order.

**Intermediate** Read Convince Me! with students. Ask students to write the following on index cards: $4z + 7 - z - 4$; $=$ ; $4z - z = 3z$; $7 - 4 = 3$; $3z + 3$. Instruct students to work with partners to retell information by putting the index cards in the correct order.

**Advanced** Instruct students to read Convince Me! Ask them to retell information by writing on index cards the steps to simplify the algebraic expression. Have students share their steps with partners.

**Summarize** What are the steps to simplifying an algebraic expression?

# DEVELOP: PROBLEM-BASED LEARNING

**COHERENCE: Engage learners by connecting prior knowledge to new ideas.**
Students extend their understanding of equivalent expressions by combining like terms to simplify an algebraic expression.

10–15 min

PEARSON realize. PearsonRealize.com

Solve

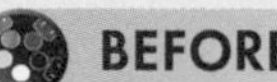

## BEFORE

1. **Pose the Solve-and-Share Problem**
**MP.1 Make Sense and Persevere** Listen and look for students who connect their previous knowledge of the parts of an expression and the properties of operations to simplify an algebraic expression.

2. **Build Understanding**
*What do you know about terms in expressions?* [Sample answer: Terms are separated by plus or minus signs.] *How many terms are in the expression?* [4] *Which terms have variables?* [$x$ and $2x$] *Which terms are numbers?* [5 and 2]

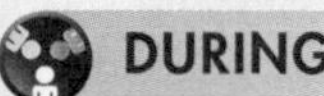

## DURING

3. **Ask Guiding Questions As Needed**
*What operation is used in the term 2x?* [Multiplication] *What other operation can you use to show multiplication?* [Repeated addition] *So, what would be another way to show 2x?* [$x + x$] *How could you use addition only to show x + 2x?* [$x + x + x$] *How could you use multiplication to show x + x + x?* [$3x$] *How would you combine the terms 5 and 2?* [Add]

## AFTER

4. **Share and Discuss Solutions**
Solve Start with students' solutions. If needed, project Estela's work to discuss how to combine the like terms in the expression.

5. **Transition to the Visual Learning Bridge**
*Terms with the same variable part are called like terms. When you combine like terms, you write a simplified equivalent expression.*

6. **Extension for Early Finishers**
*Write an expression equivalent to 4x + 8 − 2x + 3x − 1 that has no like terms.* [$5x + 7$]

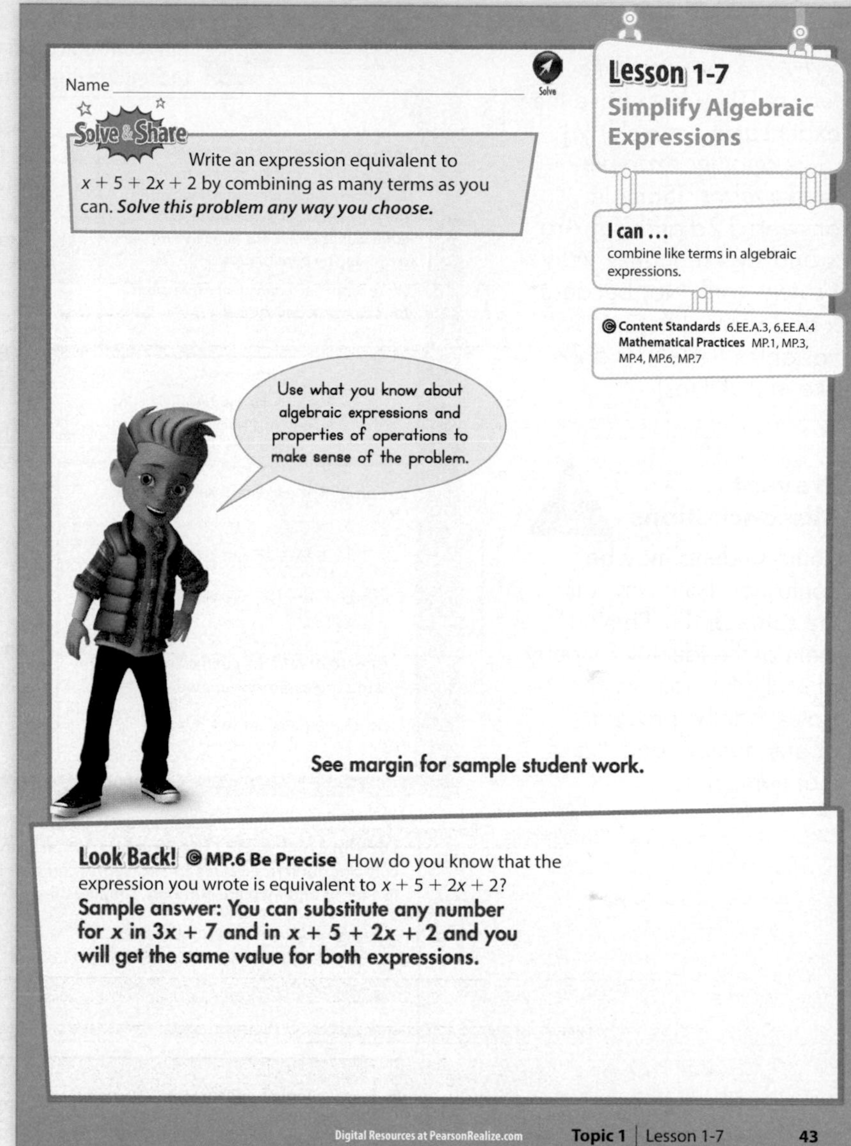

Name
Solve
Solve & Share
Write an expression equivalent to $x + 5 + 2x + 2$ by combining as many terms as you can. ***Solve this problem any way you choose.***
Lesson 1-7
Simplify Algebraic Expressions
I can …
combine like terms in algebraic expressions.
Content Standards 6.EE.A.3, 6.EE.A.4
Mathematical Practices MP.1, MP.3, MP.4, MP.6, MP.7
Use what you know about algebraic expressions and properties of operations to make sense of the problem.
**See margin for sample student work.**
**Look Back!** MP.6 Be Precise How do you know that the expression you wrote is equivalent to $x + 5 + 2x + 2$?
**Sample answer: You can substitute any number for $x$ in $3x + 7$ and in $x + 5 + 2x + 2$ and you will get the same value for both expressions.**
Digital Resources at PearsonRealize.com
Topic 1 | Lesson 1-7
43


## Analyze Student Work

Estela's Work

$$x + 5 + 2x + 2$$
$$= x + 2x + 5 + 2$$
$$= x + x + x + 7$$
$$= 3x + 7$$

Estela applies the Commutative Property to write the correct simplified expression.

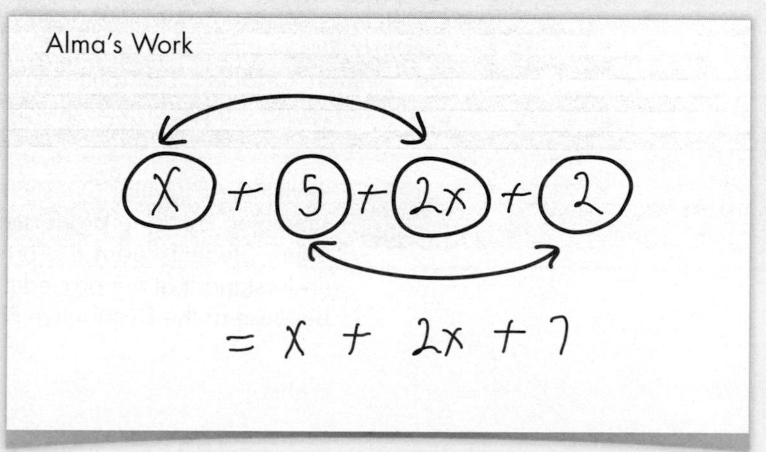


Alma correctly identifies the like terms in the expression. She adds the numbers, but does not combine $x$ and $2x$.

# DEVELOP: VISUAL LEARNING

The *Visual Learning Bridge* connects students' thinking in Solve & Share to important math ideas in the lesson. Use the *Visual Learning Bridge* to make these ideas explicit. Also available as a *Visual Learning Animation Plus* at PearsonRealize.com

Visual Learning

PEARSON realize. PearsonRealize.com

 Learn  Glossary

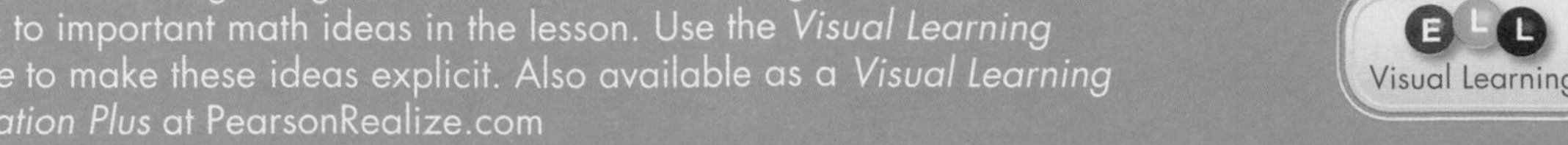

**MP.6 Be Precise**
*Why are 2y and y like terms?* [They both have the exact same variable, $y$.] *Give another example of like terms.* [Sample answer: $12d$ and $7d$] *Are x and 2y like terms? Why or why not?* [No, because $x$ and $y$ are different variables.] *Are x and 2x like terms?* [Yes]

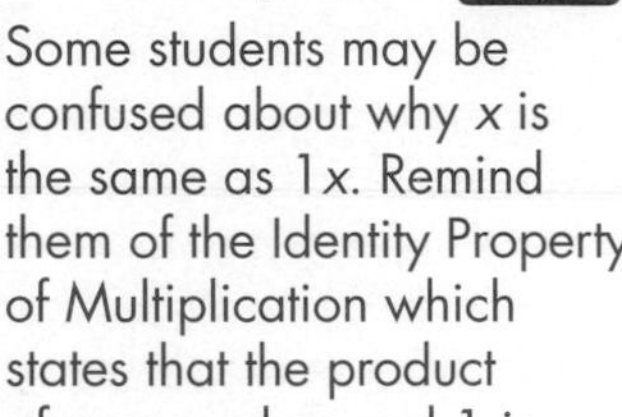

**Prevent Misconceptions**

Some students may be confused about why $x$ is the same as $1x$. Remind them of the Identity Property of Multiplication which states that the product of any number and 1 is that number.

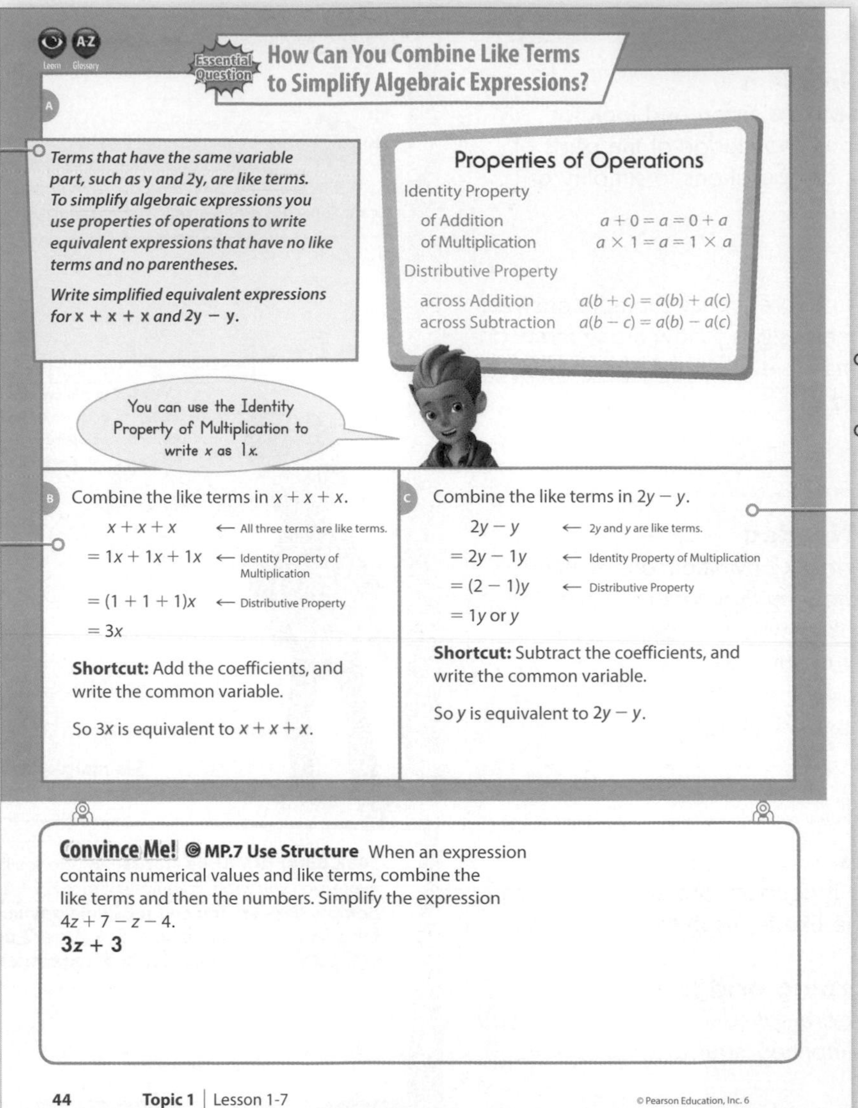

Essential Question How Can You Combine Like Terms to Simplify Algebraic Expressions?
A
Terms that have the same variable part, such as y and 2y, are like terms. To simplify algebraic expressions you use properties of operations to write equivalent expressions that have no like terms and no parentheses.
Write simplified equivalent expressions for x + x + x and 2y − y.
Properties of Operations
Identity Property
of Addition a + 0 = a = 0 + a
of Multiplication a × 1 = a = 1 × a
Distributive Property
across Addition a(b + c) = a(b) + a(c)
across Subtraction a(b − c) = a(b) − a(c)
You can use the Identity Property of Multiplication to write x as 1x.
B Combine the like terms in x + x + x.
x + x + x ← All three terms are like terms.
= 1x + 1x + 1x ← Identity Property of Multiplication
= (1 + 1 + 1)x ← Distributive Property
= 3x
Shortcut: Add the coefficients, and write the common variable.
So 3x is equivalent to x + x + x.
C Combine the like terms in 2y − y.
2y − y ← 2y and y are like terms.
= 2y − 1y ← Identity Property of Multiplication
= (2 − 1)y ← Distributive Property
= 1y or y
Shortcut: Subtract the coefficients, and write the common variable.
So y is equivalent to 2y − y.
Convince Me! MP.7 Use Structure When an expression contains numerical values and like terms, combine the like terms and then the numbers. Simplify the expression 4z + 7 − z − 4.
3z + 3
44 Topic 1 | Lesson 1-7
© Pearson Education, Inc. 6


Visual Learning Bridge

*How would you combine like terms in the expression 9g − 2g?* [Subtract 2 from 9 and write the common variable: $7g$] *Is 9g − 2g equal to (9 − 2)g? Explain.* [Yes, because of the Distributive Property]

**Convince Me! MP.7 Use Structure** *What like terms would you combine first?* [$4z$ and $-z$] *What is another way to represent −z? Explain.* [$-1z$; because of the Identity Property of Multiplication] *What property makes it possible for you to subtract the coefficients and write the common variable?* [Distributive Property] *How do you simplify the numerical terms?* [Subtract, $7 - 4 = 3$]

Revisit the Essential Question. Algebraic expressions can be simplified by using properties of operations to combine like terms. Students learn a shortcut procedure, but also need to understand that the procedure works the shortcut works because of the Distributive Property.

## QUICK CHECK

Check mark indicates items for prescribing differentiation on the next page.
Item 12 is worth 1 point. Items 30 and 31 are worth up to 2 points.

20–30 min

 Practice Buddy  Tools  Assessment

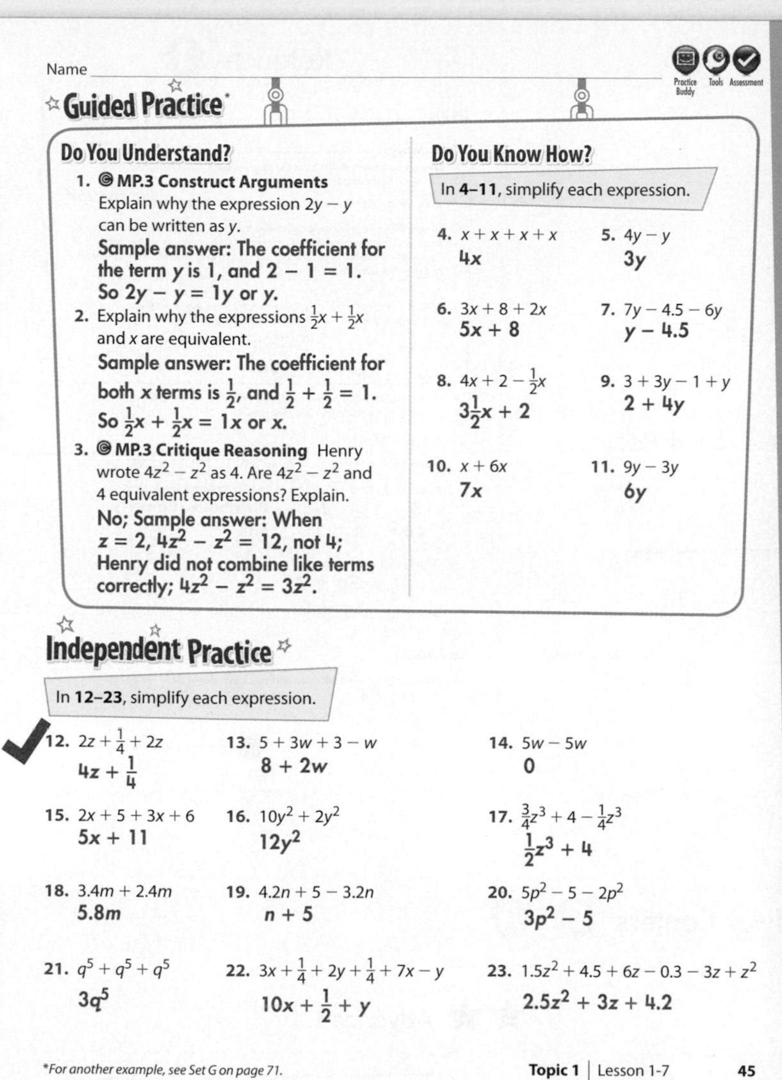

Name

### Guided Practice*

**Do You Understand?**

1. MP.3 Construct Arguments Explain why the expression $2y - y$ can be written as $y$.
   **Sample answer: The coefficient for the term $y$ is 1, and $2 - 1 = 1$. So $2y - y = 1y$ or $y$.**
2. Explain why the expressions $\frac{1}{2}x + \frac{1}{2}x$ and $x$ are equivalent.
   **Sample answer: The coefficient for both $x$ terms is $\frac{1}{2}$, and $\frac{1}{2} + \frac{1}{2} = 1$. So $\frac{1}{2}x + \frac{1}{2}x = 1x$ or $x$.**
3. MP.3 Critique Reasoning Henry wrote $4z^2 - z^2$ as 4. Are $4z^2 - z^2$ and 4 equivalent expressions? Explain.
   **No; Sample answer: When $z = 2$, $4z^2 - z^2 = 12$, not 4; Henry did not combine like terms correctly; $4z^2 - z^2 = 3z^2$.**

**Do You Know How?**

In **4–11**, simplify each expression.

4. $x + x + x + x$ **$4x$**
5. $4y - y$ **$3y$**
6. $3x + 8 + 2x$ **$5x + 8$**
7. $7y - 4.5 - 6y$ **$y - 4.5$**
8. $4x + 2 - \frac{1}{2}x$ **$3\frac{1}{2}x + 2$**
9. $3 + 3y - 1 + y$ **$2 + 4y$**
10. $x + 6x$ **$7x$**
11. $9y - 3y$ **$6y$**

### Independent Practice*

In **12–23**, simplify each expression.

12. $2z + \frac{1}{4} + 2z$ **$4z + \frac{1}{4}$**
13. $5 + 3w + 3 - w$ **$8 + 2w$**
14. $5w - 5w$ **0**
15. $2x + 5 + 3x + 6$ **$5x + 11$**
16. $10y^2 + 2y^2$ **$12y^2$**
17. $\frac{3}{4}z^3 + 4 - \frac{1}{4}z^3$ **$\frac{1}{2}z^3 + 4$**
18. $3.4m + 2.4m$ **$5.8m$**
19. $4.2n + 5 - 3.2n$ **$n + 5$**
20. $5p^2 - 5 - 2p^2$ **$3p^2 - 5$**
21. $q^5 + q^5 + q^5$ **$3q^5$**
22. $3x + \frac{1}{4} + 2y + \frac{1}{4} + 7x - y$ **$10x + \frac{1}{2} + y$**
23. $1.5z^2 + 4.5 + 6z - 0.3 - 3z + z^2$ **$2.5z^2 + 3z + 4.2$**

*For another example, see Set G on page 71.

Topic 1 | Lesson 1-7 45

### Math Practices and Problem Solving*

In **24–26**, use the diagram at the right.

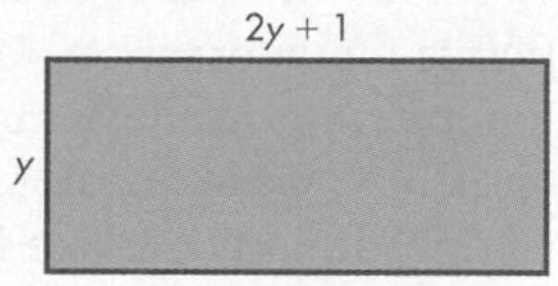

24. Write an algebraic expression for the perimeter of the rectangle.
    **Sample answer: $2y + 1 + 2y + 2y + 1$**
25. MP.7 Use Structure Write an expression equivalent to the expression you wrote for Exercise 24.
    **Sample answer: $6y + 2$**
26. What is the perimeter of the rectangle, in units, if $y = 2\frac{1}{2}$?
    **17 units**

(Diagram labels: $2y + 1$; $y$)

27. Rodney rewrote the expression $\frac{1}{2}(2x + 7)$ as $x + 3\frac{1}{2}$. Which property of operations did Rodney use?
    **Distributive Property**
28. **Number Sense** Give an example of a number, $n$, for which the inequality below is true.
    $$n > n^2$$
    **Sample answer: $n = \frac{1}{2}$**
29. MP.3 Critique Reasoning Thea said that the expressions $4x - 3x + 2$ and $x + 2$ are equivalent. Is Thea correct? Explain.
    **Yes; Sample answer: $4x$ and $3x$ are like terms so they can be combined. $4x - 3x = 1x$ or $x$, so $4x - 3x + 2$ is equivalent to $x + 2$.**
30. **Higher Order Thinking** Write an equivalent expression for the expression shown below.
    $$\frac{a}{3} + \frac{a}{3} + \frac{a}{3}$$
    **$a$; $\frac{a}{3} + \frac{a}{3} + \frac{a}{3} = \left(\frac{1}{3}\right)a + \left(\frac{1}{3}\right)a + \left(\frac{1}{3}\right)a = \left(\frac{1}{3} + \frac{1}{3} + \frac{1}{3}\right)a = 1a$**

**Common Core Assessment**

31. Write each expression below in the correct column in the table at the right to show whether the expression is equivalent to $2x + 7 + 6x - x$.

$2x + 13$
$7 + 7x$
$14x$
$7x + 7$

| Equivalent to $2x + 7 + 6x - x$ | NOT Equivalent to $2x + 7 + 6x - x$ |
|---|---|
| **$7 + 7x$** | **$2x + 13$** |
| **$7x + 7$** | **$14x$** |

46 Topic 1 | Lesson 1-7



**Error Intervention: Item 6**

**If** students simplify the expression incorrectly,

**then** remind them that only like terms may be combined. *What are the like terms in this expression?* [3x and 2x] *Why isn't the 8 also a like term?* [It does not contain the variable, x.] *So, which terms can be combined?* [3x and 2x] *What is 3x + 2x?* [5x] *Can 5x + 8 be simplified by combining like terms?* [No, because 5x and 8 are not like terms.]

**Item 23** Students need to understand that $z^2$ and $z$ are **not** like terms. You can point this out to students by substituting a value other than 0 or 1 for the variable. *If $z = 3$, what is the value of $z^2$?* [9] *So, are z and $z^2$ equivalent?* [No]

**Reteaching** Assign Reteaching Set G on p. 71.

**Item 24** Remind students that the perimeter of a rectangle is found by adding the lengths of all four sides. Students who use the formula $P = 2(\ell + w)$ might write the expression $2(2y + 1 + y)$.

**Item 25 MP.7 Use Structure** The properties of operations provide structure for generating equivalent expressions. *Once you simplify an expression, what does it mean that it is an equivalent expression?* [Sample answer: The expressions are equivalent so they represent the same value regardless of the value substituted for y.]

**Item 30 Higher Order Thinking** Students should recall that $\frac{a}{3}$ can be written as $\left(\frac{1}{3}\right)a$. They can also use their knowledge of fractions to reason that the sum of 3 thirds is one whole, so the sum of 3 thirds of $a$ equals $1a$ or $a$.

**Multi-Step Problems** *Page 46 Items 25, 26, 29–31; Page 48 Items 16–18, 20, 23*

# ASSESS AND DIFFERENTIATE

Use the **QUICK CHECK** on the previous page to prescribe differentiated instruction.

**Intervention** 0–3 points on the Quick Check

**On-Level** 4 points on the Quick Check

**Advanced** 5 points on the Quick Check

## Intervention Activity

### Simplifying Algebraic Expressions

- Write the expression $4x + 9 + 8x - 4$ on the board. Show students how to use matching underlines or circles and other shapes to indicate like terms. Then work together to combine like terms and write the simplified expression. Remind students to combine the numerical terms 9 and 4. [$12x + 5$]
- Have students use this procedure to simplify the following expressions:
  $5m + 6 - 2m - 3$ [$3m + 3$]
  $8h - 7 + h$ [$9h - 7$]
  $4a + 7b - 2a + 3b$ [$2a + 10b$]
  $6n + 7s + 2.5n - 3s$ [$8.5n + 4s$]

$6n + 7s + 2.5n - 3s = 8.5n + 4s$

## Reteach

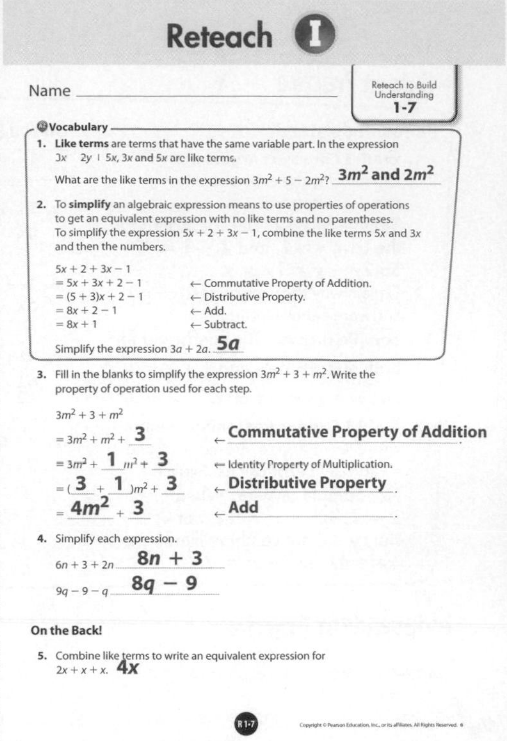

Name ______________

Reteach to Build Understanding 1-7

Vocabulary

1. **Like terms** are terms that have the same variable part. In the expression $3x + 2y + 5x$, $3x$ and $5x$ are like terms.
   What are the like terms in the expression $3m^2 + 5 - 2m^2$? **$3m^2$ and $2m^2$**

2. To **simplify** an algebraic expression means to use properties of operations to get an equivalent expression with no like terms and no parentheses. To simplify the expression $5x + 2 + 3x - 1$, combine the like terms $5x$ and $3x$ and then the numbers.

   $5x + 2 + 3x - 1$
   $= 5x + 3x + 2 - 1$ ← Commutative Property of Addition.
   $= (5 + 3)x + 2 - 1$ ← Distributive Property.
   $= 8x + 2 - 1$ ← Add.
   $= 8x + 1$ ← Subtract.

   Simplify the expression $3a + 2a$. **$5a$**

3. Fill in the blanks to simplify the expression $3m^2 + 3 + m^2$. Write the property of operation used for each step.

   $3m^2 + 3 + m^2$
   $= 3m^2 + m^2 +$ **3** ← **Commutative Property of Addition**
   $= 3m^2 +$ **1** $m^2 +$ **3** ← Identity Property of Multiplication.
   $= ($**3** $+$ **1**$)m^2 +$ **3** ← **Distributive Property**
   $=$ **$4m^2$** $+$ **3** ← **Add**

4. Simplify each expression.
   $6n + 3 + 2n$ **$8n + 3$**
   $9q - 9 - q$ **$8q - 9$**

On the Back!

5. Combine like terms to write an equivalent expression for $2x + x + x$. **$4x$**

R 1-7 Copyright © Pearson Education, Inc., or its affiliates. All Rights Reserved. 6

## On-Level and Advanced Activity Centers

### Center Games

Students work in pairs or small teams to combine like terms to simplify expressions. Have students record their work as they play the game.

★ On-Level

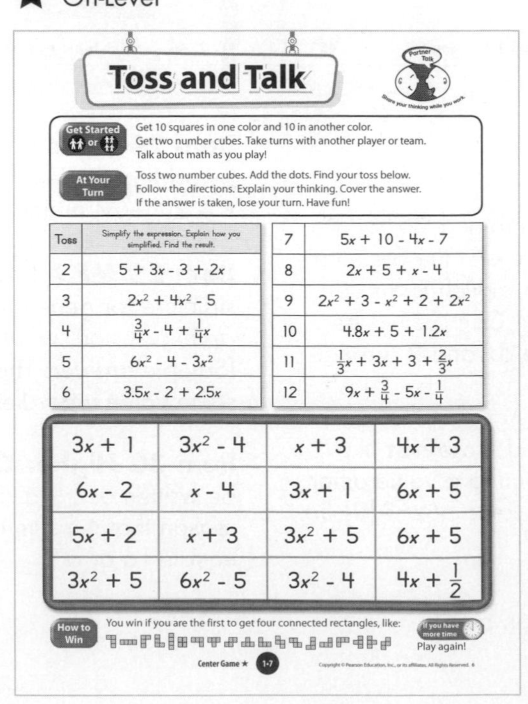

**Toss and Talk**

Partner Talk — Share your thinking while you work.

Get Started: Get 10 squares in one color and 10 in another color. Get two number cubes. Take turns with another player or team. Talk about math as you play!

At Your Turn: Toss two number cubes. Add the dots. Find your toss below. Follow the directions. Explain your thinking. Cover the answer. If the answer is taken, lose your turn. Have fun!

| Toss | Simplify the expression. Explain how you simplified. Find the result. | Toss | |
|---|---|---|---|
| 2 | $5 + 3x - 3 + 2x$ | 7 | $5x + 10 - 4x - 7$ |
| 3 | $2x^2 + 4x^2 - 5$ | 8 | $2x + 5 + x - 4$ |
| 4 | $\frac{3}{4}x - 4 + \frac{1}{4}x$ | 9 | $2x^2 + 3 - x^2 + 2 + 2x^2$ |
| 5 | $6x^2 - 4 - 3x^2$ | 10 | $4.8x + 5 + 1.2x$ |
| 6 | $3.5x - 2 + 2.5x$ | 11 | $\frac{1}{3}x + 3x + 3 + \frac{2}{3}x$ |
| | | 12 | $9x + \frac{3}{4} - 5x - \frac{1}{4}$ |

| | | | |
|---|---|---|---|
| $3x + 1$ | $3x^2 - 4$ | $x + 3$ | $4x + 3$ |
| $6x - 2$ | $x - 4$ | $3x + 1$ | $6x + 5$ |
| $5x + 2$ | $x + 3$ | $3x^2 + 5$ | $6x + 5$ |
| $3x^2 + 5$ | $6x^2 - 5$ | $3x^2 - 4$ | $4x + \frac{1}{2}$ |

How to Win: You win if you are the first to get four connected rectangles, like:

If you have more time: Play again!

Center Game ★ 1-7 Copyright © Pearson Education, Inc., or its affiliates. All Rights Reserved. 6

★★ Advanced

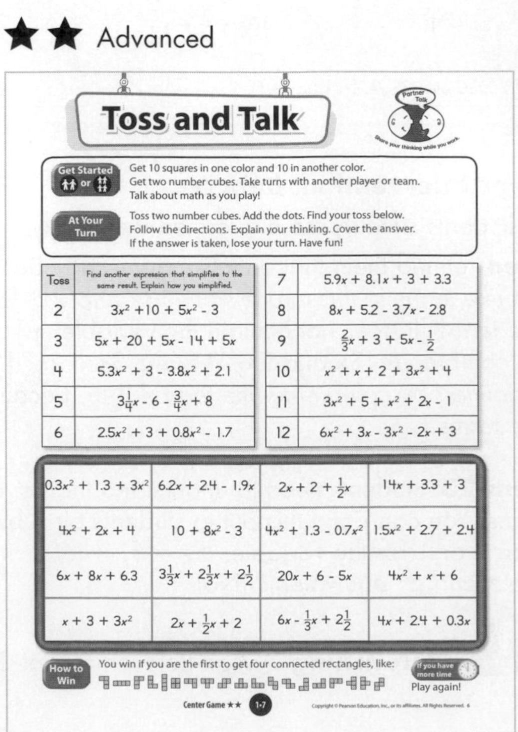

**Toss and Talk**

Partner Talk — Share your thinking while you work.

Get Started: Get 10 squares in one color and 10 in another color. Get two number cubes. Take turns with another player or team. Talk about math as you play!

At Your Turn: Toss two number cubes. Add the dots. Find your toss below. Follow the directions. Explain your thinking. Cover the answer. If the answer is taken, lose your turn. Have fun!

| Toss | Find another expression that simplifies to the same result. Explain how you simplified. | Toss | |
|---|---|---|---|
| 2 | $3x^2 + 10 + 5x^2 - 3$ | 7 | $5.9x + 8.1x + 3 + 3.3$ |
| 3 | $5x + 20 + 5x - 14 + 5x$ | 8 | $8x + 5.2 - 3.7x - 2.8$ |
| 4 | $5.3x^2 + 3 - 3.8x^2 + 2.1$ | 9 | $\frac{2}{3}x + 3 + 5x - \frac{1}{2}$ |
| 5 | $3\frac{1}{4}x - 6 - \frac{3}{4}x + 8$ | 10 | $x^2 + x + 2 + 3x^2 + 4$ |
| 6 | $2.5x^2 + 3 + 0.8x^2 - 1.7$ | 11 | $3x^2 + 5 + x^2 + 2x - 1$ |
| | | 12 | $6x^2 + 3x - 3x^2 - 2x + 3$ |

| | | | |
|---|---|---|---|
| $0.3x^2 + 1.3 + 3x^2$ | $6.2x + 2.4 - 1.9x$ | $2x + 2 + \frac{1}{2}x$ | $14x + 3.3 + 3$ |
| $4x^2 + 2x + 4$ | $10 + 8x^2 - 3$ | $4x^2 + 1.3 - 0.7x^2$ | $1.5x^2 + 2.7 + 2.4$ |
| $6x + 8x + 6.3$ | $3\frac{1}{3}x + 2\frac{1}{3}x + 2\frac{1}{2}$ | $20x + 6 - 5x$ | $4x^2 + x + 6$ |
| $x + 3 + 3x^2$ | $2x + \frac{1}{2}x + 2$ | $6x - \frac{1}{3}x + 2\frac{1}{2}$ | $4x + 2.4 + 0.3x$ |

How to Win: You win if you are the first to get four connected rectangles, like:

If you have more time: Play again!

Center Game ★★ 1-7 Copyright © Pearson Education, Inc., or its affiliates. All Rights Reserved. 6

**TIMING**

The time allocated to Step 3 will depend on the teacher's instructional decisions and differentiation routines.

15–30 min

Help

Practice Buddy

Tools

Games

### Math Tools and Math Games

A link to a specific math tools activity or math game to use with this lesson is provided at PearsonRealize.com.

## Leveled Assignment

 Items 1–9, 16–20, 23  Items 7–18, 21–23  Items 10–23

Name ________________

## Homework & Practice 1-7
### Simplify Algebraic Expressions

**Another Look!**

Simplify the expression $2x + 6 + 5x + 4$.

**Like terms** have the same variable part.
In this expression, $2x$ and $5x$ are like terms.

$2x + 6 + 5x + 4$
$= 2x + 5x + 6 + 4$ Commutative Property of Addition
$= 7x + 10$

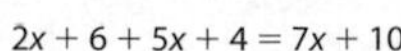

$2x + 6 + 5x + 4 = 7x + 10$

In **1–3**, combine like terms to complete the equivalent expressions.

1. $n + n + n = 1n + 1n + 1n$
$= (1 + \underline{1} + \underline{1})n$
$= \underline{\mathbf{3n}}$

2. $3n + 6 - n - 4 = (\underline{3}n - \underline{1}n) + 6 - 4$
$= \underline{2}n + \underline{2}$

3. $1\frac{1}{2}z^2 + 3\frac{1}{2} + 5z - 3 + 6z - \frac{1}{2}z^2$
$= (1\frac{1}{2}z^2 - \frac{1}{2}z^2) + (5z + 6z) + (3\frac{1}{2} - 3)$
$= \underline{1}z^2 + 11z + \frac{1}{2}$

You can combine like terms with fraction or decimal coefficients the same way you do whole number coefficients.

In **4–15**, simplify each expression.

4. $4y + 9y$
**$13y$**

5. $3z + \frac{3}{4} - 2z$
**$z + \frac{3}{4}$**

6. $25 + 5w - 10 + w$
**$15 + 6w$**

7. $7.7w - 4.6w$
**$3.1w$**

8. $\frac{1}{2}x + \frac{1}{2} + \frac{1}{2}x + \frac{1}{2}$
**$x + 1$**

9. $12y^2 - 6y^2$
**$6y^2$**

10. $3z^3 + 2\frac{1}{4} - z^3$
**$2z^3 + 2\frac{1}{4}$**

11. $6.6m + 3m$
**$9.6m$**

12. $100n - 1 - 25n$
**$75n - 1$**

13. $5x + \frac{1}{2} + 3y + \frac{1}{4} + 2x - 2y$
**$7x + \frac{3}{4} + y$**

14. $p^2 + 2.3 + 3p^2$
**$4p^2 + 2.3$**

15. $z^4 + z^4 + z^4 + z^4$
**$4z^4$**



In **16–18**, use the sign at the right.

16. **MP.4 Model with Math** At a drive-thru restaurant, Casey's family ordered a small drink and $m$ medium drinks. Anika's family ordered $m$ medium drinks and a large drink. Write an algebraic expression that shows the total cost, in dollars, of both orders.
**Sample answer: $1.10 + 1.25m + 1.25m + 1.50$**

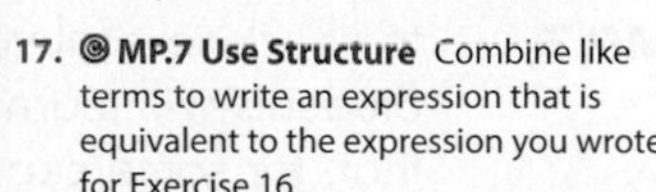

17. **MP.7 Use Structure** Combine like terms to write an expression that is equivalent to the expression you wrote for Exercise 16.
**Sample answer: $2.60 + 2.50m$**

18. What was the total cost of the drinks in both orders if $m = 3$?
**$10.10; $2.60 + 7.50 = 10.10$**

19. Jan rewrote the expression $\frac{1}{2}y \cdot 5$ as $5 \cdot \frac{1}{2}y$. Which property of operations did Jan use?
**Commutative Property of Multiplication**

20. **Number Sense** Give an example of a number, $n$, for which the inequality below is true.
$n^3 < n^2$
**Sample answer: $n = 0.25$**

21. **MP.3 Critique Reasoning** Manuel rewrote the expression $6x - x + 5$ as $6 + 5$. Are $6x - x + 5$ and $6 + 5$ equivalent expressions? Explain.
**No; Sample answer: If $x = 2$, $6x - x + 5 = 15$; $6 + 5 = 11$; $15 \neq 11$.**

22. **Higher Order Thinking** Write an equivalent expression for the expression shown below.
$\frac{b}{2} + \frac{b}{2}$
**$b$; $\frac{b}{2} + \frac{b}{2} = \left(\frac{1}{2}\right)b + \left(\frac{1}{2}\right)b = \left(\frac{1}{2} + \frac{1}{2}\right)b = 1b$**

### Common Core Assessment

23. Write each expression below in the correct column in the table at the right to show whether the expression is equivalent to $\frac{1}{2}x + 4\frac{1}{2} + \frac{1}{2}x - \frac{1}{2}$.

$\frac{1}{2}x + 4$
$x + 4\frac{1}{2}$
$x + 4$
$x - 4$

| Equivalent to $\frac{1}{2}x + 4\frac{1}{2} + \frac{1}{2}x - \frac{1}{2}$ | NOT Equivalent to $\frac{1}{2}x + 4\frac{1}{2} + \frac{1}{2}x - \frac{1}{2}$ |
|---|---|
| $x + 4$ | $\frac{1}{2}x + 4$<br>$x + 4\frac{1}{2}$<br>$x - 4$ |

# LESSON 1-8

# EQUIVALENT EXPRESSIONS

## DIGITAL RESOURCES PearsonRealize.com

eText — Student and Teacher eTexts

PD — Listen and Look For Lesson Video

Think — Today's Challenge

Solve — Solve and Share

Learn — Visual Learning Animation Plus

Glossary — Animated Glossary

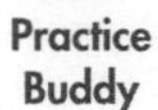
Practice Buddy — Online Personalized Practice

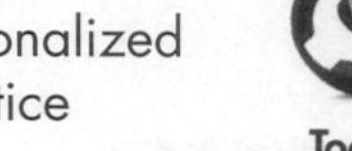

Tools — Math Tools

Assessment — Quick Check

Help — Another Look Homework Video

Games — Math Games

## LESSON OVERVIEW — FCR FOCUS • COHERENCE • RIGOR

### FOCUS

**Domain 6.EE** Expressions and Equations

**Cluster 6.EE.A** Apply and extend previous understandings of arithmetic to algebraic expressions.

**Content Standard 6.EE.A.3** Apply the properties of operations to generate equivalent expressions. *For example, apply the distributive property to the expression 3(2 + x) to produce the equivalent expression 6 + 3x; apply the distributive property to the expression 24x + 18y to produce the equivalent expression 6(4x + 3y); apply properties of operations to y + y + y to produce the equivalent expression 3y.* Also **6.EE.A.4**.

**Mathematical Practices MP.1, MP.3, MP.7, MP.8**

**Objective** Identify equivalent algebraic expressions.

**Essential Understanding** Equivalent expressions have the same value regardless of the number substituted for the variable. Properties of operations can be used to verify that expressions are equivalent.

### COHERENCE

In Lesson 1-6, students used properties of operations to write equivalent algebraic expressions. In this lesson, students apply these concepts to identify equivalent expressions from a given list of expressions. Students' experience with evaluating expressions will prepare them for checking the validity of their solutions when solving equations or inequalities in Topic 2.

### RIGOR

This lesson emphasizes **conceptual understanding**. Students explore whether two expressions are equivalent by substituting the same number for the variable in each expression. Encourage students to check several values for the variables. Students will learn in future algebra courses that, for some expressions, checking even two or three values does not guarantee the expressions are equivalent.

PD Watch the Listen and Look For Lesson Video.

## MATH ANYTIME

### Daily Common Core Review

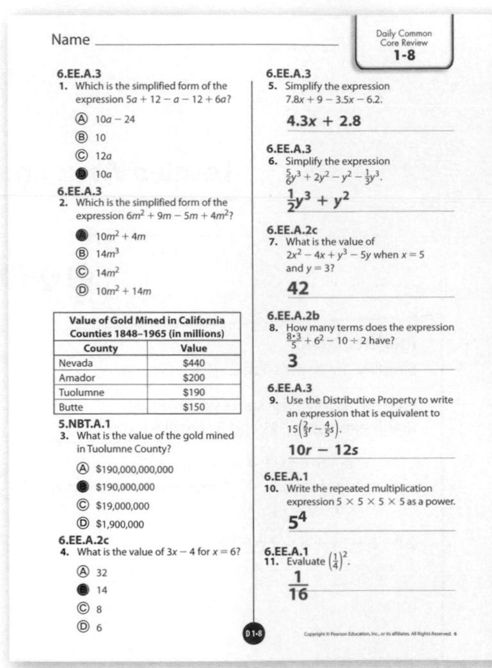

Name ____________

Daily Common Core Review 1-8

**6.EE.A.3**
1. Which is the simplified form of the expression $5a + 12 - a - 12 + 6a$?
   - Ⓐ $10a - 24$
   - Ⓑ $10$
   - Ⓒ $12a$
   - Ⓓ $10a$ (filled in)

**6.EE.A.3**
2. Which is the simplified form of the expression $6m^2 + 9m - 5m + 4m^2$?
   - Ⓐ $10m^2 + 4m$ (filled in)
   - Ⓑ $14m^3$
   - Ⓒ $14m^2$
   - Ⓓ $10m^2 + 14m$

| Value of Gold Mined in California Counties 1848–1965 (in millions) | |
|---|---|
| County | Value |
| Nevada | $440 |
| Amador | $200 |
| Tuolumne | $190 |
| Butte | $150 |

**5.NBT.A.1**
3. What is the value of the gold mined in Tuolumne County?
   - Ⓐ $190,000,000,000
   - Ⓑ $190,000,000 (filled in)
   - Ⓒ $19,000,000
   - Ⓓ $1,900,000

**6.EE.A.2c**
4. What is the value of $3x - 4$ for $x = 6$?
   - Ⓐ 32
   - Ⓑ 14 (filled in)
   - Ⓒ 8
   - Ⓓ 6

**6.EE.A.3**
5. Simplify the expression $7.8x + 9 - 3.5x - 6.2$.
   **$4.3x + 2.8$**

**6.EE.A.3**
6. Simplify the expression $\frac{5}{6}y^3 + 2y^2 - y^2 - \frac{1}{3}y^3$.
   **$\frac{1}{2}y^3 + y^2$**

**6.EE.A.2c**
7. What is the value of $2x^2 - 4x + y^3 - 5y$ when $x = 5$ and $y = 3$?
   **42**

**6.EE.A.2b**
8. How many terms does the expression $\frac{8 \cdot 3}{5} + 6^2 - 10 \div 2$ have?
   **3**

**6.EE.A.3**
9. Use the Distributive Property to write an expression that is equivalent to $15\left(\frac{2}{3}r - \frac{4}{5}s\right)$.
   **$10r - 12s$**

**6.EE.A.1**
10. Write the repeated multiplication expression $5 \times 5 \times 5 \times 5$ as a power.
   **$5^4$**

**6.EE.A.1**
11. Evaluate $\left(\frac{1}{4}\right)^2$.
   **$\frac{1}{16}$**

D 1•8



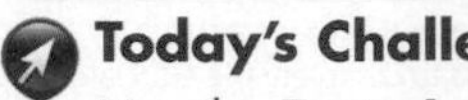
### Today's Challenge

Think Use the Topic 1 problems any time during this topic.

## ENGLISH LANGUAGE LEARNERS ELL

**Reading** Use reading supports: graphic organizers.

*Use with the Solve & Share on Student's Edition p. 49.*

Read the Solve & Share. Point to the graphic organizer. *Using a graphic organizer can help make sense of the problem.* Explain each column of the graphic organizer. *Why is it easier to understand the expressions when recording them on a graphic organizer?* Write the following expressions on the board: $8x - 4$, $4x$, $4(2x - 1)$. Instruct students to use a graphic organizer to find which of the three expressions are equivalent.

**Beginning** Read the speech bubble with the students. Draw a graphic organizer with the following column headers: $x$, $8x - 4$, $4x$, $4(2x - 1)$. Work with students to evaluate the expressions for several values of the variable and identify the equivalent expressions.

**Intermediate** Read the speech bubble with the students. Instruct student partners to draw a graphic organizer with the following column headers: $x$, $8x - 4$, $4x$, $4(2x - 1)$. Ask partners to evaluate the expressions for several values of the variable and identify the equivalent expressions.

**Advanced** Instruct students to read the speech bubble with partners. Ask partners to create a graphic organizer to evaluate the expressions for several values of the variable and identify the equivalent expressions.

**Summarize** How do graphic organizers help make sense of information when evaluating expressions?

# DEVELOP: PROBLEM-BASED LEARNING

**COHERENCE: Engage learners by connecting prior knowledge to new ideas.**
Students extend their understanding of algebraic expressions by testing whether expressions are equivalent and explaining their reasoning.

10–15 min

Solve

## BEFORE

1. **Pose the Solve-and-Share Problem**
**MP.1 Make Sense and Persevere** Listen and look for students who extend the table to evaluate the expressions using different values for the variable.

2. **Build Understanding**
*What expressions are you given?* [$8n + 6$, $2(4n + 3)$, and $14n$] *What is shown in the table?* [The table shows the value of each expression for $n = 1$, and the work it took to evaluate them.]

## DURING

3. **Ask Guiding Questions As Needed**
*If the expressions all have the same value when n = 1, does that mean the expressions are equivalent?* [Sample answer: Not necessarily. The expressions might not have the same value for a different value of $n$.] *What other value of* n *could you test in the table?* [Sample answer: $n = 2$]

## AFTER

4. **Share and Discuss Solutions**
Start with students' solutions. If needed, project Tim's work to discuss how to determine whether expressions are equivalent.

5. **Transition to the Visual Learning Bridge**
*Substituting the same values for variables is one way to help you determine whether two expressions are equivalent. You can also use properties of operations to identify equivalent expressions.*

6. **Extension for Early Finishers**
On the board, write the algebraic expressions $4(6x - 5)$ and $24x - 20$. *Are these algebraic expressions equivalent when x = 1? How about when x = 5? Explain.* [Yes, for both values. When $x = 1$, $4(6x - 5) = 4$ and $24x - 20 = 4$. When $x = 5$, $4(6x - 5) = 100$ and $24x - 20 = 100$.]

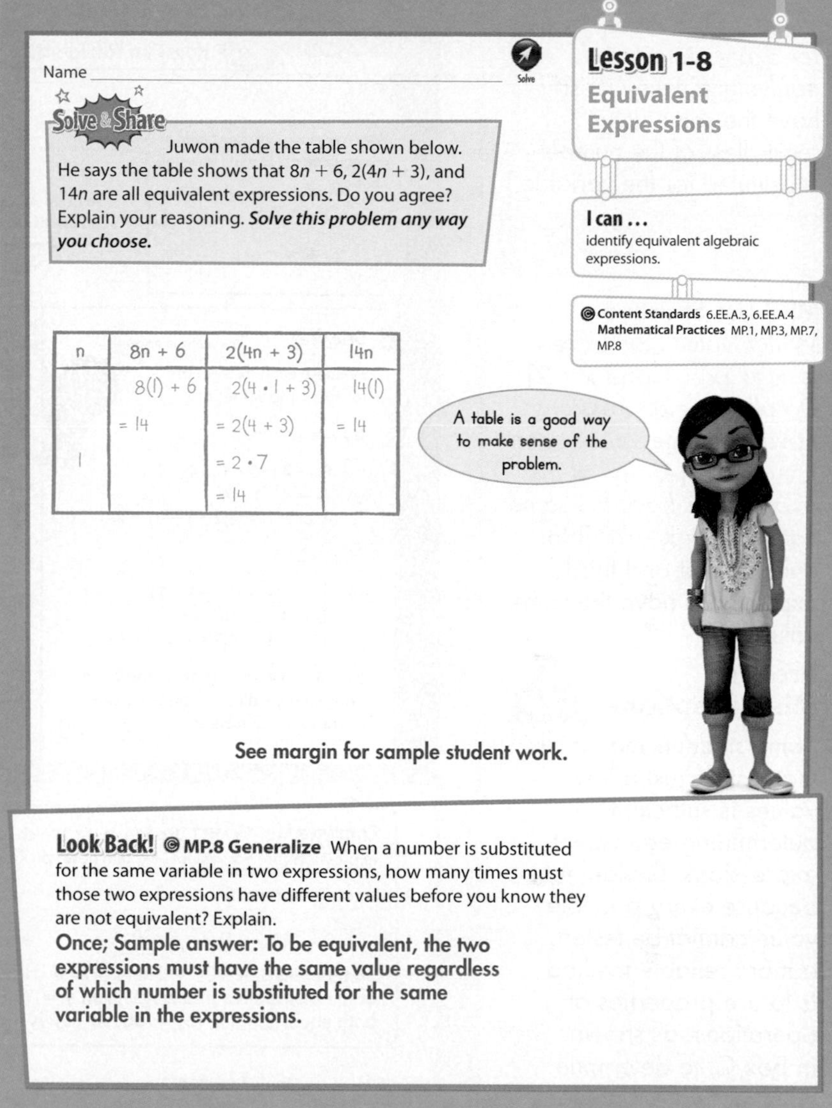

Name

Solve & Share

Juwon made the table shown below. He says the table shows that $8n + 6$, $2(4n + 3)$, and $14n$ are all equivalent expressions. Do you agree? Explain your reasoning. ***Solve this problem any way you choose.***

**Lesson 1-8**
**Equivalent Expressions**

**I can ...**
identify equivalent algebraic expressions.

**Content Standards** 6.EE.A.3, 6.EE.A.4
**Mathematical Practices** MP.1, MP.3, MP.7, MP.8

| n | 8n + 6 | 2(4n + 3) | 14n |
|---|---|---|---|
| 1 | 8(1) + 6<br>= 14 | 2(4 • 1 + 3)<br>= 2(4 + 3)<br>= 2 • 7<br>= 14 | 14(1)<br>= 14 |

A table is a good way to make sense of the problem.



See margin for sample student work.

**Look Back!** **MP.8 Generalize** When a number is substituted for the same variable in two expressions, how many times must those two expressions have different values before you know they are not equivalent? Explain.
**Once; Sample answer: To be equivalent, the two expressions must have the same value regardless of which number is substituted for the same variable in the expressions.**

Digital Resources at PearsonRealize.com **Topic 1** | Lesson 1-8 49

## Analyze Student Work

Tim's Work

| n | 8n + 6 | 2(4n + 3) | 14n |
|---|---|---|---|
| 1 | 8(1) + 6<br>= 14 | 2(4 • 1 + 3)<br>= 2(4 + 3)<br>= 2 • 7<br>= 14 | 14(1)<br>= 14 |
| 2 | 8·2+6<br>= 16 + 6<br>= 22 | 2(4·2+3)<br>= 2(8+3)<br>= 2·11<br>= 22 | 14·2<br>= 28 |

8n + 6 and 2(4n + 3) are equivalent because of the Distributive Property. 14n is not equivalent.

Tim correctly extends the table to show $14n$ is not equivalent to the other two expressions. He uses the Distributive Property to justify why $8n + 6$ and $2(4n + 3)$ are equivalent.

Marcy's Work

| n | 8n + 6 | 2(4n + 3) | 14n |
|---|---|---|---|
| 1 | 8(1) + 6<br>= 14 | 2(4 • 1 + 3)<br>= 2(4 + 3)<br>= 2 • 7<br>= 14 | 14(1)<br>= 14 |

The values of the expressions are the same for n = 1, so all three expressions are equivalent.

Marcy does not try any other values for the variable. She incorrectly concludes that all three expressions are equivalent.

# DEVELOP: VISUAL LEARNING

The *Visual Learning Bridge* connects students' thinking in Solve & Share to important math ideas in the lesson. Use the *Visual Learning Bridge* to make these ideas explicit. Also available as a *Visual Learning Animation Plus* at PearsonRealize.com

Visual Learning

PEARSON realize. PearsonRealize.com

Learn Glossary

*What does it mean for expressions to be equivalent?* [They must have the same value regardless of the number substituted for the variable.]

**MP.7 Use Structure**
*Which values for x are tested?* [$x = 1$ and $x = 2$] *Do all of the expressions have the same value when $x = 1$?* [Yes] *Do all of the expressions have the same value when $x = 2$?* [No; only the first and third expressions have the same value.]

**Prevent Misconceptions**

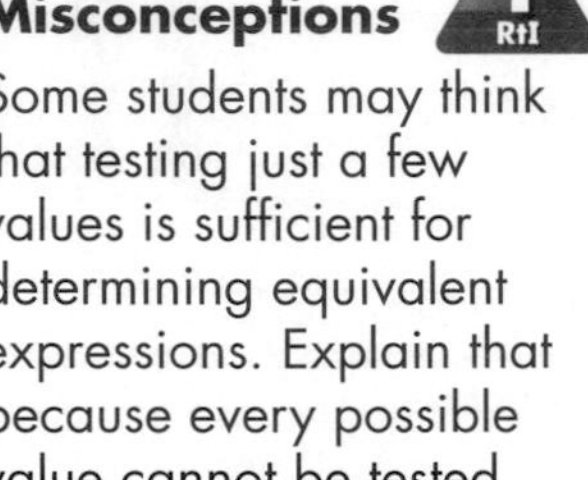

Some students may think that testing just a few values is sufficient for determining equivalent expressions. Explain that because every possible value cannot be tested, a more reliable method is to use properties of operations, as shown in Box C, to determine whether two expressions are equivalent.

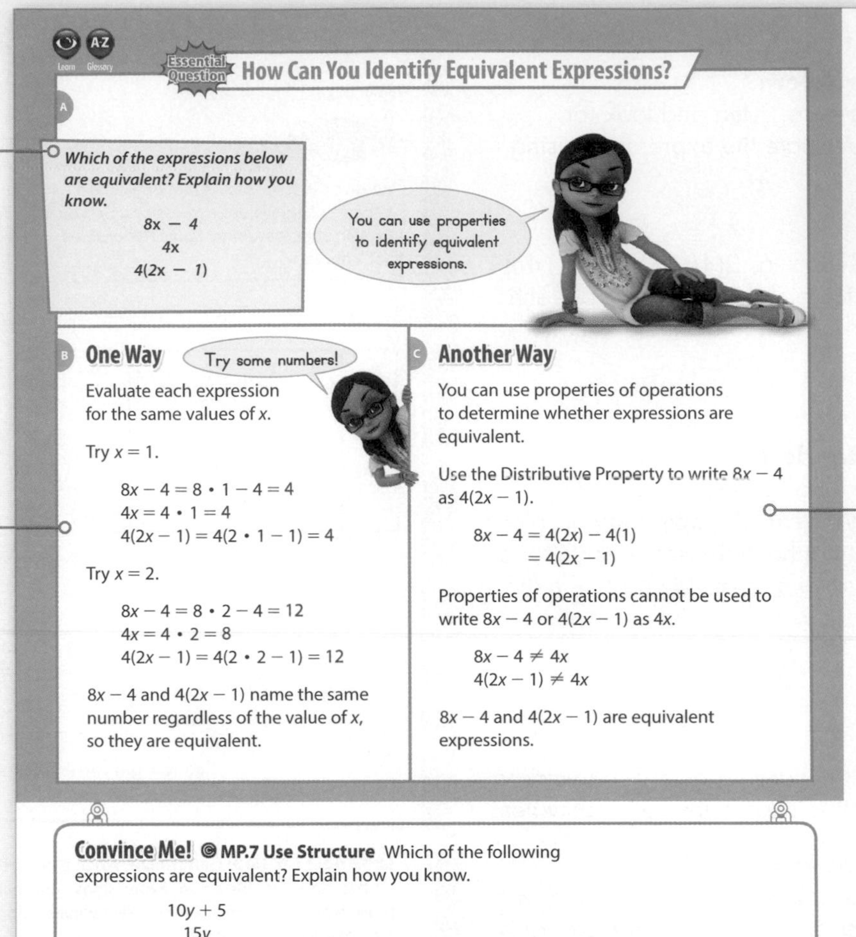

Essential Question **How Can You Identify Equivalent Expressions?**

A

***Which of the expressions below are equivalent? Explain how you know.***

$8x - 4$
$4x$
$4(2x - 1)$

You can use properties to identify equivalent expressions.

B **One Way** Try some numbers!

Evaluate each expression for the same values of $x$.

Try $x = 1$.

$8x - 4 = 8 \cdot 1 - 4 = 4$
$4x = 4 \cdot 1 = 4$
$4(2x - 1) = 4(2 \cdot 1 - 1) = 4$

Try $x = 2$.

$8x - 4 = 8 \cdot 2 - 4 = 12$
$4x = 4 \cdot 2 = 8$
$4(2x - 1) = 4(2 \cdot 2 - 1) = 12$

$8x - 4$ and $4(2x - 1)$ name the same number regardless of the value of $x$, so they are equivalent.

C **Another Way**

You can use properties of operations to determine whether expressions are equivalent.

Use the Distributive Property to write $8x - 4$ as $4(2x - 1)$.

$8x - 4 = 4(2x) - 4(1)$
$= 4(2x - 1)$

Properties of operations cannot be used to write $8x - 4$ or $4(2x - 1)$ as $4x$.

$8x - 4 \neq 4x$
$4(2x - 1) \neq 4x$

$8x - 4$ and $4(2x - 1)$ are equivalent expressions.

**Convince Me!** MP.7 Use Structure Which of the following expressions are equivalent? Explain how you know.

$10y + 5$
$15y$
$5(2y + 1)$

**Sample answer: $10y + 5$ and $5(2y + 1)$ are equivalent because of the Distributive property. When $y = 2$, $10y + 5$ and $5(2y + 1)$ both equal 25, but $15y = 30$, so $15y$ is not equivalent.**

50 Topic 1 | Lesson 1-8 © Pearson Education, Inc. 6

Visual Learning Bridge

**MP.8 Generalize**
*Why can properties of operations be used to determine whether expressions are equivalent?* [Properties of operations are always true. When you rewrite an expression using properties of operations, you produce an equivalent expression.] *Besides the Distributive Property, what other properties can be used to find equivalent expressions?* [Commutative, Associative, and Identity Properties]

**Convince Me! MP.7 Use Structure** Students can use substitution to see if any of the expressions can be eliminated. *Why is it important to test each expression with more than one value for y?* [Different values might produce different results.] *Why is it impossible to test for every value of y?* [There are infinite possible values.] *What other ways can you determine whether expressions are equivalent?* [Use properties of operations.]

Revisit the Essential Question. Expressions are equivalent if they have the same value regardless of the number substituted for the variable. Properties of operations can be used to verify that two expressions are equivalent.

## ✓ QUICK CHECK

Check mark indicates items for prescribing differentiation on the next page. Items 10 and 16 are worth 1 point. Item 15 is worth up to 3 points.

20–30 min

PEARSON realize. PearsonRealize.com

Practice Buddy

Tools

Assessment

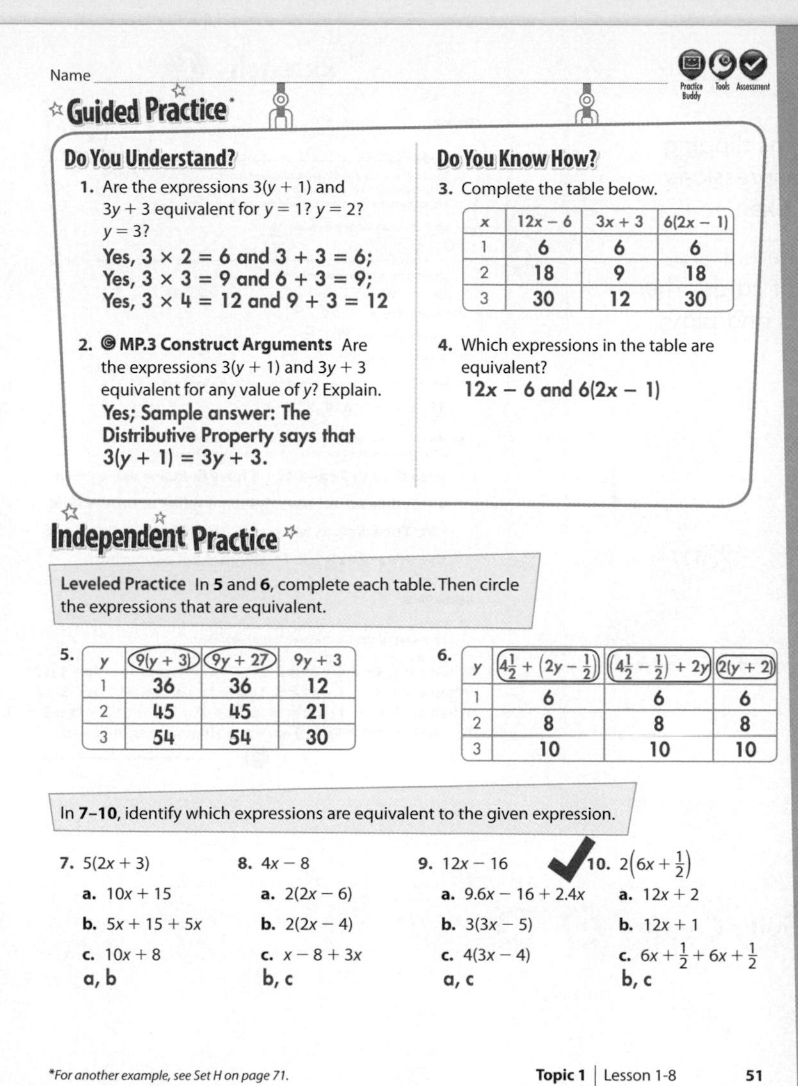

Name

### Guided Practice*

**Do You Understand?**

1. Are the expressions $3(y + 1)$ and $3y + 3$ equivalent for $y = 1$? $y = 2$? $y = 3$?
   **Yes, $3 \times 2 = 6$ and $3 + 3 = 6$; Yes, $3 \times 3 = 9$ and $6 + 3 = 9$; Yes, $3 \times 4 = 12$ and $9 + 3 = 12$**
2. **MP.3 Construct Arguments** Are the expressions $3(y + 1)$ and $3y + 3$ equivalent for any value of $y$? Explain.
   **Yes; Sample answer: The Distributive Property says that $3(y + 1) = 3y + 3$.**

**Do You Know How?**

3. Complete the table below.

| $x$ | $12x - 6$ | $3x + 3$ | $6(2x - 1)$ |
|---|---|---|---|
| 1 | **6** | **6** | **6** |
| 2 | **18** | **9** | **18** |
| 3 | **30** | **12** | **30** |

4. Which expressions in the table are equivalent?
   **$12x - 6$ and $6(2x - 1)$**

### Independent Practice

**Leveled Practice** In **5** and **6**, complete each table. Then circle the expressions that are equivalent.

5.

| $y$ | $9(y + 3)$ | $9y + 27$ | $9y + 3$ |
|---|---|---|---|
| 1 | **36** | **36** | **12** |
| 2 | **45** | **45** | **21** |
| 3 | **54** | **54** | **30** |

6.

| $y$ | $4\frac{1}{2} + (2y - \frac{1}{2})$ | $(4\frac{1}{2} - \frac{1}{2}) + 2y$ | $2(y + 2)$ |
|---|---|---|---|
| 1 | **6** | **6** | **6** |
| 2 | **8** | **8** | **8** |
| 3 | **10** | **10** | **10** |

In **7–10**, identify which expressions are equivalent to the given expression.

7. $5(2x + 3)$
   a. $10x + 15$
   b. $5x + 15 + 5x$
   c. $10x + 8$
   **a, b**
8. $4x - 8$
   a. $2(2x - 6)$
   b. $2(2x - 4)$
   c. $x - 8 + 3x$
   **b, c**
9. $12x - 16$
   a. $9.6x - 16 + 2.4x$
   b. $3(3x - 5)$
   c. $4(3x - 4)$
   **a, c**
10. ✓ $2(6x + \frac{1}{2})$
   a. $12x + 2$
   b. $12x + 1$
   c. $6x + \frac{1}{2} + 6x + \frac{1}{2}$
   **b, c**

*For another example, see Set H on page 71.

Topic 1 | Lesson 1-8 51

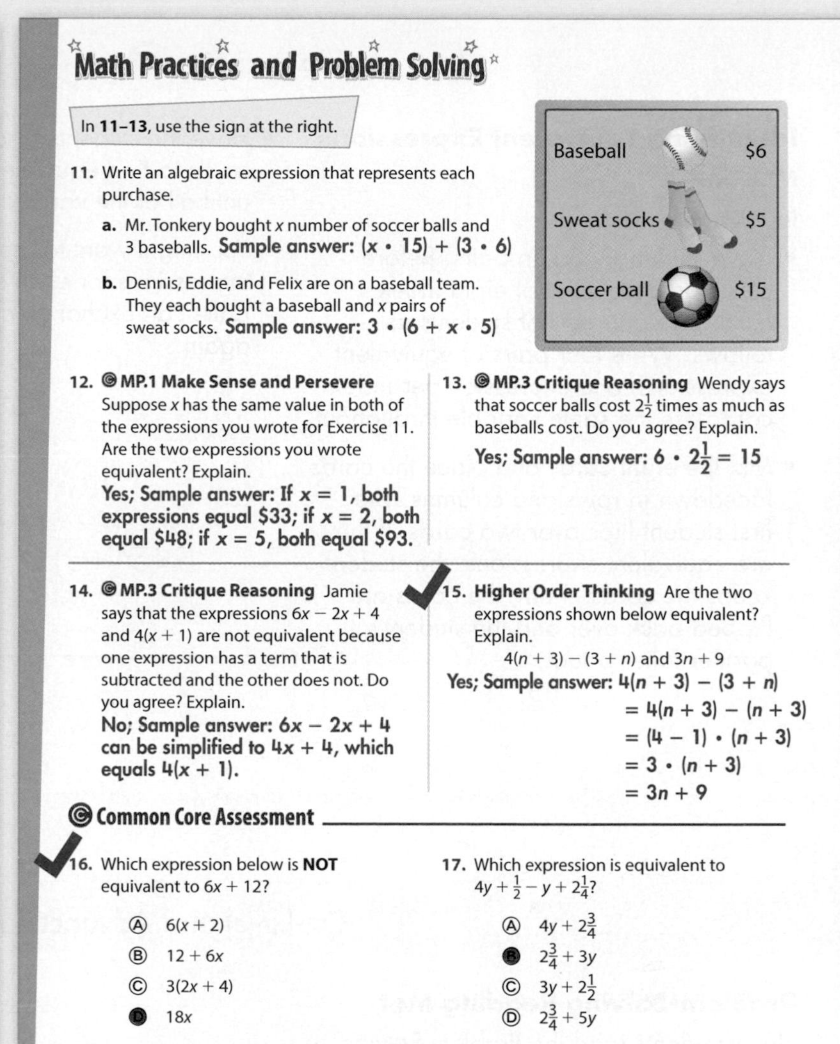

### Math Practices and Problem Solving

In **11–13**, use the sign at the right.

| Baseball | $6 |
|---|---|
| Sweat socks | $5 |
| Soccer ball | $15 |

11. Write an algebraic expression that represents each purchase.
   a. Mr. Tonkery bought $x$ number of soccer balls and 3 baseballs. **Sample answer: $(x \cdot 15) + (3 \cdot 6)$**
   b. Dennis, Eddie, and Felix are on a baseball team. They each bought a baseball and $x$ pairs of sweat socks. **Sample answer: $3 \cdot (6 + x \cdot 5)$**
12. **MP.1 Make Sense and Persevere** Suppose $x$ has the same value in both of the expressions you wrote for Exercise 11. Are the two expressions you wrote equivalent? Explain.
   **Yes; Sample answer: If $x = 1$, both expressions equal \$33; if $x = 2$, both equal \$48; if $x = 5$, both equal \$93.**
13. **MP.3 Critique Reasoning** Wendy says that soccer balls cost $2\frac{1}{2}$ times as much as baseballs cost. Do you agree? Explain.
   **Yes; Sample answer: $6 \cdot 2\frac{1}{2} = 15$**
14. **MP.3 Critique Reasoning** Jamie says that the expressions $6x - 2x + 4$ and $4(x + 1)$ are not equivalent because one expression has a term that is subtracted and the other does not. Do you agree? Explain.
   **No; Sample answer: $6x - 2x + 4$ can be simplified to $4x + 4$, which equals $4(x + 1)$.**
15. ✓ **Higher Order Thinking** Are the two expressions shown below equivalent? Explain.
   $4(n + 3) - (3 + n)$ and $3n + 9$
   **Yes; Sample answer: $4(n + 3) - (3 + n)$**
   **$= 4(n + 3) - (n + 3)$**
   **$= (4 - 1) \cdot (n + 3)$**
   **$= 3 \cdot (n + 3)$**
   **$= 3n + 9$**

**Common Core Assessment**

16. ✓ Which expression below is **NOT** equivalent to $6x + 12$?
   Ⓐ $6(x + 2)$
   Ⓑ $12 + 6x$
   Ⓒ $3(2x + 4)$
   ● $18x$
17. Which expression is equivalent to $4y + \frac{1}{2} - y + 2\frac{1}{4}$?
   Ⓐ $4y + 2\frac{3}{4}$
   ● $2\frac{3}{4} + 3y$
   Ⓒ $3y + 2\frac{1}{2}$
   Ⓓ $2\frac{3}{4} + 5y$

52 Topic 1 | Lesson 1-8

© Pearson Education, Inc. 6

**Error Intervention: Item 4**

**If** students say that all the expressions are equivalent,

**then** remind them that equivalent expressions have the same value for all values of the variable. *Look at the table you completed in Item 3. Are all of the expressions equivalent when x = 1?* [Yes] *Are all of the expressions equivalent when x = 2?* [No; only the first and third expressions have the same value.]

**Items 5 and 6** For early finishers or advanced students, you may wish to extend these items. Have students use the properties of operations to show whether the expressions are equivalent.

**Reteaching** Assign Reteaching Set H on p. 71.

**Item 12 MP.1 Make Sense and Persevere** Substituting several values for the variable suggests that the two expressions are equivalent, but the properties of operations can be used to justify that the expressions are equivalent.

**Item 15 Higher Order Thinking** Simplifying the first expression, $4(n + 3) - (3 + n)$, does not require operations with integers. First, apply the Commutative Property of Addition to $(3 + n)$ to write an equivalent expression with a common factor of $(n + 3)$. Then apply the Distributive Property in reverse order and simplify the coefficients $(4 - 1)$. Finally, apply the Distributive Property, in standard order, to write the second given expression, $3n + 9$. If students have difficulty applying the Distributive Property in reverse order, remind them that $(n + 3)$ can be rewritten as $1(n + 3)$ using the Identity Property of Multiplication.

**Multi-Step Problems** *Page 52 Items 15–17; Page 54 Items 9, 12, and 13*

# ASSESS AND DIFFERENTIATE

Use the **QUICK CHECK** on the previous page to prescribe differentiated instruction.

**Intervention**
0–3 points on the Quick Check

**On-Level**
4 points on the Quick Check

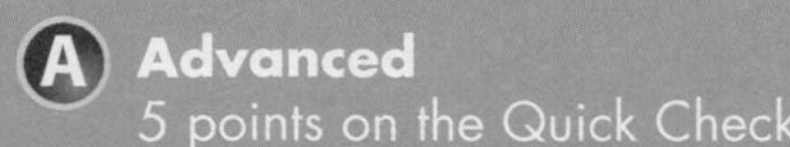

**Advanced**
5 points on the Quick Check

## Intervention Activity

### Identifying Equivalent Expressions

**Materials**

Index cards

- Have students work in pairs. Before class, prepare a set of eight index cards for each pair of students as follows: Write four pairs of equivalent expressions, one expression per index card. Use the same variable throughout.
- Mix the eight cards and place the cards facedown in rows and columns. The first student flips over two cards. If they are equivalent expressions, the student keeps the cards. If not, the cards are flipped back over and the student's partner takes a turn.
- Have the students take turns flipping cards to find equivalent expressions until all of the cards are taken.
- You might want to use different expressions for each set of cards. Then pairs can exchange cards and play again.

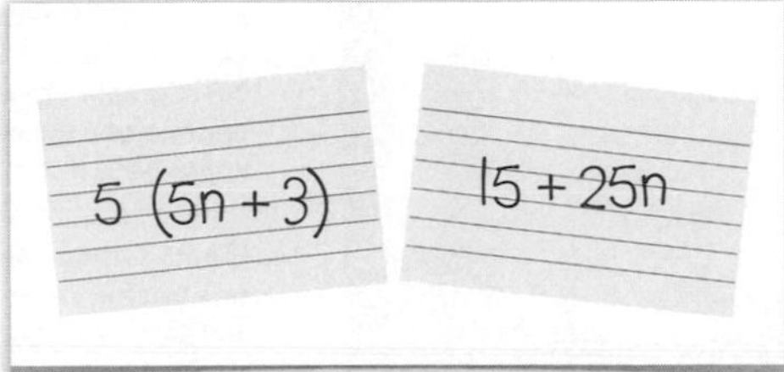


## Reteach

Name ______________________

Reteach to Build Understanding
**1-8**

**Vocabulary**

1. Two algebraic expressions are **equivalent** if they can be simplified to the same expression. For example, the expressions $3x + 2x + 1$ and $5x + 4 - 3$ are equivalent expressions because they both simplify to $5x + 1$.

   Circle the expressions that are equivalent.

   ($2x + 4$) $\quad 6x \quad$ ($2(x + 2)$)

2. Consider the following expressions.

   $10x - 8 - 4x \qquad 6x + 6 + 2 \qquad 2(3x - 4)$

   Simplify $10x - 8 - 4x$. **$6x - 8$**

   Simplify $6x + 6 + 2$. **$6x + 8$**

   Simplify $2(3x - 4)$. **$6x - 8$**

3. Which of the given expressions in Exercise 2 are equivalent?

   **$10x - 8 - 4x$ and $2(3x - 4)$**

4. When $x = 1$, the value of the expression $7x$ is 7 and the value of $4x + 3$ is 7. Explain whether $7x$ and $4x + 3$ are equivalent expressions.

   **Even though $7x$ and $4x + 3$ have the same value when $x = 1$, they do not have the same value for other values of $x$. For example, when $x = 2$, the value of $7x$ is 14, and the value of $4x + 3$ is 11. They are not equivalent.**

**On the Back!**

5. Find the values of the following expressions when $z = 1$, $z = 2$, and $z = 3$. Then identify which expressions are equivalent.

   $9z - 4 - 3z \qquad 2(3z - 2) \qquad 9z - 4z - 3$

**When $z = 1$, $9z - 4 - 3z = 2$, $2(3z - 2) = 2$, and $9z - 4z - 3 = 2$.**
**When $z = 2$, $9z - 4 - 3z = 8$, $2(3z - 2) = 8$, and $9z - 4z - 3 = 7$.**
**When $z = 3$, $9z - 4 - 3z = 14$, $2(3z - 2) = 14$, and $9z - 4z - 3 = 12$.**
**$9z - 4 - 3z$ and $2(3z - 2)$ are equivalent expressions.**

R 1-8



## On-Level and Advanced Activity Centers

### Problem-Solving Reading Mat

Have students read the Problem-Solving Reading Mat for Topic 1 and then complete Problem-Solving Reading Activity 1-8.

See the Problem-Solving Reading Activity Guide for other suggestions on how to use this mat.

TIMING

The time allocated to Step 3 will depend on the teacher's instructional decisions and differentiation routines.

15–30 min

PEARSON realize. PearsonRealize.com

 Help
 Practice Buddy
 Tools
Games

## Technology Center   

Tools Games

### Math Tools and Math Games

A link to a specific math tools activity or math game to use with this lesson is provided at PearsonRealize.com.

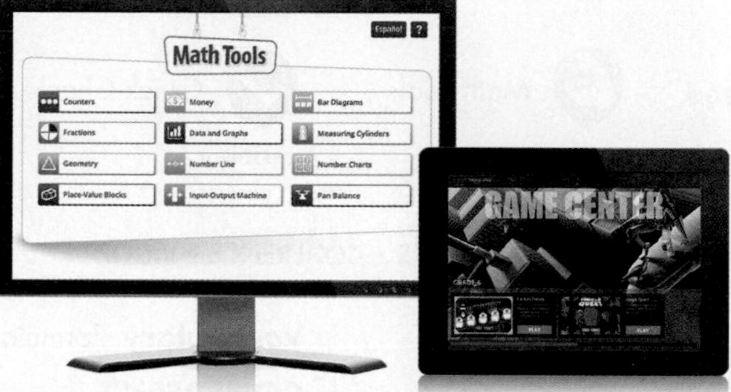


## Leveled Assignment

 Items 1–4, 9, 10, 12, 13  Items 3–8, 10–13  Items 3–8, 11–13

Name

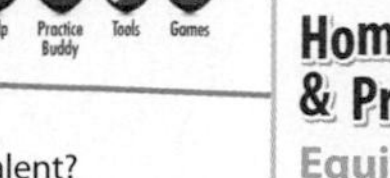


**Another Look!**

Which of the following expressions are equivalent? Explain how you know.

$2(5x + 7)$
$10x + 14$
$24x$

You can evaluate the expressions for the same values of $x$ or use properties to determine whether the expressions are equivalent.

Expressions are equivalent if they name the same number or the same value regardless of the value of the variable.

Try $x = 2$.

$2(5x + 7) = 2(5 \cdot 2 + 7) = 34$
$10x + 14 = 10(2) + 14 = 34$
$24x = 24(2) = 48$

You can use properties of operations to determine whether expressions are equivalent.

$2(5x + 7) = 2(5x) + 2(7)$ Distributive Property
$= 10x + 14$

Properties of operations cannot be used to write $2(5x + 7)$ or $10x + 14$ as $24x$.

$2(5x + 7) \neq 24x$
$10x + 14 \neq 24x$

$2(5x + 7)$ and $10x + 14$ are equivalent expressions.

In **1** and **2**, complete each table. Then circle the expressions that are equivalent.

**1.**

| $y$ | $10y - 5$ | $5y$ | $5(2y - 1)$ |
|---|---|---|---|
| 1 | 5 | 5 | 5 |
| 2 | 15 | 10 | 15 |
| 3 | 25 | 15 | 25 |

**2.**

| $y$ | $3y + 3.5 - y$ | $1.5 + 2(1 + y)$ | $3y + 2.5$ |
|---|---|---|---|
| 1 | 5.5 | 5.5 | 5.5 |
| 2 | 7.5 | 7.5 | 8.5 |
| 3 | 9.5 | 9.5 | 11.5 |

In **3–6**, identify which expressions are equivalent to the given expression.

**3.** $5x + 5$
a. $10x + 5 - 5x$
b. $10x$
c. $5(x + 1)$
a, c

**4.** $12x - 10 - 6x$
a. $6x - 10$
b. $2(3x - 5)$
c. $16x - 8 - 2$
a, b

**5.** $\frac{1}{2}x + 3 + \frac{1}{2}x$
a. $\frac{1}{2}(x + 3)$
b. $x + 3$
c. $3x + 3 - x$
b

**6.** $3(3x - 1)$
a. $6x - 2$
b. $9x - 3$
c. $15x + 6 - 6x - 3$
b, c



In **7–9**, use the sign at the right.

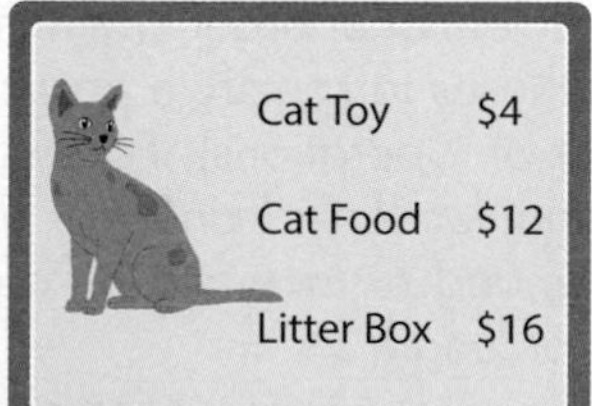


**7.** Write an algebraic expression that represents each purchase.

a. Ms. Martinez bought $x$ number of litter boxes and 8 bags of cat food for the animal shelter.
**Sample answer: $(x \cdot 16) + (8 \cdot 12)$**

b. Two sisters each bought 1 litter box, 10 cat toys, and $x$ bags of cat food.
**Sample answer: $2 \cdot (16 + 10 \cdot 4 + x \cdot 12)$**

**8.** MP.1 Make Sense and Persevere Suppose $x$ has the same value in both of the expressions you wrote for Exercise 7. Are the two expressions you wrote equivalent? Explain.
**No; Sample answer: If $x = 1$, $(x \cdot 16) + (8 \cdot 12) = \$112$, but $2 \cdot (16 + 10 \cdot 4 + x \cdot 12) = \$136$.**

**9.** MP.3 Construct Arguments Which costs the most: 12 cat toys, 4 bags of cat food, or 3 litter boxes? Explain.
**Sample answer: The costs are all the same; $12 \cdot 4 = \$48$; $4 \cdot 12 = \$48$; $3 \cdot 16 = \$48$**

**10.** MP.3 Critique Reasoning Zach says that the expressions $6x - 36$ and $3(2x - 12)$ are equivalent because of the Distributive Property. Do you agree? Explain.
**Yes; Sample answer: $3(2x - 12) = 3 \cdot 2x - 3 \cdot 12 = 6x - 36$.**

**11.** Higher Order Thinking Are the two expressions shown below equivalent? Explain.
$4n + 6m - 12k$ and $2(2n + 3m - 6k)$
**Yes; Sample answer: You can apply the Distributive Property across both addition and subtraction.**

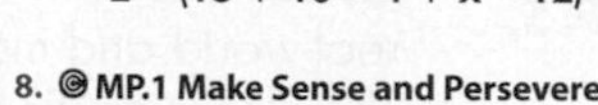
Common Core Assessment

**12.** Which expression below is **NOT** equivalent to $9x + 3x - 12$?
● $6(x - 2)$
Ⓑ $12x - 12$
Ⓒ $3(4x - 4)$
Ⓓ $4(3x - 3)$

**13.** Which expression is equivalent to $3\left(y + \frac{1}{4}\right)$?
Ⓐ $3y + 2\frac{3}{4} - 1$
Ⓑ $3y + \frac{3}{4} - y$
● $\frac{3}{4} + 3y$
Ⓓ $\frac{3}{4} - 3y$

# LESSON 1-9

# FORMULAS

## DIGITAL RESOURCES PearsonRealize.com

eText — Student and Teacher eTexts

PD — Listen and Look For Lesson Video

Think — Today's Challenge

Solve — Solve and Share

Learn — Visual Learning Animation Plus

Glossary — Animated Glossary

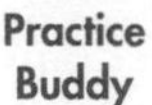
Practice Buddy — Online Personalized Practice

Tools — Math Tools

Assessment — Quick Check

Help — Another Look Homework Video

Games — Math Games

## LESSON OVERVIEW FCR FOCUS • COHERENCE • RIGOR

### FOCUS

**Domain 6.EE** Expressions and Equations

**Cluster 6.EE.A** Apply and extend previous understandings of arithmetic to algebraic expressions.

**Content Standard 6.EE.A.2c** Evaluate expressions at specific values of their variables. Include expressions that arise from formulas used in real-world problems. Perform arithmetic operations, including those involving whole-number exponents, in the conventional order when there are no parentheses to specify a particular order (Order of Operations). *For example, use the formulas* $V = s^3$ *and* $A = 6s^2$ *to find the volume and surface area of a cube with sides of length* $s = \frac{1}{2}$.

**Mathematical Practices MP.3, MP.4, MP.5, MP.6, MP.8**

**Objective** Use formulas to solve problems.

**Essential Understanding** A formula is a rule that uses symbols to relate two or more quantities. Formulas are used to solve problems in areas such as geometry, finance, and science.

**Vocabulary** Formula

### COHERENCE

In Grade 4, students learned how to apply the area and perimeter formulas for rectangles in real-world problems. In Grade 5, they extended their work with formulas to include volume. Earlier in Topic 1, students evaluated algebraic expressions and wrote equivalent expressions. In this lesson, these concepts come together as students solve problems using various new and familiar formulas. They will delve deeper into geometric formulas in Topics 13 and 14.

### RIGOR

This lesson emphasizes a blend of **procedural skill** and **application**. Students use formulas to solve a variety of real-world and mathematical problems. They learn to identify the variables in the formula, substitute the variables with known quantities, and evaluate the formula to determine the value of the unknown variable.

PD Watch the Listen and Look For Lesson Video.

## MATH ANYTIME

### Daily Common Core Review

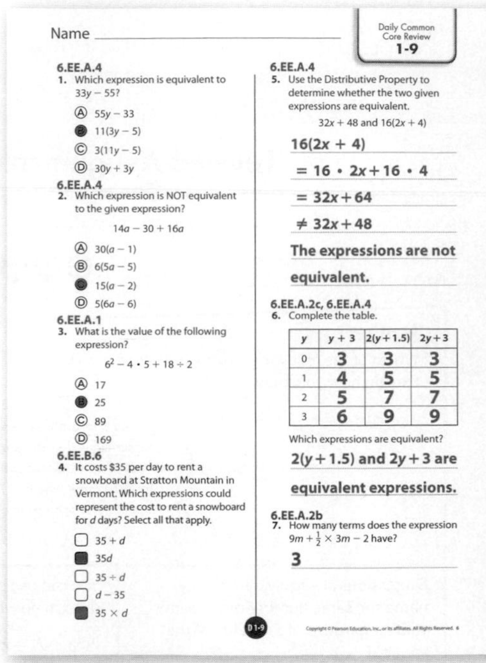
Name ______________

Daily Common Core Review 1-9

6.EE.A.4
1. Which expression is equivalent to $33y - 55$?
   Ⓐ $55y - 33$
   ● $11(3y - 5)$
   Ⓒ $3(11y - 5)$
   Ⓓ $30y + 3y$

6.EE.A.4
2. Which expression is NOT equivalent to the given expression?
   $14a - 30 + 16a$
   Ⓐ $30(a - 1)$
   Ⓑ $6(5a - 5)$
   ● $15(a - 2)$
   Ⓓ $5(6a - 6)$

6.EE.A.1
3. What is the value of the following expression?
   $6^2 - 4 \cdot 5 + 18 \div 2$
   Ⓐ 17
   ● 25
   Ⓒ 89
   Ⓓ 169

6.EE.B.6
4. It costs $35 per day to rent a snowboard at Stratton Mountain in Vermont. Which expressions could represent the cost to rent a snowboard for *d* days? Select all that apply.
   ☐ $35 + d$
   ■ $35d$
   ☐ $35 \div d$
   ☐ $d - 35$
   ■ $35 \times d$

6.EE.A.4
5. Use the Distributive Property to determine whether the two given expressions are equivalent.
   $32x + 48$ and $16(2x + 4)$
   **$16(2x + 4)$**
   **$= 16 \cdot 2x + 16 \cdot 4$**
   **$= 32x + 64$**
   **$\neq 32x + 48$**
   **The expressions are not equivalent.**

6.EE.A.2c, 6.EE.A.4
6. Complete the table.

| $y$ | $y + 3$ | $2(y + 1.5)$ | $2y + 3$ |
|---|---|---|---|
| 0 | **3** | **3** | **3** |
| 1 | **4** | **5** | **5** |
| 2 | **5** | **7** | **7** |
| 3 | **6** | **9** | **9** |

   Which expressions are equivalent?
   **$2(y + 1.5)$ and $2y + 3$ are equivalent expressions.**

6.EE.A.2b
7. How many terms does the expression $9m + \frac{1}{2} \times 3m - 2$ have?
   **3**

D 1-9



### Today's Challenge

Think Use the Topic 1 problems any time during this topic.

## ENGLISH LANGUAGE LEARNERS ELL

**Reading** Use support from peers/teachers to develop vocabulary.

*Use with the Solve & Share on Student's Edition p. 55.*

Write the word *formula*. *A formula is a rule that uses symbols to relate two or more quantities.* Read the Solve & Share. *What are the variables and what do they represent?* [$P$ = perimeter, $s$ = side length] Write the formula $P = 4s$. Demonstrate how to determine the perimeter of the smaller square using the formula.

**Beginning** Review the Solve & Share with students. Indicate the side length of the larger square. *What formula will help us solve this problem?* Have students respond using the following sentence stem: The ________ is $P = 4s$.

**Intermediate** Instruct students to read the Solve & Share with partners. Ask student pairs to define *formula*. Then have them determine the formula needed for determining the perimeter of the larger square.

**Advanced** Instruct students to read the Solve & Share. Ask them to explain to their partners how a formula helps to solve mathematical problems. Instruct students to determine the formula needed for determining the perimeter of the larger square.

**Summarize** How do formulas help solve mathematical problems?

# DEVELOP: PROBLEM-BASED LEARNING

PearsonRealize.com

**COHERENCE: Engage learners by connecting prior knowledge to new ideas.**
Students apply what they have learned about variables and algebraic expressions to solve perimeter problems by using a formula.

10–15 min

Solve

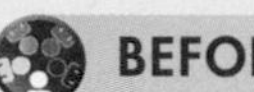 **BEFORE**

**1. Pose the Solve-and-Share Problem**
**MP.5 Use Appropriate Tools Strategically** Listen and look for students who use an appropriate tool to draw and measure the perimeter of each square, and then use the formula to check or verify their drawing and calculation.

**2. Build Understanding**
*What measuring tool would be appropriate to use to solve this problem?* [Sample answer: A ruler could be used if each inch was divided into tenths and measurements were made very carefully. A drawing tool on a computer would measure accurately.]

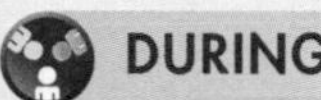 **DURING**

**3. Ask Guiding Questions As Needed**
*Tell in words what the formula P = 4s means.* [To find the perimeter of a square, multiply the length of a side by 4.] *How can you use the formula to check the perimeters you found by using a measuring tool?* [Sample answer: You can evaluate the formula by substituting the side length of each square.]

 **AFTER**

**4. Share and Discuss Solutions**
Solve Start with students' solutions. If needed, project Isaiah's and Maria's work to discuss how to use the formula to solve the problem.

**5. Transition to the Visual Learning Bridge**
*A formula is a rule that relates two or more quantities. You can use formulas to solve real-world problems.*

**6. Extension for Early Finishers**
*What is the difference between the areas of the squares? Use the formula $A = s^2$ to find the area, A, of a square with side length s.* [4.81 $in^2$]

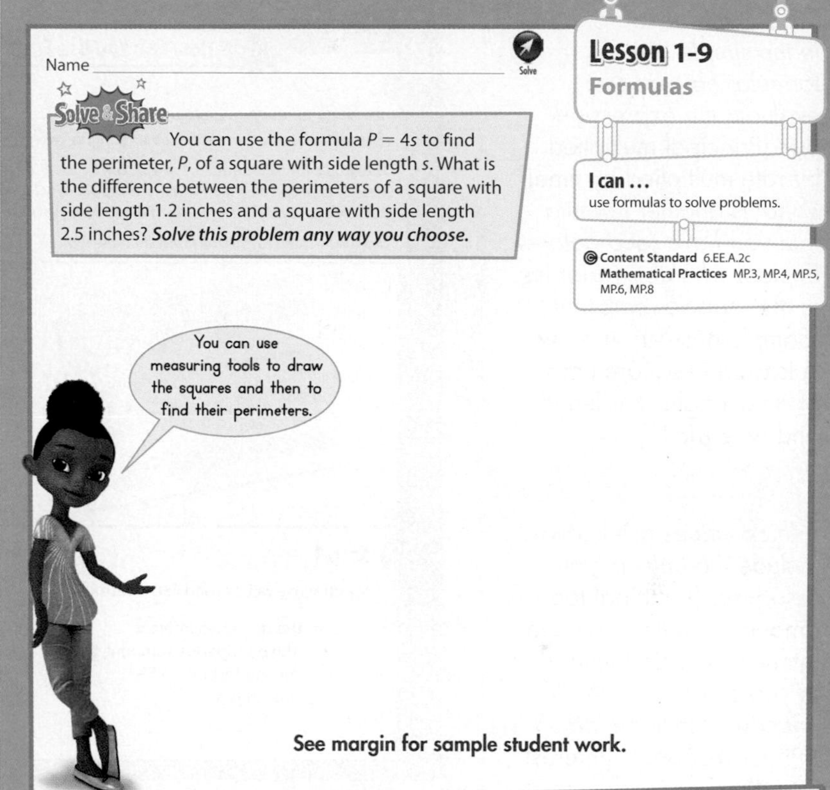

Name
Solve
Lesson 1-9
Formulas
Solve & Share
You can use the formula $P = 4s$ to find the perimeter, $P$, of a square with side length $s$. What is the difference between the perimeters of a square with side length 1.2 inches and a square with side length 2.5 inches? *Solve this problem any way you choose.*
I can ...
use formulas to solve problems.
Content Standard 6.EE.A.2c
Mathematical Practices MP.3, MP.4, MP.5, MP.6, MP.8
You can use measuring tools to draw the squares and then to find their perimeters.
See margin for sample student work.
Look Back! MP.8 Generalize How can you use the formula to find the length of each side of a square that has a perimeter of 72 inches?
Sample answer: You can substitute 72 for P and then solve for s. $72 = 4s$, $s = \frac{72}{4}$, $s = 18$ inches.
Digital Resources at PearsonRealize.com
Topic 1 | Lesson 1-9
55


## Analyze Student Work

**Isaiah's Work**

S = 1.2
P = 4 × 1.2
P = 4.8 in.

S = 2.5
P = 4 × 2.5
P = 10 in.

10.0
− 4.8
5.2 in.

The difference is 5.2 inches.

Isaiah substitutes the side lengths of each square for s and evaluates the formula to find the perimeter of each square. Then he subtracts to find the difference.

**Maria's Work**

Small square: P = 4s, P = 4 · 1.2
Big square: P = 4s, P = 4 · 2.5

Difference
(4 · 2.5) − (4 · 1.2) = 4(2.5 − 1.2)
= 4 · 1.3
= 5.2 in.

2.5 − 1.2 = 1.3
1.3 × 4 = 5.2

Maria uses the formula to write a numerical expression for each perimeter. Then she applies the Distributive Property to calculate the difference.

# DEVELOP: VISUAL LEARNING

The *Visual Learning Bridge* connects students' thinking in Solve & Share to important math ideas in the lesson. Use the *Visual Learning Bridge* to make these ideas explicit. Also available as a *Visual Learning Animation Plus* at PearsonRealize.com

ELL Visual Learning

PEARSON realize. PearsonRealize.com

 Learn  Glossary

**MP.8 Generalize** *In the simple interest formula, how do you evaluate the expression prt?* [Principal multiplied by rate multiplied by time] *What is another formula that you have used before? Explain what the variables in the formula represent.* [Sample answer: $A = \ell w$; $A$ is area in square units of a rectangle, $\ell$ is length, and $w$ is width.]

*Which values are known? Include the units in your response.* [Principal loan amount in dollars, percent interest rate, and time in years] *Which value is unknown? Include the units in your response.* [Interest in dollars]

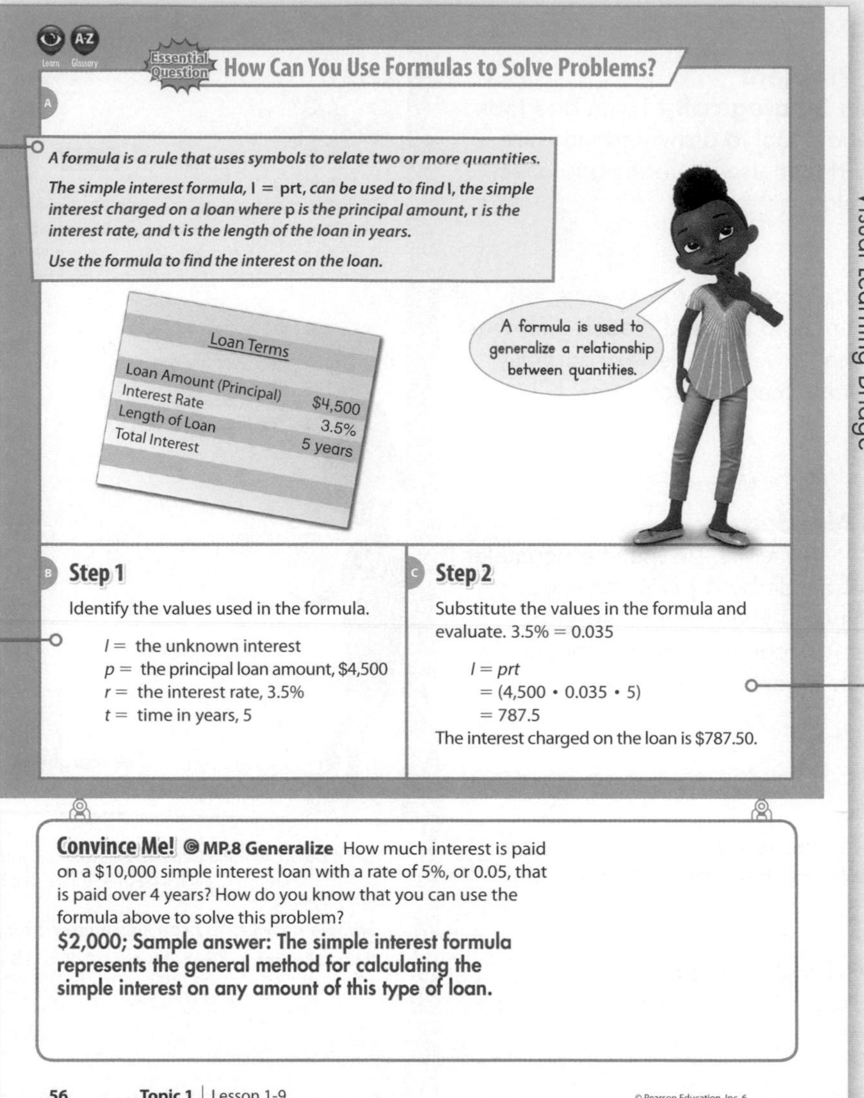

Essential Question **How Can You Use Formulas to Solve Problems?**

A

*A formula is a rule that uses symbols to relate two or more quantities.*

*The simple interest formula, I = prt, can be used to find I, the simple interest charged on a loan where p is the principal amount, r is the interest rate, and t is the length of the loan in years.*

*Use the formula to find the interest on the loan.*

| Loan Terms | |
|---|---|
| Loan Amount (Principal) | $4,500 |
| Interest Rate | 3.5% |
| Length of Loan | 5 years |
| Total Interest | |



B **Step 1**

Identify the values used in the formula.

$I$ = the unknown interest
$p$ = the principal loan amount, $4,500
$r$ = the interest rate, 3.5%
$t$ = time in years, 5

C **Step 2**

Substitute the values in the formula and evaluate. 3.5% = 0.035

$I = prt$
$= (4{,}500 \cdot 0.035 \cdot 5)$
$= 787.5$

The interest charged on the loan is $787.50.

**Convince Me!** **MP.8 Generalize** How much interest is paid on a $10,000 simple interest loan with a rate of 5%, or 0.05, that is paid over 4 years? How do you know that you can use the formula above to solve this problem?

**$2,000; Sample answer: The simple interest formula represents the general method for calculating the simple interest on any amount of this type of loan.**

56 Topic 1 | Lesson 1-9 © Pearson Education, Inc. 6

Visual Learning Bridge

**Convince Me! MP.8 Generalize** *How is this problem similar to the problem above?* [Sample answer: The principal loan amount in dollars, the percent interest rate, and the time in years are all known. The unknown amount is the interest in dollars.] *How is it different?* [Sample answer: The values of the variables are different.]

Essential Question Revisit the Essential Question. A formula is a mathematical rule that uses variables to show the relationship between two or more quantities. The relationship does not change from one specific situation to another, but the values of the variables may change. An unknown value can be found by substituting the known values into the formula and evaluating.

**MP.7 Use Structure** *Why is the order of operations important when using a formula?* [Formulas often contain parentheses and operations, which need to be done in the correct order to get the correct answer.]

Have students substitute 0.035 for *r*. Students will learn more about percent and decimal equivalents in Topic 11. If students struggle with the calculations, you may wish to provide them with four-function calculators to use. This will provide them with an opportunity to become proficient in using a four-function calculator. The point of this lesson is for students to identify variables in formulas and use substitution to solve problems.

**Prevent Misconceptions** 

Be sure students understand that $4{,}500 \cdot 0.035 \cdot 5 = 787.500$ or 787.5. The money amount is shown as $787.50.

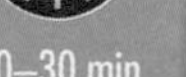


## ✓ QUICK CHECK

Check mark indicates items for prescribing differentiation on the next page.
Item 5 is worth 1 point. Items 13 and 14 are worth up to 2 points.

20–30 min

Practice Buddy | Tools | Assessment

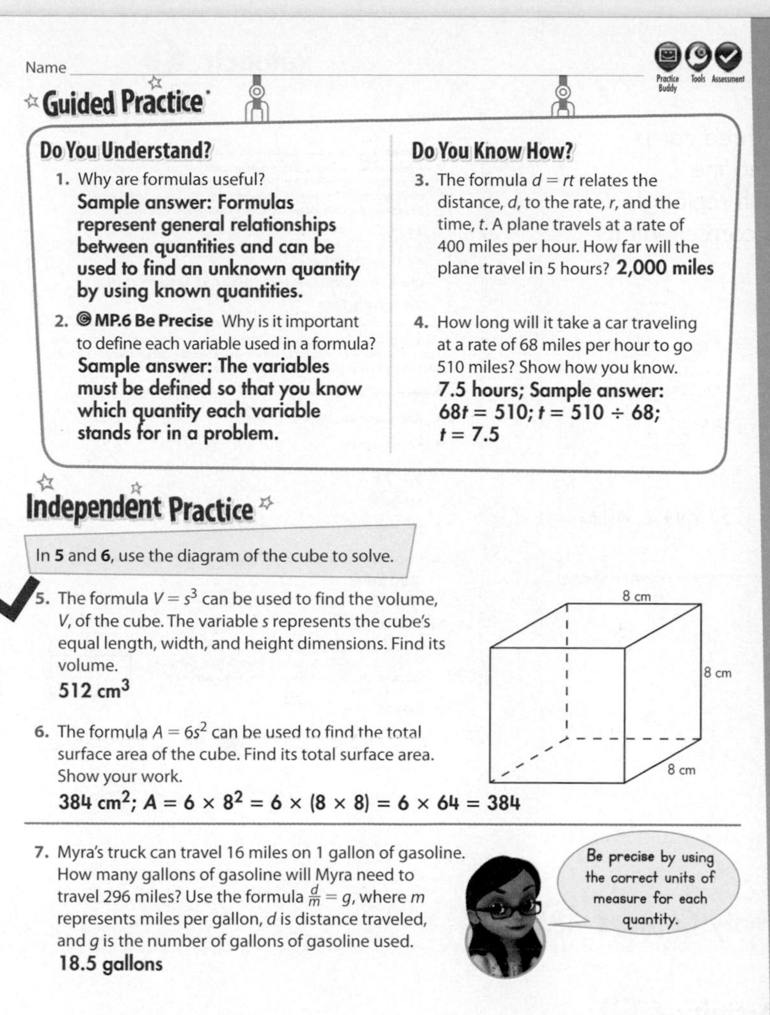

Name

### Guided Practice*

**Do You Understand?**

1. Why are formulas useful? **Sample answer: Formulas represent general relationships between quantities and can be used to find an unknown quantity by using known quantities.**
2. **MP.6 Be Precise** Why is it important to define each variable used in a formula? **Sample answer: The variables must be defined so that you know which quantity each variable stands for in a problem.**

**Do You Know How?**

3. The formula $d = rt$ relates the distance, $d$, to the rate, $r$, and the time, $t$. A plane travels at a rate of 400 miles per hour. How far will the plane travel in 5 hours? **2,000 miles**
4. How long will it take a car traveling at a rate of 68 miles per hour to go 510 miles? Show how you know. **7.5 hours; Sample answer: $68t = 510$; $t = 510 \div 68$; $t = 7.5$**

### Independent Practice

In **5** and **6**, use the diagram of the cube to solve.

5. The formula $V = s^3$ can be used to find the volume, $V$, of the cube. The variable $s$ represents the cube's equal length, width, and height dimensions. Find its volume. **512 cm³**



6. The formula $A = 6s^2$ can be used to find the total surface area of the cube. Find its total surface area. Show your work. **384 cm²; $A = 6 \times 8^2 = 6 \times (8 \times 8) = 6 \times 64 = 384$**

7. Myra's truck can travel 16 miles on 1 gallon of gasoline. How many gallons of gasoline will Myra need to travel 296 miles? Use the formula $\frac{d}{m} = g$, where $m$ represents miles per gallon, $d$ is distance traveled, and $g$ is the number of gallons of gasoline used. **18.5 gallons**



*For another example, see Set I on page 72.



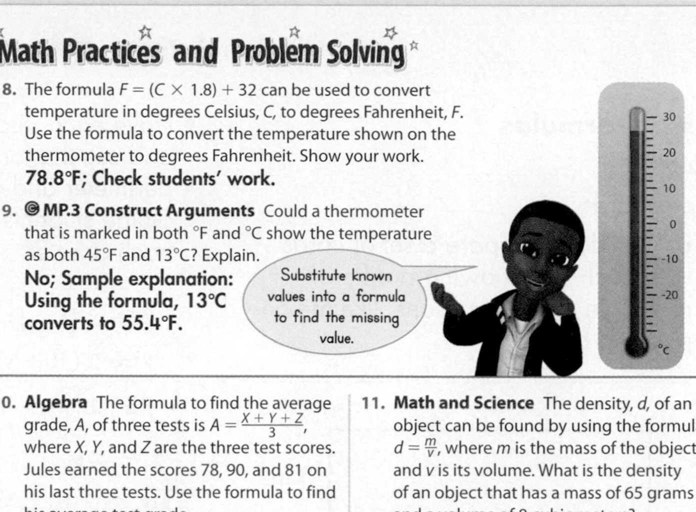

### Math Practices and Problem Solving

8. The formula $F = (C \times 1.8) + 32$ can be used to convert temperature in degrees Celsius, $C$, to degrees Fahrenheit, $F$. Use the formula to convert the temperature shown on the thermometer to degrees Fahrenheit. Show your work. **78.8°F; Check students' work.**
9. **MP.3 Construct Arguments** Could a thermometer that is marked in both °F and °C show the temperature as both 45°F and 13°C? Explain. **No; Sample explanation: Using the formula, 13°C converts to 55.4°F.**



10. **Algebra** The formula to find the average grade, $A$, of three tests is $A = \frac{X + Y + Z}{3}$, where $X$, $Y$, and $Z$ are the three test scores. Jules earned the scores 78, 90, and 81 on his last three tests. Use the formula to find his average test grade. **83**
11. **Math and Science** The density, $d$, of an object can be found by using the formula $d = \frac{m}{v}$, where $m$ is the mass of the object and $v$ is its volume. What is the density of an object that has a mass of 65 grams and a volume of 8 cubic meters? **8.125 g/cubic meters**
12. Evaluate the expression $7(3^2 + 5) - \left(\frac{81}{9}\right)$. **$7(9 + 5) - 9$ $= 63 + 35 - 9$ $= 98 - 9$ $= 89$**
13. **Higher Order Thinking** Janie knows that she will pay $696 of interest if she borrows $5,800 at a rate of 4%, or 0.04. Show how to use the formula $I = prt$ to find whether it will take Janie 2 years, 3 years, or 4 years to pay off the loan. **Sample answer: $696 = 5{,}800 \cdot 0.04 \cdot 3$; It will take Janie 3 years.**

#### Common Core Assessment

14. Jeremiah helps his neighbor with yard work for 6 hours each day for 15 days. His neighbor offers two payment options. Option 1 is to pay him $4.50 for each hour worked. Option 2 is a final payment of $350. Use the formula $p = 15 \times 4.50h$, where $p$ is the total payment after 15 days and $h$ is the hours worked each day, to decide which offer Jeremiah should choose. Justify your response.

**Sample answer: Jeremiah should choose Option 1. I know that Jeremiah helps for 6 hours each day. I used the formula to find $p = 15 \times 4.50(6) = 15 \times 27 = 405$. So, he can earn $405 by choosing Option 1 and $405 > $350.**




**Error Intervention: Item 3**

**If** students have difficulty identifying which variable represents each quantity,

**then** have them write the formula, and then list each variable and what it means in words. Then have them write each given quantity including units and match it with the appropriate variable.

**Items 5–6 Coherence** Students learned the formula for the volume of a rectangular prism in Grade 5. They will revisit these volume and surface area formulas in Topic 14.

**Item 9 MP.3 Construct Arguments** Encourage students to use math to support their argument. They can evaluate the formula for $C = 13°$ and show that the temperature is equivalent to 55.4°F, not 45°F. Remind students that they must use complete sentences and correct mathematical language when they construct arguments.

**Reteaching** Assign Reteaching Set I on p. 72.

**Item 10 Algebra** Point out that this formula works for finding the average of any three quantities. In general, when an average is calculated, the quantities are added, then the sum is divided by the number of addends.

**Item 11 Math and Science** Since the mass is given in grams, and the volume is given in cubic meters, the unit of measure for density is grams per cubic meter.

**Item 12** You may wish to review the order of operations, which students learned in Lesson 1-2. Have them discuss the order in which they need to perform the operations in the given numerical expression.

**Multi-Step Problems** *Page 58 Items 8–14; Page 60 Items 3, 4, and 7*

# ASSESS AND DIFFERENTIATE

Use the **QUICK CHECK** on the previous page to prescribe differentiated instruction.

**I Intervention** 0–3 points on the Quick Check

**O On-Level** 4 points on the Quick Check

**A Advanced** 5 points on the Quick Check

## Intervention Activity I

### Using Formulas

**Materials**

Index cards

- Before class, prepare a set of cards with each one showing a different rectangle and dimensions, like the one pictured below.

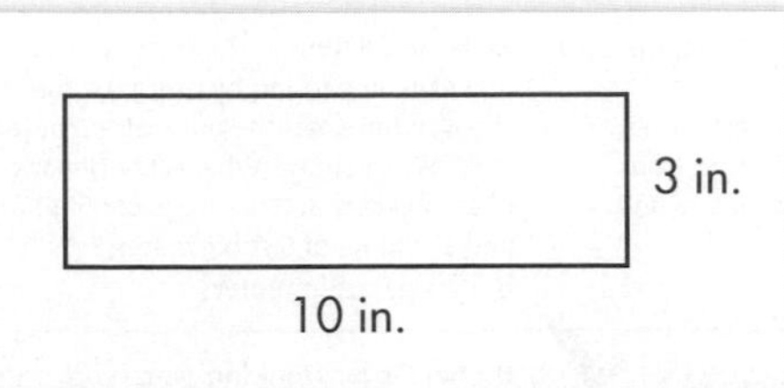


- Write the following formulas on the board and review their meaning.
  $P = 2(\ell + w)$ $\quad A = \ell w$
- Have each student select three cards and use the formulas to find the perimeter and area of each rectangle. Guide students to use the correct unit in each answer.

$P = 2(l + w)$ $\quad A = lw$
$P = 2(10 + 3)$ $\quad A = 10 \cdot 3$
$P = 2(13)$ $\quad A = 30$
$P = 26$
The Perimeter is 26 in. The area is 30 square inches.

## Reteach I

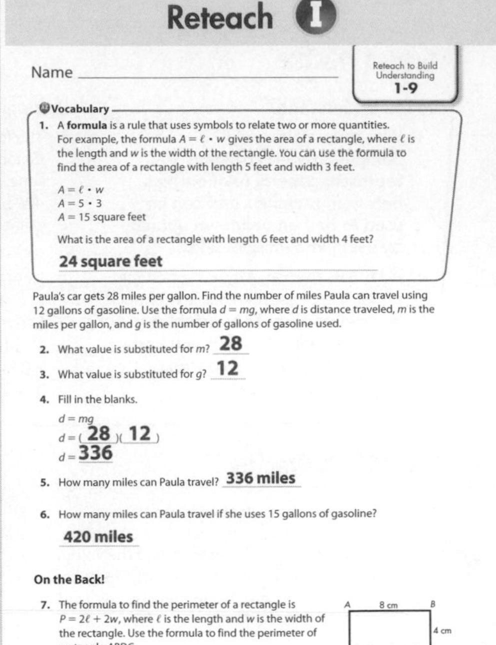

Name ______

Reteach to Build Understanding 1-9

**Vocabulary**

1. A **formula** is a rule that uses symbols to relate two or more quantities. For example, the formula $A = \ell \cdot w$ gives the area of a rectangle, where $\ell$ is the length and $w$ is the width of the rectangle. You can use the formula to find the area of a rectangle with length 5 feet and width 3 feet.
   $A = \ell \cdot w$
   $A = 5 \cdot 3$
   $A = 15$ square feet
   What is the area of a rectangle with length 6 feet and width 4 feet?
   **24 square feet**

Paula's car gets 28 miles per gallon. Find the number of miles Paula can travel using 12 gallons of gasoline. Use the formula $d = mg$, where $d$ is distance traveled, $m$ is the miles per gallon, and $g$ is the number of gallons of gasoline used.

2. What value is substituted for $m$? **28**
3. What value is substituted for $g$? **12**
4. Fill in the blanks.
   $d = mg$
   $d = ($**28**$)($**12**$)$
   $d =$ **336**
5. How many miles can Paula travel? **336 miles**
6. How many miles can Paula travel if she uses 15 gallons of gasoline? **420 miles**

**On the Back!**

7. The formula to find the perimeter of a rectangle is $P = 2\ell + 2w$, where $\ell$ is the length and $w$ is the width of the rectangle. Use the formula to find the perimeter of rectangle $ABDC$.
   **24 cm**

A 8 cm B, 4 cm, C D

R 1-9



## On-Level and Advanced Activity Centers  

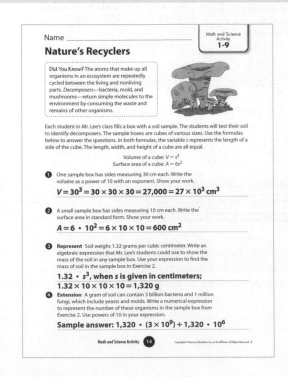

Name ______

Math and Science Activity 1-9

### Nature's Recyclers

Did You Know? The atoms that make up all organisms in an ecosystem are repeatedly cycled between the living and nonliving parts. *Decomposers*—bacteria, mold, and mushrooms—return simple molecules to the environment by consuming the waste and remains of other organisms.

Each student in Mr. Lee's class fills a box with a soil sample. The students will test their soil to identify decomposers. The sample boxes are cubes of various sizes. Use the formulas below to answer the questions. In both formulas, the variable $s$ represents the length of a side of the cube. The length, width, and height of a cube are all equal.

Volume of a cube: $V = s^3$
Surface area of a cube: $A = 6s^2$

1. One sample box has sides measuring 30 cm each. Write the volume as a power of 10 with an exponent. Show your work.
   **$V = 30^3 = 30 \times 30 \times 30 = 27{,}000 = 27 \times 10^3$ cm$^3$**
2. A small sample box has sides measuring 10 cm each. Write the surface area in standard form. Show your work.
   **$A = 6 \cdot 10^2 = 6 \times 10 \times 10 = 600$ cm$^2$**
3. **Represent** Soil weighs 1.32 grams per cubic centimeter. Write an algebraic expression that Mr. Lee's students could use to show the mass of the soil in any sample box. Use your expression to find the mass of soil in the sample box in Exercise 2.
   **$1.32 \cdot s^3$, when $s$ is given in centimeters;**
   **$1.32 \times 10 \times 10 \times 10 = 1{,}320$ g**
4. **Extension** A gram of soil can contain 3 billion bacteria and 1 million fungi, which include yeasts and molds. Write a numerical expression to represent the number of these organisms in the sample box from Exercise 2. Use powers of 10 in your expression.
   **Sample answer: $1{,}320 \cdot (3 \times 10^9) + 1{,}320 \cdot 10^6$**

Math and Science Activity 1-9



### Math and Science Activity STEM

This activity revisits the science theme, Energy and Food Chains, introduced on page 1 in the Student's Edition.

### Sample Student Work

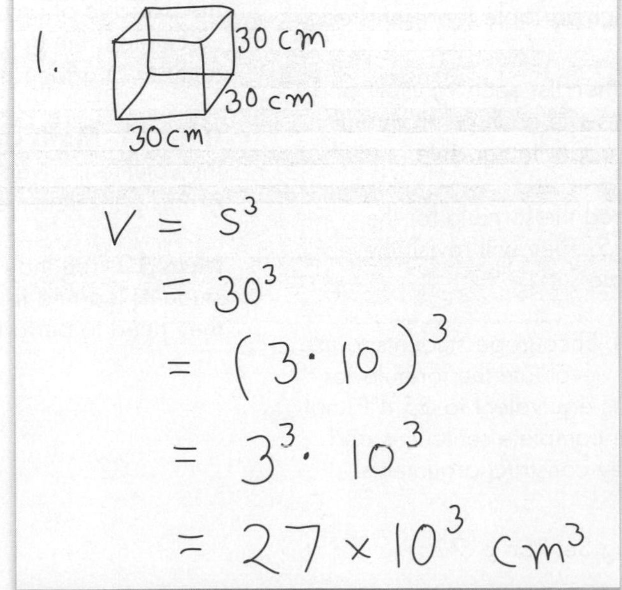

## TIMING

The time allocated to Step 3 will depend on the teacher's instructional decisions and differentiation routines.

15–30 min

Help | Practice Buddy | Tools | Games

## Technology Center

Tools Games

### Math Tools and Math Games

A link to a specific math tools activity or math game to use with this lesson is provided at PearsonRealize.com.

## Leveled Assignment

 Items 1–3, 5, 7  Items 1–3, 5–7  Items 3–7

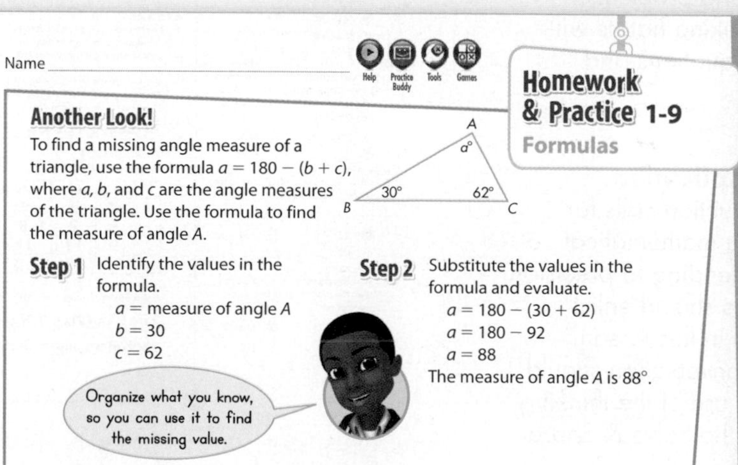

Name ______

Homework & Practice 1-9
Formulas

**Another Look!**

To find a missing angle measure of a triangle, use the formula $a = 180 - (b + c)$, where $a$, $b$, and $c$ are the angle measures of the triangle. Use the formula to find the measure of angle $A$.

**Step 1** Identify the values in the formula.
$a$ = measure of angle $A$
$b = 30$
$c = 62$

**Step 2** Substitute the values in the formula and evaluate.
$a = 180 - (30 + 62)$
$a = 180 - 92$
$a = 88$
The measure of angle $A$ is 88°.

Organize what you know, so you can use it to find the missing value.

In **1** and **2**, let $\ell$ = the length of the rectangle and $w$ = the width of the rectangle.

1. The formula to find the perimeter of a rectangle is $P = 2\ell + 2w$. Use the formula to find the perimeter of rectangle *LMNP*.
$P = 2\ell + 2w$
$= 2 \cdot 12 + 2 \cdot 8$
$= 24 + 16$
$= 40$
$P = 40$ feet

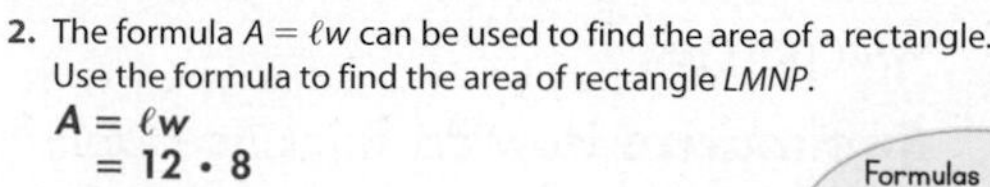

2. The formula $A = \ell w$ can be used to find the area of a rectangle. Use the formula to find the area of rectangle *LMNP*.
$A = \ell w$
$= 12 \cdot 8$
$= 96$
$A = 96$ ft²

Formulas help you model problems and show how quantities are related.

In **3** and **4**, use the formula $a = \frac{(f - s)}{t}$, where $a$ is the rate of acceleration, $f$ is the final speed, $s$ is the starting speed, and $t$ is the time.

3. A racecar goes from 44 meters per second to 77 meters per second in just 11 seconds. What is the acceleration (in meters per second squared) of the racecar? Show how you know.
$a = \frac{(77 - 44)}{11}; = \frac{33}{11}; = 3$
The car accelerates at a rate of 3 meters per second squared.

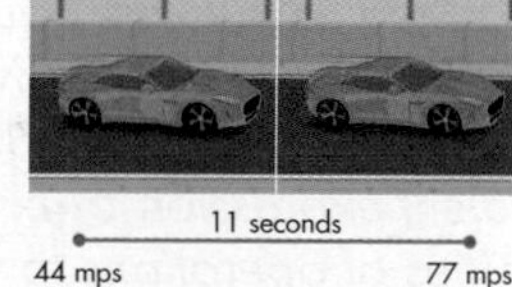


4. **MP.3 Construct Arguments** A popular car model accelerates from 0 to 26.9 meters per second in just 6.5 seconds. An advertisement for the car claims its rate of acceleration is 4 meters per second squared. Can you support this claim? Explain.
Yes; Sample answer: I can substitute given values in the formula to show that the car accelerates at a rate of 4.1 meters per second squared.
$a = \frac{(26.9 - 0)}{6.5} = \frac{26.9}{6.5} = 4.1$

5. Jenna is baking two different types of cookies. One recipe requires $\frac{3}{4}$ cup of flour. The other recipe requires $\frac{1}{2}$ cup of flour. She has 2 cups of flour. Is this enough flour to make both recipes? Explain how you know.
Yes; Sample answer: Jenna needs $1\frac{1}{4}$ cups of flour and she has 2 cups.

6. **Higher Order Thinking** Jack writes the formula $P = 2\ell + 2w$ to find the perimeter, $P$, of a rectangle with length, $\ell$, and width, $w$. Sandy says that she uses the formula $P = 2(\ell + w)$ to find the perimeter of a rectangle. Which formula is correct? Explain.
Sample answer: Jack and Sandy are both correct. The expressions for the perimeter are equivalent, $2(\ell + w) = 2\ell + 2w$.

**Common Core Assessment**

7. A European furniture maker requires that dimensions of custom orders be given in centimeters. The rectangle at the right is a model of a tabletop. One foot is equal to about 0.3 meter. Use the formula $c = 0.3f \times 100$, where $c$ is the measure in centimeters and $f$ is the measure in feet, to find the dimensions of the rectangular tabletop in centimeters.

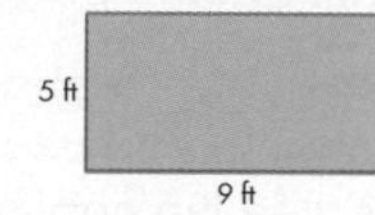


Length, $c = 0.3(9) \times 100 = 2.7 \times 100 = 270$; width, $c = 0.3(5) \times 100 = 1.5 \times 100 = 150$. The tabletop measures 270 cm by 150 cm.

# MATH PRACTICES AND PROBLEM SOLVING | LESSON 1-10

# LOOK FOR AND USE STRUCTURE

## DIGITAL RESOURCES PearsonRealize.com

eText — Student and Teacher eTexts

PD — Listen and Look For Lesson Video

Think — Today's Challenge

Solve — Solve and Share

Learn — Visual Learning Animation Plus

Glossary — Animated Glossary

Practice Buddy — Online Personalized Practice

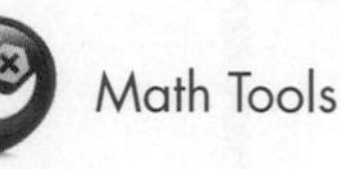
Tools — Math Tools

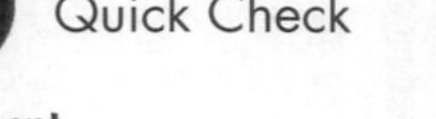
Assessment — Quick Check

Help — Another Look Homework Video

Games — Math Games

MP — Math Practices Animations

## LESSON OVERVIEW FCR FOCUS • COHERENCE • RIGOR

### FOCUS

**Mathematical Practices MP.7** Look for and make use of structure. Also **MP.2, MP.3, MP.6**.

**Domain 6.EE** Expressions and Equations

**Cluster 6.EE.A** Apply and extend previous understandings of arithmetic to algebraic expressions.

**Content Standard 6.EE.A.3** Apply the properties of operations to generate equivalent expressions. *For example, apply the distributive property to the expression $3(2 + x)$ to produce the equivalent expression $6 + 3x$; apply the distributive property to the expression $24x + 18y$ to produce the equivalent expression $6(4x + 3y)$; apply properties of operations to $y + y + y$ to produce the equivalent expression $3y$.* Also **6.EE.A.2c**.

**Objective** Solve problems by using structure to analyze algebraic expressions.

**Essential Understanding** Good math thinkers look for relationships in math to help solve problems.

### COHERENCE

Throughout Topic 1, students have looked for and used structure to solve problems. This lesson is a good opportunity to stop and focus on the Thinking Habits good problem solvers use. Students analyze algebraic expressions and use the properties of operations to evaluate and solve real-world problems. Developing these good thinking habits will prepare them for solving equations and inequalities in Topic 2.

### RIGOR

This lesson emphasizes **application**. Rigorous mathematics instruction calls for the engagement of multiple mathematical practices. For example, attending to precision, MP.6, is a practice students should enlist as they solve the problems in this lesson. However, the classroom conversation should focus on the meaning and use of the thinking habits for MP.7 shown on the Solve & Share task.

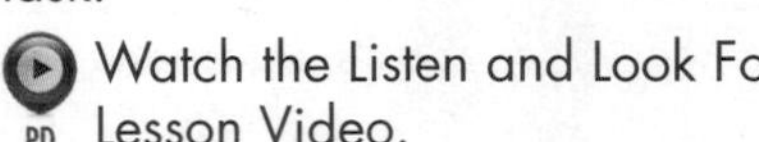
PD Watch the Listen and Look For Lesson Video.

## MATH ANYTIME

### Daily Common Core Review

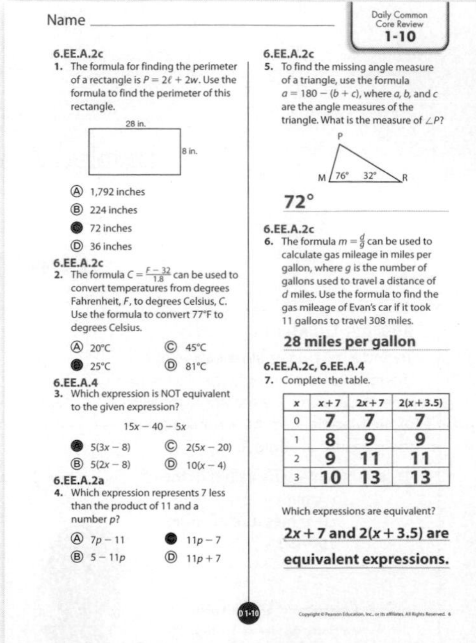
Name ____________

Daily Common Core Review 1-10

6.EE.A.2c
1. The formula for finding the perimeter of a rectangle is $P = 2\ell + 2w$. Use the formula to find the perimeter of this rectangle.



Ⓐ 1,792 inches
Ⓑ 224 inches
● 72 inches
Ⓓ 36 inches

6.EE.A.2c
2. The formula $C = \frac{F - 32}{1.8}$ can be used to convert temperatures from degrees Fahrenheit, $F$, to degrees Celsius, $C$. Use the formula to convert 77°F to degrees Celsius.

Ⓐ 20°C Ⓒ 45°C
● 25°C Ⓓ 81°C

6.EE.A.4
3. Which expression is NOT equivalent to the given expression?

$15x - 40 - 5x$

● $5(3x - 8)$ Ⓒ $2(5x - 20)$
Ⓑ $5(2x - 8)$ Ⓓ $10(x - 4)$

6.EE.A.2a
4. Which expression represents 7 less than the product of 11 and a number $p$?

Ⓐ $7p - 11$ ● $11p - 7$
Ⓑ $5 - 11p$ Ⓓ $11p + 7$

6.EE.A.2c
5. To find the missing angle measure of a triangle, use the formula $a = 180 - (b + c)$, where $a$, $b$, and $c$ are the angle measures of the triangle. What is the measure of $\angle P$?



**72°**

6.EE.A.2c
6. The formula $m = \frac{d}{g}$ can be used to calculate gas mileage in miles per gallon, where $g$ is the number of gallons used to travel a distance of $d$ miles. Use the formula to find the gas mileage of Evan's car if it took 11 gallons to travel 308 miles.

**28 miles per gallon**

6.EE.A.2c, 6.EE.A.4
7. Complete the table.

| $x$ | $x + 7$ | $2x + 7$ | $2(x + 3.5)$ |
|---|---|---|---|
| 0 | 7 | 7 | 7 |
| 1 | 8 | 9 | 9 |
| 2 | 9 | 11 | 11 |
| 3 | 10 | 13 | 13 |

Which expressions are equivalent?

**$2x + 7$ and $2(x + 3.5)$ are equivalent expressions.**

D 1-10

### Today's Challenge

Think Use the Topic 1 problems any time during this topic.

## ENGLISH LANGUAGE LEARNERS ELL

**Speaking** Express ideas.

*Use with the Solve & Share on Student's Edition p. 61.*

Read the Solve & Share. *What will Benny do to find equivalent expressions?* Read *Thinking Habits*. Use the habits to demonstrate how Benny found equivalent expressions.

**Beginning** Read Look Back! to students. Write $8g + 2$. *Let's find an equivalent expression.* Point to the first Thinking Habit. Demonstrate how it is used to find equivalent expressions. Continue with Habits 2–4. *Which habit is most helpful?* Students will express their ideas.

**Intermediate** Read Look Back! with students. Write $8g + 2$. *Let's find an equivalent expression.* Point to the first Thinking Habit. Demonstrate how it is used to find equivalent expressions. Continue with Habits 2–4. *Which habit is most helpful?* Students will express their ideas.

**Advanced** Instruct students to read Look Back! Write $8g + 2$. Ask students to work individually to find equivalent expressions, using the Thinking Habits. *Which habit is most helpful?* Students will express their ideas with partners.

**Summarize** How do *Thinking Habits* help analyze algebraic expressions?

# DEVELOP: PROBLEM-BASED LEARNING

**COHERENCE: Engage learners by connecting prior knowledge to new ideas.**
Students apply what they have learned about variables and the properties of operations to find three equivalent algebraic expressions.

10–15 min

Solve

## BEFORE

1. **Pose the Solve-and-Share Problem**
**MP.7 Use Structure** Listen and look for students who analyze the different parts of the expressions and use properties of operations to generate equivalent expressions.

2. **Build Understanding**
*What does it mean for expressions to be equivalent?* [Expressions are equivalent if they have the same value regardless of what number is substituted for the variable.] *How can you write an expression equivalent to a given expression?* [Apply the properties of operations to the given expression.]

## DURING

3. **Ask Guiding Questions As Needed**
*How are the two given expressions the same? How are they different?* [Sample answer: The expressions are alike in that both use the same variable and use the same operations. They are different in that they contain different numerical values, and only one has parentheses.] *What properties of operations can be used to find equivalent expressions?* [Commutative Properties, Identity Properties, Associative Properties, Distributive Property]

## AFTER

4. **Share and Discuss Solutions**
Solve Start with students' solutions. If needed, project Sarah's work to discuss how to generate equivalent expressions.

5. **Transition to the Visual Learning Bridge**
*You can use the structure of algebraic expressions and properties of operations to analyze and solve real-world problems.*

6. **Extension for Early Finishers**
*Simplify the expression $5(2x + 3x) + (2 \times 4)$.* [$25x + 8$]

Name

**Solve & Share**

Alicia says that $3(2b - 4)$ is equivalent to $6b - 12$. Benny says Alicia is correct but that he can think of three other expressions that are also equivalent to $3(2b - 4)$.

Think about the structure of the algebraic expression $3(2b - 4)$. Find three other equivalent algebraic expressions.

**Math Practices and Problem Solving**

**Lesson 1-10**
**Look For and Use Structure**

**I can ...**
look for and make use of structure to analyze algebraic expressions.

**Mathematical Practices** MP.7, MP.2, MP.3, MP.6
**Content Standards** 6.EE.A.3, 6.EE.A.2c

**Thinking Habits**
*Be a good thinker! These questions can help you.*
- What patterns can I see and describe?
- How can I use the patterns to solve the problem?
- Can I see expressions and objects in different ways?
- What equivalent expressions can I use?

**See margin for sample student work.**

**Look Back!** **MP.7 Use Structure** Write two expressions that are equivalent to $8g + 2$.
**Sample answers: $2 + 8g$; $2(4g + 1)$; $(4g + 1)2$**

Digital Resources at PearsonRealize.com Topic 1 | Lesson 1-10 61

## Analyze Student Work

Sarah's Work

$$3(2b - 4) = 6b - 12$$
$$= 1(6b - 12)$$
$$= (3 \cdot 2b) - (3 \cdot 4)$$
$$= (2b \cdot 3) - (4 \cdot 3)$$

Sarah uses the Identity Property of Multiplication, the Distributive Property, and the Commutative Property of Multiplication to write three equivalent expressions.

Ashley's Work

$$3(2b - 4) = 6b - 12$$
$$= (3 \cdot 2b) - (3 \cdot 4)$$

Ashley uses the Distributive Property, but writes only one equivalent expression.

# DEVELOP: VISUAL LEARNING

The *Visual Learning Bridge* connects students' thinking in Solve & Share to important math ideas in the lesson. Use the *Visual Learning Bridge* to make these ideas explicit. Also available as a *Visual Learning Animation Plus* at PearsonRealize.com

ELL Visual Learning

PEARSON realize. PearsonRealize.com

Learn Glossary

*What do the numbers in the expression represent?* [The 20 and 5 represent the amount of money earned for each job. The 10 represents the expenses. The 2 outside of the parentheses represents doubling the earnings and expenses.] *What does the variable x represent?* [The unknown number of lawns Vanna mows and rakes in a weekend]

**MP.7 Use Structure** *Can you think of this expression as a product?* [Yes] *What are the factors?* [2 and the quantity of $20x + 5x - 10$]

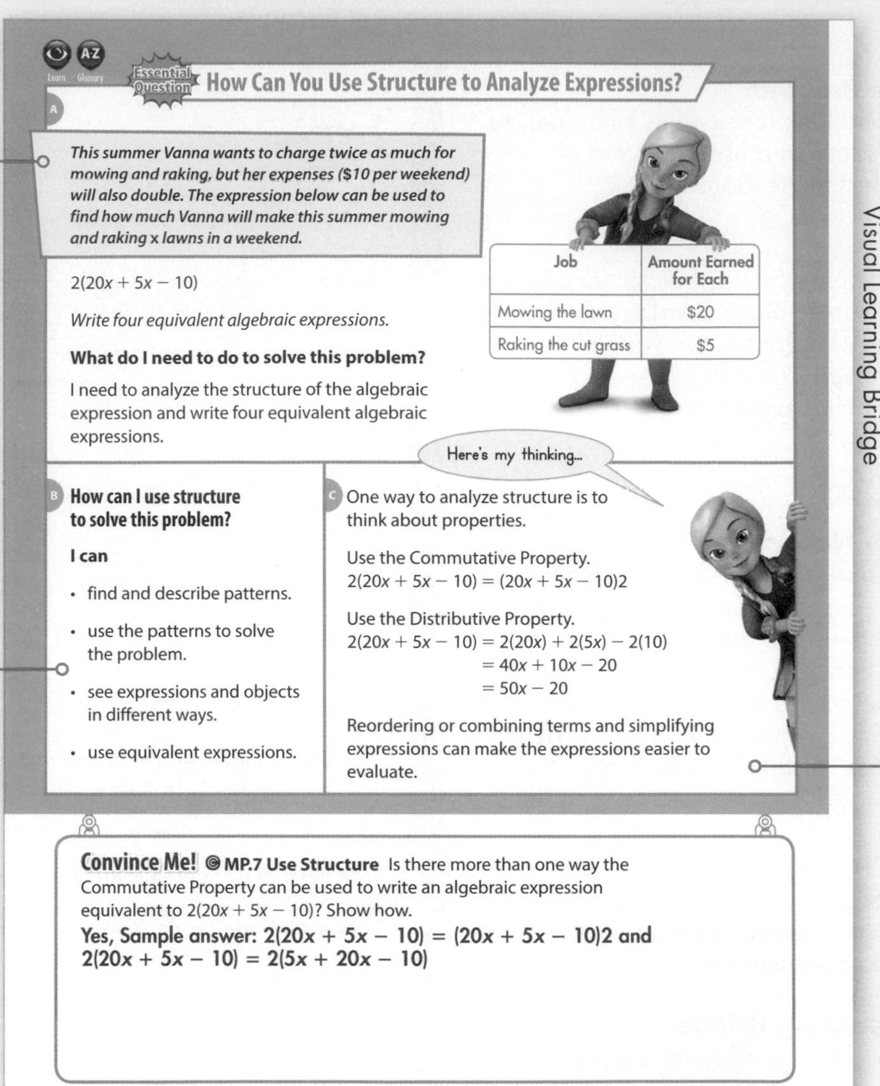

Essential Question **How Can You Use Structure to Analyze Expressions?**

A

*This summer Vanna wants to charge twice as much for mowing and raking, but her expenses ($10 per weekend) will also double. The expression below can be used to find how much Vanna will make this summer mowing and raking x lawns in a weekend.*

| Job | Amount Earned for Each |
|---|---|
| Mowing the lawn | $20 |
| Raking the cut grass | $5 |

$2(20x + 5x - 10)$

*Write four equivalent algebraic expressions.*

**What do I need to do to solve this problem?**

I need to analyze the structure of the algebraic expression and write four equivalent algebraic expressions.



B **How can I use structure to solve this problem?**

**I can**

- find and describe patterns.
- use the patterns to solve the problem.
- see expressions and objects in different ways.
- use equivalent expressions.

C One way to analyze structure is to think about properties.

Use the Commutative Property.
$2(20x + 5x - 10) = (20x + 5x - 10)2$

Use the Distributive Property.
$2(20x + 5x - 10) = 2(20x) + 2(5x) - 2(10)$
$= 40x + 10x - 20$
$= 50x - 20$

Reordering or combining terms and simplifying expressions can make the expressions easier to evaluate.

**Convince Me!** MP.7 Use Structure Is there more than one way the Commutative Property can be used to write an algebraic expression equivalent to $2(20x + 5x - 10)$? Show how.

**Yes, Sample answer: $2(20x + 5x - 10) = (20x + 5x - 10)2$ and $2(20x + 5x - 10) = 2(5x + 20x - 10)$**

62 Topic 1 | Lesson 1-10 © Pearson Education, Inc. 6

Visual Learning Bridge

*How did applying the Commutative Property change the structure of the expression?* [The order of the factors was rearranged.] *How did applying the Distributive Property change the structure of the expression?* [Each quantity inside the parentheses was multiplied by the 2 outside the parentheses.] *What was done to the expression after the Distributive Property?* [The like terms of $40x$ and $10x$ were combined.]

**Convince Me! MP.7 Use Structure** *The Commutative Property applies to which operations?* [Addition and Multiplication] *Which terms are being added?* [The $20x$ and $5x$ inside the parentheses] *What are the factors in this expression?* [2 and the set of parentheses, $(20x + 5x - 10)$]

Revisit the Essential Question. Students can apply properties of operations to change the structure of an algebraic expression while maintaining its value.

PEARSON realize.
PearsonRealize.com

## QUICK CHECK

Check mark indicates items for prescribing differentiation on the next page. Items 3 and 4 are worth 1 point. Items 5–8 are worth up to 3 points.

20–30 min

Practice Buddy

Tools

Assessment

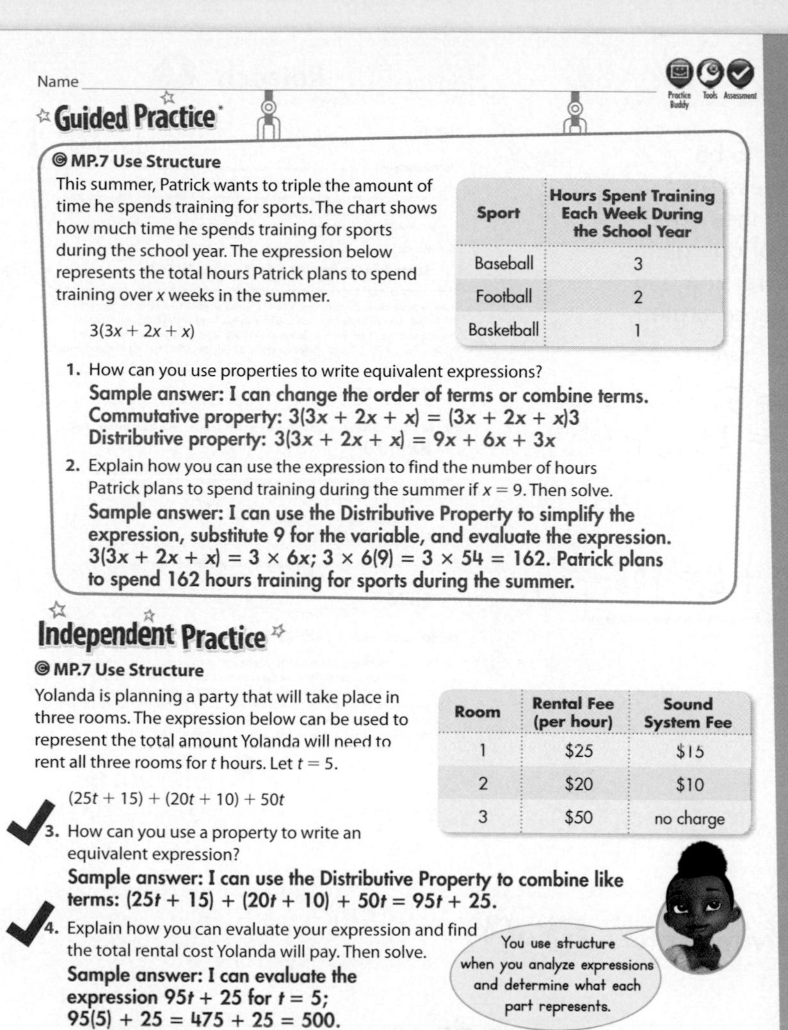

Name

### Guided Practice*

**MP.7 Use Structure**

This summer, Patrick wants to triple the amount of time he spends training for sports. The chart shows how much time he spends training for sports during the school year. The expression below represents the total hours Patrick plans to spend training over $x$ weeks in the summer.

$3(3x + 2x + x)$

| Sport | Hours Spent Training Each Week During the School Year |
|---|---|
| Baseball | 3 |
| Football | 2 |
| Basketball | 1 |

1. How can you use properties to write equivalent expressions?
   **Sample answer: I can change the order of terms or combine terms.**
   **Commutative property: $3(3x + 2x + x) = (3x + 2x + x)3$**
   **Distributive property: $3(3x + 2x + x) = 9x + 6x + 3x$**
2. Explain how you can use the expression to find the number of hours Patrick plans to spend training during the summer if $x = 9$. Then solve.
   **Sample answer: I can use the Distributive Property to simplify the expression, substitute 9 for the variable, and evaluate the expression. $3(3x + 2x + x) = 3 \times 6x$; $3 \times 6(9) = 3 \times 54 = 162$. Patrick plans to spend 162 hours training for sports during the summer.**

### Independent Practice

**MP.7 Use Structure**

Yolanda is planning a party that will take place in three rooms. The expression below can be used to represent the total amount Yolanda will need to rent all three rooms for $t$ hours. Let $t = 5$.

$(25t + 15) + (20t + 10) + 50t$

| Room | Rental Fee (per hour) | Sound System Fee |
|---|---|---|
| 1 | \$25 | \$15 |
| 2 | \$20 | \$10 |
| 3 | \$50 | no charge |

3. How can you use a property to write an equivalent expression?
   **Sample answer: I can use the Distributive Property to combine like terms: $(25t + 15) + (20t + 10) + 50t = 95t + 25$.**
4. Explain how you can evaluate your expression and find the total rental cost Yolanda will pay. Then solve.
   **Sample answer: I can evaluate the expression $95t + 25$ for $t = 5$; $95(5) + 25 = 475 + 25 = 500$. Yolanda's total cost to rent the 3 rooms for 5 hours is \$500.**

You use structure when you analyze expressions and determine what each part represents.

*For another example, see Set J on page 72.

### Math Practices and Problem Solving

**Common Core Performance Assessment**

**Construction Work**

Mrs. Hayes hired Alex and Tyrone to build doghouses for her kennel service. She paid each worker a daily overtime bonus and an hourly wage. The project took two days to complete. Mrs. Hayes used the algebraic expression $2(10 + 7x) + 2(15 + 8x)$ to calculate the total amount she paid Alex and Tyrone for working $x$ hours on each of the two days.

| Worker | Overtime Bonus (\$) | Hourly Wage (\$) |
|---|---|---|
| Alex | 10 | 7 |
| Tyrone | 15 | 8 |

5. **MP.6 Be Precise** How are each worker's earnings represented in the expression? Explain how you know.
   **Sample answer: Alex's earnings are represented by $2(10 + 7x)$ and Tyrone's earnings are represented by $2(15 + 8x)$. Both parts of the expression represent how much each worker was paid in overtime and hourly wages.**
6. **MP.3 Critique Reasoning** Is Mrs. Hayes's expression accurate? How did you decide?
   **Yes; Sample answer: She calculated the workers' daily earnings and then multiplied each amount by 2 to represent the total amount she will owe each worker after two days.**
7. **MP.2 Reasoning** Which property can you use to write an equivalent expression? Explain.
   **Sample answer: I can use the Distributive Property to combine like terms: $2(10 + 7x) + 2(15 + 8x) = 20 + 14x + 30 + 16x = 50 + 30x$**
8. **MP.7 Use Structure** Explain how you can use an equivalent expression to find the total amount Mrs. Hayes paid Alex and Tyrone if each worked 9 hours each day.
   **Sample answer: I can evaluate the expression for $x = 9$; $50 + 30(9) = 50 + 270 = 320$. Alex and Tyrone were paid a total of \$320.**

When you are precise, you can state the meaning of symbols and clarify the meaning of quantities in an expression.

**MP.7 Use Structure** Listen and look for these behaviors as evidence that students are exhibiting proficiency with MP.7.

- Analyze and describe patterns in numbers
- Analyze expressions, equations, procedures, and objects to represent, describe, and work with them in different ways

**Item 5 MP.6 Be Precise** In order for students to understand which part of the expression represents each worker's earnings, they must have a clear understanding of what the variable represents. In this case, $x$ represents the number of hours the workers worked each day. *Since the same variable, x, is used in both expressions, what do you know about the hours Alex and Tyrone worked?* [They worked the same number of hours each day.]

**Reteaching** Assign Reteaching Set J on p. 72.

**Item 6 MP.3 Critique Reasoning** Students must interpret the data in the table and make sense of the language of the Construction Work situation in order to decide whether Mrs. Hayes's algebraic expression accurately represents the total amount she paid.

**Item 7 MP.2 Reason Quantitatively** The sample answer shows how the Distributive Property can be used to combine like terms and generate an equivalent expression. However, additional equivalent expressions can be written using other properties of operations. For example, some students may apply the Commutative Property to write equivalent expressions such as $2(7x + 10) + 2(8x + 15)$, $(10 + 7x)2 + (15 + 8x)2$, and $30x + 50$.

**Item 8 MP.7 Use Structure** This item provides a good opportunity to point out some advantages of writing equivalent expressions. If students were to use the original expression to find the amount of money Mrs. Hayes paid, they would need to evaluate $2(10 + 7 \cdot 18) + 2(15 + 8 \cdot 18)$. It takes a fewer number of calculations to use an equivalent expression such as $50 + 30x$. Then the expression to evaluate is simply $50 + 30 \cdot 18$.

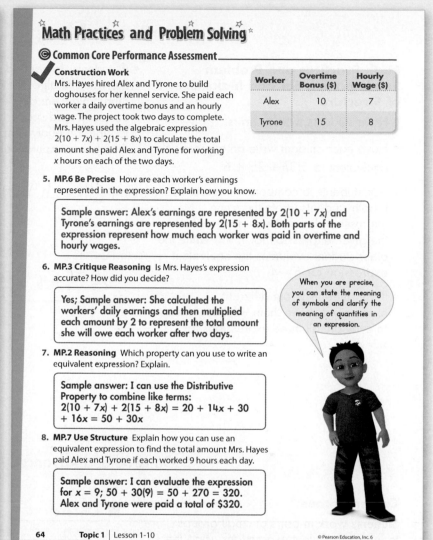

# ASSESS AND DIFFERENTIATE

Use the **QUICK CHECK** on the previous page to prescribe differentiated instruction.

**I Intervention** 0–3 points on the Quick Check

**O On-Level** 4 points on the Quick Check

**A Advanced** 5 points on the Quick Check

## Intervention Activity I

**Math Practices and Problem Solving: Look For and Make Use of Structure**

- Have students work in pairs.
- Have each student write an expression equivalent to $5(3h + 2h) + 6$.
- Ask students to compare expressions. If both students wrote the same expression, have one student evaluate the given expression for $h = 4$ while the other student evaluates the equivalent expression for $h = 4$.
- If the students wrote different expressions, have them work together to evaluate all three expressions for $h = 4$.
- If students do not find 106 to be the value of all of the expressions, then have them check that they have correctly used properties of operations to write an equivalent expression and that their computations are accurate.

$5(3h+2h)+6 = 5 \cdot 5h + 6$
$= 25h + 6$

$h = 4$

$25 \cdot 4 + 6 = 100 + 6 = 106$

## Reteach 

Name ______________________

Reteach to Build Understanding
**1-10**

**Vocabulary**

1. **Equivalent expressions** have the same value regardless of what value is substituted for the same variable in the expressions. Properties of operations can be used to write equivalent expressions. For example, $4(g + 3)$ and $(g + 3)4$ are equivalent expressions by using the Commutative Property of Multiplication.

   Write three expressions that are equivalent to $4(t + 2)$.

   **Sample answers: $4t + 8$, $(t + 2)4$, $4(2 + t)$**

Shawna and Jules work at Mrs. Hill's café. Shawna works 10 hours each week with a \$15 weekly bonus, while Jules works 8 hours each week with a \$10 weekly bonus. Shawna and Jules earn $x$ dollars per hour. Mrs. Hill uses the algebraic expression $4(10x + 15) + 4(8x + 10)$ to calculate how much she pays them for four weeks of work.

2. Which part of the expression represents the amount Shawna earns in one week?

   **$10x + 15$**

3. Which part of the expression represents the amount Jules earns in one week?

   **$8x + 10$**

4. Fill in the blanks to write an equivalent expression.

   $4(10x + 15) + 4(8x + 10)$
   $= \mathbf{40}x + \mathbf{60} + \mathbf{32}x + \mathbf{40}$
   $= \mathbf{72}x + \mathbf{100}$

5. How much does Mrs. Hill pay Shawna and Jules for four weeks of work if they both earn \$10 per hour?

   **\$820**

**On the Back!** **$6.5 \cdot (4x)$; 29.5 miles**

6. Marcus is training for a triathlon. He swims at a rate of 3 miles per hour, he runs at a rate of 6.5 miles per hour, and he cycles at a rate of 15 miles per hour. He runs for four times the amount of time that he swims and cycles twice the amount of time he swims. Marcus uses the expression $3 \cdot x + 6.5 \cdot (4x) + 15 \cdot (2x)$ to represent the total miles he travels when he swims for $x$ hours. Which term in Marcus's expression describes the total miles Marcus runs? How far does he travel in total if he swims for half an hour?

 R 1-10



## On-Level and Advanced Activity Centers O A

**Center Games**

Students work in pairs or small groups to write equivalent expressions using the properties of operations. Have students record their work and explain their thinking as they play the game.

### ★ On-Level

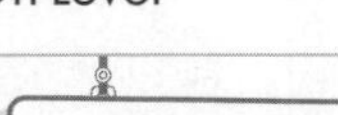

**Teamwork**

**Get Started** (2 or 4 students): Get paper and a pencil. Put 1 2 3 4 in a bag.

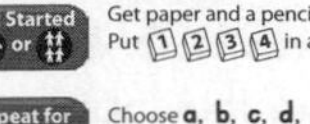

**Repeat for Each Round**: Choose **a, b, c, d, e,** or **f**. Pick a tile. Pick two tiles if your group has only two students. Do the jobs listed below in order. To find your job, find the number that matches the tile you chose.

1. **Write an equivalent expression using the Distributive Property.**
2. **Write an equivalent expression using the Commutative Property of Multiplication or Commutative Property of Addition.**
3. **Write an expression that is NOT equivalent.**
4. **Write two different equivalent expressions. State which properties you used.**

| | |
|---|---|
| a. $4(a + 2) + 4$ | b. $3(2b + 1) + 3$ |
| c. $5(2c + 10) + 5c$ | d. $7 + 21d + 28$ |
| e. $5e + 10 + 25e$ | f. $4f + 8 + 2f + 4$ |

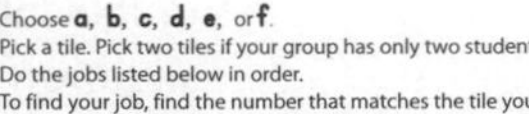

**If you have more time**: Choose different values for each variable. Evaluate your equivalent expressions from Step 4 for the values you chose to verify that your expressions are equivalent.

Center Game ★ 1-10



### ★★ Advanced

**Teamwork**

Partner Talk — Share your thinking while you work.

**Get Started** (2 or 4 students): Get paper and a pencil. Put 1 2 3 4 in a bag.

**Repeat for Each Round**: Choose **a, b, c, d, e,** or **f**. Pick a tile. Pick two tiles if your group has only two students. Do the jobs listed below in order. To find your job, find the number that matches the tile you chose.

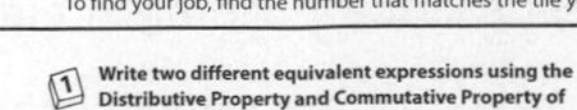

1. **Write two different equivalent expressions using the Distributive Property and Commutative Property of Addition.**
2. **Write two different equivalent expressions using the Distributive Property and the Commutative Property of Multiplication.**
3. **Write two different equivalent expressions with at least two terms with variables and no parentheses.**
4. **Write two different equivalent expressions using any properties you choose. State which properties you used.**

| | |
|---|---|
| a. $8a + 12 + 4a$ | b. $32b + 16 + 4b$ |
| c. $8 + 6(c + 4)$ | d. $3(2d + 3) + 2(3d + 6)$ |
| e. $4(e + 3) + 8e$ | f. $4(3f + 3) + 3(2f - 6)$ |

**If you have more time**: Choose several values for each variable. Evaluate your equivalent expressions for the values you chose to verify that your expressions are equivalent.

Center Game ★★ 1-10

**TIMING**

The time allocated to Step 3 will depend on the teacher's instructional decisions and differentiation routines.

15–30 min

PEARSON realize. PearsonRealize.com

Help | Practice Buddy | Tools | Games

## Technology Center I O A

Tools Games

### Math Tools and Math Games

A link to a specific math tools activity or math game to use with this lesson is provided at PearsonRealize.com.

## Leveled Assignment I Items 1–6 O Items 1–6 A Items 1–6

Name ____________________

**Homework & Practice 1-10**
**Look for and Use Structure**

### Another Look!

Shea sells bracelets at the Farmer's Market. For each bracelet she sells, she spends $1.50 on beads and $3.00 on hardware. She also pays $10 to rent her booth. The expression $4(1.50x + 3x) + 10$ represents her total expenses for selling $x$ bracelets per day in four days. Write two equivalent expressions.

**How can you use structure to solve the problem?**

When you use structure, you can see different ways of writing an expression.

- I can simplify the algebraic expression by combining like terms.
- I can use properties of operations to write equivalent expressions and solve the problem.

**Write two equivalent expressions.**

By combining like terms, I can write this expression:

$$4(1.50x + 3x) + 10 = 4[(1.50 + 3)x] + 10$$
$$= 4(4.50x) + 10$$

By using the Distributive Property, I can write this expression:

$$4(1.50x + 3x) + 10 = 4(1.50x) + 4(3x) + 10$$
$$= (4 \cdot 1.50)x + (4 \cdot 3)x + 10$$
$$= 6x + 12x + 10$$

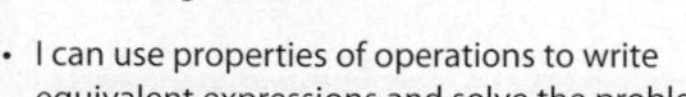

**MP.7 Use Structure**

Jose is training for a half-marathon. Each week he runs $x$ miles per day for 5 days. For 3 days of the week, he runs at a speed of 8 minutes per mile. For 2 days he runs 7-minute miles. Jose uses the expression $4(3 \cdot 8x) + 4(2 \cdot 7x)$ to represent the amount of time, in minutes, that he runs in 4 weeks.

1. Which parts of Jose's expression describe the amount of time he spends running on a given day? Explain.
**$8x$ = the time he spends running 8 minutes per mile; $7x$ = the time he spends running 7 minutes per mile.**

2. How can you use properties to write equivalent expressions?
**Sample answer: I can multiply and then use the Associative Property to combine like terms and write the equivalent expression $4(24x) + 4(14x)$.**



### Common Core Performance Assessment

**Research Project**

Josephine's math study group is doing a research project. There are 5 students in her group. In January, each group member surveyed $x$ volunteers and gave a 10-minute presentation. Each volunteer completed a follow-up survey in May. Josephine wrote the expression $5(6x + 25x + 10)$ to represent the total time in minutes that her group spent surveying volunteers and giving presentations.

**Time Spent Surveying Volunteers**

| Month | Survey Time |
|---|---|
| January | 6 |
| May | 25 |

3. **MP.6 Be Precise** Which parts of the expression represent the time each group member spent surveying volunteers? Explain.
**$6x$ represents the time spent to complete the January survey; $25x$ represents the time spent to complete the May survey.**

4. **MP.3 Critique Reasoning** Is Josephine's expression accurate? How did you decide?
**Yes; Sample answer: She added the times spent surveying to the time spent giving presentations and then multiplied the sum by 5 to represent the total time for the 5-member group.**

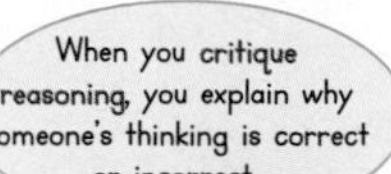

When you critique reasoning, you explain why someone's thinking is correct or incorrect.


5. **MP.2 Reasoning** How can you use properties of operations to write an equivalent expression? Explain your reasoning.
**Sample answer: I can use the Distributive Property to combine like terms and write the expression $5(31x + 10)$. This expression has fewer terms and is easier to evaluate.**

6. **MP.7 Use Structure** Explain how you can use an equivalent expression to find the total time Josephine's group spent on the research project if each worked with 20 volunteers.
**Sample answer: I can substitute 20 for the value of $x$ in the expression $5(31x + 10)$: $5(620 + 10) = 5 \cdot 630 = 3{,}150$. Josephine's groups spent 3,150 minutes on the project.**

# FLUENCY PRACTICE ACTIVITY

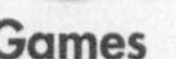

Games Practice Buddy

## FLUENCY PRACTICE ACTIVITY

Students review the Grade 5 fluency standard about multiplying multi-digit whole numbers during a partner activity that reinforces mathematical practices.

### Common Core Standards

**Content Standard 5.NBT.B.5** Fluently multiply multi-digit whole numbers using the standard algorithm.

**Mathematical Practices MP.3, MP.6, MP.7, MP.8**

**Getting Started** Ask students to work with a partner. Tell them to record their matches on their own page. Go over the directions. Both students should solve each problem and record their work. Tell students to take turns identifying the match.

**As Students Do the Activity** Remind students that each clue can be matched with only one problem. Encourage students to use estimation to help choose the matches efficiently. Some students may find all of the answers first and then match the clues. Allow this strategy as it provides the same fluency practice.

**Another Activity** Have students work together to write a new set of clues for the problems on the page. Ask them to record the new rules on a separate sheet of paper.

**Extra Challenge** *Create your own Find a Match activity. Use the same clues on your page. Write a new problem for each clue. Then trade your activity with your partner and complete your partner's Find a Match activity.*

**Online Game** The Game Center at PearsonRealize.com provides opportunities for fluency practice.

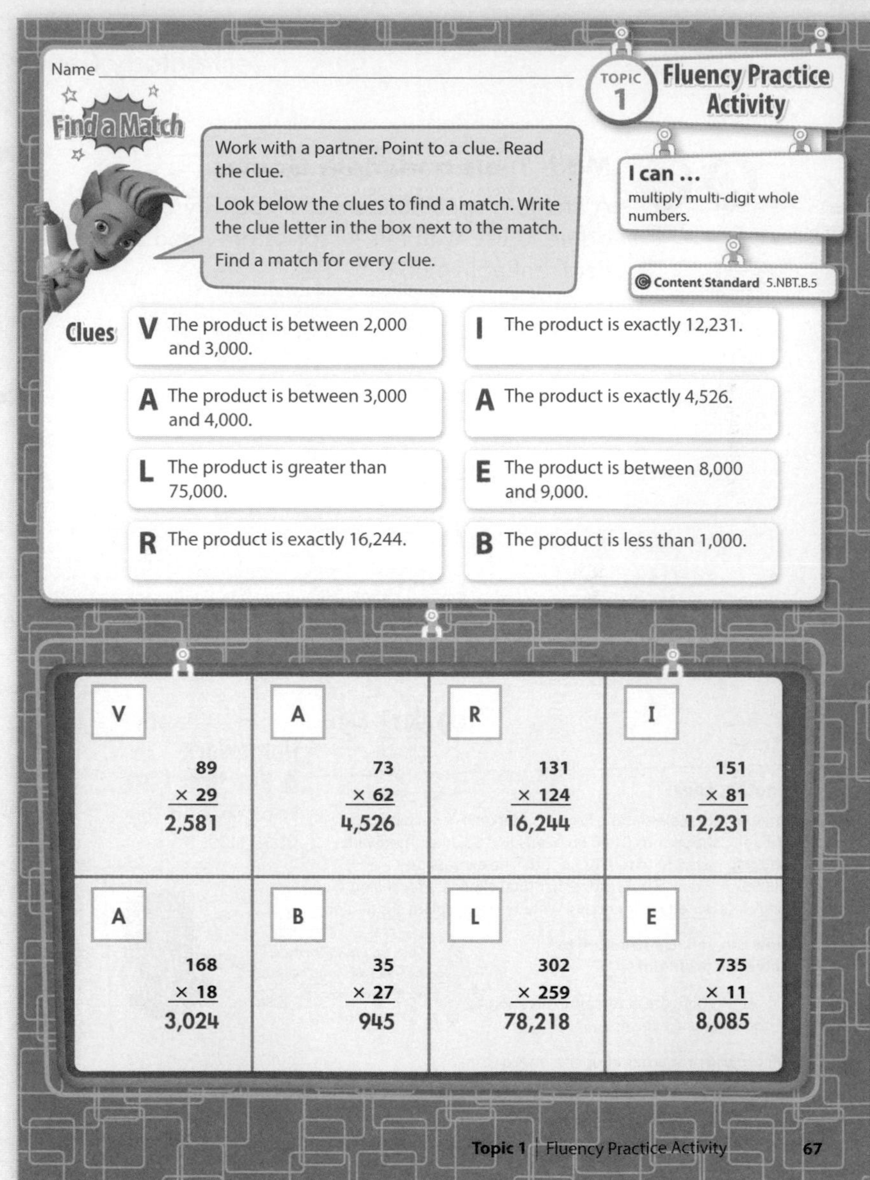

# VOCABULARY REVIEW

PEARSON realize.
PearsonRealize.com

Glossary

Games

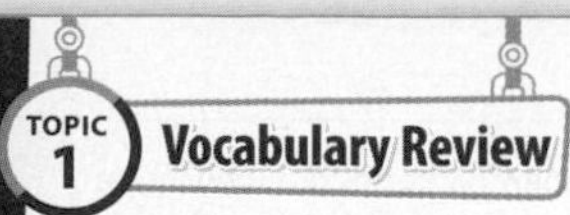


Glossary

**Understand Vocabulary**

Choose the best term from the Word List. Write it on the blank.

**Word List**
- algebraic expression
- base
- coefficient
- equivalent expressions
- evaluate
- exponent
- formula
- like terms
- power
- simplify
- substitution
- terms
- variable

**1.** The number 5 in the expression $5^3$ is the **base**.

**2.** A(n) **exponent** describes the number of times the base is used as a factor.

**3.** There are four **terms** in the expression $5k + 3 - 2k + 7$.

**4.** A **variable** is a quantity that can change or vary.

Draw a line from each expression in Column A to an *equivalent expression* in Column B.

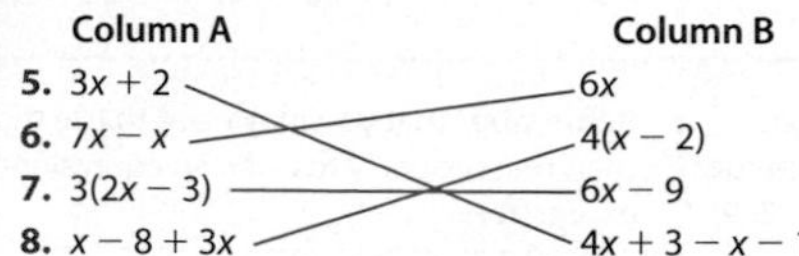

| | Column A | Column B |
|---|---|---|
| **5.** | $3x + 2$ | $6x$ |
| **6.** | $7x - x$ | $4(x - 2)$ |
| **7.** | $3(2x - 3)$ | $6x - 9$ |
| **8.** | $x - 8 + 3x$ | $4x + 3 - x - 1$ |

**9.** Look at the variables in each expression below. Write **Y** if the terms of each expression are *like terms*. Write **N** if they are NOT *like terms*.

$3a + 3z$ **N** $\quad \frac{x}{3} + \frac{x}{4}$ **Y** $\quad 4j - j + 3.8j$ **Y**

**Use Vocabulary in Writing**

**10.** Explain one way to simplify the expression $4(3q - q)$. Use at least 4 words from the Word List in your explanation.

**Sample answer: First *simplify* the *algebraic expression* inside the parentheses by combining *like terms*. Subtract the *coefficients*, $3q - 1q = (3 - 1)q = 2q$. Then multiply 4 and $2q$. The *equivalent expression* is $8q$.**

68 **Topic 1** | Vocabulary Review



## VOCABULARY REVIEW

Students review vocabulary words used in the topic.

**Oral Language** Before students complete the page, you might reinforce oral language through a class discussion involving one or more of the following activities.

- Have students define the terms in their own words.
- Have students say math sentences or math questions that use the words.
- Play a "What's My Word?" guessing game in which you or a student thinks about one of the words and says a clue that others listen to before they guess the word.
- Play a "Right or Wrong?" game in which you or a student says a sentence that uses one of the words correctly or incorrectly. Then others say "right" or "wrong."

**Writing in Math** After students complete the page, you might further reinforce writing in math by doing one or more of the following activities.

- Tell students to close their books. Then say the words and have students write them. Students trade papers to check if the words are spelled correctly.
- Have students work with a partner. Each partner writes a math question that uses one of the words. Then students trade papers and give a written answer that uses the word.

Games

**Online Game** The Game Center at PearsonRealize.com includes a vocabulary game that students can access any time.

# RETEACHING

## ALGEBRA: UNDERSTAND NUMERICAL AND ALGEBRAIC EXPRESSIONS

Name ______________________

TOPIC 1

**Reteaching**

**Set A** pages 7–12

Evaluate $6^3$.

6 is the base and 3 is the exponent.

6 is used as a factor 3 times.

$6 \times 6 \times 6 = 216$

**Remember** that any base number, except zero, with an exponent of 0 has a value of 1.

Evaluate each expression.

1. $9^2$ **81**
2. $99^1$ **99**
3. $3{,}105^0$ **1**

**Set B** pages 13–18

Use the order of operations to evaluate expressions with parentheses and brackets.

Order of Operations

1. Compute inside parentheses and brackets.
2. Evaluate terms with exponents.
3. Multiply and divide from left to right.
4. Add and subtract from left to right.

**Remember** that you can think of brackets as outside parentheses and evaluate the inside parentheses first.

Evaluate each expression.

1. $80 - 4^2 \div 8$ **78**
2. $92.3 - (3.2 \div 0.4) \times 2^3$ **28.3**
3. $\left[(2^3 \times 2.5) \div \frac{1}{2}\right] + 120$ **160**
4. $[20 + (2.5 \cdot 3)] - 3^3$ **0.5**
5. $\left[(2 \times 10^0) \div \frac{1}{3}\right] + 8$ **14**

**Set C** pages 19–24

A variable represents an unknown quantity that can change.

The expression $24 + n$ means "the sum of 24 and a number." The unknown number is a variable that is expressed by a letter, $n$.

**Operation Terms**

Addition → Sum
Subtraction → Difference
Multiplication → Product
Division → Quotient

**Remember** that you can use any letter as a variable to represent an unknown value.

Write an algebraic expression to represent each situation.

1. 22 less than 5 times a number $f$ **$5f - 22$**
2. 48 times a number of game markers, $g$ **$48g$**
3. a number of eggs, $e$, divided by 12 **$e \div 12$**
4. 3 times the sum of $m$ and 7 **$3(m + 7)$**



**Set D** pages 25–30

Each part of an expression that is separated by a plus or a minus sign is called a term.

$4x + 9 - \frac{x}{2}$ — terms

A coefficient is a number that is multiplied by a variable. In the expression above, 4 is the coefficient of $x$ in the product $4x$.

**Remember** that terms grouped inside parentheses can also be viewed as a single part of an expression.

In **1** and **2**, write the number of terms in each expression and identify any coefficients.

1. $12 + y$ **2 terms; coefficient is 1**
2. $8x + (9 \div 3) - 4.3$ **3 terms; coefficient is 8**
3. Write an expression that has four terms and includes two variables. **Sample answer: $2x + 5 - y + 9$**

**Set E** pages 31–36

What is the value of $8a \div b + 2c - d^2$, when $a = 3$, $b = 4$, $c = \frac{1}{2}$, and $d = 2$?

Evaluate the expression.

$8a \div b + 2c - d^2 =$

$8(3) \div 4 + 2(\frac{1}{2}) - 2^2 = 3$

Use substitution to replace each variable with its value.

**Remember** that using *substitution* means to replace the variables with the given values.

Evaluate each expression for $n = 7$, $x = 4$, $y = 8$, and $z = 1$.

1. $12x - 7$ **41**
2. $x^2 \div y$ **2**
3. $5z + 3n - z^3$ **25**
4. $y^2 \div 2x + 3n - z$ **28**

**Set F** pages 37–42

Equivalent expressions are expressions that have the same value. You can use the properties of operations to write the expression $4(2x + 9)$ as an equivalent expression.

$4(2x + 9) = 4(2x) + 4(9)$ ← Distributive Property

$= (4 \cdot 2)x + 36$ ← Associative Property of Multiplication

$= 8x + 36$

So $8x + 36$ is equivalent to $4(2x + 9)$.

**Remember** that you may need to use more than one property to write an equivalent expression.

Use properties of operations to complete the equivalent expressions.

1. $2(x + 4)$ and **2** $x$ + **8**
2. $5x - 45$ and 5( **$x$** − **9** )
3. $3(x + 7)$ and **3** $x$ + **21**





## RtI Item Analysis for Diagnosis and Intervention

| Reteaching Sets | Standard | MDIS | Reteaching Sets | Standard | MDIS |
|---|---|---|---|---|---|
| Set A | 6.EE.A.1 | G60 | Set F | 6.EE.A.3, 6.EE.A.4 | F59 |
| Set B | 6.EE.A.1, 6.EE.A.3 | F41 | Set G | 6.EE.A.3, 6.EE.A.4 | F59, F60 |
| Set C | 6.EE.A.2a, 6.EE.B.6 | F46 | Set H | 6.EE.A.3, 6.EE.A.4 | F42, F43 |
| Set D | 6.EE.A.2b | F58 | Set I | 6.EE.A.2c | F47 |
| Set E | 6.EE.A.2c, 6.EE.B.6 | F45 | Set J | MP.7, MP.2, MP.3, MP.6 | F42, F46 |

Name ____________________

TOPIC 1

**Reteaching**
Continued

## Set G pages 43–48

Simplify the expression $3x + 7 + 6x$.

| | |
|---|---|
| $3x + 7 + 6x$ | Identify the like terms, $3x$ and $6x$. |
| $= 3x + 6x + 7$ | Commutative Property of Addition |
| $= 9x + 7$ | Simplify. |

**Remember** that only like terms can be combined.

Simplify each expression.

1. $9y + 4 - 6y$ **$3y + 4$**
2. $3x + 5 + 7x$ **$10x + 5$**
3. $2y + 8 - y$ **$y + 8$**
4. $8x + 13 - 3x + 9$ **$5x + 22$**
5. $y^2 + 3y^2$ **$4y^2$**
6. $4x + 15 - 3x + 10$ **$x + 25$**
7. $20y - 15 - 6y$ **$14y - 15$**
8. $10x + 2x - 12x$ **0**

## Set H pages 49–54

For algebraic expressions to be equivalent, each expression must name the same value no matter what value is substituted for the variable.

| $x$ | $5x + 20$ | $5(x + 4)$ | $x + 4$ |
|---|---|---|---|
| 1 | 25 | 25 | 5 |
| 2 | 30 | 30 | 6 |
| 3 | 35 | 35 | 7 |

You can use properties of operations to determine whether expressions are equivalent.

Use the Distributive Property to write $5x + 20$ as $5(x + 4)$.

$$5x + 20 = 5 \cdot x + 5 \cdot 4$$
$$= 5(x + 4)$$

Properties of operations cannot be used to write $5x + 20$ or $5(x + 4)$ as $x + 4$.
$5x + 20$ and $5(x + 4)$ are equivalent expressions.

**Remember** that equivalent algebraic expressions must name the same number regardless of the value of the variable.

Complete the table. Then circle the expressions that are equivalent.

1.

| $y$ | $5(2.2y + 1) - 3$ (circled) | $11y + 5 - y$ | $11y + 2$ (circled) |
|---|---|---|---|
| 1 | **13** | **15** | **13** |
| 2 | **24** | **25** | **24** |
| 3 | **35** | **35** | **35** |

Write Yes or No to indicate whether the expressions are equivalent.

2. $10x - 3 + 2x - 5$ and $4(3x - 2)$ **Yes**
3. $3y + 3$ and $9\left(y + \frac{1}{3}\right)$ **No**
4. $6(3x + 1)$ and $9x + 6 + 9x$ **Yes**



## Set I pages 55–60

A formula is a rule that uses symbols to relate two or more quantities.

Find the missing angle measure of the quadrilateral by using the formula $d = 360° - (a + b + c)$, where $a$, $b$, $c$, and $d$ are the angle measures of the quadrilateral.

Identify the values in the formula. Then substitute the values in the formula and evaluate.

$$d = 360° - (a + b + c)$$
$$d = 360° - (45° + 100° + 135°)$$
$$d = 360° - 280°$$
$$d = 80°$$

The measure of angle $D$ is 80°.

**Remember** that you may need to use the order of operations to evaluate formulas.

1. The formula $F = 1.8 \times (K - 273) + 32$ can be used to convert temperature in degrees Fahrenheit, $F$, to degrees Kelvin, $K$. Use the formula to convert a temperature of 323 Kelvin to degrees Fahrenheit. **122°F**
2. Yolanda's bank offers a simple interest loan with a rate of 4%, or 0.04. She plans to borrow \$4,000. Use the formula $I = prt$ to find the amount of interest she will pay if she pays off the loan in 5 years. **\$800**
3. A formula to find the perimeter of a rectangle is $P = 2\ell + 2w$. What is the perimeter of a picture frame with a length of 6.5 centimeters and a width of 5.5 centimeters? **24 centimeters**

## Set J pages 61–66

Think about these questions to help you **look for and make use of structure.**

**Thinking Habits**

- What patterns can I see and describe?
- How can I use the patterns to solve the problem?
- Can I see expressions and objects in different ways?
- What equivalent expressions can I use?

**Remember** to use the structure of an algebraic expression to write equivalent expressions.

Each week, Michael practices his drums for 5 hours and his cello for 3 hours. To double the amount of practice time, he uses the expression $2(5x + 3x)$ to represent the total hours he will practice over $x$ weeks.

1. Describe what the quantities $5x$ and $3x$ represent in the situation.
   **Sample answer: $5x$ represents the time Michael practices the drum and $3x$ represents the cello practice time.**
2. How can Michael use structure to write an equivalent expression?
   **Sample answer: He can use the Distributive Property across Addition to write the expression as $10x + 6x$.**





## Response to Intervention

### Ongoing Intervention

- Lessons with guiding questions to assess understanding
- Support to prevent misconceptions and to reteach

### Strategic Intervention

- Targeted to small groups that need more support
- Easy to implement

### Intensive Intervention

- Instruction to accelerate progress
- Instruction focused on foundational skills

# TOPIC ASSESSMENT

## ALGEBRA: UNDERSTAND NUMERICAL AND ALGEBRAIC EXPRESSIONS

Name ______________________

TOPIC 1 Assessment

**1.** Evaluate the expression below. **1 point**

$(4.5 + 7.6) - 8 \div 2.5$

**8.9**

**2.** Large balloons are sold in packages of 12. Select the expressions that can represent the total number of balloons in $p$ packages of large balloons. **1 point**

- [ ] $12 - p$
- [x] $12 \times p$
- [ ] $p + 12$
- [ ] $p \div 12$
- [x] $12p$

In **3** and **4**, use the expression $5h + 8$.

**3.** List the terms in the expression. **1 point**

**$5h$ and 8**

**4.** What is the coefficient in the expression? **1 point**

**5**

**5.** The same digits are used for the expressions $3^4$ and $4^3$. Explain how to compare the value of each expression. **1 point**

**Sample answer:** $3^4 = 3 \times 3 \times 3 \times 3 = 81$; $4^3 = 4 \times 4 \times 4 = 64$. So $3^4 > 4^3$.

**6.** For questions 6a–6d, choose Yes or No to tell if the expressions are equivalent. **1 point**

**6a.** $6.5 \times 4 - 7.8$ and $26 - 7.8$ ● Yes ○ No

**6b.** $10.3 + (8.7 - 4.2)$ and $19 - 4.2$ ● Yes ○ No

**6c.** $(5^2 + 3.4) \div 6.8$ and $13.4 \div 6.8$ ○ Yes ● No

**6d.** $6.5 \times (12.6 - 9.3)$ and $6.5 \times 3.3$ ● Yes ○ No

**7.** Barb sells necklaces for $3 each. She spent $15 on supplies. Write an expression to show how much she earns if she sells $n$ necklaces. **1 point**

**$3n - 15$**



**8.** Mr. Parker wants to rent a cargo van for a day. It will cost the daily fee of $50 plus $0.35 per mile driven. **2 points**

**Part A**

Let $m$ = the number of miles Mr. Parker drives for the day. Write an expression that shows the amount he will pay for the van.

**Sample answer: $50 + 0.35m$**

**Part B**

Evaluate the expression you wrote to find how much Mr. Parker will pay if he drives 80 miles.

**$50 + 0.35 \cdot 80 = 50 + 28 = 78$**

**Mr. Parker will pay $78.**

**9.** Darnell's truck can travel 18 miles on 1 gallon of gasoline.

How many gallons of gasoline will Darnell need to travel 315 miles?

Use the formula $\frac{d}{m} = g$, where $m$ represents miles per gallon, $d$ is distance traveled, and $g$ is the number of gallons of gasoline used. **1 point**

Ⓐ 11 gallons
Ⓑ 14.5 gallons
● 17.5 gallons
Ⓓ 19 gallons

**10.** For questions 10a–10d, choose Yes or No to tell if the expressions are equivalent. **1 point**

**10a.** $4(5c + 3)$ and $9c + 7$ ○ Yes ● No

**10b.** $10f - 10$ and $2(8f - 5)$ ○ Yes ● No

**10c.** $12g + 21$ and $3(4g + 7)$ ● Yes ○ No

**10d.** $6(4j - 6)$ and $24 - 36j$ ○ Yes ● No

**11.** Draw lines to match each property on the left to its corresponding pair of equivalent expressions on the right. **1 point**

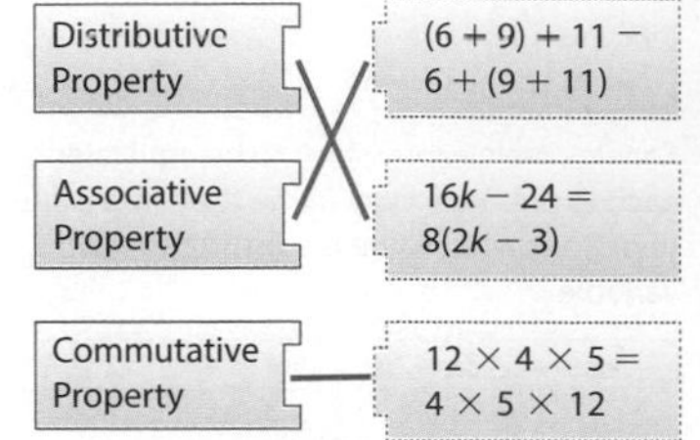


**12.** Choose all of the expressions that are equal to 243. **1 point**

- [x] $3^5$
- [ ] $5^3$
- [ ] $5 \times 5 \times 5$
- [x] $3 \times 3 \times 3 \times 3 \times 3$
- [ ] $3 \times 3 \times 3 \times 5 \times 5$





## ANSWERING THE TOPIC ESSENTIAL QUESTION

**What are expressions and how can they be written and evaluated?**

Restate the Topic Essential Question from the Topic Opener or project it from the Student's Edition eText.

Ask students to answer the Essential Question (verbally or in writing) and give examples that support their answers. The following are key elements of the answer to the Essential Question. Be sure these are made explicit when discussing students' answers.

- An expression is a mathematical phrase that uses numbers and/or variables and operations. A numerical expression contains only numbers and operations. If an expression contains a variable, it is called an algebraic expression.

  **Example:** Some examples of numerical expressions are $7 - 4$, $8^2$, and $6 + 9 \times \frac{1}{3}$. Some examples of algebraic expressions are $3z$, $4y + 8$, and $9 - x^2$.

- Evaluating an expression means finding its value. To evaluate an algebraic expression, substitute the variable with a number before performing the computations.

  **Example:** The value of the numerical expression $3^2 \times (1 + 2)$ is 27. The value of the expression $6x + 4$, when $x = 3$, is 22.

- Use the order of operations when evaluating an expression.

  **Example:** To evaluate $\left(6 + 9 \times \frac{1}{3}\right) - [(5 - y) \times 3]$ for $y = 2$, first substitute 2 for $y$ in the expression. Then follow the order of operations. Within the first pair of parentheses, multiply 9 by $\frac{1}{3}$ to get 3, and then add 6 and 3 to get 9. If the order of operations is not followed when evaluating that expression, the incorrect result for the first pair of parentheses would be 5. Within the brackets, first subtract 2 from 5 to get 3, and multiply 3 by 3 to get 9. The expression in the first pair of parentheses and the expression in the brackets are equivalent. The value of the entire expression is 0 because $9 - 9 = 0$.

## ONLINE TOPIC ASSESSMENT

An auto-scored Topic Assessment is provided at PearsonRealize.com.

## EXAMVIEW® TEST GENERATOR

ExamView can be used to create a blackline-master Topic Assessment with multiple-choice and free-response items.

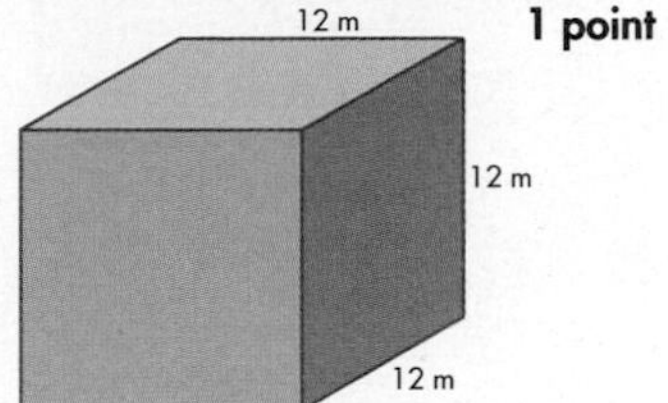


Name ______________________

TOPIC 1

Assessment Continued

**13.** On a trip, Morgan drives at an average speed of 65 miles per hour. The equation $d = 65t$ can be used to find the distance, $d$, she travels, where $t$ is the time in hours.

Fill in the table below to find the distances at different times. **1 point**

| Time, $t$ | Distance, $d$ |
|---|---|
| 3 | 195 |
| 4 | **260** |
| 6 | 390 |
| 7 | **455** |
| 10 | **650** |

**14.** Which expression is equivalent to $5b + 13 - 2b - 7$? **1 point**

● $3b + 6$
Ⓑ $7b + 6$
Ⓒ $9b$
Ⓓ $3b + 20$

**15.** Select the expressions that are equivalent to $12n - 8$. **1 point**

☐ $3n + 4 + 3n + 4 + 4n$
■ $11n + 4 + n - 12$
☐ $6(6n - 2)$
■ $4(3n - 2)$
■ $4n + 2^2 - 12 + 8n$

**16.** Use the diagram below. **3 points**

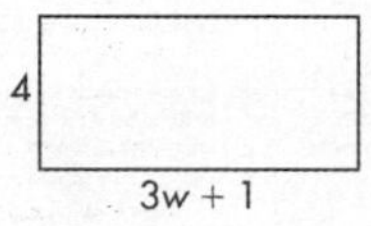

(Rectangle with side 4 and side $3w + 1$)

**Part A**

Write an algebraic expression for the perimeter of the rectangle.

**Sample answer: $4 + 4 + 3w + 1 + 3w + 1$**

**Part B**

Write an expression equivalent to the expression you wrote for Part A.

**$6w + 10$**

**Part C**

Find the perimeter of the rectangle if $w = 8$.

**58**



**17.** Quinn says that the expressions $10x - 4x + 6$ and $3(2x + 2)$ are not equivalent because one expression has a term that is subtracted and the other does not. Do you agree? Explain. **1 point**

**No; Sample answer: They are equivalent expressions. $10x - 4x + 6$ can be simplified to $6x + 6$, and $3(2x + 2)$ also equals $6x + 6$.**

**18.** Two expressions are shown below. **3 points**

$3(3x - 5)$
$6x - 15$

**Part A**

Use the Distributive Property to write an expression that is equivalent to $3(3x - 5)$.

**$9x - 15$**

**Part B**

Use the Distributive Property to write an expression that is equivalent to $6x - 15$.

**$3(2x - 5)$**

**Part C**

Explain whether the expressions are equivalent.

**Sample answer: The expressions are not equivalent. Parts A and B show that the Distributive Property cannot be used to write $3(3x - 5)$ as $6x - 15$, so the expressions are not equivalent.**

**19.** Use the formula $V = s^3$, where $V$ is the volume and $s$ is the length of each side. Which is the volume of the cube below? **1 point**

(Cube with sides 12 m, 12 m, 12 m)

Ⓐ $36\text{ m}^3$
Ⓑ $288\text{ m}^3$
Ⓒ $1{,}152\text{ m}^3$
● $1{,}728\text{ m}^3$

**20.** Write two algebraic expressions equivalent to $3(14x + 23 + 5x)$. **2 points**

**Sample answers: $3(19x + 23)$ and $3(14x) + 3(23) + 3(5x)$**





## RtI Item Analysis for Diagnosis and Intervention

| Item | Standard | DOK | MDIS |
|---|---|---|---|
| 1 | 6.EE.A.3 | 1 | F40 |
| 2 | 6.EE.A.2a, 6.EE.B.6 | 1 | F46 |
| 3 | 6.EE.A.2b | 1 | F58 |
| 4 | 6.EE.A.2b | 1 | F58 |
| 5 | 6.EE.A.1 | 2 | G60 |
| 6 | 6.EE.A.3 | 1 | F41 |
| 7 | 6.EE.A.2a, 6.EE.B.6 | 1 | F46 |
| 8 | 6.EE.A.2c, 6.EE.B.6 | 2 | F46 |
| 9 | 6.EE.A.2c | 1 | F47 |
| 10 | 6.EE.A.4 | 1 | F59, F60 |
| 11 | 6.EE.A.3 | 1 | F42, F43 |
| 12 | 6.EE.A.1 | 1 | G60 |
| 13 | 6.EE.A.2c | 1 | F47 |
| 14 | 6.EE.A.3, 6.EE.A.4 | 1 | F59, F60 |
| 15 | 6.EE.A.3, 6.EE.A.4, MP.7 | 2 | F42, F43 |
| 16 | 6.EE.A.2c, 6.EE.A.3 | 1 | F44, F60 |
| 17 | 6.EE.A.4 | 3 | F59, F60 |
| 18 | 6.EE.A.3 | 3 | F59, F60 |
| 19 | 6.EE.A.2c | 1 | F47 |
| 20 | 6.EE.A.3 | 1 | F59, F60 |

TOPIC 1

# TOPIC ASSESSMENT

## ALGEBRA: UNDERSTAND NUMERICAL AND ALGEBRAIC EXPRESSIONS

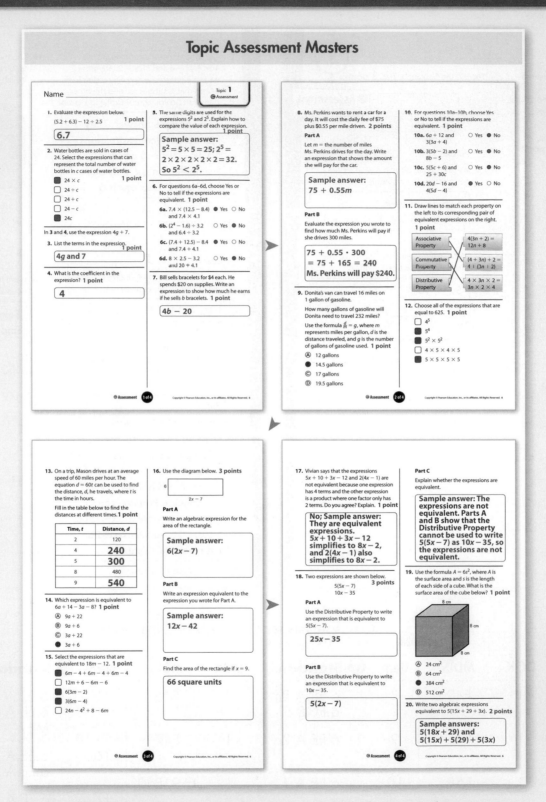

### Topic Assessment Masters

Name ______________________ Topic 1 Assessment

**1.** Evaluate the expression below. **1 point**
$(5.2 + 6.3) - 12 \div 2.5$

6.7

**2.** Water bottles are sold in cases of 24. Select the expressions that can represent the total number of water bottles in $c$ cases of water bottles. **1 point**

- ■ $24 \times c$
- □ $24 \div c$
- □ $24 + c$
- □ $24 - c$
- ■ $24c$

In **3** and **4**, use the expression $4g + 7$.

**3.** List the terms in the expression. **1 point**

$4g$ and 7

**4.** What is the coefficient in the expression? **1 point**

4

**5.** The same digits are used for the expressions $5^2$ and $2^5$. Explain how to compare the value of each expression. **1 point**

Sample answer: $5^2 = 5 \times 5 = 25$; $2^5 = 2 \times 2 \times 2 \times 2 \times 2 = 32$. So $5^2 < 2^5$.

**6.** For questions 6a–6d, choose Yes or No to tell if the expressions are equivalent. **1 point**

**6a.** $7.4 \times (12.5 - 8.4)$ and $7.4 \times 4.1$ ● Yes ○ No
**6b.** $(2^4 - 1.6) \div 3.2$ and $6.4 \div 3.2$ ○ Yes ● No
**6c.** $(7.4 + 12.5) - 8.4$ and $7.4 + 4.1$ ● Yes ○ No
**6d.** $8 \times 2.5 - 3.2$ and $20 + 4.1$ ○ Yes ● No

**7.** Bill sells bracelets for $4 each. He spends $20 on supplies. Write an expression to show how much he earns if he sells $b$ bracelets. **1 point**

$4b - 20$




**8.** Ms. Perkins wants to rent a car for a day. It will cost the daily fee of $75 plus $0.55 per mile driven. **2 points**

**Part A**

Let $m$ = the number of miles Ms. Perkins drives for the day. Write an expression that shows the amount she will pay for the car.

Sample answer: $75 + 0.55m$

**Part B**

Evaluate the expression you wrote to find how much Ms. Perkins will pay if she drives 300 miles.

$75 + 0.55 \cdot 300$
$= 75 + 165 = 240$
Ms. Perkins will pay $240.

**9.** Donita's van can travel 16 miles on 1 gallon of gasoline.

How many gallons of gasoline will Donita need to travel 232 miles?

Use the formula $\frac{d}{m} = g$, where $m$ represents miles per gallon, $d$ is the distance traveled, and $g$ is the number of gallons of gasoline used. **1 point**

- Ⓐ 12 gallons
- ● 14.5 gallons
- Ⓒ 17 gallons
- Ⓓ 19.5 gallons

**10.** For questions 10a–10b, choose Yes or No to tell if the expressions are equivalent. **1 point**

**10a.** $6a + 12$ and $3(3a + 4)$ ○ Yes ● No
**10b.** $3(5b - 2)$ and $8b - 5$ ○ Yes ● No
**10c.** $5(5c + 6)$ and $25 + 30c$ ○ Yes ● No
**10d.** $20d - 16$ and $4(5d - 4)$ ● Yes ○ No

**11.** Draw lines to match each property on the left to its corresponding pair of equivalent expressions on the right. **1 point**

| | |
|---|---|
| Associative Property | $4(3n + 2) = 12n + 8$ |
| Commutative Property | $(4 + 3n) + 2 = 4 + (3n + 2)$ |
| Distributive Property | $4 \times 3n \times 2 = 3n \times 2 \times 4$ |

**12.** Choose all of the expressions that are equal to 625. **1 point**

- □ $4^5$
- ■ $5^4$
- ■ $5^2 \times 5^2$
- □ $4 \times 5 \times 4 \times 5$
- ■ $5 \times 5 \times 5 \times 5$




**13.** On a trip, Mason drives at an average speed of 60 miles per hour. The equation $d = 60t$ can be used to find the distance, $d$, he travels, where $t$ is the time in hours.

Fill in the table below to find the distances at different times. **1 point**

| Time, $t$ | Distance, $d$ |
|---|---|
| 2 | 120 |
| 4 | 240 |
| 5 | 300 |
| 8 | 480 |
| 9 | 540 |

**14.** Which expression is equivalent to $6a + 14 - 3a - 8$? **1 point**

- Ⓐ $9a + 22$
- Ⓑ $9a + 6$
- Ⓒ $3a + 22$
- ● $3a + 6$

**15.** Select the expressions that are equivalent to $18m - 12$. **1 point**

- ■ $6m - 4 + 6m - 4 + 6m - 4$
- □ $12m + 6 - 6m - 6$
- ■ $6(3m - 2)$
- ■ $3(6m - 4)$
- □ $24n - 4^2 + 8 - 6m$

**16.** Use the diagram below. **3 points**

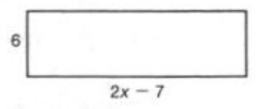


**Part A**

Write an algebraic expression for the area of the rectangle.

Sample answer: $6(2x - 7)$

**Part B**

Write an expression equivalent to the expression you wrote for Part A.

Sample answer: $12x - 42$

**Part C**

Find the area of the rectangle if $x = 9$.

66 square units




**17.** Vivian says that the expressions $5x + 10 + 3x - 12$ and $2(4x - 1)$ are not equivalent because one expression has 4 terms and the other expression is a product where one factor only has 2 terms. Do you agree? Explain. **1 point**

No; Sample answer: They are equivalent expressions. $5x + 10 + 3x - 12$ simplifies to $8x - 2$, and $2(4x - 1)$ also simplifies to $8x - 2$.

**18.** Two expressions are shown below. **3 points**
$5(5x - 7)$
$10x - 35$

**Part A**

Use the Distributive Property to write an expression that is equivalent to $5(5x - 7)$.

$25x - 35$

**Part B**

Use the Distributive Property to write an expression that is equivalent to $10x - 35$.

$5(2x - 7)$

**Part C**

Explain whether the expressions are equivalent.

Sample answer: The expressions are not equivalent. Parts A and B show that the Distributive Property cannot be used to write $5(5x - 7)$ as $10x - 35$, so the expressions are not equivalent.

**19.** Use the formula $A = 6s^2$, where $A$ is the surface area and $s$ is the length of each side of a cube. What is the surface area of the cube below? **1 point**

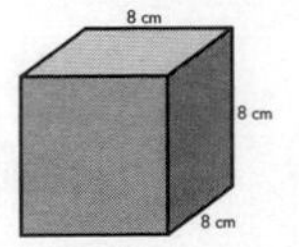


- Ⓐ 24 $cm^2$
- Ⓑ 64 $cm^2$
- ● 384 $cm^2$
- Ⓓ 512 $cm^2$

**20.** Write two algebraic expressions equivalent to $5(15x + 29 + 3x)$. **2 points**

Sample answers: $5(18x + 29)$ and $5(15x) + 5(29) + 5(3x)$




The Topic Assessment Masters assess the same content item for item as the Topic Assessment in the Student's Edition.

**ONLINE TOPIC ASSESSMENT**
An auto-scored Topic Assessment is provided at PearsonRealize.com.

**EXAMVIEW® TEST GENERATOR**
ExamView can be used to create a blackline-master Topic Assessment with multiple-choice and free-response items.

Assessment

### Scoring Guide

| Item | Points | Topic Assessment (Student's Edition and Masters) |
|---|---|---|
| 1 | 1 | Correct numerical value |
| 2 | 1 | All correct choices selected |
| 3 | 1 | Correct answers |
| 4 | 1 | Correct answer |
| 5 | 1 | Correct explanation |
| 6 | 1 | All correct choices selected |
| 7 | 1 | Correct answer |
| 8A | 1 | Correct answer |
| 8B | 1 | Correct answer |
| 9 | 1 | Correct choice selected |
| 10 | 1 | All correct choices selected |
| 11 | 1 | All matches correct |
| 12 | 1 | All correct choices selected |
| 13 | 1 | All numerical values in the correct place |
| 14 | 1 | Correct choice selected |
| 15 | 1 | All correct choices selected |
| 16A | 1 | Correct answer |
| 16B | 1 | Correct answer |
| 16C | 1 | Correct answer |
| 17 | 1 | Correct explanation |
| 18A | 1 | Correct answer |
| 18B | 1 | Correct answer |
| 18C | 1 | Correct explanation |
| 19 | 1 | Correct choice selected |
| 20 | 2<br>1 | Two correct expressions<br>One correct expression |

# TOPIC PERFORMANCE ASSESSMENT

## ALGEBRA: UNDERSTAND NUMERICAL AND ALGEBRAIC EXPRESSIONS

Name 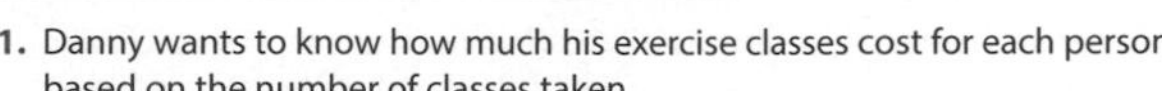

TOPIC 1

Performance Assessment

**Exercise Classes**

Danny teaches an exercise class at the local community center. He distributed a flyer with the information below to advertise the class.

| Danny's Exercise Class | |
|---|---|
| Registration (includes exercise bands) | \$5 |
| Each class | \$8 |

**1.** Danny wants to know how much his exercise classes cost for each person based on the number of classes taken.

**Part A**

Use the table above to answer the question.

Let $c$ = the number of exercise classes a person takes. Write an expression that shows the amount a person will pay to take exercise classes. **1 point**

$5 + 8c$

**Part B**

Use your expression from Part A to fill in the table below.

Fill in the table below to find the amount a person will pay for taking $c$ exercise classes. **1 point**

| Number of Exercise Classes, $c$ | $5 + 8c$ |
|---|---|
| 1 | 13 |
| 3 | 29 |
| 5 | 45 |
| 8 | 69 |
| 10 | 85 |

**Part C**

Use the table above to answer the question.

Suppose Danny drops the registration fee and increases each class by \$1. Write an expression that shows the new amount a person will pay to take exercise classes. **1 point**

$9c$



**Part D**

Use your expression from Part C to fill in the table below.

Fill in the table below to find the amount a person will pay for taking $c$ exercise classes. **1 point**

| Number of Exercise Classes, $c$ | $9c$ |
|---|---|
| 1 | 9 |
| 3 | 27 |
| 5 | 45 |
| 8 | 72 |
| 10 | 90 |

**Part E**

Use your tables from Part B and Part D to answer the question.

Will it cost more or less to attend 3 exercise classes after Danny changes the registration fee? 5 exercise classes? 10 exercise classes? **1 point**

It will cost less to attend 3 exercise classes since evaluating both expressions gives a result of \$2 less after Danny changes the registration fee; It will cost the same to attend 5 classes since evaluating both expressions gives a result of \$45; It will cost more to attend 10 exercise classes since evaluating both expressions gives a result of \$5 more after Danny changes the registration fee.

**2.** If you were running Danny's exercise class, would you prefer the plan before or after Danny changes the registration fee? Explain. **1 point**

Sample answer: I would prefer the plan after Danny changes the registration fee because after taking 5 exercise classes this plan will generate more money for the company.





### Scoring Guide

| Item | Points | Topic Performance Assessment Student's Edition |
|---|---|---|
| 1A | 1 | Correct expression |
| 1B | 1 | All correct numerical values, based on the expression from Part A |
| 1C | 1 | Correct expression |
| 1D | 1 | All correct numerical values, based on the expression from Part A |
| 1E | 1 | Correct comparisons |
| 2 | 1 | Reasonable explanation |

### RtI Item Analysis for Diagnosis and Intervention

| Item | Standard | DOK | MDIS |
|---|---|---|---|
| 1A | 6.EE.A.2a, 6.EE.B.6, MP.1, MP.4 | 2 | F46 |
| 1B | 6.EE.A.2c, 6.EE.B.6, MP.6 | 1 | F45 |
| 1C | 6.EE.A.2a, 6.EE.B.6, MP.1, MP.4 | 2 | F46 |
| 1D | 6.EE.A.2c, 6.EE.B.6, MP.6 | 1 | F44 |
| 1E | 6.EE.A.2c, MP.2, MP.3 | 3 | F45 |
| 2 | 6.EE.A.2c, MP.2, MP.3 | 4 | J20 |

## Topic Performance Assessment Masters

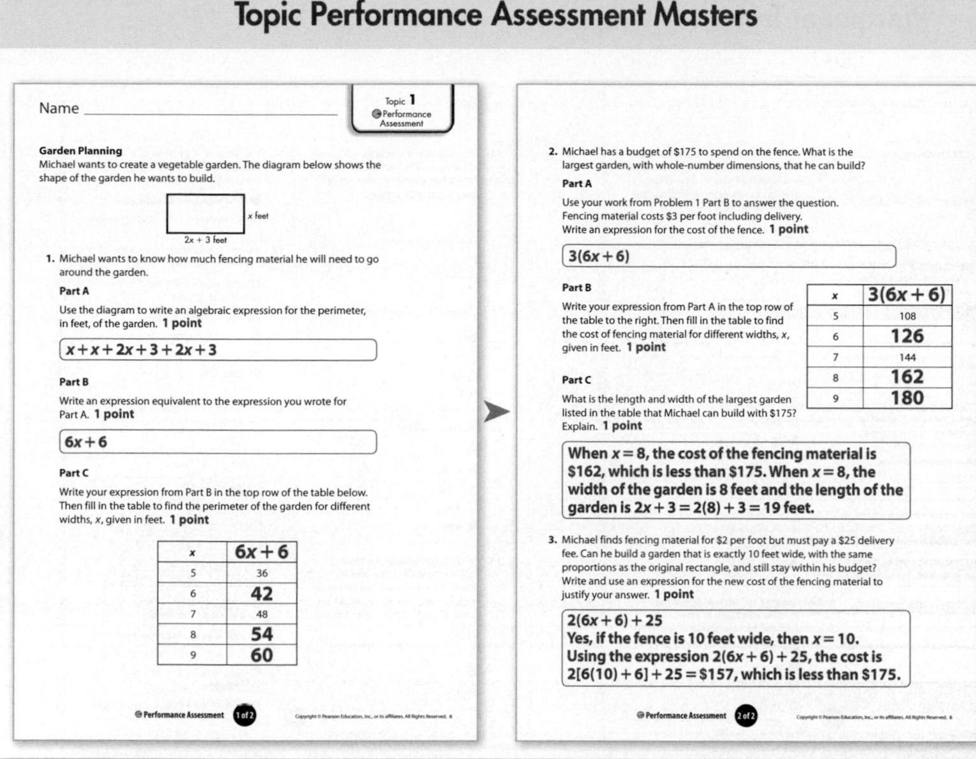

Name ______________________

Topic 1
Performance Assessment

**Garden Planning**
Michael wants to create a vegetable garden. The diagram below shows the shape of the garden he wants to build.

x feet
2x + 3 feet

1. Michael wants to know how much fencing material he will need to go around the garden.

**Part A**
Use the diagram to write an algebraic expression for the perimeter, in feet, of the garden. **1 point**

$x + x + 2x + 3 + 2x + 3$

**Part B**
Write an expression equivalent to the expression you wrote for Part A. **1 point**

$6x + 6$

**Part C**
Write your expression from Part B in the top row of the table below. Then fill in the table to find the perimeter of the garden for different widths, x, given in feet. **1 point**

| $x$ | $6x + 6$ |
|---|---|
| 5 | 36 |
| 6 | 42 |
| 7 | 48 |
| 8 | 54 |
| 9 | 60 |

Performance Assessment 1 of 2

2. Michael has a budget of $175 to spend on the fence. What is the largest garden, with whole-number dimensions, that he can build?

**Part A**
Use your work from Problem 1 Part B to answer the question. Fencing material costs $3 per foot including delivery. Write an expression for the cost of the fencing material. **1 point**

$3(6x + 6)$

**Part B**
Write your expression from Part A in the top row of the table to the right. Then fill in the table to find the cost of fencing material for different widths, x, given in feet. **1 point**

| $x$ | $3(6x + 6)$ |
|---|---|
| 5 | 108 |
| 6 | 126 |
| 7 | 144 |
| 8 | 162 |
| 9 | 180 |

**Part C**
What is the length and width of the largest garden listed in the table that Michael can build with $175? Explain. **1 point**

**When $x = 8$, the cost of the fencing material is $162, which is less than $175. When $x = 8$, the width of the garden is 8 feet and the length of the garden is $2x + 3 = 2(8) + 3 = 19$ feet.**

3. Michael finds fencing material for $2 per foot but must pay a $25 delivery fee. Can he build a garden that is exactly 10 feet wide, with the same proportions as the original rectangle, and still stay within his budget? Write and use an expression for the new cost of the fencing material to justify your answer. **1 point**

**$2(6x + 6) + 25$**
**Yes, if the fence is 10 feet wide, then $x = 10$. Using the expression $2(6x + 6) + 25$, the cost is $2[6(10) + 6] + 25 = \$157$, which is less than $175.**

Performance Assessment 2 of 2

## Scoring Guide

| Item | Points | Topic Performance Assessment Masters |
|---|---|---|
| 1A | 1 | Correct expression |
| 1B | 1 | Correct expression |
| 1C | 1 | All correct numerical values, based on the expression from Part B |
| 2A | 1 | Correct expression |
| 2B | 1 | All correct numerical values, based on the expression from Part A |
| 2C | 1 | Correct answer and reasonable explanation |
| 3 | 1 | Correct answer and reasonable explanation |

## RtI Item Analysis for Diagnosis and Intervention

| Item | Standard | DOK | MDIS |
|---|---|---|---|
| 1A | 6.EE.A.2a, 6.EE.B.6, MP.1, MP.4 | 1 | F46 |
| 1B | 6.EE.A.3, MP.7 | 1 | F59, F60 |
| 1C | 6.EE.A.2c, 6.EE.B.6, MP.6 | 2 | F45 |
| 2A | 6.EE.A.2a, 6.EE.B.6, MP.1, MP.4 | 2 | F46 |
| 2B | 6.EE.A.2c, 6.EE.B.6, MP.6 | 2 | F45 |
| 2C | 6.EE.A.2c, 6.EE.B.6, MP.2, MP.3 | 3 | F45, J20 |
| 3 | 6.EE.A.2a, 6.EE.A.2c, MP.2, MP.3 | 4 | F45, J20 |

# TOPIC 1 PLACEMENT TEST

## Placement Test

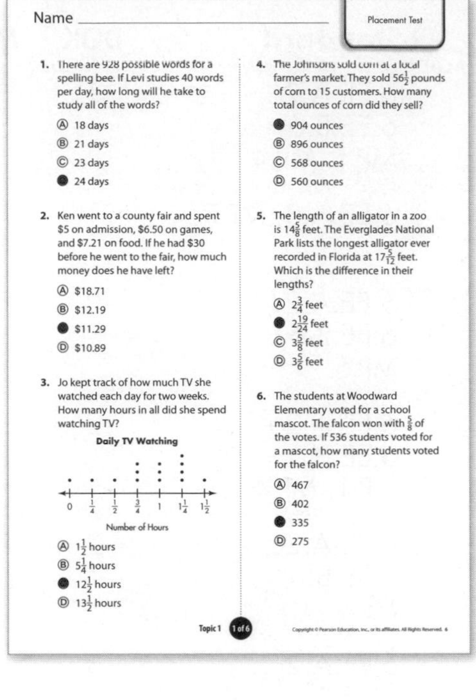

Name ____________________ Placement Test

1. There are 928 possible words for a spelling bee. If Levi studies 40 words per day, how long will he take to study all of the words?
   Ⓐ 18 days
   Ⓑ 21 days
   Ⓒ 23 days
   ● 24 days

2. Ken went to a county fair and spent \$5 on admission, \$6.50 on games, and \$7.21 on food. If he had \$30 before he went to the fair, how much money does he have left?
   Ⓐ \$18.71
   Ⓑ \$12.19
   ● \$11.29
   Ⓓ \$10.89

3. Jo kept track of how much TV she watched each day for two weeks. How many hours in all did she spend watching TV?

   Daily TV Watching

   

   Ⓐ $1\frac{1}{2}$ hours
   Ⓑ $5\frac{1}{4}$ hours
   ● $12\frac{1}{2}$ hours
   Ⓓ $13\frac{1}{2}$ hours

4. The Johnsons sold corn at a local farmer's market. They sold $56\frac{1}{2}$ pounds of corn to 15 customers. How many total ounces of corn did they sell?
   ● 904 ounces
   Ⓑ 896 ounces
   Ⓒ 568 ounces
   Ⓓ 560 ounces

5. The length of an alligator in a zoo is $14\frac{5}{8}$ feet. The Everglades National Park lists the longest alligator ever recorded in Florida at $17\frac{5}{12}$ feet. Which is the difference in their lengths?
   Ⓐ $2\frac{3}{4}$ feet
   ● $2\frac{19}{24}$ feet
   Ⓒ $3\frac{5}{8}$ feet
   Ⓓ $3\frac{5}{6}$ feet

6. The students at Woodward Elementary voted for a school mascot. The falcon won with $\frac{5}{8}$ of the votes. If 536 students voted for a mascot, how many students voted for the falcon?
   Ⓐ 467
   Ⓑ 402
   ● 335
   Ⓓ 275

Topic 1 1 of 6



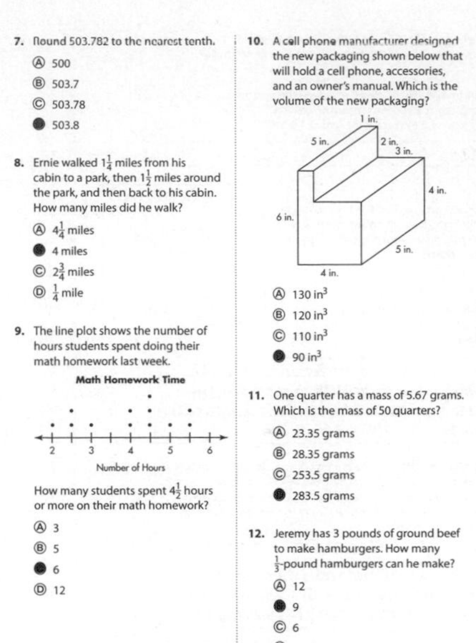

Name ____________________

7. Round 503.782 to the nearest tenth.
   Ⓐ 500
   Ⓑ 503.7
   Ⓒ 503.78
   ● 503.8

8. Ernie walked $1\frac{1}{4}$ miles from his cabin to a park, then $1\frac{1}{2}$ miles around the park, and then back to his cabin. How many miles did he walk?
   Ⓐ $4\frac{1}{4}$ miles
   ● 4 miles
   Ⓒ $2\frac{3}{4}$ miles
   Ⓓ $\frac{1}{4}$ mile

9. The line plot shows the number of hours students spent doing their math homework last week.

   Math Homework Time

   

   How many students spent $4\frac{1}{2}$ hours or more on their math homework?
   Ⓐ 3
   Ⓑ 5
   ● 6
   Ⓓ 12

10. A cell phone manufacturer designed the new packaging shown below that will hold a cell phone, accessories, and an owner's manual. Which is the volume of the new packaging?

    

    Ⓐ 130 $in^3$
    Ⓑ 120 $in^3$
    Ⓒ 110 $in^3$
    ● 90 $in^3$

11. One quarter has a mass of 5.67 grams. Which is the mass of 50 quarters?
    Ⓐ 23.35 grams
    Ⓑ 28.35 grams
    Ⓒ 253.5 grams
    ● 283.5 grams

12. Jeremy has 3 pounds of ground beef to make hamburgers. How many $\frac{1}{3}$-pound hamburgers can he make?
    Ⓐ 12
    ● 9
    Ⓒ 6
    Ⓓ 1

Topic 1 2 of 6



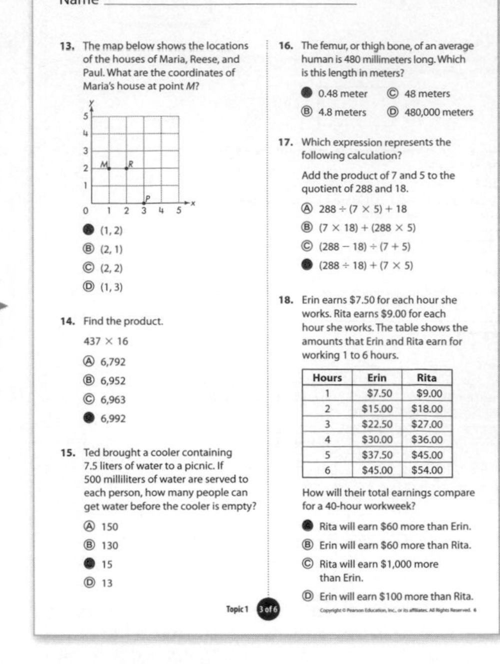

Name ____________________

13. The map below shows the locations of the houses of Maria, Reese, and Paul. What are the coordinates of Maria's house at point $M$?

    

    ● (1, 2)
    Ⓑ (2, 1)
    Ⓒ (2, 2)
    Ⓓ (1, 3)

14. Find the product.

    $437 \times 16$

    Ⓐ 6,792
    Ⓑ 6,952
    Ⓒ 6,963
    ● 6,992

15. Ted brought a cooler containing 7.5 liters of water to a picnic. If 500 milliliters of water are served to each person, how many people can get water before the cooler is empty?
    Ⓐ 150
    Ⓑ 130
    ● 15
    Ⓓ 13

16. The femur, or thigh bone, of an average human is 480 millimeters long. Which is this length in meters?
    ● 0.48 meter Ⓒ 48 meters
    Ⓑ 4.8 meters Ⓓ 480,000 meters

17. Which expression represents the following calculation?

    Add the product of 7 and 5 to the quotient of 288 and 18.

    Ⓐ $288 \div (7 \times 5) + 18$
    Ⓑ $(7 \times 18) + (288 \times 5)$
    Ⓒ $(288 - 18) \div (7 + 5)$
    ● $(288 \div 18) + (7 \times 5)$

18. Erin earns \$7.50 for each hour she works. Rita earns \$9.00 for each hour she works. The table shows the amounts that Erin and Rita earn for working 1 to 6 hours.

    | Hours | Erin | Rita |
    |---|---|---|
    | 1 | \$7.50 | \$9.00 |
    | 2 | \$15.00 | \$18.00 |
    | 3 | \$22.50 | \$27.00 |
    | 4 | \$30.00 | \$36.00 |
    | 5 | \$37.50 | \$45.00 |
    | 6 | \$45.00 | \$54.00 |

    How will their total earnings compare for a 40-hour workweek?
    ● Rita will earn \$60 more than Erin.
    Ⓑ Erin will earn \$60 more than Rita.
    Ⓒ Rita will earn \$1,000 more than Erin.
    Ⓓ Erin will earn \$100 more than Rita.

Topic 1 3 of 6



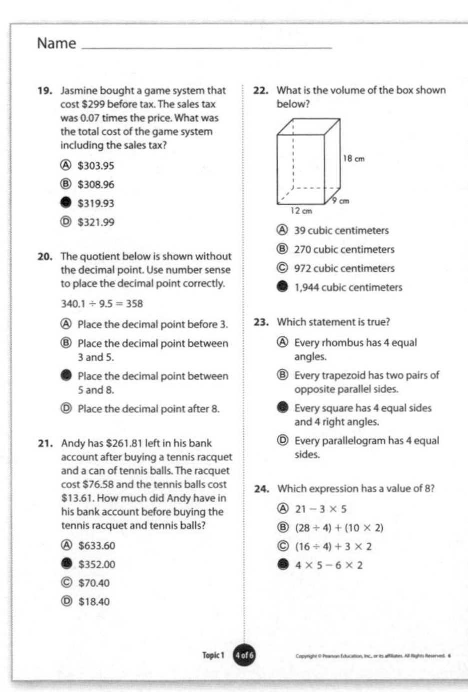

Name ____________________

19. Jasmine bought a game system that cost \$299 before tax. The sales tax was 0.07 times the price. What was the total cost of the game system including the sales tax?
    Ⓐ \$303.95
    Ⓑ \$308.96
    ● \$319.93
    Ⓓ \$321.99

20. The quotient below is shown without the decimal point. Use number sense to place the decimal point correctly.

    $340.1 \div 9.5 = 358$

    Ⓐ Place the decimal point before 3.
    Ⓑ Place the decimal point between 3 and 5.
    ● Place the decimal point between 5 and 8.
    Ⓓ Place the decimal point after 8.

21. Andy has \$261.81 left in his bank account after buying a tennis racquet and a can of tennis balls. The racquet cost \$76.58 and the tennis balls cost \$13.61. How much did Andy have in his bank account before buying the tennis racquet and tennis balls?
    Ⓐ \$633.60
    ● \$352.00
    Ⓒ \$70.40
    Ⓓ \$18.40

22. What is the volume of the box shown below?

    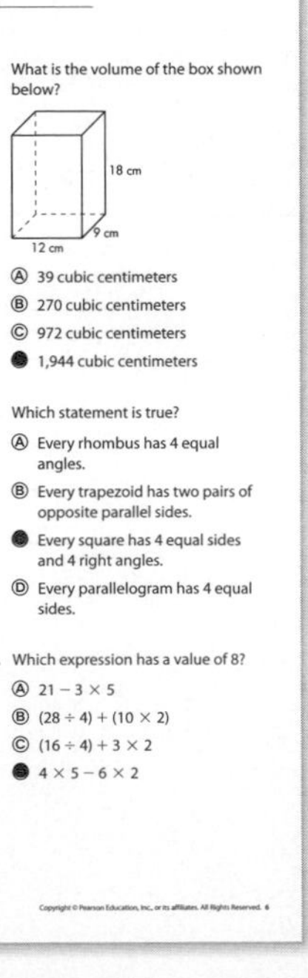

    

    Ⓐ 39 cubic centimeters
    Ⓑ 270 cubic centimeters
    Ⓒ 972 cubic centimeters
    ● 1,944 cubic centimeters

23. Which statement is true?
    Ⓐ Every rhombus has 4 equal angles.
    Ⓑ Every trapezoid has two pairs of opposite parallel sides.
    ● Every square has 4 equal sides and 4 right angles.
    Ⓓ Every parallelogram has 4 equal sides.

24. Which expression has a value of 8?
    Ⓐ $21 - 3 \times 5$
    Ⓑ $(28 \div 4) + (10 \times 2)$
    Ⓒ $(16 \div 4) + 3 \times 2$
    ● $4 \times 5 - 6 \times 2$

Topic 1 4 of 6



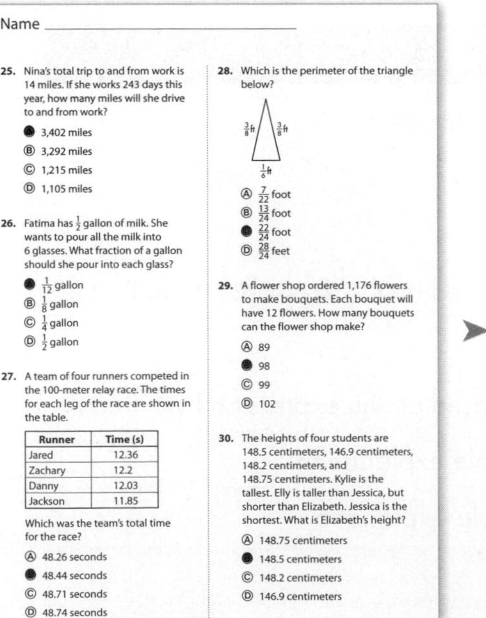

Name ____________________

25. Nina's total trip to and from work is 14 miles. If she works 243 days this year, how many miles will she drive to and from work?
    ● 3,402 miles
    Ⓑ 3,292 miles
    Ⓒ 1,215 miles
    Ⓓ 1,105 miles

26. Fatima has $\frac{1}{2}$ gallon of milk. She wants to pour all the milk into 6 glasses. What fraction of a gallon should she pour into each glass?
    ● $\frac{1}{12}$ gallon
    Ⓑ $\frac{1}{8}$ gallon
    Ⓒ $\frac{1}{4}$ gallon
    Ⓓ $\frac{1}{2}$ gallon

27. A team of four runners competed in the 100-meter relay race. The times for each leg of the race are shown in the table.

    | Runner | Time (s) |
    |---|---|
    | Jared | 12.36 |
    | Zachary | 12.2 |
    | Danny | 12.03 |
    | Jackson | 11.85 |

    Which was the team's total time for the race?
    Ⓐ 48.26 seconds
    ● 48.44 seconds
    Ⓒ 48.71 seconds
    Ⓓ 48.74 seconds

28. Which is the perimeter of the triangle below?

    

    Ⓐ $\frac{7}{22}$ foot
    Ⓑ $\frac{13}{24}$ foot
    ● $\frac{22}{24}$ foot
    Ⓓ $\frac{28}{24}$ feet

29. A flower shop ordered 1,176 flowers to make bouquets. Each bouquet will have 12 flowers. How many bouquets can the flower shop make?
    Ⓐ 89
    ● 98
    Ⓒ 99
    Ⓓ 102

30. The heights of four students are 148.5 centimeters, 146.9 centimeters, 148.2 centimeters, and 148.75 centimeters. Kylie is the tallest. Elly is taller than Jessica, but shorter than Elizabeth. Jessica is the shortest. What is Elizabeth's height?
    Ⓐ 148.75 centimeters
    ● 148.5 centimeters
    Ⓒ 148.2 centimeters
    Ⓓ 146.9 centimeters

Topic 1 5 of 6



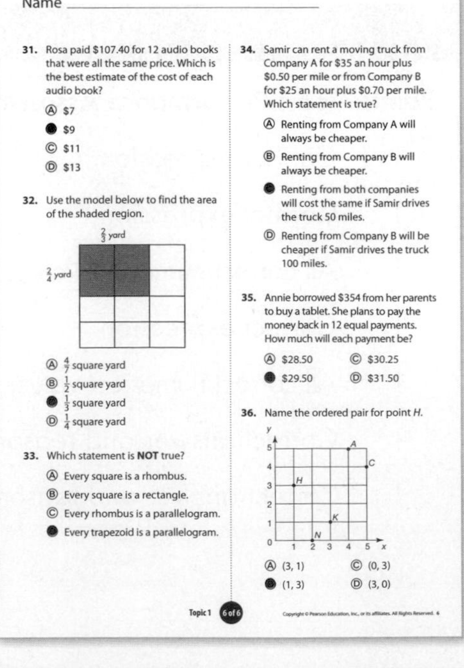

Name ____________________

31. Rosa paid \$107.40 for 12 audio books that were all the same price. Which is the best estimate of the cost of each audio book?
    Ⓐ \$7
    ● \$9
    Ⓒ \$11
    Ⓓ \$13

32. Use the model below to find the area of the shaded region.

    

    Ⓐ $\frac{4}{7}$ square yard
    Ⓑ $\frac{1}{2}$ square yard
    ● $\frac{1}{3}$ square yard
    Ⓓ $\frac{1}{4}$ square yard

33. Which statement is **NOT** true?
    Ⓐ Every square is a rhombus.
    Ⓑ Every square is a rectangle.
    Ⓒ Every rhombus is a parallelogram.
    ● Every trapezoid is a parallelogram.

34. Samir can rent a moving truck from Company A for \$35 an hour plus \$0.50 per mile or from Company B for \$25 an hour plus \$0.70 per mile. Which statement is true?
    Ⓐ Renting from Company A will always be cheaper.
    Ⓑ Renting from Company B will always be cheaper.
    ● Renting from both companies will cost the same if Samir drives the truck 50 miles.
    Ⓓ Renting from Company B will be cheaper if Samir drives the truck 100 miles.

35. Annie borrowed \$354 from her parents to buy a tablet. She plans to pay the money back in 12 equal payments. How much will each payment be?
    Ⓐ \$28.50 Ⓒ \$30.25
    ● \$29.50 Ⓓ \$31.50

36. Name the ordered pair for point $H$.

    

    Ⓐ (3, 1) Ⓒ (0, 3)
    ● (1, 3) Ⓓ (3, 0)

Topic 1 6 of 6

**ONLINE PLACEMENT TEST**

An auto-scored Placement Test is provided at PearsonRealize.com.

## RtI Item Analysis for Diagnosis and Intervention

| Item | Standard | MDIS | Item | Standard | MDIS | Item | Standard | MDIS |
|---|---|---|---|---|---|---|---|---|
| 1 | 5.NBT.B.6 | G73 | 13 | 5.G.A.2, MP.4 | F32 | 25 | 5.NBT.B.5 | G69 |
| 2 | 5.NBT.B.7 | H56, H57 | 14 | 5.NBT.B.5 | G69 | 26 | 5.NF.B.7c | H87 |
| 3 | 5.MD.B.2 | I69 | 15 | 5.MD.A.1 | I35 | 27 | 5.NBT.B.7 | H56 |
| 4 | 5.MD.A.1, MP.1 | I34 | 16 | 5.MD.A.1 | I35 | 28 | 5.NF.A.2 | I41, H42 |
| 5 | 5.NF.A.2 | H46 | 17 | 5.OA.A.2 | F37 | 29 | 5.NBT.B.6 | G73 |
| 6 | 5.NF.B.6 | H47 | 18 | 5.OA.B.3, MP.7 | F29 | 30 | 5.NBT.A.3b, MP.2 | H30 |
| 7 | 5.NBT.A.4, MP.6 | H29 | 19 | 5.NBT.B.7 | H60 | 31 | 5.NBT.B.7 | H68 |
| 8 | 5.NF.A.2 | H45 | 20 | 5.NBT.B.7, MP.2 | H69 | 32 | 5.NF.B.4b | I45 |
| 9 | 5.MD.B.2 | I69 | 21 | 5.NBT.B.7 | H56 | 33 | 5.G.B.4, MP.2 | I6 |
| 10 | 5.MD.C.5c | I72 | 22 | 5.MD.C.5b | I55 | 34 | 5.OA.B.3 | F30 |
| 11 | 5.NBT.B.7 | H60 | 23 | 5.G.B.3 | I6 | 35 | 5.NBT.B.7, MP.6 | H67 |
| 12 | 5.NF.B.7c | H86 | 24 | 5.OA.A.1, MP.6 | F40 | 36 | 5.G.A.1 | F32 |

# BASIC-FACTS TIMED TESTS

## Basic-Facts Timed Tests, 1–6

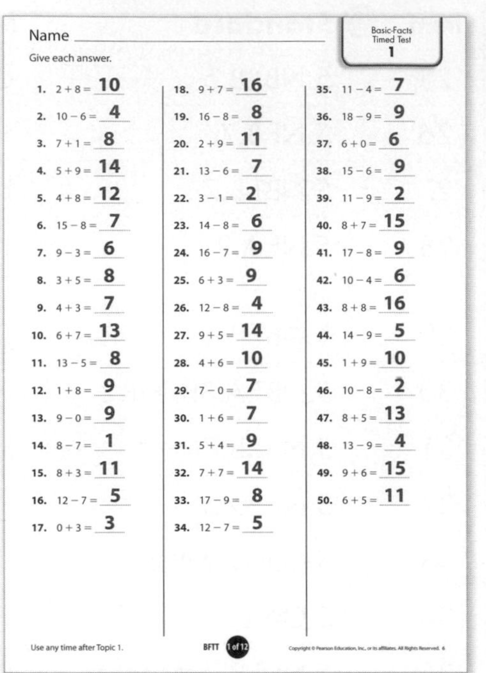

Name ______________________

Basic-Facts Timed Test 1

Give each answer.

1. $2 + 8 = 10$
2. $10 - 6 = 4$
3. $7 + 1 = 8$
4. $5 + 9 = 14$
5. $4 + 8 = 12$
6. $15 - 8 = 7$
7. $9 - 3 = 6$
8. $3 + 5 = 8$
9. $4 + 3 = 7$
10. $6 + 7 = 13$
11. $13 - 5 = 8$
12. $1 + 8 = 9$
13. $9 - 0 = 9$
14. $8 - 7 = 1$
15. $8 + 3 = 11$
16. $12 - 7 = 5$
17. $0 + 3 = 3$
18. $9 + 7 = 16$
19. $16 - 8 = 8$
20. $2 + 9 = 11$
21. $13 - 6 = 7$
22. $3 - 1 = 2$
23. $14 - 8 = 6$
24. $16 - 7 = 9$
25. $6 + 3 = 9$
26. $12 - 8 = 4$
27. $9 + 5 = 14$
28. $4 + 6 = 10$
29. $7 - 0 = 7$
30. $1 + 6 = 7$
31. $5 + 4 = 9$
32. $7 + 7 = 14$
33. $17 - 9 = 8$
34. $12 - 7 = 5$
35. $11 - 4 = 7$
36. $18 - 9 = 9$
37. $6 + 0 = 6$
38. $15 - 6 = 9$
39. $11 - 9 = 2$
40. $8 + 7 = 15$
41. $17 - 8 = 9$
42. $10 - 4 = 6$
43. $8 + 8 = 16$
44. $14 - 9 = 5$
45. $1 + 9 = 10$
46. $10 - 8 = 2$
47. $8 + 5 = 13$
48. $13 - 9 = 4$
49. $9 + 6 = 15$
50. $6 + 5 = 11$

Use any time after Topic 1. BFTT 1 of 12 

Name ______________________

Basic-Facts Timed Test 2

Give each answer.

1. $9 \times 0 = 0$
2. $7 \times 6 = 42$
3. $5 \times 9 = 45$
4. $3 \times 1 = 3$
5. $3 \times 9 = 27$
6. $8 \times 9 = 72$
7. $6 \times 9 = 54$
8. $8 \times 7 = 56$
9. $4 \times 6 = 24$
10. $7 \times 4 = 28$
11. $3 \times 3 = 9$
12. $6 \times 7 = 42$
13. $1 \times 3 = 3$
14. $5 \times 5 = 25$
15. $2 \times 8 = 16$
16. $9 \times 2 = 18$
17. $4 \times 8 = 32$
18. $3 \times 8 = 24$
19. $7 \times 2 = 14$
20. $2 \times 2 = 4$
21. $5 \times 6 = 30$
22. $0 \times 2 = 0$
23. $3 \times 4 = 12$
24. $8 \times 3 = 24$
25. $3 \times 7 = 21$
26. $9 \times 4 = 36$
27. $3 \times 2 = 6$
28. $3 \times 5 = 15$
29. $6 \times 3 = 18$
30. $2 \times 7 = 14$
31. $7 \times 5 = 35$
32. $7 \times 1 = 7$
33. $1 \times 2 = 2$
34. $5 \times 7 = 35$
35. $4 \times 2 = 8$
36. $8 \times 8 = 64$
37. $9 \times 8 = 72$
38. $6 \times 4 = 24$
39. $2 \times 5 = 10$
40. $4 \times 7 = 28$
41. $6 \times 6 = 36$
42. $1 \times 9 = 9$
43. $8 \times 5 = 40$
44. $6 \times 8 = 48$
45. $7 \times 3 = 21$
46. $4 \times 4 = 16$
47. $6 \times 5 = 30$
48. $4 \times 9 = 36$
49. $2 \times 4 = 8$
50. $0 \times 4 = 0$

Use any time after Topic 1. BFTT 2 of 12 

Name ______________________

Basic-Facts Timed Test 3

Give each answer.

1. $3 + 7 = 10$
2. $8 + 5 = 13$
3. $7 + 3 = 10$
4. $4 + 9 = 13$
5. $0 + 4 = 4$
6. $10 - 3 = 7$
7. $11 - 7 = 4$
8. $14 - 5 = 9$
9. $6 - 2 = 4$
10. $12 - 9 = 3$
11. $7 + 5 = 12$
12. $6 + 6 = 12$
13. $8 + 9 = 17$
14. $6 + 4 = 10$
15. $4 + 7 = 11$
16. $15 - 7 = 8$
17. $10 - 7 = 3$
18. $15 - 9 = 6$
19. $13 - 4 = 9$
20. $12 - 6 = 6$
21. $6 + 8 = 14$
22. $7 + 9 = 16$
23. $8 + 6 = 14$
24. $4 + 5 = 9$
25. $9 + 9 = 18$
26. $1 \times 6 = 6$
27. $7 \times 9 = 63$
28. $5 \times 4 = 20$
29. $45 \div 5 = 9$
30. $6 \times 7 = 42$
31. $72 \div 8 = 9$
32. $56 \div 7 = 8$
33. $42 \div 6 = 7$
34. $0 \times 8 = 0$
35. $35 \div 7 = 5$
36. $48 \div 6 = 8$
37. $5 \times 0 = 0$
38. $0 \div 4 = 0$
39. $6 \times 9 = 54$
40. $18 \div 6 = 3$
41. $36 \div 9 = 4$
42. $3 \times 9 = 27$
43. $6 \times 4 = 24$
44. $7 \div 7 = 1$
45. $30 \div 6 = 5$
46. $8 \times 7 = 56$
47. $9 \times 4 = 36$
48. $7 \div 1 = 7$
49. $24 \div 6 = 4$
50. $6 \times 6 = 36$

Use any time after Topic 1. BFTT 3 of 12 

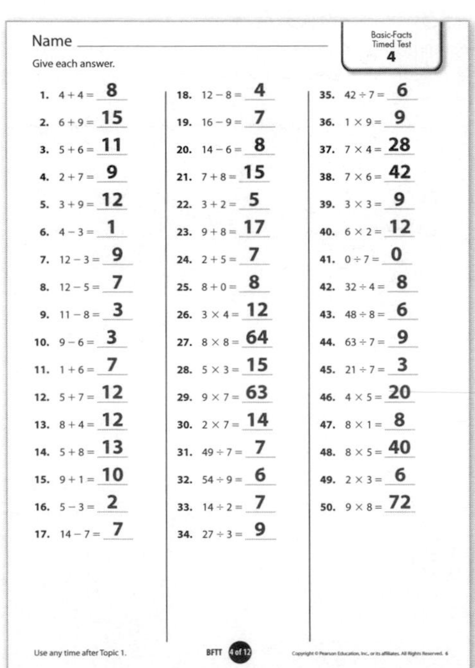

Name ______________________

Basic-Facts Timed Test 4

Give each answer.

1. $4 + 4 = 8$
2. $6 + 9 = 15$
3. $5 + 6 = 11$
4. $2 + 7 = 9$
5. $3 + 9 = 12$
6. $4 - 3 = 1$
7. $12 - 3 = 9$
8. $12 - 5 = 7$
9. $11 - 8 = 3$
10. $9 - 6 = 3$
11. $1 + 6 = 7$
12. $5 + 7 = 12$
13. $8 + 4 = 12$
14. $5 + 8 = 13$
15. $9 + 1 = 10$
16. $5 - 3 = 2$
17. $14 - 7 = 7$
18. $12 - 8 = 4$
19. $16 - 9 = 7$
20. $14 - 6 = 8$
21. $7 + 8 = 15$
22. $3 + 2 = 5$
23. $9 + 8 = 17$
24. $2 + 5 = 7$
25. $8 + 0 = 8$
26. $3 \times 4 = 12$
27. $8 \times 8 = 64$
28. $5 \times 3 = 15$
29. $9 \times 7 = 63$
30. $2 \times 7 = 14$
31. $49 \div 7 = 7$
32. $54 \div 9 = 6$
33. $14 \div 2 = 7$
34. $27 \div 3 = 9$
35. $42 \div 7 = 6$
36. $1 \times 9 = 9$
37. $7 \times 4 = 28$
38. $7 \times 6 = 42$
39. $3 \times 3 = 9$
40. $6 \times 2 = 12$
41. $0 \div 7 = 0$
42. $32 \div 4 = 8$
43. $48 \div 8 = 6$
44. $63 \div 7 = 9$
45. $21 \div 7 = 3$
46. $4 \times 5 = 20$
47. $8 \times 1 = 8$
48. $8 \times 5 = 40$
49. $2 \times 3 = 6$
50. $9 \times 8 = 72$

Use any time after Topic 1. BFTT 4 of 12 

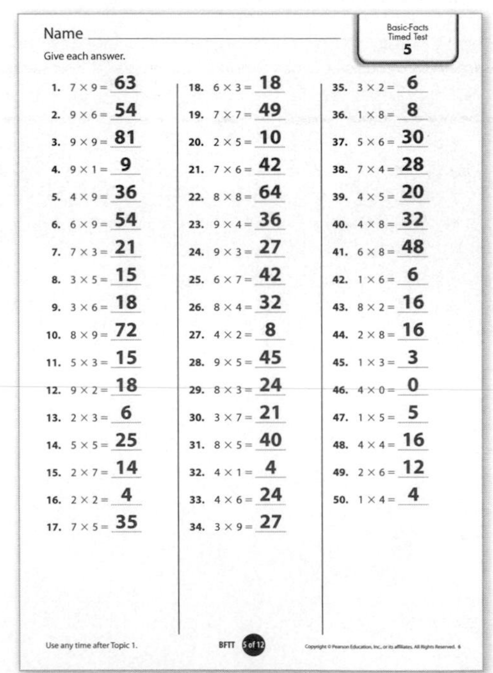

Name ______________________

Basic-Facts Timed Test 5

Give each answer.

1. $7 \times 9 = 63$
2. $9 \times 6 = 54$
3. $9 \times 9 = 81$
4. $9 \times 1 = 9$
5. $4 \times 9 = 36$
6. $6 \times 9 = 54$
7. $7 \times 3 = 21$
8. $3 \times 5 = 15$
9. $3 \times 6 = 18$
10. $8 \times 9 = 72$
11. $5 \times 3 = 15$
12. $9 \times 2 = 18$
13. $2 \times 3 = 6$
14. $5 \times 5 = 25$
15. $2 \times 7 = 14$
16. $2 \times 2 = 4$
17. $7 \times 5 = 35$
18. $6 \times 3 = 18$
19. $7 \times 7 = 49$
20. $2 \times 5 = 10$
21. $7 \times 6 = 42$
22. $8 \times 8 = 64$
23. $9 \times 4 = 36$
24. $9 \times 3 = 27$
25. $6 \times 7 = 42$
26. $8 \times 4 = 32$
27. $4 \times 2 = 8$
28. $9 \times 5 = 45$
29. $8 \times 3 = 24$
30. $3 \times 7 = 21$
31. $8 \times 5 = 40$
32. $4 \times 1 = 4$
33. $4 \times 6 = 24$
34. $3 \times 9 = 27$
35. $3 \times 2 = 6$
36. $1 \times 8 = 8$
37. $5 \times 6 = 30$
38. $7 \times 4 = 28$
39. $4 \times 5 = 20$
40. $4 \times 8 = 32$
41. $6 \times 8 = 48$
42. $1 \times 6 = 6$
43. $8 \times 2 = 16$
44. $2 \times 8 = 16$
45. $1 \times 3 = 3$
46. $4 \times 0 = 0$
47. $1 \times 5 = 5$
48. $4 \times 4 = 16$
49. $2 \times 6 = 12$
50. $1 \times 4 = 4$

Use any time after Topic 1. BFTT 5 of 12 

Name ______________________

Basic-Facts Timed Test 6

Give each answer.

1. $8 \times 3 = 24$
2. $9 \times 4 = 36$
3. $7 \times 8 = 56$
4. $6 \times 2 = 12$
5. $5 \times 9 = 45$
6. $7 \times 4 = 28$
7. $2 \times 1 = 2$
8. $3 \times 2 = 6$
9. $9 \times 9 = 81$
10. $8 \times 4 = 32$
11. $2 \times 9 = 18$
12. $8 \times 5 = 40$
13. $7 \times 7 = 49$
14. $7 \times 2 = 14$
15. $9 \times 3 = 27$
16. $1 \times 6 = 6$
17. $3 \times 0 = 0$
18. $5 \times 7 = 35$
19. $7 \times 9 = 63$
20. $9 \times 2 = 18$
21. $3 \times 3 = 9$
22. $6 \times 5 = 30$
23. $5 \times 5 = 25$
24. $8 \times 2 = 16$
25. $5 \times 8 = 40$
26. $16 \div 4 = 4$
27. $30 \div 5 = 6$
28. $10 \div 5 = 2$
29. $24 \div 3 = 8$
30. $42 \div 7 = 6$
31. $16 \div 2 = 8$
32. $6 \div 6 = 1$
33. $81 \div 9 = 9$
34. $35 \div 5 = 7$
35. $0 \div 2 = 0$
36. $21 \div 3 = 7$
37. $7 \div 1 = 7$
38. $56 \div 8 = 7$
39. $8 \div 2 = 4$
40. $27 \div 3 = 9$
41. $48 \div 6 = 8$
42. $28 \div 4 = 7$
43. $10 \div 2 = 5$
44. $15 \div 5 = 3$
45. $18 \div 3 = 6$
46. $24 \div 6 = 4$
47. $2 \div 2 = 1$
48. $24 \div 4 = 6$
49. $63 \div 7 = 9$
50. $36 \div 4 = 9$

Use any time after Topic 1. BFTT 6 of 12 

# Basic-Facts Timed Tests, 7–12

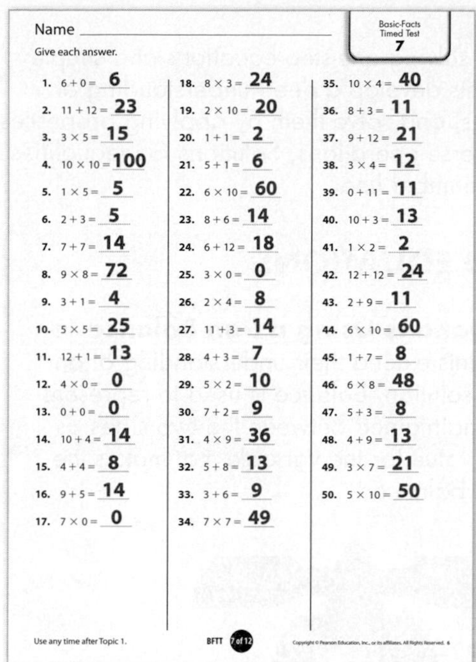

Name ____________

Basic-Facts Timed Test 7

Give each answer.

1. 6 + 0 = 6
2. 11 + 12 = 23
3. 3 × 5 = 15
4. 10 × 10 = 100
5. 1 × 5 = 5
6. 2 + 3 = 5
7. 7 + 7 = 14
8. 9 × 8 = 72
9. 3 + 1 = 4
10. 5 × 5 = 25
11. 12 + 1 = 13
12. 4 × 0 = 0
13. 0 + 0 = 0
14. 10 + 4 = 14
15. 4 + 4 = 8
16. 9 + 5 = 14
17. 7 × 0 = 0
18. 8 × 3 = 24
19. 2 × 10 = 20
20. 1 + 1 = 2
21. 5 + 1 = 6
22. 6 × 10 = 60
23. 8 + 6 = 14
24. 6 + 12 = 18
25. 3 × 0 = 0
26. 2 × 4 = 8
27. 11 + 3 = 14
28. 4 + 3 = 7
29. 5 × 2 = 10
30. 7 + 2 = 9
31. 4 × 9 = 36
32. 5 + 8 = 13
33. 3 + 6 = 9
34. 7 × 7 = 49
35. 10 × 4 = 40
36. 8 + 3 = 11
37. 9 + 12 = 21
38. 3 × 4 = 12
39. 0 + 11 = 11
40. 10 + 3 = 13
41. 1 × 2 = 2
42. 12 + 12 = 24
43. 2 + 9 = 11
44. 6 × 10 = 60
45. 1 + 7 = 8
46. 6 × 8 = 48
47. 5 + 3 = 8
48. 4 + 9 = 13
49. 3 × 7 = 21
50. 5 × 10 = 50

Use any time after Topic 1. BFTT 7 of 12



Name ____________

Basic-Facts Timed Test 8

Give each answer.

1. 3 × 3 = 9
2. 0 + 10 = 10
3. 5 × 9 = 45
4. 4 + 10 = 14
5. 3 × 6 = 18
6. 12 + 11 = 23
7. 5 + 2 = 7
8. 3 + 2 = 5
9. 6 × 9 = 54
10. 1 × 1 = 1
11. 10 + 2 = 12
12. 6 × 11 = 66
13. 10 × 9 = 90
14. 7 + 1 = 8
15. 4 × 8 = 32
16. 9 + 11 = 20
17. 2 + 10 = 12
18. 1 + 6 = 7
19. 5 × 6 = 30
20. 8 + 7 = 15
21. 8 + 2 = 10
22. 11 + 11 = 22
23. 3 + 7 = 10
24. 10 + 5 = 15
25. 8 × 4 = 32
26. 2 × 3 = 6
27. 6 + 1 = 7
28. 4 + 5 = 9
29. 11 + 4 = 15
30. 4 × 1 = 4
31. 5 + 7 = 12
32. 7 × 6 = 42
33. 7 + 8 = 15
34. 10 × 3 = 30
35. 1 + 2 = 3
36. 1 × 6 = 6
37. 4 + 2 = 6
38. 9 × 9 = 81
39. 3 × 1 = 3
40. 2 × 9 = 18
41. 12 + 2 = 14
42. 6 × 9 = 54
43. 0 + 1 = 1
44. 6 + 11 = 17
45. 3 × 6 = 18
46. 5 + 2 = 7
47. 2 + 4 = 6
48. 7 × 1 = 7
49. 5 × 1 = 5
50. 9 + 6 = 15

Use any time after Topic 1. BFTT 8 of 12



Name ____________

Basic-Facts Timed Test 9

Give each answer.

1. 5 × 8 = 40
2. 2 × 2 = 4
3. 4 × 7 = 28
4. 3 × 5 = 15
5. 1 + 8 = 9
6. 8 + 1 = 9
7. 6 × 4 = 24
8. 5 × 0 = 0
9. 9 × 10 = 90
10. 7 + 0 = 7
11. 4 + 1 = 5
12. 10 × 8 = 80
13. 0 + 2 = 2
14. 8 + 8 = 16
15. 7 + 9 = 16
16. 3 × 2 = 6
17. 1 + 3 = 4
18. 9 + 7 = 16
19. 7 × 2 = 14
20. 4 + 11 = 15
21. 6 × 6 = 36
22. 11 + 5 = 16
23. 6 + 2 = 8
24. 6 + 10 = 16
25. 2 + 5 = 7
26. 10 + 6 = 16
27. 2 × 8 = 16
28. 11 + 10 = 21
29. 8 × 5 = 40
30. 1 × 7 = 7
31. 5 + 3 = 8
32. 4 × 2 = 8
33. 3 + 3 = 6
34. 6 × 8 = 48
35. 10 + 1 = 11
36. 5 + 1 = 6
37. 12 + 10 = 22
38. 3 × 7 = 21
39. 5 + 6 = 11
40. 3 × 2 = 6
41. 2 + 11 = 13
42. 12 + 3 = 15
43. 0 + 9 = 9
44. 1 × 0 = 0
45. 10 × 2 = 20
46. 9 + 10 = 19
47. 5 × 7 = 35
48. 7 × 5 = 35
49. 4 + 6 = 10
50. 3 + 8 = 11

Use any time after Topic 1. BFTT 9 of 12



Name ____________

Basic-Facts Timed Test 10

Give each answer.

1. 4 × 6 = 24
2. 8 + 4 = 12
3. 3 × 4 = 12
4. 4 + 12 = 16
5. 6 × 0 = 0
6. 0 + 3 = 3
7. 3 + 9 = 12
8. 2 × 1 = 2
9. 10 × 7 = 70
10. 3 × 3 = 9
11. 2 + 6 = 8
12. 7 × 3 = 21
13. 5 + 4 = 9
14. 6 + 3 = 9
15. 8 + 9 = 17
16. 9 × 7 = 63
17. 9 + 8 = 17
18. 2 × 7 = 14
19. 4 × 3 = 12
20. 11 + 6 = 17
21. 10 × 1 = 10
22. 1 × 8 = 8
23. 12 + 9 = 21
24. 12 + 4 = 16
25. 7 + 3 = 10
26. 11 + 9 = 20
27. 5 × 3 = 15
28. 10 + 7 = 17
29. 5 × 8 = 40
30. 8 × 6 = 48
31. 6 + 9 = 15
32. 3 × 8 = 24
33. 6 × 7 = 42
34. 4 + 0 = 4
35. 7 + 10 = 17
36. 0 + 8 = 8
37. 1 × 3 = 3
38. 6 × 5 = 30
39. 3 + 4 = 7
40. 2 + 12 = 14
41. 5 + 0 = 5
42. 9 + 9 = 18
43. 6 × 3 = 18
44. 7 × 4 = 28
45. 1 + 9 = 10
46. 3 × 1 = 3
47. 5 + 9 = 14
48. 10 + 0 = 10
49. 1 + 4 = 5
50. 4 + 7 = 11

Use any time after Topic 1. BFTT 10 of 12



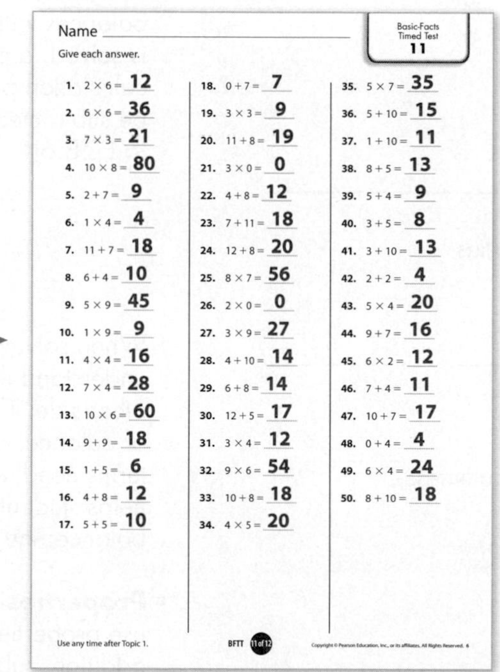

Name ____________

Basic-Facts Timed Test 11

Give each answer.

1. 2 × 6 = 12
2. 6 × 6 = 36
3. 7 × 3 = 21
4. 10 × 8 = 80
5. 2 + 7 = 9
6. 1 × 4 = 4
7. 11 + 7 = 18
8. 6 + 4 = 10
9. 5 × 9 = 45
10. 1 × 9 = 9
11. 4 × 4 = 16
12. 7 × 4 = 28
13. 10 × 6 = 60
14. 9 + 9 = 18
15. 1 + 5 = 6
16. 4 + 8 = 12
17. 5 + 5 = 10
18. 0 + 7 = 7
19. 3 × 3 = 9
20. 11 + 8 = 19
21. 3 × 0 = 0
22. 4 + 8 = 12
23. 7 + 11 = 18
24. 12 + 8 = 20
25. 8 × 7 = 56
26. 2 × 0 = 0
27. 3 × 9 = 27
28. 4 + 10 = 14
29. 6 + 8 = 14
30. 12 + 5 = 17
31. 3 × 4 = 12
32. 9 × 6 = 54
33. 10 + 8 = 18
34. 4 × 5 = 20
35. 5 × 7 = 35
36. 5 + 10 = 15
37. 1 + 10 = 11
38. 8 + 5 = 13
39. 5 + 4 = 9
40. 3 + 5 = 8
41. 3 + 10 = 13
42. 2 + 2 = 4
43. 5 × 4 = 20
44. 9 + 7 = 16
45. 6 × 2 = 12
46. 7 + 4 = 11
47. 10 + 7 = 17
48. 0 + 4 = 4
49. 6 × 4 = 24
50. 8 + 10 = 18

Use any time after Topic 1. BFTT 11 of 12



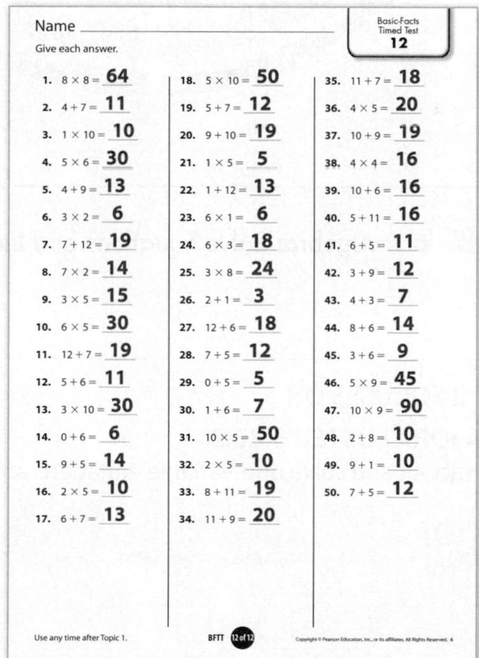

Name ____________

Basic-Facts Timed Test 12

Give each answer.

1. 8 × 8 = 64
2. 4 + 7 = 11
3. 1 × 10 = 10
4. 5 × 6 = 30
5. 4 + 9 = 13
6. 3 × 2 = 6
7. 7 + 12 = 19
8. 7 × 2 = 14
9. 3 × 5 = 15
10. 6 × 5 = 30
11. 12 + 7 = 19
12. 5 + 6 = 11
13. 3 × 10 = 30
14. 0 + 6 = 6
15. 9 + 5 = 14
16. 2 × 5 = 10
17. 6 + 7 = 13
18. 5 × 10 = 50
19. 5 + 7 = 12
20. 9 + 10 = 19
21. 1 × 5 = 5
22. 1 + 12 = 13
23. 6 × 1 = 6
24. 6 × 3 = 18
25. 3 × 8 = 24
26. 2 + 1 = 3
27. 12 + 6 = 18
28. 7 + 5 = 12
29. 0 + 5 = 5
30. 1 + 6 = 7
31. 10 × 5 = 50
32. 2 × 5 = 10
33. 8 + 11 = 19
34. 11 + 9 = 20
35. 11 + 7 = 18
36. 4 × 5 = 20
37. 10 + 9 = 19
38. 4 × 4 = 16
39. 10 + 6 = 16
40. 5 + 11 = 16
41. 6 + 5 = 11
42. 3 + 9 = 12
43. 4 + 3 = 7
44. 8 + 6 = 14
45. 3 + 6 = 9
46. 5 × 9 = 45
47. 10 × 9 = 90
48. 2 + 8 = 10
49. 9 + 1 = 10
50. 7 + 5 = 12

Use any time after Topic 1. BFTT 12 of 12

# MAJOR CLUSTER 6.EE.B

## MATH BACKGROUND: FOCUS

FCR FOCUS | COHERENCE | RIGOR

 MAJOR CLUSTER  SUPPORTING CLUSTER  ADDITIONAL CLUSTER

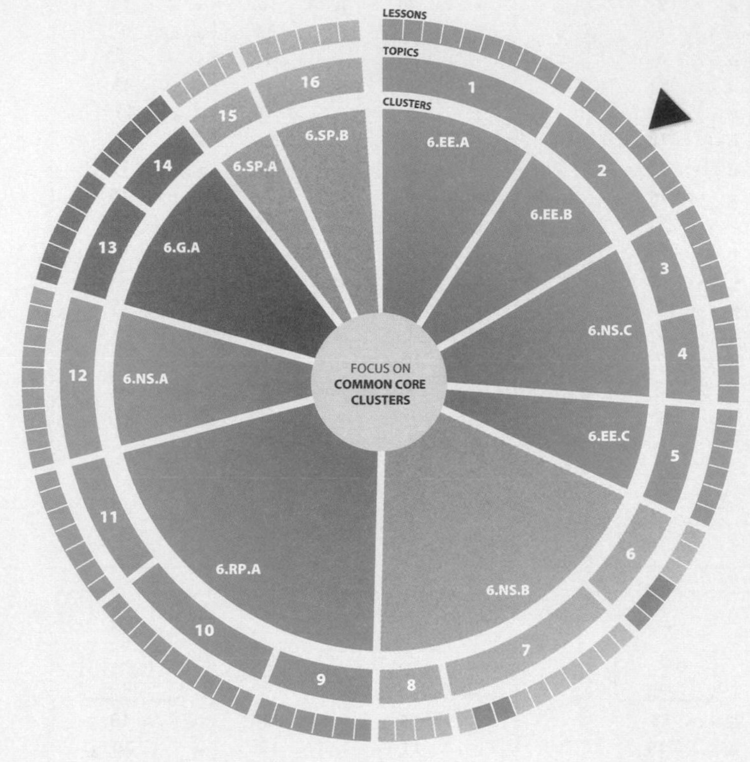


**TOPIC 2** **Algebra: Solve Equations and Inequalities**

TOPIC 2 FOCUSES ON

 **MAJOR CLUSTER 6.EE.B**

Reason about and solve one-variable equations and inequalities.

**Content Focus in enVisionmath2.0**

Topic 2 focuses on solving one-step equations and simple inequalities. Students develop a deep understanding of algebraic equations, and solve them by applying properties of equality and inverse operations. Solutions to inequalities are graphed on a number line.

## UNDERSTAND EQUATIONS

- **Represent Equations Using a Pan Balance** In Lesson 2-1, students extend their understanding of an equation and its solution. Balance is used to represent how equality is maintained between the two sides as students find the value for the variable that makes the equation true, or balanced.

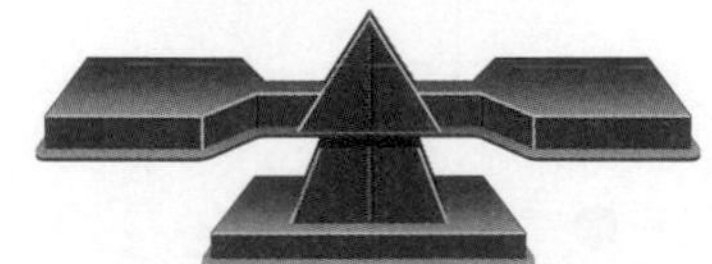

In Lesson 2-3, the idea is formalized that an unknown balances with the value of its solution. When an equation is solved, a pan balance representation can replicate the calculation physically. For example, equal quantities can be subtracted from both sides while maintaining balance. (6.EE.B.6)

$$\begin{aligned} x + 24 &= 42 \\ x + 24 - 24 &= 42 - 24 \\ x &= 42 - 24 \\ x &= 18 \end{aligned}$$

When solving an equation, it is important to know and understand that one side of the equation is equal to the other side. Thus, the equal sign (=) serves as an indicator of balance, or equality. Bar diagrams can represent the terms needing to be balanced in an equation. Substitution helps students determine the value that achieves this balance: the solution of the equation. (6.EE.B.5, 6.EE.B.7)

- **Properties of Equality** In Lesson 2-2, students use properties to write equivalent equations involving addition, subtraction, multiplication, and division. This lesson builds on the previous lesson's concept that the two sides of an equation must balance. These properties are foundational for using operations to solve equations. (6.EE.B.6)

- **Solve Equations** Lesson 2-3 focuses on solving addition and subtraction equations, and Lesson 2-4 focuses on solving multiplication and division equations. Addition and subtraction have an inverse relationship and multiplication and division have an inverse relationship. These ideas connect with the properties of equality previously presented in Lesson 2-2. A pan balance is once again used to represent the solving of equations. Lessons 2-3 and 2-4 provide a natural connection to Lessons 2-1 and 2-2, which are more focused on understanding equations and properties of equality. (6.EE.B.5, 6.EE.B.6)

  In Lesson 2-5, students solve equations with fractions and mixed numbers. As in their work with whole-number equations, students use inverse operations and properties of equality to solve equations with fractions and mixed numbers. Students also learn how to use reciprocals to solve multiplication equations involving fractions. To solve an equation such as $\frac{3}{8}n = 15$, instead of dividing both sides of the equation by $\frac{3}{8}$, we multiply both sides by the reciprocal, $\frac{8}{3}$, because multiplying by the reciprocal is equivalent to dividing by a fraction. (6.EE.B.7)

$$\frac{3}{8}n = 15$$

$$\left(\frac{8}{3}\right)\frac{3}{8}n = \left(\frac{8}{3}\right)15$$

$$n = \frac{8}{\cancel{3}_1} \times \frac{\cancel{15}^5}{1}$$

$$n = 40$$

## UNDERSTAND INEQUALITIES

- **Write and Solve Inequalities** In Lessons 2-6 and 2-7, students write and solve inequalities. While students have used the $<$, $=$, and $>$ symbols since the primary grades, they have had limited experience with the use of the $\leq$ (less than or equal to), $\geq$ (greater than or equal to), and $\neq$ (not equal) symbols.

  Both Lessons 2-6 and 2-7 represent "first time" opportunities to consider inequalities both conceptually and abstractly for this grade level and are important as a foundation for algebra. (6.EE.B.5, 6.EE.B.8)

- **Number Lines and Inequalities** In Lesson 2-6, the number line is used to show some of the solutions to an inequality. In Lesson 2-7, the number line is used as a graphing representation of all solutions to an inequality. (6.EE.B.8)

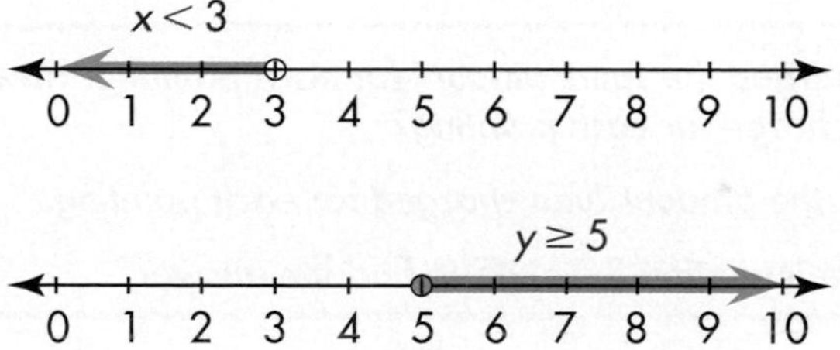


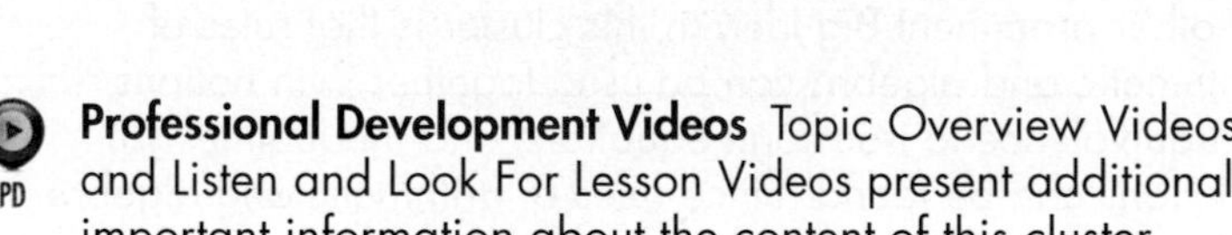


**Professional Development Videos** Topic Overview Videos and Listen and Look For Lesson Videos present additional important information about the content of this cluster.

# MAJOR CLUSTER 6.EE.B

## MATH BACKGROUND: COHERENCE

FOCUS | FCR COHERENCE | RIGOR

### Content Coherence in enVisionmath2.0

Students learn best when ideas are connected in a coherent curriculum. This coherence is achieved through various types of connections including connections within clusters, across clusters, across domains, and across grades.

**BIG IDEAS IN GRADES K–6**

Big Ideas are the conceptual underpinnings of **enVision**math**2.0** and provide conceptual cohesion of the content. Big Ideas connect Essential Understandings throughout the program.

While there are several Big Ideas that connect many of the lessons within this cluster, the most prominent are the ones that involve equations and inequalities.

One such Big Idea is that variables can be used to stand for numbers. Many mathematical and real-world situations can be represented using variables, operations, and numbers in expressions and equations. Below is an example.

> ***Juan charged the same amount for each painting. How much did he charge for each painting?***
>
> ***Let x = the amount Juan charged for each painting.***
>
> ***Solve the equation 3x = 45 to find the answer.***

Another prominent Big Idea in this cluster is that rules of arithmetic and algebra can be used together with notions of equivalence to transform equations and inequalities so solutions can be found. Since rules of arithmetic and algebra were applied to $3x = 45$, below, all three of the equations are equivalent. The last one reveals the solution.

$$3x = 45$$
$$3x \div 3 = 45 \div 3$$
$$x = 15$$

Students come to understand these Big Ideas as the foundation for their work with equations and inequalities.

For a complete list of Big Ideas, see pages 110–111 in the *Teacher's Edition Program Overview.*

### LOOK BACK

*How does Topic 2 connect to what students learned earlier?*

**GRADE 5**

- **Write and Interpret Numerical Expressions** In Topic 13, students developed their understanding of numerical expressions. This prepared students to become proficient with equations, comparing and ordering numbers, and operations with whole numbers and fractions. engages students in multiple lessons involving numerical expressions. (5.OA.A.1)

Mrs. Katz is planning her family's trip to the museum. She made a list of the expenses. Then she wrote the following expression to show how she can calculate the total cost.

$6 \times (4.20 + 8 + 12 + 3.50)$

How many people do you think are in the family? How can you tell?

**EARLIER IN GRADE 6**

- **Numerical and Algebraic Expressions** In Topic 1, students developed understanding of algebraic expressions, including the concepts of equivalent expressions, simplifying expressions, and formulas. (6.EE.A)

## TOPIC 2

*How is content connected within Topic 2?*

- **Understand Equations and Properties of Equations** In Lesson 2-1, students develop an understanding of how to ensure that one side of an equation balances with the other side. In Lesson 2-2, students learn how properties of equality are helpful in solving equations. These two lessons provide the conceptual understanding needed for Lessons 2-3, 2-4, and 2-5, which all involve solving equations. (6.EE.B.5)
- **Solve Equations** In Lessons 2-3, 2-4, and 2-5, students apply their understanding of equations to solve equations that involve addition and subtraction, multiplication and division, and fractions and mixed numbers. (6.EE.B.7)

| Addition Equation | Subtraction Equation |
|---|---|
| $h + \frac{3}{5} = \frac{2}{3}$ | $y - \frac{2}{3} = \frac{4}{9}$ |
| $h + \frac{3}{5} - \frac{3}{5} = \frac{2}{3} - \frac{3}{5}$ | $y - \frac{2}{3} + \frac{2}{3} = \frac{4}{9} + \frac{2}{3}$ |
| $h = \frac{1}{15}$ | $y = 1\frac{1}{9}$ |
| **Multiplication Equation** | **Division Equation** |
| $\frac{3}{4}t = 9$ | $\frac{r}{5} = 14$ |
| $\frac{4}{3} \cdot \frac{3}{4}t = \frac{4}{3} \cdot \frac{9}{1}$ | $\frac{5}{1} \cdot \frac{1}{5}r = \frac{5}{1} \cdot \frac{14}{1}$ |
| $t = 12$ | $r = 70$ |

- **Inequalities** In Lessons 2-6 and 2-7, students extend prior work with expressions and equations to include writing and solving inequalities. Students also use number lines to graph inequalities. (6.EE.B.8)

## LOOK AHEAD

*How does Topic 2 connect to what students will learn later?*

### LATER IN GRADE 6

- **Graphs of Equations** In Topic 5, students will graph equations. (6.EE.C)

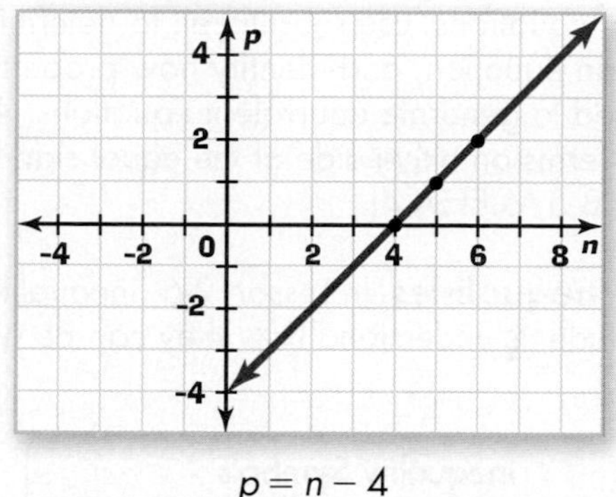


$p = n - 4$

- **Expressions and Equations Involving Division** In Topic 6, students will evaluate expressions involving division and solve equations involving division. (6.EE.A.2c, 6.EE.B.7)

| x | 2 | 3 | 5 | 7 | 9 |
|---|---|---|---|---|---|
| $\frac{48x + 16 + 35}{3}$ | 49 | 65 | 97 | 129 | 161 |

- **Expressions and Equations Involving Decimals** In Topic 7, students will evaluate expressions involving decimals and solve equations involving decimals. (6.EE.A.2c, 6.EE.B.7)

$$13m = 7.15$$
$$13m \div 13 = 7.15 \div 13$$
$$m = 0.55$$

Content Rigor in enVisionmath2.0

A rigorous curriculum emphasizes conceptual understanding, procedural skill and fluency, and applications.

### CONCEPTUAL UNDERSTANDING

- **Understand Equations and Properties of Equality** In Lessons 2-1 and 2-2, students learn the conceptual prerequisites for solving equations. Students understand the definition of equations, use substitution to determine the solution to an equation, and identify how properties of equality are used to generate equivalent equations. A key concept is that terms on either side of the equal sign (=) must balance. (6.EE.B.5, 6.EE.A.4)

- **Understand Inequalities** In Lesson 2-6, inequalities are defined, and students understand how they can be written. (6.EE.B.8)

| Inequality Symbols | |
|---|---|
| Symbol | Meaning |
| $<$ | is less than |
| $\leq$ | is less than or equal to |
| $>$ | is greater than |
| $\geq$ | is greater than or equal to |
| $\neq$ | is not equal to |

### PROCEDURAL SKILL AND FLUENCY

There are no standards in this cluster that call for fluency.

- **Solve Addition and Subtraction Equations** In Lesson 2-3, students use the concepts of equations and equality to solve addition and subtraction equations. Students recognize that one operation has an inverse relationship with the other. (6.EE.B.7)

$$n - 19 = 34$$
$$n - 19 + 19 = 34 + 19$$
$$n = 53$$

- **Solve Multiplication and Division Equations** In Lesson 2-4, students use concepts of equations and equality to solve multiplication and division equations. Once again, students recognize that one operation is the inverse of the other. (6.EE.B.7)

- **Solve Equations with Fractions and Mixed Numbers** In Lesson 2-5, students use and extend the concepts of equations and equality to solve addition, subtraction, multiplication, and division equations involving fractions and mixed numbers. (6.EE.B.7)

- **Solve Inequalities** In Lesson 2-7, students use the conceptual understandings related to writing inequalities to solve inequalities. Number lines are used as a representational tool for graphing inequalities. (6.EE.B.8)

### APPLICATIONS

- **Use Equations and Inequalities to Solve Problems** Throughout Topic 2, students write and solve equations and inequalities to solve problems that place the mathematics learned within a real-world context. (6.EE.B.7, 6.EE.B.8)

# MATH PRACTICES

MP

**Connecting Math Practices and Content Standards in enVisionmath2.0**

Math practices and content standards are connected within all lessons including lessons that focus on math practices.

## MATH PRACTICES WITHIN LESSONS

- **MP.1 Make sense of problems and persevere in solving them.**

  Students make sense of problems and then persevere by using expressions and equations to help move toward a solution. (e.g., p. 127, Items 1 and 2)

- **MP.2 Reason abstractly and quantitatively.**

  Students use abstract and quantitative reasoning as they solve equations and inequalities. (e.g., p. 119, Look Back!)

- **MP.3 Construct viable arguments and critique the reasoning of others.**

  Students construct arguments to justify solutions to equations and inequalities. (e.g., p. 86, Item 17)

- **MP.4 Model with mathematics.**

  Students model with mathematics when they draw on the math they know to write equations and inequalities. (e.g., p. 94, Item 9)

- **MP.5 Use appropriate tools strategically.**

  Students use tools such as pan balances, bar diagrams, and number lines to help represent equations and inequalities. (e.g., p. 119, Solve and Share)

- **MP.6 Attend to precision.**

  Students attend to precision when they recognize that an equation has one solution, and that an inequality may have an infinite number of solutions. (e.g., p. 113, Look Back!)

- **MP.7 Look for and make use of structure.**

  Students understand the general structure of equations and inequalities they use to solve pre-algebraic problems. (e.g., p. 89, Look Back!)

- **MP.8 Look for and express regularity in repeated reasoning.**

  Students use repeated reasoning when they generalize their work with equations and inequalities to all operations and to whole numbers and fractions. (e.g., p. 109, Item 1)

## LESSON THAT FOCUSES ON MATH PRACTICES

- **Lesson 2-8** This lesson focuses on MP.1. Making sense of problems and persevering in their solution is the key focus of this lesson, which involves writing and solving equations in the problem solving process.

### Thinking Habits

*Be a good thinker! These questions can help you.*

- What do I need to find?
- What do I know?
- What's my plan for solving the problem?
- What else can I try if I get stuck?
- How can I check that my solution makes sense?

Revisit the information about MP.1 in these other resources:

- **Math Practices and Problem Solving Handbook** before Topic 1; includes Math Practices Proficiency Rubrics.
- **Math Practices Posters** to display in your classroom
- MP **Math Practices Animations,** one for each math practice, available at PearsonRealize.com.

# MAJOR CLUSTER 6.EE.B

## DIFFERENTIATED INSTRUCTION

 Intervention  On-Level  Advanced

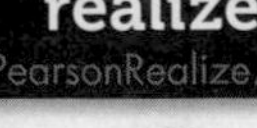

 Learn  Practice Buddy  Tools  Assessment Games

### Ongoing Intervention

**During the core lesson,** monitor progress, reteach as needed, and extend students' thinking.

**Guiding Questions**

- **In the Teacher's Edition** Guiding questions are used to monitor understanding during instruction.

**Online Guiding Questions** Guiding questions are also in the online Visual Learning Animation Plus.

**Prevent Misconceptions**
This feature in the Teacher's Edition is embedded in the guiding questions.

**Error Intervention: If... then...**
This feature in the Teacher's Edition is provided during Guided Practice. It spotlights common errors and gives suggestions for addressing them.

**Reteaching**
Reteaching sets are at the end of the topic in the Student's Edition. They provide additional examples, reminders, and practice. Use these sets as needed before students do the Independent Practice.

**Higher Order Thinking**
These problems require students to think more deeply about the rich, conceptual knowledge developed in the lesson.

**Practice Buddy Online**

Online auto-scored practice is provided for each lesson. On-screen learning aids include Help Me Solve This and View an Example.

### Strategic Intervention

**At the end of the lesson,** assess to identify students' strengths and needs and then provide appropriate support.

**Quick Check**

**In the Student's Edition** Assess the lesson using 3 items checked in the Teacher's Edition.

**Online Quick Check** You can also assess the lesson using 5 online, machine-scored items.

**Intervention Activity** I
Teachers work with struggling students.

**Reteach to Build Understanding** I
This is a page of guided reteaching.

**Technology Center** I O A

**Digital Math Tools Activities** reinforce the lesson content or previously taught content using a suite of digital math tools.

**Online Games** provide practice on the lesson content or previously taught content.

**Homework and Practice** I O A
Use the leveled assignment to provide differentiated homework and practice.

*Additional resources to support differentiated instruction for on-level and advanced students include:*

**On-Level and Advanced Activity Centers** O A

- **Center Games** are provided in on-level and advanced versions.
- **Math and Science Activity** is related to the topic science theme introduced at the start of the topic.
- **Problem-Solving Reading Mat** is used with a lesson-specific activity.

### Intensive Intervention

**As needed,** provide more instruction that is on or below grade level for students who are struggling.

**Math Diagnosis and Intervention System 2.0**

- **Diagnosis** Use the diagnostic tests in the system. Also, use the item analysis charts given with program assessments at the start of a grade or topic, or at the end of a topic, group of topics, or the year.
- **Intervention Lessons** These two-page lessons include guided instruction followed by practice. The system includes lessons below, on, and above grade level.
- **Teacher Support** Teacher Notes provide the support needed to conduct a short lesson. The lesson focuses on vocabulary, concept development, and practice. The Teacher's Guide contains individual and class record forms and correlations to Student's Edition lessons.

**Resources for Fluency Success**

- A variety of print and digital resources are provided to ensure success on Common Core fluency standards. See Steps to Fluency Success on pages 271K–271N and 317E–317H.

# THE LANGUAGE OF MATH

PEARSON realize
PearsonRealize.com

Glossary

Games

## English Language Learners

**Provide ELL support** through visual learning throughout the program, ELL instruction in every lesson, and additional ideas in an ELL Toolkit.

### Visual Learning

The visual learning that is infused in **enVision**math**2.0** provides support for English language learners. This support includes a Visual Learning Animation Plus and a Visual Learning Bridge for each lesson.

### English Language Learners Instruction

Lessons provide instruction for English language learners at Beginning, Intermediate, and Advanced levels of English proficiency.

### English Language Learners Toolkit

This resource provides professional development and resources for supporting English language learners.

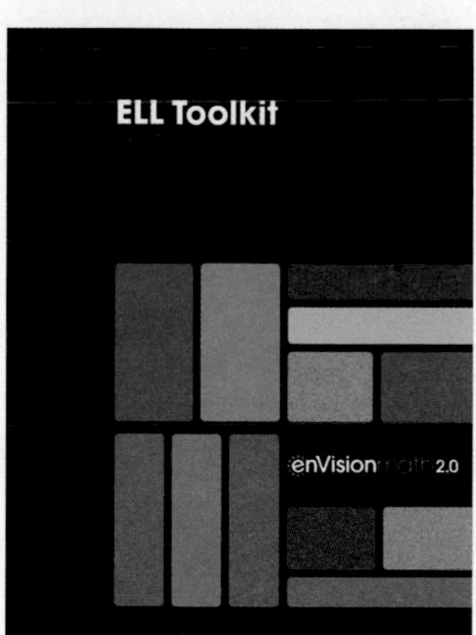
ELL Toolkit
enVision math 2.0

## Math Vocabulary

**Build math vocabulary** using the vocabulary cards, vocabulary activities, vocabulary review, and glossary plus the online glossary and vocabulary game.

### My Word Cards

Vocabulary cards for a topic are provided in the Student's Edition. Students use the example on the front of the card to complete the definition on the back.

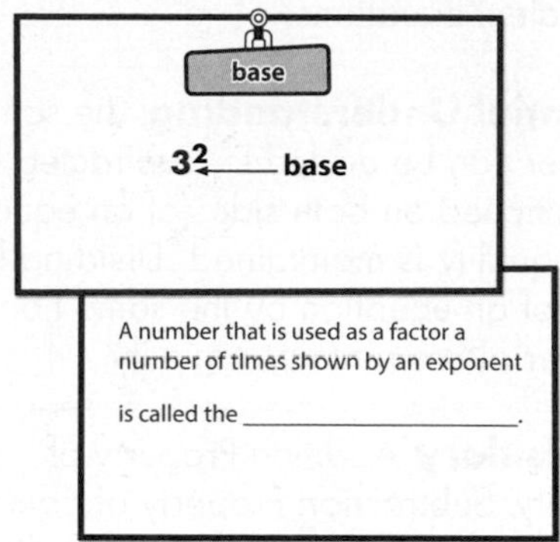
base
$3^2$ base
A number that is used as a factor a number of times shown by an exponent is called the ______.

### Vocabulary Activities

The Teacher's Edition provides vocabulary activities at the start of topics. These include activities for vocabulary in My Word Cards and/or activities for vocabulary in Review What You Know.

### Vocabulary Review

A page of vocabulary review is provided at the end of each topic. It reviews vocabulary used in the topic.

### Glossary

A glossary is provided at the back of the Student's Edition.

### Animated Glossary

Glossary

An online, bilingual, animated glossary uses motion and sound to build understanding of math vocabulary.

### Online Vocabulary Game

Games

An online vocabulary game is available in the Game Center.

## Math and Reading

**Connect reading and math** using a data-filled reading mat for the topic with accompanying activity masters and guide.

### Problem-Solving Reading Mats

There is a large, beautiful mat for each topic. At the start of the topic, help students become familiar with the mat and the vocabulary used by reading the mat aloud as students follow along. Use the Problem-Solving Reading Activity Guide for suggestions about how to use the mat.

### Problem-Solving Reading Activity

At the end of some lessons, a Problem-Solving Reading Activity provides a page of math problems to solve by using the data on the mat.

# TOPIC PLANNER

## ALGEBRA: SOLVE EQUATIONS AND INEQUALITIES

### Lesson 2-1

**UNDERSTAND EQUATIONS AND SOLUTIONS** pp. 83–88

**Content Standard 6.EE.B.5**
**Mathematical Practices MP.2, MP.3, MP.4, MP.6, MP.7, MP.8**

**Objective** Use substitution to find solutions to equations.

**Essential Understanding** A solution to an equation is a value for the variable that makes the equation true. An equation is true when the expressions or numbers on both sides of the equal sign have the same value.

**Vocabulary** Equation

**ELL Reading:** Use contextual support to develop vocabulary.

**Materials** Number cube

**On-Level and Advanced Activity Centers**
- Center Games

### Lesson 2-2

**PROPERTIES OF EQUALITY** pp. 89–94

**Content Standards 6.EE.A.4, 6.EE.B.7**
**Mathematical Practices MP.2, MP.3, MP.4, MP.7**

**Objective** Identify equivalent expressions and use the properties of equality to write equivalent equations.

**Essential Understanding** The same number can be added to, subtracted from, or multiplied on both sides of an equation and equality is maintained. Dividing both sides of an equation by the same non-zero number also maintains equality.

**Vocabulary** Addition Property of Equality, Subtraction Property of Equality, Multiplication Property of Equality, Division Property of Equality

**ELL Speaking:** Explain content area information.

**Materials** Number cube

**On-Level and Advanced Activity Centers**
- Problem-Solving Reading Mat

### Lesson 2-3

**SOLVE ADDITION AND SUBTRACTION EQUATIONS** pp. 95–100

**Content Standards 6.EE.B.7, 6.EE.B.6**
**Mathematical Practices MP.2, MP.3, MP.4, MP.5**

**Objective** Use inverse relationships and properties of equality to solve one-step addition and subtraction equations.

**Essential Understanding** Solving an equation involves finding the value of the variable that makes the equation true.

**Vocabulary** Inverse relationship

**ELL Listening:** Use visual support to confirm understanding.

**Materials** None

**On-Level and Advanced Activity Centers**
- Center Games

## LESSON RESOURCES

Digital

Print

- Student's Edition
- Daily Common Core Review
- Reteach to Build Understanding
- Center Games
- Math and Science Activity
- Problem-Solving Reading Mat
- Problem-Solving Reading Activity

Digital

- Listen and Look For PD Lesson Video
- Student's Edition eText
- Today's Challenge
- Solve & Share
- Visual Learning Animation Plus
- Animated Glossary
- Math Tools
- Practice Buddy Online Practice
- Quick Check
- Another Look Homework Video
- Math Games

Digital

## Lesson 2-4

SOLVE MULTIPLICATION AND DIVISION EQUATIONS pp. 101–106

**Content Standards 6.EE.B.7, 6.EE.B.6**
**Mathematical Practices MP.1, MP.4, MP.6, MP.7, MP.8**

**Objective** Use inverse relationships and properties of equality to solve one-step multiplication and division equations.

**Essential Understanding** Solving an equation involves finding the value of the variable that makes the equation true.

**Vocabulary** None

**ELL Listening:** Demonstrate listening comprehension by retelling.

**Materials** None

**On-Level and Advanced Activity Centers**
- Math and Science Activity

## Lesson 2-5

SOLVE EQUATIONS WITH FRACTIONS pp. 107–112

**Content Standards 6.EE.B.7, 6.EE.B.6**
**Mathematical Practices MP.1, MP.2, MP.4, MP.6, MP.7, MP.8**

**Objective** Solve one-step equations involving fractions and mixed numbers.

**Essential Understanding** Inverse relationships and properties of equality can be used to solve equations with fractions and mixed numbers.

**Vocabulary** Reciprocal

**ELL Learning Strategies:** Use and reuse academic language in meaningful ways when speaking.

**Materials** Index cards

**On-Level and Advanced Activity Centers**
- Center Games

## Lesson 2-6

WRITE INEQUALITIES pp. 113–118

**Content Standards 6.EE.B.8, 6.EE.B.5**
**Mathematical Practices MP.2, MP.3, MP.4, MP.6, MP.8**

**Objective** Write inequalities to describe mathematical or real-world situations.

**Essential Understanding** An inequality is a mathematical sentence that contains the inequality symbol $<$ (is less than), $>$ (is greater than), $\leq$ (is less than or equal to), $\geq$ (is greater than or equal to), or $\neq$ (is not equal to). An inequality describes a situation that has an infinite number of numerical possibilities.

**Vocabulary** Inequality

**ELL Learning Strategies:** Use prior experiences to understand meanings.

**Materials** Index cards, Number lines (TT 13)

**On-Level and Advanced Activity Centers**
- Problem-Solving Reading Mat

## TOPIC RESOURCES

Digital

Print

**Start of Topic**
- Math and Science Project
- Home-School Connection
- Review What You Know
- My Word Cards

**End of Topic**
- Fluency Practice Activity
- Vocabulary Review
- Reteaching
- Topic Assessment
- Topic Performance Assessment

Digital

**Start of Topic**
- Topic Overview PD Video

**End of Topic**
- Math Practices Animations
- Online Topic Assessment
- ExamView® Test Generator
- Practice Buddy Fluency Practice/Assessment

PearsonRealize.com

TOPIC 2

# TOPIC PLANNER

## ALGEBRA: SOLVE EQUATIONS AND INEQUALITIES

### Lesson 2-7

SOLVE INEQUALITIES pp. 119–124

Content Standards **6.EE.B.5, 6.EE.B.8**
Mathematical Practices **MP.2, MP.4, MP.5, MP.7**

**Objective** Describe solutions to an inequality and represent them on a number line.

**Essential Understanding** An inequality is a mathematical sentence that contains the inequality symbol $<$ (is less than), $>$ (is greater than), $\leq$ (is less than or equal to), $\geq$ (is greater than or equal to), or $\neq$ (is not equal to). An inequality describes a situation that has an infinite number of numerical possibilities.

**Vocabulary** None

**ELL Reading:** Expand comprehension by making conclusions.

**Materials** Index cards, number cube, Number lines (TT 13)

**On-Level and Advanced Activity Centers**
- Center Games

### Lesson 2-8

MATH PRACTICES AND PROBLEM SOLVING: MAKE SENSE AND PERSEVERE pp. 125–130

Mathematical Practices **MP.1 Also MP.2, MP.4, MP.6, MP.8**
Content Standards **6.EE.B.7, 6.EE.B.6**

**Objective** Use equations to make sense of problems and persevere in solving them.

**Essential Understanding** Good math thinkers make sense of problems and think of ways to solve them. If they get stuck, they don't give up.

**Vocabulary** None

**ELL Reading:** Demonstrate comprehension by responding to questions.

**Materials** None

**On-Level and Advanced Activity Centers**
- Math and Science Activity

**Notes**

Digital

# TOPIC OPENER

## ALGEBRA: SOLVE EQUATIONS AND INEQUALITIES

### TOPIC ESSENTIAL QUESTION

**What procedures can be used to solve equations and inequalities?**

Revisit the Topic Essential Question throughout the topic, and see a note about answering the question in the Teacher's Edition for the Topic Assessment.

### MATH AND SCIENCE PROJECT STEM

**Science Theme** The science theme for this project is **Reduce, Reuse, Recycle**. This theme will be revisited in the Math and Science Activities in Lessons 2-4 and 2-8 and in some lesson exercises.

Have students help you list items they reuse and recycle. Ask for products made from recycled material. [Fleece jackets from plastic drink bottles, park benches from milk jugs, plastic molding and trim from polystyrene packaging, newsprint from magazines, tissues from office paper]

Explain that renewable resources are natural resources that can be replenished over time.

**Project-Based Learning** Have students work on the **Math and Science Project** over the course of several days.

### EXTENSION

Have students collect data on an additional type of waste. Ask them to weigh the material, or a representative sample. Students should use their data to predict the amount of time it would take their family to recycle 1,000 pounds of the waste.

TOPIC 2 Algebra: Solve Equations and Inequalities

**Essential Question:** What procedures can be used to solve equations and inequalities?

Digital Resources

Solve Learn Glossary Practice Buddy Tools Assessment Help Games

Do you know that recycled materials can be used to make houses?
Some places recycle as much of their trash as possible, and what's left over, they turn into fuel.
So recycling prevents pollution, makes new stuff, and produces energy. Here's a project on recycling and solving equations.



**Math and Science Project:** Reduce, Reuse, Recycle

**Do Research** Use the Internet or other sources to learn about what goes into landfills. How much of the waste stream could be recycled? Think about the stuff you throw out. What would happen if you recycled just one type of waste, such as cloth, food, paper, plastic, or metal?

**Journal: Write a Report** Include what you found. Also in your report:

- Outline a plan for reducing and recycling waste.
- Write and solve an equation to find how many weeks it would take the average family of four to recycle 1,000 pounds of one type of waste.

Topic 2 79

### Sample Student Work for Math and Science Project

The average soda drinker drinks 2.5 cans of soda everyday.
For a family of 4, that is 10 cans per day or 70 cans per week.
The average aluminum can weighs 0.5 ounces.

Aluminum collected each week

$70 \times 0.5$ ounces $= 35$ ounces per week

16 ounces = 1 pound, so $\frac{35}{16}$ or about 2.2 pounds of aluminum are collected each week.

Time needed to collect 1000 pounds

$\frac{1{,}000}{2.2} = 454.5$ weeks

It will take about 455 weeks to collect 1000 pounds of aluminum.

### Home-School Connection

Send this page home at the start of Topic 2 to give families an overview of the content in the topic.

Name ____________________

Home-School Connection Topic 2

**Algebra: Solve Equations and Inequalities**

**Topic 2 Standards**

6.EE.A.4, 6.EE.B.5, 6.EE.B.6, 6.EE.B.7, 6.EE.B.8

*See the front of the Student's Edition for complete standards.*

Dear Family,

Your child is learning how to write and solve algebraic equations involving addition, subtraction, multiplication, and division, and how to write and solve one-step inequalities. He or she will learn to use variables to represent numbers when solving real-world and mathematical problems. Your child will also learn the properties of equality and use them to solve equations.

Here is an activity that you can do to help your child understand equations and inequalities.

**How Much Is That?**

Look for ads in newspapers that give prices of groceries, electronics, toys, sporting goods, and other items that are of interest to your child. Use the ads to have your child write an equation. Suppose an ad shows a bicycle on sale for $80. Examples of equations are shown below.

If you save $5 each week, what equation shows how long it would take to save enough money to buy the bike? $5x = 80$, where $x$ represents the number of weeks.

If you already have $25, what equation shows how much more you will need to buy the bicycle? $y + 25 = 80$, where $y$ represents dollars still needed to buy the bicycle.

Help your child solve each of the equations. ($x = 16$ weeks, $y = \$55$)

Then state that you need at least $80 to buy the bicycle. Ask your child to write an inequality to represent this situation. (Let $m$ represent the amount of money a person has if they can buy the bicycle; $m \geq 80$.)

**Observe Your Child**

**Focus on Mathematical Practice 5**
Use appropriate tools strategically.

Help your child become proficient with Mathematical Practice 5. A number line is an appropriate tool to use to describe the possible solutions of an inequality. Ask your child to represent the inequality from the activity above on a number line. Ask him or her to explain why the solution arrow points in one direction, and why he or she used an open or closed circle on the number-line graph.

Name ____________________

**Vocabulary**

Choose the best term from the box.
Write it on the blank.

| • algebraic expression | • evaluate |
|---|---|
| • coefficient | • variable |

1. In $6x$, $x$ is a(n) **variable**.
2. $x + 5$ is an example of a(n) **algebraic expression**.
3. **Evaluate** an expression to find its value.

**Equality**

Tell whether the equation is true or false.

4. $6 + 2 = 2 + 6$ **True**
5. $2.5 - 1 = 1 - 2.5$ **False**
6. $\frac{1}{2} \times 3 = 3 \times \frac{1}{2}$ **True**
7. $\frac{3}{4} \div 5 = \frac{3}{4} \times \frac{1}{5}$ **True**
8. $5 \div \frac{1}{3} = \frac{5}{3}$ **False**
9. $\frac{2}{3} \times 5 = \frac{10}{15}$ **False**

**Expressions**

Evaluate each expression.

10. $x - 2$ for $x = 8$ **6**
11. $2b$ for $b = 9$ **18**
12. $3\frac{3}{4} + y$ for $y = \frac{5}{6}$ **$4\frac{7}{12}$**
13. $\frac{15}{x}$ for $x = 3$ **5**
14. $5.6t$ for $t = 0.7$ **3.92**
15. $4x$ for $x = \frac{1}{2}$ **2**

**Order of Operations**

16. In which order should you compute the operations in the expression? Then evaluate the expression.

$[(33 \div 3) + 1] - 2^2$

**You perform the operation in parentheses first, and then the brackets. Simplify the exponent next and finally, subtract. 8**




## RtI Item Analysis for Diagnosis and Intervention

| Item | Standard | MDIS |
|---|---|---|
| 1–3 | 6.EE.A.2 | F44 |
| 4–6 | 6.EE.A.3 | F43 |
| 7–9 | 5.NF.B.4<br>5.NF.B.7 | H47, H49 |
| 10–15 | 6.EE.A.2c | F44 |
| 16 | 6.EE.A.1 | F41 |

## Topic 2 Vocabulary Words Activity

Use the Topic 1 activity on p. 3–4 with the Topic 2 words at the right.

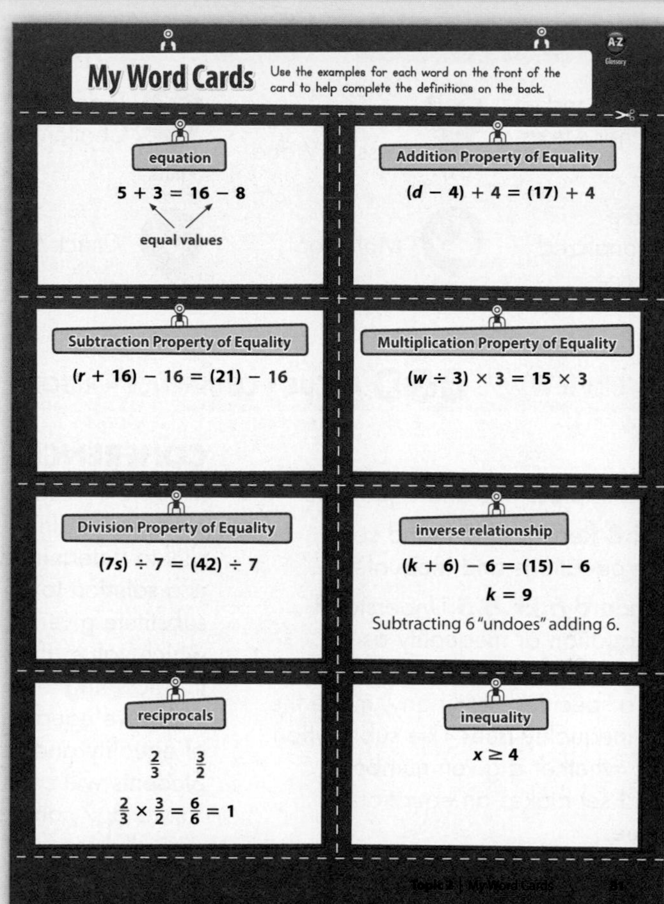

**My Word Cards** Use the examples for each word on the front of the card to help complete the definitions on the back.

**equation**
$5 + 3 = 16 - 8$
equal values

**Addition Property of Equality**
$(d - 4) + 4 = (17) + 4$

**Subtraction Property of Equality**
$(r + 16) - 16 = (21) - 16$

**Multiplication Property of Equality**
$(w \div 3) \times 3 = 15 \times 3$

**Division Property of Equality**
$(7s) \div 7 = (42) \div 7$

**inverse relationship**
$(k + 6) - 6 = (15) - 6$
$k = 9$
Subtracting 6 "undoes" adding 6.

**reciprocals**
$\frac{2}{3}$ $\frac{3}{2}$
$\frac{2}{3} \times \frac{3}{2} = \frac{6}{6} = 1$

**inequality**
$x \geq 4$

Topic 2 | My Word Cards 81

**My Word Cards** Complete each definition. Extend learning by writing your own definitions.

The property that states that the two sides of an equation remain equal when the same amount is added to both sides of the equation is called the **Addition Property of Equality**.

A mathematical sentence with equal values on either side of an equal sign (=) is called an **equation**.

The property that states that the two sides of an equation remain equal when both sides of the equation are multiplied by the same amount is called the **Multiplication Property of Equality**.

The property that states that the two sides of an equation remain equal when the same amount is subtracted from both sides of the equation is called the **Subtraction Property of Equality**.

Operations that undo each other have an **inverse relationship**.

The property that states that the two sides of an equation remain equal when both sides of the equation are divided by the same amount is called the **Division Property of Equality**.

A mathematical sentence that contains < (less than), > (greater than), ≤ (less than or equal to), ≥ (greater than or equal to), or ≠ (is not equal to) is called an **inequality**.

Two numbers whose product is 1 are called **reciprocals**.

82 Topic 2 | My Word Cards

# LESSON 2-1

# UNDERSTAND EQUATIONS AND SOLUTIONS

## DIGITAL RESOURCES PearsonRealize.com

Student and Teacher eTexts — eText

Listen and Look For Lesson Video — PD

Today's Challenge — Think

Solve and Share — Solve

Visual Learning Animation Plus — Learn

Animated Glossary — Glossary

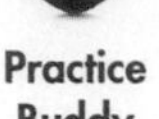
Online Personalized Practice — Practice Buddy

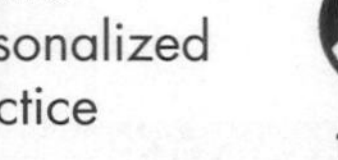

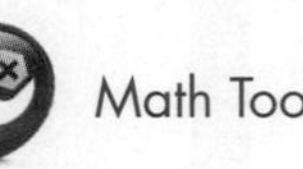
Math Tools — Tools

Quick Check — Assessment

Another Look Homework Video — Help

Math Games — Games

## LESSON OVERVIEW FCR FOCUS • COHERENCE • RIGOR

### FOCUS

**Domain 6.EE** Expressions and Equations

**Cluster 6.EE.B** Reason about and solve one-variable equations and inequalities.

**Content Standard 6.EE.B.5** Understand solving an equation or inequality as a process of answering a question: which values from a specified set, if any, make the equation or inequality true? Use substitution to determine whether a given number in a specified set makes an equation or inequality true.

**Mathematical Practices MP.2, MP.3, MP.4, MP.6, MP.7, MP.8**

**Objective** Use substitution to find solutions to equations.

**Essential Understanding** A solution to an equation is a value for the variable that makes the equation true. An equation is true when the expressions or numbers on both sides of the equal sign have the same value.

**Vocabulary** Equation

### COHERENCE

In Topic 1, students evaluated algebraic expressions. In this lesson, students use that skill to determine whether a given number is a solution to an equation. They learn to substitute given values for the variable to see which value, if any, makes the equation true. In upcoming lessons in this topic, students will solve equations by applying properties of equality and using inverse operations. Students will continue to solve equations in Topics 6, 7, and 12, which involve multi-digit division, decimals, and fractions.

### RIGOR

This lesson emphasizes **conceptual understanding**. For any work with equations, students need to have a solid understanding that a solution to an equation is a value for the variable that makes the equation true. While students will learn later that equations may have no solution, one solution, or more than one solution, this lesson focuses on equations that have exactly one variable and one solution.

PD Watch the Listen and Look For Lesson Video.

## MATH ANYTIME

### Daily Common Core Review

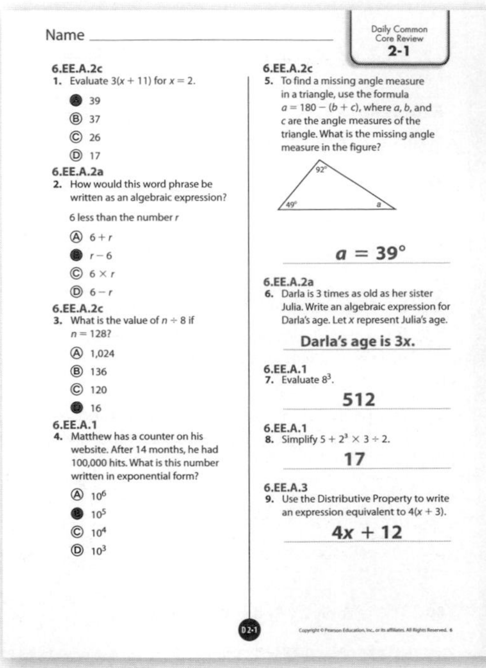

Name ______________

Daily Common Core Review 2-1

6.EE.A.2c
1. Evaluate $3(x + 11)$ for $x = 2$.
- Ⓐ 39 (filled)
- Ⓑ 37
- Ⓒ 26
- Ⓓ 17

6.EE.A.2a
2. How would this word phrase be written as an algebraic expression?

6 less than the number $r$
- Ⓐ $6 + r$
- Ⓑ $r - 6$ (filled)
- Ⓒ $6 \times r$
- Ⓓ $6 - r$

6.EE.A.2c
3. What is the value of $n \div 8$ if $n = 128$?
- Ⓐ 1,024
- Ⓑ 136
- Ⓒ 120
- Ⓓ 16 (filled)

6.EE.A.1
4. Matthew has a counter on his website. After 14 months, he had 100,000 hits. What is this number written in exponential form?
- Ⓐ $10^6$
- Ⓑ $10^5$ (filled)
- Ⓒ $10^4$
- Ⓓ $10^3$

6.EE.A.2c
5. To find a missing angle measure in a triangle, use the formula $a = 180 - (b + c)$, where $a$, $b$, and $c$ are the angle measures of the triangle. What is the missing angle measure in the figure?

92°, 49°, a

$a = 39°$

6.EE.A.2a
6. Darla is 3 times as old as her sister Julia. Write an algebraic expression for Darla's age. Let $x$ represent Julia's age.

Darla's age is $3x$.

6.EE.A.1
7. Evaluate $8^3$.

512

6.EE.A.1
8. Simplify $5 + 2^3 \times 3 \div 2$.

17

6.EE.A.3
9. Use the Distributive Property to write an expression equivalent to $4(x + 3)$.

$4x + 12$

D 2-1



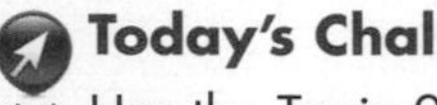

### Today's Challenge

Think Use the Topic 2 problems any time during this topic.

## ENGLISH LANGUAGE LEARNERS 

**Reading** Use contextual support to develop vocabulary.

*Use with the Visual Learning Bridge on Student's Edition p. 84.*

Read Box A. Instruct students to circle important information for solving the problem. Read Box B. *The context of the problem can be used to understand the meaning of words.*

**Beginning** Reread Box B to students. Circle *equation*. Underline *equal sign* and *two expressions*. *An equation has an equal sign and two expressions.* Write $\$4.50 + x = \$15.00$. Instruct students to point to the equal sign. Then point to $\$4.50 + x$ and $\$15.00$. *These are two expressions.* Have students summarize using the sentence stem: An equation has an ____ and two ________.

**Intermediate** Reread Box B with students. Instruct students to circle *equation* and underline *equal sign* and *two expressions*. *An equation has an equal sign and two expressions.* Write $\$4.50 + x = \$15.00$. Ask students to show partners the equal sign and two expressions. Provide the sentence stem for students to summarize: An equation has ______.

**Advanced** Instruct students to reread Box B with partners. Ask students to identify the parts of an equation. Write $\$4.50 + x = \$15.00$. Have students identify the equal sign and two expressions. Then have students explain the term *equation* to partners.

**Summarize** What is an *equation*?

# DEVELOP: PROBLEM-BASED LEARNING

**COHERENCE: Engage learners by connecting prior knowledge to new ideas.**
Students use their previous understanding of equality to explain how balance can be achieved using a pan balance.

10–15 min

Solve

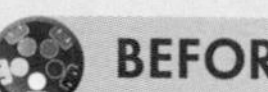

## BEFORE

1. **Pose the Solve-and-Share Problem**
**MP.4 Model with Math** Listen and look for students who represent the situation with an equation. Discuss how the situation and equation are related.

2. **Build Understanding**
*Why does the picture show that the pans are not balanced?* [The pan on the right has more cubes than the pan on the left.] *In general, when would the pans balance?* [When each pan has the same number of cubes]

## DURING

3. **Ask Guiding Questions As Needed**
*How could you add cubes to one side to make the pans balance?* [Add 6 cubes to the side with fewer cubes.] *How could you remove cubes from one side to make the pans balance?* [Remove 6 cubes from the side with more cubes.] *What do you notice about the number of cubes you would need to add to or remove from one side to keep the pans in balance?* [The number of cubes is the same.]

## AFTER

4. **Share and Discuss Solutions**
Start with students' solutions. If needed, project Roberto's and Erin's work to discuss two ways to balance the pans.

5. **Transition to the Visual Learning Bridge**
*A pan balance can be used to represent an equation. An equation is true when the values on both sides of the equal sign are the same.*

6. **Extension for Early Finishers**
*Suppose a pan balance has 5 cubes on one pan and 13 cubes on the other. Write an equation using the variable x to represent adding some cubes to one side to balance the pans.* [$5 + x = 13$] *What value of x makes the equation true?* [$x = 8$]

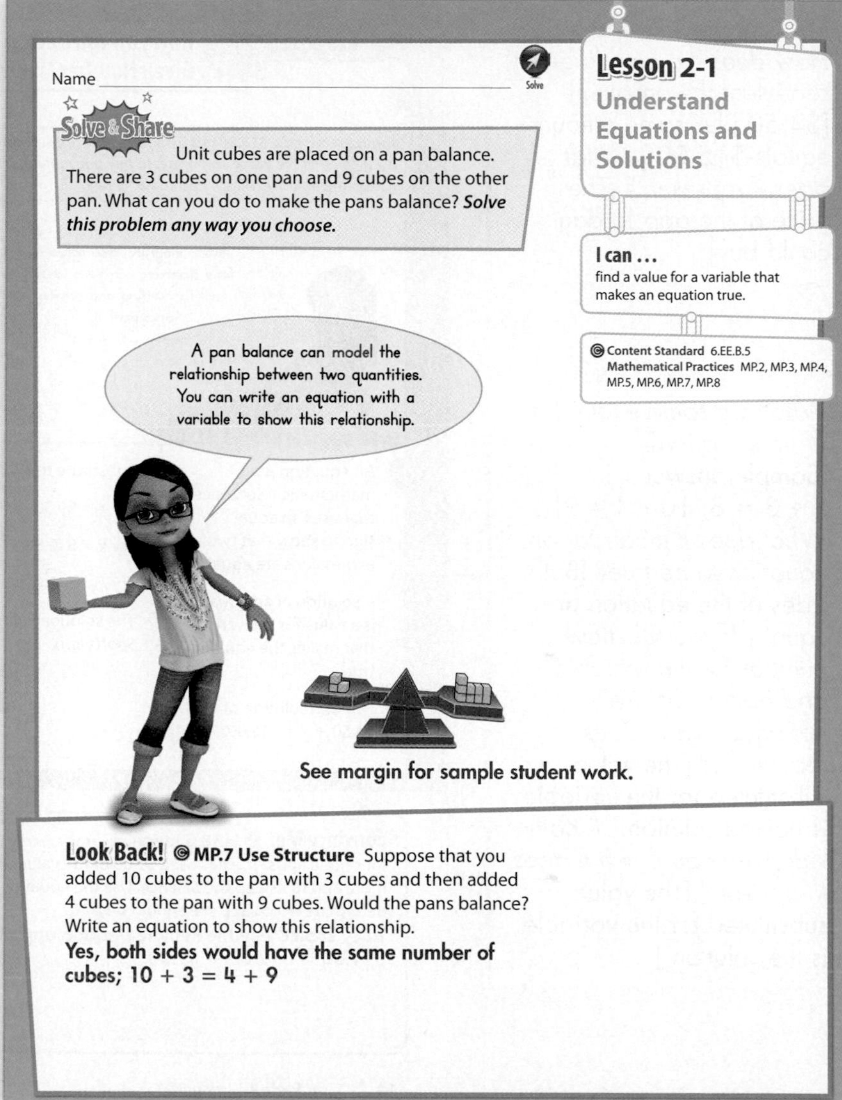

Name
Solve & Share
Unit cubes are placed on a pan balance. There are 3 cubes on one pan and 9 cubes on the other pan. What can you do to make the pans balance? *Solve this problem any way you choose.*
Lesson 2-1
Understand Equations and Solutions
I can ...
find a value for a variable that makes an equation true.
Content Standard 6.EE.B.5
Mathematical Practices MP.2, MP.3, MP.4, MP.5, MP.6, MP.7, MP.8
A pan balance can model the relationship between two quantities. You can write an equation with a variable to show this relationship.
See margin for sample student work.
Look Back! MP.7 Use Structure Suppose that you added 10 cubes to the pan with 3 cubes and then added 4 cubes to the pan with 9 cubes. Would the pans balance? Write an equation to show this relationship.
Yes, both sides would have the same number of cubes; 10 + 3 = 4 + 9
Digital Resources at PearsonRealize.com
Topic 2 | Lesson 2-1
83


## Analyze Student Work

**Roberto's Work**

x is the number of cubes I need to add to the pan with 3 cubes.
$3 + x = 9$

If I add 6 cubes to the side with 3 cubes, then both sides have 9 cubes and the pans balance.
So, $x = 6$.

Roberto writes an equation to represent the situation and explains how to balance the pans.

**Erin's Work**

$9 - c = 3$

If I take 6 cubes off of the pan with 9 cubes, then $c = 6$. The pans balance because $9 - 6 = 3$.

Erin writes a different equation to represent the situation and explains another way to balance the pans.

# DEVELOP: VISUAL LEARNING

The *Visual Learning Bridge* connects students' thinking in Solve & Share to important math ideas in the lesson. Use the *Visual Learning Bridge* to make these ideas explicit. Also available as a *Visual Learning Animation Plus* at PearsonRealize.com

Visual Learning

Learn Glossary

**MP.4 Model with Math** *How does the bar diagram represent the problem?* [$4.50 plus some amount equals $15.00.] *What does x represent?* [The price of the app Jordan could buy]

*What are some examples of an equation?* [Sample answer: $5 + 3 = 8$; $10 - 1 = 9$] *What does it mean for an equation to be true?* [Both sides of the equation are equal.] *If you substitute a number for the variable and both sides are not equal, what does that mean?* [The value substituted for the variable is not the solution.] *If both sides are equal, what does that mean?* [The value substituted for the variable is the solution.]

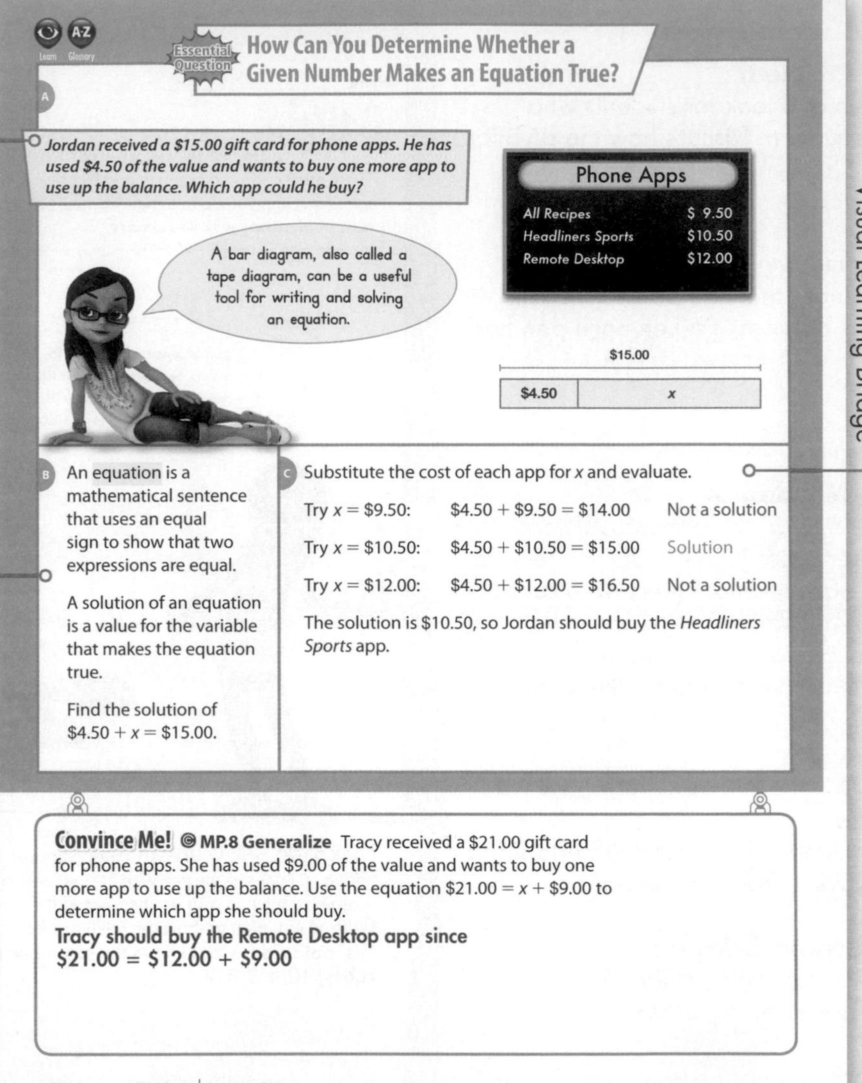

Visual Learning Bridge

**Essential Question** How Can You Determine Whether a Given Number Makes an Equation True?

A *Jordan received a $15.00 gift card for phone apps. He has used $4.50 of the value and wants to buy one more app to use up the balance. Which app could he buy?*

A bar diagram, also called a tape diagram, can be a useful tool for writing and solving an equation.

| Phone Apps | |
|---|---|
| All Recipes | $ 9.50 |
| Headliners Sports | $10.50 |
| Remote Desktop | $12.00 |



B An equation is a mathematical sentence that uses an equal sign to show that two expressions are equal.

A solution of an equation is a value for the variable that makes the equation true.

Find the solution of $4.50 + x = 15.00$.

C Substitute the cost of each app for *x* and evaluate.

| | | |
|---|---|---|
| Try $x = \$9.50$: | $\$4.50 + \$9.50 = \$14.00$ | Not a solution |
| Try $x = \$10.50$: | $\$4.50 + \$10.50 = \$15.00$ | Solution |
| Try $x = \$12.00$: | $\$4.50 + \$12.00 = \$16.50$ | Not a solution |

The solution is $10.50, so Jordan should buy the *Headliners Sports* app.

**Convince Me!** **MP.8 Generalize** Tracy received a $21.00 gift card for phone apps. She has used $9.00 of the value and wants to buy one more app to use up the balance. Use the equation $\$21.00 = x + \$9.00$ to determine which app she should buy.

**Tracy should buy the Remote Desktop app since $\$21.00 = \$12.00 + \$9.00$**

84 **Topic 2** | Lesson 2-1 © Pearson Education, Inc. 6

**MP.2 Reason Quantitatively** *How do you know that $9.50 is not the solution?* [$4.50 plus $9.50 does not equal $15.00, so when you substitute $9.50 for *x*, the equation is not true.] *How do you know that $10.50 is a solution?* [$\$4.50 + \$10.50 = \$15.00$, so when you substitute $10.50 for *x*, the equation is true.] *How do you know that $12.00 is not the solution?* [$4.50 plus $12.00 does not equal $15.00, so when you substitute $12.00 for *x*, the equation is not true.] *Could there be other solutions to the equation in this situation? Explain.* [No; in this case, only $x = \$10.50$ makes the equation true.]

**Convince Me!** **MP.8 Generalize** Point out the similarities between this problem and the problem in the Visual Learning Bridge. *How can you use the equation to determine which app Tracy should buy?* [You can use the same method of substituting given values for the variable to see which one makes the equation true.]

**Coherence** In the phone app problem, students learn that they can use substitution to determine whether a given value for the variable makes the equation true. Students should be familiar with the process of substitution from their previous work in Topic 1, when they evaluated algebraic expressions. Throughout their work in middle school math and algebra, students will continue to use substitution to check whether they have solved an equation correctly.

Revisit the Essential Question. Substitute given values for a variable into an equation to see which value makes the equation true. If the equation is not true for any of the values tested, then the solution is not among the given values.

## QUICK CHECK

Check mark indicates items for prescribing differentiation on the next page. Item 14 is worth 1 point. Items 18 and 21 are worth up to 2 points.

20–30 min

Practice Buddy | Tools | Assessment

Name ____________

### Guided Practice*

**Do You Understand?**

1. When is an equation true?
   **When both sides are equal**
2. **MP.2 Reasoning** Ben says that $n = 5$ is the solution of the equation $7n = 45$. How can you check whether he is correct?
   **Sample answer: Substitute 5 for $n$ to see if the equation is true. $7 \times 5 = 35$, so 5 is not the solution. Ben is not correct.**
3. There are 3 cubes on one pan and 11 cubes on the other pan. Lucy thinks she should add 7, 8, 9, or 10 cubes to make the pans balance. How can you use the equation $3 + c = 11$ to find the number of cubes Lucy should add?
   **Sample answer: Substitute each value for $c$ to see when the equation is true. $3 + 8 = 11$, so 8 is the solution of the equation. Lucy should add 8 cubes.**

**Do You Know How?**

In **4–7**, substitute each value of the variable to find the solution of each equation.

4. $d + 9 = 35$  $d = 16, 22, 26, 36$
   **26**
5. $13.4 - g = 8.1$  $g = 4.3, 5.3, 5.5, 6.5$
   **5.3**
6. $4 = 36 \div m$  $m = 4, 6, 8, 9$
   **9**
7. $c - 17 = 3.4$  $c = 13.4, 14.6, 18.4, 21.4$
   **No solution is given in the set of values.**

In **8** and **9**, tell if each equation is true or false for $n = 8$.

8. $n = 54 - 36$
   **False**
9. $5n = 40$
   **True**

### Independent Practice*

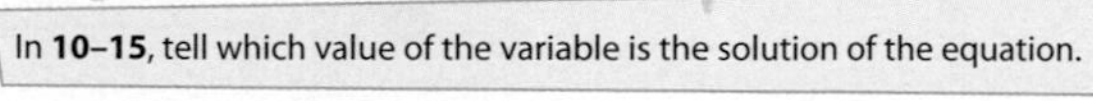

In **10–15**, tell which value of the variable is the solution of the equation.

10. $t - 2.1 = 0$  $t = 2.1, 2.4, 2.6, 2.8$
    **2.1**
11. $49 = 7r$  $r = 3, 6, 7, 9$
    **7**
12. $24 \div h = 6$  $h = 1, 3, 6, 8$
    **No solution is given in the set of values.**
13. $8.9 + a = 9.7$  $a = 0.7, 0.8, 0.9, 1.2$
    **0.8**

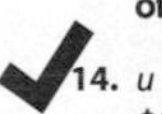

14. $u + \$8.44 = \$12.00$  $u = \$2.56, \$2.66, \$3.46, \$3.56$
    **\$3.56**
15. $\$4.10 = \$16.25 - y$  $y = \$12.15, \$12.95, \$13.05, \$13.15$
    **\$12.15**

*For another example, see Set A on page 133.



### Math Practices and Problem Solving*

16. There are 27 pennies on one pan of a pan balance and 18 pennies on the other. To make the pans balance, Hillary thinks 5 pennies should be added to the higher pan, Sean thinks 8 pennies should be added, and Rachel thinks 9 pennies should be added. Use the equation $27 = 18 + p$ to determine who is correct.
    **Rachel**
17. **MP.3 Construct Arguments** Gerard spent \$5.12 for a drink and a sandwich. His drink cost \$1.30. Did he have a ham sandwich for \$3.54, a tuna sandwich for \$3.82, or a turkey sandwich for \$3.92? Use the equation $s + 1.30 = 5.12$ to justify your answer. **Tuna sandwich for \$3.82. Sample answer: Substitute the price of each sandwich for $s$. $\$3.82 + \$1.30 = \$5.12$**
18. **Higher Order Thinking** Write an equation that has 12 for a solution. Show how you know that 12 is the solution.
    **Sample answer: $n + 10 = 22$. Substitute 12 for $n$. $12 + 10 = 22$, so the solution is 12.**

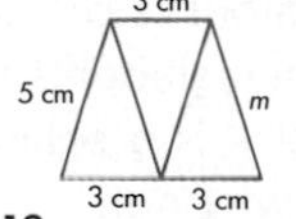

The variable in an equation can be represented with any letter you choose.


19. Gina's family is driving 255 miles to visit Sacramento. After driving for a while, they pass a sign that says "Sacramento: 124 miles." Substitute the values $m = 111, 121, 131$, and $141$ in the equation $255 - m = 124$ to find the number of miles the family has already driven.
    **131 miles**
20. **Algebra** Alisa is making a quilt that uses a pattern of triangles like the one shown. Write an equation that represents the missing side length if the perimeter is 19 centimeters.
    (Figure labels: 3 cm, 5 cm, m, 3 cm, 3 cm)
    **Sample answer: $5 + 3 + 3 + 3 + m = 19$.**

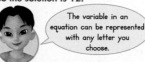

**Common Core Assessment**

21. Trish has \$26.00 to spend at a craft store. She buys fabric that costs \$18.62. She also wants to buy knitting needles for \$7.32, silk flowers for \$7.38, or oil paints for \$8.48.
    Use the equation $\$18.62 + c = \$26.00$, where $c$ is the item cost, to find the most expensive item she can buy. Explain how you found the answer.
    **\$7.38; Sample answer: Substitute \$7.38 for c, $\$18.62 + \$7.38 = \$26.00$. So, the most expensive item Trish can buy is the silk flowers for \$7.38.**




**Error Intervention: Item 8**

**If** students are unsure about what they should do after substituting 8 for the variable,

**then** explain that they should perform all calculations to determine whether the expressions on both sides of the equal sign have the same value. *What is 54 – 36?* [18] *Does 8 equal 18?* [No] *So, is the equation true or false?* [False] *Is n = 8 a solution of the equation?* [No]

**Item 12** Tell students that there may be no solution in the set of values given. *Which of the four values results in an equation in which both sides are equal?* [None] *What does that tell you about the values?* [There is no solution in the set of values.]

**Reteaching** Assign Reteaching Set A on p. 133.

**Item 16** Encourage students to think about solving this problem in terms of solving an equation. *How will you know who is correct?* [The number he or she chooses will make the equation true.] *Does Sean's number make the equation true? Why or why not?* [No; 18 plus 8 does not equal 27.]

**Item 17 MP.3 Construct Arguments** Remind students that mathematically proficient students use correct mathematical language and equations to justify solutions.

**Item 18 Higher Order Thinking** Suggest that students begin by writing an equation with no variable that has the number 12 as one of the terms. [Sample answer: $12 + 10 = 22$] *What does the equation look like if you replace the 12 with a variable?* [$n + 10 = 22$] *How can you show that 12 is the solution?* [You can check by substituting 12 back into the equation for *n*.]

**Multi-Step Problems** *Page 86 Items 16, 17, 19, and 21; Page 88 Items 13, 14, and 17*

# ASSESS AND DIFFERENTIATE

Use the **QUICK CHECK** on the previous page to prescribe differentiated instruction.

**I Intervention** 0–3 points on the Quick Check

**O On-Level** 4 points on the Quick Check

**A Advanced** 5 points on the Quick Check

## Intervention Activity I

### Understand Equations and Solutions

**Materials**

Number cube

- Have students work in pairs.
- Write the following equations on the board.
  1. $5m = 20$
  2. $26 - g = 21$
  3. $y + 21 = 24$
  4. $60 \div n = 10$
- For each equation, each student rolls the number cube and tests to see whether that number is a solution of the equation. Then students tell their partners whether it is a solution and explain why or why not.

5m = 20
5 • 3 = 15
3 is not a solution.

## Reteach I

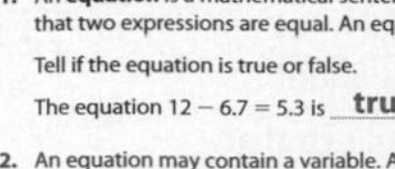

Name ______________________

Reteach to Build Understanding 2-1

**Vocabulary**

1. An **equation** is a mathematical sentence that uses an equal sign to show that two expressions are equal. An equation is true when both sides are equal.

   Tell if the equation is true or false.

   The equation $12 - 6.7 = 5.3$ is **true**.

2. An equation may contain a variable. A **solution** of an equation is a value of the variable that makes the equation true.

   What is the solution of the equation $8m = 72$? **9**

3. Tell if the equation $35 \div r = 5$ is true or false for $r = 7$. **true**

   What is the solution of this equation? **7**

4. You can determine if a number is a solution of an equation by substituting that number for the variable in the equation.

   Substitute each value in the set for the variable to determine whether it is the solution of the equation $16.6 - t = 11.9$.

   $t = 3.6, 4.4, 4.7, 5.4$

   Try 3.6.
   $16.6 - 3.6 = 13$, so 3.6 is not the solution.

   Try 4.4.
   $16.6 -$ **4.4** $= 12.2$, so 4.4 **is not** the solution.

   Try 4.7. Show your work.
   **16.6 − 4.7 = 11.9 is true, so 4.7 is the solution.**

   Try 5.4. Show your work.
   **16.6 − 5.4 = 11.2, so 5.4 is not the solution.**

   The solution of the equation $16.6 - t = 11.9$ is **4.7**.

**On the Back!**

5. Tell which value of the variable is the solution of the equation.
   $9.4 = k + 5.07$ $k = 3.33, 4.33, 4.47, 14.47$ **4.33**

R 2•1



## On-Level and Advanced Activity Centers O A

### Center Games

Students work in pairs or small groups to use mental math to match equations with their solutions. Have students justify their answers and record their work as they play the game.

★ On-Level

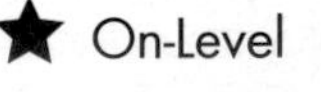

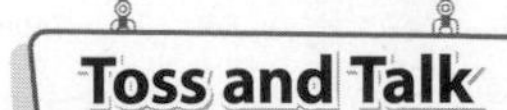

**Toss and Talk**

Partner Talk — Share your thinking while you work.

**Get Started** Get 10 squares in one color and 10 in another color. Get two number cubes. Take turns with another player or team. Talk about math as you play!

**At Your Turn** Toss two number cubes. Add the dots. Find your toss below. Follow the directions. Explain your thinking. Cover the answer. If the answer is taken, lose your turn. Have fun!

| Toss | Which value of *y* makes the equation true? Use mental math. |
|---|---|
| 2 | $7y = 21$ |
| 3 | $y - 18 = 9$ |
| 4 | $18.2 - y = 8.2$ |
| 5 | $4y = 20$ |
| 6 | $11.5 + y = 23.5$ |
| 7 | $y \div 2 = 15$ |
| 8 | $4y = 36$ |
| 9 | $42 = 7y$ |
| 10 | $y \div 5 = 5$ |
| 11 | $4y = 16$ |
| 12 | $y + 7 = 77$ |

| | | | |
|---|---|---|---|
| $y = 6$ | $y = 3$ | $y = 25$ | $y = 70$ |
| $y = 12$ | $y = 70$ | $y = 10$ | $y = 12$ |
| $y = 27$ | $y = 9$ | $y = 6$ | $y = 5$ |
| $y = 30$ | $y = 5$ | $y = 4$ | $y = 9$ |

**How to Win** You win if you are the first to get four connected rectangles, like:

**If you have more time** Play again!

Center Game ★ 2•1



★★ Advanced

**Toss and Talk**

Partner Talk — Share your thinking while you work.

**Get Started** Get 10 squares in one color and 10 in another color. Get two number cubes. Take turns with another player or team. Talk about math as you play!

**At Your Turn** Toss two number cubes. Add the dots. Find your toss below. Follow the directions. Explain your thinking. Cover the answer. If the answer is taken, lose your turn. Have fun!

| Toss | Use mental math. Find an equation that has this solution. Explain why the equation has this solution. |
|---|---|
| 2 | $n = 10$ |
| 3 | $n = 1$ |
| 4 | $n = 100$ |
| 5 | $n = 6$ |
| 6 | $n = 0$ |
| 7 | $n = 20$ |
| 8 | $n = 12$ |
| 9 | $n = 2$ |
| 10 | $n = 30$ |
| 11 | $n = 8$ |
| 12 | $n = 5$ |

| | | | |
|---|---|---|---|
| $7n = 35$ | $3n = 60$ | $12 - n = 0$ | $9n = 0$ |
| $n \div 2 = 1$ | $4n = 24$ | $5n = 60$ | $16.8 - n = 11.8$ |
| $n \div 1 = 1$ | $9n = 18$ | $6n = 36$ | $n - 50 = 50$ |
| $150n = 0$ | $5n = 40$ | $n - 3 = 27$ | $8n = 80$ |

**How to Win** You win if you are the first to get four connected rectangles, like:

**If you have more time** Play again!

Center Game ★★ 2•1

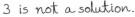

## TIMING

The time allocated to Step 3 will depend on the teacher's instructional decisions and differentiation routines.

15–30 min

realize.
PearsonRealize.com
Help
Practice Buddy
Tools
Games

## Technology Center I O A

### Math Tools and Math Games

A link to a specific math tools activity or math game to use with this lesson is provided at PearsonRealize.com.

Math Tools
GAME CENTER

## Leveled Assignment

I Items 1–6, 15–17 O Items 1–4, 9, 13, 14, 16, 17 A Items 7–14, 16, 17

Name ______________

### Homework & Practice 2-1

**Understand Equations and Solutions**

**Another Look!**

Anton walked 8.9 miles of his 13.5-mile goal for this week. Which path should Anton walk so he meets his goal for the week?

| Path Lengths | |
|---|---|
| Meadow Path | 3.2 miles |
| Circle Path | 4.2 miles |
| Oak Tree Path | 4.6 miles |

13.5: $m$ | 8.9

Find the solution of $m + 8.9 = 13.5$
Substitute the different values for the variable, $m$.

Try $m = 3.2$: $3.2 + 8.9$ miles $= 12.1$ miles Not a solution
Try $m = 4.2$: $4.2 + 8.9$ miles $= 13.1$ miles Not a solution
Try $m = 4.6$: $4.6 + 8.9$ miles $= 13.5$ miles Solution

Since the solution to the equation is 4.6 miles, Anton should walk the Oak Tree Path to complete his 13.5-mile goal for the week.

In **1–12**, tell which value of the variable is the solution of the equation.

1. $5.6 = l + 4.09$ $l = 0.7, 0.97, 1.51, 9.69$ **1.51**
2. $5k = 65$ $k = 11, 12, 13, 14$ **13**
3. $t - \$5.60 = \$1.04$ $t = \$6.00, \$6.10, \$6.64, \$7.00$ **$6.64**
4. $133 \div y = 19$ $y = 6, 7, 8, 9$ **7**
5. $14 = \frac{u}{6}$ $u = 78, 81, 84, 90$ **84**
6. $9 + a = 46$ $a = 37, 39, 41, 55$ **37**
7. $6.8 = 2.89 + m$ $m = 3.9, 3.91, 4, 4.11$ **3.91**
8. $8c = 64$ $c = 6, 7, 8, 9$ **8**
9. $0.06 = n - 4.4$ $n = 4.406, 4.46, 4.64, 5$ **4.46**
10. $\frac{176}{g} = 16$ $g = 10, 11, 12, 13$ **11**
11. $25.54 = 83.1 - b$ $b = 57, 57.47, 57.56, 57.65$ **57.56**
12. $\$19.25p = \$115.50$ $p = \$5.25, \$6.00, \$6.50, \$7.00$ **$6.00**

In **13** and **14**, use the table.

| Cost of Popcorn | |
|---|---|
| Small | $2.85 |
| Medium | $3.75 |
| Large | $4.75 |
| Extra Large | $4.85 |

13. **Higher Order Thinking** James bought a movie ticket and popcorn for $12.20. The movie ticket cost $8.45. Use the equation $c + \$8.45 = \$12.20$ to find which size popcorn James bought. How much change did he get back if he paid with a $20 bill? **$\$3.75 + \$8.45 = \$12.20$, so $c = \$3.75$. James got $7.80 in change.**

14. **MP.2 Reasoning** Kyle bought a movie ticket for $8.45 and a drink for $1.80. He only had enough money to buy the large popcorn. How much money did Kyle have to start with? Write an equation to show your reasoning. **Sample answer: Let $s$ = the amount of money Kyle started with. $s = \$8.45 + \$1.80 + \$4.75$; $s = \$15.00$. Kyle had $15.00 to start with.**

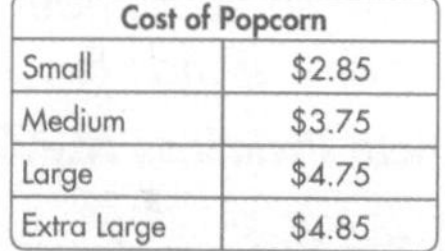

Be precise when you write an equation. Remember to define the variable in the equation.

15. Nadia made 56 muffins. She wants to fill each treat bag with 8 muffins. Nadia bought 7 bags. Use the equation $56 \div b = 8$ to explain whether Nadia bought enough bags. **Substitute 7 for $b$ in the equation. $56 \div 7 = 8$, so Nadia bought enough bags.**

16. **MP.7 Use Structure** The students in Mrs. Johnson's class are running a race. Let $g$ represent the number of girl runners and $b$ represent the number of boy runners. Write an algebraic expression that describes the total number of students in the race. **$g + b$**

### Common Core Assessment

17. Jerry built a table with a square top. The perimeter of the tabletop is 18 feet. He knows that each side of the table is 3, $3\frac{1}{2}$, 4, or $4\frac{1}{2}$ feet long. Use the equation $18 = 4s$, where $s$ is the side length of the table, to determine which is the length of the tabletop.

**$18 = 4s$**
**Try $s = 3$: $18 \neq 4(3)$ Not a solution**
**Try $s = 3\frac{1}{2}$: $18 \neq 4(3\frac{1}{2})$ Not a solution**
**Try $s = 4$: $18 \neq 4(4)$ Not a solution**
**Try $s = 4\frac{1}{2}$: $18 = 4(4\frac{1}{2})$ Solution**
**The length of the tabletop is $4\frac{1}{2}$ feet.**

# LESSON 2-2

# PROPERTIES OF EQUALITY

## DIGITAL RESOURCES PearsonRealize.com

 Student and Teacher eTexts
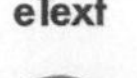 eText

 Listen and Look For Lesson Video
 PD

Today's Challenge
 Think

 Solve and Share
 Solve

 Visual Learning Animation Plus
Learn

 Animated Glossary
 Glossary

Online Personalized Practice
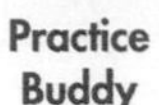 Practice Buddy

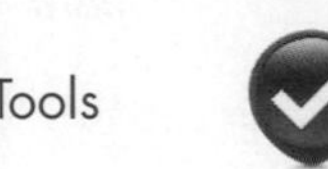 Math Tools
Tools

Quick Check
Assessment

 Another Look Homework Video
Help

 Math Games
Games

## LESSON OVERVIEW FCR FOCUS • COHERENCE • RIGOR

### FOCUS

**Domain 6.EE** Expressions and Equations

**Cluster 6.EE.A** Apply and extend previous understandings of arithmetic to algebraic expressions.

**Content Standard 6.EE.A.4** Identify when two expressions are equivalent (i.e., when the two expressions name the same number regardless of which value is substituted into them). *For example, the expressions* $y + y + y$ *and* $3y$ *are equivalent because they name the same number regardless of which number* $y$ *stands for.* Also **6.EE.B.7**.

**Mathematical Practices MP.2, MP.3, MP.4, MP.7**

**Objective** Identify equivalent expressions and use the properties of equality to write equivalent equations.

**Essential Understanding** The same number can be added to, subtracted from, or multiplied on both sides of an equation and equality is maintained. Dividing both sides of an equation by the same non-zero number also maintains equality.

**Vocabulary** Addition Property of Equality, Subtraction Property of Equality, Multiplication Property of Equality, Division Property of Equality

### COHERENCE

In Topic 1, students wrote and identified equivalent expressions. In this lesson, students examine equivalent expressions in an equation and learn how to write equivalent equations. They develop an understanding that equality is maintained when one or more properties of equality are applied. In the next three lessons in this topic and in later topics, students will solve equations by using properties of equality to isolate the variable on one side of the equal sign.

### RIGOR

This lesson emphasizes **conceptual understanding**. The concepts developed in this lesson form the basis for the procedures used to solve algebraic equations.

PD Watch the Listen and Look For Lesson Video.

## MATH ANYTIME

### Daily Common Core Review

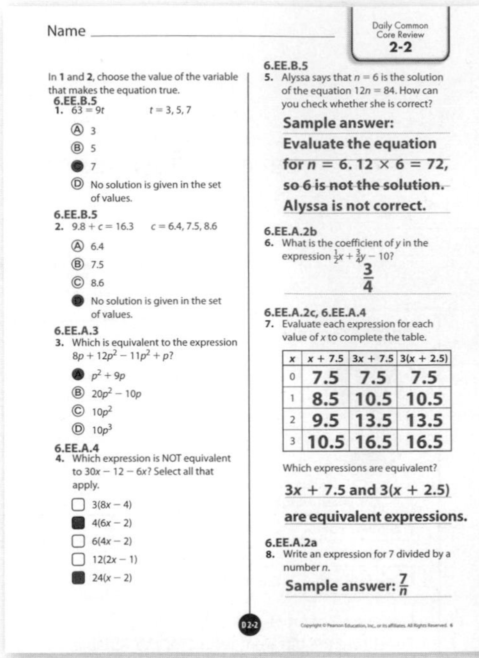

Name ______

Daily Common Core Review **2-2**

In **1** and **2**, choose the value of the variable that makes the equation true.

**6.EE.B.5**
1. $63 = 9t$ $t = 3, 5, 7$
   - Ⓐ 3
   - Ⓑ 5
   - ● 7
   - Ⓓ No solution is given in the set of values.

**6.EE.B.5**
2. $9.8 + c = 16.3$ $c = 6.4, 7.5, 8.6$
   - Ⓐ 6.4
   - Ⓑ 7.5
   - Ⓒ 8.6
   - ● No solution is given in the set of values.

**6.EE.A.3**
3. Which is equivalent to the expression $8p + 12p^2 - 11p^2 + p$?
   - ● $p^2 + 9p$
   - Ⓑ $20p^2 - 10p$
   - Ⓒ $10p^2$
   - Ⓓ $10p^3$

**6.EE.A.4**
4. Which expression is NOT equivalent to $30x - 12 - 6x$? Select all that apply.
   - ☐ $3(8x - 4)$
   - ■ $4(6x - 2)$
   - ☐ $6(4x - 2)$
   - ☐ $12(2x - 1)$
   - ■ $24(x - 2)$

**6.EE.B.5**
5. Alyssa says that $n = 6$ is the solution of the equation $12n = 84$. How can you check whether she is correct?
   **Sample answer: Evaluate the equation for $n = 6$. $12 \times 6 = 72$, so 6 is not the solution. Alyssa is not correct.**

**6.EE.A.2b**
6. What is the coefficient of $y$ in the expression $\frac{1}{2}x + \frac{3}{4}y - 10$?
   $\frac{3}{4}$

**6.EE.A.2c, 6.EE.A.4**
7. Evaluate each expression for each value of $x$ to complete the table.

| $x$ | $x + 7.5$ | $3x + 7.5$ | $3(x + 2.5)$ |
|---|---|---|---|
| 0 | 7.5 | 7.5 | 7.5 |
| 1 | 8.5 | 10.5 | 10.5 |
| 2 | 9.5 | 13.5 | 13.5 |
| 3 | 10.5 | 16.5 | 16.5 |

Which expressions are equivalent?
**$3x + 7.5$ and $3(x + 2.5)$ are equivalent expressions.**

**6.EE.A.2a**
8. Write an expression for 7 divided by a number $n$.
   **Sample answer: $\frac{7}{n}$**

D 2-2



### Today's Challenge

Think Use the Topic 2 problems any time during this topic.

## ENGLISH LANGUAGE LEARNERS 

**Speaking** Explain content area information.

*Use with the Solve & Share on Student's Edition p. 89.*

Read the Solve & Share. Ask students to work with partners. *What are the parts of an equation?* Write $4 + 8 = 12$. Partners should see if the equation has two expressions with the same value, with an equal sign between them. Point to the chart. Read the first computation.

**Beginning** *Add 5 to both sides.* Demonstrate by writing $4 + 8 + 5 = 12 + 5$. Underline $4 + 8 + 5$. *What is the value of this expression?* Underline $12 + 5$. *What is the value of this expression? Is the equation* $4 + 8 + 5 = 12 + 5$ *true?* Have partners share information using the sentence stem: The ______ is true. Continue this process with the remaining computations.

**Intermediate** Instruct students to rewrite the given equation by adding 5 to each side and to find the value of each expression. *Is the equation* $4 + 8 + 5 = 12 + 5$ *true?* Have partners share information by using the sentence stem: The ______ is true because ______. Continue this process with the remaining computations.

**Advanced** Instruct students to rewrite the given equation by adding 5 to each side and to find the value of each expression. *Is the equation* $4 + 8 + 5 = 12 + 5$ *true?* Have partners share information by explaining why the equation is or is not true. Continue this process with the remaining computations.

**Summarize** What makes an equation true?

# DEVELOP: PROBLEM-BASED LEARNING

**COHERENCE: Engage learners by connecting prior knowledge to new ideas.**
Students use their prior understanding about evaluating numerical expressions to examine which computations in a given set maintain equality in an equation.

10–15 min

Solve

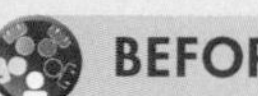

## BEFORE

1. **Pose the Solve-and-Share Problem**
**MP.2 Reason Quantitatively** Listen and look for students who use reasoning rather than calculations to determine which of the computations will keep the equation true.

2. **Build Understanding**
*How do you know that the equation $4 + 8 = 12$ is true?* [The expressions on both sides of the equal sign have the same value, 12.] *How will you tell whether the computation keeps the equation true?* [If the expressions on both sides of the equation are equal after the computation, the equation is still true.]

## DURING

3. **Ask Guiding Questions As Needed**
*What equation shows adding 5 to both sides of $4 + 8 = 12$?* [$4 + 8 + 5 = 12 + 5$] *What is the value of the left side of the new equation?* [17] *What is the value of the right side of the new equation?* [17] *What do you notice about the computations that keep the equation true?* [The computations are the same.]

## AFTER

4. **Share and Discuss Solutions**
Solve Start with students' solutions. If needed, project Amanda's work to discuss which computations keep the equation true.

5. **Transition to the Visual Learning Bridge**
*When the same computation is done to the expressions on both sides of an equation, the equation stays true.*

6. **Extension for Early Finishers**
Write $20 - 2 = 15 + 3$. *Show a way to do the same computation to both sides of this equation so that the resulting equation is true.* [Sample answer: $(20 - 2) + 10 = (15 + 3) + 10$]

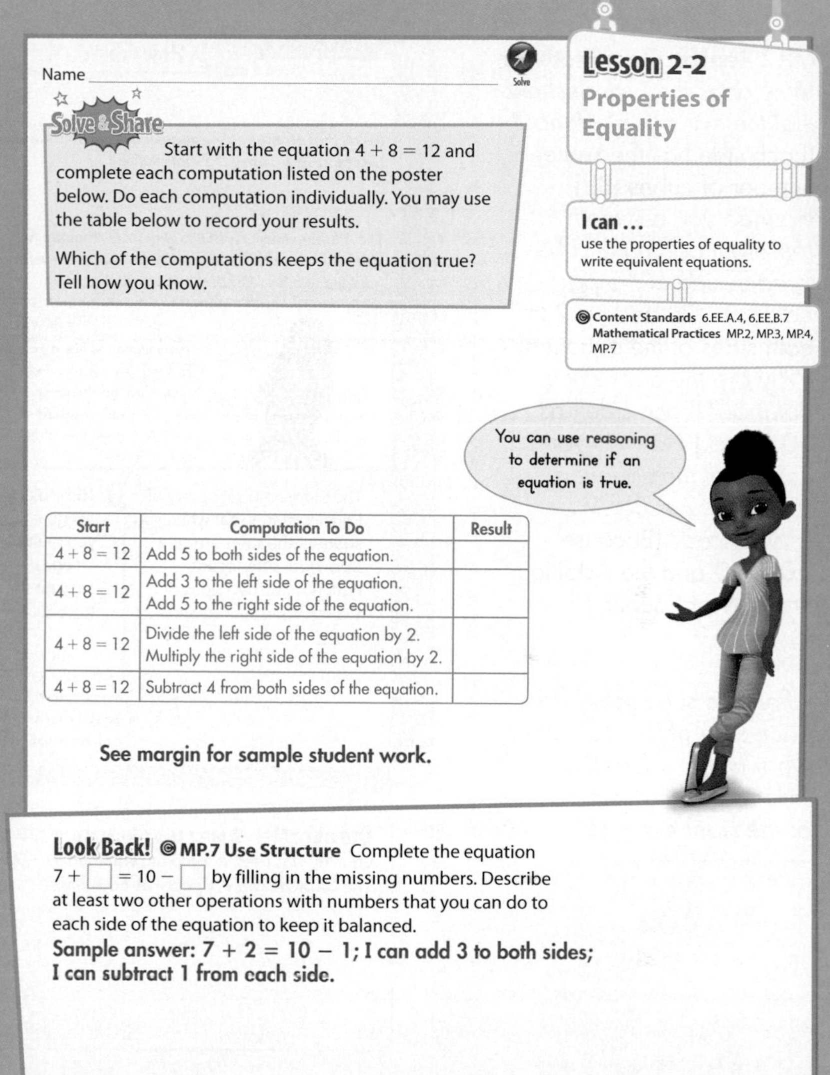

Name

Solve & Share

Start with the equation $4 + 8 = 12$ and complete each computation listed on the poster below. Do each computation individually. You may use the table below to record your results.

Which of the computations keeps the equation true? Tell how you know.

**Lesson 2-2**
**Properties of Equality**

**I can ...**
use the properties of equality to write equivalent equations.

Content Standards 6.EE.A.4, 6.EE.B.7
Mathematical Practices MP.2, MP.3, MP.4, MP.7

You can use reasoning to determine if an equation is true.

| Start | Computation To Do | Result |
|---|---|---|
| $4 + 8 = 12$ | Add 5 to both sides of the equation. | |
| $4 + 8 = 12$ | Add 3 to the left side of the equation.<br>Add 5 to the right side of the equation. | |
| $4 + 8 = 12$ | Divide the left side of the equation by 2.<br>Multiply the right side of the equation by 2. | |
| $4 + 8 = 12$ | Subtract 4 from both sides of the equation. | |

**See margin for sample student work.**

**Look Back!** **MP.7 Use Structure** Complete the equation $7 + \square = 10 - \square$ by filling in the missing numbers. Describe at least two other operations with numbers that you can do to each side of the equation to keep it balanced.
**Sample answer: $7 + 2 = 10 - 1$; I can add 3 to both sides; I can subtract 1 from each side.**

Digital Resources at PearsonRealize.com Topic 2 | Lesson 2-2 89

## Analyze Student Work

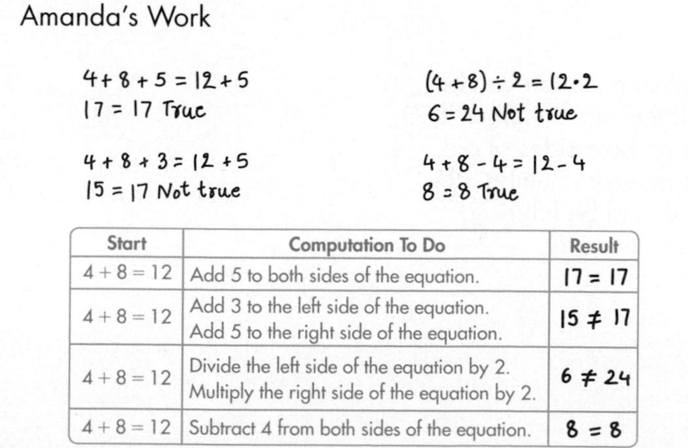

Amanda's Work

$4 + 8 + 5 = 12 + 5$
$17 = 17$ True

$(4 + 8) \div 2 = 12 \cdot 2$
$6 = 24$ Not true

$4 + 8 + 3 = 12 + 5$
$15 = 17$ Not true

$4 + 8 - 4 = 12 - 4$
$8 = 8$ True

| Start | Computation To Do | Result |
|---|---|---|
| $4 + 8 = 12$ | Add 5 to both sides of the equation. | $17 = 17$ |
| $4 + 8 = 12$ | Add 3 to the left side of the equation.<br>Add 5 to the right side of the equation. | $15 \neq 17$ |
| $4 + 8 = 12$ | Divide the left side of the equation by 2.<br>Multiply the right side of the equation by 2. | $6 \neq 24$ |
| $4 + 8 = 12$ | Subtract 4 from both sides of the equation. | $8 = 8$ |

Amanda correctly completes each computation and then states whether the resulting equation is true.

Nick's Work

The equation stays true if you add 5 to both sides or subtract 4 from both sides.

Nick tells which computations maintain equality, but he does not tell how he knows.

# DEVELOP: VISUAL LEARNING

The *Visual Learning Bridge* connects students' thinking in Solve & Share to important math ideas in the lesson. Use the *Visual Learning Bridge* to make these ideas explicit. Also available as a *Visual Learning Animation Plus* at PearsonRealize.com

ELL Visual Learning

PEARSON realize. PearsonRealize.com

Learn Glossary

**MP.2 Reason Quantitatively** *Why does the picture show that the two pans balance?* [Each side has the same number of cubes (8).] *How do you use math to represent adding 2 cubes to each side of the pan balance?* [By adding 2 to both sides of the equation] *Why are the pans still in balance?* [Each side has 10 cubes.] *How do you know that the equation $(5 + 3) + 2 = 8 + 2$ is balanced?* [Because $10 = 10$ and the Addition Property of Equality]

*After 2 is subtracted from each side of the equation, what is the value of the left side?* [6] *What is the value of the right side?* [6]

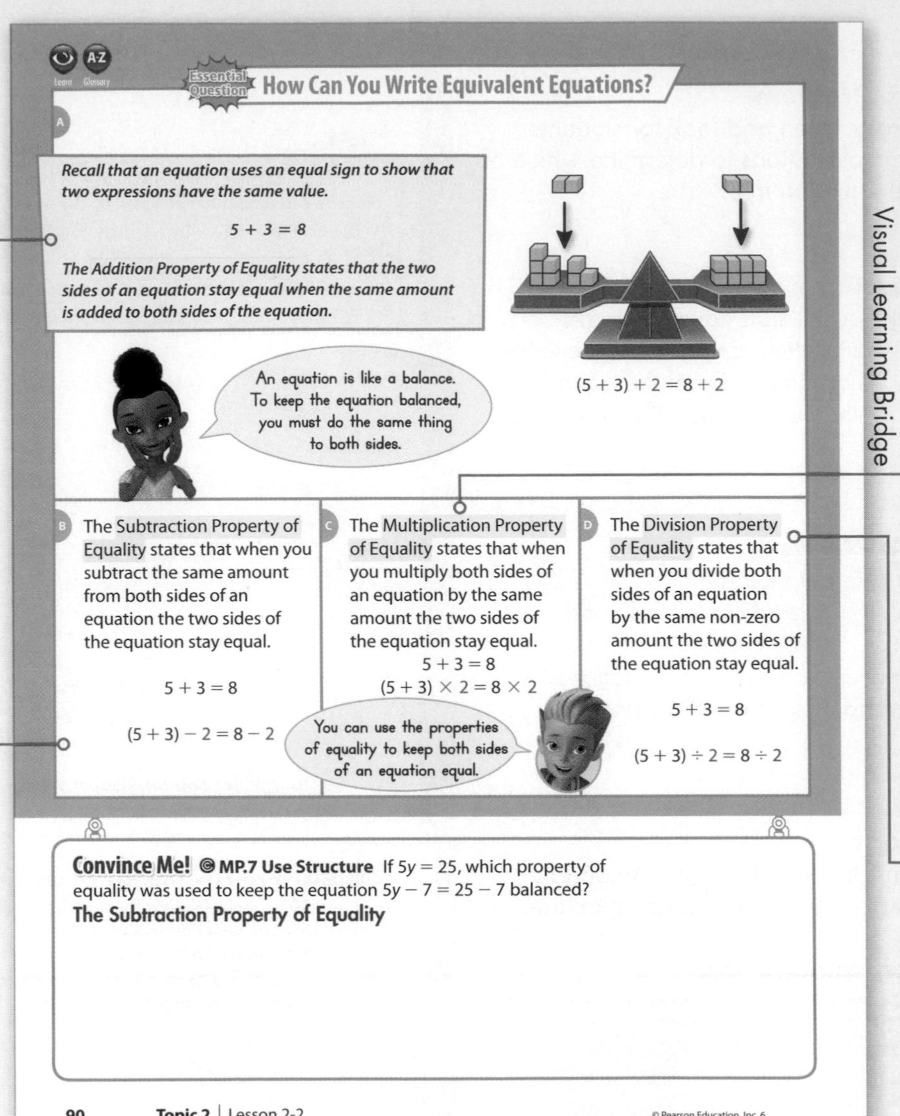

Essential Question **How Can You Write Equivalent Equations?**

A

*Recall that an equation uses an equal sign to show that two expressions have the same value.*

$5 + 3 = 8$

*The Addition Property of Equality states that the two sides of an equation stay equal when the same amount is added to both sides of the equation.*

$(5 + 3) + 2 = 8 + 2$



B The Subtraction Property of Equality states that when you subtract the same amount from both sides of an equation the two sides of the equation stay equal.

$5 + 3 = 8$

$(5 + 3) - 2 = 8 - 2$

C The Multiplication Property of Equality states that when you multiply both sides of an equation by the same amount the two sides of the equation stay equal.

$5 + 3 = 8$

$(5 + 3) \times 2 = 8 \times 2$



D The Division Property of Equality states that when you divide both sides of an equation by the same non-zero amount the two sides of the equation stay equal.

$5 + 3 = 8$

$(5 + 3) \div 2 = 8 \div 2$

**Convince Me!** MP.7 Use Structure If $5y = 25$, which property of equality was used to keep the equation $5y - 7 = 25 - 7$ balanced?
**The Subtraction Property of Equality**

90 Topic 2 | Lesson 2-2 © Pearson Education, Inc. 6

Visual Learning Bridge

*After each side is multiplied by 2, what is the value of the left side?* [16] *What is the value of the right side?* [16]

*Is the expression $(5 + 3) \div 2$ equal to $5 + 3 \div 2$? How do you know?* [No; using the order of operations, $(5 + 3) \div 2$ has a value of 4, but $5 + 3 \div 2$ has a value of 6.5.]

**Prevent Misconceptions** 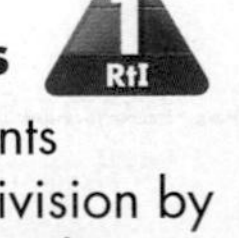
Be sure that students understand that division by 0 is undefined. Dividing the expressions on both sides of the equal sign by any other number maintains equality.

**Convince Me! MP.7 Use Structure** The properties of equality hold for any equation, including those that contain variables. *What math was done to both sides of the first equation to result in the second equation?* [The number 7 was subtracted.]

Essential Question Revisit the Essential Question. An equivalent equation can be written using the properties of equality. If the same number is added to, subtracted from, or multiplied on both sides of an equation, or if both sides are divided by the same non-zero number, the resulting equation is true. The order of operations should be followed when evaluating expressions on each side of the equal sign.

## QUICK CHECK

Check mark indicates items for prescribing differentiation on the next page.
Items 8 and 16 are worth 1 point. Item 13 is worth up to 3 points.

20–30 min

PEARSON realize. PearsonRealize.com

 Practice Buddy  Tools  Assessment

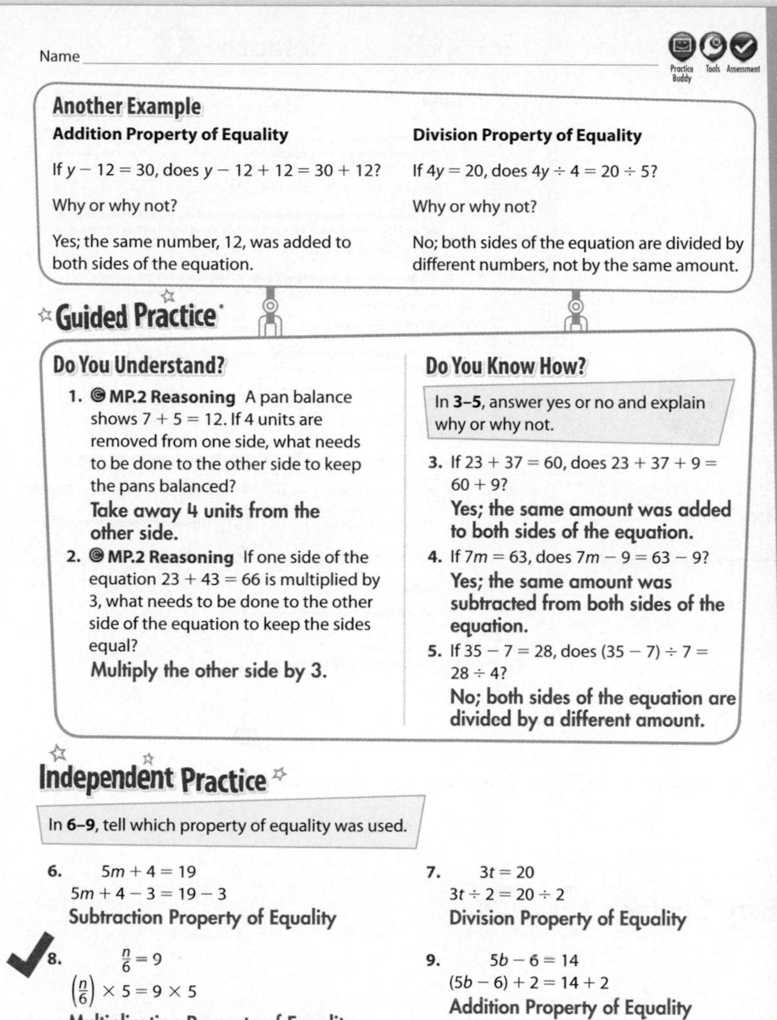

Name

### Another Example

**Addition Property of Equality**

If $y - 12 = 30$, does $y - 12 + 12 = 30 + 12$?

Why or why not?

Yes; the same number, 12, was added to both sides of the equation.

**Division Property of Equality**

If $4y = 20$, does $4y \div 4 = 20 \div 5$?

Why or why not?

No; both sides of the equation are divided by different numbers, not by the same amount.

### Guided Practice*

**Do You Understand?**

1. **MP.2 Reasoning** A pan balance shows $7 + 5 = 12$. If 4 units are removed from one side, what needs to be done to the other side to keep the pans balanced?
   **Take away 4 units from the other side.**
2. **MP.2 Reasoning** If one side of the equation $23 + 43 = 66$ is multiplied by 3, what needs to be done to the other side of the equation to keep the sides equal?
   **Multiply the other side by 3.**

**Do You Know How?**

In **3–5**, answer yes or no and explain why or why not.

3. If $23 + 37 = 60$, does $23 + 37 + 9 = 60 + 9$?
   **Yes; the same amount was added to both sides of the equation.**
4. If $7m = 63$, does $7m - 9 = 63 - 9$?
   **Yes; the same amount was subtracted from both sides of the equation.**
5. If $35 - 7 = 28$, does $(35 - 7) \div 7 = 28 \div 4$?
   **No; both sides of the equation are divided by a different amount.**

### Independent Practice*

In **6–9**, tell which property of equality was used.

6. $5m + 4 = 19$
   $5m + 4 - 3 = 19 - 3$
   **Subtraction Property of Equality**
7. $3t = 20$
   $3t \div 2 = 20 \div 2$
   **Division Property of Equality**
8. ✓ $\frac{n}{6} = 9$
   $\left(\frac{n}{6}\right) \times 5 = 9 \times 5$
   **Multiplication Property of Equality**
9. $5b - 6 = 14$
   $(5b - 6) + 2 = 14 + 2$
   **Addition Property of Equality**

*For another example, see Set B on page 133.



### Math Practices and Problem Solving

10. Bobbie wrote $y + 6 = 15$. Then she wrote $(y + 6) \div 3 = 15$. Explain why the second equation is not equivalent to the first. What can Bobbie do to make the two equations equivalent?
    **The second equation is not equivalent because only one side is divided by 3. Bobbie needs to divide 15 by 3 to balance the equations equivalent.**
11. **MP.2 Reasoning** Rolanda is planning a sleep-over. It will start at 7:30 P.M. and end at 11:15 A.M. the next morning. How long will the sleep-over last?
    **15 h 45 min**
12. **MP.3 Construct Arguments** Scientists often use a pan balance to measure mass when doing experiments. The equation $4 + 3 - 1 = 7 - 1$ represents when a scientist takes one unit of mass from each side of a pan balance. Construct an argument to explain how the scientist knows that the pans are still in balance.
    **Sample answer: The same amount of mass was removed from both pans, so the mass in the pans remain equal and so the pans stay in balance.**
13. ✓ **Higher Order Thinking** Emil has \$1 and a quarter in his pile. Jade has 5 quarters in her pile. If Emil gives Jade \$1 and Jade gives Emil 4 quarters, will the two piles still be equal in value? Explain.
    **Sample answer: Yes, \$1 = 4 quarters. Emil and Jade subtracted the value of \$1 and then added the same amount to each pile. The value of each pile is still equal.**
14. **Vocabulary** If $7w = 49$, which property of equality was used to find the equivalent equation $7w \div 7 = 49 \div 7$?
    **The Division Property of Equality**
15. **MP.3 Construct Arguments** John wrote that $5 + 5 = 10$. Then he wrote that $5 + 5 + n = 10 + n$. Are the equations John wrote equivalent? Explain.
    **Yes; John added a variable that represents the same quantity to each side, so the equations are equivalent.**

**Common Core Assessment**

16. ✓ Which equation is equivalent to $n + 4 = 11$?
    Ⓐ $(n + 4) \times 2 = 11$
    Ⓑ $(n + 4) \times 2 = 11 \div 2$
    Ⓒ $(n + 4) \times 2 = 11 \times 4$
    **Ⓓ** $(n + 4) \times 2 = 11 \times 2$
17. Which of the equations is **NOT** equivalent to $8p = 12$?
    Ⓐ $8p \div 8 = 12 \div 8$
    **Ⓑ** $8p \div 8 = 12 \div 12$
    Ⓒ $8p + 4 = 12 + 4$
    Ⓓ $8p - 2 = 12 - 2$





**Another Example** *Write an equation to illustrate the Division Property of Equality. Start with the equation $4y = 20$.* [Sample answer: $4y \div 2 = 20 \div 2$]

**Error Intervention: Item 4**

**If** students are uncertain about the equation because it contains a variable,

**then** point out that the properties of equality hold for all equations. *In the second equation, what is being subtracted from 7m?* [9] *What is being subtracted from 63?* [9] *So, is $7m - 9 = 63 - 9$ a true equation? Explain.* [Yes, the Subtraction Property of Equality was used.]

**Reteaching** Assign Reteaching Set B on p. 133.

**Items 6–9** Encourage students to identify how the expressions on each side of the equal sign change and which operation is used.

**Item 13 Higher Order Thinking** The original piles can be modeled by the equation $1 + 0.25 = 5 \times 0.25$. Emil gives away \$1 and gains 4 quarters while Jade gains \$1 and gives away 4 quarters. This exchange can be represented by the equation $(1 + 0.25) - 1 + (4 \times 0.25) = (5 \times 0.25) + 1 - (4 \times 0.25)$. Evaluating both sides gives the resulting equation $1.25 = 1.25$.

**Item 15 MP.3 Construct Arguments** While $n$ can represent any number, every instance of $n$ within the same equation must represent the same number. So, when $n$ is added to both sides of the equation, the same number is added to both sides of the equation.

**Multi-Step Problems** *Page 92 Item 13; Page 94 Item 12*

# ASSESS AND DIFFERENTIATE

Use the **QUICK CHECK** on the previous page to prescribe differentiated instruction.

**I Intervention** 0–3 points on the Quick Check

**O On-Level** 4 points on the Quick Check

**A Advanced** 5 points on the Quick Check

## Intervention Activity 

### Properties of Equality

**Materials**

Number cube

- Have students work in pairs. Ask them to write the equation $13 + 7 = 20$.
- The first student rolls the number cube and shows how to use that number to add, subtract, multiply, or divide on both sides of the equation. Have students verify that equality is maintained. Then the other student identifies the property of equality that was used.
- Have students switch roles and repeat the procedure for $48 \div 2 = 24$.
- Then have students repeat the activity for $12x = 36$ and $m - 6 = 15$.

$13 + 7 = 20$

$(13 + 7) \div 2 = 20 \div 2$

$10 = 10$

Division Property of Equality

## Reteach I

Name ______________

Reteach to Build Understanding 2-2

**Vocabulary**

1. The **Addition Property of Equality** states that when you add the same amount to both sides of an equation, the two sides of the equation stay equal.
   $22 - 7 = 15$, so $(22 - 7) + 10 = 15 +$ **10**.
2. The **Subtraction Property of Equality** states that when you subtract the same amount from both sides of an equation, the two sides of the equation stay equal.
   $25 + 12 = 37$, so $(25 + 12) - 9 = 37 -$ **9**.
3. The **Multiplication Property of Equality** states that when you multiply both sides of an equation by the same amount, the two sides of the equation stay equal.
   $18 - 4 = 14$, so $(18 - 4) \times 3 = 14 \times$ **3**.
4. The **Division Property of Equality** states that when you divide both sides of an equation by the same non-zero amount, the two sides of the equation stay equal.
   $8 + 6 = 14$, so $(8 + 6) \div 7 = 14 \div$ **7**.

Complete the statements. Then write the property of equality that is illustrated by the statement.

5. If $\frac{y}{8} = 4$, then $\frac{y}{8} \cdot 8 = 4 \cdot$ **8**. **Multiplication Property of Equality**
6. If $4 + x = 34$, then $4 + x - 4 = 34 -$ **4**. **Subtraction Property of Equality**
7. If $3.5m = 14$, then $3.5m \div 3.5 = 14 \div$ **3.5**. **Division Property of Equality**
8. If $g - 6 = 10$, then $g - 6 + 6 = 10 +$ **6**. **Addition Property of Equality**

**On the Back!**

9. Tell which property of equality was used.
   $6z = 90$
   $6z \div 6 = 90 \div 6$
   **Division Property of Equality**

R 2•2



## On-Level and Advanced Activity Centers  

### Problem-Solving Reading Mat

Have students read the Problem-Solving Reading Mat for Topic 2 and then complete Problem-Solving Reading Activity 2-2.

See the Problem-Solving Reading Activity Guide for other suggestions on how to use this mat.

## TIMING

The time allocated to Step 3 will depend on the teacher's instructional decisions and differentiation routines.

15–30 min

PEARSON realize. PearsonRealize.com

Help

Practice Buddy

Tools

Games

## Technology Center    

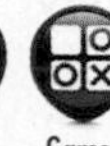
Tools Games

### Math Tools and Math Games

A link to a specific math tools activity or math game to use with this lesson is provided at PearsonRealize.com.

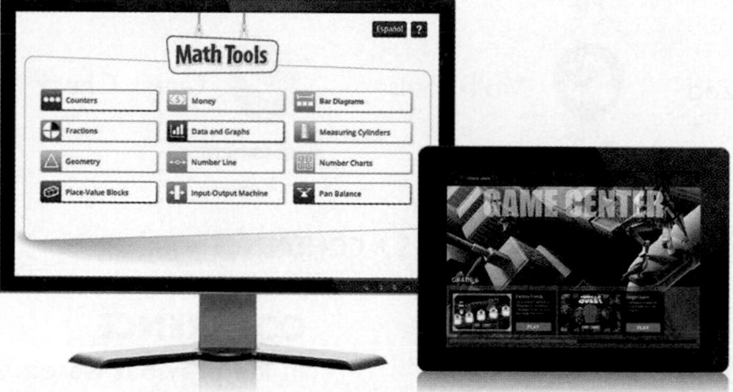


## Leveled Assignment

 Items 1–3, 5, 6, 9, 10, 12, 14, 15  Items 3–10, 12–15  Items 3–6, 10–15

Name ________________

### Homework & Practice 2-2

Properties of Equality

**Another Look!**

You can use the properties of equality to write equivalent equations.


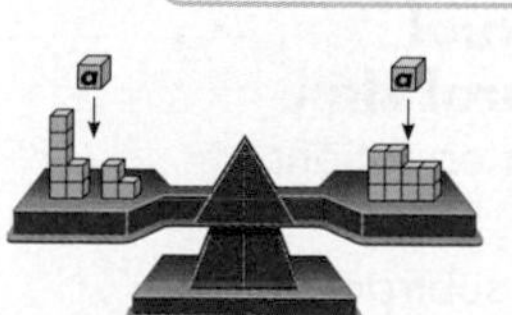

How can you use the properties of equality and $a$ to write four equations that are equivalent to $7 + 3 = 10$?

| | |
|---|---|
| Add the same number to each side. | $7 + 3 = 10$, so $(7 + 3) + a = 10 + a$ |
| Subtract the same number from each side. | $7 + 3 = 10$, so $(7 + 3) - a = 10 - a$ |
| Multiply each side by the same number. | $7 + 3 = 10$, so $(7 + 3) \times a = 10 \times a$ |
| Divide each side by the same number. | $7 + 3 = 10$, so $(7 + 3) \div a = 10 \div a$ |

In **1–4**, tell which property of equality was used.

**1.** $49 = \frac{245}{v}$
$49 \times 65 = \left(\frac{245}{v}\right) \times 65$
**Multiplication Property of Equality**

**2.** $14 + s = 28$
$(14 + s) - 2 = 28 - 2$
**Subtraction Property of Equality**

**3.** $4y = 48$
$4y \div 4 = 48 \div 4$
**Division Property of Equality**

**4.** $88 = 33 + 5x$
$88 - 33 = (33 + 5x) - 33$
**Subtraction Property of Equality**

In **5–8**, answer yes or no and explain why or why not.

**5.** If $10 \times 3 = 30$, does $10 \times 3 + 4 = 30 + 5$?
**No, because a different number is added to each side.**

**6.** If $8n = 180$, does $8n \div 8 = 180 \div 8$?
**Yes, because each side is divided by the same number.**

**7.** If $d \div 3 = 10$, does $d \div 3 + 3 = 10 + 3$?
**Yes, because the same number is added to each side.**

**8.** If $12 - 2 = 10$, does $12 - 2 - 3 = 10 - 2$?
**No, because a different number is subtracted from each side.**



**9. MP.4 Model with Math** Wayne has 6 times the number of songs on an MP3 player as his mom. If Wayne has 1,800 songs, what equation could you write to find the number of songs, $s$, his mom has on her MP3 player?
**$6s = 1{,}800$**

Remember, the expressions on each side of an equation are equal, or equivalent.

**10. MP.3 Construct Arguments** Maggie said she could add 8 to both sides of any equation and the expressions on both sides of the equation would still be equal. Do you agree? Explain why or why not.
**Maggie is correct. Sample answer: The Addition Property of Equality states that if the same number is added to both sides of an equation, then the sides stay equal.**

**11.** James multiplies one side of the equation $56 + 124 = 180$ by a number $n$. What does he need to do to balance the equation?
**Multiply the other side of the equation by $n$.**

**12. Number Sense** Write the next three numbers in this pattern. Then describe the pattern.
6, 10, 8, 12, 10, 14, 12, 16, 14
**18, 16, 20; The pattern is add 4, subtract 2.**

**13. Higher Order Thinking** A store sells 3 pens in a package. There are 12 packages of pens in a box. Write an equation to model the number of pens in a box. Use the equation to write another equation that uses the Subtraction Property of Equality. Explain how the equation is balanced.
**$3 \times 12 = 36$; Sample answer: $(3 \times 12) - 6 = 36 - 6$; I subtracted 6 from both sides of the equation.**

An equation is balanced when the same number is subtracted from each side.

**Common Core Assessment**

**14.** Which equation is **NOT** equivalent to $5 + n = 10$?

Ⓐ $5 + n - n = 10 - n$
● $5 + n - 5 = 10 - 10$
Ⓒ $5 + n - 5 = 10 - 5$
Ⓓ $5 + n + 3 = 10 + 3$

**15.** Which equation is equivalent to $5 = 95 \div x$?

Ⓐ $5 = (95 \div x) + 6$
● $5 + 6 = (95 \div x) + 6$
Ⓒ $5 + 6 = (95 \div x) \times 6$
Ⓓ $5 \div 6 = (95 \div x) + 6$

# LESSON 2-3

# SOLVE ADDITION AND SUBTRACTION EQUATIONS

## DIGITAL RESOURCES PearsonRealize.com

eText — Student and Teacher eTexts

PD — Listen and Look For Lesson Video

Think — Today's Challenge

Solve — Solve and Share

Learn — Visual Learning Animation Plus

Glossary — Animated Glossary

Practice Buddy — Online Personalized Practice

Tools — Math Tools

Assessment — Quick Check

Help — Another Look Homework Video

Games — Math Games

## LESSON OVERVIEW FCR FOCUS • COHERENCE • RIGOR

### FOCUS

**Domain 6.EE** Expressions and Equations

**Cluster 6.EE.B** Reason about and solve one-variable equations and inequalities.

**Content Standard 6.EE.B.7** Solve real-world and mathematical problems by writing and solving equations of the form $x + p = q$ and $px = q$ for cases in which $p$, $q$ and $x$ are all nonnegative rational numbers. Also **6.EE.B.6**.

**Mathematical Practices MP.2, MP.3, MP.4, MP.5**

**Objective** Use inverse relationships and properties of equality to solve one-step addition and subtraction equations.

**Essential Understanding** Solving an equation involves finding the value of the variable that makes the equation true.

**Vocabulary** Inverse relationship

### COHERENCE

In the previous lesson, students learned that when a property of equality is applied to an equation, the equation remains true. This lesson focuses on using the Addition and Subtraction Properties of Equality to isolate the variable on one side of an equation of the form $x + p = q$, where $x$, $p$, and $q$ are rational numbers, to solve for the unknown. In the next lesson, students will use this procedure to solve multiplication and division equations.

### RIGOR

This lesson emphasizes **conceptual understanding** and **procedural skill**. Solving addition and subtraction equations involves two important concepts. First, students learn that addition and subtraction have an inverse relationship: addition *undoes* subtraction and subtraction *undoes* addition. Second, students understand that the properties of equality ensure that adding or subtracting the same value on both sides of an equation maintains equality.

PD Watch the Listen and Look For Lesson Video.

## MATH ANYTIME

### Daily Common Core Review

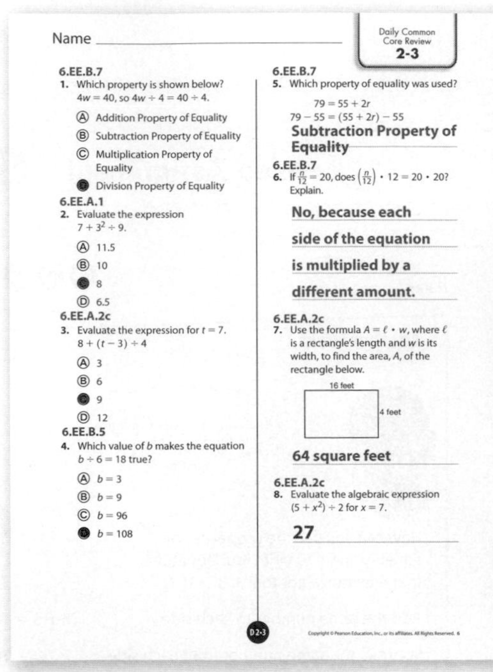
Name ________

Daily Common Core Review 2-3

6.EE.B.7
1. Which property is shown below? $4w = 40$, so $4w \div 4 = 40 \div 4$.
   Ⓐ Addition Property of Equality
   Ⓑ Subtraction Property of Equality
   Ⓒ Multiplication Property of Equality
   ● Division Property of Equality

6.EE.A.1
2. Evaluate the expression $7 + 3^2 \div 9$.
   Ⓐ 11.5
   Ⓑ 10
   ● 8
   Ⓓ 6.5

6.EE.A.2c
3. Evaluate the expression for $t = 7$. $8 + (t - 3) \div 4$
   Ⓐ 3
   Ⓑ 6
   ● 9
   Ⓓ 12

6.EE.B.5
4. Which value of $b$ makes the equation $b \div 6 = 18$ true?
   Ⓐ $b = 3$
   Ⓑ $b = 9$
   Ⓒ $b = 96$
   ● $b = 108$

6.EE.B.7
5. Which property of equality was used?
   $79 = 55 + 2r$
   $79 - 55 = (55 + 2r) - 55$
   **Subtraction Property of Equality**

6.EE.B.7
6. If $\frac{n}{12} = 20$, does $\left(\frac{n}{12}\right) \cdot 12 = 20 \cdot 20$? Explain.
   **No, because each side of the equation is multiplied by a different amount.**

6.EE.A.2c
7. Use the formula $A = \ell \cdot w$, where $\ell$ is a rectangle's length and $w$ is its width, to find the area, $A$, of the rectangle below.
   16 feet
   4 feet
   **64 square feet**

6.EE.A.2c
8. Evaluate the algebraic expression $(5 + x^2) \div 2$ for $x = 7$.
   **27**

D2-3



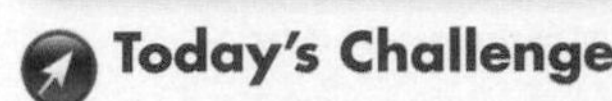

### Today's Challenge

Think Use the Topic 2 problems any time during this topic.

## ENGLISH LANGUAGE LEARNERS 

**Listening** Use visual support to confirm understanding.

*Use with the Visual Learning Bridge on Student's Edition p. 96.*

Read Box A. Ask students to listen to and share important information needed to solve the problem. *How would using cubes on the pan balance help solve the problem?*

**Beginning** Write $n + 7 = 25$. Read Box B as students listen. Point to the first pan balance. *Take 7 cubes from each side.* Point to the second pan balance. *What is left?* Point to $n + 7 = 25$. *$n = 18$.* Then write $y + 8 = 22$. Ask students to work together to draw pan balances as visual support to demonstrate how to find the value of $y$.

**Intermediate** Write $n + 7 = 25$. Read Box B as students listen. Point to each side of the first pan balance. *What happened on each side of the pan balance?* Point to the second pan balance. *What is left? What is the value of* n? Then write $y + 8 = 22$. Have students draw pan balances as visual support to show how to find the value of $y$.

**Advanced** Instruct students to read Box B as partners listen. Have students listen to partners explain why 7 cubes were removed from each side of the pan balance. *What is the value of* n? Then write $y + 8 = 22$. Ask students to listen as partners explain how to use a pan balance to determine the value of $y$.

**Summarize** How does using cubes on a pan balance help solve equations?

# DEVELOP: PROBLEM-BASED LEARNING

**COHERENCE: Engage learners by connecting prior knowledge to new ideas.**
Students extend their understanding of properties of equality to find the value of an unknown in an addition situation. They can use a pan balance to help them represent and solve the problem.

10–15 min

Solve

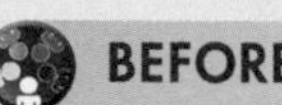

## BEFORE

1. **Pose the Solve-and-Share Problem**
   **MP.5 Use Appropriate Tools Strategically** Listen and look for students who use a pan balance to solve the problem.

2. **Build Understanding**
   *What quantities are represented on the pan balance?* [The 16 students picked up at the last stop and the 25 students on the bus when it arrived at school] *What quantity is not represented on the pan balance?* [The number of students on the bus before the last stop] *How can you represent this unknown quantity in order to balance the pans?* [Add a cube labeled $n$ to the left pan.]

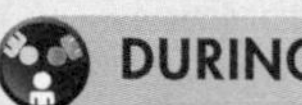

## DURING

3. **Ask Guiding Questions As Needed**
   *How many cubes must you subtract from the left pan to get the n cube alone?* [16] *How many cubes must you subtract from the right to keep the pans balanced?* [16] *What property of equality does this represent?* [Subtraction Property of Equality]

## AFTER

4. **Share and Discuss Solutions**
   Start with students' solutions. If needed, project Hugo's work to discuss how to reason about the pan balance to solve.

5. **Transition to the Visual Learning Bridge**
   *If two pans of cubes balance, they will stay in balance if you add or subtract the same number of cubes on both sides. You can use algebra to represent this situation.*

6. **Extension for Early Finishers**
   *Write an equation to represent the problem about the school bus. Tell what the variable represents.* [Sample answer: $16 + x = 25$; $x =$ the number of students on the bus before the last stop]

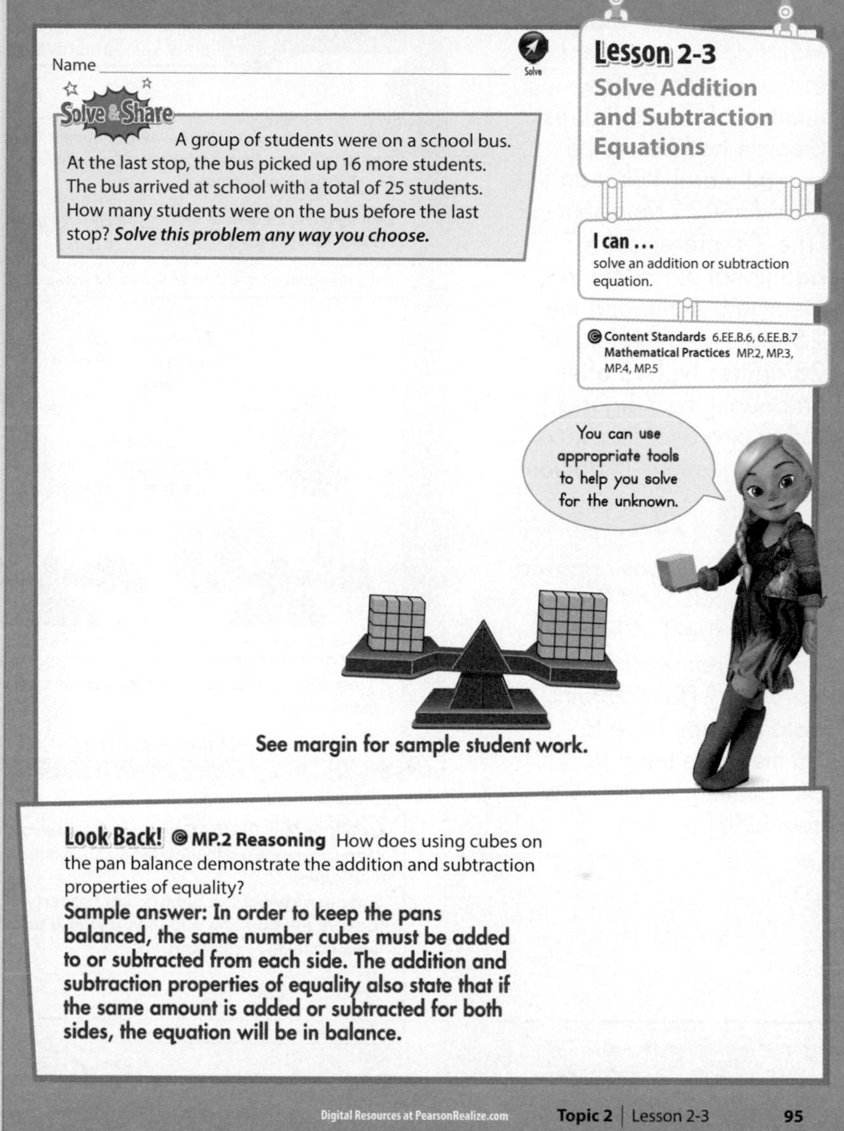

Name
Solve & Share
A group of students were on a school bus. At the last stop, the bus picked up 16 more students. The bus arrived at school with a total of 25 students. How many students were on the bus before the last stop? *Solve this problem any way you choose.*
Lesson 2-3
Solve Addition and Subtraction Equations
I can …
solve an addition or subtraction equation.
Content Standards 6.EE.B.6, 6.EE.B.7
Mathematical Practices MP.2, MP.3, MP.4, MP.5
You can use appropriate tools to help you solve for the unknown.
See margin for sample student work.
Look Back! MP.2 Reasoning How does using cubes on the pan balance demonstrate the addition and subtraction properties of equality?
Sample answer: In order to keep the pans balanced, the same number cubes must be added to or subtracted from each side. The addition and subtraction properties of equality also state that if the same amount is added or subtracted for both sides, the equation will be in balance.
Digital Resources at PearsonRealize.com
Topic 2 | Lesson 2-3
95


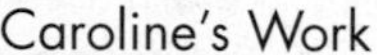

## Analyze Student Work

**Hugo's Work**

n = (cubes)

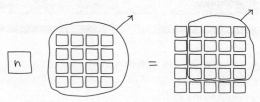

I used a pan balance to show that there were n students, then 16 more got on, and then there were 25 in all. I got n by itself when I removed 16 cubes from each side. That left n balancing with 9 cubes, so n = 9. There were 9 students on the bus before the last stop.

Hugo uses a pan balance to represent and solve the problem.

**Caroline's Work**

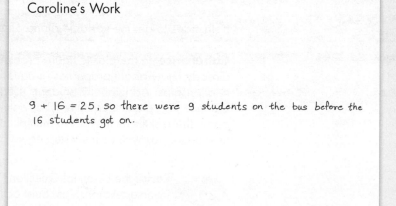

9 + 16 = 25, so there were 9 students on the bus before the the 16 students got on.

Caroline writes an addition equation to solve the problem.

# DEVELOP: VISUAL LEARNING

The *Visual Learning Bridge* connects students' thinking in Solve & Share to important math ideas in the lesson. Use the *Visual Learning Bridge* to make these ideas explicit. Also available as a *Visual Learning Animation Plus* at PearsonRealize.com

Visual Learning

PEARSON realize. PearsonRealize.com

Learn

Glossary

**MP.4 Model with Math** *What does n represent in the equation?* [The number of plastic figures George had before he bought more] *What do the 7 and the 25 represent?* [The 7 represents the 7 additional plastic figures George bought, and the 25 represents the total of 25 figures he had after he bought the 7 figures.] *What operation is shown in the equation?* [Addition]

*Why are 7 cubes removed from the left pan?* [To get *n* by itself] *Why are 7 cubes removed from the right pan?* [To maintain balance, you have to do the same thing to both sides.] *What is the solution?* [$n = 18$]

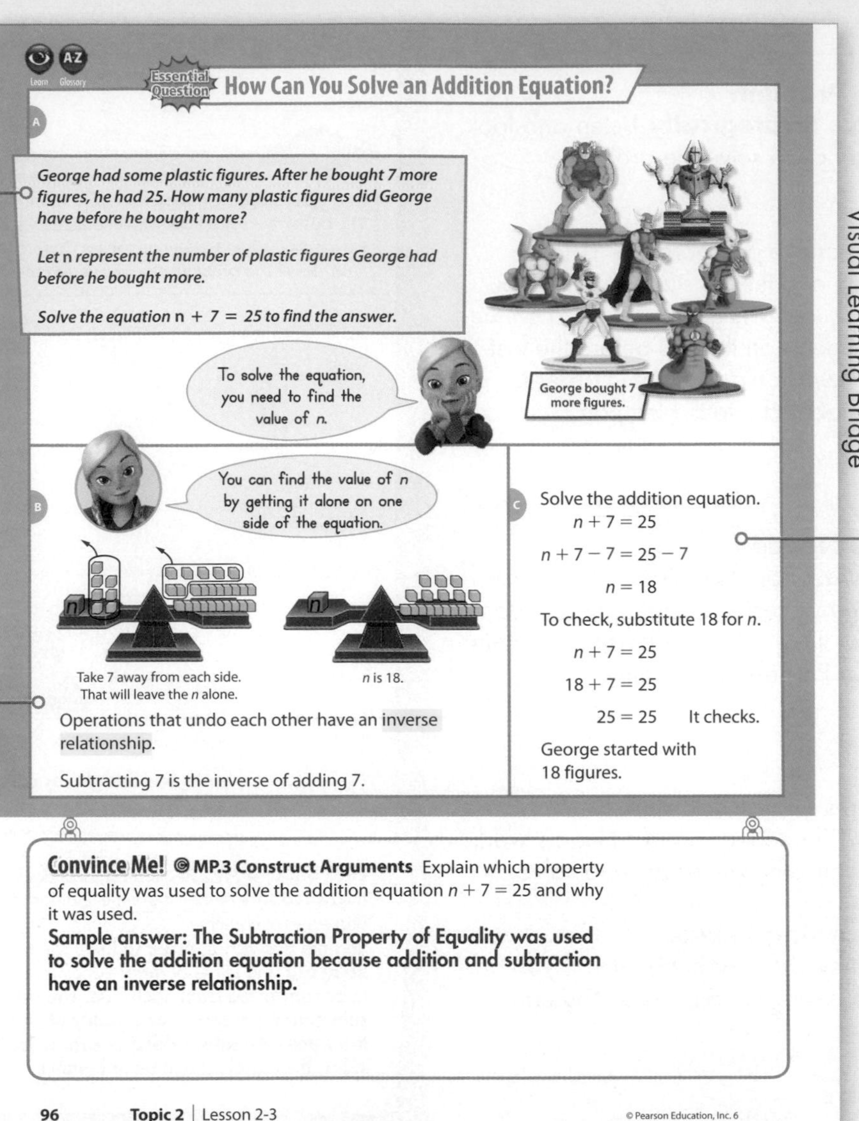


*How would you know if the solution did not check?* [You would not get the same value on both sides of the equal sign, so the equation would be false.]

**Prevent Misconceptions**  Be sure students remember that whatever computation they do on one side of an equation must be done on the other side in order to maintain equality.

**Convince Me! MP.3 Construct Arguments** Help students understand which property of equality is used to solve addition equations. *What operation has an inverse relationship with addition?* [Subtraction] *What is done to both sides of the addition equation? Why?* [7 is subtracted from both sides to get the variable alone on one side of the equation.

**Coherence** In the plastic figure problem, students connect what they already know about properties of equality with the concept of inverse relationships. Additionally, students use the familiar model of a pan balance to represent equality when solving an equation. Students will apply these skills as they solve multiplication and division equations in the next lesson, as well as multi-step equations in Grade 7.

Revisit the Essential Question. To solve an addition equation, use inverse relationships. Subtraction *undoes* addition, so subtract the same quantity from both sides of the equation to solve for the unknown.

## ✓ QUICK CHECK

Check mark indicates items for prescribing differentiation on the next page.
Item 10 is worth 1 point. Items 17 and 19 are worth up to 2 points.

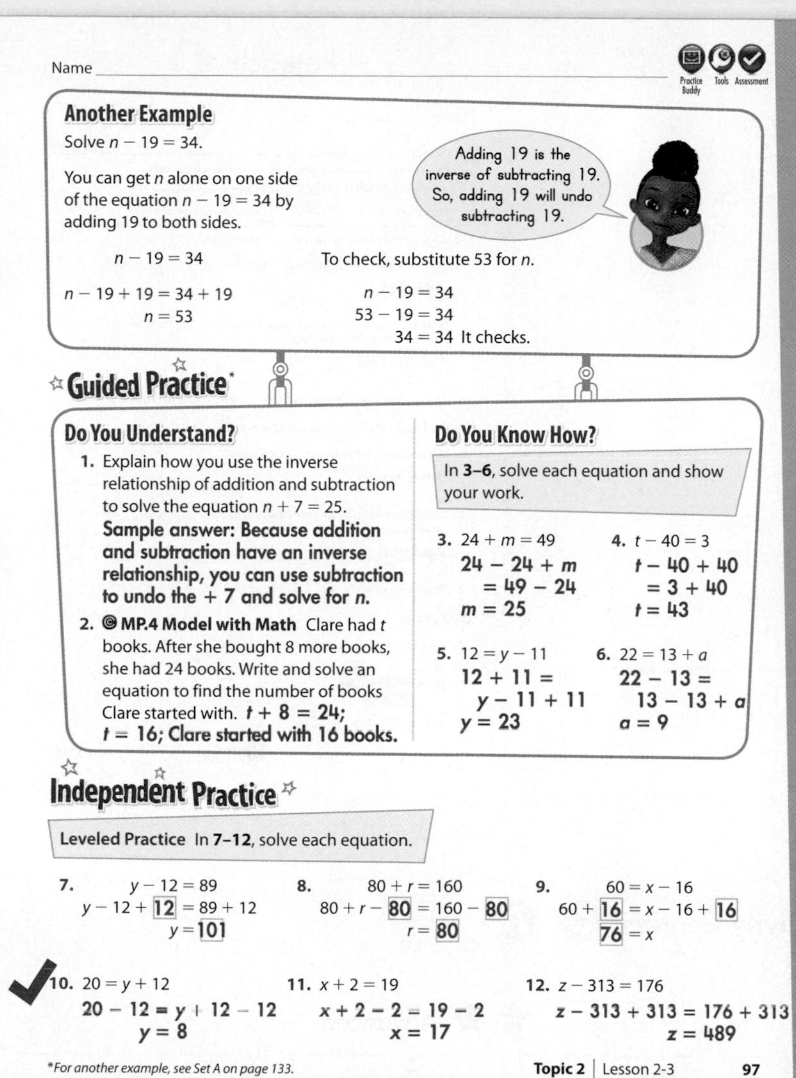

Name

### Another Example

Solve $n - 19 = 34$.

You can get $n$ alone on one side of the equation $n - 19 = 34$ by adding 19 to both sides.

$n - 19 = 34$

$n - 19 + 19 = 34 + 19$

$n = 53$

To check, substitute 53 for $n$.

$n - 19 = 34$

$53 - 19 = 34$

$34 = 34$ It checks.

Adding 19 is the inverse of subtracting 19. So, adding 19 will undo subtracting 19.



### Guided Practice*

**Do You Understand?**

1. Explain how you use the inverse relationship of addition and subtraction to solve the equation $n + 7 = 25$.
**Sample answer: Because addition and subtraction have an inverse relationship, you can use subtraction to undo the + 7 and solve for *n*.**

2. MP.4 Model with Math Clare had $t$ books. After she bought 8 more books, she had 24 books. Write and solve an equation to find the number of books Clare started with. **$t + 8 = 24$; $t = 16$; Clare started with 16 books.**

**Do You Know How?**

In **3–6**, solve each equation and show your work.

3. $24 + m = 49$
**$24 - 24 + m = 49 - 24$**
**$m = 25$**

4. $t - 40 = 3$
**$t - 40 + 40 = 3 + 40$**
**$t = 43$**

5. $12 = y - 11$
**$12 + 11 = y - 11 + 11$**
**$y = 23$**

6. $22 = 13 + a$
**$22 - 13 = 13 - 13 + a$**
**$a = 9$**

### Independent Practice*

Leveled Practice In **7–12**, solve each equation.

7. $y - 12 = 89$
$y - 12 + \boxed{12} = 89 + 12$
$y = \boxed{101}$

8. $80 + r = 160$
$80 + r - \boxed{80} = 160 - \boxed{80}$
$r = \boxed{80}$

9. $60 = x - 16$
$60 + \boxed{16} = x - 16 + \boxed{16}$
$\boxed{76} = x$

✓ 10. $20 = y + 12$
**$20 - 12 = y + 12 - 12$**
**$y = 8$**

11. $x + 2 = 19$
**$x + 2 - 2 = 19 - 2$**
**$x = 17$**

12. $z - 313 = 176$
**$z - 313 + 313 = 176 + 313$**
**$z = 489$**

*For another example, see Set A on page 133.

Topic 2 | Lesson 2-3 97

### Math Practices and Problem Solving

13. MP.2 Reasoning Jeremy bought lunch at school. He had a sandwich and a drink that cost him \$7. His drink cost \$1.75. Solve the equation $7 = s + 1.75$ to find the cost of Jeremy's sandwich, $s$.
**$s = 5.25$; Jeremy's sandwich cost \$5.25.**

14. MP.4 Model with Math Joy added 26 new contacts to her phone list. She had to delete 15 old contacts before she could add any more. Joy now has a total of 100 contacts. Let $c$ represent how many contacts she had on her phone list before she updated it. Write an equation and then solve for $c$.
**$c + 26 - 15 = 100$; $c = 89$**

15. A triathlon is about 51 kilometers. One participant completed two of the three legs of the race and has traveled 42 kilometers. Solve the equation $42 + d = 51$ for the distance, $d$, of the third leg of the race.
**$d = 9$; The distance of the third leg is 9 km.**

16. Eve's allowance is \$25 per week. She is saving money to buy a bike for \$109, a helmet for \$14, and a pair of shoes for \$47. How many weeks does Eve have to save her entire allowance to have enough money for everything she would like to buy?
**It will take Eve about 7 weeks to save enough money.**

✓ 17. **Higher Order Thinking** In the equation $6 + 3y = 4y + 2$ the variable $y$ represents the same value. Is $y = 2, 3, 4,$ or 5 the solution of this equation? Explain how you know.
**$6 + 3(4) = 4(4) + 2$; $18 = 18$; $y = 4$; Substitute 4 for $y$, so the solution is 4.**

What do you need to solve first?

18. When ten is subtracted from four times a number the result is six. Write an equation that represents this sentence. Use any letter variable you choose.
**Sample answer: $4n - 10 = 6$.**

**Common Core Assessment**

✓ 19. Select all the equations that have $g = 6$ as the solution.

- ☐ $g + 2 = 10$
- ☐ $g - 1 = 10$
- ■ $g - 2 = 4$
- ☐ $58 + g = 60$

20. Select all the equations that have $x = 4$ as the solution.

- ■ $42 = 38 + x$
- ■ $x + 15 = 19$
- ☐ $18 = x - 2$
- ■ $36 = x + 32$

98 Topic 2 | Lesson 2-3



**Another Example** *What operation is used in the equation n − 19 = 34?* [Subtraction] *How do you know that you can add 19 to both sides of the equation to solve?* [Sample answer: Addition and subtraction have an inverse relationship. So, adding 19 undoes the subtraction.]

**Error Intervention: Item 5**

**If** students are uncertain about the equation because the variable is on the right side of the equal sign,

**then** point out that they should use the same approach as for other equations. *What number is being subtracted from y?* [11] *What operation undoes subtraction?* [Addition] *Add 11 to both sides of the equation to get y alone.* Tell students that as long as the variable is by itself, it can be on the left or the right of the equal sign. However, algebraic solutions are typically written with the variable on the left side of the equation. For example, $23 = y$ can be rewritten as $y = 23$.

**Reteaching** Assign Reteaching Set A on p. 133.

**Items 7–12 Coherence** Explain to students that it is important for them to record each step as they solve an equation. This will help prevent errors, and it also allows the students or others to review their work and understand what was done to find the solution. As equations become more complicated, showing the steps in a solution process becomes even more important. Developing the good habit of showing work will benefit students now and in the future.

**Item 14 MP.4 Model with Math** In an equation such as $c + 26 - 15 = 100$, point out that the left side of the equation can be simplified to $c + 11 = 100$ before applying the Subtraction Property of Equality.

**Items 19–20** Students have two efficient methods for solving equations. They can use substitution to test the given value in each equation, or they can use properties of equality and operations with inverse relationships to isolate the variable.

**Multi-Step Problems** *Page 98 Items 14, 16, and 17; Page 100 Items 9–12*

# ASSESS AND DIFFERENTIATE

Use the **QUICK CHECK** on the previous page to prescribe differentiated instruction.

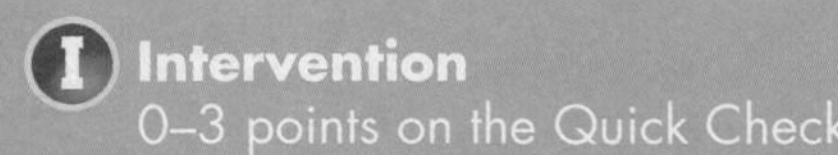

**Intervention**
0–3 points on the Quick Check

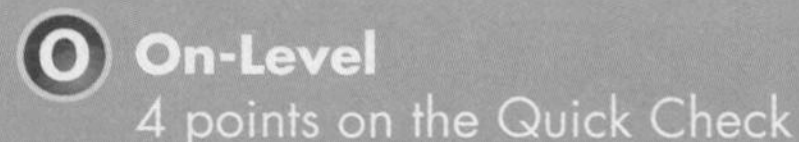

**On-Level**
4 points on the Quick Check

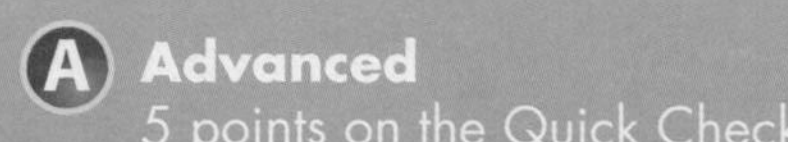

**Advanced**
5 points on the Quick Check

## Intervention Activity 

### Solve Addition and Subtraction Equations

- Have students work in pairs. Ask each pair to write the equation $x + 17 = 22$.
- The first student describes the operation used in the equation. For example, "17 is added to *x*."
- The second student describes how to undo that operation. For example, "Subtracting 17 undoes adding 17."
- Have each student show how to subtract 17 from both sides of the equation and then write the solution. Then have them use substitution to check the solution.
- Have students switch roles and repeat the activity for $x - 8 = 19$.

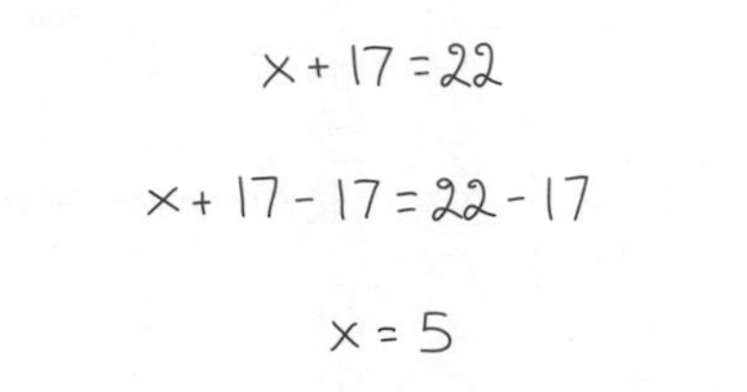


## Reteach I

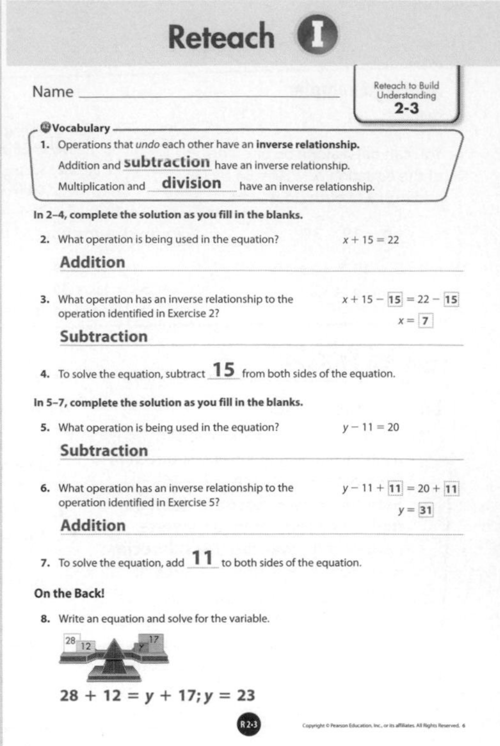

Name ____________________

Reteach to Build Understanding
2-3

**Vocabulary**

1. Operations that *undo* each other have an **inverse relationship.**
   Addition and **subtraction** have an inverse relationship.
   Multiplication and **division** have an inverse relationship.

**In 2–4, complete the solution as you fill in the blanks.**

2. What operation is being used in the equation? $x + 15 = 22$
   **Addition**
3. What operation has an inverse relationship to the operation identified in Exercise 2? $x + 15 - 15 = 22 - 15$; $x = 7$
   **Subtraction**
4. To solve the equation, subtract **15** from both sides of the equation.

**In 5–7, complete the solution as you fill in the blanks.**

5. What operation is being used in the equation? $y - 11 = 20$
   **Subtraction**
6. What operation has an inverse relationship to the operation identified in Exercise 5? $y - 11 + 11 = 20 + 11$; $y = 31$
   **Addition**
7. To solve the equation, add **11** to both sides of the equation.

**On the Back!**

8. Write an equation and solve for the variable.
   **28 + 12 = y + 17; y = 23**

R 2-3



## On-Level and Advanced Activity Centers  

### Center Games

Students work in pairs or small groups to solve addition and subtraction equations using properties of equality. Ask students to record their work on a separate sheet of paper and to provide a check for any equation they solve.

★ On-Level

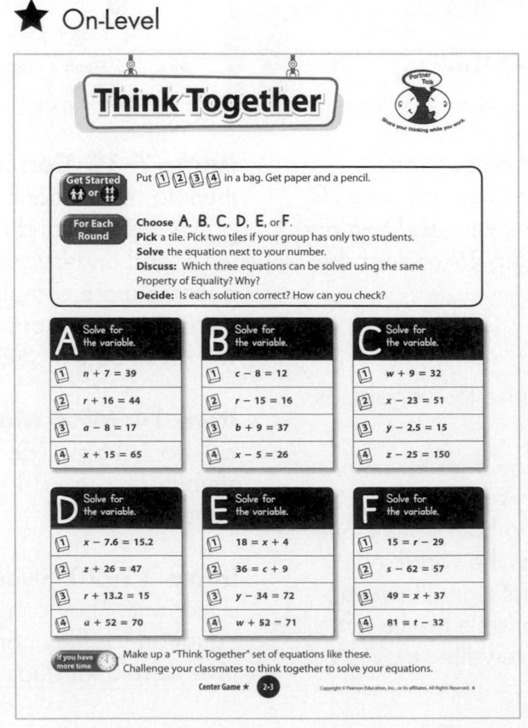

**Think Together**

Partner Talk — Share your thinking while you work.

**Get Started** Put 1 2 3 4 in a bag. Get paper and a pencil.

**For Each Round** Choose A, B, C, D, E, or F.
**Pick** a tile. Pick two tiles if your group has only two students.
**Solve** the equation next to your number.
**Discuss:** Which three equations can be solved using the same Property of Equality? Why?
**Decide:** Is each solution correct? How can you check?

| | A Solve for the variable. | B Solve for the variable. | C Solve for the variable. |
|---|---|---|---|
| 1 | $n + 7 = 39$ | $c - 8 = 12$ | $w + 9 = 32$ |
| 2 | $r + 16 = 44$ | $r - 15 = 16$ | $x - 23 = 51$ |
| 3 | $a - 8 = 17$ | $b + 9 = 37$ | $y - 2.5 = 15$ |
| 4 | $x + 15 = 65$ | $x - 5 = 26$ | $z - 25 = 150$ |

| | D Solve for the variable. | E Solve for the variable. | F Solve for the variable. |
|---|---|---|---|
| 1 | $x - 7.6 = 15.2$ | $18 = x + 4$ | $15 = r - 29$ |
| 2 | $z + 26 = 47$ | $36 = c + 9$ | $s - 62 = 57$ |
| 3 | $r + 13.2 = 15$ | $y - 34 = 72$ | $49 = x + 37$ |
| 4 | $a + 52 = 70$ | $w + 52 - 71$ | $81 = t - 32$ |

**If you have more time** Make up a "Think Together" set of equations like these. Challenge your classmates to think together to solve your equations.

Center Game ★ 2-3



★★ Advanced

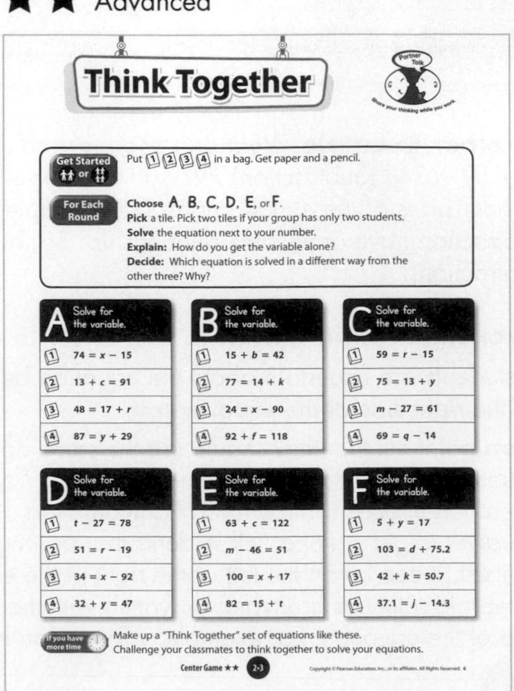

**Think Together**

Partner Talk — Share your thinking while you work.

**Get Started** Put 1 2 3 4 in a bag. Get paper and a pencil.

**For Each Round** Choose A, B, C, D, E, or F.
**Pick** a tile. Pick two tiles if your group has only two students.
**Solve** the equation next to your number.
**Explain:** How do you get the variable alone?
**Decide:** Which equation is solved in a different way from the other three? Why?

| | A Solve for the variable. | B Solve for the variable. | C Solve for the variable. |
|---|---|---|---|
| 1 | $74 = x - 15$ | $15 + b = 42$ | $59 = r - 15$ |
| 2 | $13 + c = 91$ | $77 = 14 + k$ | $75 = 13 + y$ |
| 3 | $48 = 17 + r$ | $24 = x - 90$ | $m - 27 = 61$ |
| 4 | $87 = y + 29$ | $92 + f = 118$ | $69 = q - 14$ |

| | D Solve for the variable. | E Solve for the variable. | F Solve for the variable. |
|---|---|---|---|
| 1 | $t - 27 = 78$ | $63 + c = 122$ | $5 + y = 17$ |
| 2 | $51 = r - 19$ | $m - 46 = 51$ | $103 = d + 75.2$ |
| 3 | $34 = x - 92$ | $100 = x + 17$ | $42 + k = 50.7$ |
| 4 | $32 + y = 47$ | $82 = 15 + t$ | $37.1 = j - 14.3$ |

**If you have more time** Make up a "Think Together" set of equations like these. Challenge your classmates to think together to solve your equations.

Center Game ★★ 2-3

**TIMING**

The time allocated to Step 3 will depend on the teacher's instructional decisions and differentiation routines.

15–30 min

Help | Practice Buddy | Tools | Games

## Technology Center

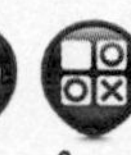

Tools Games

### Math Tools and Math Games

A link to a specific math tools activity or math game to use with this lesson is provided at PearsonRealize.com.

## Leveled Assignment

 Items 1–6, 9, 12–16  Items 2–6, 9–16  Items 3–8, 10–16

Name ______________

### Homework & Practice 2-3

**Solve Addition and Subtraction Equations**

**Another Look!**

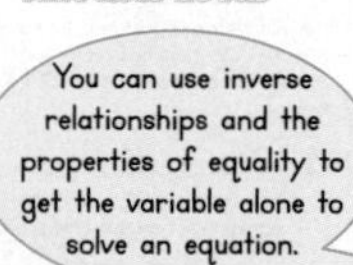

You can use inverse relationships and the properties of equality to get the variable alone to solve an equation.

Remember, you need to do the same thing to both sides of the equation to keep it balanced.


**Addition Equation**

Let $c$ represent the unknown.

Solve the equation $5 + c = 15$.

To get $c$ alone, undo adding 5 by subtracting 5 from both sides.

$$5 + c = 15$$
$$5 + c - 5 = 15 - 5$$
$$c = 10$$

Check your solution by substituting 10 for $c$ in the equation.

$$5 + c = 15$$
$$5 + 10 = 15$$
$$15 = 15 \quad \text{It checks.}$$

**Subtraction Equation**

Let $m$ represent the unknown.

Solve the equation $m - 20 = 16$.

To get $m$ alone, undo subtracting 20 by adding 20 to both sides.

$$m - 20 = 16$$
$$m - 20 + 20 = 16 + 20$$
$$m = 36$$

Check your solution by substituting 36 for $m$ in the equation.

$$m - 20 = 16$$
$$36 - 20 = 16$$
$$16 = 16 \quad \text{It checks.}$$

In **1** and **2**, write an equation and solve for the variable.

1. 
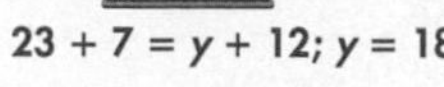

**$23 + 7 = y + 12$; $y = 18$**

2. 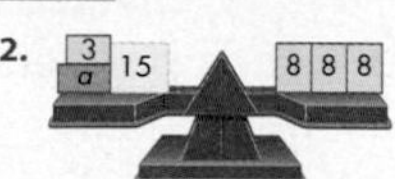

**$3 + a + 15 = 8 + 8 + 8$; $a = 6$**

In **3–8**, solve each equation and check your answer.

3. $g - 8 = 25$ **$g = 33$**

4. $25 + y = 42$ **$y = 17$**

5. $r + 82 = 97$ **$r = 15$**

6. $30 = m - 18$ **$m = 48$**

7. $150 = e + 42$ **$e = 108$**

8. $a - 51 = 12$ **$a = 63$**



9. Let $a$ equal the measure of angle $A$. The equation $360° = a + 90° + 135° + 75°$ represents the sum of the angles in the quadrilateral. Find the missing angle measure by solving the equation.
**$a = 60°$.**

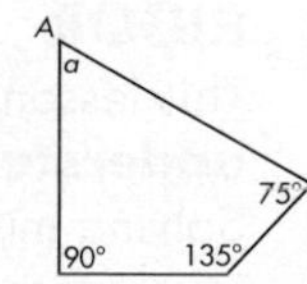


10. **Higher Order Thinking** In the equation $8x - 1 = 3x + 4$ the variable $x$ represents the same value. Which value of $x$ is the solution of the equation; $x = 0, 1, 2,$ or $3$? Explain how you know the solution.
**$8(1) - 1 = 3(1) + 4$; $7 = 7$; $x = 1$; Substitute 1 for $x$, so the solution is 1.**

The value of a variable remains the same throughout the equation.


11. Cameron has a dog-walking service. He just added 2 more dogs to the 14 dogs he walks each week. Now 10 of the dogs are small dogs. What fraction describes the number of small dogs Cameron walks? **$\frac{10}{16}$ or $\frac{5}{8}$**

12. **MP.4 Model with Math** Jorge hiked 15.4 miles on Monday. He hiked 20.6 miles on Tuesday, and the rest of the 50-mile trail on Wednesday. If $m$ represents the miles Jorge hiked on Wednesday, write an equation to show the total number of miles Jorge hiked and solve for $m$.
**$15.4 + 20.6 + m = 50$; $m = 14$; Jorge hiked 14 miles on Wednesday.**

13. **Vocabulary** If $8t = 72$, which property was used to write $8t \div 8 = 72 \div 8$?
**The Division Property of Equality**

14. **MP.3 Construct Arguments** Explain how to find $n$ in the equation $n + 25 = 233$.
**Subtract 25 from both sides. $n = 208$.**

**Common Core Assessment**

15. Select all the equations that represent the bar diagram.

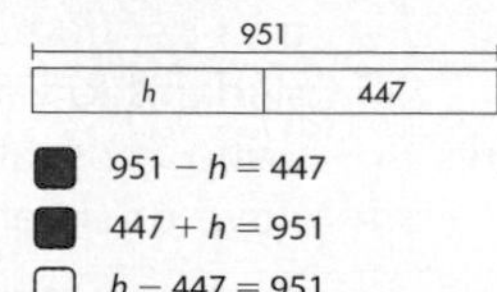


- [x] $951 - h = 447$
- [x] $447 + h = 951$
- [ ] $h - 447 = 951$
- [ ] $447h = 951$

16. Select all the equations that have $x = 49$ as the solution.

- [x] $42 = 38 + x$
- [x] $x + 15 = 19$
- [ ] $18 = x - 2$
- [x] $36 = x + 32$

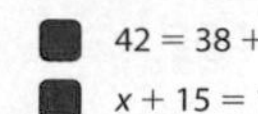
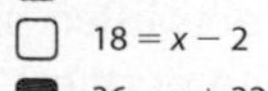
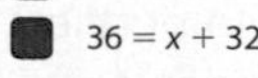

# LESSON 2-4

# SOLVE MULTIPLICATION AND DIVISION EQUATIONS

## DIGITAL RESOURCES PearsonRealize.com

eText — Student and Teacher eTexts

PD — Listen and Look For Lesson Video

Think — Today's Challenge

Solve — Solve and Share

Learn — Visual Learning Animation Plus

Glossary — Animated Glossary

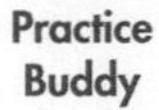
Practice Buddy — Online Personalized Practice

Tools — Math Tools

Assessment — Quick Check

Help — Another Look Homework Video

Games — Math Games

## LESSON OVERVIEW FCR FOCUS • COHERENCE • RIGOR

### FOCUS

**Domain 6.EE** Expressions and Equations

**Cluster 6.EE.B** Reason about and solve one-variable equations and inequalities.

**Content Standard 6.EE.B.7** Solve real-world and mathematical problems by writing and solving equations of the form $x + p = q$ and $px = q$ for cases in which $p$, $q$ and $x$ are all nonnegative rational numbers. Also **6.EE.B.6**.

**Mathematical Practices MP.1, MP.4, MP.6, MP.7, MP.8**

**Objective** Use inverse relationships and properties of equality to solve one-step multiplication and division equations.

**Essential Understanding** Solving an equation involves finding the value of the variable that makes the equation true.

### COHERENCE

In the previous lesson, students used the Addition and Subtraction Properties of Equality to isolate variables and solve equations. This lesson focuses on a similar approach in which students use the Multiplication Property of Equality or the Division Property of Equality to solve equations of the form $px = q$, where $p$, $q$, and $x$ are nonnegative rational numbers. Students will generalize this procedure of isolating the variable to solve more complex equations in Grade 7 and beyond.

### RIGOR

This lesson emphasizes **conceptual understanding** and **procedural skill**. Solving multiplication and division equations involves the understanding that multiplication and division have an inverse relationship: multiplication *undoes* division and division *undoes* multiplication. Students apply their understanding of inverse relationships and properties of equality to solve equations.

PD Watch the Listen and Look For Lesson Video.

## MATH ANYTIME

### Daily Common Core Review

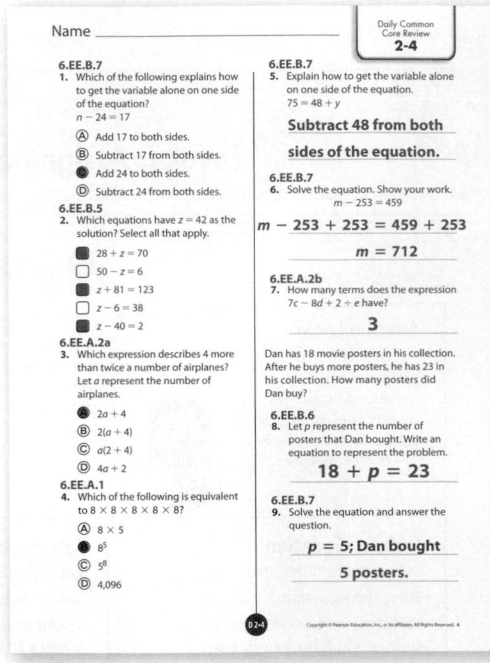
Name ______

Daily Common Core Review 2-4

6.EE.B.7
1. Which of the following explains how to get the variable alone on one side of the equation?
$n - 24 = 17$
- Ⓐ Add 17 to both sides.
- Ⓑ Subtract 17 from both sides.
- ● Add 24 to both sides.
- Ⓓ Subtract 24 from both sides.

6.EE.B.5
2. Which equations have $z = 42$ as the solution? Select all that apply.
- ■ $28 + z = 70$
- □ $50 - z = 6$
- ■ $z + 81 = 123$
- □ $z - 6 = 38$
- ■ $z - 40 = 2$

6.EE.A.2a
3. Which expression describes 4 more than twice a number of airplanes? Let $a$ represent the number of airplanes.
- ● $2a + 4$
- Ⓑ $2(a + 4)$
- Ⓒ $a(2 + 4)$
- Ⓓ $4a + 2$

6.EE.A.1
4. Which of the following is equivalent to $8 \times 8 \times 8 \times 8 \times 8$?
- Ⓐ $8 \times 5$
- ● $8^5$
- Ⓒ $5^8$
- Ⓓ 4,096

6.EE.B.7
5. Explain how to get the variable alone on one side of the equation.
$75 = 48 + y$
**Subtract 48 from both sides of the equation.**

6.EE.B.7
6. Solve the equation. Show your work.
$m - 253 = 459$
$m - 253 + 253 = 459 + 253$
$m = 712$

6.EE.A.2b
7. How many terms does the expression $7c - 8d + 2 \div e$ have?
**3**

Dan has 18 movie posters in his collection. After he buys more posters, he has 23 in his collection. How many posters did Dan buy?

6.EE.B.6
8. Let $p$ represent the number of posters that Dan bought. Write an equation to represent the problem.
$18 + p = 23$

6.EE.B.7
9. Solve the equation and answer the question.
**$p = 5$; Dan bought 5 posters.**

D 2-4



### Today's Challenge

Think Use the Topic 2 problems any time during this topic.

## ENGLISH LANGUAGE LEARNERS 

**Listening** Demonstrate listening comprehension by retelling.

*Use with the Visual Learning Bridge on Student's Edition p. 102.*

Read Box A as students listen. Instruct students to retell information to partners. *What information is needed to solve the problem?* Write $3x = 45$. Read Box B as students listen.

**Beginning** Point to three $x$'s in the left pan of the first balance as you say, *3x*. Point to the 45 cubes as you say, *= 45*. Write $3x \div 3 = 45 \div 3$. Point to one $x$ in the left pan of the second balance as you say, *3x ÷ 3 = 1x*. Point to the 15 cubes as you say, *45 ÷ 3 = 15*. Read Box C. *Multiplication and division have an inverse relationship.* Ask students to listen to partners retell information using the sentence stem: _____ and _____ have an inverse relationship.

**Intermediate** Point to the first pan balance. Instruct students to listen to partners explain how the balance represents $3x = 45$. Point to $1x$ and 15 cubes in the second balance as you say, *3x ÷ 3 = 1x and 45 ÷ 3 = 15*. Read Box C. *Multiplication and division have an inverse relationship.* Ask students to listen to partners retell information using the sentence stem: _____ and _____ have an _____ relationship because _____.

**Advanced** Point to each of the balances. Instruct students to listen to partners explain how the balances represent $3x = 45$ and $x = 15$. Read Box C. Ask students to listen to partners retell information about using inverse relationships of operations.

**Summarize** How are multiplication and division related?

# DEVELOP: PROBLEM-BASED LEARNING

**COHERENCE: Engage learners by connecting prior knowledge to new ideas.**
Students extend their understanding of properties of equality and inverse relationships to solve a multiplication equation. They can use a pan balance to help them visualize the problem and write an equation to solve the problem.

10–15 min

Solve

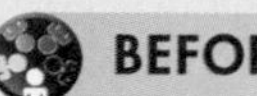

## BEFORE

1. **Pose the Solve-and-Share Problem**
**MP.6 Be Precise** Listen and look for students who define a variable, write an equation, and solve with a property of equality.

2. **Build Understanding**
*Who has more pencils, David or Linda?* [David] *How can you use the pan balance to represent the problem?* [Sample answer: Use the left side of the balance for David's 18 pencils and the right side for Linda's unknown number of pencils.] *How are the 18 pencils related to the number of pencils Linda has?* [18 is twice the number of pencils Linda has.]

## DURING

3. **Ask Guiding Questions As Needed**
*Define a variable for the unknown quantity.* [Sample answer: Let $p$ = the number of pencils Linda has.] *How could you use the variable to describe the number of pencils David has?* [$2p$] *What equation represents the situation?* [$2p = 18$]

## AFTER

4. **Share and Discuss Solutions**
Solve: Start with students' solutions. If needed, project Isabelle's work to discuss how to use an equation to find the solution.

5. **Transition to the Visual Learning Bridge**
*Use what you know about inverse relationships and properties of equality to solve multiplication and division equations.*

6. **Extension for Early Finishers**
*Solve the equation $r \div 3 = 24$. Tell which property of equality you used to solve it.* [$r = 72$; Multiplication Property of Equality]

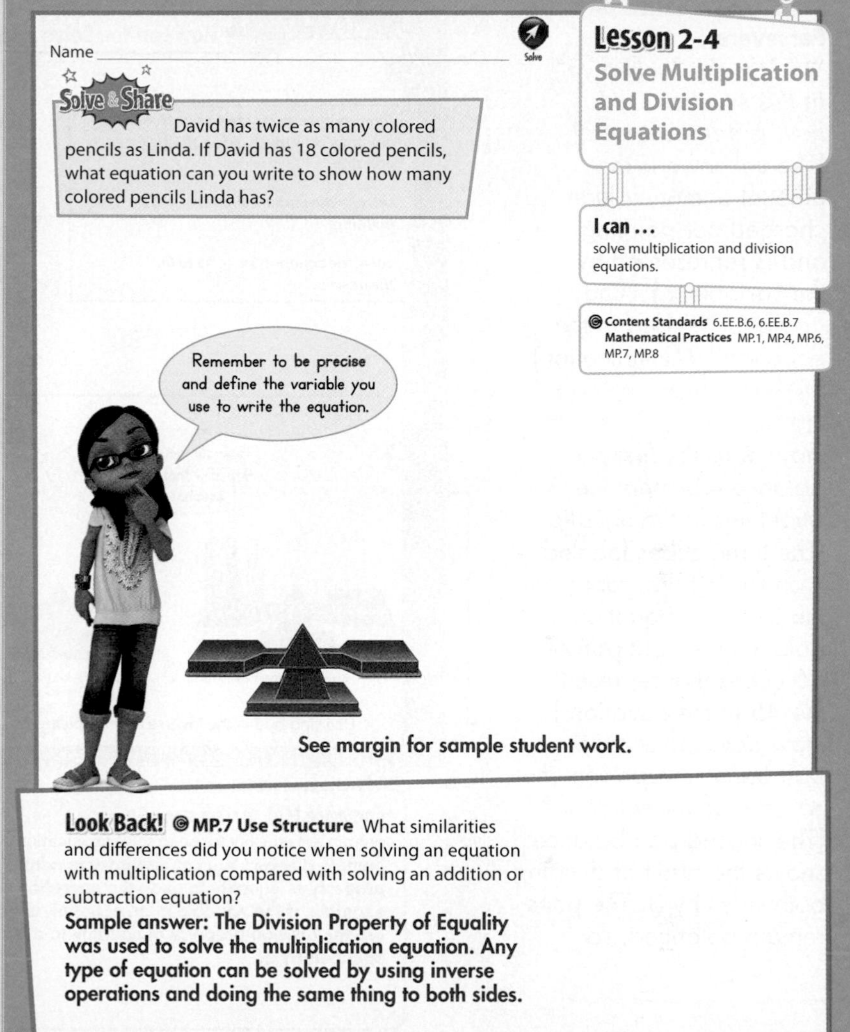

Name
Solve & Share
David has twice as many colored pencils as Linda. If David has 18 colored pencils, what equation can you write to show how many colored pencils Linda has?
Lesson 2-4
Solve Multiplication and Division Equations
I can ...
solve multiplication and division equations.
Content Standards 6.EE.B.6, 6.EE.B.7
Mathematical Practices MP.1, MP.4, MP.6, MP.7, MP.8
Remember to be precise and define the variable you use to write the equation.
See margin for sample student work.
Look Back! MP.7 Use Structure What similarities and differences did you notice when solving an equation with multiplication compared with solving an addition or subtraction equation?
Sample answer: The Division Property of Equality was used to solve the multiplication equation. Any type of equation can be solved by using inverse operations and doing the same thing to both sides.
Digital Resources at PearsonRealize.com
Topic 2 | Lesson 2-4
101


## Analyze Student Work

**Isabelle's Work**

p stands for the number of pencils Linda has.

$2p = 18$

$2p \div 2 = 18 \div 2$

$p = 9$

Linda has 9 pencils.

Isabelle represents the problem with a multiplication equation. She defines the variable and uses the Division Property of Equality to solve.

**Bobby's Work**

$2 \times ? = 18$

Linda has 9 pencils.

Bobby finds the correct solution to the problem. However, he does not write an equation with a letter variable or show how he determined the value of the unknown.

# DEVELOP: VISUAL LEARNING

The *Visual Learning Bridge* connects students' thinking in Solve & Share to important math ideas in the lesson. Use the *Visual Learning Bridge* to make these ideas explicit. Also available as a *Visual Learning Animation Plus* at PearsonRealize.com

Visual Learning

PEARSON realize. PearsonRealize.com

Learn Glossary

**MP.1 Make Sense and Persevere** *What is the "unknown" in this situation and how is it represented?* [The unknown is the amount of money Juan charged per painting and is represented by the variable *x*.] *What operation is used in the equation?* [Multiplication]

*How does the first pan balance represent the quantities in the equation?* [The three cubes labeled *x* on the left pan represent the 3*x* in the equation and balance the right pan of 45 cubes that represent the 45 in the equation.] *How does the second pan balance represent the solution of the equation?* [The second pan balance shows the result of dividing both sides by 3. The pans remain balanced, so $x = 15$.]

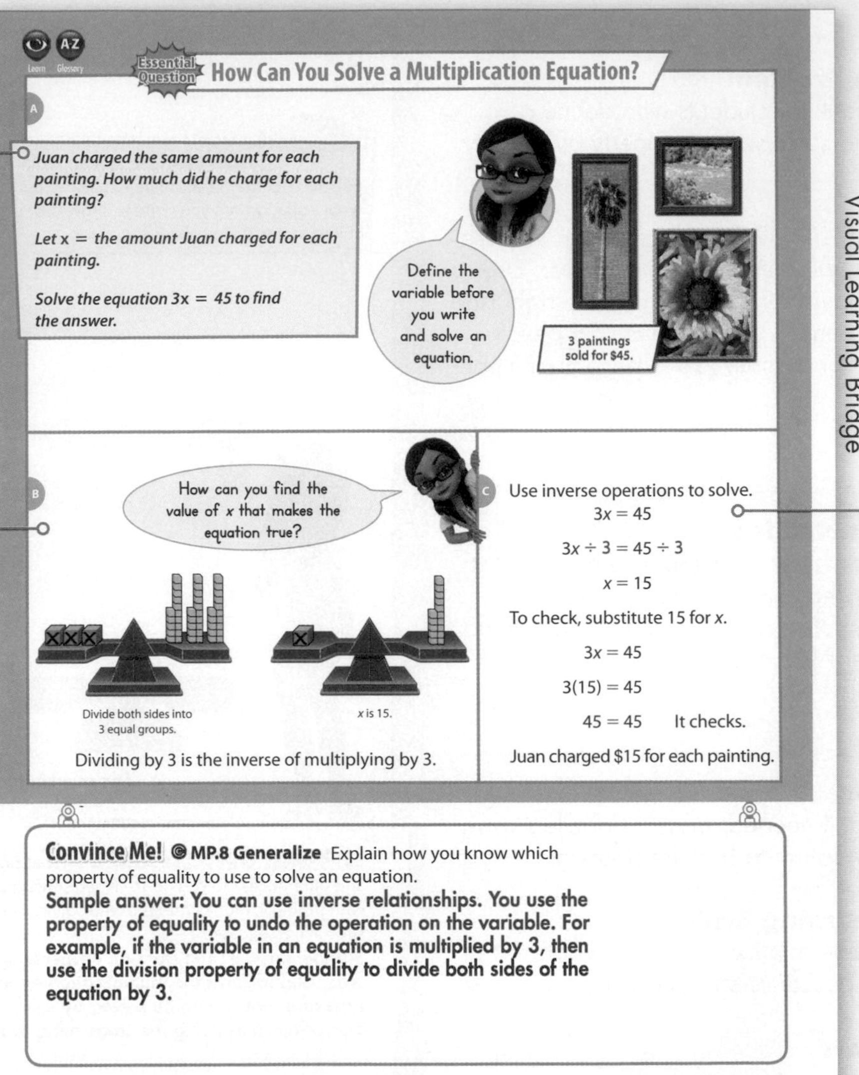

Essential Question
How Can You Solve a Multiplication Equation?
Juan charged the same amount for each painting. How much did he charge for each painting?
Let x = the amount Juan charged for each painting.
Solve the equation 3x = 45 to find the answer.
Define the variable before you write and solve an equation.
3 paintings sold for $45.
How can you find the value of x that makes the equation true?
Divide both sides into 3 equal groups.
x is 15.
Dividing by 3 is the inverse of multiplying by 3.
Use inverse operations to solve.
3x = 45
3x ÷ 3 = 45 ÷ 3
x = 15
To check, substitute 15 for x.
3x = 45
3(15) = 45
45 = 45 It checks.
Juan charged $15 for each painting.
Convince Me! MP.8 Generalize Explain how you know which property of equality to use to solve an equation.
Sample answer: You can use inverse relationships. You use the property of equality to undo the operation on the variable. For example, if the variable in an equation is multiplied by 3, then use the division property of equality to divide both sides of the equation by 3.
102 Topic 2 | Lesson 2-4
© Pearson Education, Inc. 6
Visual Learning Bridge


*Why is 15 substituted for x in the check?* [The solution that was determined is $x = 15$. So you substitute 15 for *x* to see whether the equation is true.] *What does the solution represent in the problem situation?* [Juan charged $15 per painting. Three paintings at $15 each equals the total amount of $45.]

**Convince Me! MP.8 Generalize** Guide students to generalize their prior work. *Without seeing a specific equation, how could you explain to a friend how to solve it?* [Sample answer: Figure out which operation has an inverse relationship to the operation in the equation. Perform that operation on both sides of the equation to undo the operation shown in the equation.] *So, without seeing an equation, how could you decide which property of equality is used to solve it?* [The inverse operation performed on both sides of the equal sign which has an inverse relationship to the operation in the equation, is the type of property of equality used.]

**Coherence** Solving equations of the form $px = q$ builds coherence by extending students' work with solving addition and subtraction equations of the form $x + p = q$ and $x - p = q$. Students continue to use what they know about inverse relationships and how to apply the properties of equality to isolate the variable and solve equations.

Revisit the Essential Question. Students may begin to generalize that equations containing one operation can be solved by applying properties of equality and using inverse operations.

PEARSON realize.
PearsonRealize.com

## QUICK CHECK

Check mark indicates items for prescribing differentiation on the next page. Item 15 is worth 1 point. Items 17 and 22 are worth up to 2 points.

20–30 min

Practice Buddy
Tools
Assessment

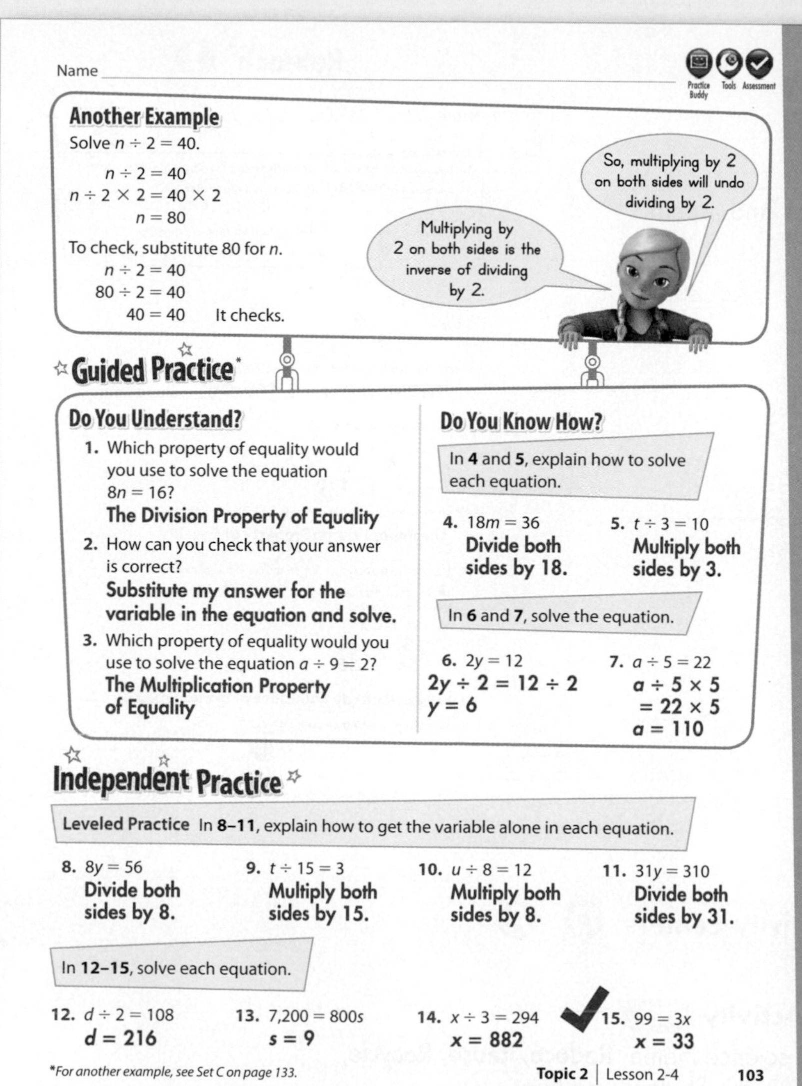

Name

**Another Example**

Solve $n \div 2 = 40$.

$n \div 2 = 40$
$n \div 2 \times 2 = 40 \times 2$
$n = 80$

To check, substitute 80 for $n$.

$n \div 2 = 40$
$80 \div 2 = 40$
$40 = 40$ It checks.

So, multiplying by 2 on both sides will undo dividing by 2.
Multiplying by 2 on both sides is the inverse of dividing by 2.

**Guided Practice***

**Do You Understand?**

1. Which property of equality would you use to solve the equation $8n = 16$? **The Division Property of Equality**
2. How can you check that your answer is correct? **Substitute my answer for the variable in the equation and solve.**
3. Which property of equality would you use to solve the equation $a \div 9 = 2$? **The Multiplication Property of Equality**

**Do You Know How?**

In **4** and **5**, explain how to solve each equation.

4. $18m = 36$ **Divide both sides by 18.**
5. $t \div 3 = 10$ **Multiply both sides by 3.**

In **6** and **7**, solve the equation.

6. $2y = 12$ **$2y \div 2 = 12 \div 2$; $y = 6$**
7. $a \div 5 = 22$ **$a \div 5 \times 5 = 22 \times 5$; $a = 110$**

**Independent Practice**

**Leveled Practice** In **8–11**, explain how to get the variable alone in each equation.

8. $8y = 56$ **Divide both sides by 8.**
9. $t \div 15 = 3$ **Multiply both sides by 15.**
10. $u \div 8 = 12$ **Multiply both sides by 8.**
11. $31y = 310$ **Divide both sides by 31.**

In **12–15**, solve each equation.

12. $d \div 2 = 108$ **$d = 216$**
13. $7{,}200 = 800s$ **$s = 9$**
14. $x \div 3 = 294$ **$x = 882$**
15. ✓ $99 = 3x$ **$x = 33$**

*For another example, see Set C on page 133.

Topic 2 | Lesson 2-4 103

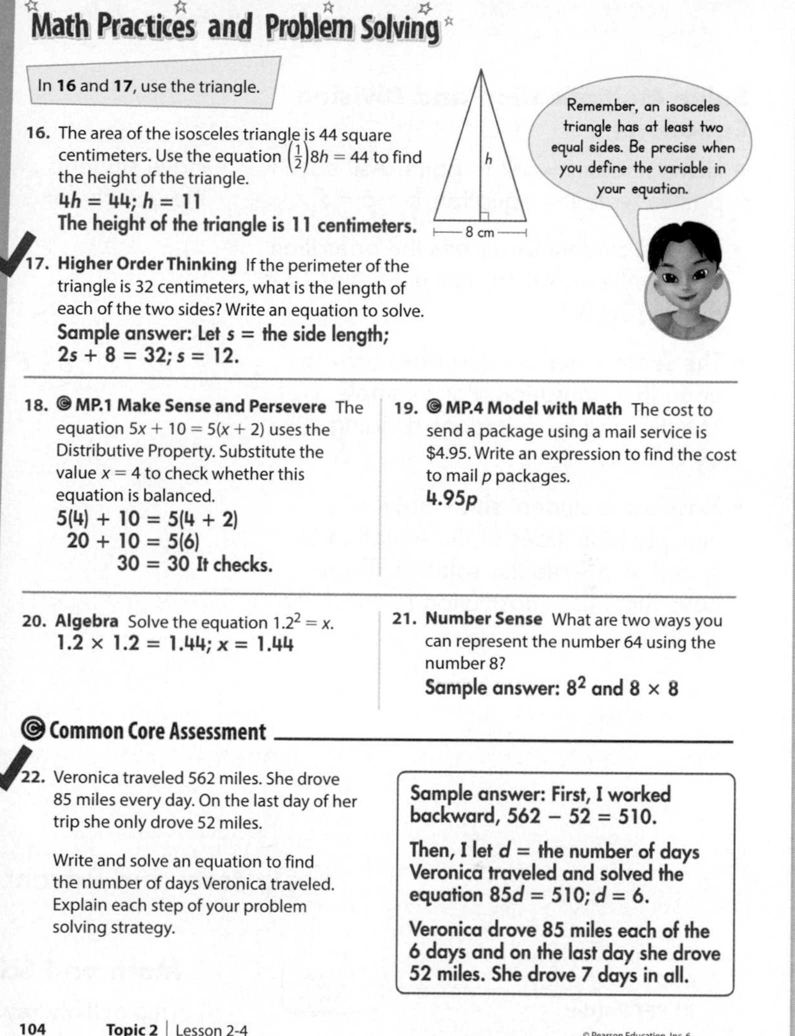

**Math Practices and Problem Solving***

In **16** and **17**, use the triangle.

16. The area of the isosceles triangle is 44 square centimeters. Use the equation $\left(\frac{1}{2}\right)8h = 44$ to find the height of the triangle. **$4h = 44$; $h = 11$ The height of the triangle is 11 centimeters.**
17. ✓ **Higher Order Thinking** If the perimeter of the triangle is 32 centimeters, what is the length of each of the two sides? Write an equation to solve. **Sample answer: Let $s$ = the side length; $2s + 8 = 32$; $s = 12$.**

h
8 cm
Remember, an isosceles triangle has at least two equal sides. Be precise when you define the variable in your equation.

18. **MP.1 Make Sense and Persevere** The equation $5x + 10 = 5(x + 2)$ uses the Distributive Property. Substitute the value $x = 4$ to check whether this equation is balanced. **$5(4) + 10 = 5(4 + 2)$; $20 + 10 = 5(6)$; $30 = 30$ It checks.**
19. **MP.4 Model with Math** The cost to send a package using a mail service is \$4.95. Write an expression to find the cost to mail $p$ packages. **$4.95p$**
20. **Algebra** Solve the equation $1.2^2 = x$. **$1.2 \times 1.2 = 1.44$; $x = 1.44$**
21. **Number Sense** What are two ways you can represent the number 64 using the number 8? **Sample answer: $8^2$ and $8 \times 8$**

**Common Core Assessment**

22. ✓ Veronica traveled 562 miles. She drove 85 miles every day. On the last day of her trip she only drove 52 miles.

Write and solve an equation to find the number of days Veronica traveled. Explain each step of your problem solving strategy.

**Sample answer: First, I worked backward, $562 - 52 = 510$.**
**Then, I let $d$ = the number of days Veronica traveled and solved the equation $85d = 510$; $d = 6$.**
**Veronica drove 85 miles each of the 6 days and on the last day she drove 52 miles. She drove 7 days in all.**

104 Topic 2 | Lesson 2-4

**Another Example** *What operation is used in the equation?* [Division] *What operation do you use to undo division?* [Multiplication] Use this opportunity to point out that $n \div 2$ can also be written as $\frac{n}{2}$. Students should be able to recognize both forms as division.

**Error Intervention: Items 1 and 3**

**If** students are uncertain about which property of equality to use, **then** point out that they should first identify the operation in the equation. *In Item 1, what operation is shown in the equation?* [Multiplication] *What operation has an inverse relationship with multiplication?* [Division] *So, which property of equality should you use?* [Division Property of Equality]

1
RtI

**Reteaching** Assign Reteaching Set C on p. 133.

**Items 12–15 Coherence** As they did with addition and subtraction equations in the previous lesson, it is important for students to write out each step as they solve the multiplication and division equations. Suggest, too, that they check each solution by using substitution.

**Item 17 Higher Order Thinking** Remind students that an isosceles triangle has two sides of equal length. You may want to point out that they already know that the length of one side of the triangle is 8 cm. The perimeter is 32 cm, so the lengths of the other two sides must add to 32 – 8, or 24 cm.

**Item 18 MP.1 Make Sense and Persevere** Listen and look for students who recognize that the equation will remain balanced for any value of $x$ because the Distributive Property was used to write an equivalent expression.

**Multi-Step Problems** *Page 104 Items 16–18 and 22; Page 106 Items 15–18*

STEP 3

# ASSESS AND DIFFERENTIATE

Use the **QUICK CHECK** on the previous page to prescribe differentiated instruction.

**I Intervention** 0–3 points on the Quick Check

**O On-Level** 4 points on the Quick Check

**A Advanced** 5 points on the Quick Check

## Intervention Activity I

### Solve Multiplication and Division Equations

- Have students work in pairs. Ask each pair to write the equation $b \div 6 = 7$.
- The first student describes the operation used in the equation. For example, "$b$ is divided by 6."
- The second student describes how to undo that operation. For example, "Multiplying by 6 undoes dividing by 6."
- Have each student show how to multiply both sides of the equation by 6 and then write the solution. Then have them use substitution to check the solution.
- Have students switch roles and repeat the activity for $9s = 36$.

$$b \div 6 = 7$$
$$b \div 6 \times 6 = 7 \times 6$$
$$b = 42$$

## Reteach I

Name ______________ Reteach to Build Understanding 2-4

**Vocabulary**

1. Two operations have an **inverse relationship** if they *undo* each other.
   Addition and **subtraction** have an inverse relationship.
   $n + 3 - 3 = n$ $t - 8 +$ **8** $= t$
   Multiplication and **division** have an inverse relationship.
   $4d \div 4 =$ **d** $g \div 7 \cdot$ **7** $= g$
2. Solve the equation $9p = 54$.
   $9p = 54$
   $9p \div 9 = 54 \div$ **9**
   $p =$ **6**
   Which property of equality did you use to solve the equation?
   **The Division Property of Equality**
3. Solve the equation $x \div 4 = 30$.
   $x \div 4 = 30$
   $x \div 4 \cdot$ **4** $= 30 \cdot$ **4**
   $x =$ **120**
   Which property of equality did you use to solve the equation?
   **The Multiplication Property of Equality**
4. Maria solved the equation $7d = 56$ and found the solution $d = 8$.
   She can check her solution by substituting **8** for $d$ in the original equation.
   $7d = 56$
   $7 \cdot$ **8** $=$ **56**
   **56** $=$ **56** It checks.

On the Back! **Multiply both sides of the equation by 12.**

5. Explain how to solve the equation $8 = \frac{p}{12}$.

R2-4 Copyright © Pearson Education, Inc., or its affiliates. All Rights Reserved. 6

## On-Level and Advanced Activity Centers O A

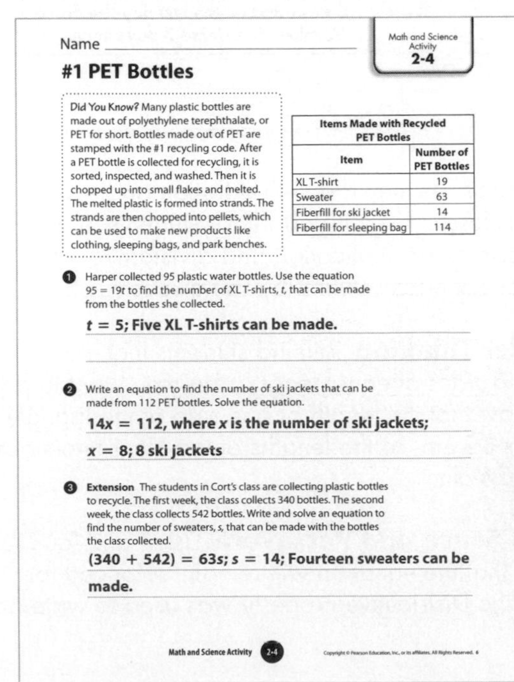
Name ______________ Math and Science Activity 2-4

**#1 PET Bottles**

Did You Know? Many plastic bottles are made out of polyethylene terephthalate, or PET for short. Bottles made out of PET are stamped with the #1 recycling code. After a PET bottle is collected for recycling, it is sorted, inspected, and washed. Then it is chopped up into small flakes and melted. The melted plastic is formed into strands. The strands are then chopped into pellets, which can be used to make new products like clothing, sleeping bags, and park benches.

**Items Made with Recycled PET Bottles**

| Item | Number of PET Bottles |
|---|---|
| XL T-shirt | 19 |
| Sweater | 63 |
| Fiberfill for ski jacket | 14 |
| Fiberfill for sleeping bag | 114 |

1. Harper collected 95 plastic water bottles. Use the equation $95 = 19t$ to find the number of XL T-shirts, $t$, that can be made from the bottles she collected.
   **$t = 5$; Five XL T-shirts can be made.**
2. Write an equation to find the number of ski jackets that can be made from 112 PET bottles. Solve the equation.
   **$14x = 112$, where $x$ is the number of ski jackets;**
   **$x = 8$; 8 ski jackets**
3. **Extension** The students in Cort's class are collecting plastic bottles to recycle. The first week, the class collects 340 bottles. The second week, the class collects 542 bottles. Write and solve an equation to find the number of sweaters, $s$, that can be made with the bottles the class collected.
   **$(340 + 542) = 63s$; $s = 14$; Fourteen sweaters can be made.**

Math and Science Activity 2-4 Copyright © Pearson Education, Inc., or its affiliates. All Rights Reserved. 6

### Math and Science Activity STEM

This activity revisits the science theme, **Reduce, Reuse, Recycle,** introduced on page 79 in the Student's Edition.

### Sample Student Work

2. $x$ = the number of ski jackets
   $14x$ = the number of PET bottles to make 14 ski jackets
   $$\frac{14x}{14} = \frac{112}{14}$$
   $$x = 8$$

## TIMING

The time allocated to Step 3 will depend on the teacher's instructional decisions and differentiation routines.

Help

Practice Buddy

Tools

Games

## Technology Center   

 Tools  Games

### Math Tools and Math Games

A link to a specific math tools activity or math game to use with this lesson is provided at PearsonRealize.com.

## Leveled Assignment  Items 1–8, 13–16, 18  Items 1, 3, 5–8, 13–18  Items 5–12, 15–18

Name ______

Help Practice Buddy Tools Games

### Homework & Practice 2-4

### Solve Multiplication and Division Equations

#### Another Look!

You can multiply or divide both sides of an equation by the same number and it will remain balanced.

Remember, inverse operations undo each other.

**Multiplication Equation**

Let $m$ represent the unknown.

Solve the equation $9m = 54$.

To get $m$ alone, divide both sides by 9.

$$9m = 54$$
$$9m \div 9 = 54 \div 9$$
$$m = 6$$

Check your solution by substituting 6 for $m$ in the equation.

$$9m = 54$$
$$9(6) = 54$$
$$54 = 54 \quad \text{It checks.}$$

**Division Equation**

Let $p$ represent the unknown.

Solve the equation $p \div 8 = 7$.

To get $p$ alone, multiply both sides by 8.

$$p \div 8 = 7$$
$$p \div 8 \times 8 = 7 \times 8$$
$$p = 56$$

Check your solution by substituting 56 for $p$ in the equation.

$$p \div 8 = 7$$
$$56 \div 8 = 7$$
$$7 = 7 \quad \text{It checks.}$$

In **1–4**, explain how to solve each equation.

1. $81 = \frac{m}{9}$ **Multiply both sides by 9.**
2. $h \div 3 = 12$ **Multiply both sides by 3.**
3. $4r = 20$ **Divide both sides by 4.**
4. $34 = 17b$ **Divide both sides by 17.**

In **5–12**, solve each equation. Check your answers.

5. $\frac{t}{35} = 42$ **$t = 1{,}470$**
6. $1 = \frac{u}{2}$ **$u = 2$**
7. $7s = 245$ **$s = 35$**
8. $600a = 2{,}400$ **$a = 4$**
9. $936 = 78p$ **$p = 12$**
10. $29 = k \div 5$ **$k = 145$**
11. $16d = 2{,}864$ **$d = 179$**
12. $180 = \frac{g}{12}$ **$g = 2{,}160$**



13. **MP.4 Model with Math** Teddy is seven times older than Bella. If Teddy is 42 years old, how old is Bella? Write an equation to solve for Bella's age.
**Let $a$ = the age of Bella; $7a = 42$; $a = 6$. Bella is 6 years old.**

14. A cheese farmer distributes 672 ounces of cheese each day. The cheese is packaged in 16-ounce containers. Find the number of containers of cheese distributed each day by solving the equation $16c = 672$.
**$c = 42$**

15. **MP.1 Make Sense and Persevere** Kris left the library at 4:30 P.M. She had been studying at the library for 45 minutes. It takes her 12 minutes to walk to the library from her home. At what time did Kris leave home to walk to the library?
**3:33 P.M.**

16. **Math and Science** In Science class, Krissy labeled 26 vertebrae bones on a diagram of an adult human. Doug labeled 1 bone in the throat and 6 bones of the inner ear for both ears. Most adult humans have 206 bones. Write an equation to solve for the number of bones left in the diagram that need to be labeled.
**Let $b$ = the number of bones; $b + [26 + 1 + 6] = 206$; $b + 39 = 206$; $b = 167$ bones.**

17. **Higher Order Thinking** Stanley bought 108 feet of fencing to put around his backyard. The backyard is a perfect square. Write an equation to find the dimensions of his backyard. Is the area big enough for a pool that is 800 feet$^2$?
**Let $s$ = the sides of Stanley's backyard; $4s = 108$; $s = 27$. No, the backyard is not big enough because it is only 729 feet$^2$.**

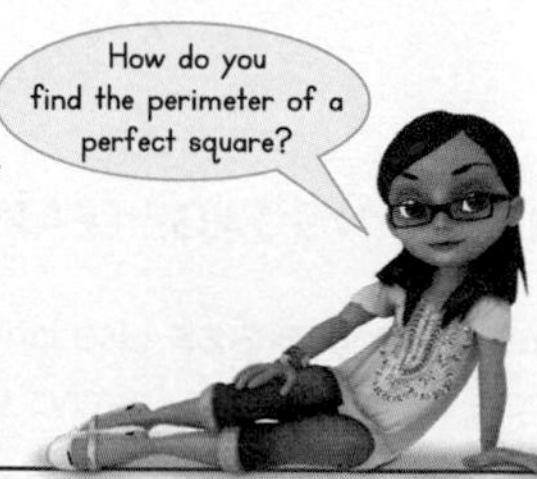

How do you find the perimeter of a perfect square?

#### Common Core Assessment

18. Maggie brought $188.50 to spend on her 7-day vacation. After 4 days of her vacation, she spent $107.50. The last 3 days, she spent the remaining money in the same amount each day.

Write an equation to find how much money Maggie spent each of the remaining 3 days of her vacation.

**Let $m$ = the amount of money Maggie spent each day.**
**$3m = 188.50 - 107.50$**
**$3m = 81$**
**$m = 27$.**
**Maggie spent $27 each of the last 3 days of her vacation.**

# LESSON 2-5

# SOLVE EQUATIONS WITH FRACTIONS

## DIGITAL RESOURCES PearsonRealize.com

Student and Teacher eTexts
eText

Listen and Look For Lesson Video
PD

Today's Challenge
Think

Solve and Share
Solve

Visual Learning Animation Plus
Learn

Animated Glossary
Glossary

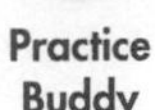
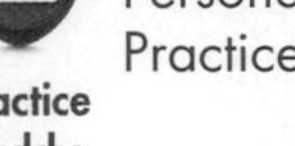
Online Personalized Practice
Practice Buddy

Math Tools
Tools

Quick Check
Assessment

Another Look Homework Video
Help

Math Games
Games

## LESSON OVERVIEW FCR FOCUS • COHERENCE • RIGOR

### FOCUS

**Domain 6.EE** Expressions and Equations

**Cluster 6.EE.B** Reason about and solve one-variable equations and inequalities.

**Content Standard 6.EE.B.7** Solve real-world and mathematical problems by writing and solving equations of the form $x + p = q$ and $px = q$ for cases in which $p$, $q$ and $x$ are all nonnegative rational numbers. Also **6.EE.B.6**.

**Mathematical Practices MP.1, MP.2, MP.4, MP.6, MP.7, MP.8**

**Objective** Solve one-step equations involving fractions and mixed numbers.

**Essential Understanding** Inverse relationships and properties of equality can be used to solve equations with fractions and mixed numbers.

**Vocabulary** Reciprocal

### COHERENCE

In Lessons 2-3 and 2-4, students used inverse relationships and properties of equality to solve one-step equations involving whole numbers. In this lesson, students continue this approach to solve equations that contain fractions or mixed numbers. Students also apply what they learned in Grade 5 about operations with fractions to solve equations. Students will revisit solving equations with fractions in Topic 12, when they learn more about dividing fractions and mixed numbers.

### RIGOR

This lesson emphasizes **conceptual understanding** and **procedural skill**. Students learn to use reciprocals to solve multiplication and division equations. Because the product of a fraction and its reciprocal is 1, multiplying both sides of a multiplication or division equation by the reciprocal of the variable's coefficient isolates the variable on one side of the equation.

PD Watch the Listen and Look For Lesson Video.

## MATH ANYTIME

### Daily Common Core Review

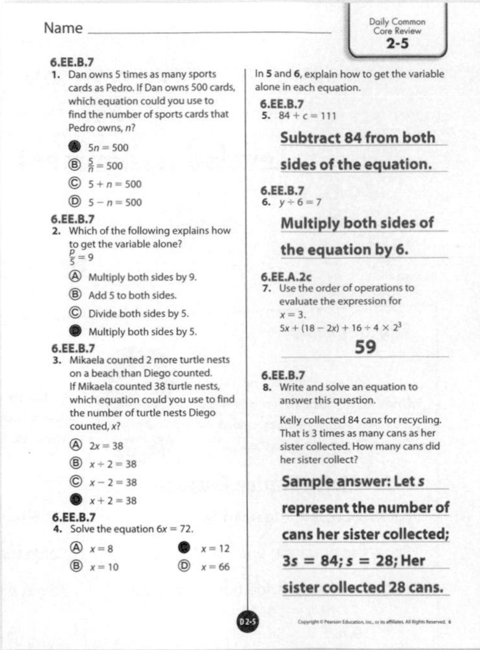

Name ____________

Daily Common Core Review 2-5

6.EE.B.7
1. Dan owns 5 times as many sports cards as Pedro. If Dan owns 500 cards, which equation could you use to find the number of sports cards that Pedro owns, $n$?
   Ⓐ $5n = 500$ (filled)
   Ⓑ $\frac{5}{n} = 500$
   Ⓒ $5 + n = 500$
   Ⓓ $5 - n = 500$

6.EE.B.7
2. Which of the following explains how to get the variable alone?
   $\frac{p}{5} = 9$
   Ⓐ Multiply both sides by 9.
   Ⓑ Add 5 to both sides.
   Ⓒ Divide both sides by 5.
   Ⓓ Multiply both sides by 5. (filled)

6.EE.B.7
3. Mikaela counted 2 more turtle nests on a beach than Diego counted. If Mikaela counted 38 turtle nests, which equation could you use to find the number of turtle nests Diego counted, $x$?
   Ⓐ $2x = 38$
   Ⓑ $x \div 2 = 38$
   Ⓒ $x - 2 = 38$
   Ⓓ $x + 2 = 38$ (filled)

6.EE.B.7
4. Solve the equation $6x = 72$.
   Ⓐ $x = 8$
   Ⓑ $x = 10$
   Ⓒ $x = 12$ (filled)
   Ⓓ $x = 66$

In **5** and **6**, explain how to get the variable alone in each equation.

6.EE.B.7
5. $84 + c = 111$
   **Subtract 84 from both sides of the equation.**

6.EE.B.7
6. $y \div 6 = 7$
   **Multiply both sides of the equation by 6.**

6.EE.A.2c
7. Use the order of operations to evaluate the expression for $x = 3$.
   $5x + (18 - 2x) + 16 \div 4 \times 2^3$
   **59**

6.EE.B.7
8. Write and solve an equation to answer this question.
   Kelly collected 84 cans for recycling. That is 3 times as many cans as her sister collected. How many cans did her sister collect?
   **Sample answer: Let $s$ represent the number of cans her sister collected; $3s = 84$; $s = 28$; Her sister collected 28 cans.**

D2-5



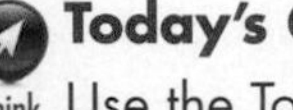

### Today's Challenge

Think Use the Topic 2 problems any time during this topic.

## ENGLISH LANGUAGE LEARNERS ELL

**Learning Strategies** Use and reuse academic language in meaningful ways when speaking.

*Use with the Visual Learning Bridge on Student's Edition p. 108.*

Read Boxes A and B. Instruct students to write *equation, inverse relationships,* and *properties of equality* on index cards.

**Beginning** Instruct students to hold up correct cards when words/phrases are heard. *$3\frac{3}{4} + x = 6$ is an equation.* Read Box C. Write $3\frac{3}{4} + x = 6$. Circle the plus sign. Write $3\frac{3}{4} + x - 3\frac{3}{4} = 6 - 3\frac{3}{4}$. Point to the subtraction sign. *Addition and subtraction have an inverse relationship.* Circle $-3\frac{3}{4}$ on both sides of the equal sign. *Use the Subtraction Property of Equality to subtract $3\frac{3}{4}$ from both sides of the equation.*

**Intermediate** Instruct students to hold up correct cards when words/phrases are heard. *$3\frac{3}{4} + x = 6$ is an equation.* Read Box C. Write $3\frac{3}{4} + x = 6$ and subtract $3\frac{3}{4}$ on both sides of the equal sign. Circle $-3\frac{3}{4}$ on both sides. *Addition and subtraction have an inverse relationship. The Subtraction Property of Equality is used to subtract $3\frac{3}{4}$ from both sides of the equation.* Have students describe each word/phrase.

**Advanced** Read Box C with students. Instruct students to explain how *equation, inverse relationships,* and *property of equality* are used to solve the problem. Ask students to hold up one index card at a time for their partners to describe.

**Summarize** How can inverse relationships and properties of equality help you solve equations?

# DEVELOP: PROBLEM-BASED LEARNING

**COHERENCE: Engage learners by connecting prior knowledge to new ideas.**
Students extend their understanding about solving equations with whole numbers to solving an equation that involves fractions and mixed numbers.

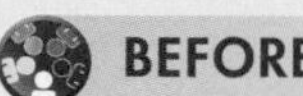

## BEFORE

**1. Pose the Solve-and-Share Problem**
**MP.2 Reason Quantitatively** Listen and look for students who write and solve an equation with fractions.

**2. Build Understanding**
*What operation can you use to solve this problem?* [Sample answer: Addition or subtraction can be used, depending on the equation you write.]

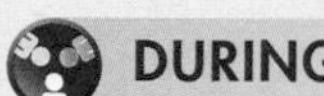

## DURING

**3. Ask Guiding Questions As Needed**
*How much rain fell in the morning?* [$\frac{3}{8}$ inch] *What is the total amount of rain that fell the entire day?* [$1\frac{1}{4}$ inches] *How can you tell?* [It is shown in the rain gauge.] *What equation could you write to represent this situation?* [Sample answer: $\frac{3}{8} + n = 1\frac{1}{4}$] *How would you solve the equation?* [Subtract $\frac{3}{8}$ from both sides.]

## AFTER

**4. Share and Discuss Solutions**
Solve Start with students' solutions. If needed, project Nathan's work to discuss how to write and solve an equation with fractions to find the solution to the problem.

**5. Transition to the Visual Learning Bridge**
*Inverse relationships and the properties of equality are used to solve equations with fractions and mixed numbers in the same way they are used to solve equations with whole numbers.*

**6. Extension for Early Finishers**
*Solve the equation* $n - 3\frac{1}{3} = 5\frac{2}{5}$. [$n = 8\frac{11}{15}$]

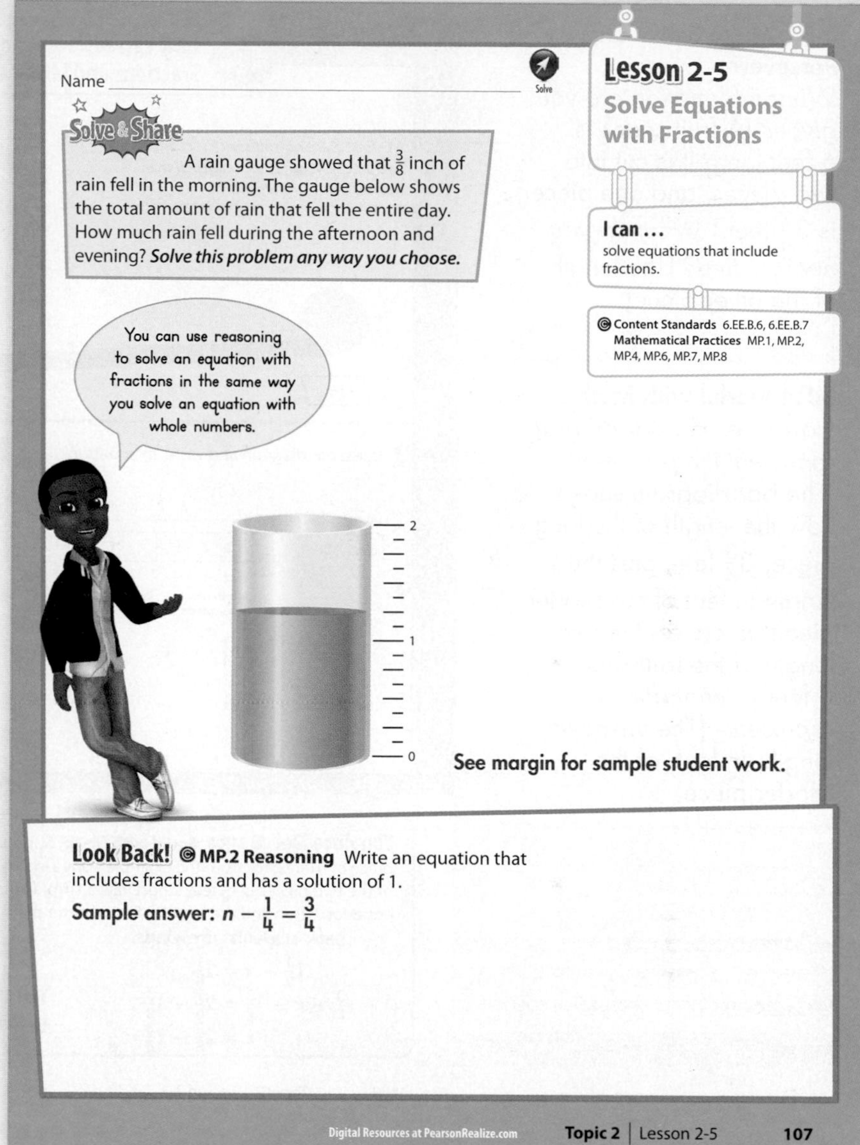

Name

**Solve & Share**

A rain gauge showed that $\frac{3}{8}$ inch of rain fell in the morning. The gauge below shows the total amount of rain that fell the entire day. How much rain fell during the afternoon and evening? ***Solve this problem any way you choose.***

**Lesson 2-5**
**Solve Equations with Fractions**

**I can ...**
solve equations that include fractions.

Content Standards 6.EE.B.6, 6.EE.B.7
Mathematical Practices MP.1, MP.2, MP.4, MP.6, MP.7, MP.8

You can use reasoning to solve an equation with fractions in the same way you solve an equation with whole numbers.
2
1
0



See margin for sample student work.

**Look Back!** MP.2 Reasoning Write an equation that includes fractions and has a solution of 1.

**Sample answer:** $n - \frac{1}{4} = \frac{3}{4}$

Digital Resources at PearsonRealize.com  **Topic 2** | Lesson 2-5  **107**

## Analyze Student Work

Nathan's Work

$n + \frac{3}{8} = 1\frac{1}{4}$

$n + \frac{3}{8} - \frac{3}{8} = 1\frac{1}{4} - \frac{3}{8}$

$n + \frac{7}{8}$

$\frac{7}{8}$ inch of rain fell later that day.

$1\frac{1}{4} - \frac{3}{8}$

$1\frac{2}{8} - \frac{3}{8}$

$\frac{10}{8} - \frac{3}{8}$

$\frac{7}{8}$

Nathan represents the problem with an addition equation. He correctly solves the equation using the Subtraction Property of Equality.

Karin's Work

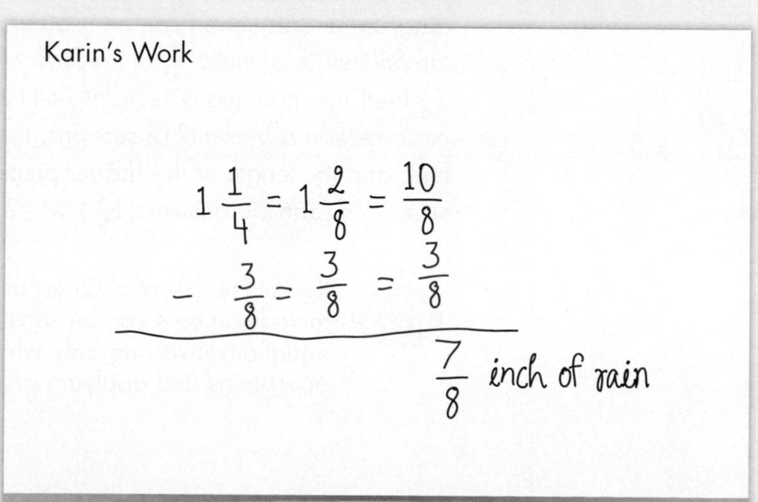

$1\frac{1}{4} = 1\frac{2}{8} = \frac{10}{8}$
$- \frac{3}{8} = \frac{3}{8} = \frac{3}{8}$
$\frac{7}{8}$ inch of rain


Karin uses subtraction to find the correct solution to the problem.

# DEVELOP: VISUAL LEARNING

The *Visual Learning Bridge* connects students' thinking in Solve & Share to important math ideas in the lesson. Use the *Visual Learning Bridge* to make these ideas explicit. Also available as a *Visual Learning Animation Plus* at PearsonRealize.com

Visual Learning

PEARSON realize. PearsonRealize.com

Learn Glossary

**MP.1 Make Sense and Persevere**
*What information are you given?* [A fruit snack is 6 feet long. It is cut into two pieces, and one piece is $3\frac{3}{4}$ feet.] *What do you need to find?* [The length of the other piece]

**MP.4 Model with Math**
*How does the bar diagram represent the problem?* [The bar diagram shows how the length of the long piece, $3\frac{3}{4}$ feet, plus the length in feet of the shorter piece, *x*, equals the total length of the fruit snack, 6 feet.] *What does x represent?* [The unknown length, in feet, of the shorter piece]

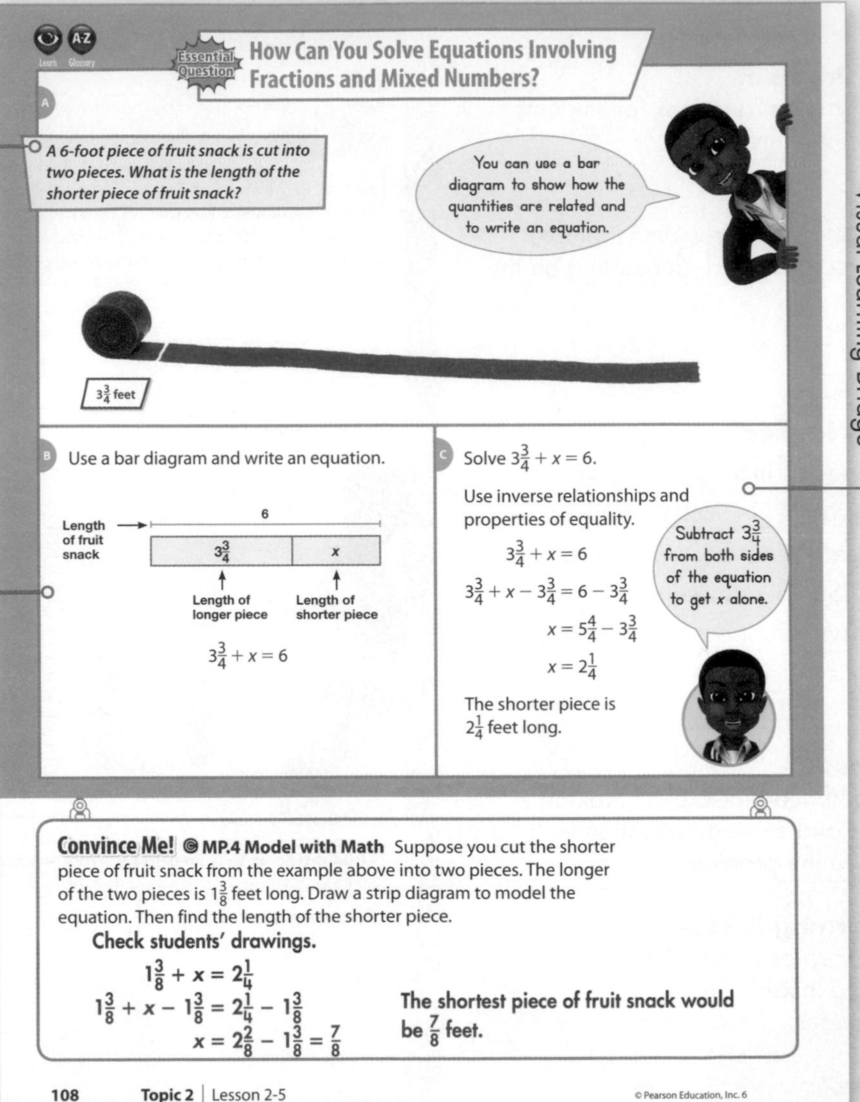

Essential Question
How Can You Solve Equations Involving Fractions and Mixed Numbers?
A 6-foot piece of fruit snack is cut into two pieces. What is the length of the shorter piece of fruit snack?
You can use a bar diagram to show how the quantities are related and to write an equation.
$3\frac{3}{4}$ feet
Use a bar diagram and write an equation.
Length of fruit snack
6
$3\frac{3}{4}$
x
Length of longer piece
Length of shorter piece
$3\frac{3}{4} + x = 6$
Solve $3\frac{3}{4} + x = 6$.
Use inverse relationships and properties of equality.
$3\frac{3}{4} + x = 6$
$3\frac{3}{4} + x - 3\frac{3}{4} = 6 - 3\frac{3}{4}$
$x = 5\frac{4}{4} - 3\frac{3}{4}$
$x = 2\frac{1}{4}$
Subtract $3\frac{3}{4}$ from both sides of the equation to get x alone.
The shorter piece is $2\frac{1}{4}$ feet long.
Convince Me! MP.4 Model with Math Suppose you cut the shorter piece of fruit snack from the example above into two pieces. The longer of the two pieces is $1\frac{3}{8}$ feet long. Draw a strip diagram to model the equation. Then find the length of the shorter piece.
Check students' drawings.
$1\frac{3}{8} + x = 2\frac{1}{4}$
$1\frac{3}{8} + x - 1\frac{3}{8} = 2\frac{1}{4} - 1\frac{3}{8}$
$x = 2\frac{2}{8} - 1\frac{3}{8} = \frac{7}{8}$
The shortest piece of fruit snack would be $\frac{7}{8}$ feet.
108 Topic 2 | Lesson 2-5
© Pearson Education, Inc. 6
Visual Learning Bridge


*Why do you rewrite 6 as $5\frac{4}{4}$?* [So you can subtract $\frac{3}{4}$ from $\frac{4}{4}$]

**Convince Me! MP.4 Model with Math** Help students see that this problem is similar to the original fruit snack problem above, so a strip diagram and equation can be used to represent the situation. *What will the full length of the diagram represent?* [The length of the shorter piece, $2\frac{1}{4}$ feet] *Into how many sections will the diagram be divided? What will each section represent?* [2 sections; the length of the longer piece or $1\frac{3}{8}$ feet, and the length of the shorter piece] *What equation represents this situation?* [Sample answers: $1\frac{3}{8} + x = 2\frac{1}{4}$, $x = 2\frac{1}{4} - 1\frac{3}{8}$]

Revisit the Essential Question. Equations involving fractions and mixed numbers can be solved using the same approach as with equations involving only whole numbers—by using inverse operations and applying properties of equality.

PearsonRealize.com

## QUICK CHECK

Check mark indicates items for prescribing differentiation on the next page.
Item 6 is worth 1 point. Items 16 and 19 are worth up to 2 points.

20–30 min

Practice Buddy

Tools

Assessment

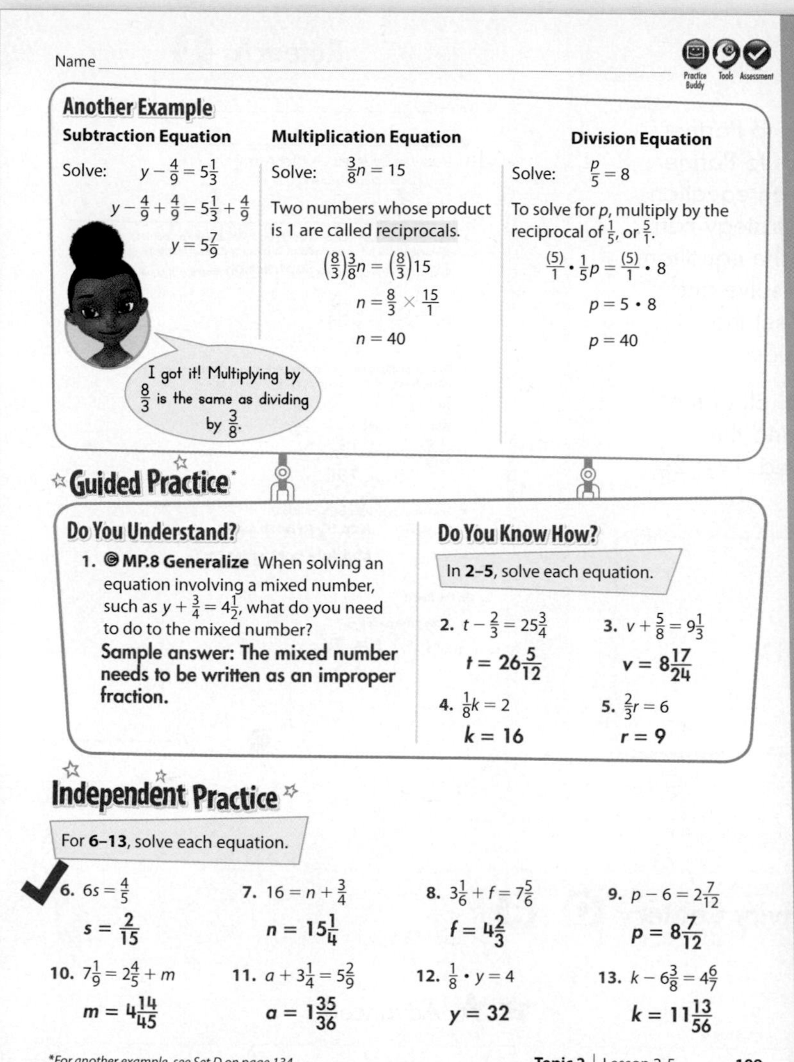

Name

### Another Example

**Subtraction Equation**

Solve: $y - \frac{4}{9} = 5\frac{1}{3}$

$y - \frac{4}{9} + \frac{4}{9} = 5\frac{1}{3} + \frac{4}{9}$

$y = 5\frac{7}{9}$

**Multiplication Equation**

Solve: $\frac{3}{8}n = 15$

Two numbers whose product is 1 are called reciprocals.

$\left(\frac{8}{3}\right)\frac{3}{8}n = \left(\frac{8}{3}\right)15$

$n = \frac{8}{3} \times \frac{15}{1}$

$n = 40$

**Division Equation**

Solve: $\frac{p}{5} = 8$

To solve for $p$, multiply by the reciprocal of $\frac{1}{5}$, or $\frac{5}{1}$.

$\frac{(5)}{1} \cdot \frac{1}{5}p = \frac{(5)}{1} \cdot 8$

$p = 5 \cdot 8$

$p = 40$

I got it! Multiplying by $\frac{8}{3}$ is the same as dividing by $\frac{3}{8}$.



### Guided Practice

**Do You Understand?**

1. MP.8 Generalize When solving an equation involving a mixed number, such as $y + \frac{3}{4} = 4\frac{1}{2}$, what do you need to do to the mixed number?
**Sample answer: The mixed number needs to be written as an improper fraction.**

**Do You Know How?**

In **2–5**, solve each equation.

2. $t - \frac{2}{3} = 25\frac{3}{4}$ **$t = 26\frac{5}{12}$**
3. $v + \frac{5}{8} = 9\frac{1}{3}$ **$v = 8\frac{17}{24}$**
4. $\frac{1}{8}k = 2$ **$k = 16$**
5. $\frac{2}{3}r = 6$ **$r = 9$**

### Independent Practice

For **6–13**, solve each equation.

6. $6s = \frac{4}{5}$ **$s = \frac{2}{15}$**
7. $16 = n + \frac{3}{4}$ **$n = 15\frac{1}{4}$**
8. $3\frac{1}{6} + f = 7\frac{5}{6}$ **$f = 4\frac{2}{3}$**
9. $p - 6 = 2\frac{7}{12}$ **$p = 8\frac{7}{12}$**
10. $7\frac{1}{9} = 2\frac{4}{5} + m$ **$m = 4\frac{14}{45}$**
11. $a + 3\frac{1}{4} = 5\frac{2}{9}$ **$a = 1\frac{35}{36}$**
12. $\frac{1}{8} \cdot y = 4$ **$y = 32$**
13. $k - 6\frac{3}{8} = 4\frac{6}{7}$ **$k = 11\frac{13}{56}$**

*For another example, see Set D on page 134.

Topic 2 | Lesson 2-5 109

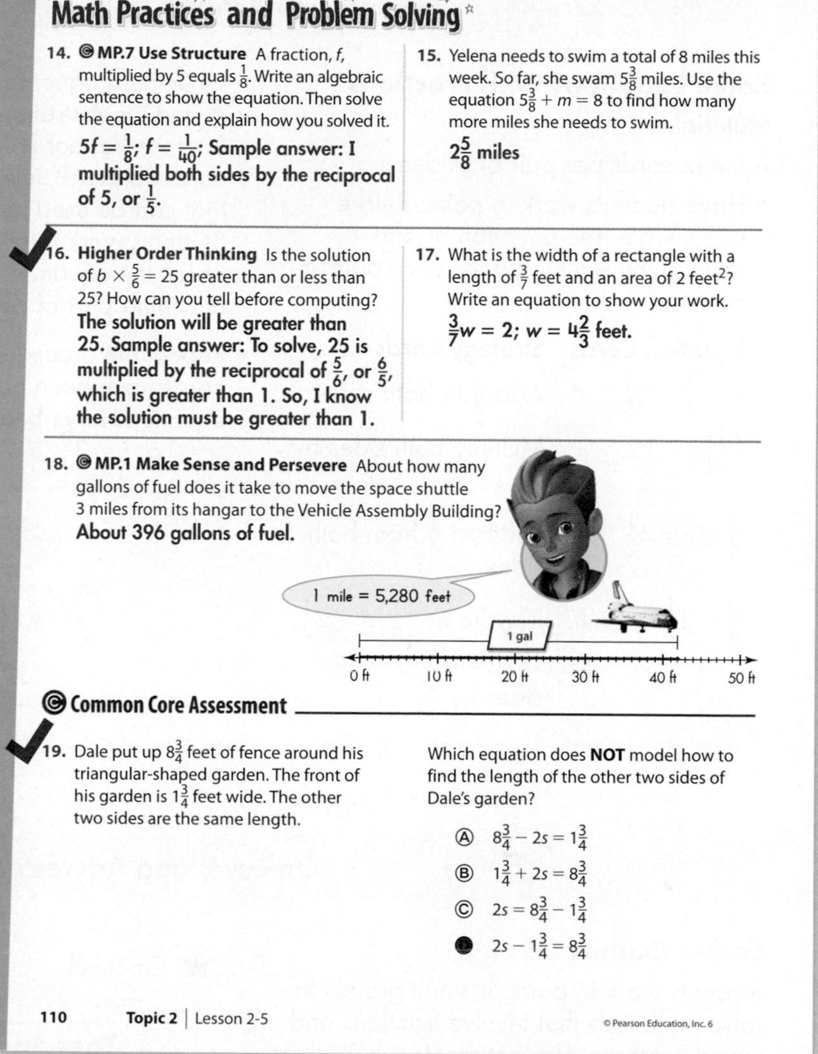

### Math Practices and Problem Solving

14. MP.7 Use Structure A fraction, $f$, multiplied by 5 equals $\frac{1}{8}$. Write an algebraic sentence to show the equation. Then solve the equation and explain how you solved it.
**$5f = \frac{1}{8}$; $f = \frac{1}{40}$; Sample answer: I multiplied both sides by the reciprocal of 5, or $\frac{1}{5}$.**

15. Yelena needs to swim a total of 8 miles this week. So far, she swam $5\frac{3}{8}$ miles. Use the equation $5\frac{3}{8} + m = 8$ to find how many more miles she needs to swim.
**$2\frac{5}{8}$ miles**

16. Higher Order Thinking Is the solution of $b \times \frac{5}{6} = 25$ greater than or less than 25? How can you tell before computing?
**The solution will be greater than 25. Sample answer: To solve, 25 is multiplied by the reciprocal of $\frac{5}{6}$, or $\frac{6}{5}$, which is greater than 1. So, I know the solution must be greater than 1.**

17. What is the width of a rectangle with a length of $\frac{3}{7}$ feet and an area of 2 feet$^2$? Write an equation to show your work.
**$\frac{3}{7}w = 2$; $w = 4\frac{2}{3}$ feet.**

18. MP.1 Make Sense and Persevere About how many gallons of fuel does it take to move the space shuttle 3 miles from its hangar to the Vehicle Assembly Building?
**About 396 gallons of fuel.**



### Common Core Assessment

19. Dale put up $8\frac{3}{4}$ feet of fence around his triangular-shaped garden. The front of his garden is $1\frac{3}{4}$ feet wide. The other two sides are the same length.

Which equation does **NOT** model how to find the length of the other two sides of Dale's garden?

Ⓐ $8\frac{3}{4} - 2s = 1\frac{3}{4}$
Ⓑ $1\frac{3}{4} + 2s = 8\frac{3}{4}$
Ⓒ $2s = 8\frac{3}{4} - 1\frac{3}{4}$
● $2s - 1\frac{3}{4} = 8\frac{3}{4}$

110 Topic 2 | Lesson 2-5

© Pearson Education, Inc. 6

**Another Example** To undo the fraction multiplication in the multiplication equation example, you can divide both sides by $\frac{3}{8}$. Any non-zero number divided by itself is 1, so $\frac{3}{8} \div \frac{3}{8} = 1$. The result of $\frac{3}{8} \times \frac{8}{3}$ is also 1, so you can also multiply both sides of the equation by the reciprocal $\frac{8}{3}$. Dividing by any fraction $\frac{a}{b}$ is the same as multiplying by its reciprocal $\frac{b}{a}$. Students will formally build conceptual understanding of fraction division in Topic 12.

**Error Intervention: Item 4**

**If** students are uncertain about how to solve this equation,

**then** remind students that $\frac{1}{8}k$ is the same as $k \div 8$, and rewrite the equation as $k \div 8 = 2$. *How do you get* k *alone on one side of the equation?* [Multiply both sides by 8.]

**Reteaching** Assign Reteaching Set D on p. 134.

**Items 2–13** Remind students to write out each step as they solve the equations. Suggest, too, that they check each solution.

**Item 14 MP.7 Use Structure** Students use the structure of expressions to write the word phrase *a fraction* f *multiplied by 5* as the algebraic expression $5f$. The expressions $5f$ and $\frac{1}{8}$ are equivalent so $5f = \frac{1}{8}$. Students apply properties of equality to generate equivalent expressions to solve the equation.

**Item 16 Coherence** In their previous work with fractions in Grade 5, students explored the concept that multiplying a given number by a fraction greater than 1 results in a product greater than the given number and that multiplying a given number by a fraction less than 1 results in a product smaller than the given number.

**Multi-Step Problems** *Page 110 Items 18 and 19; Page 112 Items 16, 20, and 21*

# STEP 3 ASSESS AND DIFFERENTIATE

Use the **QUICK CHECK** on the previous page to prescribe differentiated instruction.

**I Intervention** 0–3 points on the Quick Check

**O On-Level** 4 points on the Quick Check

**A Advanced** 5 points on the Quick Check

## Intervention Activity I

### Solve Equations with Fractions

**Materials**

8 index cards per pair of students

- Have students work in pairs. Before class, write one equation or one strategy on each card for each pair of students.

| Equation Cards | Strategy Cards |
|---|---|
| $x - \frac{3}{4} = 2\frac{1}{8}$ | Add $\frac{3}{4}$ to both sides. |
| $\left(\frac{3}{4}\right)y = 12$ | Multiply both sides by $\frac{4}{3}$. |
| $\frac{3}{4} + r = 4\frac{1}{2}$ | Subtract $\frac{3}{4}$ from both sides. |
| $\frac{d}{4} = 2\frac{1}{2}$ | Rewrite as $\left(\frac{1}{4}\right)d = 2\frac{1}{2}$. Then multiply both sides by $\frac{4}{1}$. |

- Give the 4 equation cards to Partner A and the 4 strategy cards to Partner B. Have Partner A reveal an equation card. Partner B selects a strategy card that can be used to solve the equation. Students work together to solve and check the equation. Then set the matching pair of cards aside.
- Repeat the procedure until all of the cards have been paired and the equations have been solved. [$x = 2\frac{7}{8}$; $y = 16$; $r = 3\frac{3}{4}$; $d = 10$]

$$\left(\frac{3}{4}\right)y = 12$$

$$\left(\frac{4}{3}\right)\left(\frac{3}{4}\right)y = \left(\frac{4}{3}\right)12$$

$$y = 16$$

## Reteach I

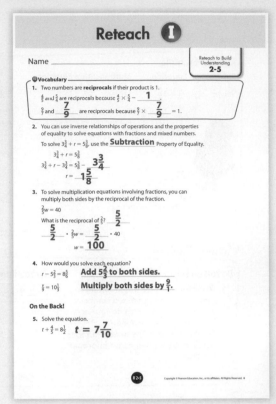

Name ______________________

Reteach to Build Understanding
**2-5**

**Vocabulary**

1. Two numbers are **reciprocals** if their product is 1.
$\frac{4}{5}$ and $\frac{5}{4}$ are reciprocals because $\frac{4}{5} \times \frac{5}{4} =$ **1**.
$\frac{9}{7}$ and **$\frac{7}{9}$** are reciprocals because $\frac{9}{7} \times$ **$\frac{7}{9}$** $= 1$.

2. You can use inverse relationships of operations and the properties of equality to solve equations with fractions and mixed numbers.
To solve $3\frac{3}{4} + r = 5\frac{3}{8}$, use the **Subtraction** Property of Equality.
$3\frac{3}{4} + r = 5\frac{3}{8}$
$3\frac{3}{4} + r - 3\frac{3}{4} = 5\frac{3}{8} -$ **$3\frac{3}{4}$**
$r =$ **$1\frac{5}{8}$**

3. To solve multiplication equations involving fractions, you can multiply both sides by the reciprocal of the fraction.
$\frac{2}{5}w = 40$
What is the reciprocal of $\frac{2}{5}$? **$\frac{5}{2}$**
**$\frac{5}{2}$** $\cdot \frac{2}{5}w =$ **$\frac{5}{2}$** $\cdot 40$
$w =$ **100**

4. How would you solve each equation?
$r - 5\frac{2}{3} = 8\frac{5}{6}$ **Add $5\frac{2}{3}$ to both sides.**
$\frac{v}{9} = 10\frac{1}{3}$ **Multiply both sides by $\frac{9}{1}$.**

**On the Back!**

5. Solve the equation.
$t + \frac{4}{5} = 8\frac{1}{2}$ **$t = 7\frac{7}{10}$**

R 2-5



## On-Level and Advanced Activity Centers O A

### Center Games

Students work in pairs or small groups to solve equations that involve fractions and mixed numbers. Have students record their work for each problem as they play the game.

★ On-Level

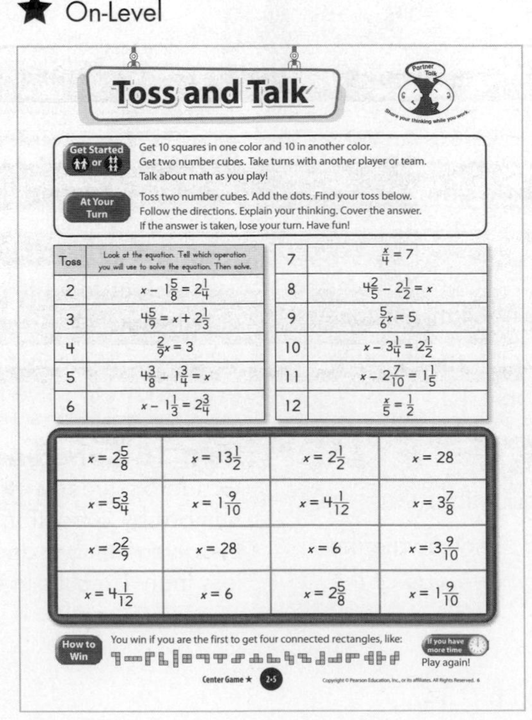

**Toss and Talk**



**Get Started** Get 10 squares in one color and 10 in another color. Get two number cubes. Take turns with another player or team. Talk about math as you play!

**At Your Turn** Toss two number cubes. Add the dots. Find your toss below. Follow the directions. Explain your thinking. Cover the answer. If the answer is taken, lose your turn. Have fun!

| Toss | Look at the equation. Tell which operation you will use to solve the equation. Then solve. |
|---|---|
| 2 | $x - 1\frac{5}{8} = 2\frac{1}{4}$ |
| 3 | $4\frac{5}{9} = x + 2\frac{1}{3}$ |
| 4 | $\frac{2}{9}x = 3$ |
| 5 | $4\frac{3}{8} - 1\frac{3}{4} = x$ |
| 6 | $x - 1\frac{1}{3} = 2\frac{3}{4}$ |
| 7 | $\frac{x}{4} = 7$ |
| 8 | $4\frac{2}{5} - 2\frac{1}{2} = x$ |
| 9 | $\frac{5}{6}x = 5$ |
| 10 | $x - 3\frac{1}{4} = 2\frac{1}{2}$ |
| 11 | $x - 2\frac{7}{10} = 1\frac{1}{5}$ |
| 12 | $\frac{x}{5} = \frac{1}{2}$ |

| | | | |
|---|---|---|---|
| $x = 2\frac{5}{8}$ | $x = 13\frac{1}{2}$ | $x = 2\frac{1}{2}$ | $x = 28$ |
| $x = 5\frac{3}{4}$ | $x = 1\frac{9}{10}$ | $x = 4\frac{1}{12}$ | $x = 3\frac{7}{8}$ |
| $x = 2\frac{2}{9}$ | $x = 28$ | $x = 6$ | $x = 3\frac{9}{10}$ |
| $x = 4\frac{1}{12}$ | $x = 6$ | $x = 2\frac{5}{8}$ | $x = 1\frac{9}{10}$ |

**How to Win** You win if you are the first to get four connected rectangles, like:

**If you have more time** Play again!

Center Game ★ 2-5



★★ Advanced

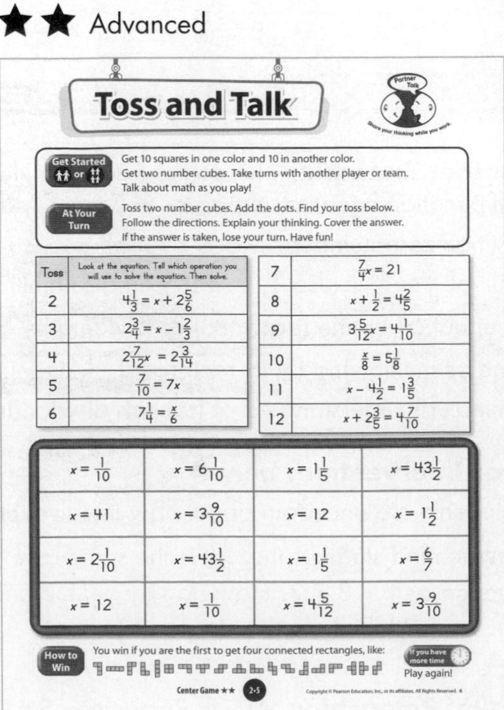

**Toss and Talk**



**Get Started** Get 10 squares in one color and 10 in another color. Get two number cubes. Take turns with another player or team. Talk about math as you play!

**At Your Turn** Toss two number cubes. Add the dots. Find your toss below. Follow the directions. Explain your thinking. Cover the answer. If the answer is taken, lose your turn. Have fun!

| Toss | Look at the equation. Tell which operation you will use to solve the equation. Then solve. |
|---|---|
| 2 | $4\frac{1}{3} = x + 2\frac{5}{6}$ |
| 3 | $2\frac{3}{4} = x - 1\frac{2}{3}$ |
| 4 | $2\frac{7}{12}x = 2\frac{3}{14}$ |
| 5 | $\frac{7}{10} = 7x$ |
| 6 | $7\frac{1}{4} = \frac{x}{6}$ |
| 7 | $\frac{7}{4}x = 21$ |
| 8 | $x + \frac{1}{2} = 4\frac{2}{5}$ |
| 9 | $3\frac{5}{12}x = 4\frac{1}{10}$ |
| 10 | $\frac{x}{8} = 5\frac{1}{8}$ |
| 11 | $x - 4\frac{1}{2} = 1\frac{3}{5}$ |
| 12 | $x + 2\frac{3}{5} = 4\frac{7}{10}$ |

| | | | |
|---|---|---|---|
| $x = \frac{1}{10}$ | $x = 6\frac{1}{10}$ | $x = 1\frac{1}{5}$ | $x = 43\frac{1}{2}$ |
| $x = 41$ | $x = 3\frac{9}{10}$ | $x = 12$ | $x = 1\frac{1}{2}$ |
| $x = 2\frac{1}{10}$ | $x = 43\frac{1}{2}$ | $x = 1\frac{1}{5}$ | $x = \frac{6}{7}$ |
| $x = 12$ | $x = \frac{1}{10}$ | $x = 4\frac{5}{12}$ | $x = 3\frac{9}{10}$ |

**How to Win** You win if you are the first to get four connected rectangles, like:

**If you have more time** Play again!

Center Game ★★ 2-5

## TIMING

The time allocated to Step 3 will depend on the teacher's instructional decisions and differentiation routines.

15–30 min

PEARSON realize. PearsonRealize.com

Help | Practice Buddy | Tools | Games

## Technology Center    

Tools Games

### Math Tools and Math Games

A link to a specific math tools activity or math game to use with this lesson is provided at PearsonRealize.com.

## Leveled Assignment

 Items 1–9, 16–18, 21  Items 5–12, 16–18, 20, 21  Items 7–15, 18–21

Name ______________________

## Homework & Practice 2-5

### Solve Equations with Fractions

### Another Look!

Solve each equation below.

| Addition Equation | Subtraction Equation | Multiplication Equation | Division Equation |
|---|---|---|---|
| $h + \frac{3}{5} = \frac{2}{3}$ | $y - \frac{2}{3} = \frac{4}{9}$ | $\frac{3}{4}t = 9$ | $\frac{r}{5} = 14$ |
| $h + \frac{3}{5} - \frac{3}{5} = \frac{2}{3} - \frac{3}{5}$ | $y - \frac{2}{3} + \frac{2}{3} = \frac{4}{9} + \frac{2}{3}$ | $\frac{(4)}{3} \cdot \frac{3}{4}t = \frac{(4)}{3} \cdot \frac{9}{1}$ | $\frac{(5)}{1} \cdot \frac{1}{5}r = \frac{(5)}{1} \cdot \frac{14}{1}$ |
| $h = \frac{1}{15}$ | $y = 1\frac{1}{9}$ | $t = 12$ | $r = 70$ |

For **1–12**, solve each equation.

1. $s + \frac{1}{4} = 12\frac{1}{2}$
   **$s = 12\frac{1}{4}$**
2. $2\frac{2}{3} + y = 4\frac{1}{4}$
   **$y = 1\frac{7}{12}$**
3. $a - 4\frac{3}{8} = 2\frac{1}{2}$
   **$a = 6\frac{7}{8}$**
4. $\frac{2}{7}q = 3$
   **$q = 10\frac{1}{2}$**
5. $14\frac{1}{6} = d + 12\frac{3}{4}$
   **$d = 1\frac{5}{12}$**
6. $7f = \frac{1}{12}$
   **$f = \frac{1}{84}$**
7. $\frac{t}{3} = 6\frac{1}{2}$
   **$t = 19\frac{1}{2}$**
8. $u + 2\frac{7}{8} = 6\frac{1}{6}$
   **$u = 3\frac{7}{24}$**
9. $7\frac{1}{5} = m - \frac{2}{3}$
   **$m = 7\frac{13}{15}$**
10. $\frac{8}{9} = 13p$
    **$p = \frac{8}{117}$**
11. $9\frac{1}{12} = \frac{k}{9}$
    **$k = 81\frac{3}{4}$**
12. $x + \frac{1}{3} = \frac{2}{5}$
    **$x = \frac{1}{15}$**
13. $n - 5\frac{3}{8} = \frac{1}{5}$
    **$n = 5\frac{23}{40}$**
14. $\frac{3}{5} = 12g$
    **$g = \frac{1}{20}$**
15. $h + \frac{11}{12} = 120\frac{1}{2}$
    **$h = 119\frac{7}{12}$**



For **16–18**, use the information given in the recipe.

| Sam's Fruit Party Punch | |
|---|---|
| $\frac{2}{3}$ cup | pineapple juice |
| $\frac{1}{2}$ cup | orange juice |
| $\frac{3}{4}$ cup | lemon/lime juice |
| $\frac{1}{3}$ cup | ginger ale |

16. **MP.6 Be Precise** Sam needs a bowl to mix her punch. She has a 2-cup bowl, 4-cup bowl, and a 6-cup bowl. What is the smallest bowl she can use to make her punch? Explain.
    **The 4-cup bowl is the smallest bowl she can use because the recipe makes $2\frac{1}{4}$ cups of punch.**

17. The recipe makes 1 serving of punch. If Sam used 2 cups of pineapple juice to make her punch, how many servings did she make? Use the equation $\frac{2}{3}m = 2$ to find the number of servings.
    **$m = 3$ servings**

18. **Algebra** Sam needs $7\frac{1}{2}$ cups of orange juice to make punch for a group of her friends. She only has $5\frac{1}{3}$ cups. Write an equation to represent how many more cups of orange juice Sam needs. Then solve.
    **$5\frac{1}{3} + j = 7\frac{1}{2}$; $j = 2\frac{1}{6}$ cups more orange juice.**

19. There are 6 people seated equally along a counter. If each person has $1\frac{7}{8}$ feet of counter space, how long is the counter? Tell how you can check that your answer is reasonable.
    **The counter is $11\frac{1}{4}$ feet long. Sample answer: I can estimate with compatible numbers. $1\frac{7}{8}$ feet is close to 2 feet. So, $2 \times 6 = 12$, which is close to $11\frac{1}{4}$ feet. My answer is reasonable.**

20. **Higher Order Thinking** A bus left New York City and arrived in Philadelphia after $2\frac{1}{3}$ hours. From there, it took $1\frac{3}{4}$ hours to travel to Baltimore. It took another $\frac{5}{6}$ hour to go from Baltimore to Washington. If the bus arrived in Washington at 10:05 P.M., what time did it leave New York City? Tell how you know.
    **The bus left New York City at 5:10 P.M. Sample answer: I worked backwards to find the time.**

### Common Core Assessment

21. Abigail participated in an 18-mile race. She ran $6\frac{3}{4}$ miles, climbed a $\frac{1}{4}$-mile trail on a mountain, and then swam and biked an equal number of miles to complete the race.

    Which equation models how to find the number of miles Abigail swam and biked in the race?

    Ⓐ $18 = \frac{1}{2}r$
    **● $2r = 11$**
    Ⓒ $\frac{r}{2} = 11$
    Ⓓ $r + 7 = 18$

# LESSON 2-6

# WRITE INEQUALITIES

## DIGITAL RESOURCES PearsonRealize.com

eText — Student and Teacher eTexts

PD — Listen and Look For Lesson Video

Think — Today's Challenge

Solve — Solve and Share

Learn — Visual Learning Animation Plus

Glossary — Animated Glossary

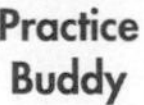
Practice Buddy — Online Personalized Practice

Tools — Math Tools

Assessment — Quick Check

Help — Another Look Homework Video

Games — Math Games

## LESSON OVERVIEW FCR FOCUS • COHERENCE • RIGOR

### FOCUS

**Domain 6.EE** Expressions and Equations

**Cluster 6.EE.B** Reason about and solve one-variable equations and inequalities.

**Content Standard 6.EE.B.8** Write an inequality of the form $x > c$ or $x < c$ to represent a constraint or condition in a real-world or mathematical problem. Recognize that inequalities of the form $x > c$ or $x < c$ have infinitely many solutions; represent solutions of such inequalities on number line diagrams. Also **6.EE.B.5**.

**Mathematical Practices MP.2, MP.3, MP.4, MP.6, MP.8**

**Objective** Write inequalities to describe mathematical or real-world situations.

**Essential Understanding** An inequality is a mathematical sentence that contains the inequality symbol $<$ (is less than), $>$ (is greater than), $\leq$ (is less than or equal to), $\geq$ (is greater than or equal to), or $\neq$ (is not equal to). An inequality describes a situation that has an infinite number of numerical possibilities.

**Vocabulary** Inequality

### COHERENCE

In Grades 1 through 5, students used the symbols $<$, $>$, and $=$ to compare whole numbers, fractions, and decimals. Earlier in this topic, students wrote and solved equations representing mathematical or real-world situations. The content in this lesson connects and extends this previous learning, focusing on writing inequalities to represent mathematical or real-world situations. In Grade 7, students will write multi-step inequalities to represent such situations.

### RIGOR

This lesson emphasizes **conceptual understanding**. Students learn that they can write an inequality to represent a situation that contains a limitation or constraint. They differentiate between the symbols $<$ and $\leq$, as well as $>$ and $\geq$. The inequality $x < 12$ might represent "children younger than 12 years old," whereas $x \leq 12$ would represent "children 12 years old and younger."

PD Watch the Listen and Look For Lesson Video.

## MATH ANYTIME

### Daily Common Core Review

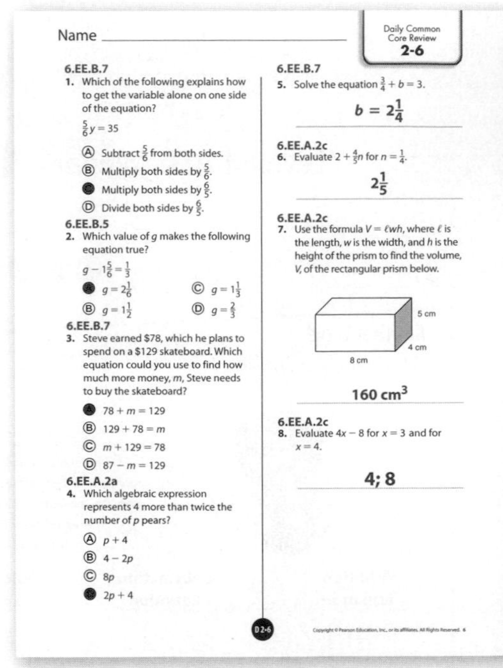
Name ______

Daily Common Core Review 2-6

6.EE.B.7
1. Which of the following explains how to get the variable alone on one side of the equation?

$\frac{5}{6}y = 35$

Ⓐ Subtract $\frac{5}{6}$ from both sides.
Ⓑ Multiply both sides by $\frac{5}{6}$.
● Multiply both sides by $\frac{6}{5}$.
Ⓓ Divide both sides by $\frac{6}{5}$.

6.EE.B.5
2. Which value of $g$ makes the following equation true?

$g - 1\frac{5}{6} = \frac{1}{3}$

● $g = 2\frac{1}{6}$
Ⓑ $g = 1\frac{1}{2}$
Ⓒ $g = 1\frac{1}{3}$
Ⓓ $g = \frac{2}{3}$

6.EE.B.7
3. Steve earned $78, which he plans to spend on a $129 skateboard. Which equation could you use to find how much more money, $m$, Steve needs to buy the skateboard?

● $78 + m = 129$
Ⓑ $129 + 78 = m$
Ⓒ $m + 129 = 78$
Ⓓ $87 - m = 129$

6.EE.A.2a
4. Which algebraic expression represents 4 more than twice the number of $p$ pears?

Ⓐ $p + 4$
Ⓑ $4 - 2p$
Ⓒ $8p$
● $2p + 4$

6.EE.B.7
5. Solve the equation $\frac{3}{4} + b = 3$.

$b = 2\frac{1}{4}$

6.EE.A.2c
6. Evaluate $2 + \frac{4}{5}n$ for $n = \frac{1}{4}$.

$2\frac{1}{5}$

6.EE.A.2c
7. Use the formula $V = \ell wh$, where $\ell$ is the length, $w$ is the width, and $h$ is the height of the prism to find the volume, $V$, of the rectangular prism below.



$160 \text{ cm}^3$

6.EE.A.2c
8. Evaluate $4x - 8$ for $x = 3$ and for $x = 4$.

4; 8

D 2-6



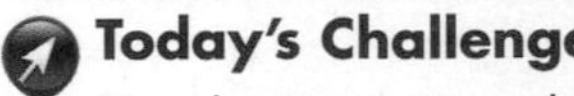

### Today's Challenge

Think Use the Topic 2 problems any time during this topic.

## ENGLISH LANGUAGE LEARNERS ELL

**Learning Strategies** Use prior experiences to understand meanings.

*Use with the Solve & Share on Student's Edition p. 113.*

Ask students to write $>$, $<$, $\geq$, and $\leq$ on index cards and share prior experiences using the symbols. Read the Solve & Share. Instruct students to identify important information for solving the problem. Write on the board: Record Time = 24.49 seconds.

**Beginning** *Camilla wants to swim faster than 24.49 s.* Write $< 24.49$ and circle $<$. *Is this greater than or less than?* Point to the 50-Meter Free Style chart. Write 26.56. *Is 26.56 $>$, $<$, $\geq$, or $\leq$ 24.49?* Ask students to hold up the correct card and respond using the sentence stem: 26.56 is ____ 24.49. Continue this process with the remaining times.

**Intermediate** Ask students what record Camilla wants to beat. Write $< 24.49$ and circle $<$. *Is this greater than or less than 24.49?* Point to the 50-Meter Free Style chart, and write 26.56. *Is 26.56 $>$, $<$, $\geq$, or $\leq$ 24.49?* Ask students to hold up the correct card and respond using the sentence stem: 26.56 is ____ 24.49 because ____. Continue this process with the remaining times.

**Advanced** Write $< 24.49$. Ask students to share prior experiences using the term *less than*. Instruct students to look at the first row in the 50-Meter Free Style chart. *Is 26.56 $>$, $<$, $\geq$, or $\leq$ 24.49?* Have students show the correct card and explain to partners why the card was chosen. Continue this process with the remaining times.

**Summarize** What do the symbols $>$, $<$, $\geq$, and $\leq$ mean?

# DEVELOP: PROBLEM-BASED LEARNING

**COHERENCE: Engage learners by connecting prior knowledge to new ideas.**
Students extend their understanding of comparing numbers to find numbers less than a given number in a real-world situation.

10–15 min

Solve

## BEFORE

**1. Pose the Solve-and-Share Problem**
**MP.2 Reason Quantitatively** Listen and look for students who write an inequality to show times less than 24.49 seconds.

**2. Build Understanding**
*A math sentence such as 5 < 8 or 10 ≥ 3 is called an inequality. What do the symbols < and > mean?* ["Less than" and "greater than"] *What do the symbols ≤ and ≥ mean?* ["Less than or equal to" and "greater than or equal to"] *When would you use the symbols ≤ and ≥?* [When you want to include the number in the inequality]

## DURING

**3. Ask Guiding Questions As Needed**
*Use an inequality to compare Swimmer A's time to 24.49 seconds.* [Sample answers: 26.56 > 24.49, 24.49 < 26.56] *Use an inequality to compare Swimmer C's time to 24.49 seconds.* [24.49 ≤ 24.49 or 24.49 ≥ 24.49]

## AFTER

**4. Share and Discuss Solutions**
Solve Start with students' solutions. If needed, project Claudia's work to discuss how to use inequalities to find possible times.

**5. Transition to the Visual Learning Bridge**
*Inequalities can be used to show how quantities compare to a given value.*

**6. Extension for Early Finishers**
*Which inequality best describes the number of eggs that could be in a carton that holds 1 dozen eggs: x < 12, x ≤ 12, x > 12, or x ≥ 12? Explain.* [x ≤ 12; a full carton has 12 eggs, but there could be fewer eggs.]

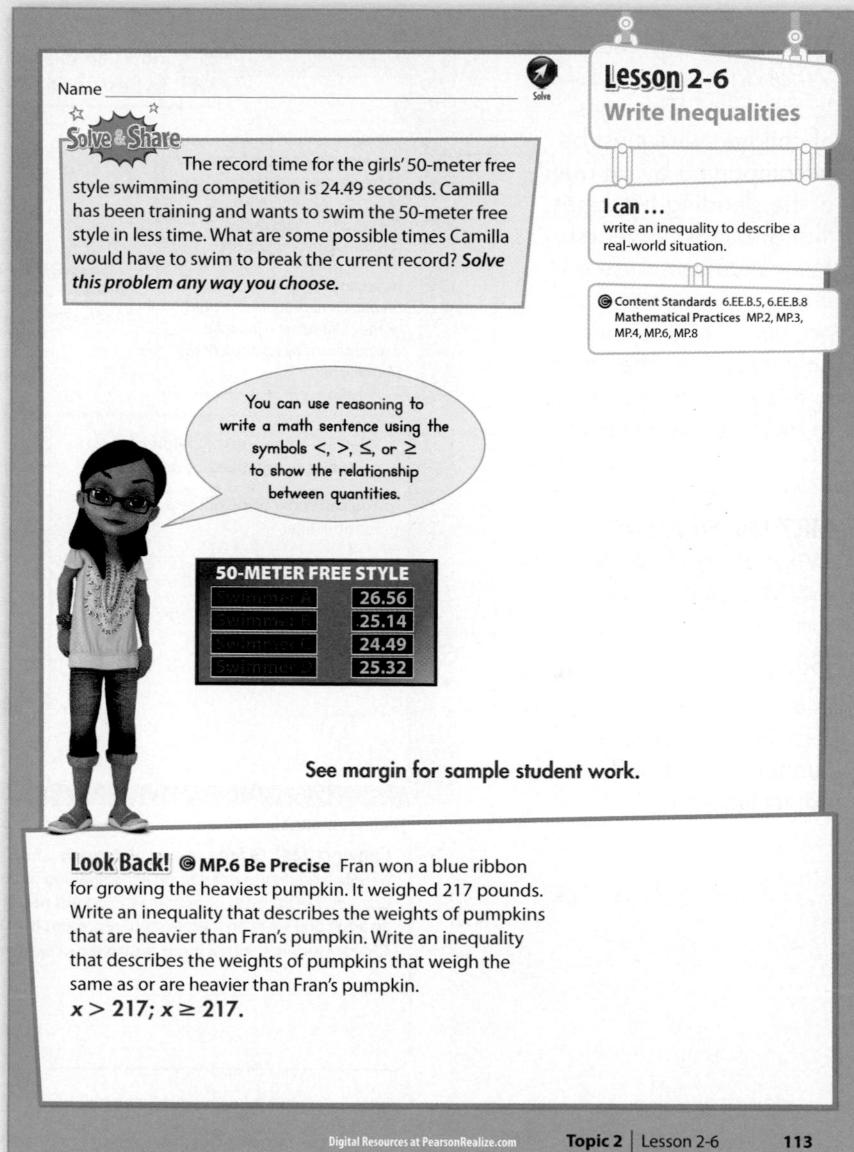

Name

Solve

Solve & Share

The record time for the girls' 50-meter free style swimming competition is 24.49 seconds. Camilla has been training and wants to swim the 50-meter free style in less time. What are some possible times Camilla would have to swim to break the current record? ***Solve this problem any way you choose.***

**Lesson 2-6**
**Write Inequalities**

**I can ...**
write an inequality to describe a real-world situation.

Content Standards 6.EE.B.5, 6.EE.B.8
Mathematical Practices MP.2, MP.3, MP.4, MP.6, MP.8

You can use reasoning to write a math sentence using the symbols <, >, ≤, or ≥ to show the relationship between quantities.

| 50-METER FREE STYLE | |
|---|---|
| Swimmer A | 26.56 |
| Swimmer B | 25.14 |
| Swimmer C | 24.49 |
| Swimmer D | 25.32 |

**See margin for sample student work.**

**Look Back!** **MP.6 Be Precise** Fran won a blue ribbon for growing the heaviest pumpkin. It weighed 217 pounds. Write an inequality that describes the weights of pumpkins that are heavier than Fran's pumpkin. Write an inequality that describes the weights of pumpkins that weigh the same as or are heavier than Fran's pumpkin.
**x > 217; x ≥ 217.**

Digital Resources at PearsonRealize.com Topic 2 | Lesson 2-6 113

## Analyze Student Work

**Claudia's Work**

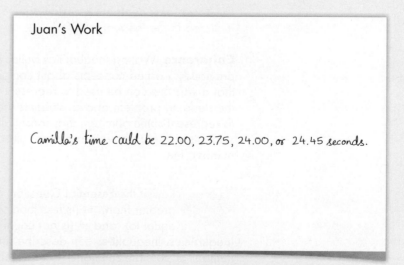

24 < 24.49
23.55 < 24.49
24.25 < 24.49

Camilla could break the record if her time is 24, 23.55, or 24.25 seconds.

Claudia finds times that are less than 24.49 seconds by writing inequalities that compare each time to 24.49.

**Juan's Work**

Camilla's time could be 22.00, 23.75, 24.00, or 24.45 seconds.

Juan states times that are less than 24.49 seconds, but he does not use inequalities to show how these times compare to 24.49.

# DEVELOP: VISUAL LEARNING

The *Visual Learning Bridge* connects students' thinking in Solve & Share to important math ideas in the lesson. Use the *Visual Learning Bridge* to make these ideas explicit. Also available as a *Visual Learning Animation Plus* at PearsonRealize.com

ELL Visual Learning

PEARSON realize. PearsonRealize.com

Learn Glossary

**MP.4 Model with Math**
*What ages are you asked to describe?* [The ages of children who must be accompanied by an adult at the sledding hill; ages that are under 8 years]
*Why should you use an inequality instead of an equation?* [An equation only describes one value. In this situation, you need to describe many values.]

**MP.7 Use Structure**
*What are some other ages that you could show on the number line?*
[Sample answer: 1, $4\frac{1}{2}$, 7]
*Is 8 one of the possibilities? Explain.* [No; children "under the age of 8" does not include 8.]

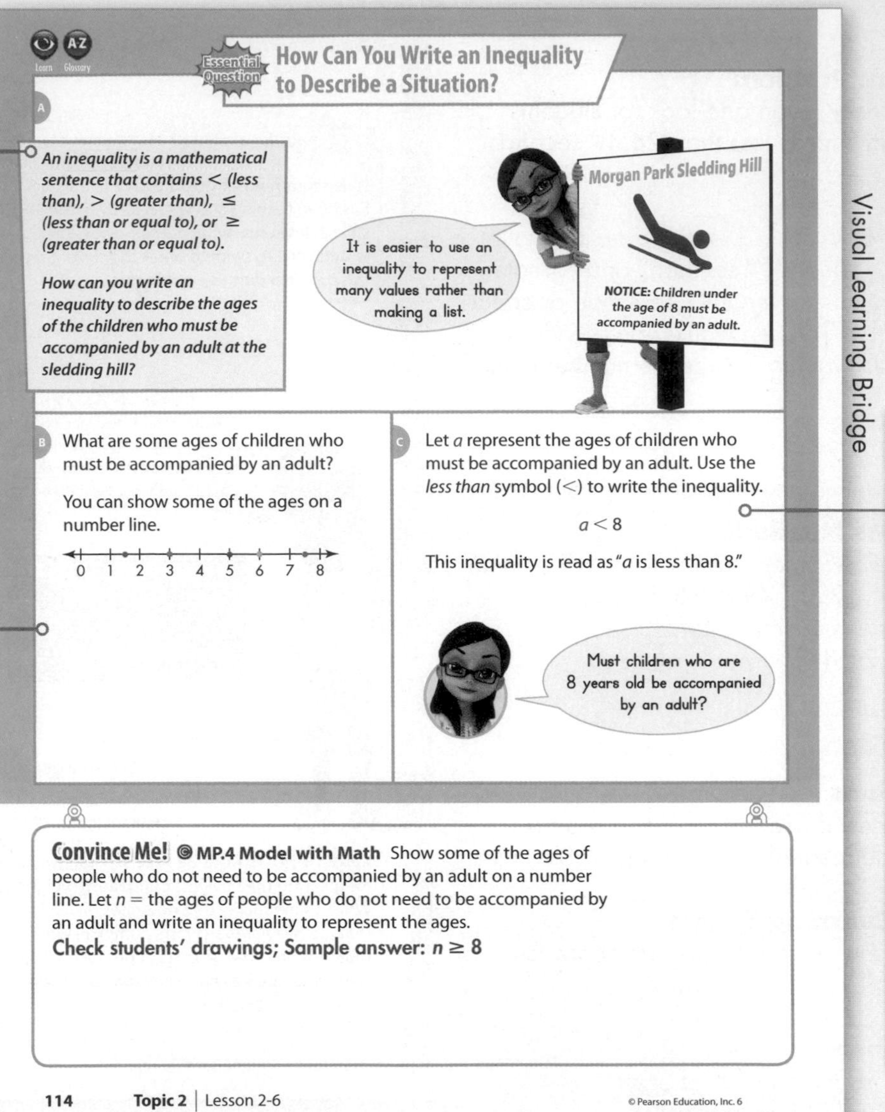


*If the sign had read "children 8 years old or younger," how would that change the inequality? Explain.* [You would need to use the $\leq$ symbol: $a \leq 8$; now, 8 is included as one of the ages.]

**Prevent Misconceptions**

Be sure students understand that < designates numbers less than a given value, while $\leq$ designates numbers less than *or equal to* the given value. Point out that the $\leq$ symbol contains part of an equal sign.

**Convince Me! MP.4 Model with Math** *What is the "cut-off" age that determines whether children need to be accompanied by an adult?* [8] *Do 8-year olds need to be accompanied by an adult?* [No] *So, is 8 included in the inequality?* [Yes]

**Coherence** Writing inequalities builds coherence by integrating previously learned concepts about comparing numbers with the concept that a variable can be used to represent an unknown quantity. In Box B of the sledding problem above, students see how a number line can be used to represent some numbers that satisfy an inequality. In the next lesson, students will learn how to represent all solutions of an inequality on a number line.

Essential Question Revisit the Essential Question. The symbols < (is less than), > (is greater than), $\leq$ (is less than or equal to), $\geq$ (is greater than or equal to), and $\neq$ (is not equal to) can be used to write inequalities. Inequalities can describe situations that have an infinite number of possible solutions. To represent a constraint or boundary that is included in the solution, write the inequality using $\leq$ or $\geq$.

## QUICK CHECK

Check mark indicates items for prescribing differentiation on the next page.
Item 4 is worth 1 point. Items 10 and 12 are worth up to 2 points.

20–30 min

Practice Buddy

Tools

Assessment

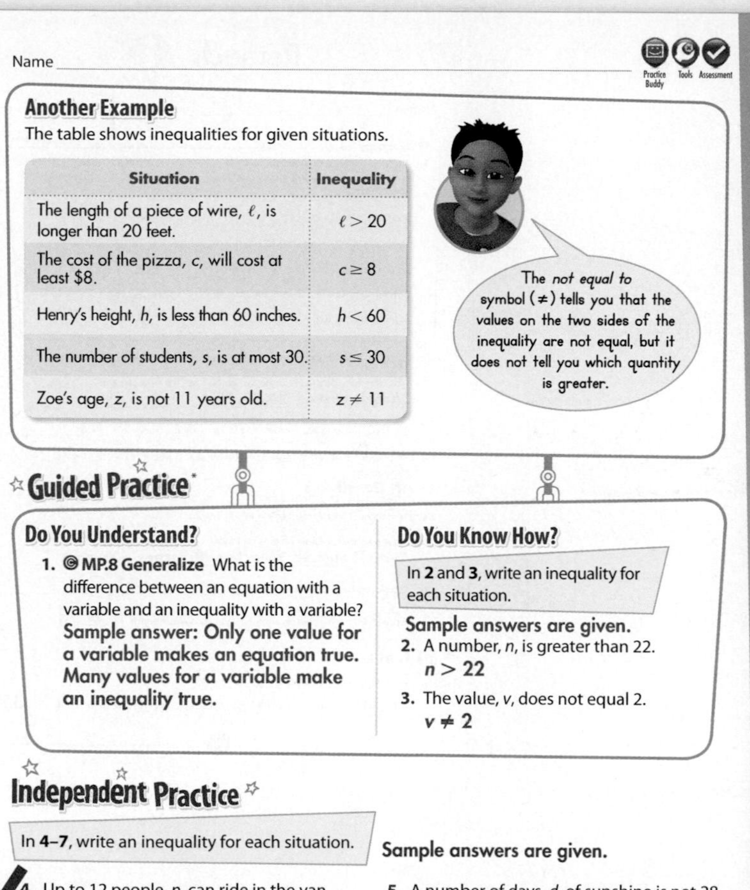

Name ____

### Another Example

The table shows inequalities for given situations.

| Situation | Inequality |
|---|---|
| The length of a piece of wire, $\ell$, is longer than 20 feet. | $\ell > 20$ |
| The cost of the pizza, $c$, will cost at least \$8. | $c \geq 8$ |
| Henry's height, $h$, is less than 60 inches. | $h < 60$ |
| The number of students, $s$, is at most 30. | $s \leq 30$ |
| Zoe's age, $z$, is not 11 years old. | $z \neq 11$ |

The *not equal to* symbol ($\neq$) tells you that the values on the two sides of the inequality are not equal, but it does not tell you which quantity is greater.

### Guided Practice*

**Do You Understand?**

**1.** **MP.8 Generalize** What is the difference between an equation with a variable and an inequality with a variable?
**Sample answer: Only one value for a variable makes an equation true. Many values for a variable make an inequality true.**

**Do You Know How?**

In **2** and **3**, write an inequality for each situation.

**Sample answers are given.**

**2.** A number, $n$, is greater than 22.
$n > 22$

**3.** The value, $v$, does not equal 2.
$v \neq 2$

### Independent Practice

In **4–7**, write an inequality for each situation. **Sample answers are given.**

**4.** Up to 12 people, $p$, can ride in the van.
$p \leq 12$

**5.** A number of days, $d$, of sunshine is not 28.
$d \neq 28$

**6.** The distance of the race, $r$, is farther than 6.2 miles.
$r > 6.2$

**7.** The value, $v$, of the bracelet is less than \$85.
$v < 85$

*For another example, see Set E on page 134.

Topic 2 | Lesson 2-6 115

### Math Practices and Problem Solving

**8.** The record for the city's greatest 1-day snowfall is 19.7 inches. Write an inequality to represent a snowfall that would beat this record.
**Sample answer: Let $s$ = the number of inches of snow. Then $s > 19.7$**

**9.** **Algebra** The first bookshelf in the literature section of a library can hold 2,492 books. The bookshelf has 7 shelves. Each shelf can hold the same number of books. How many books can each shelf hold? Write an equation to help you solve.
**Sample answer: Let $b$ = the number of books on a shelf. Then $7b = 2{,}492$; $b = 356$.**

**10.** **Higher Order Thinking** Bryan said he is 9 inches shorter than the top of a 6-foot ladder. Allen said he is taller than Bryan because he is 63 inches tall. Is Allen correct? Explain why or why not.
**Allen is incorrect. Sample answer: Bryan is 9 inches shorter than 6 feet, which is 5 feet 3 inches. Allen is 63 inches, which is also 5 feet 3 inches. So, Allen and Bryan are the exact same height.**

**11.** **MP.3 Construct Arguments** To ride a certain roller coaster, a rider must be more than 42 inches tall. To represent this situation, Elias wrote $h \geq 42$ and Nina wrote $h > 42$. Who is correct? Explain your thinking.
**Nina is correct. The riders must be taller than 42 inches, so the variable cannot be equal to 42.**

**Common Core Assessment**

**12.** Miguel earns extra money working two weekends with his dad. He is saving to buy a new bike that costs \$140.

Heather says that Miguel needs to earn more than \$6 each hour he works to have enough money to buy the bike. Her work is shown below. Explain why she is incorrect.

Heather's Solution

Weekend 1: 16 hours
Weekend 2: + 7 hours
23 hours

\$140 ÷ 23 hours ≥ \$6.00 per hour

Miguel has to earn more than \$6.00 per hour.

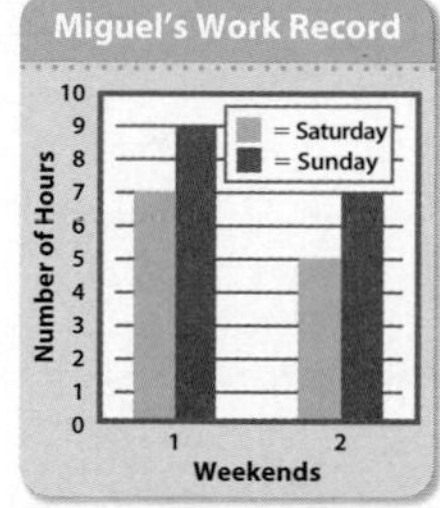

Miguel's Work Record
Number of Hours
0
1
2
3
4
5
6
7
8
9
10
= Saturday
= Sunday
1
2
Weekends

**Sample answer: Heather did not include the hours Miguel worked on Saturday in week 2. Miguel worked 28 hours in 2 weeks. \$140 ÷ 28 = \$5. Miguel has to earn at least \$5 each hour to have enough money to buy the bike. $m \geq 5$.**

116 Topic 2 | Lesson 2-6

**Another Example** *If a pizza costs "at least" 8 dollars, what does that mean?* [The cost could be \$8 or more than \$8.] *If there are "at most" 30 students, what does that mean?* [There could be 30 students or fewer than 30 students.] *Name two possible values for Zoe's age. Explain your thinking.* [Sample answer: 10 and 12; Zoe's age could be less than 11 years or greater than 11 years.]

**Error Intervention: Item 2**

**If** students use the ≥ symbol instead of the > symbol,

**then** ask them if 22 is greater than 22. [No] *Does n ≥ 22 or n > 22 represent this situation?* [$n > 22$]

**Reteaching** Assign Reteaching Set E on p. 134.

**Item 8** Suggest that students rephrase the problem to help them choose the correct inequality symbol to use. For example, "Write an inequality to represent a snowfall that is greater than the record."

**Item 10 Higher Order Thinking** Students should recall their work with measurement conversions in Grades 4 and 5 to convert 6 feet to inches. Then they can reason about how the measurements in the problem compare.

**Item 11 MP.3 Construct Arguments** Be sure students provide a complete and clear explanation of their thinking. *What solution is included in the inequality that Elias wrote that is not included in the inequality that Nina wrote?* [Exactly 42 inches tall] *Can a person who is exactly 42 inches tall ride the roller coaster?* [No]

**Multi-Step Problems** *Page 116 Items 10 and 12; Page 118 Items 11, 13, and 15*

# ASSESS AND DIFFERENTIATE

Use the **QUICK CHECK** on the previous page to prescribe differentiated instruction.

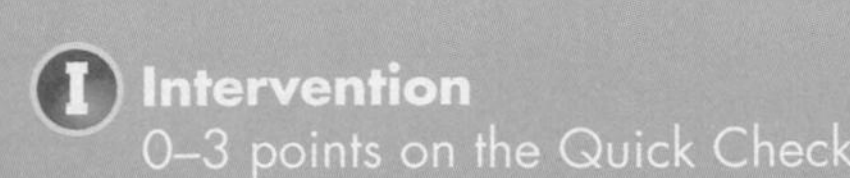

**Intervention** 0–3 points on the Quick Check

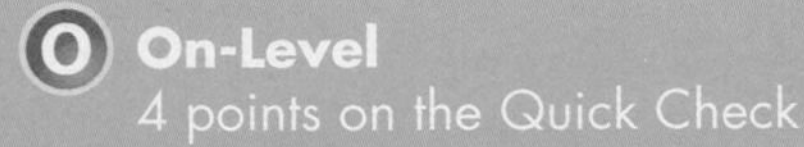

**On-Level** 4 points on the Quick Check

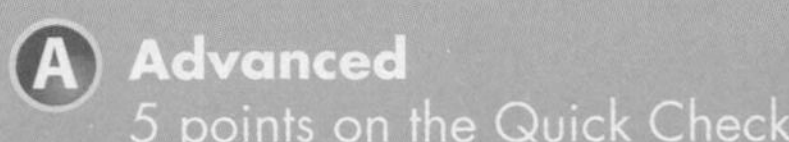

**Advanced** 5 points on the Quick Check

## Intervention Activity (I)

**Solutions of Inequalities**

**Materials**

Number lines (Teaching Tool 13)

- Ask students to use a number line to show four numbers that represent the inequality $x > 6$. If the number is included in the solution, have them show that on the number line.
- Have students repeat the procedure for each these situations using separate number lines:

  $x \leq 9$

  $x < 5$

  $x \geq 3$

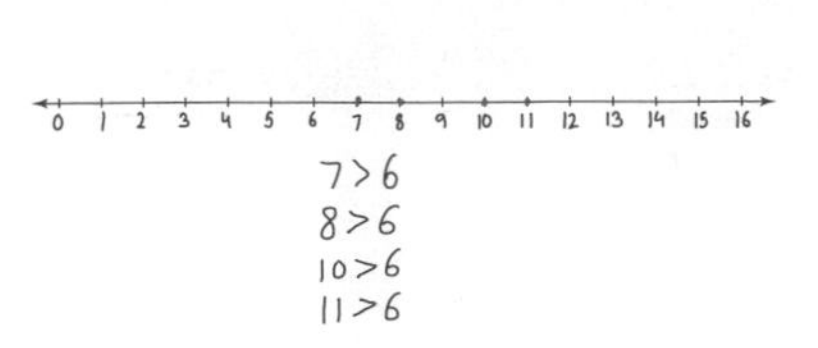


## Reteach (I)

Name ____________________

Reteach to Build Understanding
**2-6**

**Vocabulary**

1. A mathematical sentence that contains < (less than), > (greater than), ≤ (less than or equal to), ≥ (greater than or equal to), or ≠ (not equal to) is an **inequality**.

   Use an inequality symbol to complete each statement.

   A number, $n$, is less than 50. $n < 50$

   A number, $p$, is greater than 37. $p > 37$

   Erin's age, $e$, is greater than or equal to 12. $e \geq 12$

   Gabriel's age, $g$, is less than or equal to 15. $g \leq 15$

   Ramon's test score, $r$, is not 85. $r \neq 85$

Morgan ate at least 20 blueberries. Let $m =$ the number of blueberries that Morgan ate.

2. What are three possible numbers of blueberries that Morgan ate?
   **Sample answer: 20, 21, 30**
3. Can the number of blueberries that Morgan ate be exactly 20? **Yes**
4. Write an inequality that represents the possible number of blueberries that Morgan ate.
   $m \geq 20$

Kayla is at most 56 inches tall. Let $k =$ Kayla's height.

5. What are three possible heights for Kayla?
   **Sample answer: 36 inches, 48 inches, 50 inches**
6. Can Kayla's height be exactly 56 inches? **Yes**
7. Write an inequality that represents Kayla's possible heights. $k \leq 56$

**On the Back!**

8. Write an inequality for the situation.
   The number of teachers, $t$, at Riverside Middle School is greater than 35. $t > 35$

R 2•6



## On-Level and Advanced Activity Centers (O) (A)

**Problem-Solving Reading Mat**

Have students read the Problem-Solving Reading Mat for Topic 2 and then complete Problem-Solving Reading Activity 2-6.

See the Problem-Solving Reading Activity Guide for other suggestions on how to use this mat.

PEARSON realize.
PearsonRealize.com

## TIMING

The time allocated to Step 3 will depend on the teacher's instructional decisions and differentiation routines.

15–30 min

 Help  Practice Buddy  Tools  Games

## Technology Center   

 Tools  Games

### Math Tools and Math Games

A link to a specific math tools activity or math game to use with this lesson is provided at PearsonRealize.com.

## Leveled Assignment  Items 1–7, 11, 12, 14, 15  Items 3–8, 11–15  Items 5–15

Name ______________________ Help Practice Buddy Tools Games

## Homework & Practice 2-6

### Write Inequalities

### Another Look!

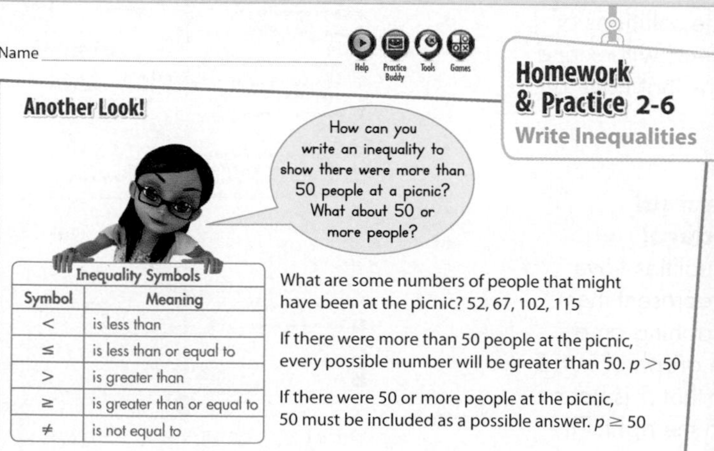

How can you write an inequality to show there were more than 50 people at a picnic? What about 50 or more people?


Inequality Symbols

| Symbol | Meaning |
|---|---|
| < | is less than |
| ≤ | is less than or equal to |
| > | is greater than |
| ≥ | is greater than or equal to |
| ≠ | is not equal to |

What are some numbers of people that might have been at the picnic? 52, 67, 102, 115

If there were more than 50 people at the picnic, every possible number will be greater than 50. $p > 50$

If there were 50 or more people at the picnic, 50 must be included as a possible answer. $p \geq 50$

In **1–10**, write an inequality for each situation.

**Sample answers are given.**

1. The number of students the bus holds, $s$, is less than 40.
**$s < 40$**

2. The weight limit, $w$, on the bridge is 12 tons.
**$w \leq 12$**

3. The distance, $d$, is at least 110 miles.
**$d \geq 110$**

4. The depth of the swimming pool, $d$, cannot be deeper than $3\frac{1}{2}$ feet.
**$d \leq 3\frac{1}{2}$**

5. The least amount of water, $w$, that hikers must bring is 30 ounces.
**$w \geq 30$**

6. The least number of minutes, $m$, that a player must practice per day is 45 minutes.
**$m \geq 45$**

7. Tim's age, $t$, is not 21 years old.
**$t \neq 21$**

8. The cost, $c$, is less than $45.
**$c < 45$**

9. The length of the driveway, $d$, is longer than $\frac{1}{5}$ mile.
**$d > \frac{1}{5}$**

10. The height of the sunflower, $s$, is not $45\frac{5}{6}$ inches tall.
**$s \neq 45\frac{5}{6}$**



11. **MP.6 Be Precise** A test has 50 questions, with 25 questions worth 1 point each and 25 questions worth 3 points each. Julia had no more than 20 points subtracted from the total possible points. Write an inequality that shows the possible points, $p$, that Julia earned.
**$p \geq 80$**

12. Lorraine practices piano for 1 hour every week and dances for $h$ hours 3 times every week. Evaluate $3h + 1$ for $h = 2, 5,$ and 9 to see how many hours Lorraine could spend practicing piano and dancing each week.
**$h = 7, 16,$ and 28 hours.**

13. **Higher Order Thinking** In 4th grade, Richard read 37 books. In 5th grade, he read 9 more books than the year before. This year in 6th grade, Richard plans to read at least 12 more books than the total number of books read in both 4th and 5th grades. Richard writes the inequality $b \geq 180$ to show the total number of books he will have read in 4th, 5th, and 6th grade. Is his inequality correct? Why or why not?
**No, Richard is not correct. $37 + (37 + 9) + (37 + 37 + 9 + 12) = 178$. Sample answer: He should write $b \geq 178$.**

14. **Math and Science** The waste-to-energy process generates energy in the form of electricity, heat, or fuel from the incineration of waste. Converting non-recyclable waste materials into electricity, heat, or fuel generates a renewable energy source. The 86 facilities in the United States have the capacity to produce 2,720 megawatts of power per year by processing more than 28 million tons of waste per year. Write an inequality to show the possible power, $p$, the waste-to-energy facilities in the United States are capable of producing.
**$p \leq 2720$**

### Common Core Assessment

15. The Cruz family shares a family cell phone plan. The plan is for 3,200 cell phone minutes each month. The father has used 1,200 minutes. The mother has used at least 600 minutes. The two children have used 675 minutes each.

Write an inequality that shows the number of minutes the Cruz family has used. Explain your reasoning.

**Sample answer: Let $m$ = the number of minutes. Then $m \geq 3,150$; The father and the two children have used 2,550 minutes. The mother has used at least 600 minutes. So, the amount of minutes the family has used is greater than or equal to 3,150.**

# LESSON 2-7

# SOLVE INEQUALITIES

## DIGITAL RESOURCES PearsonRealize.com

eText — Student and Teacher eTexts

PD — Listen and Look For Lesson Video

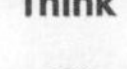
Think — Today's Challenge

Solve — Solve and Share

Learn — Visual Learning Animation Plus

Glossary — Animated Glossary

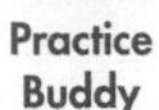
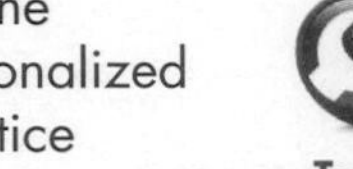
Practice Buddy — Online Personalized Practice

Tools — Math Tools

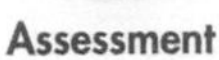
Assessment — Quick Check

Help — Another Look Homework Video

Games — Math Games

## LESSON OVERVIEW 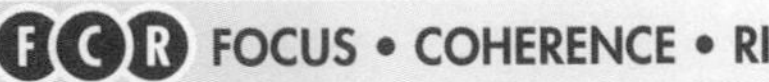

### FOCUS

**Domain 6.EE** Expressions and Equations

**Cluster 6.EE.B** Reason about and solve one-variable equations and inequalities.

**Content Standard 6.EE.B.5** Understand solving an equation or inequality as a process of answering a question: which values from a specified set, if any, make the equation or inequality true? Use substitution to determine whether a given number in a specified set makes an equation or inequality true. Also **6.EE.B.8**.

**Mathematical Practices MP.2, MP.4, MP.5, MP.7**

**Objective** Describe solutions to an inequality and represent them on a number line.

**Essential Understanding** An inequality is a mathematical sentence that contains the inequality symbol $<$ (is less than), $>$ (is greater than), $\leq$ (is less than or equal to), $\geq$ (is greater than or equal to), or $\neq$ (is not equal to). An inequality describes a situation that has an infinite number of numerical possibilities.

**Materials** Number lines (Teaching Tool 13) (optional)

### COHERENCE

In the first half of Topic 2, students found solutions to equations. In the previous lesson, they wrote inequalities. In this lesson, students extend these skills as they learn to represent solutions to inequalities. Their prior experience with locating, comparing, and ordering numbers on a number line will help students as they graph the solutions of inequalities. In Grade 8, students will extend this understanding to equations that have an infinite number of solutions.

### RIGOR

This lesson emphasizes **conceptual understanding** and **procedural skill**. Students learn that inequalities have infinitely many solutions and represent them algebraically as well as by graphing on a number line. For example, the graph of $x > 5$ is an open circle at 5 to show that 5 is not a solution, and a ray pointing to the right. The graph of $x \geq 5$ is the same, but with a solid circle at 5.

PD Watch the Listen and Look For Lesson Video.

## MATH ANYTIME

### Daily Common Core Review

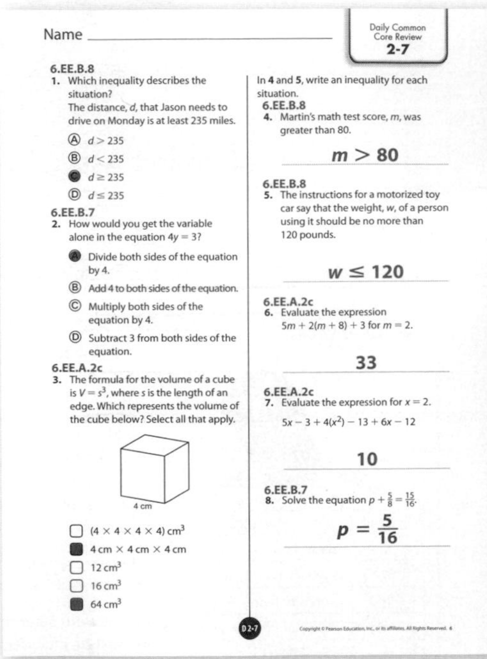
Name ____________

Daily Common Core Review **2-7**

6.EE.B.8
1. Which inequality describes the situation?
The distance, $d$, that Jason needs to drive on Monday is at least 235 miles.
Ⓐ $d > 235$
Ⓑ $d < 235$
● $d \geq 235$
Ⓓ $d \leq 235$

6.EE.B.7
2. How would you get the variable alone in the equation $4y = 3$?
● Divide both sides of the equation by 4.
Ⓑ Add 4 to both sides of the equation.
Ⓒ Multiply both sides of the equation by 4.
Ⓓ Subtract 3 from both sides of the equation.

6.EE.A.2c
3. The formula for the volume of a cube is $V = s^3$, where $s$ is the length of an edge. Which represents the volume of the cube below? Select all that apply.

4 cm

☐ $(4 \times 4 \times 4 \times 4)$ cm$^3$
■ 4 cm × 4 cm × 4 cm
☐ 12 cm$^3$
☐ 16 cm$^3$
■ 64 cm$^3$

In **4** and **5**, write an inequality for each situation.

6.EE.B.8
4. Martin's math test score, $m$, was greater than 80.

$m > 80$

6.EE.B.8
5. The instructions for a motorized toy car say that the weight, $w$, of a person using it should be no more than 120 pounds.

$w \leq 120$

6.EE.A.2c
6. Evaluate the expression $5m + 2(m + 8) + 3$ for $m = 2$.

33

6.EE.A.2c
7. Evaluate the expression for $x = 2$.
$5x - 3 + 4(x^2) - 13 + 6x - 12$

10

6.EE.B.7
8. Solve the equation $p + \frac{5}{8} = \frac{15}{16}$.

$p = \frac{5}{16}$

D 2-7



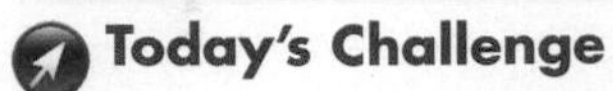
### Today's Challenge

Think Use the Topic 2 problems any time during this topic.

## ENGLISH LANGUAGE LEARNERS 

**Reading** Expand comprehension by making conclusions.

*Use with the Solve & Share on Student's Edition p. 119.*

Read the Solve & Share. *What conclusions can be made about q < 17?*

**Beginning** Read the speech bubble to students. Label a number line 0–20. Write $q < 17$. Point to 17 in the inequality and on the number line. Draw an open circle around 17 and say, *< 17*. Ask students to point to the direction that indicates < 17. Start at the open circle and shade in solutions. *We can conclude that all the numbers to the left of 17 are < 17.*

**Intermediate** Read the speech bubble with students. Instruct students to label the number line by adding numbers 0–20. Write $q < 17$. Draw an open circle around 17. *We're looking for numbers < 17.* Ask students to share with partners the direction that indicates < 17. Start at the open circle and shade in solutions. *What conclusions can be made about the solution?* Have students respond with the sentence stem: All numbers to the ___ are less than 17 because ___.

**Advanced** Instruct students to read the speech bubble with partners. Ask students to label the number line by adding numbers 0–20 and to draw an open circle around 17. Have students shade the numbers that are less than 17. Ask students to share with partners any conclusions that can be made about $q < 17$.

**Summarize** What does the < symbol indicate about an inequality graphed on a number line?

# DEVELOP: PROBLEM-BASED LEARNING

**COHERENCE: Engage learners by connecting prior knowledge to new ideas.**
Students extend their understanding of inequalities to find the solutions to a given inequality.

10–15 min

Solve

## BEFORE

**1. Pose the Solve-and-Share Problem**
You may wish to provide number lines (Teaching Tool 13).
**MP.5 Use Appropriate Tool Strategically** Listen and look for students who use a number line to represent the solution.

**2. Build Understanding**
*Are you able to list all of the numbers that make the inequality $q < 17$ true? Explain.* [No; there are an infinite number of solutions.] *What tool could you use to show all of the solutions?* [Sample answer: A number line]

## DURING

**3. Ask Guiding Questions As Needed**
*Could q equal 17? Explain.* [No; 17 is not less than 17.] *Could q be a fraction or a decimal? Give examples.* [Yes; Sample answer: $q$ could be 16.5 or $10\frac{1}{2}$.] *Compared to 17, in which direction on the number line are the solutions located?* [To the left of 17] *How might you show that all the numbers to the left of 17 are solutions?* [Sample answer: Draw a line over the solutions.]

## AFTER

**4. Share and Discuss Solutions**
Start with students' solutions. If needed, project Michael's work to illustrate the inequality's solutions on a number line.

**5. Transition to the Visual Learning Bridge**
*An inequality has an infinite number of solutions. You can use a number line to show solutions of inequalities.*

**6. Extension for Early Finishers**
*Which numbers on a number line are solutions to $x > 8$?* [All the numbers to the right of 8 on the number line are solutions.]

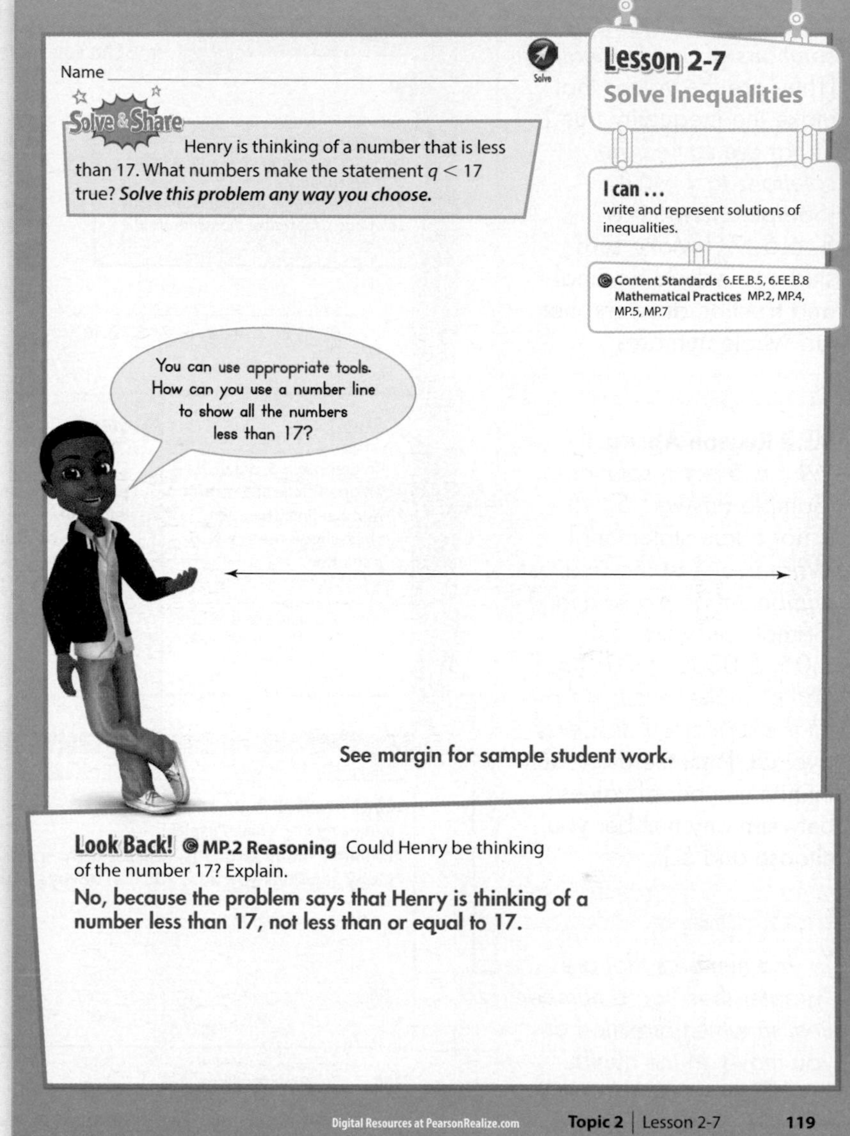

Name
Solve & Share
Henry is thinking of a number that is less than 17. What numbers make the statement $q < 17$ true? *Solve this problem any way you choose.*
Lesson 2-7
Solve Inequalities
I can ...
write and represent solutions of inequalities.
Content Standards 6.EE.B.5, 6.EE.B.8
Mathematical Practices MP.2, MP.4, MP.5, MP.7
You can use appropriate tools. How can you use a number line to show all the numbers less than 17?
See margin for sample student work.
Look Back! MP.2 Reasoning Could Henry be thinking of the number 17? Explain.
No, because the problem says that Henry is thinking of a number less than 17, not less than or equal to 17.
Digital Resources at PearsonRealize.com
Topic 2 | Lesson 2-7 119


## Analyze Student Work

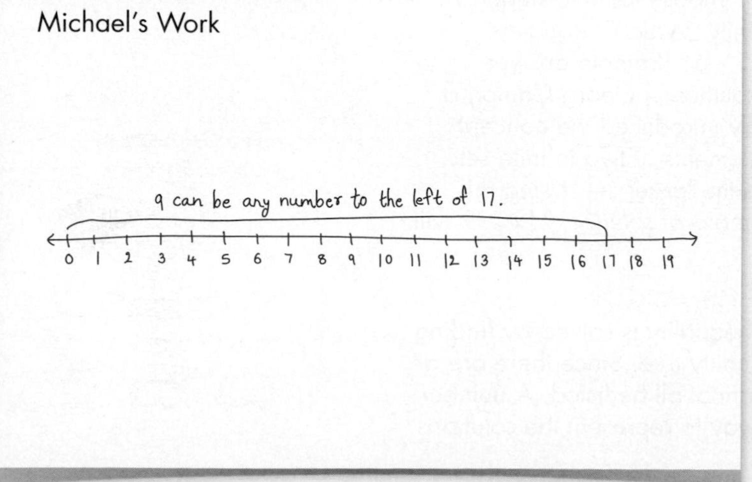


Michael uses a number line to help him describe all of the solutions. On the next page, he will learn the conventional way to graph the solutions on a number line.

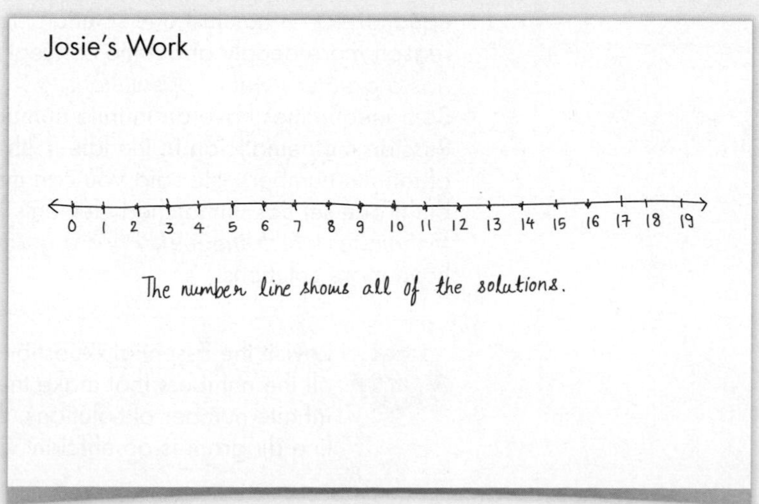


Josie also uses a number line, but she shows only whole-number solutions.

# DEVELOP: VISUAL LEARNING

PearsonRealize.com

Learn Glossary

The *Visual Learning Bridge* connects students' thinking in Solve & Share to important math ideas in the lesson. Use the *Visual Learning Bridge* to make these ideas explicit. Also available as a *Visual Learning Animation Plus* at PearsonRealize.com

*What is true about the solutions of any inequality?* [They are the values that make the inequality true.] *What are some other solutions to $x > 5$?* [Sample answers: 6, 8, 6.5, $7\frac{1}{4}$] Make sure students include decimal and fraction answers, not just whole numbers.

**MP.2 Reason Abstractly**
*Why is 5 not a solution?* [Sample answer: $5 > 5$ is not a true statement.] *What is one of the smallest numbers that is a solution?* [Sample answers: 5.1, 5.05, 5.00001] *Can you find a smaller number than all the suggested answers? Explain.* [Yes; there are an infinite number of values between any number you choose and 5.]

*To find numbers that are "greater than" on a number line, in which direction do you move on the number line?* [To the right] *Are the numbers that are plotted located to the right or to the left of 5?* [They are to the right.]

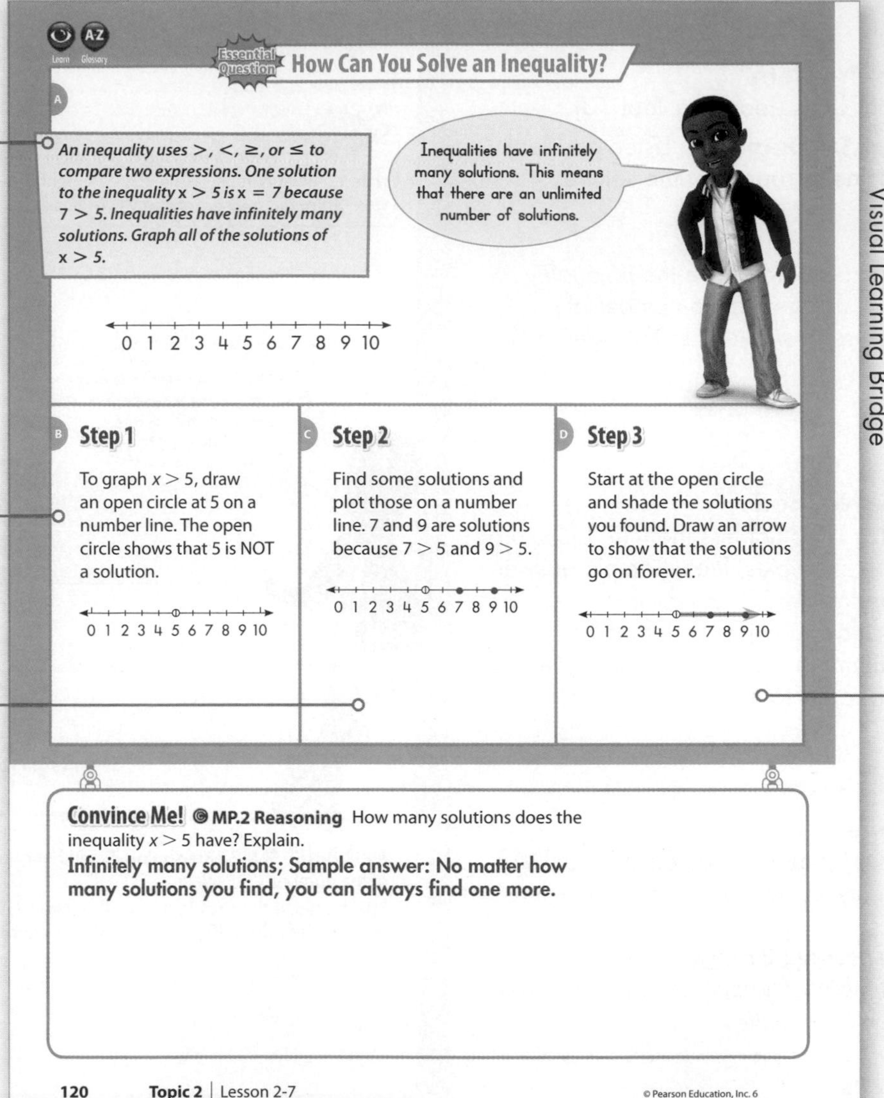

Essential Question **How Can You Solve an Inequality?**

A

*An inequality uses $>$, $<$, $\geq$, or $\leq$ to compare two expressions. One solution to the inequality $x > 5$ is $x = 7$ because $7 > 5$. Inequalities have infinitely many solutions. Graph all of the solutions of $x > 5$.*

Inequalities have infinitely many solutions. This means that there are an unlimited number of solutions.

0 1 2 3 4 5 6 7 8 9 10

Visual Learning Bridge

B **Step 1**

To graph $x > 5$, draw an open circle at 5 on a number line. The open circle shows that 5 is NOT a solution.

0 1 2 3 4 5 6 7 8 9 10

C **Step 2**

Find some solutions and plot those on a number line. 7 and 9 are solutions because $7 > 5$ and $9 > 5$.

0 1 2 3 4 5 6 7 8 9 10

D **Step 3**

Start at the open circle and shade the solutions you found. Draw an arrow to show that the solutions go on forever.

0 1 2 3 4 5 6 7 8 9 10

**Convince Me!** **MP.2 Reasoning** How many solutions does the inequality $x > 5$ have? Explain.
**Infinitely many solutions; Sample answer: No matter how many solutions you find, you can always find one more.**

120 **Topic 2** | Lesson 2-7 © Pearson Education, Inc. 6

*How do you indicate there are solutions that are not whole numbers?* [Trace over the number line by drawing an arrow connecting the whole numbers.]

**Prevent Misconceptions**

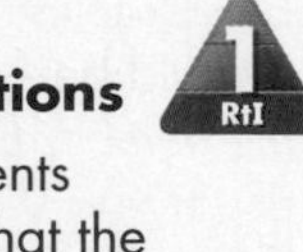


Be sure students understand that the numbers on a number line never end even though we can only see some of them. *The last whole number shown on the number line is 10. Is 10 the greatest solution to the inequality $x > 5$? Explain.* [No; the arrow pointing to the right shows that the solutions go on forever, but only part of the number line fits on the page.]

**Convince Me!** **MP.2 Reason Abstractly** Be sure students understand that the inequality $x > 5$ has an infinite number of solutions, but the equation $x = 5$ has just one solution. You may choose to have students reason more deeply about the concept of infinity. *Which inequality has a greater number of solutions: $x > 5$ or $x > 6$?* [Sample answer: Both inequalities have an infinite number of solutions.] Georg Cantor, a Russian mathematician in the late 19th century introduced the concept of infinite numbers. He said you can match elements of two infinite sets, but if one set has unmatched elements, that is the larger set. *Using this technique, which inequality has a greater number of solutions?* [$x > 5$ will have more solutions.]

Revisit the Essential Question. An inequality is solved by finding all the numbers that make the inequality true. Since there are an infinite number of solutions, they cannot all be listed. A number line diagram is an efficient visual way to represent the solutions.

## ✓ QUICK CHECK

Check mark indicates items for prescribing differentiation on the next page.
Item 4 is worth 1 point. Items 10 and 13 are worth up to 2 points.

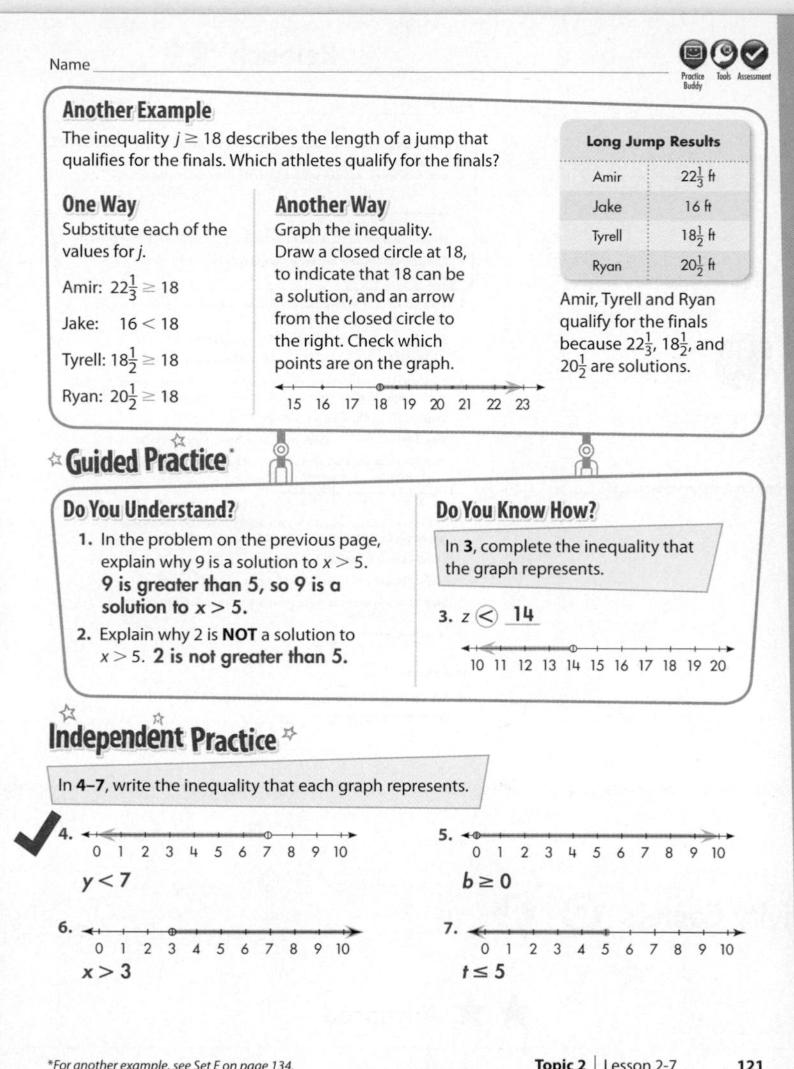

Name ______________________

### Another Example

The inequality $j \geq 18$ describes the length of a jump that qualifies for the finals. Which athletes qualify for the finals?

| Long Jump Results | |
|---|---|
| Amir | $22\frac{1}{3}$ ft |
| Jake | 16 ft |
| Tyrell | $18\frac{1}{2}$ ft |
| Ryan | $20\frac{1}{2}$ ft |

**One Way**

Substitute each of the values for *j*.

Amir: $22\frac{1}{3} \geq 18$

Jake: $16 < 18$

Tyrell: $18\frac{1}{2} \geq 18$

Ryan: $20\frac{1}{2} \geq 18$

**Another Way**

Graph the inequality. Draw a closed circle at 18, to indicate that 18 can be a solution, and an arrow from the closed circle to the right. Check which points are on the graph.

15 16 17 18 19 20 21 22 23

Amir, Tyrell and Ryan qualify for the finals because $22\frac{1}{3}$, $18\frac{1}{2}$, and $20\frac{1}{2}$ are solutions.

### Guided Practice*

**Do You Understand?**

1. In the problem on the previous page, explain why 9 is a solution to $x > 5$.
**9 is greater than 5, so 9 is a solution to $x > 5$.**

2. Explain why 2 is **NOT** a solution to $x > 5$. **2 is not greater than 5.**

**Do You Know How?**

In **3**, complete the inequality that the graph represents.

3. $z$ (<) 14

10 11 12 13 14 15 16 17 18 19 20

### Independent Practice*

In **4–7**, write the inequality that each graph represents.

✓ 4. 0 1 2 3 4 5 6 7 8 9 10
$y < 7$

5. 0 1 2 3 4 5 6 7 8 9 10
$b \geq 0$

6. 0 1 2 3 4 5 6 7 8 9 10
$x > 3$

7. 0 1 2 3 4 5 6 7 8 9 10
$t \leq 5$

*For another example, see Set E on page 134.



### Math Practices and Problem Solving

8. The number line below represents the solutions of the inequality $x > 7$. Is 7.1 a solution? Is 7.01 a solution? Explain how you can tell.

0 1 2 3 4 5 6 7 8 9 10

**Sample answer: Both 7.1 and 7.01 are greater than 7 and are solutions on the graphed line.**

9. **MP.4 Model with Math** Death Valley is the hottest place in the United States. The highest temperature ever recorded there was 134°F. The lowest temperature recorded there was 15°F. Write two inequalities that would describe the temperature, in °F, in Death Valley at any time since temperatures have been recorded.
**$t \leq 134$ and $t \geq 15$**

✓ 10. **Higher Order Thinking** Francine received a gift card to buy cell phone apps. She says the card's value is enough to buy any of the apps shown at the right. Let *v* be the dollar value of the gift card. Write an inequality that best describes the value of the gift card.
**$v \geq 12$**

| Phone Apps | |
|---|---|
| All Recipes | $ 9.50 |
| Headliners Sports | $10.50 |
| Remote Desktop | $12.00 |

11. The maximum load in a freight elevator is 1,500 pounds. Let $w$ = the weight in the elevator. Write an inequality to describe the allowable weight in the elevator.
**$w \leq 1{,}500$**

12. **Algebra** A chessboard is made up of 64 square places. Let $s$ = the side length of each square on a chessboard. Evaluate the expression $64s^2$ to find the area of a chessboard for which $s = 1\frac{1}{2}$ inches.
**144 in$^2$**

### Common Core Assessment

✓ 13. Tania started a graph to show the inequality $y < 3.7$. Finish labeling the number line and draw the graph.

3.0 3.1 3.2 3.3 3.4 3.5 3.6 3.7 3.8 3.9 4.0

14. Bill started a graph to show the inequality $x \leq 25$. Finish labeling the number line and draw the graph.

20 21 22 23 24 25 26 27 28 29 30





**Another Example** *On a number line, what is the difference between an open circle and a closed circle?* [An open circle shows that the number is *not* a solution. A closed circle shows that the number *is* a solution.] *Why is 18 a solution to the inequality?* [$18 \geq 18$ is a true statement.] *What type of circle would you use when graphing the solutions to $j \geq 18$? Explain.* [A closed circle; 18 is included as a solution.]

**Error Intervention: Item 3**

**If** students are unsure which inequality symbol to use,

**then** ask: *Is 14 a solution? How do you know?* [No; 14 has an open circle, so it is not a solution.] *So, does the graph show numbers "less than" 14 or numbers "less than or equal to" 14?* [Less than] *Which symbol do you use for "less than"?* [<]

**Reteaching** Assign Reteaching Set E on p. 134.

**Item 9 MP.4 Model with Math** Suggest to students that they think carefully about whether 134 and 15 are solutions to the inequalities they write. That should help them decide whether to use < or ≤, and whether to use > or ≥.

**Item 10 Higher Order Thinking** *What are some values that are greater than 12 but are not part of the solution set? Explain.* [Sample answer: Numbers such as $\frac{62}{3}$, 15.567, and 25.008 are greater than 12, but they do not describe dollar values.] *Can you represent this solution set by drawing a ray on a number line? Explain.* [No; you would need to draw dots at each dollar value, such as 12.00, 12.01, 12.02, 12.03, and so on. There are an infinite number of values between each of these numbers, and they are not included in this solution set because *v* represents an amount of money.]

**Items 13 and 14** Remind students that any scale and any interval of numbers can be shown on a number line.

**Multi-Step Problems** *Page 122 Item 12; Page 124 Item 18*

# ASSESS AND DIFFERENTIATE

Use the **QUICK CHECK** on the previous page to prescribe differentiated instruction.

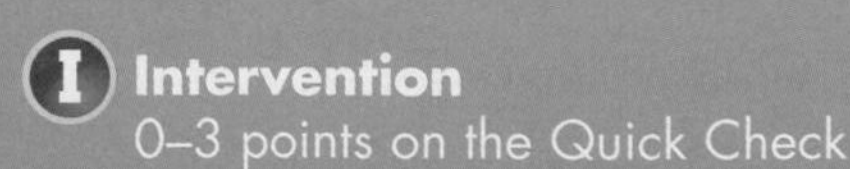


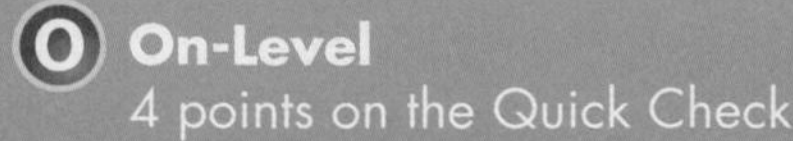


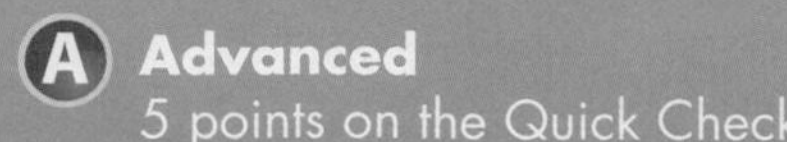


## Intervention Activity (I)

### Solve Inequalities

**Materials**

4 index cards per pair, number cube, Number lines (Teaching Tool 13)

- Before class, write each of these symbols on a different index card: $<, \leq, >, \geq$.
- Have students work in pairs. Mix the cards and place them facedown. Partner A selects a card and rolls the number cube. Partner B writes an inequality using the chosen symbol and number, and then states three solutions. Together, students graph all the solutions on a number line.
- Have students switch roles and repeat the activity.

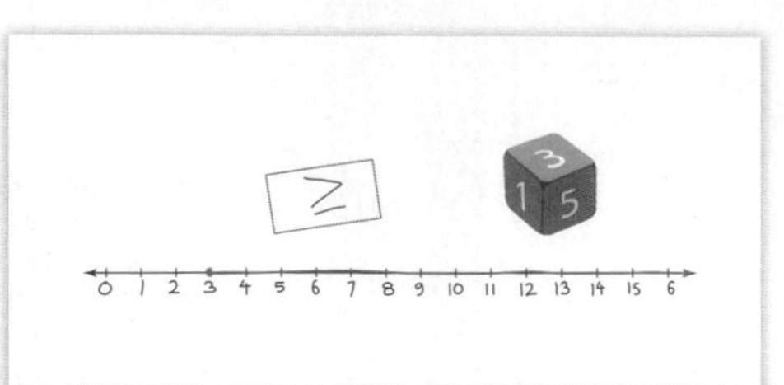


## Reteach (I)

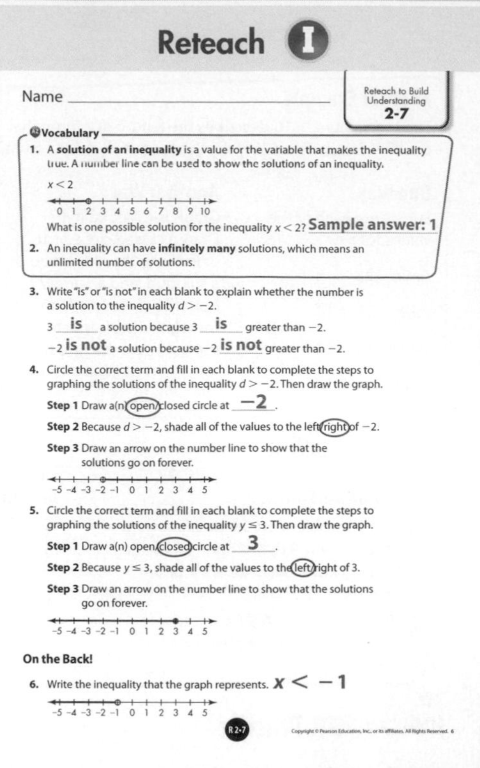

Name ______________

Reteach to Build Understanding
**2-7**

**Vocabulary**

1. A **solution of an inequality** is a value for the variable that makes the inequality true. A number line can be used to show the solutions of an inequality.

   $x < 2$

   0 1 2 3 4 5 6 7 8 9 10

   What is one possible solution for the inequality $x < 2$? **Sample answer: 1**

2. An inequality can have **infinitely many** solutions, which means an unlimited number of solutions.

3. Write "is" or "is not" in each blank to explain whether the number is a solution to the inequality $d > -2$.

   3 **is** a solution because 3 **is** greater than $-2$.

   $-2$ **is not** a solution because $-2$ **is not** greater than $-2$.

4. Circle the correct term and fill in each blank to complete the steps to graphing the solutions of the inequality $d > -2$. Then draw the graph.

   **Step 1** Draw a(n) open/closed circle at **$-2$**.

   **Step 2** Because $d > -2$, shade all of the values to the left/right of $-2$.

   **Step 3** Draw an arrow on the number line to show that the solutions go on forever.

   –5 –4 –3 –2 –1 0 1 2 3 4 5

5. Circle the correct term and fill in each blank to complete the steps to graphing the solutions of the inequality $y \leq 3$. Then draw the graph.

   **Step 1** Draw a(n) open/closed circle at **3**.

   **Step 2** Because $y \leq 3$, shade all of the values to the left/right of 3.

   **Step 3** Draw an arrow on the number line to show that the solutions go on forever.

   –5 –4 –3 –2 –1 0 1 2 3 4 5

**On the Back!**

6. Write the inequality that the graph represents. $x < -1$

   –5 –4 –3 –2 –1 0 1 2 3 4 5

R 2-7



## On-Level and Advanced Activity Centers (O) (A)

### Center Games

Students work individually or in pairs to match number line diagrams with inequalities. Suggest to students that they discuss and record several possible values for the variable as they play the game.

★ On-Level

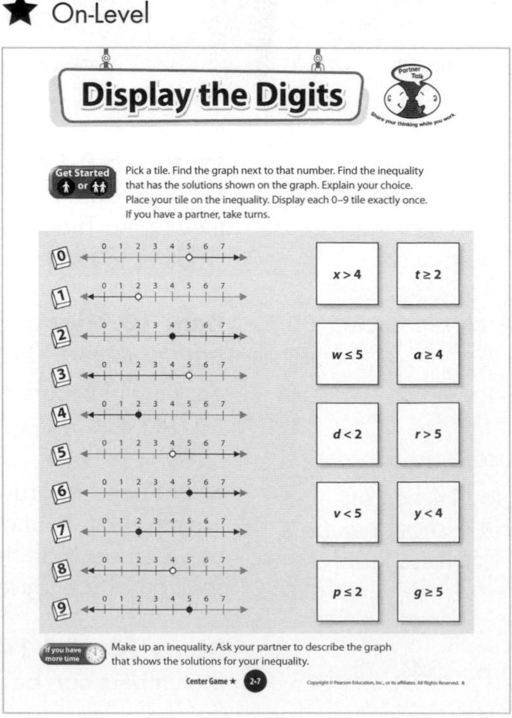

**Display the Digits**

Partner Talk
Share your thinking while you work.

Get Started: Pick a tile. Find the graph next to that number. Find the inequality that has the solutions shown on the graph. Explain your choice. Place your tile on the inequality. Display each 0–9 tile exactly once. If you have a partner, take turns.

0 1 2 3 4 5 6 7

| | |
|---|---|
| $x > 4$ | $t \geq 2$ |
| $w \leq 5$ | $a \geq 4$ |
| $d < 2$ | $r > 5$ |
| $v < 5$ | $y < 4$ |
| $p \leq 2$ | $g \geq 5$ |

If you have more time: Make up an inequality. Ask your partner to describe the graph that shows the solutions for your inequality.

Center Game ★ 2-7



★★ Advanced

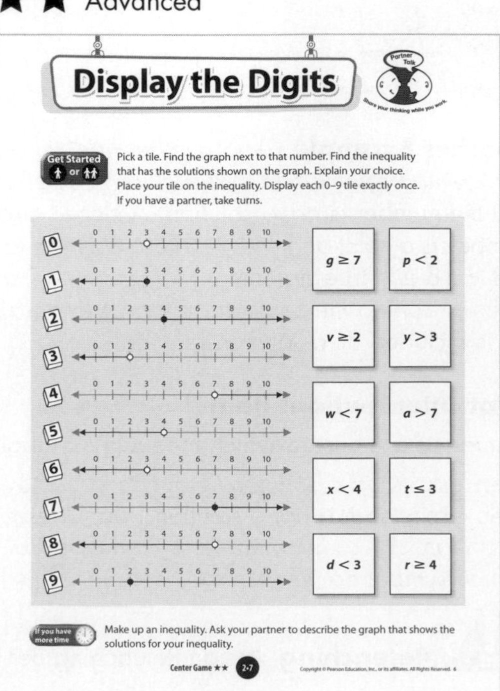

**Display the Digits**

Partner Talk
Share your thinking while you work.

Get Started: Pick a tile. Find the graph next to that number. Find the inequality that has the solutions shown on the graph. Explain your choice. Place your tile on the inequality. Display each 0–9 tile exactly once. If you have a partner, take turns.

0 1 2 3 4 5 6 7 8 9 10

| | |
|---|---|
| $g \geq 7$ | $p < 2$ |
| $v \geq 2$ | $y > 3$ |
| $w < 7$ | $a > 7$ |
| $x < 4$ | $t \leq 3$ |
| $d < 3$ | $r \geq 4$ |

If you have more time: Make up an inequality. Ask your partner to describe the graph that shows the solutions for your inequality.

Center Game ★★ 2-7

**TIMING**

The time allocated to Step 3 will depend on the teacher's instructional decisions and differentiation routines.

15–30 min

PEARSON realize. PearsonRealize.com

Help

Practice Buddy

Tools

Games

## Technology Center

Tools Games

### Math Tools and Math Games

A link to a specific math tools activity or math game to use with this lesson is provided at PearsonRealize.com.

## Leveled Assignment

 Items 1–7, 10, 15–17, 19–21  Items 1–6, 8–10, 16–21 (A) Items 3–6, 11–14, 16–21

Name ______________________

Help Practice Buddy Tools Games

**Homework & Practice 2-7**
**Solve Inequalities**

**Another Look!**

Graph the solutions of the inequalities $x < 3$ and $x \geq 5$.

Draw an open circle at 3. The values of $x$ are less than 3, so shade to the left on the number line.

$x < 3$

0 1 2 3 4 5 6 7 8 9 10

Draw a closed circle at 5. The values of $y$ are greater than 5, so shade to the right on the number line.

$y \geq 5$

0 1 2 3 4 5 6 7 8 9 10

An inequality uses <, >, ≤, and ≥, to compare two expressions.

In **1–4**, write the inequality that each graph represents.

**1.** 5 6 7 8 9 10 11 12 13 14 15
**$x < 11$**

**2.** 0 1 2 3 4 5 6 7 8 9 10
**$f \geq 5$**

**3.** 0 1 2 3 4 5 6 7 8 9 10
**$y > 0$**

**4.** 0 1 2 3 4 5 6 7 8 9 10
**$b \leq 9$**

In **5** and **6**, graph each inequality on a number line.

**5.** $x < 7$

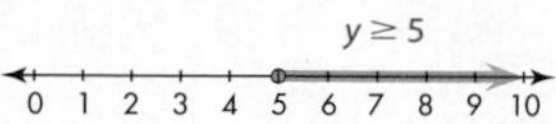

0 1 2 3 4 5 6 7 8 9 10

**6.** $x \geq 7$

0 1 2 3 4 5 6 7 8 9 10

In **7–14**, name three solutions of each inequality. **Sample answers are given.**

**7.** $x < 9$ **6, 7, 8**
**8.** $x < 6$ **3, 4, 5**
**9.** $y > 2$ **3, 4, 5**
**10.** $y \geq 100$ **100, 102, 103**
**11.** $z < 8$ **5, 6, 7**
**12.** $x \geq 77$ **78, 79, 80**
**13.** $u > 10.9$ **11, 12, 13**
**14.** $u \leq 13.99$ **11, 12, 13**



**15. MP.7 Use Structure** The number line below represents the solutions of the inequality $y < 6$. How many solutions are there? Write three of the solutions that are greater than 5.

0 1 2 3 4 5 6 7 8 9 10

**There are infinitely many solutions; Sample answer: 5.2, 5.5, and 5.9 are solutions.**

**16. MP.4 Model with Math** In 1992, the women's world record in the pole vault was officially recognized as 4.05 meters. The most recent world record, set in 2009, is 5.06 meters. What inequality can you write that would describe a new world record in the women's pole vault?
**Sample answer: $v > 5.06$**

**17.** At the right is a portion of the menu at a diner. The inequality $m < 5$ represents the amount of money, $m$, that Elizabeth has to spend on lunch at the diner. Which items can she choose for lunch?
**Elizabeth can choose a turkey sandwich, Italian beef sandwich, or one or two slices of cheese pizza.**

| Diner | |
|---|---|
| Turkey Sandwich | \$3.99 |
| Tuna Sandwich with Fruit | \$5.45 |
| Italian Beef Sandwich | \$4.75 |
| Slice of Cheese Pizza | \$2.25 |
| Grilled Chicken Sandwich | \$6.00 |

**18. Higher Order Thinking** The width of a youth soccer field must be at least 45 meters, but cannot exceed 60 meters. Write two inequalities that describe the width, $w$, of a youth soccer field. Then write two integers that are solutions of the inequalities.
**$w \geq 45$ and $w \leq 60$; Sample answer: $w = 52$, $w = 55$**

**19. MP.2 Reasoning** Two friends split the cost of 1 medium pizza equally. Each friend's share of the cost was \$5.60. If 4 friends split the cost of 2 medium pizzas equally, how much would each friend's share of the cost be? Explain how you know without calculating.
**\$5.60; Sample answer: If two friends share the cost of 1 medium and you double the cost and double the number of shares, the cost each person shares stays the same.**

**Common Core Assessment**

**20.** Andy started a graph to show the inequality $z > 0.4$. Finish labeling the number line and draw the graph.

0 0.1 0.2 0.3 0.4 0.5 0.6 0.7 0.8 0.9 1.0

**21.** Tricia started a graph to show the inequality $x \geq 12$. Finish labeling the number line and draw the graph.

10 11 12 13 14 15 16 17 18 19 20

MATH PRACTICES AND PROBLEM SOLVING | LESSON **2-8**

# MAKE SENSE AND PERSEVERE

## DIGITAL RESOURCES PearsonRealize.com

 Student and Teacher eTexts
 eText

 Listen and Look For Lesson Video
 PD

 Today's Challenge
Think

 Solve and Share
 Solve

 Visual Learning Animation Plus
Learn

 Animated Glossary
Glossary

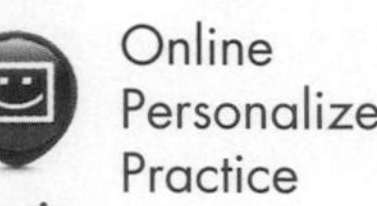 Online Personalized Practice
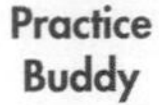 Practice Buddy

Math Tools
Tools

 Quick Check
Assessment

 Another Look Homework Video
Help

 Math Games
Games

 Math Practices Animations
MP

## LESSON OVERVIEW  FOCUS • COHERENCE • RIGOR

### FOCUS

**Mathematical Practices MP.1** Make sense of problems and persevere in solving them. Also **MP.2, MP.4, MP.6, MP.8**

**Domain 6.EE** Expressions and Equations

**Cluster 6.EE.B** Reason about and solve one-variable equations and inequalities.

**Content Standard 6.EE.B.7** Solve real-world and mathematical problems by writing and solving equations of the form $x + p = q$ and $px = q$ for cases in which $p$, $q$ and $x$ are all nonnegative rational numbers. Also **6.EE.B.6**.

**Objective** Use equations to make sense of problems and persevere in solving them.

**Essential Understanding** Good math thinkers make sense of problems and think of ways to solve them. If they get stuck, they don't give up.

### COHERENCE

Students have engaged MP.1 throughout their work in Topics 1 and 2, and will continue to do so throughout Grade 6. Although the content used in this lesson was developed in this topic, instruction should focus on reinforcing good thinking habits to develop students' proficiency with MP.1, as they make sense and persevere in solving problems.

### RIGOR

This lesson emphasizes **application**. All of the problems in this lesson elicit the use of multiple mathematical practices while applying skills students have learned in this topic. Any mathematical practice that is employed in the work of this lesson should be explicitly discussed. However, the main focus of classroom conversation should be the development of the Thinking Habits shown in the Solve & Share task for MP.1.

 PD Watch the Listen and Look For Lesson Video.

## MATH ANYTIME

### Daily Common Core Review

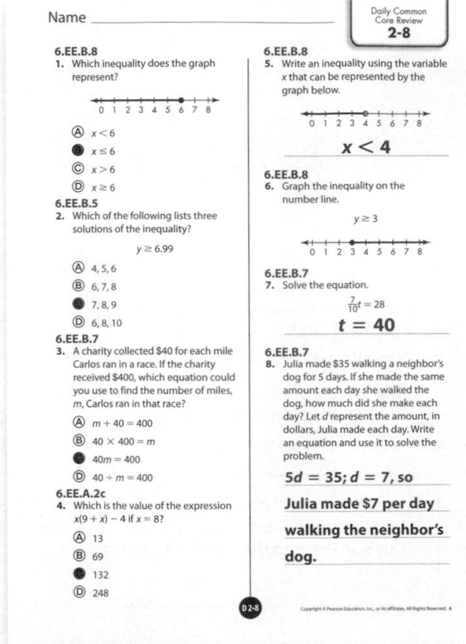

Name ____________

Daily Common Core Review **2-8**

**6.EE.B.8**
**1.** Which inequality does the graph represent?

Ⓐ $x < 6$
● $x \le 6$
Ⓒ $x > 6$
Ⓓ $x \ge 6$

**6.EE.B.5**
**2.** Which of the following lists three solutions of the inequality?

$y \ge 6.99$

Ⓐ 4, 5, 6
Ⓑ 6, 7, 8
● 7, 8, 9
Ⓓ 6, 8, 10

**6.EE.B.7**
**3.** A charity collected $40 for each mile Carlos ran in a race. If the charity received $400, which equation could you use to find the number of miles, $m$, Carlos ran in that race?

Ⓐ $m + 40 = 400$
Ⓑ $40 \times 400 = m$
● $40m = 400$
Ⓓ $40 \div m = 400$

**6.EE.A.2c**
**4.** Which is the value of the expression $x(9 + x) - 4$ if $x = 8$?

Ⓐ 13
Ⓑ 69
● 132
Ⓓ 248

**6.EE.B.8**
**5.** Write an inequality using the variable $x$ that can be represented by the graph below.

$x < 4$

**6.EE.B.8**
**6.** Graph the inequality on the number line.

$y \ge 3$

**6.EE.B.7**
**7.** Solve the equation.

$\frac{7}{10}t = 28$

$t = 40$

**6.EE.B.7**
**8.** Julia made $35 walking a neighbor's dog for 5 days. If she made the same amount each day she walked the dog, how much did she make each day? Let $d$ represent the amount, in dollars, Julia made each day. Write an equation and use it to solve the problem.

$5d = 35$; $d = 7$, so Julia made $7 per day walking the neighbor's dog.

D 2-8

 **Today's Challenge**

Think Use the Topic 2 problems any time during this topic.

## ENGLISH LANGUAGE LEARNERS 

**Reading** Demonstrate comprehension by responding to questions.

*Use with the Solve & Share on Student's Edition p. 125.*

Read the Solve & Share. Ask students to identify important information needed to solve the problem.

**Beginning** Read *Thinking Habits* Bullet 1. Model thinking aloud. *What do I need to find? I need to find the ages of Barb and the twins.* Read Bullet 2. *What do I know? I know Barb is 3 times older than the twins, and the sum is 55.* Read Bullet 3. *What is my plan?* Write $x + x$. *Allie and Sam are each x years old, so x + x represents the sum of the twins' ages.* Write $3x$. *This is Barb's age.* Point to 55 in the Solve & Share. *This is the sum of their ages.* Write $x + x + 3x = 55$. Demonstrate solving the problem with the age recommended by students. Read Bullet 4. Continue the process until the correct solution is found.

**Intermediate** Read *Thinking Habits* Bullet 1. *What do I need to find?* Students will respond with simple sentences. Continue the process with Bullets 2 and 3. Write $x + x + 3x = 55$. Instruct students to work with partners to solve the problem with the age recommended by students. Read Bullet 4. Continue the process until the correct solution is found.

**Advanced** Read *Thinking Habits* Bullets 1–3, pausing after each question for students to respond. Write $x + x + 3x = 55$. Instruct students to work with partners to solve the problem.

**Summarize** How do the *Thinking Habits* questions help make sense of word problems?

# DEVELOP: PROBLEM-BASED LEARNING

realize.
PearsonRealize.com

Solve

**COHERENCE: Engage learners by connecting prior knowledge to new ideas.**
Students extend their understanding of equations to help them make sense of a real-world problem and persevere in solving it.

10–15 min

## BEFORE

**1. Pose the Solve-and-Share Problem**
**MP.1 Make Sense and Persevere** Listen and look for students who write an equation to represent the problem and then solve to answer the question.

**2. Build Understanding**
*What operation will you use to solve the problem?* [Addition]
*How many people's ages are involved in this problem?* [3]

## DURING

**3. Ask Guiding Questions As Needed**
*Suppose Allie is n years old. How old is Sam? Why?* [Sam is $n$ years old; Allie and Sam are twins, so they are the same age.] *How could you represent Barb's age with an expression that contains n?* [$3n$] *What equation would show that the sum of the three ages is 55?* [$n + n + 3n = 55$] *How can you check your answer?* [Substitute the value of $n$ into the original equation. The equation should be true.]

## AFTER

**4. Share and Discuss Solutions**
Solve Start with students' solutions. If needed, project Elena's work to discuss show how to define and use a variable, write an equation, and find the solution to the problem.

**5. Transition to the Visual Learning Bridge**
*Defining a variable and writing an equation can help you make sense of the information needed to solve a problem.*

**6. Extension for Early Finishers**
*In the future, when Barb is twice as old as the twins, the sum of their ages will be 88. Write and solve an equation to find out how old each person will be then.* [$f + f + 2f = 88$, where $f$ represents the age of the twins; Allie and Sam will be 22, and Barb will be 44.]

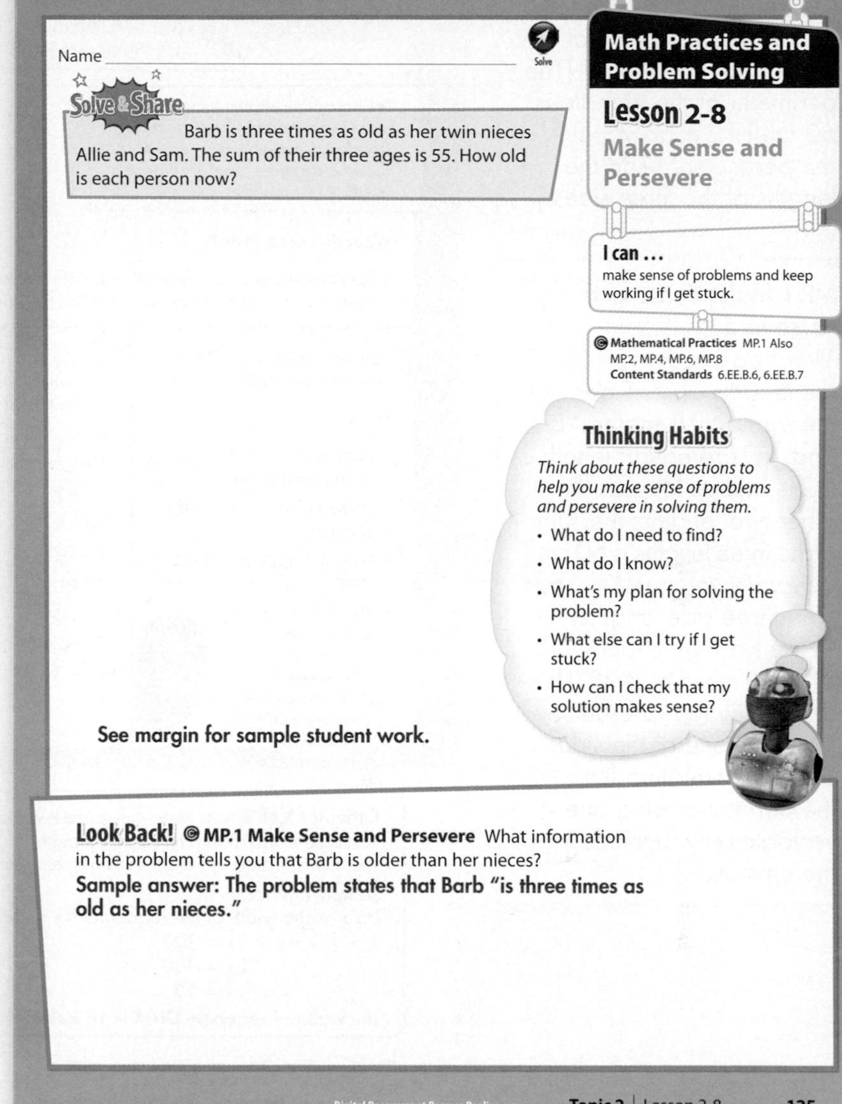

Name

Solve & Share

Barb is three times as old as her twin nieces Allie and Sam. The sum of their three ages is 55. How old is each person now?

**Math Practices and Problem Solving**

**Lesson 2-8**
**Make Sense and Persevere**

**I can ...**
make sense of problems and keep working if I get stuck.

**Mathematical Practices** MP.1 Also MP.2, MP.4, MP.6, MP.8
**Content Standards** 6.EE.B.6, 6.EE.B.7

**Thinking Habits**
*Think about these questions to help you make sense of problems and persevere in solving them.*
- What do I need to find?
- What do I know?
- What's my plan for solving the problem?
- What else can I try if I get stuck?
- How can I check that my solution makes sense?

**See margin for sample student work.**

**Look Back!** **MP.1 Make Sense and Persevere** What information in the problem tells you that Barb is older than her nieces?
**Sample answer: The problem states that Barb "is three times as old as her nieces."**

Digital Resources at PearsonRealize.com | Topic 2 | Lesson 2-8 | 125

## Analyze Student Work

**Elena's Work**

n = Allie's age and n = Sam's age.
3n = Barb's age

$n + n + 3n = 55$
$5n = 55$
$5n \div 5 = 55 \div 5$
$n = 11$
Allie and Sam are 11. Barb is 3 times as old, so she's 33.

Elena uses an equation to represent the information given in the problem. Then she solves the equation and uses the solution to find the ages of the three people.

**Richard's Work**

a = Allie's age
s = Sam's age
b = Barb's age

$a + s + b = 55$

Richard uses a different variable for each person's age and gets stuck; he cannot solve the equation. He should persevere by trying a different approach to solving the problem.

# DEVELOP: VISUAL LEARNING

The *Visual Learning Bridge* connects students' thinking in Solve & Share to important math ideas in the lesson. Use the *Visual Learning Bridge* to make these ideas explicit. Also available as a *Visual Learning Animation Plus* at PearsonRealize.com

ELL Visual Learning

PEARSON realize. PearsonRealize.com

Learn

Glossary

*What information is given in the picture that is not stated in the problem?* [The perimeter of the triangle is 60 cm.] *How do you find the perimeter?* [Add the lengths of the three sides.]

**MP.1 Make Sense and Persevere**
*What do you know about the lengths of the sides of the triangle?* [Lengths *AB* and *AC* are equal; length *BC* is half as long as the other two lengths; the sum of the three lengths is 60 cm.] *What do you need to find?* [The three side lengths] *What strategy might work to solve the problem?* [Use a variable to represent the length of one of the sides. Write an equation for the perimeter using one variable only. Solve for the unknown.]

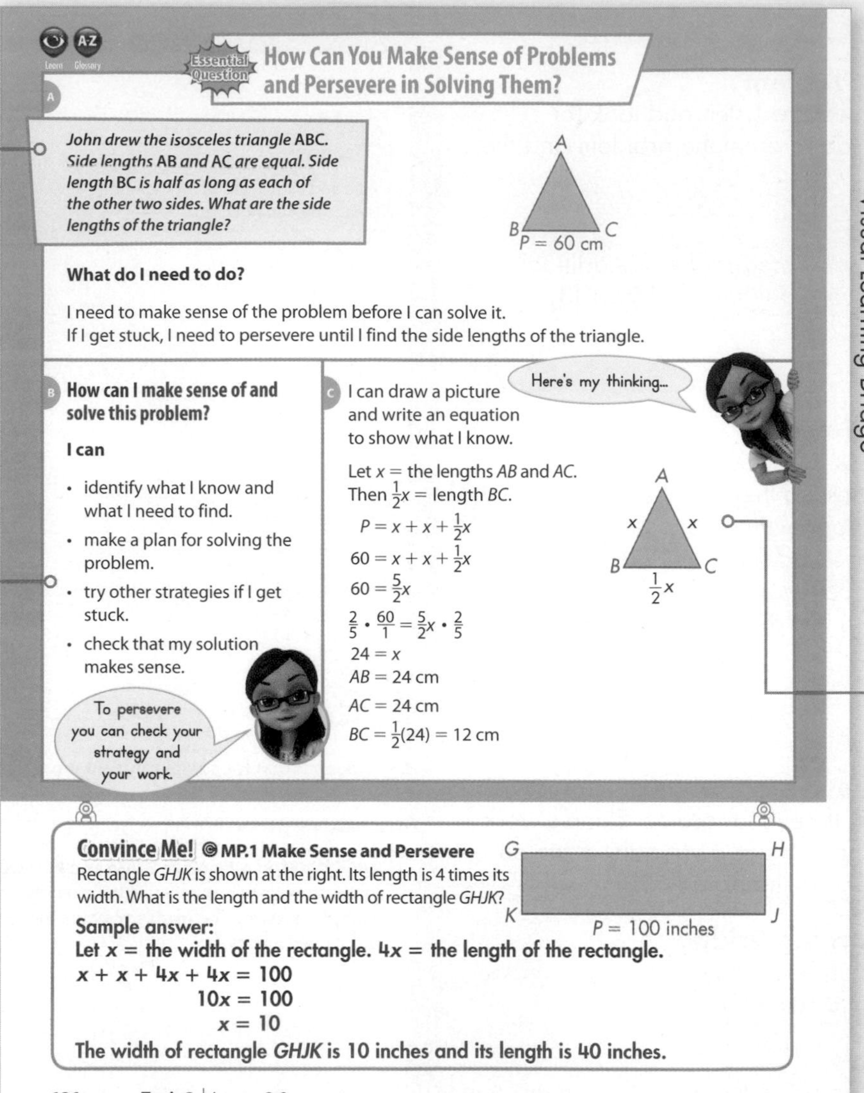

Essential Question **How Can You Make Sense of Problems and Persevere in Solving Them?**

A

*John drew the isosceles triangle ABC. Side lengths AB and AC are equal. Side length BC is half as long as each of the other two sides. What are the side lengths of the triangle?*



**What do I need to do?**

I need to make sense of the problem before I can solve it.
If I get stuck, I need to persevere until I find the side lengths of the triangle.

B **How can I make sense of and solve this problem?**

**I can**

- identify what I know and what I need to find.
- make a plan for solving the problem.
- try other strategies if I get stuck.
- check that my solution makes sense.



C I can draw a picture and write an equation to show what I know.



Let $x$ = the lengths *AB* and *AC*.
Then $\frac{1}{2}x$ = length *BC*.

$P = x + x + \frac{1}{2}x$
$60 = x + x + \frac{1}{2}x$
$60 = \frac{5}{2}x$
$\frac{2}{5} \cdot \frac{60}{1} = \frac{5}{2}x \cdot \frac{2}{5}$
$24 = x$
$AB = 24$ cm
$AC = 24$ cm
$BC = \frac{1}{2}(24) = 12$ cm



Visual Learning Bridge

**Convince Me!** MP.1 Make Sense and Persevere
Rectangle *GHJK* is shown at the right. Its length is 4 times its width. What is the length and the width of rectangle *GHJK*?



**Sample answer:**
**Let $x$ = the width of the rectangle. $4x$ = the length of the rectangle.**
$x + x + 4x + 4x = 100$
$10x = 100$
$x = 10$
**The width of rectangle *GHJK* is 10 inches and its length is 40 inches.**

126 Topic 2 | Lesson 2-8 © Pearson Education, Inc. 6

*How does the picture help?* [Sample answer: It shows how the side lengths can be represented using a variable.] *How can you check that the solution to the equation is correct?* [Substitute 24 for $x$ in the original equation and do the computations to see if the equation is true.] *Does the solution meet the conditions of the problem? Explain.* [Yes. *AB* and *AC* are each 24 cm, so they are equal lengths. *BC* is 12 cm, which is half the length of *AB* and *AC*. The perimeter is 60 cm: $24 + 24 + 12 = 60$.]

**Convince Me! MP.1 Make Sense and Persevere** *What do you know about the lengths of the sides of a rectangle?* [A rectangle has two pairs of sides of equal length.] *If the width of the rectangle is x, how do you represent that the length is 4 times its width?* [4x] *How many sides will measure x?* [2] *How many sides will measure 4x?* [2]

Essential Question Revisit the Essential Question. Writing an equation to represent a problem helps you analyze and understand the information in the problem. The plan for solving the problem is built into the steps for solving the equation. If a solution does not make sense within the context of the problem, persevere to reexamine and try writing a different equation to represent the information in the problem correctly.

## QUICK CHECK

Check mark indicates items for prescribing differentiation on the next page.
Items 3 and 5 are worth 1 point. Items 6–9 are worth up to 3 points.

PEARSON realize. PearsonRealize.com

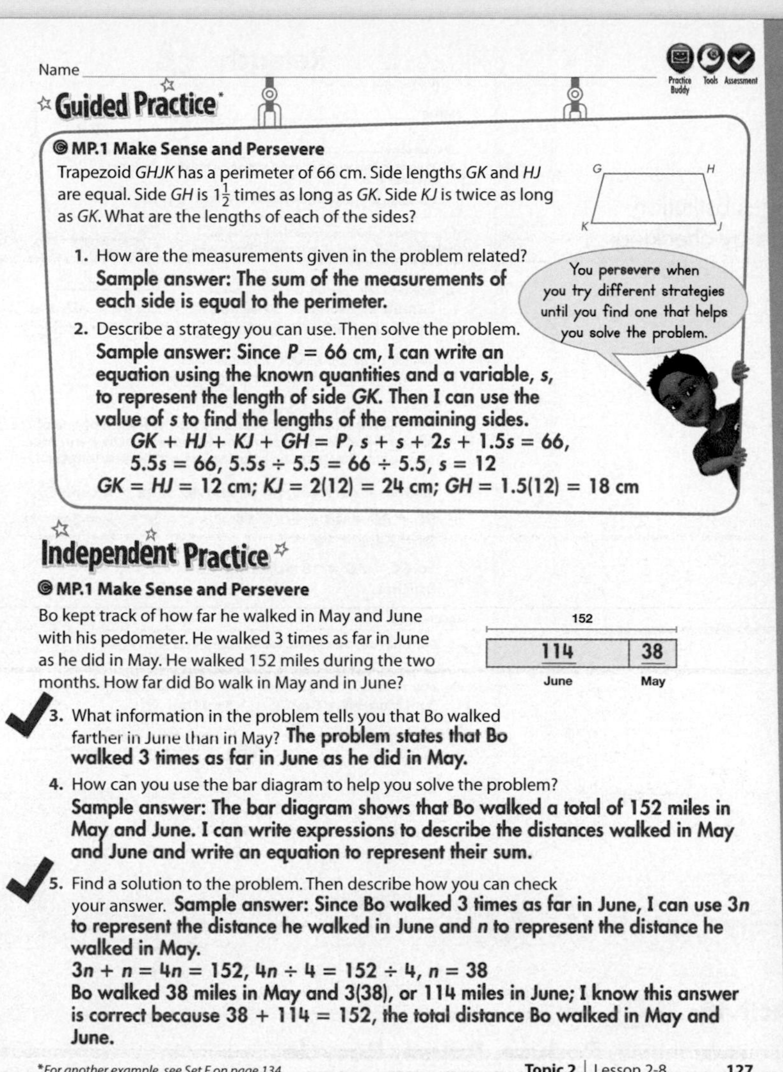

Name

### Guided Practice*

MP.1 Make Sense and Persevere

Trapezoid *GHJK* has a perimeter of 66 cm. Side lengths *GK* and *HJ* are equal. Side *GH* is $1\frac{1}{2}$ times as long as *GK*. Side *KJ* is twice as long as *GK*. What are the lengths of each of the sides?

1. How are the measurements given in the problem related? **Sample answer: The sum of the measurements of each side is equal to the perimeter.**
2. Describe a strategy you can use. Then solve the problem. **Sample answer: Since $P = 66$ cm, I can write an equation using the known quantities and a variable, $s$, to represent the length of side $GK$. Then I can use the value of $s$ to find the lengths of the remaining sides.**
   **$GK + HJ + KJ + GH = P$, $s + s + 2s + 1.5s = 66$, $5.5s = 66$, $5.5s \div 5.5 = 66 \div 5.5$, $s = 12$**
   **$GK = HJ = 12$ cm; $KJ = 2(12) = 24$ cm; $GH = 1.5(12) = 18$ cm**

You persevere when you try different strategies until you find one that helps you solve the problem.



### Independent Practice

MP.1 Make Sense and Persevere

Bo kept track of how far he walked in May and June with his pedometer. He walked 3 times as far in June as he did in May. He walked 152 miles during the two months. How far did Bo walk in May and in June?



3. What information in the problem tells you that Bo walked farther in June than in May? **The problem states that Bo walked 3 times as far in June as he did in May.**
4. How can you use the bar diagram to help you solve the problem? **Sample answer: The bar diagram shows that Bo walked a total of 152 miles in May and June. I can write expressions to describe the distances walked in May and June and write an equation to represent their sum.**
5. Find a solution to the problem. Then describe how you can check your answer. **Sample answer: Since Bo walked 3 times as far in June, I can use $3n$ to represent the distance he walked in June and $n$ to represent the distance he walked in May.**
   **$3n + n = 4n = 152$, $4n \div 4 = 152 \div 4$, $n = 38$**
   **Bo walked 38 miles in May and 3(38), or 114 miles in June; I know this answer is correct because $38 + 114 = 152$, the total distance Bo walked in May and June.**

*For another example, see Set F on page 134.

Topic 2 | Lesson 2-8 127

### Math Practices and Problem Solving

**Common Core Performance Assessment**

**Berry Smoothie**

A berry smoothie recipe is made with 24 pieces of fruit. There are 4 times as many strawberries as blackberries, and twice as many banana slices as blackberries. There is the same number of blueberries as blackberries. How many of each fruit are used to make this berry smoothie?

6. **MP.1 Make Sense and Persevere** What do you know? How is the known information related?
   **There are 24 pieces of fruit. There are 4 times as many strawberries as blackberries, twice as many banana slices as blackberries, and an equal number of blueberries and blackberries. The numbers of each type of fruit used have to have a sum of 24.**
7. **MP.4 Model with Math** How can you use a variable to help you represent the situation?
   **Sample answer: I can let $n =$ the number of blackberries in the smoothie.**
   **$4n =$ the number of strawberries**
   **$2n =$ the number of banana slices**
   **$n =$ number of blueberries**
8. **MP.2 Reasoning** Ben says that you need 2 blueberries, 2 blackberries, 4 banana slices, and 12 strawberries to make the berry smoothie. Describe how you know that Ben's answer is incorrect.
   **Sample answer: Ben has the right total number of pieces of fruit, but the number of strawberries should be 4 times the number of blackberries. His answer has 6 times as many strawberries as blackberries.**
9. **MP.6 Use Precision** Solve the problem. Explain how you can check your answer.
   **12 strawberries, 6 banana slices, 3 blueberries, and 3 blackberries. I can check my answer by finding the sum: $12 + 6 + 3 + 3 = 24$**

To make sense of a problem, identify what you know and look for relationships.

128 Topic 2 | Lesson 2-8



**MP.1 Make Sense and Persevere** Listen and look for these behaviors as evidence that students are exhibiting proficiency with MP.1.

- Identifies the information in a problem and the question to be answered
- Selects and implements tools and strategies
- Perseveres and tries other strategies when stumped
- Checks that answers make sense

**Items 1–5 MP.1 Make Sense and Persevere** As students read and synthesize the information given in each problem situation, have them think about which quantity would make sense to represent with a variable. Encourage them to think about the known and unknown quantities in the problem and their relationships within the problem situation.

**Reteaching** Assign Reteaching Set F on p. 134.

**Item 6 MP.1 Make Sense and Persevere** Have students describe the relationships between the various types of fruit.

**Item 7 MP.4 Model with Math** Students should use one variable to represent all the quantities of fruit in the problem. *Which fruit is used to describe all of the other fruits?* [Blackberries] Explain that since the number of strawberries, banana slices, and blueberries are all described in terms of the number of blackberries, a variable can be used to represent the number of blackberries.

**Item 8 MP.2 Reason Quantitatively** Students should check Ben's solution against the constraints by answering the following questions. Are there 24 pieces of fruit? Are there 4 times as many strawberries as blackberries? Are there twice as many banana slices as blackberries? Is there an equal number of blueberries and blackberries?

**Item 9 MP.6 Be Precise** A thorough check of the solution includes checking that the sum of the pieces of fruit is 24, as well as checking that there are 4 times as many strawberries as blackberries, twice as many banana slices as blackberries, and the same number of blueberries and blackberries.

# ASSESS AND DIFFERENTIATE

Use the **QUICK CHECK** on the previous page to prescribe differentiated instruction.

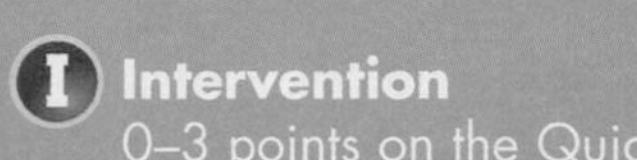

**Intervention**
0–3 points on the Quick Check

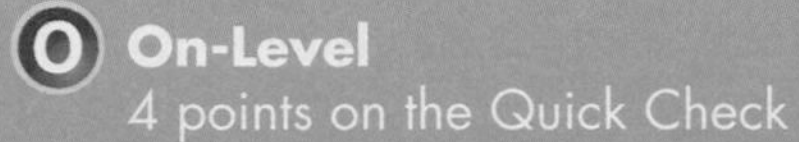

**On-Level**
4 points on the Quick Check

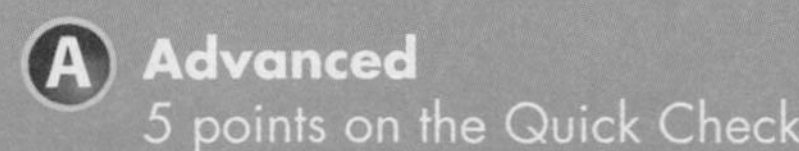

**Advanced**
5 points on the Quick Check

## Intervention Activity 

### Math Practices and Problem Solving: Make Sense and Persevere

Write the following problem on the board: Shawna, Ben, and Jason paid \$60 to buy a birthday present. Shawna contributed twice as much money as Ben, and Jason contributed 3 times as much money as Ben. How much did each person contribute?

Have students work in pairs to complete each of the following steps:

- Discuss the given information and what they need to find.
- Represent the quantities and relationships described in the problem using one variable.
- Write and solve an equation. State the answer to the problem.
- Check the solution by using substitution in the original equation and by checking that the conditions in the problem have been met.

d = Ben's contribution
2d = Shawna's contribution
3d = Jason's contribution
$d + 2d + 3d = 60$
$6d = 60$
$6d \div 6 = 60 \div 6$
$d = 10$
Ben: \$10, Shawna: \$20, Jason: \$30

## Reteach

Name ______

Reteach to Build Understanding
2-8

**Vocabulary**

1. To **persevere** means that you keep trying even though the problem may be difficult.
   A synonym for persevere is **Sample answer: persist**

The perimeter of parallelogram *ABCD* is 54 inches. The shorter sides of *ABCD* are half as long as the longer sides. What are the side lengths of *ABCD*?

2. Make sense of the problem. What do you know?
   **Sample answer: $P = 54$ inches, $AB = CD$, $BC = AD$, and the shorter sides are half as long as the longer sides**
3. Make sense of the problem. What do you need to find?
   **Sample answer: The side lengths of *ABCD***
4. What is your plan to solve the problem?
   **Sample answer: Assign a variable for the length of one of the longer sides. Write an equation to represent the perimeter and solve. Then use the solution to find the side lengths.**
5. Solve the problem.
   **Sample answer: Let $x = BC$ and $AD$, so $\frac{1}{2}x = AB$ and $CD$.**
   **$BC + AD + AB + CD = 54$; $x + x + \frac{1}{2}x + \frac{1}{2}x = 54$; $3x = 54$; $x = 18$**
   **So, $BC = AD = 18$ inches and $AB = CD = \frac{1}{2}(18) =$ 9 inches.**

**On the Back!**

6. Dan ran five days last week. On Tuesday, he ran twice as far as on Monday. On Wednesday, he ran the same distance as on Monday. On Thursday and Friday, he ran half the distance he ran on Monday. If Dan ran a total of 15 miles last week, how far did he run each day?
   **3 mi Mon, Wed; 6 mi Tues; 1.5 mi Thur, Fri**

R 2•8



## On-Level and Advanced Activity Centers

Name ______

Math and Science Activity
2-8

### Biodegradable Materials

*Did You Know?* It can take up to 1 million years for a glass bottle to biodegrade. Man-made materials, especially materials made from fossil fuels, can take centuries to biodegrade. Some plastics never biodegrade. But these materials can be recyclable! By definition, biodegradable material can dissolve quickly into raw materials of the natural environment. Any material that comes from nature, like a leaf or an eggshell, is biodegradable.

1. The length of time, *t*, it takes a sheet of paper to biodegrade is at least 2 weeks. Write an inequality to represent the time it takes a sheet of paper to biodegrade.
   **$t \geq 2$**
2. A plastic bag takes at least 10 years to biodegrade, but no more than 20 years. Write two inequalities that describe the length of time, *b*, it takes a plastic bag to biodegrade. Then write two integers that are solutions of both inequalities.
   **$b \geq 10$ and $b \leq 20$; Sample answers: 11, 19**
3. **Extension** A foam cup takes 10 times as long as a milk carton takes to biodegrade. The sole of a rubber boot takes 16 times as long as a milk carton takes to biodegrade. The sum of the years it takes for all three items to biodegrade is 135 years. How long does it take for each item to biodegrade? Show your work.
   **Let $y =$ years for the milk carton to biodegrade, $10y =$ years for the foam cup to biodegrade, and $16y =$ years for the sole to biodegrade.**
   **$10y + 16y + y = 135$; $27y = 135$; $y = 5$**
   **It takes 5 years for the milk carton, 50 years for the foam cup, and 80 years for the sole to biodegrade.**

Math and Science Activity 2•8



### Math and Science Activity STEM

This activity revisits the science theme, **Reduce, Reuse, Recycle,** introduced on page 79 in the Student's Edition.

### Sample Student Work

3.
$10y + 16y + y = 135$
$(10 + 16 + 1)y = 135$
$27y = 135$
$27y \div 27 = 135 \div 27$
$y = 5$

**TIMING**

The time allocated to Step 3 will depend on the teacher's instructional decisions and differentiation routines.

15–30 min

PEARSON realize. PearsonRealize.com

Help

Practice Buddy

Tools

Games

## Technology Center    

Tools

Games

### Math Tools and Math Games

A link to a specific math tools activity or math game to use with this lesson is provided at PearsonRealize.com.

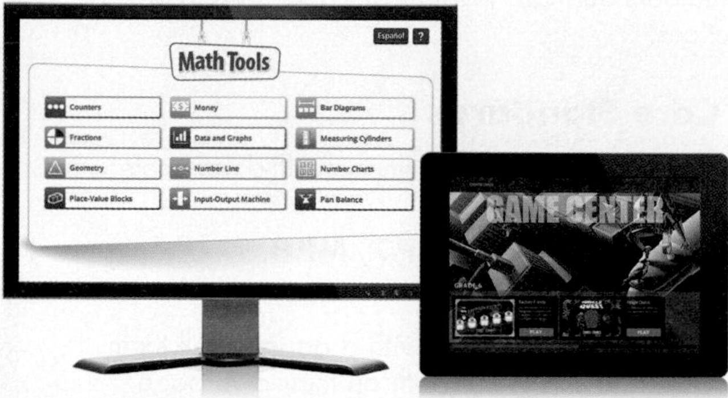


## Leveled Assignment  Items 1–9  Items 1–9  Items 1–9

Name ______________________

Help Practice Buddy Tools Games

**Homework & Practice 2-8**
**Make Sense and Persevere**

### Another Look!

Harold downloads a song, a movie, and a game onto his tablet. The game uses 5 times as many megabytes of storage as the song. The movie takes up 100 times the storage space as the game. The total storage needed for all 3 downloads is 4,048 MB. How many megabytes of storage are needed for each download?

| Make Sense of the Problem | Plan | Solve |
|---|---|---|
| **What You Know** Harold uses 4,048 MB of storage on downloads. game = 5 times the song movie = 100 times the game **What You Need to Find** The storage amount needed for each download | Define a variable and then use the relationships between the quantities to write an equation. $x$ = song storage $5x$ = game storage $100(5x) = 500x$ = movie storage | $x + 5x + 500x = 4{,}048$ $506x = 4{,}048$ $506x \div 506 = 4{,}048 \div 506$ $x = 8$ $5x = 5 \cdot 8 = 40$ $500x = 500 \cdot 8 = 4{,}000$ The song uses 8 MB, the game uses 40 MB, and the movie uses 4,000 MB of storage space. |

**MP.1 Make Sense and Persevere**
Vi walks five days each week. She walks the same distance on the first two days. On days three and four, Vi walks twice as long as on each of the first two days. On day five, she walks half as far as on day one. If Vi walks 13 miles each week, how far does she walk each day?

1. Write expressions to represent the distance Vi walks each day. Then write an equation to represent how far she walks each week.
   **$n$ = distance walked on Days 1 and 2;**
   **$2n$ = distance walked on Days 3 and 4;**
   **$\frac{1}{2}n$ = distance walked on Day 5;**
   **$n + n + 2n + 2n + \frac{1}{2}n = 13$**

2. Solve the problem.
   **On days 1 and 2, Vi walks 2 miles. On each of days 3 and 4, she walks 4 miles. Vi walks 1 mile on the fifth day.**



### Common Core Performance Assessment

**Zoo Keeper**
A local zoo budgets $750,000 for salaries and benefits of all of its employees. The salaries are estimated at $35,000 per employee and benefits at $15,000 per employee. What is the greatest number of employees the zoo can have without going over budget?

3. **MP.2 Reasoning** Can the zoo have 10 employees? Explain how you know.
   **Yes; The salaries and benefits per employee are about $50,000. $50,000 × 10 = $500,000, which is under the total budget of $750,000.**

4. **MP.4 Model with Math** Model the problem situation. You can use a bar model, drawing, or equation.
   **Sample answer: Let $e$ = the number of employees the zoo can have on staff. Then, $35{,}000e$ = total cost of employee salaries $15{,}000e$ = total cost of employee benefits So, $35{,}000e + 15{,}000e = 750{,}000$**

5. **MP.1 Make Sense and Persevere** Find the greatest number of employees the zoo could have without going over budget. Show two ways you know your answer is correct.
   **The zoo can have 15 employees.**
   **Sample answer: $35{,}000e + 15{,}000e = 750{,}000$; $35{,}000(15) + 15{,}000(15) = 525{,}000 + 225{,}000 = 750{,}0000$**
   **$50{,}000 \times 15 = 750{,}000$**

There are many ways to model with math. Choose a model that helps you visualize the problem situation.

6. **MP.8 Repeated Reasoning** Suppose the zoo received a budget increase to $1,000,000. How many additional employees could the zoo hire? Explain your reasoning.
   **5 more employees; I know that $50,000 is budgeted for each employee. $1,000,000 is an increase of $250,000 over the original budget. $250,000 ÷ 50,000 = 5**

# TOPIC 2 FLUENCY PRACTICE ACTIVITY

## FLUENCY PRACTICE ACTIVITY

Students review the Grade 5 fluency standard about multiplying multi-digit whole numbers during a partner activity that reinforces mathematical practices.

### Common Core Standards

**Content Standard 5.NBT.B.5** Fluently multiply multi-digit whole numbers using the standard algorithm.

**Mathematical Practices MP.3, MP.6, MP.7, MP.8**

**Getting Started** Ask students to work with a partner. Tell them to record their answers and shade the path on their own page. Go over the directions.

Both students should solve each problem and record their work on a separate sheet of paper. Tell students to take turns choosing which square to try next.

**As Students Do the Activity** Remind students that the path may go up, down, left, or right. There may be several options they must try before they find the square with the problem that follows the rule. Remind students to compare and discuss their answers.

Encourage students to use estimation to help choose the squares that are likely to be on the path.

**Another Activity** Ask students to find the answers to all of the problems in the remaining squares. Have students record the answers in each square.

**Extra Challenge** *Look at all of the answers in the squares. Write a new rule that results in a different path from start to finish. Your path may go up, down, left, right, or diagonally. Shade the new path in a different color.*

**Online Game** The Game Center at PearsonRealize.com provides opportunities for fluency practice.

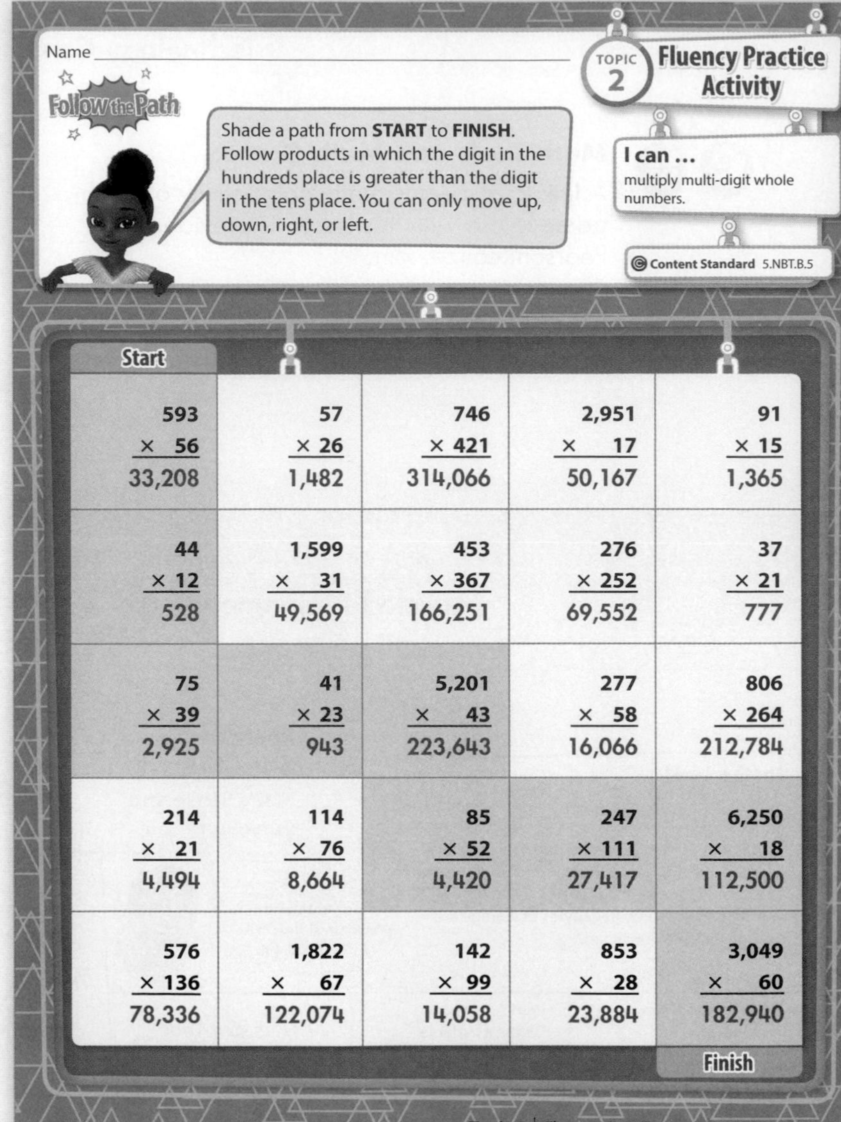

Name

TOPIC 2 Fluency Practice Activity



Shade a path from **START** to **FINISH**. Follow products in which the digit in the hundreds place is greater than the digit in the tens place. You can only move up, down, right, or left.

**I can ...** multiply multi-digit whole numbers.

Content Standard 5.NBT.B.5

| Start | | | | |
|---|---|---|---|---|
| 593<br>× 56<br>33,208 | 57<br>× 26<br>1,482 | 746<br>× 421<br>314,066 | 2,951<br>× 17<br>50,167 | 91<br>× 15<br>1,365 |
| 44<br>× 12<br>528 | 1,599<br>× 31<br>49,569 | 453<br>× 367<br>166,251 | 276<br>× 252<br>69,552 | 37<br>× 21<br>777 |
| 75<br>× 39<br>2,925 | 41<br>× 23<br>943 | 5,201<br>× 43<br>223,643 | 277<br>× 58<br>16,066 | 806<br>× 264<br>212,784 |
| 214<br>× 21<br>4,494 | 114<br>× 76<br>8,664 | 85<br>× 52<br>4,420 | 247<br>× 111<br>27,417 | 6,250<br>× 18<br>112,500 |
| 576<br>× 136<br>78,336 | 1,822<br>× 67<br>122,074 | 142<br>× 99<br>14,058 | 853<br>× 28<br>23,884 | 3,049<br>× 60<br>182,940 |
| | | | | Finish |

Topic 2 | Fluency Practice Activity 131

Glossary Games

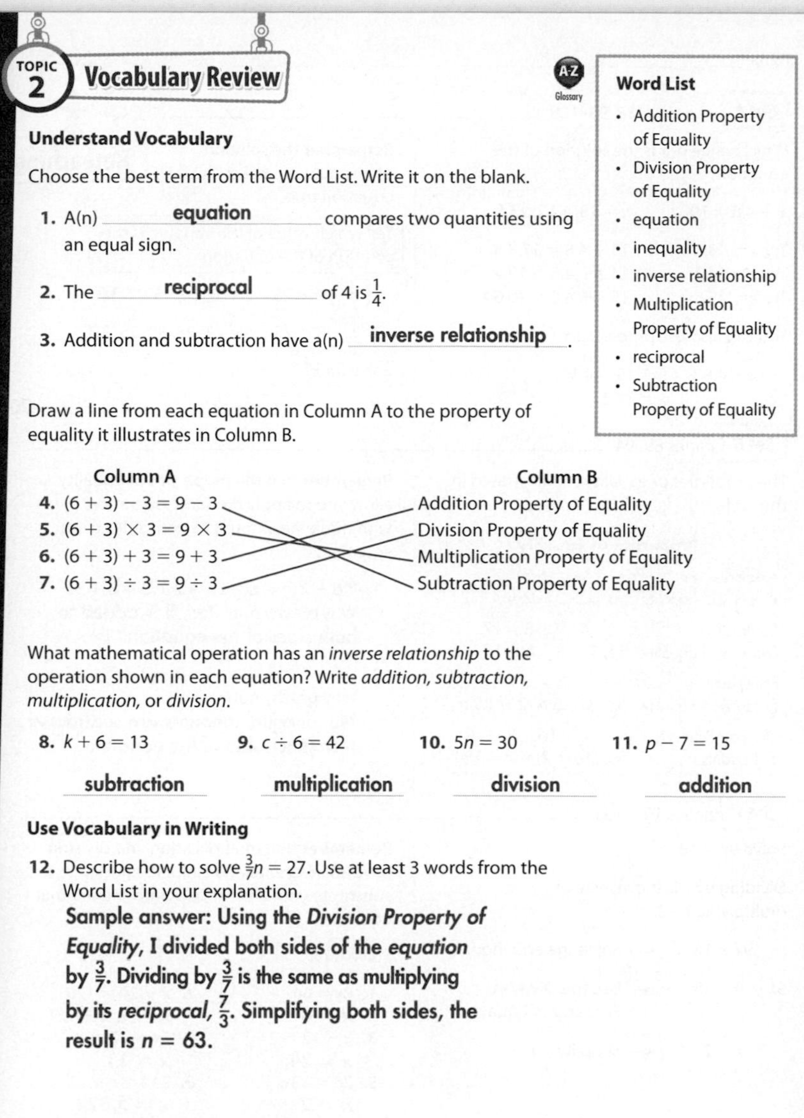

TOPIC 2 **Vocabulary Review**

**Word List**

- Addition Property of Equality
- Division Property of Equality
- equation
- inequality
- inverse relationship
- Multiplication Property of Equality
- reciprocal
- Subtraction Property of Equality

**Understand Vocabulary**

Choose the best term from the Word List. Write it on the blank.

1. A(n) **equation** compares two quantities using an equal sign.
2. The **reciprocal** of 4 is $\frac{1}{4}$.
3. Addition and subtraction have a(n) **inverse relationship**.

Draw a line from each equation in Column A to the property of equality it illustrates in Column B.

| Column A | Column B |
|---|---|
| 4. $(6 + 3) - 3 = 9 - 3$ | Addition Property of Equality |
| 5. $(6 + 3) \times 3 = 9 \times 3$ | Division Property of Equality |
| 6. $(6 + 3) + 3 = 9 + 3$ | Multiplication Property of Equality |
| 7. $(6 + 3) \div 3 = 9 \div 3$ | Subtraction Property of Equality |

What mathematical operation has an *inverse relationship* to the operation shown in each equation? Write *addition, subtraction, multiplication,* or *division.*

8. $k + 6 = 13$ **subtraction**
9. $c \div 6 = 42$ **multiplication**
10. $5n = 30$ **division**
11. $p - 7 = 15$ **addition**

**Use Vocabulary in Writing**

12. Describe how to solve $\frac{3}{7}n = 27$. Use at least 3 words from the Word List in your explanation.
**Sample answer: Using the *Division Property of Equality*, I divided both sides of the *equation* by $\frac{3}{7}$. Dividing by $\frac{3}{7}$ is the same as multiplying by its *reciprocal*, $\frac{7}{3}$. Simplifying both sides, the result is $n = 63$.**

132 Topic 2 | Vocabulary Review © Pearson Education, Inc. 6

## VOCABULARY REVIEW

Students review vocabulary words used in the topic.

**Oral Language** Before students complete the page, you might reinforce oral language through a class discussion involving one or more of the following activities.

- Have students define the terms in their own words.
- Have students work in pairs or small groups to make up a riddle that either uses topic vocabulary or riddles about topic vocabulary. Have students read their riddles and ask classmates to solve them.
- Play a "What's My Word?" guessing game in which you or a student thinks about one of the words and says a clue that others listen to before they guess the word.
- Have students build acrostics for one or more terms in the Word List and then share them with the class. You may choose to make this a whole-class activity, which allows for brainstorming and the sharing of ways to represent and describe topic vocabulary.

**Writing in Math** After students complete the page, you might further reinforce writing in math by doing one or more of the following activities.

- Have students work independently to create a crossword puzzle using the terms in the Word List. Provide grid paper or allow students to use an online crossword puzzle maker. Encourage students to use words, pictures, and examples for clues.
- Have students work with a partner. Each partner writes a math question that uses one of the words. Then students trade papers and give a written answer that uses the word.

Games

**Online Game** The Game Center at PearsonRealize.com includes a vocabulary game that students can access any time.

# RETEACHING

## ALGEBRA: SOLVE EQUATIONS AND INEQUALITIES

### RtI Item Analysis for Diagnosis and Intervention

| Reteaching Sets | Standard | MDIS |
|---|---|---|
| Set A | 6.EE.B.5, 6.EE.B.6, 6.EE.B.7 | F49 |
| Set B | 6.EE.A.4, 6.EE.B.7 | F48 |
| Set C | 6.EE.B.7, 6.EE.B.6 | F50 |
| Set D | 6.EE.B.7, 6.EE.B.6 | F55 |
| Set E | 6.EE.B.5, 6.EE.B.8 | F61, F62 |
| Set F | MP.1, MP.2, MP.4, MP.6, MP.8 | J13 |

Name ______

TOPIC 2

**Reteaching**

**Set A** pages 83–88, 95–100

Which value of $x$ is the solution of the equation?

$x + 4.8 = 19$ $x = 13, 14.2, 15.8$

Try $x = 13$: $13 + 4.8 = 17.8$ ✗
Try $x = 14.2$: $14.2 + 4.8 = 19$ ✓
Try $x = 15.8$: $15.8 + 4.8 = 20.6$ ✗

You can also use properties to solve.

$x + 4.8 - 4.8 = 19 - 4.8$
$x = 14.2$

**Remember** the solution of an equation makes the equation true.

Tell which value of the variable is the solution of the equation.

1. $d + 9 = 25$ $d = 6, 14, 16, 21$ **16**
2. $c - 8 = 25$ $c = 17, 28, 33, 35$ **33**

Solve for $x$.

3. $x + 2 = 11$ **$x = 9$** 4. $x - 17 = 13$ **$x = 30$**

**Set B** pages 89–94

The properties of equality are illustrated in the table.

| Properties of Equality | |
|---|---|
| Addition Property of Equality | $4 + 3 = 7$<br>So, $4 + 3 + 2 = 7 + 2$ |
| Subtraction Property of Equality | $9 + 8 = 17$<br>So, $9 + 8 - 5 = 17 - 5$ |
| Multiplication Property of Equality | $3 \times 5 = 15$<br>So, $3 \times 5 \times 2 = 15 \times 2$ |
| Division Property of Equality | $16 + 2 = 18$<br>So, $(16 + 2) \div 2 = 18 \div 2$ |

**Remember** that the properties of equality allow you to apply the same operation with the same amount to both sides of an equation.

1. If $6 + 2 = 8$, does $6 + 2 + 3 = 8 + 3$? Why or why not? **Yes, 3 is added to both sides of the equation.**
2. If $8 - 1 = 7$, does $8 - 1 - 2 = 7 - 3$? Why or why not? **No, unequal amounts are subtracted from each side of the equation.**

**Set C** pages 101–106

Solve $9x = 18$.

Dividing by 9 is the inverse of multiplying by 9.

$9x = 18$ ← Solve the equation.

$9x \div 9 = 18 \div 9$ ← Use the Division Property of Equality.

$x = 2$ ← Simplify.

**Remember** that multiplication and division have an inverse relationship. To check, substitute your answer back into the original equation.

Solve for $x$.

1. $8x = 64$ **$x = 8$**
2. $x \div 20 = 120$ **$x = 2{,}400$**
3. $x \div 12 = 2$ **$x = 24$**
4. $7x = 77$ **$x = 11$**
5. $26 = 13x$ **$x = 2$**
6. $242 = x \div 22$ **$x = 5{,}324$**

Topic 2 | Reteaching 133

**Set D** pages 107–112

Find $w + 4\frac{1}{3} = 7$.

Subtract $4\frac{1}{3}$ from both sides.

$w + 4\frac{1}{3} - 4\frac{1}{3} = 7 - 4\frac{1}{3}$

$w = 2\frac{2}{3}$

**Remember** that you can use inverse relationships and properties of equality to solve each equation.

1. $g + 3\frac{5}{8} = 7\frac{1}{4}$
   $g = 3\frac{5}{8}$

2. $b \div 15 = 8\frac{1}{3}$
   $b = 125$

**Set E** pages 113–118, 119–124

Molly is less than 15 years old is represented by the inequality $x < 15$.

To graph the inequality on a number line, draw an open circle at 15 and shade any solutions that you found. Draw an arrow to show all numbers less than 15.

10 11 12 13 14 15 16 17 18 19 20

**Remember** you use an open circle for $<$ or $>$ and a closed circle for $\leq$ or $\geq$.

Write the inequality that each graph represents.

1. 5 6 7 8 9 10 11 12 13 14 15
   $s < 10$

2. 0 1 2 3 4 5 6 7 8 9 10
   $m > 5$

**Set F** pages 125–130

Think about these questions to help you **make sense of problems and persevere** in solving them.

**Thinking Habits**

- What do I need to find?
- What do I know?
- What is my plan for solving the problem?
- What else can I try if I get stuck?
- How can I check that my solution makes sense?

**Remember** you can try different strategies to solve a problem. Then check that your solution makes sense.

Lee is thinking of two numbers. One number is 12 less than the other number. The sum of the two numbers is 208. What two numbers is Lee thinking of?

1. Explain how you can use what you know to decide how to solve the problem.
   **Sample answer: I can write an equation to represent how the quantities are related and solve.**

2. Solve the problem.
   **Sample answer: Let $n$ equal one number, then $n - 12$ equals the other number. $n + (n - 12) = 208$, $2n - 12 = 208$, $n = 110$. Lee is thinking of 110 and 98.**





## Response to Intervention

### Ongoing Intervention

- Lessons with guiding questions to assess understanding
- Support to prevent misconceptions and to reteach

### Strategic Intervention

- Targeted to small groups that need more support
- Easy to implement

### Intensive Intervention

- Instruction to accelerate progress
- Instruction focused on foundational skills

# TOPIC 2 TOPIC ASSESSMENT

# ALGEBRA: SOLVE EQUATIONS AND INEQUALITIES

Name ____________________

TOPIC 2

Assessment

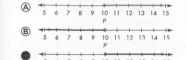

**1.** The local animal shelter has 3 times as many cats as dogs. There are 27 cats at the shelter. Let $x$ = the number of dogs at the shelter. Solve the equation $3x = 27$ to find the number of dogs at the shelter. **1 point**

Ⓐ $x = 81$

Ⓑ $x = 30$

Ⓒ $x = 24$

● $x = 9$

**2.** Solve each equation. Then write the equation in the appropriate box below.

$8x = 56$ $\quad x + 5\frac{3}{4} = 8\frac{3}{4}$ $\quad \frac{x}{2} = 3.5$

$2\frac{1}{4} + x = 9\frac{1}{8}$ $\quad x - 2.56 = 0.44$

**2 points**

| Equations with solution $x = 3$ | Equations with solution $x = 7$ | Neither |
|---|---|---|
| $x + 5\frac{3}{4} = 8\frac{3}{4}$; $x - 2.56 = 0.44$ | $8x = 56$; $\frac{x}{2} = 3.5$ | $2\frac{1}{4} + x = 9\frac{1}{8}$ |

**3.** Ed's birthday is less than 16 days away. Ann writes the inequality $d \leq 16$, where $d$ equals the number of days, to represent this. Is Ann correct? Explain. **2 points**

**No; Sample explanation: Ann used ≤, so 16 is a possible number of days until Ed's birthday, $d < 16$.**

**4.** Choose all the equations that are true if $x = 9$. **1 point**

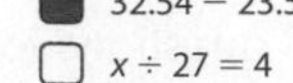

■ $32.54 - 23.54 = x$

☐ $x \div 27 = 4$

■ $\frac{3}{8}x = 3\frac{3}{8}$

☐ $8.7 + x = 17$

■ $5x = 45$

**5.** The library carries a total of 750 biography, mystery, fantasy, and science fiction books. There are 3 times as many science fiction books as fantasy books, twice as many mystery books as fantasy books, and four times as many biographies as fantasy books. **3 points**

Write an equation that describes the number of each type of book in the library.

**Sample answer: $4x + 3x + 2x + x = 750$**

How many of each genre is there in the library?

Biography **300** books

Fantasy **75** books

Mystery **150** books

Science Fiction **225** books

**6.** Write an algebraic equation that represents the total weight ($W$) of five boxes of blueberries, if $b$ equals the weight of one box of blueberries. **1 point**

**Sample answer: $W = 5b$**



**7.** Which graph represents the solutions of the inequality $p \geq 10$? **1 point**

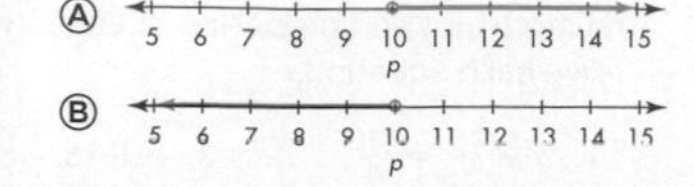

Ⓐ Ⓑ ● Ⓓ

**8.** Read each of the following problem situations. Draw lines to match each equation to the situation it represents. **2 points**

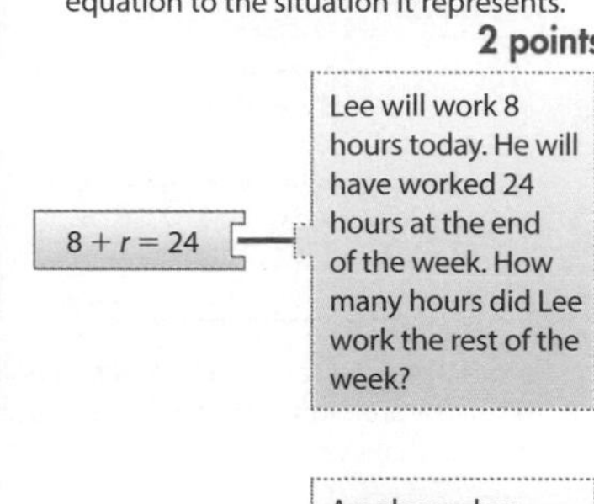

8 + r = 24
Lee will work 8 hours today. He will have worked 24 hours at the end of the week. How many hours did Lee work the rest of the week?
8x = 24
A polygon has a perimeter of 24 centimeters. Each side is 8 centimeters long. How many sides does the polygon have?

**9.** The choir had 50 members after 3 students joined. The equation $x + 3 = 50$ can be used to find the membership, $x$, before the students joined. What step should be taken to get $x$ alone on one side of the equation? **1 point**

Ⓐ Multiply each side of the equation by 3.

Ⓑ Add 3 to each side of the equation.

● Subtract 3 from each side of the equation.

Ⓓ Divide each side of the equation by 3.

**10.** Noah wrote that $6 + 6 = 12$. Then he wrote that $6 + 6 - n = 12 - n$. Are his equations balanced? Explain. **1 point**

**Yes; Sample answer: Noah subtracted the same variable from each side, so the equations are balanced.**

**11.** Mr. Daniels is organizing a class trip on a budget of \$900. The bus rental costs \$600. Mr. Daniels will also buy tickets that cost \$9.50 per student. **1 point**

Write an inequality to represent the number of students, $y$, that Mr. Daniels can bring on the trip.

**$9.5y \leq 300$**





## ANSWERING THE TOPIC ESSENTIAL QUESTION

**What procedures can be used to solve equations and inequalities?**

Restate the Topic Essential Question from the Topic Opener or project it from the Student's Edition eText.

Ask students to answer the Essential Question (verbally or in writing) and give examples that support their answers. The following are key elements of the answer to the Essential Question. Be sure these are made explicit when discussing students' answers.

- An equation is a mathematical sentence that uses an equal sign to show that two expressions have the same value. A solution is a value for the variable that makes the equation true.

  **Example:** Some examples of numeric equations are $7 - 4 = 3$ and $3.5 + 14 = 20 - 2.5$. Some examples of algebraic equations are $4 + x = 12$ and $\frac{y}{3} = 15$. The equation $3.5 + 14 = x - 2.5$ has a solution of $x = 20$ because $3.5 + 14 = 20 - 2.5$.

- Properties of equality and inverse relationships are used to solve algebraic equations.

  **Example:** To solve the equation $7x = 42$, get $x$ alone on one side of the equal sign. Undo the multiplication $7x$ by dividing the expressions on each side of the equal sign by 7. $7x \div 7 = 42 \div 7$; $x = 6$.

- An inequality is a mathematical sentence that uses the symbols $<$, $>$, $\leq$, $\geq$, or $\neq$ to compare two expressions. An inequality may have many solutions, so the solutions are often represented on a number line.

  **Example:** There are infinitely many solutions to the inequality $z \geq 7$. To graph the possible values for $z$ on a number line, fill in a circle at $z = 7$. Because the values of $z$ are greater than or equal to 7, draw an arrow in the direction of values greater than 7. The arrow shows that the solutions go beyond the values shown on the number line.

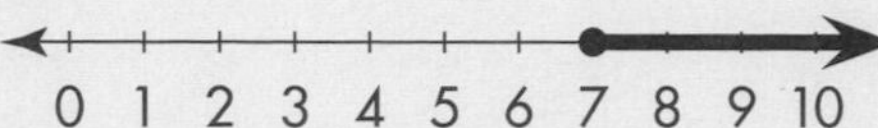

Assessment

## ONLINE TOPIC ASSESSMENT

An auto-scored Topic Assessment is provided at PearsonRealize.com.

## EXAMVIEW® TEST GENERATOR

ExamView can be used to create a blackline-master Topic Assessment with multiple-choice and free-response items.

## Topic Assessment Masters

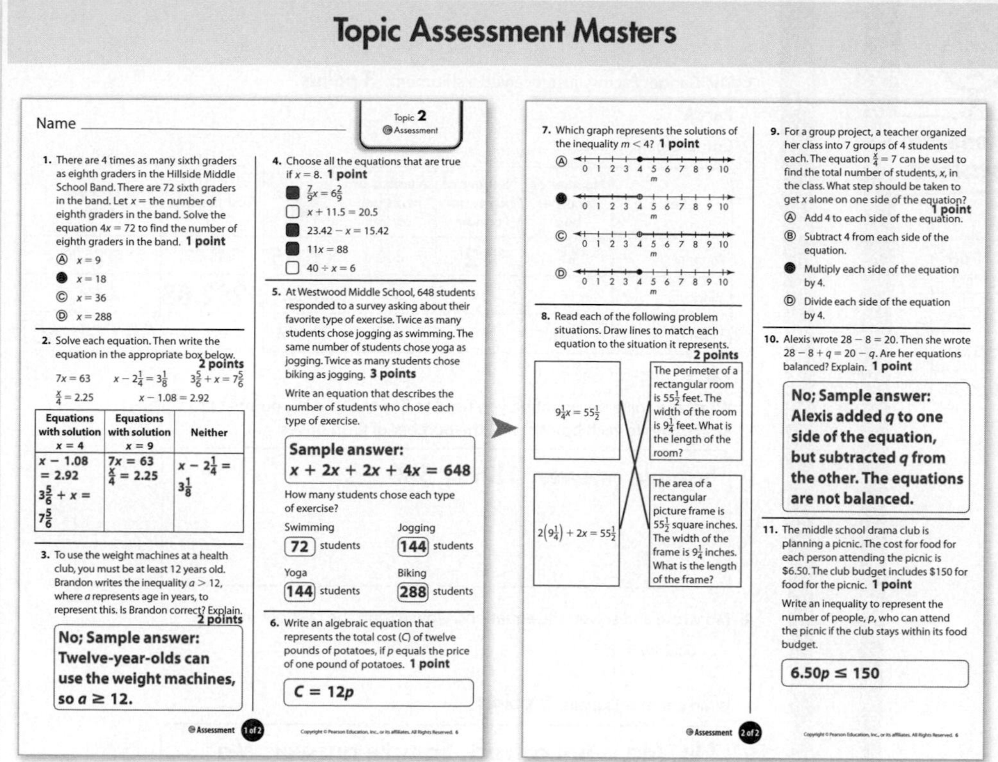

Name ______________________

Topic 2 Assessment

1. There are 4 times as many sixth graders as eighth graders in the Hillside Middle School Band. There are 72 sixth graders in the band. Let $x$ = the number of eighth graders in the band. Solve the equation $4x = 72$ to find the number of eighth graders in the band. **1 point**
   - Ⓐ $x = 9$
   - ● $x = 18$
   - Ⓒ $x = 36$
   - Ⓓ $x = 288$

2. Solve each equation. Then write the equation in the appropriate box below. **2 points**

   $7x = 63$ $\quad x - 2\frac{1}{4} = 3\frac{1}{8}$ $\quad 3\frac{5}{6} + x = 7\frac{5}{6}$ $\quad \frac{x}{4} = 2.25$ $\quad x - 1.08 = 2.92$

| Equations with solution $x = 4$ | Equations with solution $x = 9$ | Neither |
|---|---|---|
| $x - 1.08 = 2.92$<br>$3\frac{5}{6} + x = 7\frac{5}{6}$ | $7x = 63$<br>$\frac{x}{4} = 2.25$ | $x - 2\frac{1}{4} = 3\frac{1}{8}$ |

3. To use the weight machines at a health club, you must be at least 12 years old. Brandon writes the inequality $a > 12$, where $a$ represents age in years, to represent this. Is Brandon correct? Explain. **2 points**

   **No; Sample answer: Twelve-year-olds can use the weight machines, so $a \geq 12$.**

4. Choose all the equations that are true if $x = 8$. **1 point**
   - ■ $\frac{7}{9}x = 6\frac{2}{9}$
   - □ $x + 11.5 = 20.5$
   - ■ $23.42 - x = 15.42$
   - ■ $11x = 88$
   - □ $40 \div x = 6$

5. At Westwood Middle School, 648 students responded to a survey asking about their favorite type of exercise. Twice as many students chose jogging as swimming. The same number of students chose yoga as jogging. Twice as many students chose biking as jogging. **3 points**

   Write an equation that describes the number of students who chose each type of exercise.

   **Sample answer: $x + 2x + 2x + 4x = 648$**

   How many students chose each type of exercise?

   Swimming **72** students Jogging **144** students

   Yoga **144** students Biking **288** students

6. Write an algebraic equation that represents the total cost ($C$) of twelve pounds of potatoes, if $p$ equals the price of one pound of potatoes. **1 point**

   **$C = 12p$**

Assessment 1 of 2



7. Which graph represents the solutions of the inequality $m < 4$? **1 point**
   - Ⓐ number line 0–10, $m$
   - ● number line 0–10, $m$
   - Ⓒ number line 0–10, $m$
   - Ⓓ number line 0–10, $m$

8. Read each of the following problem situations. Draw lines to match each equation to the situation it represents. **2 points**

   $9\frac{1}{4}x = 55\frac{1}{2}$

   $2\left(9\frac{1}{4}\right) + 2x = 55\frac{1}{2}$

   The perimeter of a rectangular room is $55\frac{1}{2}$ feet. The width of the room is $9\frac{1}{4}$ feet. What is the length of the room?

   The area of a rectangular picture frame is $55\frac{1}{2}$ square inches. The width of the frame is $9\frac{1}{4}$ inches. What is the length of the frame?

9. For a group project, a teacher organized her class into 7 groups of 4 students each. The equation $\frac{x}{4} = 7$ can be used to find the total number of students, $x$, in the class. What step should be taken to get $x$ alone on one side of the equation? **1 point**
   - Ⓐ Add 4 to each side of the equation.
   - Ⓑ Subtract 4 from each side of the equation.
   - ● Multiply each side of the equation by 4.
   - Ⓓ Divide each side of the equation by 4.

10. Alexis wrote $28 - 8 = 20$. Then she wrote $28 - 8 + q = 20 - q$. Are her equations balanced? Explain. **1 point**

    **No; Sample answer: Alexis added $q$ to one side of the equation, but subtracted $q$ from the other. The equations are not balanced.**

11. The middle school drama club is planning a picnic. The cost for food for each person attending the picnic is \$6.50. The club budget includes \$150 for food for the picnic. **1 point**

    Write an inequality to represent the number of people, $p$, who can attend the picnic if the club stays within its food budget.

    **$6.50p \leq 150$**

Assessment 2 of 2



## RtI Item Analysis for Diagnosis and Intervention

| Item | Standard | DOK | MDIS |
|---|---|---|---|
| 1 | 6.EE.B.7 | 1 | F50 |
| 2 | 6.EE.B.7 | 2 | F51, F52, F55 |
| 3 | 6.EE.B.8 | 1 | F38 |
| 4 | 6.EE.B.5 | 1 | F51, F52, F55 |
| 5 | 6.EE.B.6, 6.EE.B.7 | 2 | F54 |
| 6 | 6.EE.B.7 | 1 | F54 |
| 7 | 6.EE.B.8 | 1 | F38 |
| 8 | 6.EE.B.6 | 2 | F53, F54 |
| 9 | 6.EE.B.7, MP.1 | 1 | F51 |
| 10 | 6.EE.A.4 | 1 | F48 |
| 11 | 6.EE.B.8 | 2 | F38, F54 |

The Topic Assessment Masters assess the same content item for item as the Topic Assessment in the Student's Edition.

## Scoring Guide

| Item | Points | Topic Assessment (Student's Edition and Masters) |
|---|---|---|
| 1 | 1 | Correct choice selected |
| 2 | 2 | All five equations in appropriate boxes |
|  | 1 | At least two equations in appropriate boxes |
| 3 | 2 | Correct answer and inequality |
|  | 1 | Correct answer or inequality |
| 4 | 1 | All correct choices selected |
| 5 | 3 | Correct equation and all four correct answers |
|  | 2 | Correct equation and one or two correct answers |
|  | 1 | Correct answers based on incorrect equation |
| 6 | 1 | Correct equation |
| 7 | 1 | Correct choice selected |
| 8 | 2 | Two correct matches |
|  | 1 | One correct match |
| 9 | 1 | Correct choice selected |
| 10 | 1 | Correct answer and explanation |
| 11 | 1 | Correct inequality |

TOPIC 2

# TOPIC PERFORMANCE ASSESSMENT

## ALGEBRA: SOLVE EQUATIONS AND INEQUALITIES

Name ______________________________

Performance Assessment

**The Gadget Factory**

The Gadget Factory makes all kinds of electronic gadgets. The sales managers at the Gadget Factory keep track of the items and their prices in the chart below.

Items at the Gadget Factory

| Item | Number of items per box | Number of boxes per carton | Number of items per carton | Cost per item | Cost per box | Cost per carton |
|---|---|---|---|---|---|---|
| Key Chain | 4 | 8 | 32 | \$0.32 | \$1.28 | \$10.24 |
| Batteries | 6 | 10 | 60 | \$0.53 | \$3.18 | \$31.80 |
| Mini Alarm Clock | 10 | 14 | 140 | \$3.73 | \$37.30 | \$522.20 |

1. Janie buys some cartons of key chains. She spends \$51.20. **2 points**

**Part A**

Write an algebraic equation to represent the total number of cartons of key chains, $x$, that Janie buys.

**$10.24x = 51.2$**

**Part B**

Solve for $x$. How many cartons does Janie buy?

**5 cartons**

2. Sam owns a clock store and wants to buy some boxes of mini alarm clocks from The Gadget Factory. He has a budget of \$200. Write an inequality to represent the number of boxes of alarm clocks, $a$, Sam can buy. What is the greatest number of boxes of alarm clocks Sam can buy? **2 points**

**$37.3a \leq 200$**
**$a \leq 5.36$**
**Sam can buy 5 boxes at most.**



3. The Gadget Factory just received a shipment. **3 points**

**Part A**

Complete the chart.

| Item | Number of items per box | Number of boxes per carton | Number of items per carton | Cost per item | Cost per box | Cost per carton |
|---|---|---|---|---|---|---|
| Magnet | 25 | **12** | 300 | **\$2.65** | \$66.25 | \$795.00 |
| Binoculars | 16 | 19 | 304 | \$17.68 | **\$282.88** | \$5,374.72 |
| Flash Drive | **30** | 18 | 540 | \$14.99 | \$449.70 | **\$8,094.60** |

**Part B**

Write and solve the equation you used to find the missing number of flash drives in each box. Let $n$ = the number of flash drives.

**Sample answer: $18n = 540$**

4. Mo wrote and solved the equation below to find the cost per magnet.

$66.25w = 795$
$w = 12$

Is Mo correct? Explain. **2 points**

**No, Mo is not correct. Sample answer: Mo found the number of boxes per carton by solving that equation. The correct equation is $25w = 66.25$. $w = 2.65$, so the cost per magnet is \$2.65.**





### Scoring Guide

| Item | Points | Topic Performance Assessment in the Student's Edition |
|---|---|---|
| 1A | 1 | Correct equation |
| 1B | 1 | Correct solution |
| 2 | 2 | Correct inequality and solution |
| | 1 | Correct inequality or solution |
| 3A | 2 | Four correct answers in columns 3, 5, 6, and 7 |
| | 1 | Three correct answers in columns 3, 5, 6, and 7 |
| 3B | 1 | Correct equation and solution |
| 4 | 2 | Correct answer and complete explanation |
| | 1 | Correct answer with partial or no explanation |

### RtI Item Analysis for Diagnosis and Intervention

| Item | Standard | DOK | MDIS |
|---|---|---|---|
| 1A | 6.EE.B.7, MP.4 | 2 | F54 |
| 1B | 6.EE.B.7, MP.6 | 1 | F50 |
| 2 | 6.EE.B.8, MP.2 | 3 | F61, F62 |
| 3A | 6.EE.B.7, MP.7 | 2 | F50 |
| 3B | 6.EE.B.7, MP.4 | 2 | F54 |
| 4 | 6.EE.B.6, 6.EE.B.7, MP.3 | 3 | F50, F54 |

## Topic Performance Assessment Masters

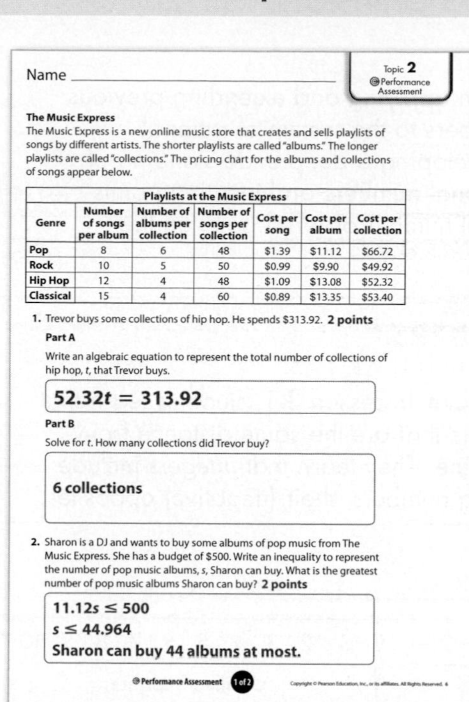

Name ________________________

Topic 2
Performance Assessment

**The Music Express**

The Music Express is a new online music store that creates and sells playlists of songs by different artists. The shorter playlists are called "albums." The longer playlists are called "collections." The pricing chart for the albums and collections of songs appear below.

**Playlists at the Music Express**

| Genre | Number of songs per album | Number of albums per collection | Number of songs per collection | Cost per song | Cost per album | Cost per collection |
|---|---|---|---|---|---|---|
| Pop | 8 | 6 | 48 | \$1.39 | \$11.12 | \$66.72 |
| Rock | 10 | 5 | 50 | \$0.99 | \$9.90 | \$49.92 |
| Hip Hop | 12 | 4 | 48 | \$1.09 | \$13.08 | \$52.32 |
| Classical | 15 | 4 | 60 | \$0.89 | \$13.35 | \$53.40 |

1. Trevor buys some collections of hip hop. He spends \$313.92. **2 points**

**Part A**

Write an algebraic equation to represent the total number of collections of hip hop, $t$, that Trevor buys.

**$52.32t = 313.92$**

**Part B**

Solve for $t$. How many collections did Trevor buy?

**6 collections**

2. Sharon is a DJ and wants to buy some albums of pop music from The Music Express. She has a budget of \$500. Write an inequality to represent the number of pop music albums, $s$, Sharon can buy. What is the greatest number of pop music albums Sharon can buy? **2 points**

**$11.12s \leq 500$**
**$s \leq 44.964$**
**Sharon can buy 44 albums at most.**

Performance Assessment 1 of 2



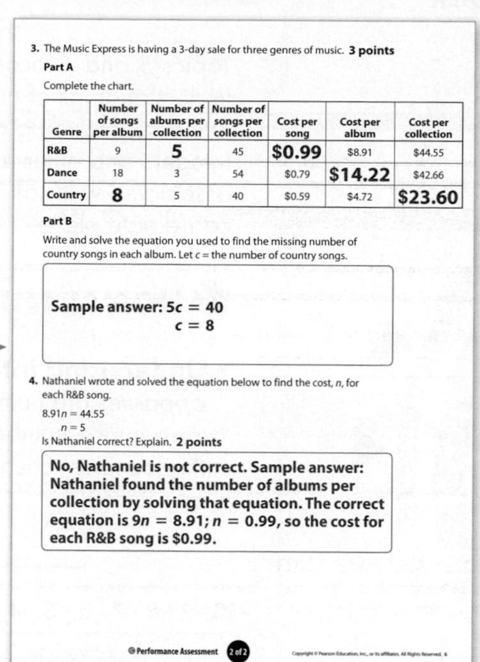

3. The Music Express is having a 3-day sale for three genres of music. **3 points**

**Part A**

Complete the chart.

| Genre | Number of songs per album | Number of albums per collection | Number of songs per collection | Cost per song | Cost per album | Cost per collection |
|---|---|---|---|---|---|---|
| R&B | 9 | **5** | 45 | **\$0.99** | \$8.91 | \$44.55 |
| Dance | 18 | 3 | 54 | \$0.79 | **\$14.22** | \$42.66 |
| Country | **8** | 5 | 40 | \$0.59 | \$4.72 | **\$23.60** |

**Part B**

Write and solve the equation you used to find the missing number of country songs in each album. Let $c$ = the number of country songs.

**Sample answer: $5c = 40$**
**$c = 8$**

4. Nathaniel wrote and solved the equation below to find the cost, $n$, for each R&B song.

$8.91n = 44.55$
$n = 5$

Is Nathaniel correct? Explain. **2 points**

**No, Nathaniel is not correct. Sample answer: Nathaniel found the number of albums per collection by solving that equation. The correct equation is $9n = 8.91$; $n = 0.99$, so the cost for each R&B song is \$0.99.**

Performance Assessment 2 of 2



## Scoring Guide

| Item | Points | Topic Performance Assessment Masters |
|---|---|---|
| 1A | 1 | Correct equation |
| 1B | 1 | Correct solution |
| 2 | 2 | Correct inequality and solution |
| | 1 | Correct inequality or solution |
| 3A | 2 | Four correct answers in columns 3, 5, 6, and 7 |
| | 1 | Three correct answers in columns 3, 5, 6, and 7 |
| 3B | 1 | Correct equation and solution |
| 4 | 2 | Correct answer and complete explanation |
| | 1 | Correct answer with partial or no explanation |

## RtI Item Analysis for Diagnosis and Intervention

| Item | © Standard | DOK | MDIS |
|---|---|---|---|
| 1A | 6.EE.B.7, MP.4 | 2 | F54 |
| 1B | 6.EE.B.7, MP.6 | 1 | F50 |
| 2 | 6.EE.B.8, MP.2 | 3 | F61, F62 |
| 3A | 6.EE.B.7, MP.7 | 2 | F50 |
| 3B | 6.EE.B.7, MP.4 | 2 | F54 |
| 4 | 6.EE.B.6, 6.EE.B.7, MP.3 | 3 | F50, F54 |

# MAJOR CLUSTER 6.NS.C

## MATH BACKGROUND: FOCUS

FOCUS | COHERENCE | RIGOR

MAJOR CLUSTER | SUPPORTING CLUSTER | ADDITIONAL CLUSTER

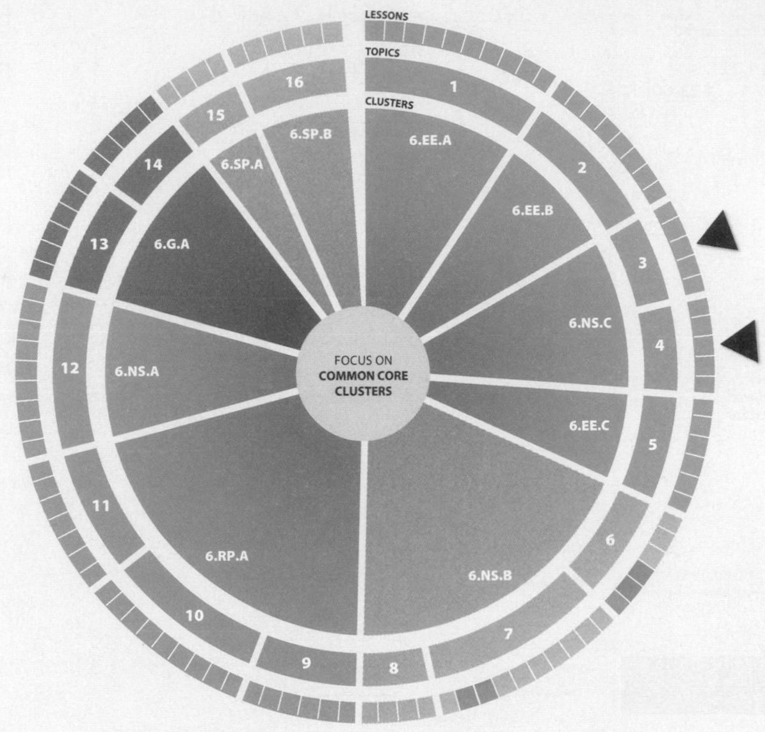


**TOPIC 3** **Rational Numbers**

**TOPIC 4** **Algebra: Coordinate Geometry**

TOPICS 3 AND 4 FOCUS ON

**MAJOR CLUSTER 6.NS.C**

Apply and extend previous understandings of numbers to the system of rational numbers.

### Content Focus in enVisionmath2.0

Topics 3 and 4 focus on applying and extending previous understandings of numbers to the system of rational numbers, including developing a deep understanding of integers and other rational numbers and locating points associated with rational number ordered pairs on the coordinate plane.

## RATIONAL NUMBERS

- **Understand Integers** In Lesson 3-1, students learn that *opposites* are numbers that are the same distance from zero on the number line. They learn that *integers* include the (positive) counting numbers, their (negative) opposites, and zero.

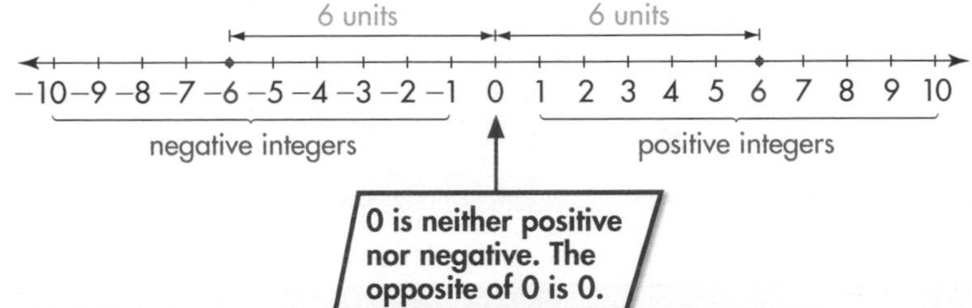


Students also use horizontal and vertical number lines in real-world contexts to understand positive and negative numbers. (6.NS.C.5, 6.NS.C.6a, 6.NS.C.6c)

- **Understand Rational Numbers** A rational number is any number that can be written as the quotient of two integers, that is, as a fraction $\frac{a}{b}$ or $-\frac{a}{b}$ where $a$ and $b$ are integers and $b$ is not equal to zero.

  $-1.5$ is a rational number because it can be written as $-\frac{3}{2}$.

  In Lesson 3-2, students build on previous understandings of fractions, decimals, and integers to focus on finding and positioning rational numbers on horizontal and vertical number lines. (6.NS.C.6c)

- **Compare and Order Rational Numbers** In Lesson 3-3, students use number lines to compare and order rational numbers, and they relate the comparison to real-world contexts. (6.NS.C.7a, 6.NS.C.7b)

  Since $-7$ is located to the left of $-3$ on a number line, $-7 < -3$ and $-7$°C is colder than $-3$°C.

PD



- **Absolute Value** In Lesson 3-4, students learn to represent and interpret absolute value in mathematical and real-world situations. Absolute value is the distance a number is from zero on a number line. Since distance cannot be negative, absolute value is always greater than or equal to zero. (6.NS.C.7c, 6.NS.C.7d)

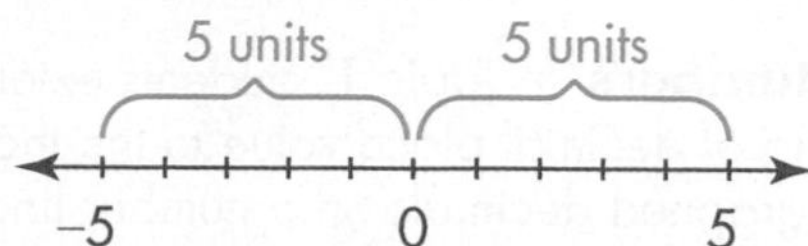


The absolute value of 5 is written $|5|$.
The absolute value of −5 is written as $|-5|$.

$|-5| = 5 \quad |5| = 5$

Students also learn that absolute value represents magnitude in real-world situations and learn to interpret comparisons of absolute value.

**Another Example**

Negative numbers sometimes represent debts. The table shows three account balances that represent debts. Tell which account balance is the least number. Then use absolute value to find which account represents the greatest debt.

| Account | Balance ($) |
|---|---|
| A | −35 |
| B | −50 |
| C | −12 |

On a number line, −50 is farther from 0 than either −35 or −12 are. So −50 is the least number.

$50 is the greatest amount of money owed. So Account B represents the greatest debt.

The money owed is the absolute value of each balance.

| **Account A** | **Account B** | **Account C** |
|---|---|---|
| $\|-35\| = \$35$ | $\|-50\| = \$50$ | $\|-12\| = \$12$ |

## COORDINATE GEOMETRY

- **Integers on the Coordinate Plane** In Lesson 4-1, students learn how to graph points with integer coordinates. They review and learn terms, including coordinate plane, *x*-axis, *y*-axis, origin, quadrants, and ordered pair. Students also learn that when the coordinates of two points differ only by the signs, the points are a reflection of each other across one or both axes. (6.NS.C.6b, 6.NS.C.6c)

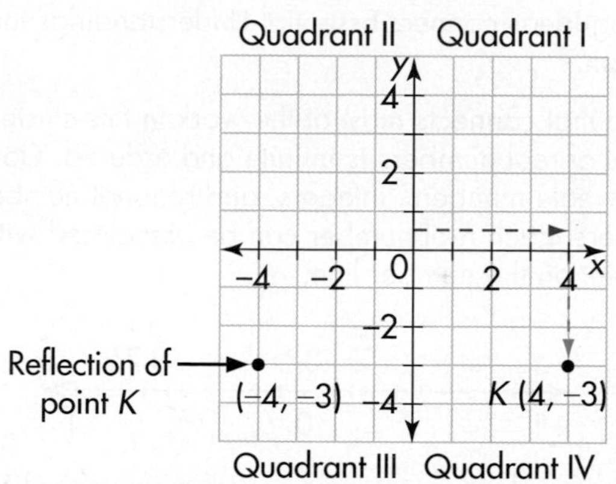


- **Rational Numbers on the Coordinate Plane** In Lesson 4-2, students extend the coordinate plane to include rational numbers other than integers. (6.NS.C.6b, 6.NS.C.6c)

- **Distance and Polygons on the Coordinate Plane** In Lesson 4-3, students apply their understanding of absolute value of integers to find the distance between points on a coordinate plane when the points have either the same first coordinate or the same second coordinate. Lesson 4-4 builds on each of the concepts explored in this topic as students find the distances of the sides of polygons graphed on a coordinate plane and solve problems involving perimeter. (6.NS.C.8, 6.G.A.3)

PD **Professional Development Videos** Topic Overview Videos and Listen and Look For Lesson Videos present additional important information about the content of this cluster.

# MAJOR CLUSTER 6.NS.C

## MATH BACKGROUND: COHERENCE

FOCUS | FCR COHERENCE | RIGOR

Content Coherence in enVisionmath2.0

Students learn best when ideas are connected in a coherent curriculum. This coherence is achieved through various types of connections including connections within clusters, across clusters, across domains, and across grades.

### BIG IDEAS IN GRADES K–6

Big Ideas are the conceptual underpinnings of **enVision**math**2.0** and provide conceptual cohesion of the content. Big Ideas connect Essential Understandings throughout the program.

A Big Idea that connects most of the work in this cluster is that the set of real numbers is infinite and ordered. Counting numbers, whole numbers, integers, and rational numbers are real numbers. Each real number can be associated with a unique point on the number line.

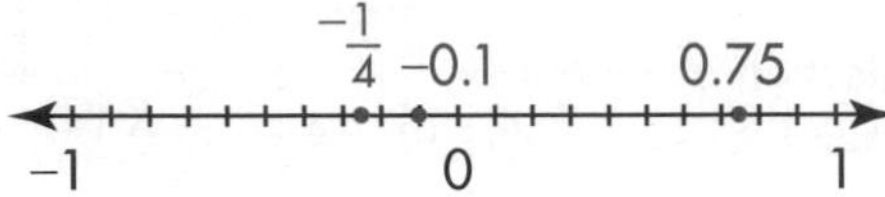


The coordinate plane is an extension of the number line to two dimensions. So, any point with real-number coordinates can be graphed on a coordinate plane.

For a complete list of Big Ideas, see pages 110–111 in the *Teacher's Edition Program Overview.*

### LOOK BACK

*How do Topics 3 and 4 connect to what students learned earlier?*

### GRADE 5

- **Rational Numbers** In Topic 1, students extended their understanding of decimal place value to the thousandths place. They graphed decimals on a number line to help them compare and round decimals. (5.NBT.A.3a, 5.NBT.A.3b) They also extended their ability to do computations with rational numbers to include adding and subtracting decimals in Topic 2, multiplying decimals in Topic 4, dividing decimals in Topic 6, adding and subtracting fractions in Topic 7, multiplying fractions in Topic 8, and dividing fractions in Topic 9. (5.NBT.A.2, 5.NBT.B.7, 5.NF.A.1, 5.NF.A.2, 5.NF.B.3, 5.NF.B.4, 5.NF.B.6, 5.NF.B.7)
- **Graph Points on the Coordinate Plane** In Topic 14, students learned about the coordinate plane and graphed points in the first quadrant to solve real-world and mathematical problems. (5.G.A.1, 5.G.A.2)

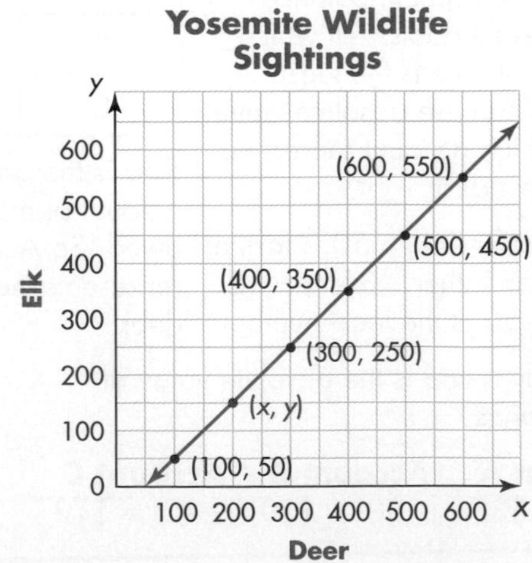


The point marked $(x, y)$ has coordinates (200, 150). When 200 deer were sighted, 150 elk were sighted.

### EARLIER IN GRADE 6

- **Rational Numbers** Students worked with positive rational numbers in decimal and fraction forms as they wrote and evaluated expressions in Topic 1 and solved equations in Topic 2. (6.EE.A, 6.EE.B.6, 6.EE.B.7)

## TOPICS 3 AND 4

*How is content connected within Topics 3 and 4?*

- **Rational Numbers** In Lesson 3-2, students extend their understanding of integers from Lesson 3-1 to all rational numbers. It is important for students to understand that integers are a special type of rational number. They further extend their understanding of rational numbers in Lesson 3-3 to comparing them and in Lesson 3-4 to absolute value. (6.NS.C.5, 6.NS.C.6a, 6.NS.C.6b, 6.NS.C.7)
- **Coordinate Plane** In Lessons 4-1 and 4-2, students apply the understanding of integers and rational numbers gained in Topic 3 to graph points on the coordinate plane with these numbers as coordinates. (6.NS.C.6b, 6.NS.C.6c) Students then solve problems by finding distances between points on the coordinate plane, graphing points to form a polygon, and then finding the perimeter of the polygon. (6.NS.C.8, 6.G.A.3)

***An archaeologist used a coordinate plane to map a dig site. She marked the corners of a building with flags as shown. How much rope does she need to go around the building?***

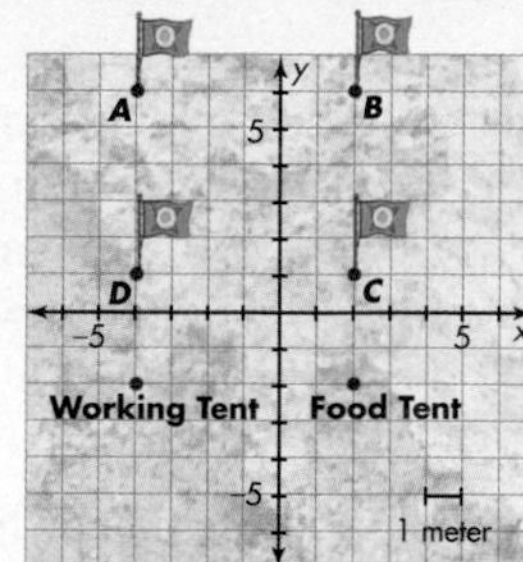


Use the coordinates of the vertices of the rectangle; $A(-4, 6)$, $B(2, 6)$, $C(2, 1)$, and $D(-4, 1)$.

- The distance from $A$ to $B = |-4| + |2|$
  $= 4 + 2 = 6$ m
- The distance from $B$ to $C = |6| - |1|$
  $= 6 - 1 = 5$ m
- The distance from $C$ to $D = |2| + |-4|$
  $= 2 + 4 = 6$ m
- The distance from $A$ to $D = |6| - |1|$
  $= 6 - 1 = 5$ m

Perimeter $= 6$ m $+ 5$ m $+ 6$ m $+ 5$ m
$= 22$ meters

- **Polygons** Topic 4 also develops content from Supporting Cluster 6.G.A on solving problems related to polygons graphed on a coordinate plane. (6.G.A.3)

## LOOK AHEAD

*How do Topics 3 and 4 connect to what students will learn later?*

### LATER IN GRADE 6

- **Graph Equations** In Topic 5, students will graph equations in the coordinate plane. (6.EE.C.9)
- **Fractions, Decimals, and Percents** In Topic 11, students will get a deeper understanding of rational numbers as they change forms between fractions, decimals, and percents. (6.RP.A.3c)

Write $\frac{3}{5}$ as a decimal and as a percent.

$$\begin{array}{r} 0.6 \\ 5\overline{)3.0} \\ -3\,0 \\ \hline 0 \end{array}$$

$\frac{3}{5}$ can be written as 0.6 or 0.60.

$$\frac{3}{5} = \frac{x}{100}$$

$$\frac{3 \times 20}{5 \times 20} = \frac{60}{100}$$

$\frac{3}{5}$ can be written as $\frac{60}{100}$ or 60%.

- **Area of Polygons on the Coordinate Plane** In Topic 13, students will apply their skill in graphing polygons and finding distances on a coordinate plane to solve problems involving area of polygons on a coordinate plane. (6.G.A.1, 6.G.A.3, 6.NS.C.6c, 6.NS.C.8)

### GRADE 7

- **Operations with Rational Numbers** Students will add, subtract, multiply, and divide both positive and negative rational numbers. They will solve multi-step problems involving operations on rational numbers, changing forms as appropriate. (7.NS.A.1, 7.NS.A.2, 7.NS.A.3, 7.EE.B.3)

# MATH BACKGROUND: RIGOR



## Content Rigor in enVisionmath2.0

A rigorous curriculum emphasizes conceptual understanding, procedural skill and fluency, and applications.

### CONCEPTUAL UNDERSTANDING

- **Extend Understandings of Numbers to the System of Rational Numbers** In Lesson 3-1, students encounter negative numbers. Integers are introduced with the idea of opposites, which indicates two numbers can have the same magnitude, or distance from zero, with different directions on a number line. They learn that the opposite of an opposite is the number itself. (6.NS.C.5, 6.NS.C.6a, 6.NS.C.6c)

  $$-(-6) = 6$$

  The opposite of negative six is six.

  In Lesson 3-2, students extend this understanding to include other rational numbers and locate positive and negative integers, fractions, and decimals on a number line. (6.NS.C.6c)

- **Absolute Value and Ordering of Rational Numbers** In Lesson 3-3, students learn how to compare and order rational numbers. 3 is left of 5 on the number line, so $3 < 5$. In the same way, the opposite of 3 is right of the opposite of 5, so $-5 < -3$. (6.NS.C.7a, 6.NS.C.7b)

  $-5 < -3$ $3 < 5$

  −6 −5 −4 −3 −2 −1 0 1 2 3 4 5 6

  In Lesson 3-4, students gain an understanding of absolute value as the magnitude of a number or its distance from zero on a number line. (6.NS.C.7c, 6.NS.C.7d)

- **Locating Points on a Coordinate Plane** In Topic 4, students combine their understanding of graphing in the first quadrant with their understanding of rational numbers having distance and direction to locate points in all 4 quadrants of the coordinate plane. (6.NS.C.6b, 6.NS.C.8)

### PROCEDURAL SKILL AND FLUENCY

There are no standards in this cluster that call for fluency.

- **Use Understanding of Rational Numbers** In Topics 3 and 4, students use conceptual understandings of integers and rational numbers to name the opposite of a number, find absolute value, locate and graph points on a number line and on the coordinate plane, and find the distance between two points. (6.NS.C)

### APPLICATIONS

- **Integer and Rational Number Situations** Throughout Topic 3, students use concepts related to integers and rational numbers to solve problems involving elevation, temperature, credits/debits, and the charge of atoms. They interpret absolute value as the magnitude of a situation and distinguish between comparisons of rational numbers and comparisons of their absolute value. (6.NS.C.5, 6.NS.C.7b, 6.NS.C.7c, 6.NS.C.7d)

  When starting from the same temperature, a change of −6°C makes it colder than a change of −4°C because $-6 < -4$. However, −6°C represents a greater change than −4°C because $|-6| > |-4|$.

- **Distance and Perimeter Situations** In Topic 4, students use their conceptual understanding of absolute value to explore situations involving distance between locations (points) and perimeter on the coordinate plane. (6.NS.C.8)

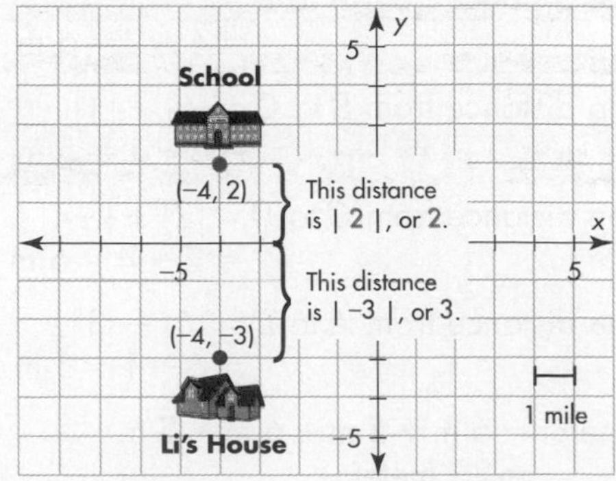


The distance from Li's house to school is $|2| + |-3| = 2 + 3 = 5$ miles.

# MATH PRACTICES

MP

**Connecting Math Practices and Content Standards in enVisionmath2.0**

Math practices and content standards are connected within all lessons including the lessons that focus on math practices.

## MATH PRACTICES WITHIN LESSONS

- **MP.1 Make sense of problems and persevere in solving them.**

  Students persevere as they solve problems involving integers and rational numbers and determine if their solution makes sense. (e.g., p. 212, Item 6)

- **MP.2 Reason abstractly and quantitatively.**

  Students use reasoning as they compare and order two or more rational numbers and compare their absolute values. (e.g., p. 143, Look Back!)

- **MP.3 Construct viable arguments and critique the reasoning of others.**

  Students critique the strategies of others as they compare and order integers and rational numbers. (e.g., p. 158, Item 12)

- **MP.4 Model with mathematics.**

  Students apply known math when they represent problems using integers and rational numbers. (e.g., p. 170, Item 7)

- **MP.5 Use appropriate tools strategically.**

  Students use tools such as number lines to solve problems involving locating, comparing, and ordering integers and rational numbers. (e.g., p. 143, Solve and Share)

- **MP.6 Attend to precision.**

  Students attend to precision when they locate and graph points on number lines and coordinate planes. (e.g., p. 191, Look Back!)

- **MP.7 Look for and make use of structure.**

  Students look for structure when they use absolute value to find distances between points on coordinate planes. (e.g., p. 198, Convince Me!)

- **MP.8 Look for and express regularity in repeated reasoning.**

  Students generalize about similarities and differences between plotting rational numbers. (e.g., p. 149, Look Back!)

## LESSONS THAT FOCUS ON MATH PRACTICES

- **Lesson 3-5** This lesson focuses on MP.2. Students use reasoning to identify known quantities, draw number line diagrams to show relationships, and apply what they know about integers to solve problems.

### Thinking Habits

*Be a good thinker! These questions can help you.*

- What do the numbers and symbols in the problem mean?
- How are the numbers or quantities related?
- How can I represent a word problem using pictures, numbers, or equations?

- **Lesson 4-5** This lesson focuses on MP.3. Students construct arguments using what they know about finding distances on the coordinate plane. They use definitions, graphs, calculations, and math words to construct and justify their arguments.

  For a list of Thinking Habits for MP.3, see p. F25 in the Math Practices and Problem Solving Handbook.

Revisit the information about MP.2 and MP.3 in these other resources:

- **Math Practices and Problem Solving Handbook** before Topic 1; includes Math Practices Proficiency Rubrics.
- **Math Practices Posters** to display in your classroom
- MP **Math Practices Animations,** one for each math practice, available at PearsonRealize.com.

# MAJOR CLUSTER 6.NS.C

## DIFFERENTIATED INSTRUCTION

 Intervention  On-Level  Advanced

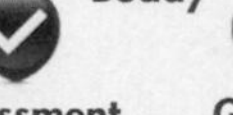


### Ongoing Intervention

**During the core lesson,** monitor progress, reteach as needed, and extend students' thinking.

**Guiding Questions**

- **In the Teacher's Edition** Guiding questions are used to monitor understanding during instruction.

**Online Guiding Questions** Guiding questions are also in the online Visual Learning Animation Plus.

**Prevent Misconceptions**
This feature in the Teacher's Edition is embedded in the guiding questions.

**Error Intervention: If... then...**
This feature in the Teacher's Edition is provided during Guided Practice. It spotlights common errors and gives suggestions for addressing them.

**Reteaching**
Reteaching sets are at the end of the topic in the Student's Edition. They provide additional examples, reminders, and practice. Use these sets as needed before students do the Independent Practice.

**Higher Order Thinking**
These problems require students to think more deeply about the rich, conceptual knowledge developed in the lesson.

**Practice Buddy Online**

Online auto-scored practice is provided for each lesson. On-screen learning aids include Help Me Solve This and View an Example.

### Strategic Intervention

**At the end of the lesson,** assess to identify students' strengths and needs and then provide appropriate support.

**Quick Check**

**In the Student's Edition** Assess the lesson using 3 items checked in the Teacher's Edition.

**Online Quick Check** You can also assess the lesson using 5 online, machine-scored items.

**Intervention Activity** I
Teachers work with struggling students.

**Reteach to Build Understanding** I
This is a page of guided reteaching.

**Technology Center** 

**Digital Math Tools Activities** reinforce the lesson content or previously taught content using a suite of digital math tools.

**Online Games** provide practice on the lesson content or previously taught content.

**Homework and Practice** I O A
Use the leveled assignment to provide differentiated homework and practice.

*Additional resources to support differentiated instruction for on-level and advanced students include:*

**On-Level and Advanced Activity Centers** O A

- **Center Games** are provided in on-level and advanced versions.
- **Math and Science Activity** is related to the topic science theme introduced at the start of the topic.
- **Problem-Solving Reading Mat** is used with a lesson-specific activity.

### Intensive Intervention

**As needed,** provide more instruction that is on or below grade level for students who are struggling.

**Math Diagnosis and Intervention System 2.0**

- **Diagnosis** Use the diagnostic tests in the system. Also, use the item analysis charts given with program assessments at the start of a grade or topic, or at the end of a topic, group of topics, or the year.
- **Intervention Lessons** These two-page lessons include guided instruction followed by practice. The system includes lessons below, on, and above grade level.
- **Teacher Support** Teacher Notes provide the support needed to conduct a short lesson. The lesson focuses on vocabulary, concept development, and practice. The Teacher's Guide contains individual and class record forms and correlations to Student's Edition lessons.

**Resources for Fluency Success**

- A variety of print and digital resources are provided to ensure success on Common Core fluency standards. See Steps to Fluency Success on pages 271K–271N and 317E–317H.

# THE LANGUAGE OF MATH

PEARSON realize.
PearsonRealize.com

A-Z
Glossary

Games

## English Language Learners

**Provide ELL support** through visual learning throughout the program, ELL instruction in every lesson, and additional ideas in an ELL Toolkit.

**Visual Learning**
The visual learning that is infused in **enVision**math**2.0** provides support for English language learners. This support includes a Visual Learning Animation Plus and a Visual Learning Bridge for each lesson.

**English Language Learners Instruction** 
Lessons provide instruction for English language learners at Beginning, Intermediate, and Advanced levels of English proficiency.

**English Language Learners Toolkit**
This resource provides professional development and resources for supporting English language learners.

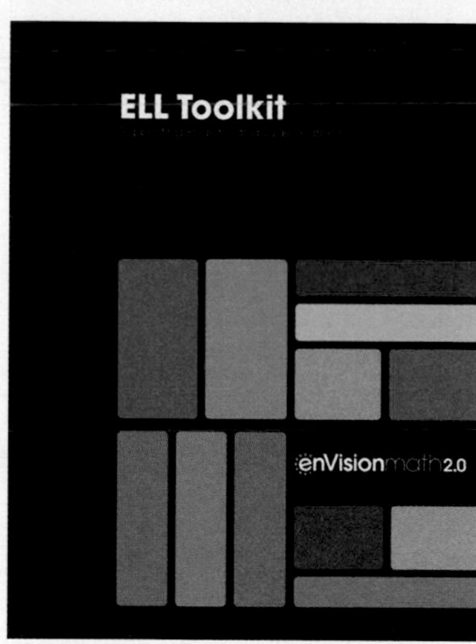
ELL Toolkit
enVisionmath2.0

## Math Vocabulary

**Build math vocabulary** using the vocabulary cards, vocabulary activities, vocabulary review, and glossary plus the online glossary and vocabulary game.

**My Word Cards**
Vocabulary cards for a topic are provided in the Student's Edition. Students use the example on the front of the card to complete the definition on the back.

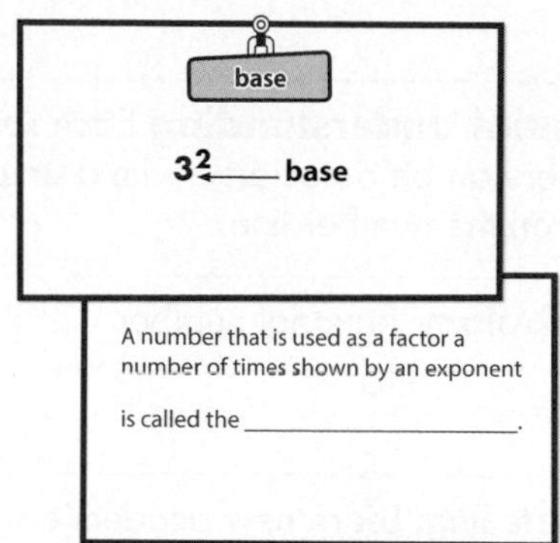
base
3² base
A number that is used as a factor a number of times shown by an exponent
is called the ______.

**Vocabulary Activities**
The Teacher's Edition provides vocabulary activities at the start of topics. These include activities for vocabulary in My Word Cards and/or activities for vocabulary in Review What You Know.

**Vocabulary Review**
A page of vocabulary review is provided at the end of each topic. It reviews vocabulary used in the topic.

**Glossary**
A glossary is provided at the back of the Student's Edition.

**Animated Glossary**

Glossary
An online, bilingual, animated glossary uses motion and sound to build understanding of math vocabulary.

**Online Vocabulary Game**

Games
An online vocabulary game is available in the Game Center.

## Math and Reading

**Connect reading and math** using a data-filled reading mat for the topic with accompanying activity masters and guide.

**Problem-Solving Reading Mats**
There is a large, beautiful mat for each topic. At the start of the topic, help students become familiar with the mat and the vocabulary used by reading the mat aloud as students follow along. Use the Problem-Solving Reading Activity Guide for suggestions about how to use the mat.

**Problem-Solving Reading Activity**
At the end of some lessons, a Problem-Solving Reading Activity provides a page of math problems to solve by using the data on the mat.

TOPIC 3

# TOPIC PLANNER

## RATIONAL NUMBERS

| Lesson 3-1 | Lesson 3-2 | Lesson 3-3 |
|---|---|---|
| **UNDERSTAND INTEGERS** pp. 143–148 | **RATIONAL NUMBERS ON A NUMBER LINE** pp. 149–154 | **COMPARE AND ORDER RATIONAL NUMBERS** pp. 155–160 |
| Content Standards **6.NS.C.5, 6.NS.C.6a, 6.NS.C.6c** Mathematical Practices **MP.2, MP.5, MP.8** | Content Standard **6.NS.C.6c** Mathematical Practices **MP.2, MP.3, MP.6, MP.8** | Content Standards **6.NS.C.7a, 6.NS.C.7b** Mathematical Practices **MP.1, MP.2, MP.3, MP.4, MP.5, MP.8** |
| **Objective** Use positive and negative integers. | **Objective** Find and position rational numbers on a number line. | **Objective** Compare and order rational numbers. |
| **Essential Understanding** Integers are the counting numbers, their opposites, and zero. | **Essential Understanding** Each rational number can be associated with a unique point on the number line. | **Essential Understanding** A number to the right of another on the number line is the greater number. |
| **Vocabulary** Integer, Opposite | **Vocabulary** Rational number | **Vocabulary** None |
| **ELL Listening:** Listen to information. | **ELL Listening:** Learn new academic expressions. | **ELL Speaking:** Express opinions. |
| **Materials** Masking or colored tape, index cards, marker, Number lines (TT 13) (optional), Thermometers (or TT 34) (optional) | **Materials** Markers, masking tape, Number lines (TT 13) (optional) | **Materials** Markers, masking tape, notecards, Number lines (TT 13) (optional) |
| **On-Level and Advanced Activity Centers** • Problem-Solving Reading Mat | **On-Level and Advanced Activity Centers** • Math and Science Activity | **On-Level and Advanced Activity Centers** • Center Games |

## LESSON RESOURCES

Digital

Print

- Student's Edition
- Daily Common Core Review
- Reteach to Build Understanding
- Center Games
- Math and Science Activity
- Problem-Solving Reading Mat
- Problem-Solving Reading Activity

Digital

- Listen and Look For PD Lesson Video
- Student's Edition eText
- Today's Challenge
- Solve & Share
- Visual Learning Animation Plus
- Animated Glossary
- Math Tools
- Practice Buddy Online Practice
- Quick Check
- Another Look Homework Video
- Math Games

Digital

## Lesson 3-4

**ABSOLUTE VALUE** pp. 161–166

Content Standards **6.NS.C.7c, 6.NS.C.7d**

Mathematical Practices **MP.1, MP.2, MP.3, MP.8**

**Objective** Interpret absolute value in mathematics and real-world situations.

**Essential Understanding** Absolute value is the magnitude of a positive or negative quantity. It can be described as a number's distance from 0 on the number line.

**Vocabulary** Absolute value

**ELL Reading:** Use contextual support to develop vocabulary.

**Materials** Number lines (TT 13)

**On-Level and Advanced Activity Centers**

- Problem-Solving Reading Mat

## Lesson 3-5

**MATH PRACTICES AND PROBLEM SOLVING: REASONING** pp. 167–172

Mathematical Practices **MP.2 Also MP.1, MP.4, MP.6**

Content Standards **6.NS.C.5, 6.NS.C.6**

**Objective** Make sense of quantities and relationships in problem situations.

**Essential Understanding** Good math thinkers know how to think about words and numbers to solve problems.

**Vocabulary** None

**ELL Speaking:** Describe information.

**Materials** Index cards, drawing paper (optional), Number lines (TT 13) (optional)

**On-Level and Advanced Activity Centers**

- Math and Science Activity

## TOPIC RESOURCES

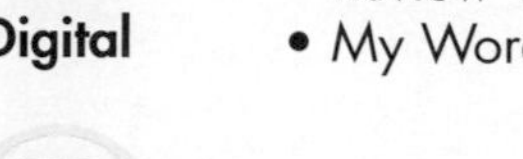

Digital

Print

**Start of Topic**

- Math and Science Project
- Home-School Connection
- Review What You Know
- My Word Cards

**End of Topic**

- Fluency Practice Activity
- Vocabulary Review
- Reteaching
- Topic Assessment
- Topic Performance Assessment

Digital

**Start of Topic**

- Topic Overview PD Video

**End of Topic**

- Math Practices Animations
- Online Topic Assessment
- ExamView® Test Generator
- Practice Buddy Fluency Practice/Assessment

PearsonRealize.com

TOPIC 3

# TOPIC OPENER

## RATIONAL NUMBERS

### TOPIC ESSENTIAL QUESTIONS

**What are integers and rational numbers? How can you compare and order rational numbers?**

Revisit the Topic Essential Questions throughout the topic, and see a note about answering the questions in the Teacher's Edition for the Topic Assessment.

### MATH AND SCIENCE PROJECT STEM

**Science Theme** The science theme for this project is **Elevation and Boiling Point**. This theme will be revisited in the Math and Science Activities in Lessons 3-2 and 3-5 and in some lesson exercises.

At sea level, liquid water freezes at 0°C and turns into ice. Liquid water boils at 100°C and turns into water vapor. But temperature is not the only thing that affects phase changes. Pressure does, too.

Explain that air pressure makes it harder for liquid water molecules to expand and break away as water vapor. The higher the altitude, the lower the air pressure. So, the boiling point is lower at higher altitudes.

**Project-Based Learning** Have students work on the **Math and Science Project** over the course of several days.

### EXTENSION

Have students research the boiling points of other substances and present these temperatures in degrees Celsius and degrees Farenheit.

**Sample Student Work for Math and Science Project**

Mount Everest is the highest point above sea level on Earth. Water boils on Mount Everest at 72°C.

$°C \cdot \frac{9}{5} + 32 = °F$

$72 \cdot \frac{9}{5} + 32 = °F$

$= 161.6°F$

Water boils on Mount Everest at 161.6°F.

**Math and Science Project:** Elevation and Boiling Point

**Do Research** Use the Internet or other sources to learn about the highest and lowest elevations in the United States and the highest and lowest elevations recorded on Earth. Then, find information about the boiling point of water at sea level and at the different elevations on land that you found.

**Journal: Write a Report** Include what you found. Also in your report:

- Identify the elevations using positive and negative numbers.
- Present the boiling points of water in degrees Fahrenheit and in degrees Celsius.
- Compare the boiling points based on elevation.
- What generalization can you make about elevation and the boiling point of water?

Topic 3 139

### Home-School Connection

Send this page home at the start of Topic 3 to give families an overview of the content in the topic.

Name ____________________

Home-School Connection Topic 3

**Rational Numbers**

**Topic 3 Standards**

6.NS.C.5, 6.NS.C.6, 6.NS.C.6a, 6.NS.C.6c, 6.NS.C.7a, 6.NS.C.7b, 6.NS.C.7c, 6.NS.C.7d

*See the front of the Student's Edition for complete standards.*

Dear Family,

Your child is learning to use integers and other rational numbers to solve problems. A part of this is learning the meanings of integers and how to use them to describe quantities that have opposite directions or values. He or she is also learning how to compare and order these numbers.

You can help your child understand the concept of negative integers by playing the following game.

**What Integer Am I?**

Draw a number line on a large sheet of paper.

–10 –8 –6 –4 –2 0 2 4 6 8 10

**Step 1** Player 1 places a token on any number on the number line. Positive numbers, negative numbers, and zero are all fair game.

**Step 2** Player 2 says, "What is my name?" "What is my opposite?" and "How many units am I away from 0?"

**Step 3** Player 1 then gives the name of the integer, its opposite, and tells its distance from 0.

**Step 4** Trade roles and play again.

*Alternate Gameplay: Draw a number line that shows halves and whole numbers from −5 to 5. Place tokens at any location on the number line to talk about positive and negative fractions and decimals.*

**Observe Your Child**

**Focus on Mathematical Practice 5**
Use appropriate tools strategically.

Help your child become proficient with Mathematical Practice 5. After drawing the number line for the activity above, ask your child where he or she might have seen or used a number line before. Suggest a thermometer or football field if your child has trouble coming up with an idea.

Name ______

## Review What You Know

### Vocabulary

Choose the best term from the box. Write it on the blank.

- decimal
- fraction
- denominator
- numerator

1. A **fraction** names part of a whole, part of a set, or a location on a number line.
2. The number above the fraction bar that represents the part of the whole is the **numerator**.
3. The number below the fraction bar that represents the total number of equal parts in one whole is the **denominator**.

### Fractions and Decimals

Write each fraction as a decimal.

4. $\frac{2}{5}$ **0.4**
5. $\frac{3}{4}$ **0.75**
6. $\frac{10}{4}$ **2.5**
7. $\frac{12}{5}$ **2.4**
8. $\frac{3}{5}$ **0.6**
9. $\frac{15}{3}$ **5.0**

### Division

Divide.

10. $1.25 \div 0.5$ **2.5**
11. $13 \div 0.65$ **20**
12. $12.2 \div 0.4$ **30.5**
13. $21.6 \div 5.4$ **4**
14. $26.35 \div 4.25$ **6.2**
15. $28.71 \div 8.7$ **3.3**

### Explain

16. Les said that the quotient of $3.9 \div 0.75$ is 0.52. Explain how you know Les is incorrect without completing the division.
**Sample answer: I can use estimation to determine that $3.9 \div 0.75$ is close to $4 \div 1$. Since $4 \div 1 = 4$, then the quotient of $3.9 \div 0.75$ is about 4. Les's answer of 0.52 is not close to the estimate.**




## Item Analysis for Diagnosis and Intervention

| Item | Standard | MDIS |
|---|---|---|
| 1–3 | 5.NF.B.3 | H2 |
| 4–9 | 5.NF.B.3 | H34 |
| 10–15 | 5.NBT.B.7 | H69 |
| 16 | 5.NBT.A.4 | H28, H68 |

## Topic 3 Vocabulary Words Activity

Use the Topic 1 activity on p. 3–4 with the Topic 3 words at the right.

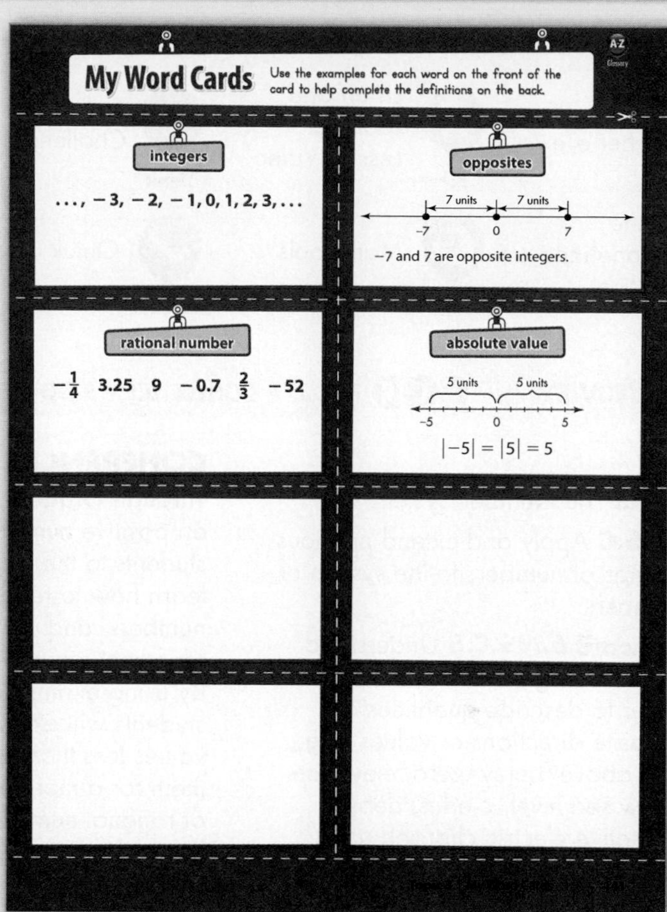

My Word Cards
Use the examples for each word on the front of the card to help complete the definitions on the back.
integers
..., −3, −2, −1, 0, 1, 2, 3, ...
opposites
7 units
7 units
−7
0
7
−7 and 7 are opposite integers.
rational number
$-\frac{1}{4}$ 3.25 9 −0.7 $\frac{2}{3}$ −52
absolute value
5 units
5 units
−5
0
5
|−5| = |5| = 5


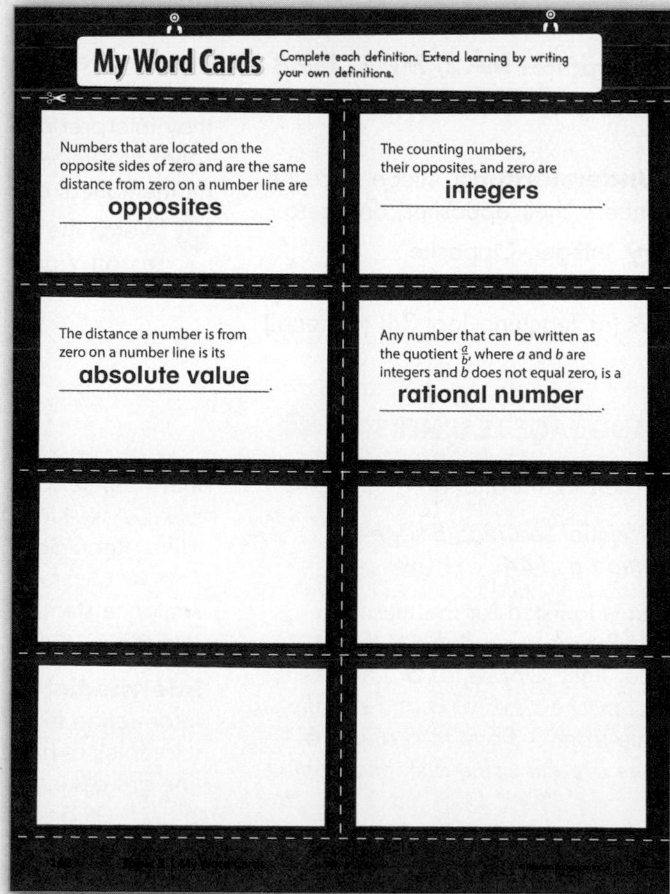

My Word Cards
Complete each definition. Extend learning by writing your own definitions.
Numbers that are located on the opposite sides of zero and are the same distance from zero on a number line are opposites.
The counting numbers, their opposites, and zero are integers.
The distance a number is from zero on a number line is its absolute value.
Any number that can be written as the quotient $\frac{a}{b}$, where a and b are integers and b does not equal zero, is a rational number.

# LESSON 3-1

# UNDERSTAND INTEGERS

## DIGITAL RESOURCES PearsonRealize.com

eText — Student and Teacher eTexts

PD — Listen and Look For Lesson Video

Think — Today's Challenge

Solve — Solve and Share

Learn — Visual Learning Animation Plus

Glossary — Animated Glossary

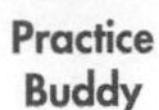
Practice Buddy — Online Personalized Practice

Tools — Math Tools

Assessment — Quick Check

Help — Another Look Homework Video

Games — Math Games

## LESSON OVERVIEW FCR FOCUS • COHERENCE • RIGOR

### FOCUS

**Domain 6.NS** The Number System

**Cluster 6.NS.C** Apply and extend previous understandings of numbers to the system of rational numbers.

**Content Standard 6.NS.C.5** Understand that positive and negative numbers are used together to describe quantities having opposite directions or values (e.g., temperature above/below zero, elevation above/below sea level, credits/debits, positive/negative electric charge); use positive and negative numbers to represent quantities in real-world contexts, explaining the meaning of 0 in each situation. Also **6.NS.C.6a, 6.NS.C.6c**.

**Mathematical Practices MP.2, MP.5, MP.8**

**Objective** Use positive and negative integers.

**Essential Understanding** Integers are the counting numbers, their opposites, and zero.

**Vocabulary** Integer, Opposite

**Materials** Number lines (Teaching Tool 13), Thermometers (or Teaching Tool 34) (optional)

### COHERENCE

Through Grade 5, students focused solely on positive numbers. This lesson introduces students to the concept of integers. They learn how to read and write negative numbers, and use negative numbers to represent quantities in real-world contexts. By using examples such as thermometers, students will extend a number line to include values less than zero. This will prepare them for a more thorough study of the set of rational numbers in the next lesson and beyond.

### RIGOR

This lesson emphasizes **conceptual understanding**. Students understand how integers are used to describe quantities and apply the definition of *opposite* as they interpret and generate integers. They solve problems using integers in both mathematical and real-world contexts.

PD Watch the Listen and Look For Lesson Video.

## MATH ANYTIME

### Daily Common Core Review

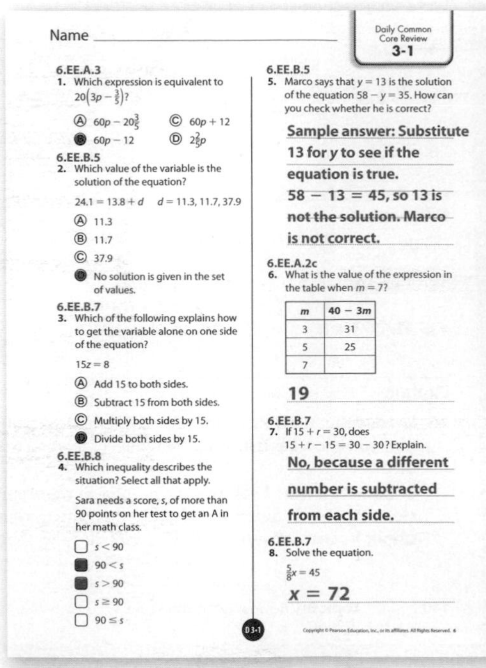
Name ______

Daily Common Core Review 3-1

6.EE.A.3
1. Which expression is equivalent to $20\left(3p - \frac{3}{5}\right)$?
Ⓐ $60p - 20\frac{3}{5}$ Ⓑ $60p - 12$ Ⓒ $60p + 12$ Ⓓ $2\frac{2}{5}p$

6.EE.B.5
2. Which value of the variable is the solution of the equation?
$24.1 = 13.8 + d$ $d = 11.3, 11.7, 37.9$
Ⓐ 11.3
Ⓑ 11.7
Ⓒ 37.9
Ⓓ No solution is given in the set of values.

6.EE.B.7
3. Which of the following explains how to get the variable alone on one side of the equation?
$15z = 8$
Ⓐ Add 15 to both sides.
Ⓑ Subtract 15 from both sides.
Ⓒ Multiply both sides by 15.
Ⓓ Divide both sides by 15.

6.EE.B.8
4. Which inequality describes the situation? Select all that apply.
Sara needs a score, $s$, of more than 90 points on her test to get an A in her math class.
☐ $s < 90$
■ $90 < s$
■ $s > 90$
☐ $s \geq 90$
☐ $90 \leq s$

6.EE.B.5
5. Marco says that $y = 13$ is the solution of the equation $58 - y = 35$. How can you check whether he is correct?
**Sample answer: Substitute 13 for $y$ to see if the equation is true. $58 - 13 = 45$, so 13 is not the solution. Marco is not correct.**

6.EE.A.2c
6. What is the value of the expression in the table when $m = 7$?

| $m$ | $40 - 3m$ |
|---|---|
| 3 | 31 |
| 5 | 25 |
| 7 | |

**19**

6.EE.B.7
7. If $15 + r = 30$, does $15 + r - 15 = 30 - 30$? Explain.
**No, because a different number is subtracted from each side.**

6.EE.B.7
8. Solve the equation.
$\frac{5}{8}x = 45$
**$x = 72$**

D3-1



### Today's Challenge

Think Use the Topic 3 problems any time during this topic.

## ENGLISH LANGUAGE LEARNERS ELL

**Listening** Listen to information.

*Use with the Visual Learning Bridge on Student's Edition p. 144.*

Instruct students to listen for the meaning of *integers* as Box A is read. Point to the 0 on the number line. *Opposites are numbers located on opposite sides of 0 and are the same distance from 0.* Point to 6 and −6. *These integers are the same distance from 0.* Read Box B.

**Beginning** Ask students to listen to the information in Box B. Point to the 0's on the thermometer and number line. *These are alike.* Ask students to discuss how they are alike. Read Box C. *What is the opposite integer of 6?* Ask students to complete the sentence stem: "The opposite of 6 is the integer ___." Continue the process with −6.

**Intermediate** Ask students to listen to the information in Box B. Instruct students to share examples of how the thermometer and number line are alike. *How do you know the integers 6 and −6 are the same distance from 0 on both the thermometer and number line?* Read Box C. Ask students to complete the sentence stem: "The opposite of 6 is the integer ___." Continue the process with −6.

**Advanced** Divide students into groups of 2. Ask Student A to listen to information as Student B explains how the number line and thermometer are alike. Ask Student B to listen as Student A explains how the integers 6 and −6 are the same distance from 0. Read Box C. Instruct students to explain why 6 and −6 are opposites.

**Summarize** What are *integers*?

# DEVELOP: PROBLEM-BASED LEARNING

**COHERENCE: Engage learners by connecting prior knowledge to new ideas.**
Students use their knowledge of reading temperatures on a thermometer to locate a number, its opposite, and zero. They associate the thermometer with a vertical number line that includes negative integers.

10–15 min

Solve

## BEFORE

1. **Pose the Solve-and-Share Problem**
**MP.5 Use Appropriate Tools Strategically** Listen and look for students who recognize the relationship between the thermometer and a vertical number line.

2. **Build Understanding**
*How do you read the temperature on a thermometer?* [Accept all reasonable answers.] *What does it mean when the temperature goes up or down?* [When the temperature goes up, the thermometer reading increases; it gets warmer. When the temperature goes down, the thermometer reading decreases; it gets cooler.]

## DURING

3. **Ask Guiding Questions As Needed**
*What numbers are already labeled on the thermometer?* [20, 10, 0, −10, −20] *What do these numbers represent?* [Degrees Celsius] *What does each small interval on the thermometer represent?* [2°C]

## AFTER

4. **Share and Discuss Solutions**
Solve Start with students' solutions. If needed, project Alisha's work to discuss how to locate numbers on the thermometer.

5. **Transition to the Visual Learning Bridge**
*A thermometer measures temperatures above and below 0°. Numbers located on opposite sides of 0 and the same distance from 0 on a number line are called opposites.*

6. **Extension for Early Finishers**
*What is the opposite of −5°C?* [5°C] *In general, what sign is opposite of a positive number?* [Negative] *Opposite of a negative number?* [Positive]

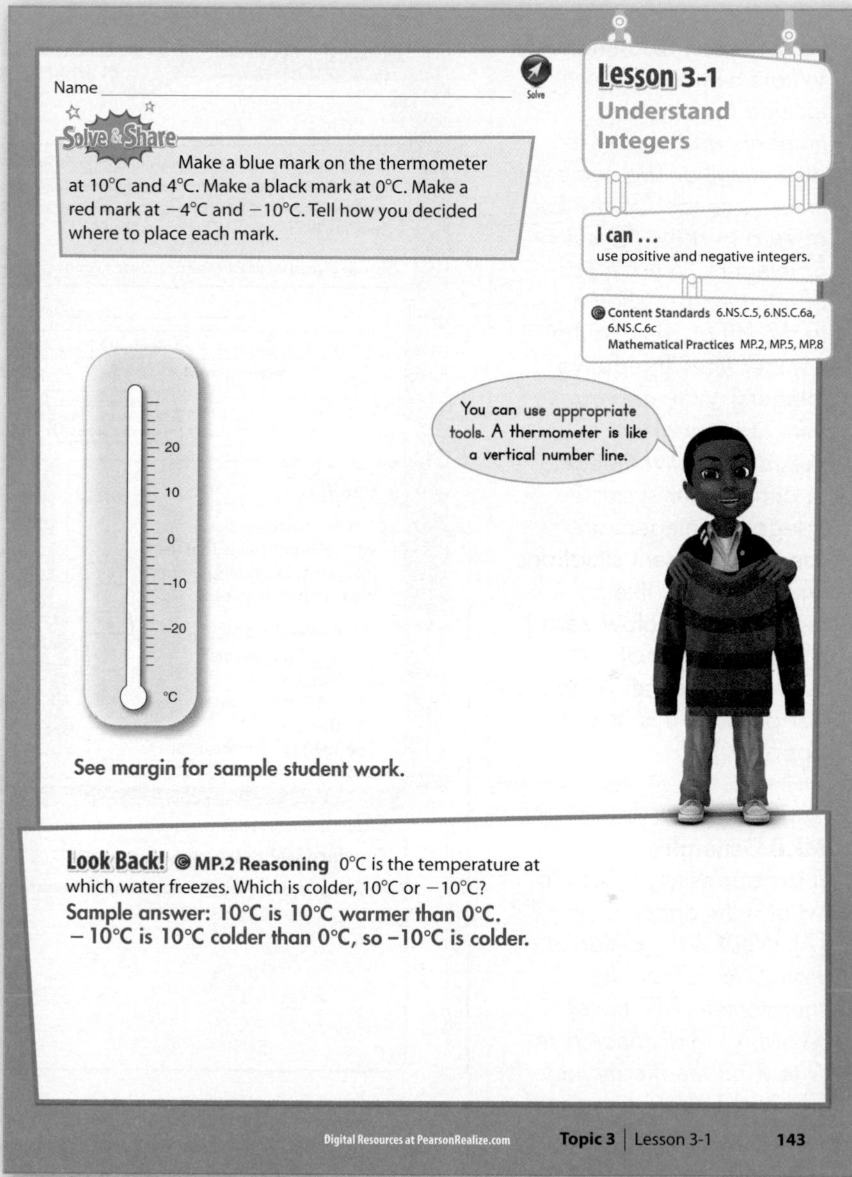

Name
Solve & Share
Make a blue mark on the thermometer at 10°C and 4°C. Make a black mark at 0°C. Make a red mark at −4°C and −10°C. Tell how you decided where to place each mark.
Lesson 3-1
Understand Integers
I can ...
use positive and negative integers.
Content Standards 6.NS.C.5, 6.NS.C.6a, 6.NS.C.6c
Mathematical Practices MP.2, MP.5, MP.8
You can use appropriate tools. A thermometer is like a vertical number line.
20
10
0
−10
−20
°C
See margin for sample student work.
Look Back! MP.2 Reasoning 0°C is the temperature at which water freezes. Which is colder, 10°C or −10°C?
Sample answer: 10°C is 10°C warmer than 0°C. −10°C is 10°C colder than 0°C, so −10°C is colder.
Digital Resources at PearsonRealize.com
Topic 3 | Lesson 3-1
143


## Analyze Student Work

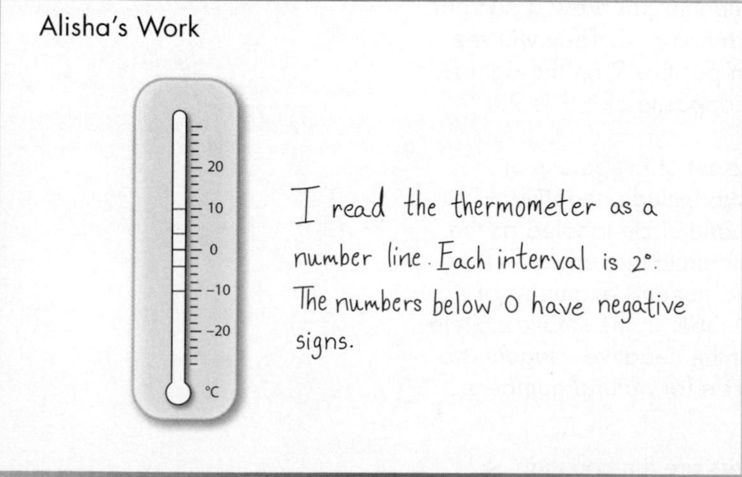

Alisha's Work
20
10
0
−10
−20
°C
I read the thermometer as a number line. Each interval is 2°. The numbers below 0 have negative signs.


Alisha correctly marks all five temperatures and explains how she did it.

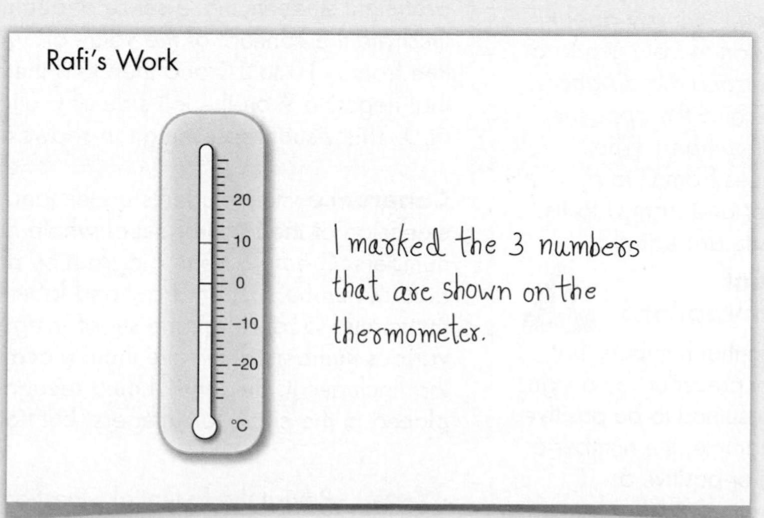

Rafi's Work
20
10
0
−10
−20
°C
I marked the 3 numbers that are shown on the thermometer.


Rafi correctly marks only the three temperatures that have corresponding labels.

# DEVELOP: VISUAL LEARNING

The *Visual Learning Bridge* connects students' thinking in Solve & Share to important math ideas in the lesson. Use the *Visual Learning Bridge* to make these ideas explicit. Also available as a *Visual Learning Animation Plus* at PearsonRealize.com

ELL Visual Learning

PEARSON realize.
PearsonRealize.com

Learn

Glossary

**MP.2 Reason Quantitatively** *Whole numbers, which include the counting numbers and zero, are also integers. The number line is extended to the left of zero to show the set of integers. What types of numbers are shown to the left of zero on the number line?* [Negative integers] *Why do you think it is important to include negative integers in our number system?* [Negative integers are used to represent situations less than zero, like temperatures below zero.] *What is unique about zero?* [It is neither negative nor positive. It is its own opposite.]

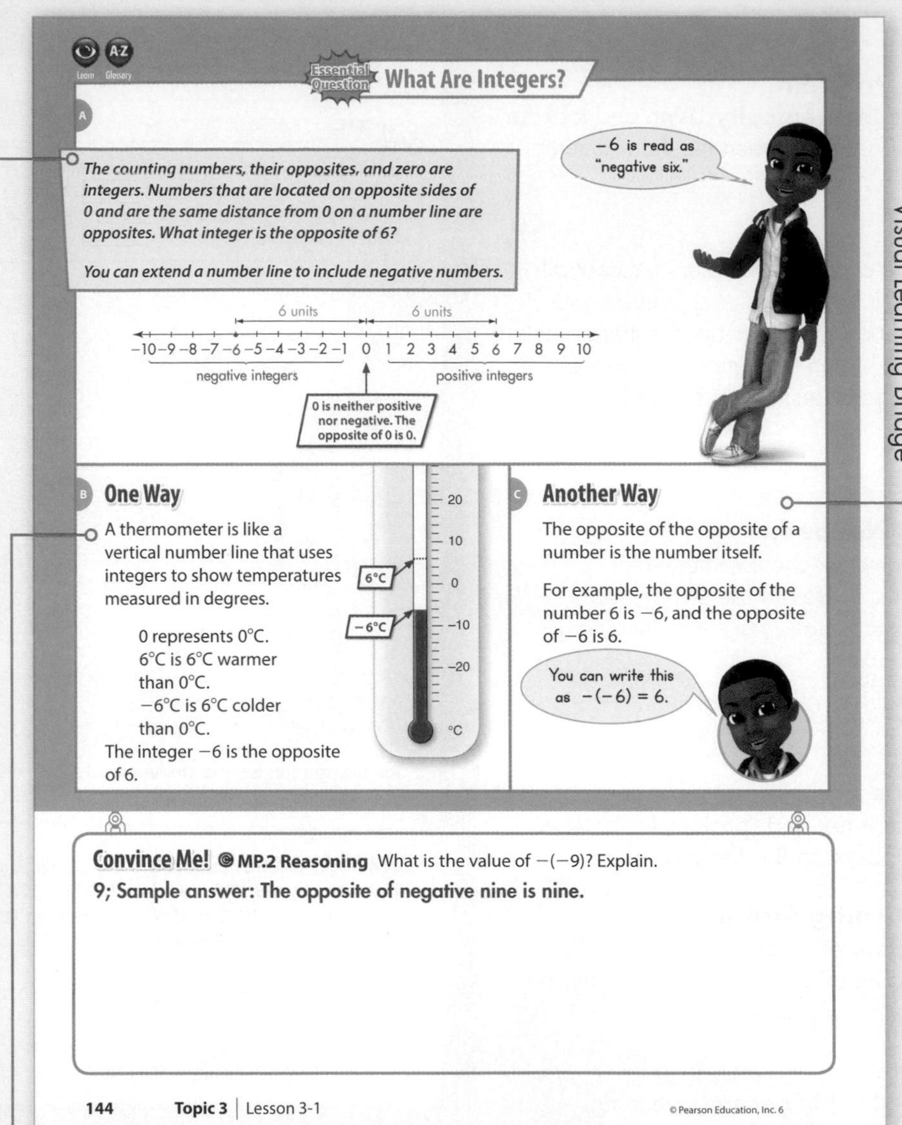

Essential Question **What Are Integers?**

A

*The counting numbers, their opposites, and zero are integers. Numbers that are located on opposite sides of 0 and are the same distance from 0 on a number line are opposites. What integer is the opposite of 6?*

*You can extend a number line to include negative numbers.*



B **One Way**

A thermometer is like a vertical number line that uses integers to show temperatures measured in degrees.

0 represents 0°C.
6°C is 6°C warmer than 0°C.
−6°C is 6°C colder than 0°C.

The integer −6 is the opposite of 6.



C **Another Way**

The opposite of the opposite of a number is the number itself.

For example, the opposite of the number 6 is −6, and the opposite of −6 is 6.



**Convince Me!** MP.2 Reasoning What is the value of −(−9)? Explain.

**9; Sample answer: The opposite of negative nine is nine.**





Visual Learning Bridge

*How would you write the opposite of the opposite of ten?* [−(−10)] *What is its value?* [10]

**Prevent Misconceptions** 

Explain that—unlike in English composition—it is acceptable to use double negatives in math. A negative sign can also be called an opposite sign. It may be easier for students to think of −(−10) as the opposite of negative ten.

**MP.8 Generalize** *If the opposite of 6 is −6, what is the opposite of −7?* [7] *What is the distance from 0 to −7 on the thermometer?* [7 units] *What is the distance from 0 to 7 on the thermometer?* [7 units] *What can you conclude about the two distances from 0?* [They are the same.] *In general, what can you say about the distance from 0 and a number and the distance from 0 and the opposite of that number?* [The distances from 0 to a number and from 0 to its opposite are equal.]

**Prevent Misconceptions** 1 RtI

Explain that numbers that are not preceded by a sign are presumed to be positive. For example, the number 6 is +6, or positive 6.

**Convince Me! MP.2 Reason Quantitatively** Mathematically proficient students make sense of quantities and their relationships. To illustrate the concept of the value of −(−9), students can draw a number line from −10 to 10 and then fold the paper in half at 0. They will see that negative 9 on the left side of 0 aligns with positive 9 on the right side of 0. This visual representation shows that the opposite of −9 is 9.

**Coherence** Help students understand that the set of integers is an extension of the familiar set of whole numbers to include negative numbers. Create a Venn diagram by drawing one circle labeled as the *natural numbers*. Then draw and label a larger circle that encloses the first circle, to represent the set of *integers*. Give students examples of various numbers and have them place each number in the smallest circle that includes it. Students should recognize that the negative integers are placed in the circle for *integers*, but not the circle for *natural numbers*.

Revisit the Essential Question. Integers are the counting numbers, their opposites, and zero. Just as there are infinitely many counting numbers, there are infinitely many negative integers.

**QUICK CHECK**

Check mark indicates items for prescribing differentiation on the next page.
Items 10 and 34 are worth 1 point. Item 32 is worth up to 3 points.

20–30 min

Practice Buddy

Tools

Assessment

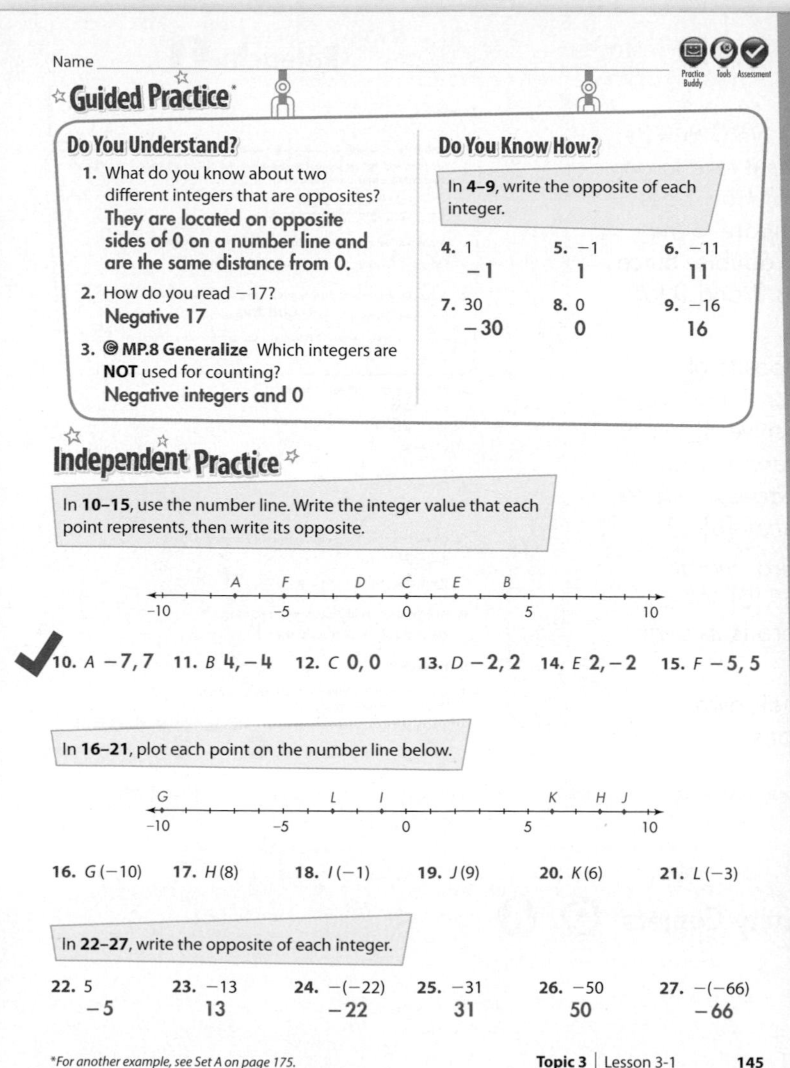

Name ______

## Guided Practice*

**Do You Understand?**

1. What do you know about two different integers that are opposites?
**They are located on opposite sides of 0 on a number line and are the same distance from 0.**
2. How do you read −17?
**Negative 17**
3. **MP.8 Generalize** Which integers are **NOT** used for counting?
**Negative integers and 0**

**Do You Know How?**

In **4–9**, write the opposite of each integer.

4. 1 **−1**
5. −1 **1**
6. −11 **11**
7. 30 **−30**
8. 0 **0**
9. −16 **16**

## Independent Practice

In **10–15**, use the number line. Write the integer value that each point represents, then write its opposite.

10. *A* **−7, 7**
11. *B* **4, −4**
12. *C* **0, 0**
13. *D* **−2, 2**
14. *E* **2, −2**
15. *F* **−5, 5**

In **16–21**, plot each point on the number line below.

16. *G*(−10)
17. *H*(8)
18. *I*(−1)
19. *J*(9)
20. *K*(6)
21. *L*(−3)

In **22–27**, write the opposite of each integer.

22. 5 **−5**
23. −13 **13**
24. −(−22) **−22**
25. −31 **31**
26. −50 **50**
27. −(−66) **−66**

*For another example, see Set A on page 175.

Topic 3 | Lesson 3-1 145

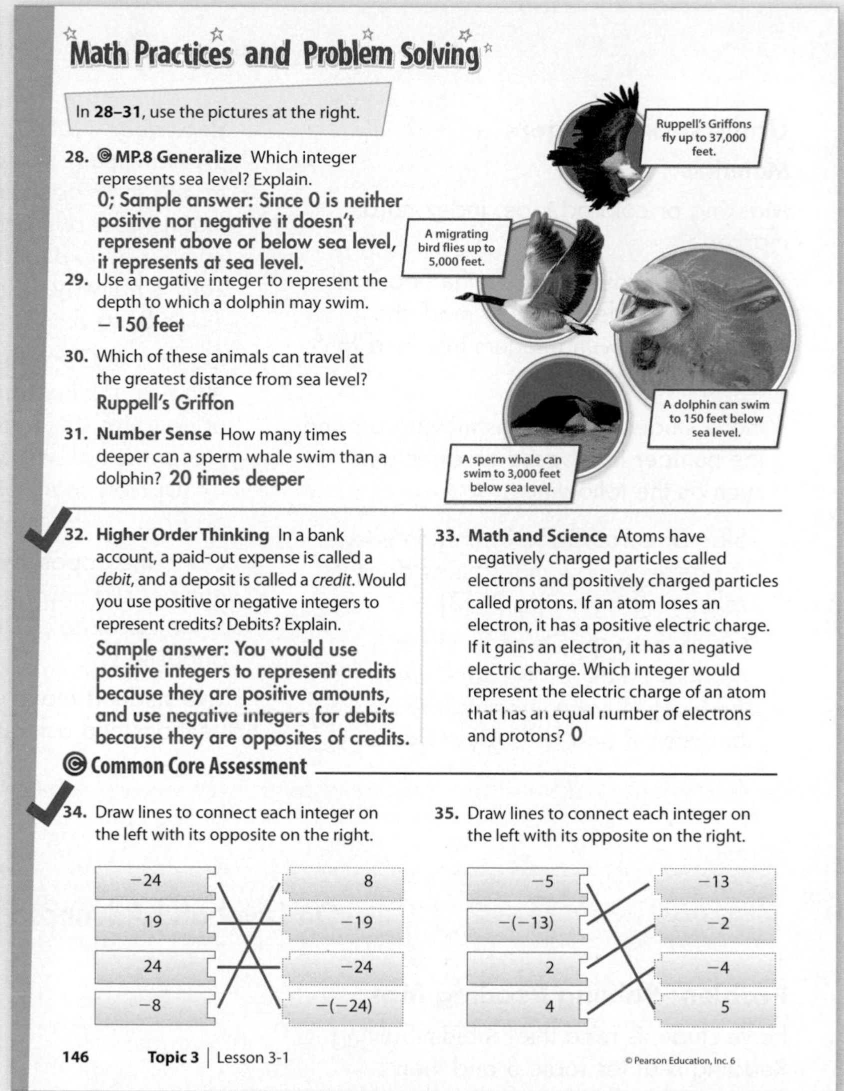

## Math Practices and Problem Solving

In **28–31**, use the pictures at the right.



28. **MP.8 Generalize** Which integer represents sea level? Explain.
**0; Sample answer: Since 0 is neither positive nor negative it doesn't represent above or below sea level, it represents at sea level.**
29. Use a negative integer to represent the depth to which a dolphin may swim.
**−150 feet**
30. Which of these animals can travel at the greatest distance from sea level?
**Ruppell's Griffon**
31. **Number Sense** How many times deeper can a sperm whale swim than a dolphin? **20 times deeper**
32. **Higher Order Thinking** In a bank account, a paid-out expense is called a *debit*, and a deposit is called a *credit*. Would you use positive or negative integers to represent credits? Debits? Explain.
**Sample answer: You would use positive integers to represent credits because they are positive amounts, and use negative integers for debits because they are opposites of credits.**
33. **Math and Science** Atoms have negatively charged particles called electrons and positively charged particles called protons. If an atom loses an electron, it has a positive electric charge. If it gains an electron, it has a negative electric charge. Which integer would represent the electric charge of an atom that has an equal number of electrons and protons? **0**

**Common Core Assessment**

34. Draw lines to connect each integer on the left with its opposite on the right.

| | |
|---|---|
| −24 | 8 |
| 19 | −19 |
| 24 | −24 |
| −8 | −(−24) |

35. Draw lines to connect each integer on the left with its opposite on the right.

| | |
|---|---|
| −5 | −13 |
| −(−13) | −2 |
| 2 | −4 |
| 4 | 5 |

146 Topic 3 | Lesson 3-1

© Pearson Education, Inc. 6

**Error Intervention: Item 8**

**If** students have difficulty finding the opposite of 0,

**then** ask: *Is there any number other than 0 located at the center of the number line between positive and negative numbers?* [No] Explain that instead of saying 0 has no opposite, you can say that 0 is its own opposite.

**Item 28 MP.8 Generalize** Some students may make a comparison with a thermometer. If 0°C is freezing, you can talk about temperatures that are above freezing or below freezing. Similarly, elevation can be described as above sea level or below sea level. So sea level should be represented by the integer 0.

**Reteaching** Assign Reteaching Set A on p. 175.

**Item 31 Number Sense** Students may note that 150 can be doubled to 300. This is a compatible number with 3,000. 3,000 is 10 times greater than 300. Since 150 was doubled, you can double 10 to answer the question. So, the sperm whale can swim 20 times deeper.

**Item 32 Higher Order Thinking** This problem helps students think about using integers to represent quantities in real-world contexts. Here, they make the connection between integers and financial terms such as *credit* and *debit*.

**Item 33 Math and Science** Students reason that a neutral particle that has neither a positive nor a negative charge can be represented by the integer 0.

**Items 32 and 33 Coherence** If students struggle to represent real-world contexts using integers, have them apply and extend what they know about number lines to help them model each situation.

**Multi-Step Problems** *Page 146 Item 31; Page 148 Item 17*

# ASSESS AND DIFFERENTIATE

Use the **QUICK CHECK** on the previous page to prescribe differentiated instruction.

**Intervention** 0–3 points on the Quick Check

**On-Level** 4 points on the Quick Check

**Advanced** 5 points on the Quick Check

## Intervention Activity 

### Understand Integers

**Materials**

Masking or colored tape, index cards, marker

- Create a number line on the floor with tape. Use index cards to mark the number line with integers from −6 to 6, at one-foot intervals.
- Have students take turns moving around the number line based on directions such as the following:

  Start at zero. Go to 3. *If each integer is one step, how many steps does it take to go from 0 to 3?* [3]

  Go to the opposite of 3. *What is another name for the opposite of 3?* [−3] *What number is halfway between 3 and −3?* [0] *How many steps does it take to go from 0 to −3?* [3] *How many steps does it take to go from 3 to its opposite?* [6] *How does that number of steps compare to the number 3? Explain.* [It is double. Since zero is halfway, 3 to 0 is 3 and 0 to −3 is 3, so 3 + 3 = 6.]

  Go to −4. Go to the opposite of −4. *What is another name for the opposite of negative 4?* [4, or positive 4] *What number is halfway between −4 and 4?* [0] *How many steps does it take to go from −4 to its opposite?* [8]

  Go to the opposite of zero. *What number did you land on?* [0] *What is the opposite of 0?* [Zero is its own opposite.]
- Have students make up their own directions and ask questions.

## Reteach I

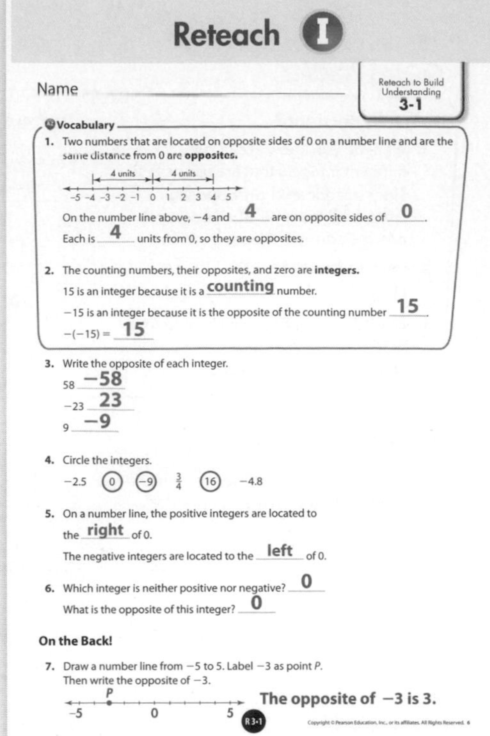

Name

Reteach to Build Understanding 3-1

**Vocabulary**

1. Two numbers that are located on opposite sides of 0 on a number line and are the same distance from 0 are **opposites.**

   4 units 4 units

   −5 −4 −3 −2 −1 0 1 2 3 4 5

   On the number line above, −4 and **4** are on opposite sides of **0**.
   Each is **4** units from 0, so they are opposites.

2. The counting numbers, their opposites, and zero are **integers.**
   15 is an integer because it is a **counting** number.
   −15 is an integer because it is the opposite of the counting number **15**.
   −(−15) = **15**

3. Write the opposite of each integer.
   58 **−58**
   −23 **23**
   9 **−9**

4. Circle the integers.
   −2.5 (0) (−9) $\frac{3}{4}$ (16) −4.8

5. On a number line, the positive integers are located to the **right** of 0.
   The negative integers are located to the **left** of 0.

6. Which integer is neither positive nor negative? **0**
   What is the opposite of this integer? **0**

**On the Back!**

7. Draw a number line from −5 to 5. Label −3 as point *P*. Then write the opposite of −3.

   P
   −5 0 5

   **The opposite of −3 is 3.**

R 3•1



## On-Level and Advanced Activity Centers 

### Problem-Solving Reading Mat

Have students read the Problem-Solving Reading Mat for Topic 3 and then complete Problem-Solving Reading Activity 3-1.

See the Problem-Solving Reading Activity Guide for other suggestions on how to use this mat.

**TIMING**

The time allocated to Step 3 will depend on the teacher's instructional decisions and differentiation routines.

 Help  Practice Buddy  Tools  Games

## Technology Center   

Tools Games

### Math Tools and Math Games

A link to a specific math tools activity or math game to use with this lesson is provided at PearsonRealize.com.

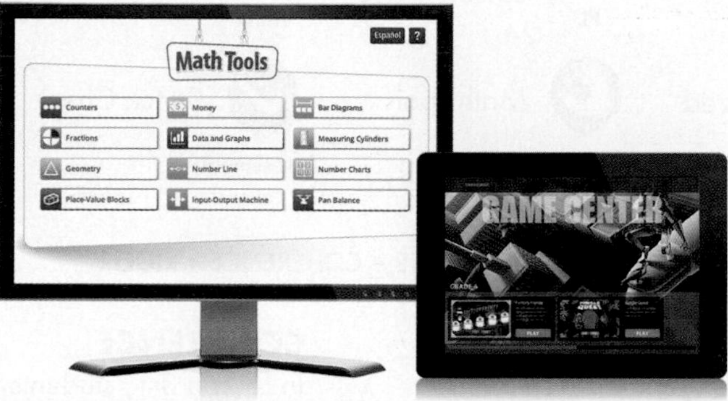


## Leveled Assignment  Items 1–16, 19–21  Items 4–13, 16–21  Items 4–21

Name ______

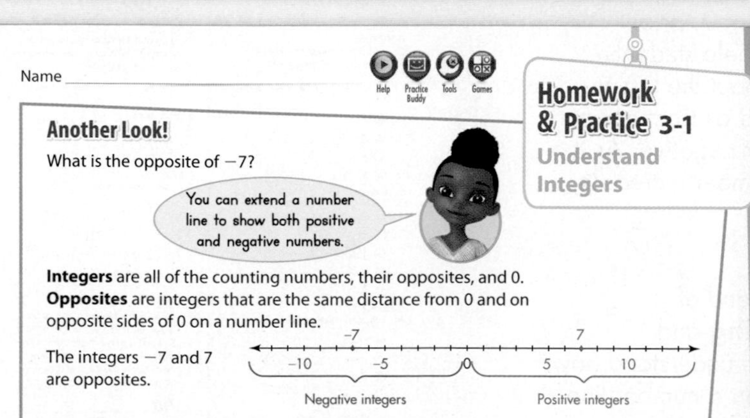
**Homework & Practice 3-1**
**Understand Integers**

**Another Look!**

What is the opposite of −7?



**Integers** are all of the counting numbers, their opposites, and 0.
**Opposites** are integers that are the same distance from 0 and on opposite sides of 0 on a number line.

The integers −7 and 7 are opposites.



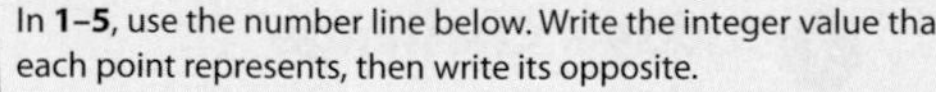
In **1–5**, use the number line below. Write the integer value that each point represents, then write its opposite.

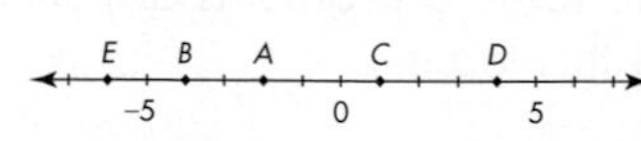

**1.** *A* **−2, 2** **2.** *B* **−4, 4** **3.** *C* **1, −1** **4.** *D* **4, −4** **5.** *E* **−6, 6**

In **6–10**, plot each point on the number line below.

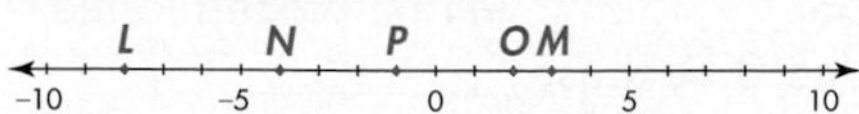


**6.** *L*(−8) **7.** *M*(3) **8.** *N*(−4) **9.** *O*(2) **10.** *P*(−1)

In **11–15**, write the opposite of each integer.

**11.** −12 **12**
**12.** 63 **−63**
**13.** −(−10) **−10**
**14.** 33 **−33**
**15.** −101 **101**



Mauna Loa, in Hawaii, is the largest above-sea-level volcano. In **16–17**, use the diagram of Mauna Loa.

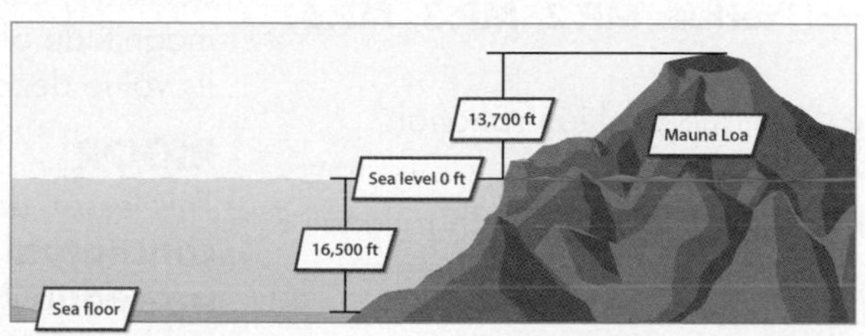


**16.** **MP.2 Reasoning** Use a negative integer to represent the depth, in feet, of the sea floor. **− 16,500**

**17.** Mauna Loa depresses the sea floor, resulting in 26,400 more feet added to its height. What is the total height of Mauna Loa? **56,600 ft**

**18.** **Higher Order Thinking** In math, a letter such as *p* can be assigned as a variable to represent an unknown value. Give an example of a value for *p* that results in −*p* being a positive integer. Explain your reasoning.
**Sample answer: *p* = −3; then −*p* is the opposite of −3, which is 3.**

**19.** Evaluate the expression $2\ell + 2w$ to find the perimeter of the rectangle.

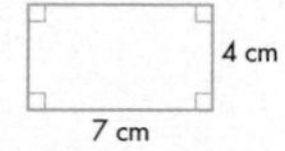


**2 • 7 + 2 • 4 = 14 + 8 = 22; The perimeter of the rectangle is 22 cm.**

### Common Core Assessment

**20.** Draw lines to connect each integer on the left with its opposite on the right.

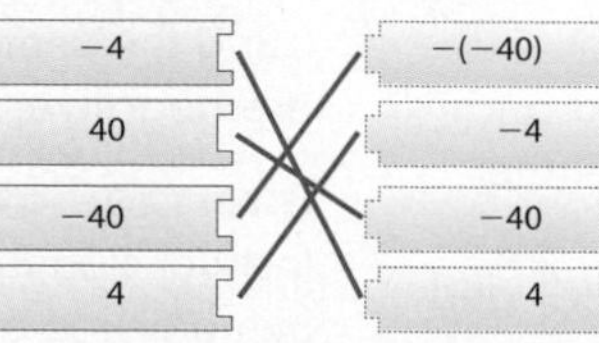

| | |
|---|---|
| −4 | −(−40) |
| 40 | −4 |
| −40 | −40 |
| 4 | 4 |

**21.** Draw lines to connect each integer on the left with its opposite on the right.

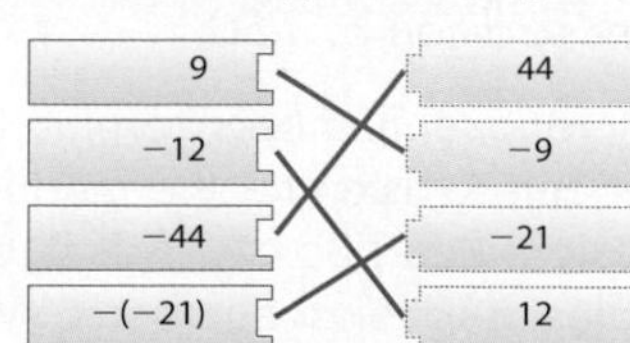

| | |
|---|---|
| 9 | 44 |
| −12 | −9 |
| −44 | −21 |
| −(−21) | 12 |

 

# LESSON 3-2

# RATIONAL NUMBERS ON A NUMBER LINE

## DIGITAL RESOURCES PearsonRealize.com

 eText — Student and Teacher eTexts

 PD — Listen and Look For Lesson Video

 Think — Today's Challenge

 Solve — Solve and Share

 Learn — Visual Learning Animation Plus

 Glossary — Animated Glossary

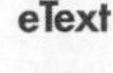 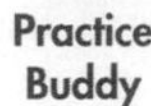 Practice Buddy — Online Personalized Practice

  Tools — Math Tools

 Assessment — Quick Check

 Help — Another Look Homework Video

 Games — Math Games

## LESSON OVERVIEW — FOCUS • COHERENCE • RIGOR

### FOCUS

**Domain 6.NS** The Number System

**Cluster 6.NS.C** Apply and extend previous understandings of numbers to the system of rational numbers.

**Content Standard 6.NS.C.6c** Find and position integers and other rational numbers on a horizontal or vertical number line diagram; find and position pairs of integers and other rational numbers on a coordinate plane.

**Mathematical Practices MP.2, MP.3, MP.6, MP.8**

**Objective** Find and position rational numbers on a number line.

**Essential Understanding** Each rational number can be associated with a unique point on the number line.

**Vocabulary** Rational number

**Materials** Number lines (Teaching Tool 13) (optional)

### COHERENCE

In Lesson 3-1, students located integers on a number line and used integers to describe real-world situations. In this lesson, students extend these skills to include other rational numbers. Since all rational numbers can be written as the fraction $\frac{a}{b}$, where $a$ and $b$ are integers and $b \neq 0$, prior knowledge of fractions will help students build understanding throughout the lesson. Rational numbers, expressed as fractions or decimals, can be positive or negative. As the magnitude of a negative number increases, its value decreases.

### RIGOR

This lesson emphasizes a blend of **conceptual understanding** and **procedural skill**. Students understand how to locate rational numbers on a number line. They learn to move left or right from zero, depending on the sign and magnitude of the number.

 PD Watch the Listen and Look For Lesson Video.

## MATH ANYTIME

### Daily Common Core Review

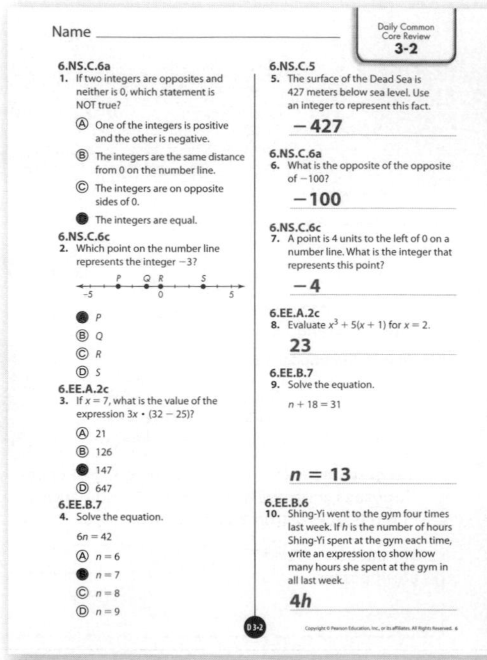

Name ____________

Daily Common Core Review 3-2

**6.NS.C.6a**

1. If two integers are opposites and neither is 0, which statement is NOT true?

   Ⓐ One of the integers is positive and the other is negative.

   Ⓑ The integers are the same distance from 0 on the number line.

   Ⓒ The integers are on opposite sides of 0.

   ● The integers are equal.

**6.NS.C.6c**

2. Which point on the number line represents the integer −3?

   

   ● P

   Ⓑ Q

   Ⓒ R

   Ⓓ S

**6.EE.A.2c**

3. If $x = 7$, what is the value of the expression $3x \cdot (32 - 25)$?

   Ⓐ 21

   Ⓑ 126

   ● 147

   Ⓓ 647

**6.EE.B.7**

4. Solve the equation.

   $6n = 42$

   Ⓐ $n = 6$

   ● $n = 7$

   Ⓒ $n = 8$

   Ⓓ $n = 9$

**6.NS.C.5**

5. The surface of the Dead Sea is 427 meters below sea level. Use an integer to represent this fact.

   **−427**

**6.NS.C.6a**

6. What is the opposite of the opposite of −100?

   **−100**

**6.NS.C.6c**

7. A point is 4 units to the left of 0 on a number line. What is the integer that represents this point?

   **−4**

**6.EE.A.2c**

8. Evaluate $x^3 + 5(x + 1)$ for $x = 2$.

   **23**

**6.EE.B.7**

9. Solve the equation.

   $n + 18 = 31$

   $n = 13$

**6.EE.B.6**

10. Shing-Yi went to the gym four times last week. If $h$ is the number of hours Shing-Yi spent at the gym each time, write an expression to show how many hours she spent at the gym in all last week.

   **4h**

D 3-2



### Today's Challenge

Think Use the Topic 3 problems any time during this topic.

## ENGLISH LANGUAGE LEARNERS

**Listening** Learn new academic expressions.

*Use with the Visual Learning Bridge on Student's Edition p. 150.*

Write "*rational numbers*" on the board and tell students to listen for the meaning of the expression. Read Box A. Ask students to give examples of rational numbers. Write $-\frac{4}{3}$ and $-1.5$. *Are $-\frac{4}{3}$ and $-1.5$ rational numbers?*

**Beginning** Reread Box A to students. Draw the horizontal number line. Point to $-\frac{4}{3}$ and $-1.5$. *On which side of the 0 will these rational numbers be placed?* Students will respond by pointing to the left of 0. *Why?* Instruct students to listen to partners respond using the sentence stem: "The _____ _____ are negative."

**Intermediate** Reread Box A with students. Instruct students to draw the horizontal number line and write $-\frac{4}{3}$ and $-1.5$ in their notes. Ask students to share with partners which side of the 0 the numbers will be placed on. *Why?* Instruct students to listen to partners respond using the sentence stem: "The ____ _____ will be placed to the_____ of the 0 because __________."

**Advanced** Instruct students to reread Box A with partners. Ask students to draw the horizontal number line and write $-\frac{4}{3}$ and $-1.5$ in their notes. Ask students to listen to partners explain which side of the 0 the rational numbers $-\frac{4}{3}$ and $-1.5$ will be placed on and why.

**Summarize** What are *rational numbers?*

# DEVELOP: PROBLEM-BASED LEARNING

**COHERENCE: Engage learners by connecting prior knowledge to new ideas.**
Students extend what they know about locating integers and positive fractions on a number line to locate a negative rational number on a number line.

10–15 min

Solve

## BEFORE

**1. Pose the Solve-and-Share Problem**
**MP.2 Reason Quantitatively** Listen and look for students who move down from zero on the vertical number line to plot the negative rational number. They reason quantitatively to locate the position three-fourths of the distance to $-1$ in order to plot $-\frac{3}{4}$.

**2. Build Understanding**
*Using fraction terminology, explain the meaning of $\frac{3}{4}$ in relation to a whole.* [The denominator, 4, means the whole is divided into four equal parts. The numerator, 3, indicates three of the four parts.] *How do you represent a fraction on the number line?* [Sample answer: Divide each whole unit into the correct number of equal parts and mark the intervals to represent the fraction.]

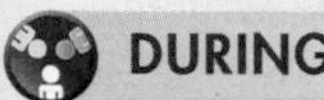

## DURING

**3. Ask Guiding Questions As Needed**
*What does the negative sign in front of $\frac{3}{4}$ mean?* [The opposite of $\frac{3}{4}$] *Where do you find negative numbers on a vertical number line?* [Below the 0]

## AFTER

**4. Share and Discuss Solutions**
Start with students' solutions. If needed, project Cordell's work to discuss how to plot negative fractions on a number line.

**5. Transition to the Visual Learning Bridge**
*Just like a counting number, a positive fraction has an opposite that can be associated with a unique point on the negative part of a number line.*

**6. Extension for Early Finishers**
*How would you write $-\frac{3}{4}$ as a decimal?* [$-0.75$]

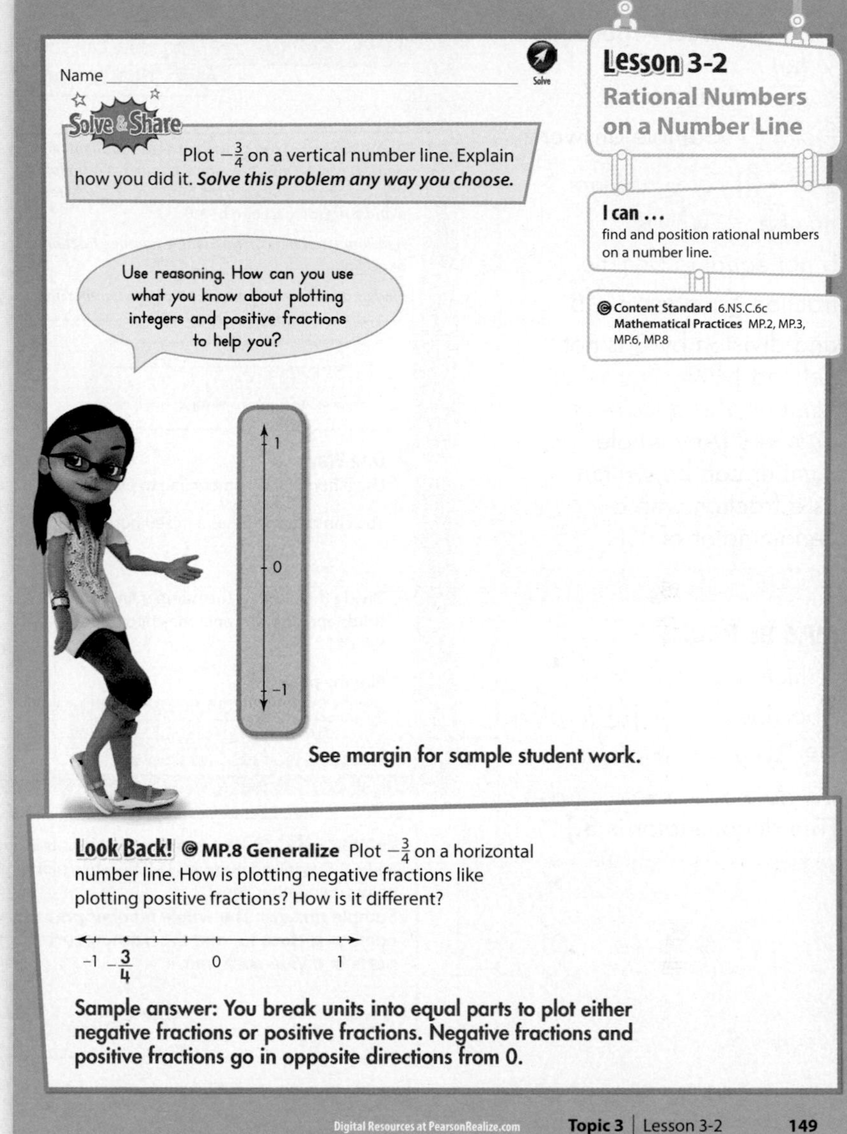

Name
Solve & Share
Plot $-\frac{3}{4}$ on a vertical number line. Explain how you did it. *Solve this problem any way you choose.*
Lesson 3-2
Rational Numbers on a Number Line
I can ...
find and position rational numbers on a number line.
Content Standard 6.NS.C.6c
Mathematical Practices MP.2, MP.3, MP.6, MP.8
Use reasoning. How can you use what you know about plotting integers and positive fractions to help you?
1
0
-1
See margin for sample student work.
Look Back! MP.8 Generalize Plot $-\frac{3}{4}$ on a horizontal number line. How is plotting negative fractions like plotting positive fractions? How is it different?
-1 $-\frac{3}{4}$ 0 1
Sample answer: You break units into equal parts to plot either negative fractions or positive fractions. Negative fractions and positive fractions go in opposite directions from 0.
Digital Resources at PearsonRealize.com
Topic 3 | Lesson 3-2
149


### Analyze Student Work

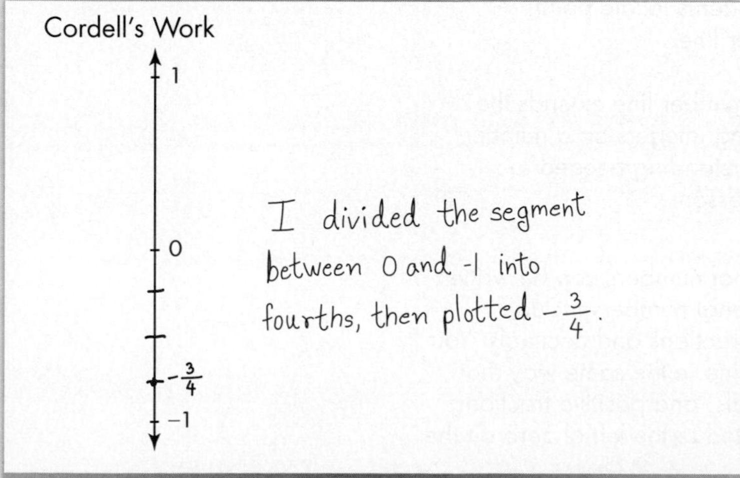

Cordell's Work
1
0
$-\frac{3}{4}$
-1
I divided the segment between 0 and -1 into fourths, then plotted $-\frac{3}{4}$.


Cordell correctly plots $-\frac{3}{4}$, dividing the unit into fourths, and gives a complete explanation.

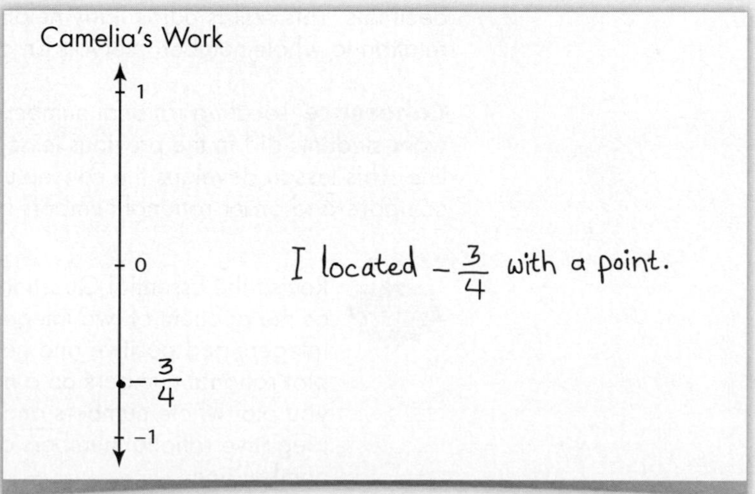


Camelia also correctly plots $-\frac{3}{4}$, but her process and explanation are less precise.

# DEVELOP: VISUAL LEARNING

The *Visual Learning Bridge* connects students' thinking in Solve & Share to important math ideas in the lesson. Use the *Visual Learning Bridge* to make these ideas explicit. Also available as a *Visual Learning Animation Plus* at PearsonRealize.com

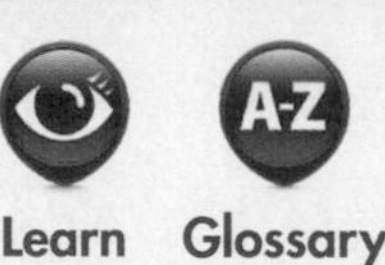


**MP.3 Construct Arguments** *What is an example of a number that is in the form $\frac{a}{b}$ or $-\frac{a}{b}$?* [Sample answers: $\frac{3}{5}$ or $-\frac{8}{9}$] *For a rational number $\frac{a}{b}$, why is b not equal to 0?* [The fraction $\frac{a}{b}$ means $a \div b$, and division by 0 is not defined.] *Why is a whole number also a rational number?* [Any whole number can be written as a fraction with a denominator of 1.]

**MP.6 Be Precise** *Which number is the opposite of $-\frac{4}{3}$?* [$\frac{4}{3}$] *To plot $-\frac{4}{3}$, why is it helpful to divide the units into thirds?* [The denominator is 3.]

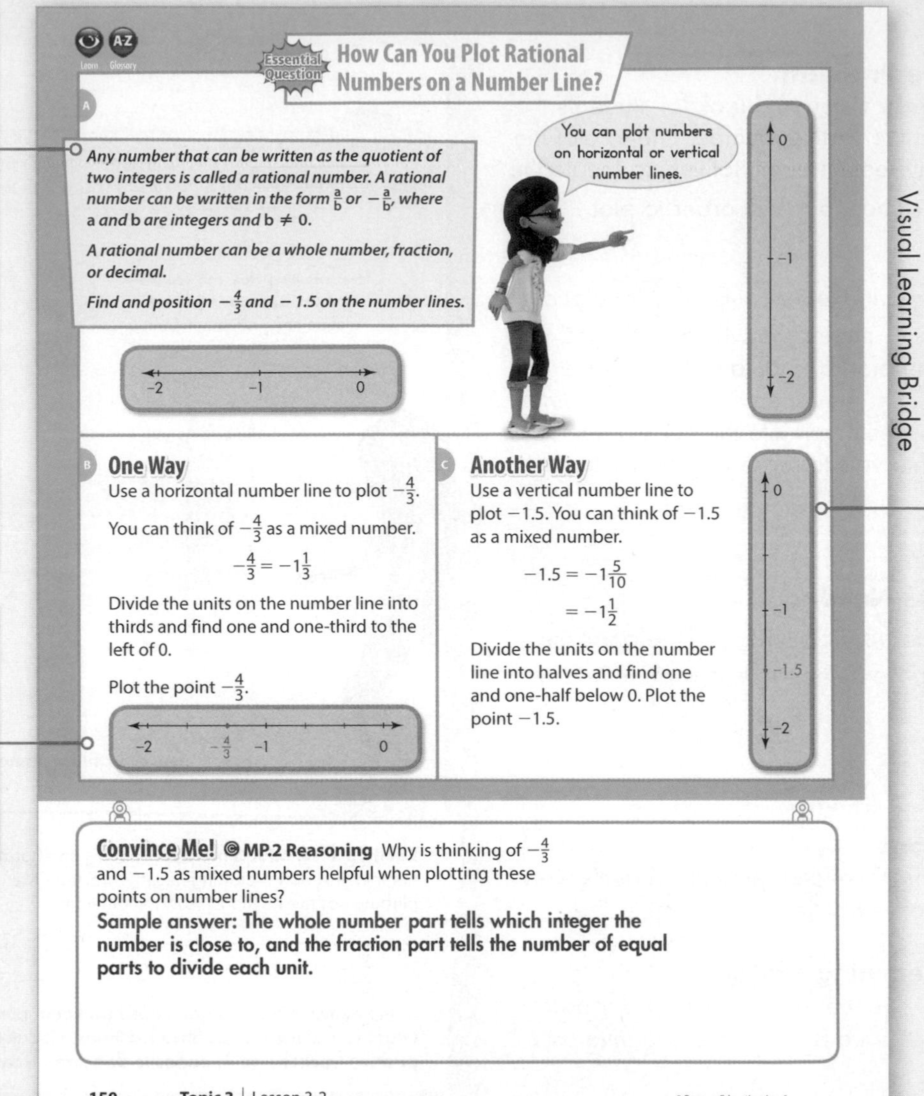

Essential Question **How Can You Plot Rational Numbers on a Number Line?**

A

*Any number that can be written as the quotient of two integers is called a rational number. A rational number can be written in the form $\frac{a}{b}$ or $-\frac{a}{b}$, where a and b are integers and $b \neq 0$.*

*A rational number can be a whole number, fraction, or decimal.*

*Find and position $-\frac{4}{3}$ and $-1.5$ on the number lines.*

You can plot numbers on horizontal or vertical number lines.

B **One Way**
Use a horizontal number line to plot $-\frac{4}{3}$.

You can think of $-\frac{4}{3}$ as a mixed number.

$$-\frac{4}{3} = -1\frac{1}{3}$$

Divide the units on the number line into thirds and find one and one-third to the left of 0.

Plot the point $-\frac{4}{3}$.

C **Another Way**
Use a vertical number line to plot $-1.5$. You can think of $-1.5$ as a mixed number.

$$-1.5 = -1\frac{5}{10}$$
$$= -1\frac{1}{2}$$

Divide the units on the number line into halves and find one and one-half below 0. Plot the point $-1.5$.

**Convince Me!** MP.2 Reasoning Why is thinking of $-\frac{4}{3}$ and $-1.5$ as mixed numbers helpful when plotting these points on number lines?
**Sample answer: The whole number part tells which integer the number is close to, and the fraction part tells the number of equal parts to divide each unit.**

150 Topic 3 | Lesson 3-2 © Pearson Education, Inc. 6

Visual Learning Bridge

**MP.3 Construct Arguments** *Why is $-1.5$ a rational number?* [It can be written as the quotient of two integers, $-\frac{3}{2}$.]

**Prevent Misconceptions** (RtI 1)
Explain that rational numbers are associated with unique points on a number line. Each unique point can be written as either a fraction or as a decimal. Equivalent fractions and decimals are different ways of writing the same number.

**Convince Me! MP.2 Reason Quantitatively** Mathematically proficient students can convert between fractions, mixed numbers, and decimals. This skill is particularly helpful as students locate points in relation to whole-number intervals on a number line.

**Coherence** Locating rational numbers on a number line extends the work students did in the previous lesson locating integers on a number line. This lesson develops the conceptual understanding needed to compare and order rational numbers in later lessons.

Revisit the Essential Question. Rational numbers can be written as the quotient of two integers. Rational numbers include integers and positive and negative fractions and decimals. You plot rational numbers on a number line in the same way that you plot whole numbers and decimals, and positive fractions. Negative rational numbers are located to the left of zero on the number line.

PEARSON realize. PearsonRealize.com

Practice Buddy  Tools  Assessment

20–30 min

**QUICK CHECK**

Check mark indicates items for prescribing differentiation on the next page. Item 8 is worth 1 point. Items 20 and 21 are worth up to 2 points.

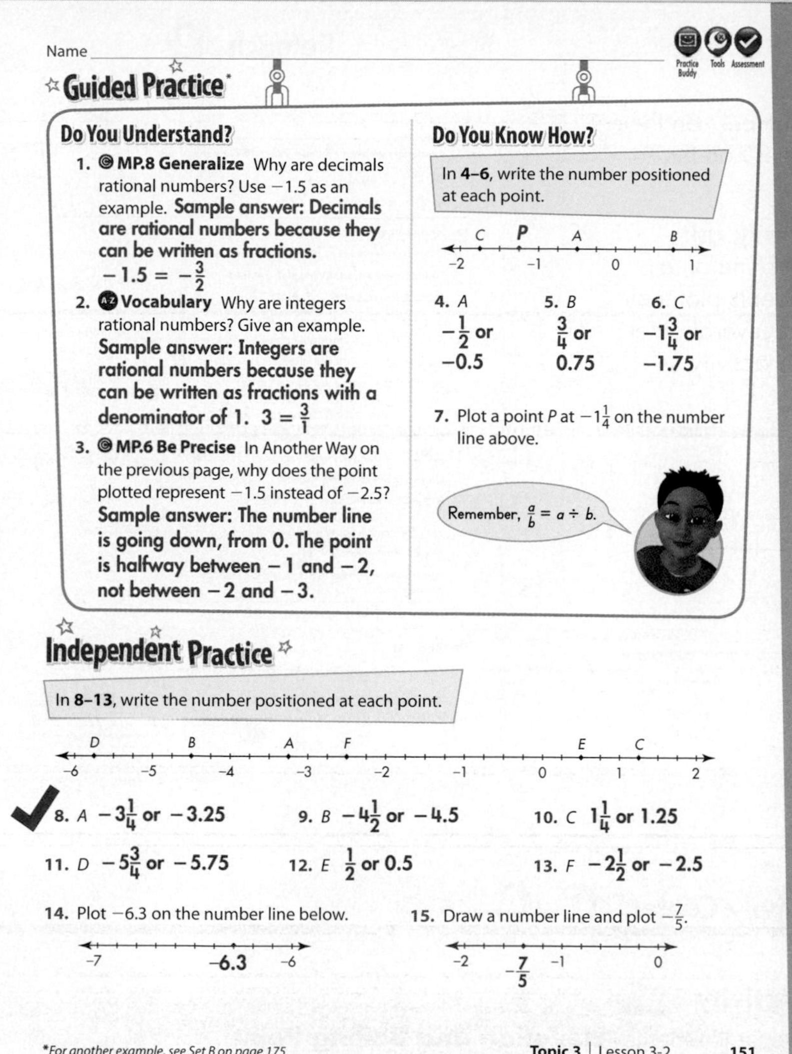

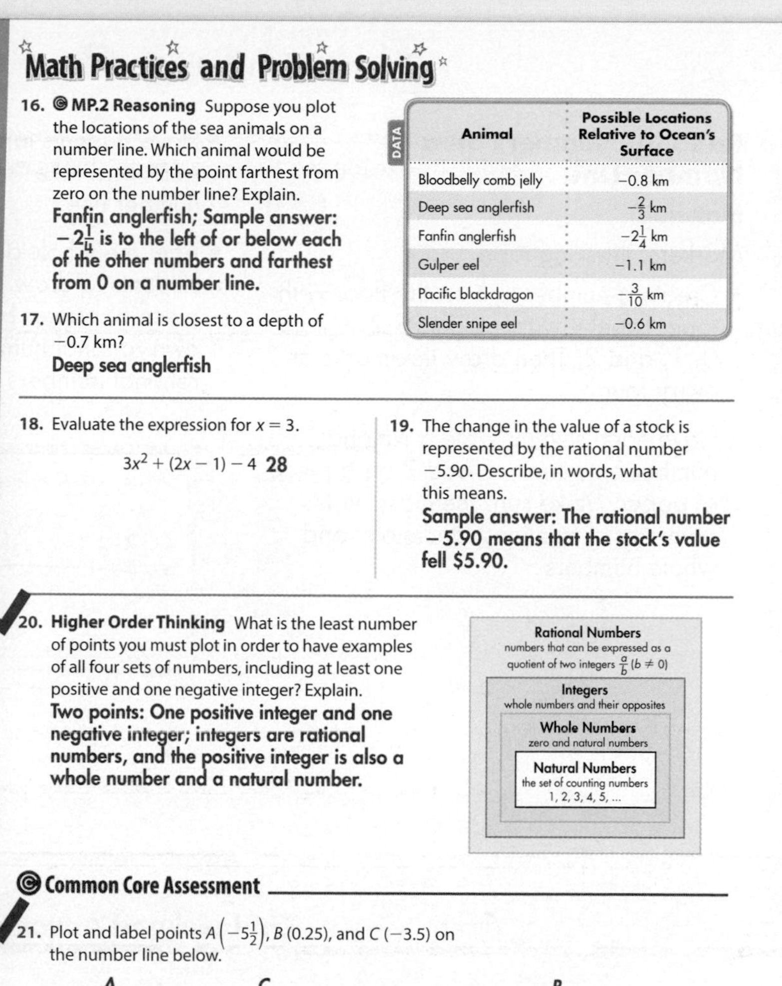

### Error Intervention: Item 2

**If** students have difficulty finding an example,

**then** have them read the definition of a rational number. *Why does a whole number not appear to meet the definition of a rational number?* [Sample answers: It is not a fraction. It is missing a denominator.] *How can you write the whole number 3 as an equivalent fraction?* [Sample answers: $\frac{6}{2}$, $\frac{12}{4}$, $\frac{3}{1}$]

**Reteaching** Assign Reteaching Set B on p. 175.

**Item 16 MP.2 Reason Quantitatively** Because the table includes only negative numbers, students will reason that they should identify the least number. The least negative number will have the greatest magnitude. The problem suggests an understanding of absolute value, which is a concept that will be formalized later in this topic.

**Items 16 and 19 Coherence** In the previous lesson, students used integers to describe quantities in real-world situations. These items further develop students' ability to relate positive and negative numbers to the real world.

**Item 20 Higher Order Thinking** This item checks whether students understand the subsets of rational numbers. They should conclude that a positive integer is both a whole number and a natural number.

**Multi-Step Problems** *Page 152 Items 18 and 20; Page 154 Item 21*

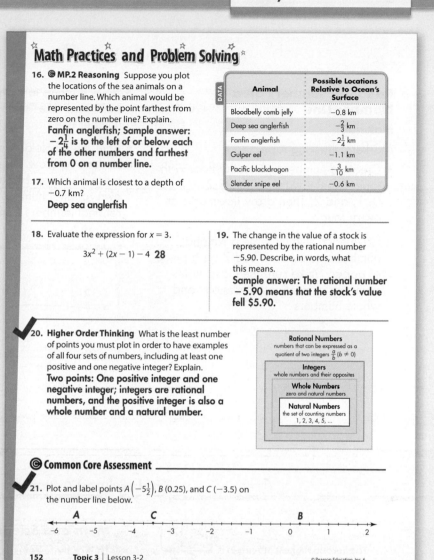

# ASSESS AND DIFFERENTIATE

Use the **QUICK CHECK** on the previous page to prescribe differentiated instruction.

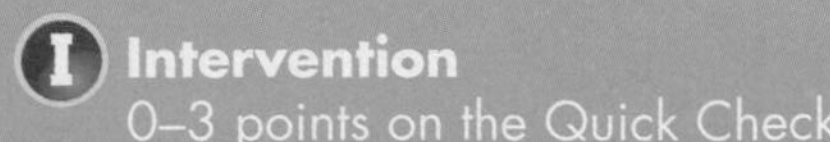

**Intervention**
0–3 points on the Quick Check

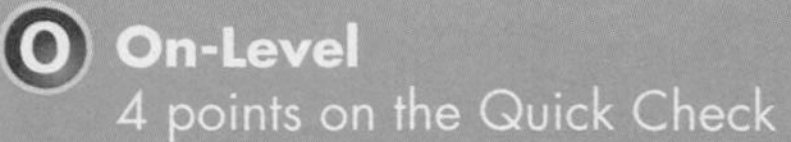

**On-Level**
4 points on the Quick Check

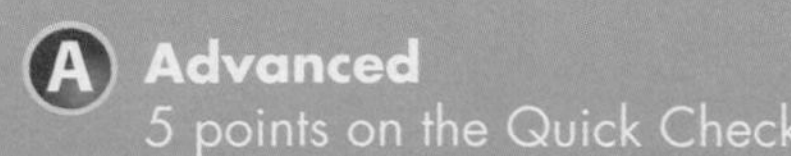

**Advanced**
5 points on the Quick Check

## Intervention Activity 

### Rational Numbers on a Number Line

**Materials**

Markers, masking tape

- Create a number line on the floor with tape. Label it with integers −2, −1, 0, 1, and 2. Then draw tick marks at every fourth.
- Have each student write a rational number between −2 and 2 on a piece of paper. Make sure the class writes a variety of fractions, decimals, and whole numbers.
- Have students tape the numbers on their shirts and take "their places" on the number line.
- After the whole-group activity, ask students to draw a number line on a piece of paper. Have students plot their own rational number and several other rational numbers from the activity.

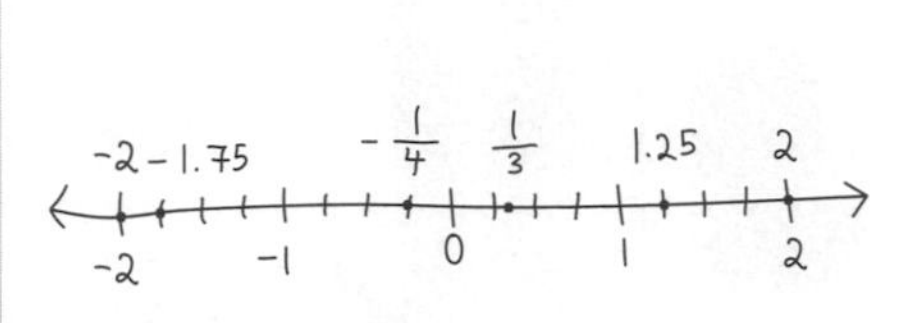


## Reteach I

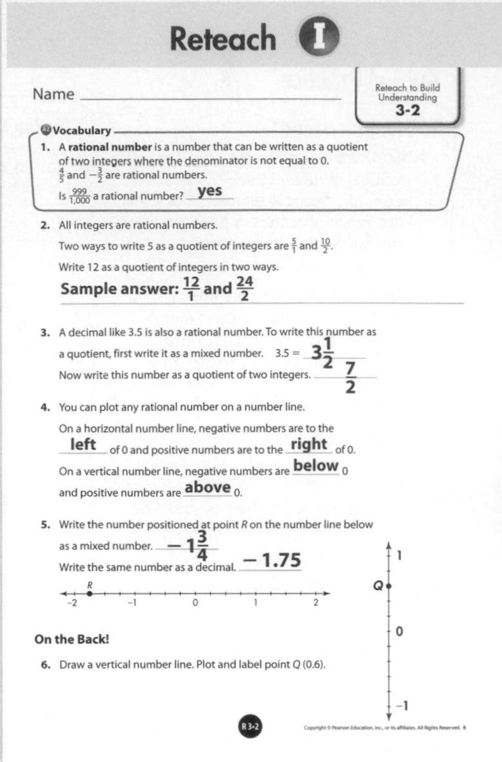

Name ______________

Reteach to Build Understanding 3-2

**Vocabulary**

1. A **rational number** is a number that can be written as a quotient of two integers where the denominator is not equal to 0. $\frac{4}{5}$ and $-\frac{3}{2}$ are rational numbers.
   Is $\frac{999}{1{,}000}$ a rational number? **yes**
2. All integers are rational numbers.
   Two ways to write 5 as a quotient of integers are $\frac{5}{1}$ and $\frac{10}{2}$.
   Write 12 as a quotient of integers in two ways.
   **Sample answer: $\frac{12}{1}$ and $\frac{24}{2}$**
3. A decimal like 3.5 is also a rational number. To write this number as a quotient, first write it as a mixed number. 3.5 = **$3\frac{1}{2}$**
   Now write this number as a quotient of two integers. **$\frac{7}{2}$**
4. You can plot any rational number on a number line.
   On a horizontal number line, negative numbers are to the **left** of 0 and positive numbers are to the **right** of 0.
   On a vertical number line, negative numbers are **below** 0 and positive numbers are **above** 0.
5. Write the number positioned at point *R* on the number line below as a mixed number. **$-1\frac{3}{4}$**
   Write the same number as a decimal. **−1.75**

**On the Back!**

6. Draw a vertical number line. Plot and label point *Q* (0.6).

R 3-2

Copyright © Pearson Education, Inc., or its affiliates. All Rights Reserved.

## On-Level and Advanced Activity Centers  

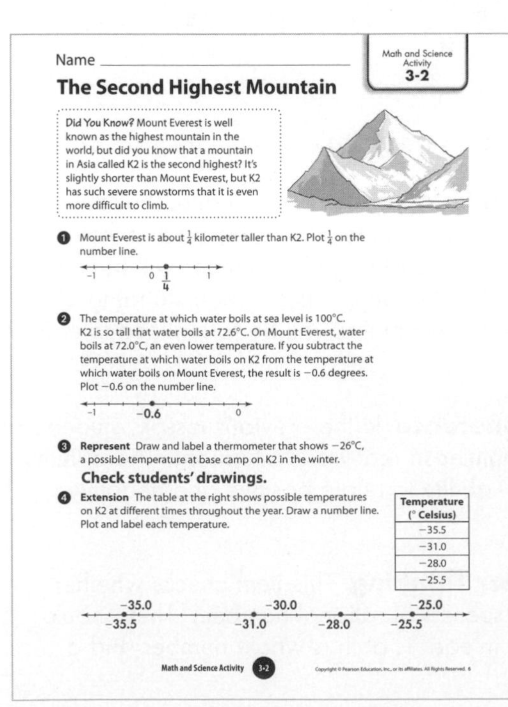

Name ______________

Math and Science Activity 3-2

**The Second Highest Mountain**

**Did You Know?** Mount Everest is well known as the highest mountain in the world, but did you know that a mountain in Asia called K2 is the second highest? It's slightly shorter than Mount Everest, but K2 has such severe snowstorms that it is even more difficult to climb.

1. Mount Everest is about $\frac{1}{4}$ kilometer taller than K2. Plot $\frac{1}{4}$ on the number line.
2. The temperature at which water boils at sea level is 100°C. K2 is so tall that water boils at 72.6°C. On Mount Everest, water boils at 72.0°C, an even lower temperature. If you subtract the temperature at which water boils on K2 from the temperature at which water boils on Mount Everest, the result is −0.6 degrees. Plot −0.6 on the number line.
3. **Represent** Draw and label a thermometer that shows −26°C, a possible temperature at base camp on K2 in the winter.
   **Check students' drawings.**
4. **Extension** The table at the right shows possible temperatures on K2 at different times throughout the year. Draw a number line. Plot and label each temperature.

| Temperature (° Celsius) |
|---|
| −35.5 |
| −31.0 |
| −28.0 |
| −25.5 |

Math and Science Activity 3-2

Copyright © Pearson Education, Inc., or its affiliates. All Rights Reserved.

### Math and Science Activity STEM

This activity revisits the science theme, **Elevation and Boiling Point**, introduced on page 139 in the Student's Edition.

### Sample Student Work

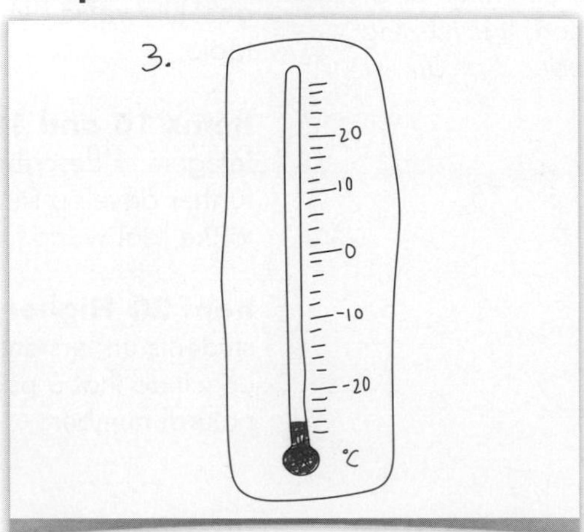

**TIMING**

The time allocated to Step 3 will depend on the teacher's instructional decisions and differentiation routines.

15–30 min

realize. PearsonRealize.com

 Help  Practice Buddy Tools  Games

## Technology Center   

 Tools 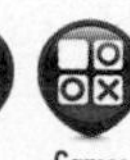 Games

### Math Tools and Math Games

A link to a specific math tools activity or math game to use with this lesson is provided at PearsonRealize.com.

## Leveled Assignment

 Items 1–10, 17–19, 22, 24  Items 5–12, 17–20, 22–24  Items 5–8, 13–16, 18–24

Name ______________________

Help Practice Buddy Tools Games

**Homework & Practice 3-2**
**Rational Numbers on a Number Line**

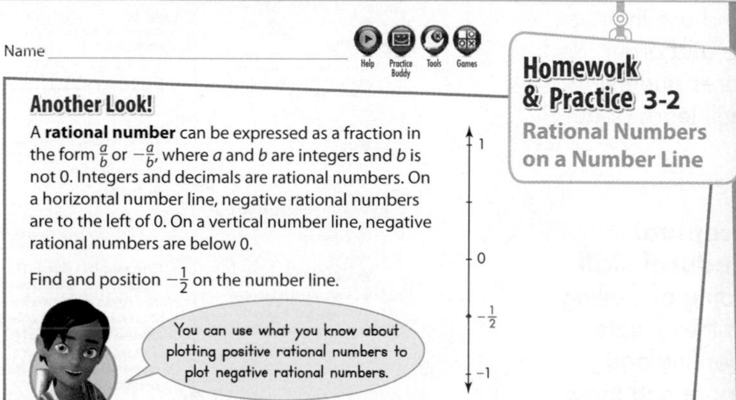

**Another Look!**

A **rational number** can be expressed as a fraction in the form $\frac{a}{b}$ or $-\frac{a}{b}$, where $a$ and $b$ are integers and $b$ is not 0. Integers and decimals are rational numbers. On a horizontal number line, negative rational numbers are to the left of 0. On a vertical number line, negative rational numbers are below 0.

Find and position $-\frac{1}{2}$ on the number line.



In **1–8**, write the number positioned at each point on the number line at the right.

1. $A$ $\frac{3}{4}$ **or 0.75**
2. $B$ $1\frac{1}{2}$ **or 1.5**
3. $C$ $-2\frac{3}{4}$ **or −2.75**
4. $D$ $-1\frac{1}{4}$ **or −1.25**
5. $E$ $2\frac{1}{2}$ **or 2.5**
6. $F$ $-\frac{1}{4}$ **or −0.25**
7. $G$ $-2\frac{1}{4}$ **or −2.25**
8. $H$ $\frac{1}{2}$ **or 0.5**

In **9–16**, plot each point on the number line at the right.

9. $S(2.75)$
10. $T\left(\frac{1}{4}\right)$
11. $U\left(-2\frac{1}{2}\right)$
12. $V(2.25)$
13. $W\left(1\frac{3}{4}\right)$
14. $X(-0.75)$
15. $Y$ −1.75
16. $Z\left(-\frac{3}{1}\right)$

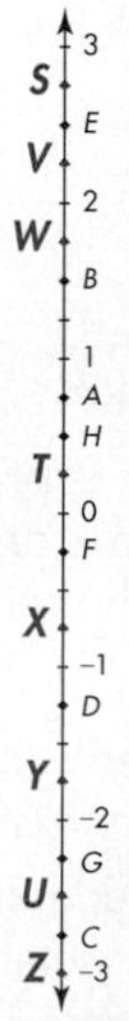

Number line (vertical): S, 3, E, V, 2, W, B, 1, A, H, T, 0, F, X, −1, D, Y, −2, G, U, C, Z, −3

17. Plot −8.7 on the number line below.

−9 **−8.7** −8

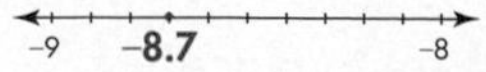

18. Draw a number line and plot $-\frac{5}{3}$.

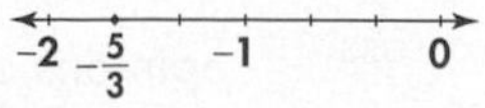

**−2 $-\frac{5}{3}$ −1 0**



19. **MP.2 Reasoning** Suppose you plot the lengths in the table on a number line. Which track member's long jump length would be represented by the point closest, but not equal to, zero on the number line? Explain.
**Ann; Sample answer: The other lengths are farther than +2 units from zero.**

DATA

| Track Members | Long Jump Length Relative to State Qualifying Distance |
|---|---|
| Theresa | −5.625 in. |
| Ann | 2 in. |
| Shirley | −3 in. |
| Delia | 0 in. |

20. Delia's relative long jump length was recorded as 0. What does this mean?
**Sample answer: This means that there was no difference in the lengths of Delia's long jump and the state qualifying jump.**

21. **MP.3 Construct Arguments** Which track members did **NOT** qualify for the state championship? Construct an argument to explain how you know.
**Theresa and Shirley; Their relative jumps were negative, which means that they were shorter than the qualifying distance.**

22. **MP.2 Reasoning** Find a number that has exactly 7 different prime factors. Explain how you found it.
**Sample answer: 510,510; I multiplied the first 7 prime numbers.**
**$2 \cdot 3 \cdot 5 \cdot 7 \cdot 11 \cdot 13 \cdot 17 = 510{,}510$**

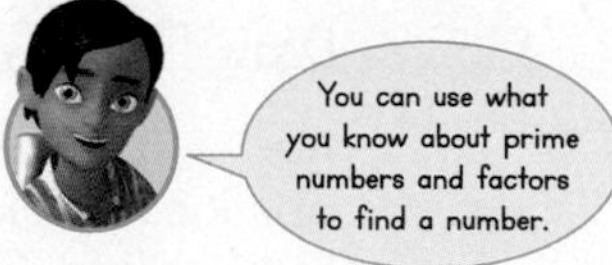

You can use what you know about prime numbers and factors to find a number.

23. **Higher Order Thinking** Tom is thinking of a number. He says that the opposite of the opposite of the number is −12.4. Write the number Tom is thinking of as a mixed number. Explain.
**$-12\frac{2}{5}$; Sample answer: The opposite of the opposite is the number itself; $-12.4 = -12\frac{4}{10}$ or $-12\frac{2}{5}$.**

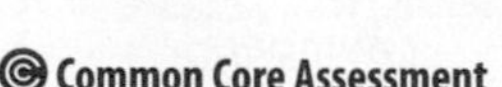

**Common Core Assessment**

24. Plot and label points $X\left(-4\frac{1}{4}\right)$, $Y(-2.75)$, and $Z\left(1\frac{1}{2}\right)$ on the number line below.

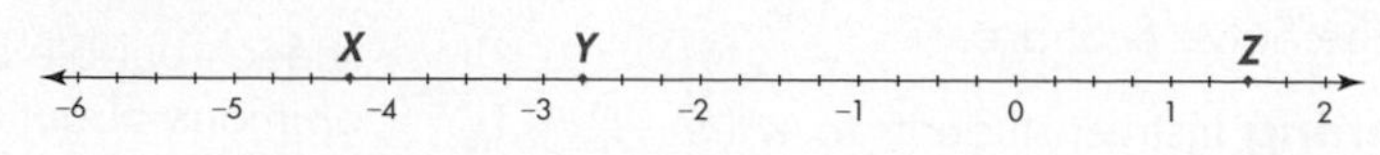

# LESSON 3-3

# COMPARE AND ORDER RATIONAL NUMBERS

## DIGITAL RESOURCES PearsonRealize.com

Student and Teacher eTexts (eText)

Listen and Look For Lesson Video (PD)

Today's Challenge (Think)

Solve and Share (Solve)

Visual Learning Animation Plus (Learn)

Animated Glossary (Glossary)

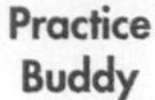
Online Personalized Practice (Practice Buddy)

Math Tools (Tools)

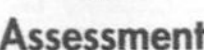
Quick Check (Assessment)

Another Look Homework Video (Help)

Math Games (Games)

## LESSON OVERVIEW  FOCUS • COHERENCE • RIGOR

### FOCUS

**Domain 6.NS** The Number System

**Cluster 6.NS.C** Apply and extend previous understandings of numbers to the system of rational numbers.

**Content Standard 6.NS.C.7a** Interpret statements of inequality as statements about the relative position of two numbers on a number line diagram. *For example, interpret $-3 > -7$ as a statement that $-3$ is located to the right of $-7$ on a number line oriented from left to right.* Also **6.NS.C.7b**.

**Mathematical Practices MP.1, MP.2, MP.3, MP.4, MP.5, MP.8**

**Objective** Compare and order rational numbers.

**Essential Understanding** A number to the right of another on the number line is the greater number.

**Materials** Number lines (Teaching Tool 13) (optional)

### COHERENCE

In Grades 3 and 4, students used visual models, such as a number line, to understand, compare, and order fractions. In this lesson, students apply and extend these skills as they examine rational numbers in both fraction and decimal forms. They use what they know about plotting rational numbers on a number line and use their relative positions to compare and order rational numbers. This prepares students for Lesson 3-4, where they will learn about absolute value.

### RIGOR

This lesson emphasizes **conceptual understanding** and **procedural skill**. Students use their understanding of plotting integers on a number line as they locate rational numbers on a number line and use the visual model to compare and order them. They apply this understanding as they use rational numbers to represent real-world situations.

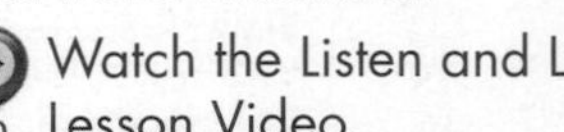
Watch the Listen and Look For Lesson Video.

## MATH ANYTIME

### Daily Common Core Review

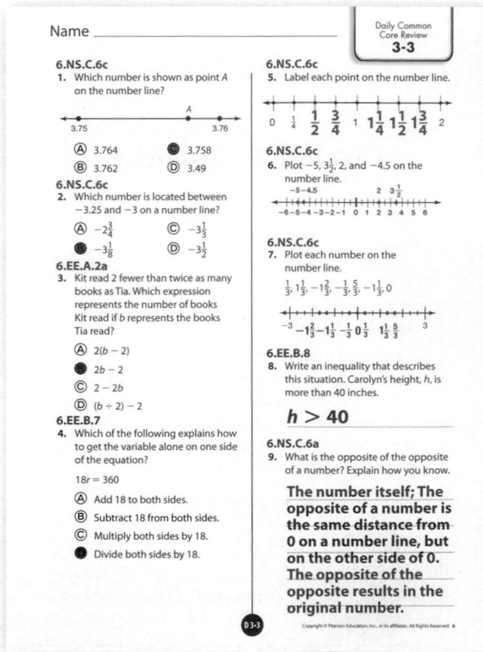
Name ______

Daily Common Core Review 3-3

6.NS.C.6c
1. Which number is shown as point $A$ on the number line?

3.75 — A — 3.76

Ⓐ 3.764 ● 3.758
Ⓑ 3.762 Ⓓ 3.49

6.NS.C.6c
2. Which number is located between $-3.25$ and $-3$ on a number line?

Ⓐ $-2\frac{3}{4}$ Ⓒ $-3\frac{1}{3}$
● $-3\frac{1}{8}$ Ⓓ $-3\frac{1}{2}$

6.EE.A.2a
3. Kit read 2 fewer than twice as many books as Tia. Which expression represents the number of books Kit read if $b$ represents the books Tia read?

Ⓐ $2(b - 2)$
● $2b - 2$
Ⓒ $2 - 2b$
Ⓓ $(b \div 2) - 2$

6.EE.B.7
4. Which of the following explains how to get the variable alone on one side of the equation?

$18r = 360$

Ⓐ Add 18 to both sides.
Ⓑ Subtract 18 from both sides.
Ⓒ Multiply both sides by 18.
● Divide both sides by 18.

6.NS.C.6c
5. Label each point on the number line.

0 $\frac{1}{4}$ $\frac{1}{2}$ $\frac{3}{4}$ 1 $1\frac{1}{4}$ $1\frac{1}{2}$ $1\frac{3}{4}$ 2

6.NS.C.6c
6. Plot $-5$, $3\frac{1}{2}$, 2, and $-4.5$ on the number line.

$-5$ $-4.5$ 2 $3\frac{1}{2}$
$-6$ $-5$ $-4$ $-3$ $-2$ $-1$ 0 1 2 3 4 5 6

6.NS.C.6c
7. Plot each number on the number line.

$\frac{1}{3}$, $1\frac{1}{3}$, $-1\frac{2}{3}$, $-\frac{1}{3}$, $\frac{5}{3}$, $-1\frac{1}{3}$, 0

$-3$ $-1\frac{2}{3}$ $-1\frac{1}{3}$ $-\frac{1}{3}$ 0 $\frac{1}{3}$ $1\frac{1}{3}$ $\frac{5}{3}$ 3

6.EE.B.8
8. Write an inequality that describes this situation. Carolyn's height, $h$, is more than 40 inches.

$h > 40$

6.NS.C.6a
9. What is the opposite of the opposite of a number? Explain how you know.

**The number itself; The opposite of a number is the same distance from 0 on a number line, but on the other side of 0. The opposite of the opposite results in the original number.**

D 3-3



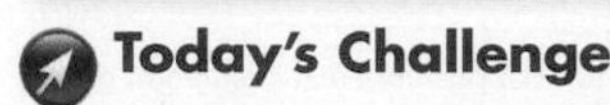
### Today's Challenge

Think Use the Topic 3 problems any time during this topic.

## ENGLISH LANGUAGE LEARNERS 

**Speaking** Express opinions.

*Use with the Solve & Share on Student's Edition p. 155.*

Instruct students to share information about positive and negative rational numbers. *Are negative rational numbers greater than 0? Is 0 a positive or negative rational number?* Read the Solve & Share.

**Beginning** Instruct students to write $-\frac{2}{3}$, $-1$, $\frac{1}{4}$, and $-0.5$ on index cards, and divide them into stacks of negative and positive numbers. Read the speech bubble aloud. Draw $-1$ 0 1. Hold up $-\frac{2}{3}$. *Where does $-\frac{2}{3}$ go?* Ask students to express their opinions by placing their cards on the number line. Continue with the remaining numbers.

**Intermediate** Instruct students to write $-\frac{2}{3}$, $-1$, $\frac{1}{4}$, and $-0.5$ on index cards. Read the speech bubble aloud. Ask students to express opinions about how to use a number line to determine where the numbers should be placed. Draw $-1$ 0 1. Hold up $-\frac{2}{3}$. *Where does $-\frac{2}{3}$ go?* Ask students to express their opinions about where to place $-\frac{2}{3}$. Continue with the remaining numbers.

**Advanced** Read the speech bubble aloud. Ask students to express opinions about how to use a number line to determine where the numbers should be placed. Draw $-1$ 0 1. Ask students to express their opinions about where to place $-\frac{2}{3}$, $-1$, $\frac{1}{4}$, and $-0.5$.

**Summarize** How is a number line used to order rational numbers?

# DEVELOP: PROBLEM-BASED LEARNING

**COHERENCE: Engage learners by connecting prior knowledge to new ideas.**
Students extend their knowledge of how to locate integers on a number line to an overall understanding of how to compare and order rational numbers.

10–15 min

Solve

## BEFORE

**1. Pose the Solve-and-Share Problem**
**MP.5 Use Appropriate Tools Strategically** Listen and look for students who draw and use a number line to order rational numbers.

**2. Build Understanding**
*When you read a horizontal number line from left to right, how are the numbers ordered?* [From least to greatest] *Where will the greatest number be located on the number line?* [Farthest to the right]

## DURING

**3. Ask Guiding Questions As Needed**
*Which tile has the greatest number? Tell how you know.* [$\frac{1}{4}$; it is the only positive number.] *Which tile's number is farthest away from 0? Explain.* [$-1$; it is one unit away from zero whereas the fractions are closer than one unit.]

## AFTER

**4. Share and Discuss Solutions**
Solve — Start with students' solutions. If needed, project Davonte's work to discuss how he ordered the rational numbers.

**5. Transition to the Visual Learning Bridge**
*A number to the right of another on a horizontal number line is the greater number. You can use a number line to help you compare and order rational numbers.*

**6. Extension for Early Finishers**
*Write three rational numbers between $-1$ and $-2$, and order them from greatest to least. Use a fraction, a mixed number, and a decimal.* [Sample answer: $-1\frac{1}{4}$, $-\frac{3}{2}$, $-1.75$]

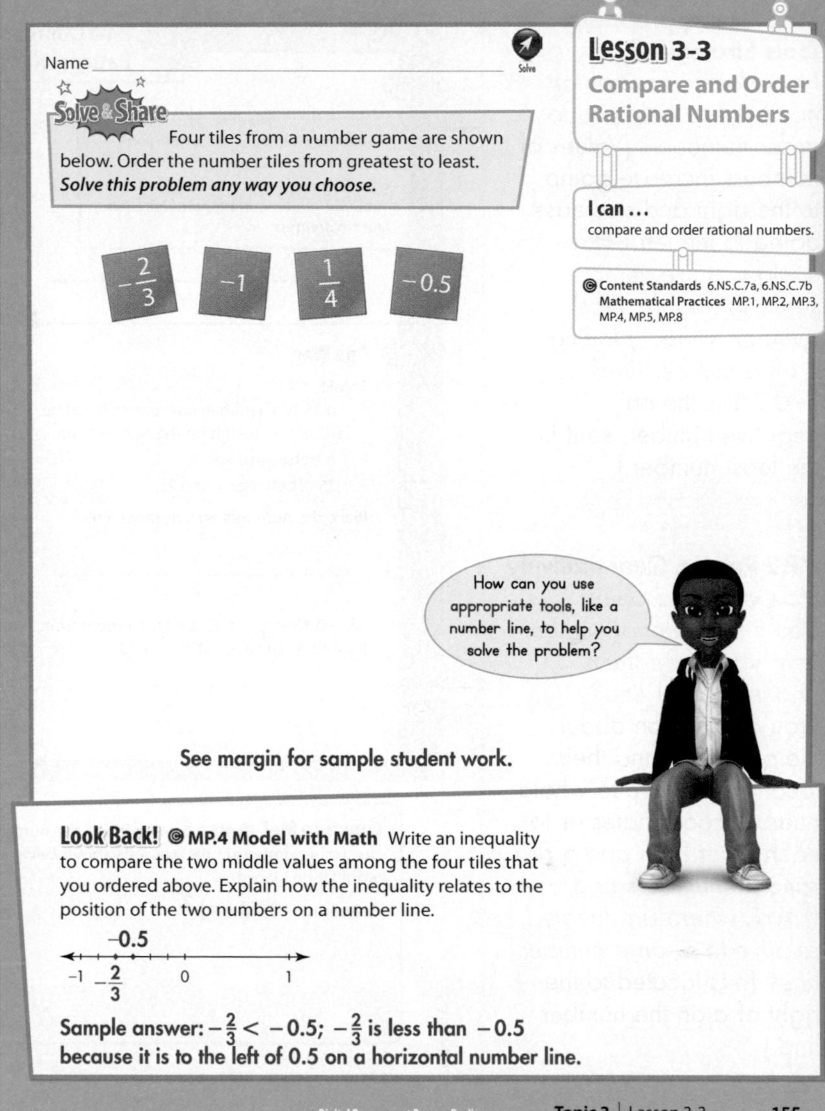

Name
Solve & Share
Four tiles from a number game are shown below. Order the number tiles from greatest to least. Solve this problem any way you choose.
Lesson 3-3
Compare and Order Rational Numbers
I can … compare and order rational numbers.
Content Standards 6.NS.C.7a, 6.NS.C.7b Mathematical Practices MP.1, MP.2, MP.3, MP.4, MP.5, MP.8
$-\frac{2}{3}$
$-1$
$\frac{1}{4}$
$-0.5$
How can you use appropriate tools, like a number line, to help you solve the problem?
See margin for sample student work.
Look Back! MP.4 Model with Math Write an inequality to compare the two middle values among the four tiles that you ordered above. Explain how the inequality relates to the position of the two numbers on a number line.
-0.5
-1
$-\frac{2}{3}$
0
1
Sample answer: $-\frac{2}{3} < -0.5$; $-\frac{2}{3}$ is less than $-0.5$ because it is to the left of 0.5 on a horizontal number line.
Digital Resources at PearsonRealize.com
Topic 3 | Lesson 3-3
155


## Analyze Student Work

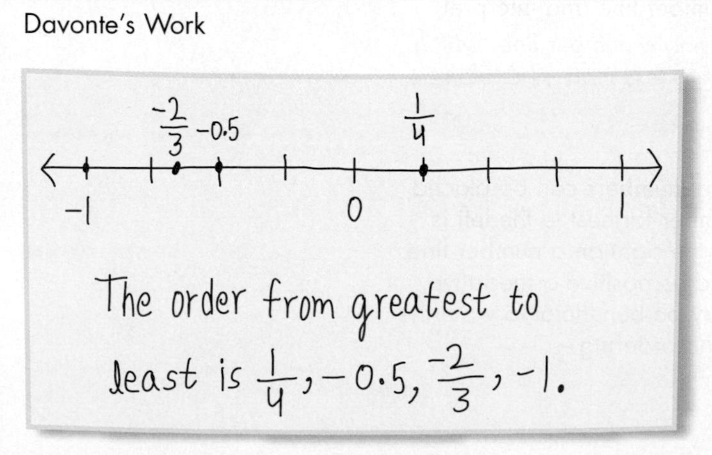


Davonte draws a number line and plots the numbers. He uses the number line to order the numbers from greatest to least.

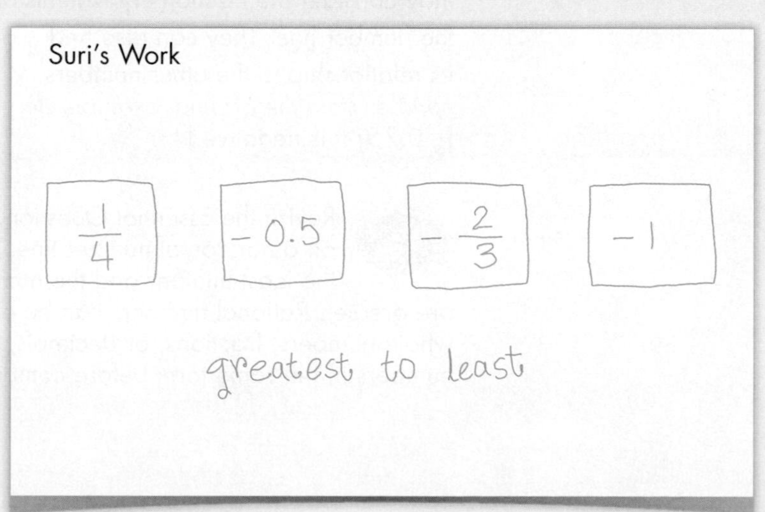


Suri uses number sense to draw the tiles in order from greatest to least, but does not use a number line to position the numbers.

# DEVELOP: VISUAL LEARNING

The *Visual Learning Bridge* connects students' thinking in Solve & Share to important math ideas in the lesson. Use the *Visual Learning Bridge* to make these ideas explicit. Also available as a *Visual Learning Animation Plus* at PearsonRealize.com

Visual Learning

PEARSON realize. PearsonRealize.com

Learn Glossary

**MP.5 Use Appropriate Tools Strategically**
*How does a horizontal number line help you to order numbers?* [Values of numbers increase going to the right and decrease going to the left.] *How could you use number sense to find the least number without plotting it on a number line?* [−0.75 is the only negative number, so it is the least number.]

**MP.2 Reason Quantitatively**
*How does reasoning about the rational numbers help you place them on the number line?* [You can reason about the quantities and their locations relative to whole-number coordinates or to each other.] *If n and a are rational numbers and n > a, where is n located, relative to a, on a number line?* [*n* is located to the right of *a* on the number line.]

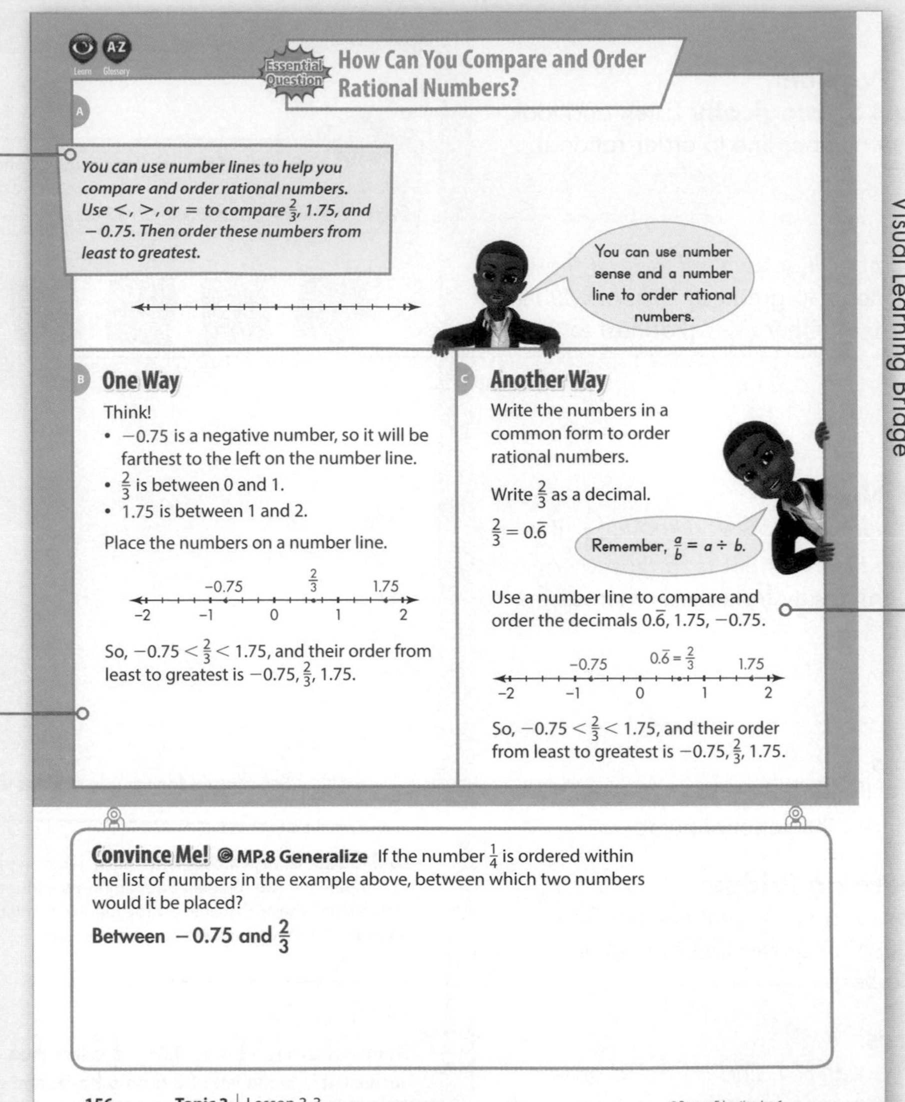

Essential Question **How Can You Compare and Order Rational Numbers?**

A

*You can use number lines to help you compare and order rational numbers. Use <, >, or = to compare $\frac{2}{3}$, 1.75, and −0.75. Then order these numbers from least to greatest.*



B **One Way**

Think!

- −0.75 is a negative number, so it will be farthest to the left on the number line.
- $\frac{2}{3}$ is between 0 and 1.
- 1.75 is between 1 and 2.

Place the numbers on a number line.



So, $-0.75 < \frac{2}{3} < 1.75$, and their order from least to greatest is $-0.75, \frac{2}{3}, 1.75$.

C **Another Way**

Write the numbers in a common form to order rational numbers.

Write $\frac{2}{3}$ as a decimal.

$\frac{2}{3} = 0.\overline{6}$



Use a number line to compare and order the decimals $0.\overline{6}$, 1.75, −0.75.



So, $-0.75 < \frac{2}{3} < 1.75$, and their order from least to greatest is $-0.75, \frac{2}{3}, 1.75$.

**Convince Me!** MP.8 Generalize If the number $\frac{1}{4}$ is ordered within the list of numbers in the example above, between which two numbers would it be placed?

**Between −0.75 and $\frac{2}{3}$**

Visual Learning Bridge

156 Topic 3 | Lesson 3-3 © Pearson Education, Inc. 6

**MP.2 Reason Quantitatively**
*What is another way of writing the numbers in common form?* [Write −0.75 and 1.75 as fractions, $-\frac{3}{4}$ and $1\frac{3}{4}$.] *Why are the fractions $-\frac{3}{4}$ and $1\frac{3}{4}$ easy to plot on the given number line?* [The denominator is four and the units on the number line are divided into fourths.]

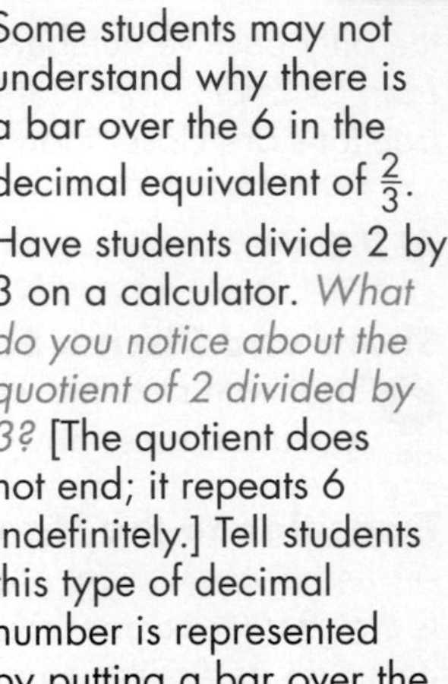

**Prevent Misconceptions** RtI 1

Some students may not understand why there is a bar over the 6 in the decimal equivalent of $\frac{2}{3}$. Have students divide 2 by 3 on a calculator. *What do you notice about the quotient of 2 divided by 3?* [The quotient does not end; it repeats 6 indefinitely.] Tell students this type of decimal number is represented by putting a bar over the repeating digit(s).

**Convince Me! MP.8 Generalize** Mathematically proficient students may consider the fraction equivalents of the decimal numbers marked on the number line. They can also find $\frac{1}{4}$ on the number line and interpret its relationship to the other numbers. *Without using a number line, which number from the original example do you know is less than $\frac{1}{4}$? Explain.* [−0.75; it is negative.]

Essential Question Revisit the Essential Question. Rational numbers can be placed on a horizontal number line. The number farthest to the left is the least number and the numbers to the right on a number line are greater. Rational numbers can be expressed as positive or negative whole numbers, fractions, or decimals, so it may be beneficial to write the numbers in the same form before comparing and ordering.

realize.
PearsonRealize.com

## ✓ QUICK CHECK

Check mark indicates items for prescribing differentiation on the next page. Item 5 is worth 1 point. Items 15 and 16 are worth up to 2 points.

20–30 min

Practice Buddy

Tools

Assessment

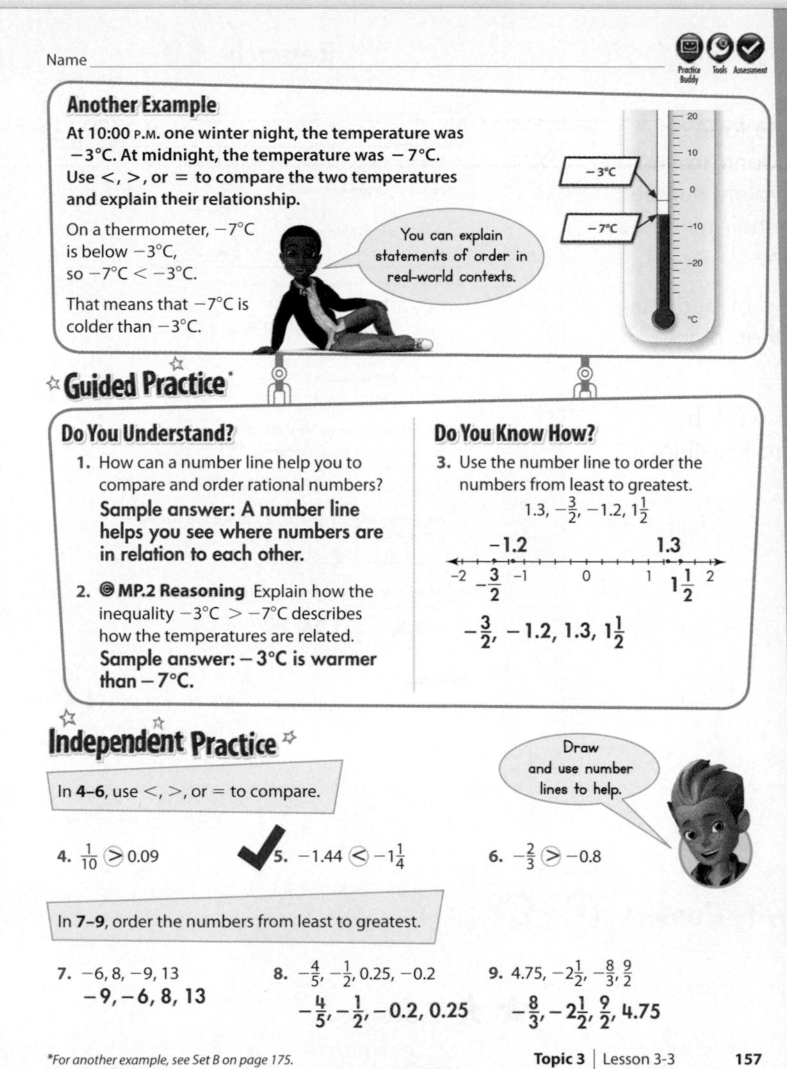

Name ____________

### Another Example

**At 10:00 P.M. one winter night, the temperature was −3°C. At midnight, the temperature was − 7°C. Use <, >, or = to compare the two temperatures and explain their relationship.**

On a thermometer, −7°C is below −3°C, so −7°C < −3°C.

That means that −7°C is colder than −3°C.

−3°C
−7°C
20
10
0
−10
−20
°C
You can explain statements of order in real-world contexts.

### Guided Practice*

**Do You Understand?**

1. How can a number line help you to compare and order rational numbers? **Sample answer: A number line helps you see where numbers are in relation to each other.**
2. MP.2 Reasoning Explain how the inequality −3°C > −7°C describes how the temperatures are related. **Sample answer: − 3°C is warmer than − 7°C.**

**Do You Know How?**

3. Use the number line to order the numbers from least to greatest.
$1.3, -\frac{3}{2}, -1.2, 1\frac{1}{2}$
(number line from −2 to 2 labeled −1.2, 1.3, $-\frac{3}{2}$, $1\frac{1}{2}$)
$\mathbf{-\frac{3}{2}, -1.2, 1.3, 1\frac{1}{2}}$

### Independent Practice

Draw and use number lines to help.

In **4–6**, use <, >, or = to compare.

4. $\frac{1}{10}$ (>) 0.09
5. ✓ −1.44 (<) $-1\frac{1}{4}$
6. $-\frac{2}{3}$ (>) −0.8

In **7–9**, order the numbers from least to greatest.

7. −6, 8, −9, 13
**−9, −6, 8, 13**
8. $-\frac{4}{5}, -\frac{1}{2}, 0.25, -0.2$
$\mathbf{-\frac{4}{5}, -\frac{1}{2}, -0.2, 0.25}$
9. $4.75, -2\frac{1}{2}, -\frac{8}{3}, \frac{9}{2}$
$\mathbf{-\frac{8}{3}, -2\frac{1}{2}, \frac{9}{2}, 4.75}$

*For another example, see Set B on page 175.

### Math Practices and Problem Solving*

For **10** and **11**, use the table of daily low temperatures.

| Day | Temperature |
|---|---|
| Monday | 3°C |
| Tuesday | −6°C |
| Wednesday | 5°C |
| Thursday | 1°C |
| Friday | −5°C |

10. **MP.4 Model with Math** Compare the low temperature on Tuesday with the low temperature on Friday. Then explain the real-world meaning in words.
**−6°C < −5°C; Sample answer: It got colder on Tuesday than on Friday.**
11. Order the days from warmest to coldest.
**Wed., Mon., Thurs., Fri., Tues.**
12. **MP.3 Construct Arguments** A classmate ordered these numbers from greatest to least. Is he correct? Construct an argument to justify your answer.
4.4, 4.2, −4.42, −4.24
**No; Sample answer: −4.42 is farther away from 0 on a number line than −4.24. He should have switched the last two numbers.**
13. **MP.1 Make Sense and Persevere** Order $-3.25, -3\frac{1}{8}, -3\frac{3}{4}$, and −3.1 from least to greatest. Explain how you decided.
$\mathbf{-3\frac{3}{4}, -3.25, -3\frac{1}{8}, -3.1}$**; Sample answer: I wrote the decimals as fractions and used number sense to compare and order.**
14. The San Francisco–Oakland Bay Bridge, opened in 2013, allows for five traffic lanes totaling 57.5 feet across. Write this width as a fraction.
**Sample answer:** $\mathbf{\frac{115}{2}}$ **ft**
15. ✓ **Higher Order Thinking** Suppose $\frac{a}{b}, \frac{c}{d}$, and $\frac{e}{f}$ represent three rational numbers. If $\frac{a}{b}$ is less than $\frac{c}{d}$, and $\frac{c}{d}$ is less than $\frac{e}{f}$, compare $\frac{a}{b}$ and $\frac{e}{f}$. Explain your reasoning.
$\mathbf{\frac{a}{b} < \frac{e}{f}}$**; Sample answer: On a number line,** $\frac{a}{b}$ **is to the left of** $\frac{c}{d}$**, and** $\frac{c}{d}$ **is to the left of** $\frac{e}{f}$**. So,** $\frac{a}{b}$ **is also to the left of** $\frac{e}{f}$**.**

#### Common Core Assessment

16. ✓ Which inequality is **NOT** true?
● $4\frac{1}{2} > \frac{25}{4}$
Ⓑ $-4\frac{1}{2} > -\frac{25}{4}$
Ⓒ $-6 < -5$
Ⓓ $-\frac{1}{2} < \frac{1}{2}$
17. The numbers below are listed in order from greatest to least. Which could be a value for *n*?
$1.2, 0, n, -\frac{1}{5}$
Ⓐ $-\frac{1}{2}$
Ⓑ $-\frac{1}{3}$
Ⓒ $-\frac{1}{4}$
● $-\frac{1}{6}$

**Another Example** *How can you read the thermometer as a number line?* [The thermometer is like a vertical number line where values increase as numbers go from bottom to top.] *Where on a vertical number line will the greater number be, in relation to the lesser number?* [The greater number will be located above the lesser number on a vertical number line.]

**Error Intervention: Item 3**

**If** students get stuck ordering the values,

**then** have them rewrite each number so they all have the same decimal or fraction form. *How could you rewrite all the numbers as decimals?* [1.3, −1.5, −1.2, 1.5] *How could you rewrite all the numbers as fractions?* [Sample answer: $\frac{13}{10}, -\frac{3}{2}, -\frac{12}{10}, \frac{3}{2}$]. *Instead of fourths, how might you divide the units on the number line? Explain.* [Sample answer: In tenths; the decimal numbers are to the tenths place, and the equivalent fractions could be written with 10 in the denominators.]

**Reteaching** Assign Reteaching Set B on p. 175.

**Item 10 MP.4 Model with Math** Students model with math as they write an inequality to compare two temperatures. Students may write the inequality as −6°C < −5°C or −5°C > −6°C. They may interpret and explain their comparison statement by saying that Tuesday was cooler than Friday, or that Friday did not get as cold as Tuesday did. Accept all reasonable explanations for this real-world context.

**Item 15 Higher Order Thinking** Rational numbers can always be written as fractions and the three given numbers are represented as fractions. Since none of the letters is duplicated, students could simplify the problem by using singular variables. Let *x*, *y*, and *z* represent the fractions. An algebraic expression that represents their relationship is $x < y < z$. Rewrite the expression by substituting the fractions for the variables. The ability to simplify problems is a skill that makes problems easier to solve.

**Item 17** Encourage students to compare answer choices. *Which answers have denominators less than 5?* [A, B, C] *Are any of these fractions greater than* $-\frac{1}{5}$*? Why?* [They are all less than $-\frac{1}{5}$ since they are located farther away from 0.]

**Multi-Step Problems** *Page 158 Items 12 and 15; Page 160 Items 17 and 19*

# ASSESS AND DIFFERENTIATE

Use the **QUICK CHECK** on the previous page to prescribe differentiated instruction.

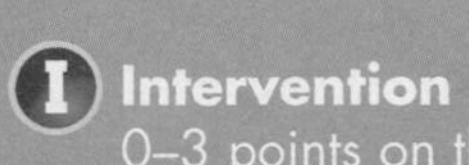

**Ⓘ Intervention**
0–3 points on the Quick Check

**Ⓞ On-Level**
4 points on the Quick Check

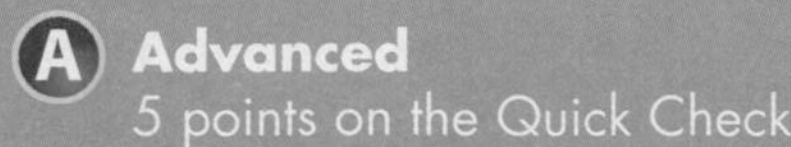

**Ⓐ Advanced**
5 points on the Quick Check

## Intervention Activity 

### Order Rational Numbers on a Number Line

**Materials**

Markers, masking tape, notecards

- Tape a number line from $-5$ to 5 on the floor or across the board. Draw tick marks at every fourth.
- On two notecards write equivalent rational numbers between $-5$ and 5, such as $-1.25$ and $-\frac{5}{4}$. Make enough pairs for several rounds of this activity.
- Give each student a card to tape on his or her shirt. Instruct students to find their partner with an equivalent number. Together they should tape their numbers correctly on the number line.
- Alternatively, a small group of students can match the cards and then place them on the number line.
- Have students record their work by drawing a number line and labeling the points.

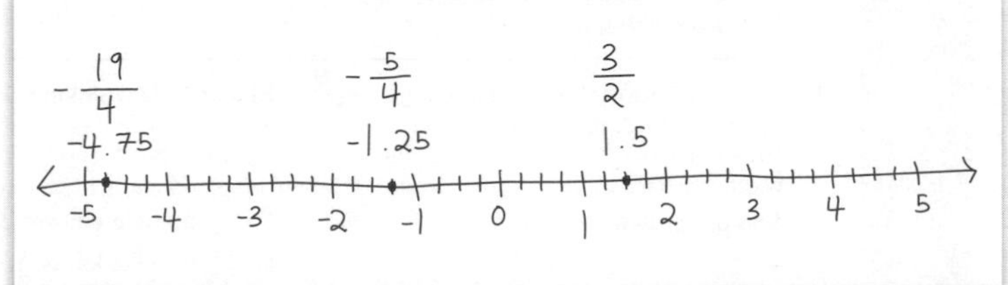


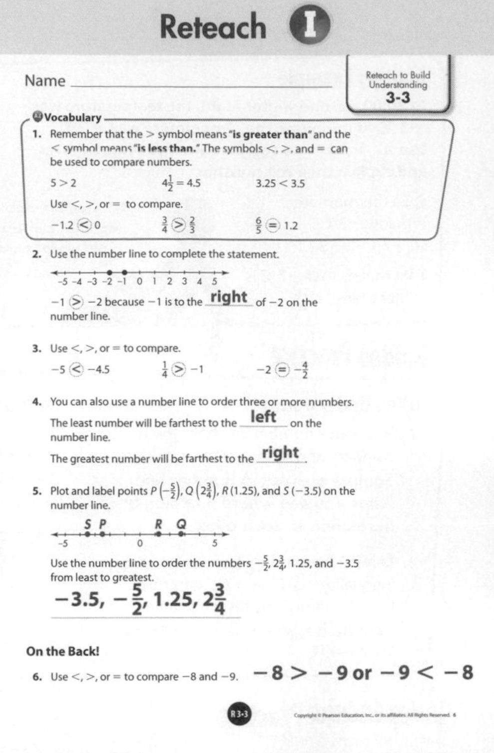

## Reteach Ⓘ

Name ______________________

Reteach to Build Understanding
**3-3**

**Vocabulary**

1. Remember that the > symbol means **"is greater than"** and the < symbol means **"is less than."** The symbols <, >, and = can be used to compare numbers.

   $5 > 2$ $4\frac{1}{2} = 4.5$ $3.25 < 3.5$

   Use <, >, or = to compare.

   $-1.2$ (<) 0 $\frac{3}{4}$ (>) $\frac{2}{3}$ $\frac{6}{5}$ (=) 1.2

2. Use the number line to complete the statement.

   $-5$ $-4$ $-3$ $-2$ $-1$ 0 1 2 3 4 5

   $-1$ (>) $-2$ because $-1$ is to the **right** of $-2$ on the number line.

3. Use <, >, or = to compare.

   $-5$ (<) $-4.5$ $\frac{1}{4}$ (>) $-1$ $-2$ (=) $-\frac{4}{2}$

4. You can also use a number line to order three or more numbers.

   The least number will be farthest to the **left** on the number line.

   The greatest number will be farthest to the **right**.

5. Plot and label points $P\left(-\frac{5}{2}\right)$, $Q\left(2\frac{3}{4}\right)$, $R(1.25)$, and $S(-3.5)$ on the number line.

   S P R Q
   $-5$ 0 5

   Use the number line to order the numbers $-\frac{5}{2}$, $2\frac{3}{4}$, 1.25, and $-3.5$ from least to greatest.

   **$-3.5, -\frac{5}{2}, 1.25, 2\frac{3}{4}$**

**On the Back!**

6. Use <, >, or = to compare $-8$ and $-9$. **$-8 > -9$ or $-9 < -8$**

R 3-3



## On-Level and Advanced Activity Centers  Ⓐ

### Center Games

Students work in pairs or small groups to compare and order rational numbers. Have students discuss their thinking and record their work on a number line.

★ On-Level

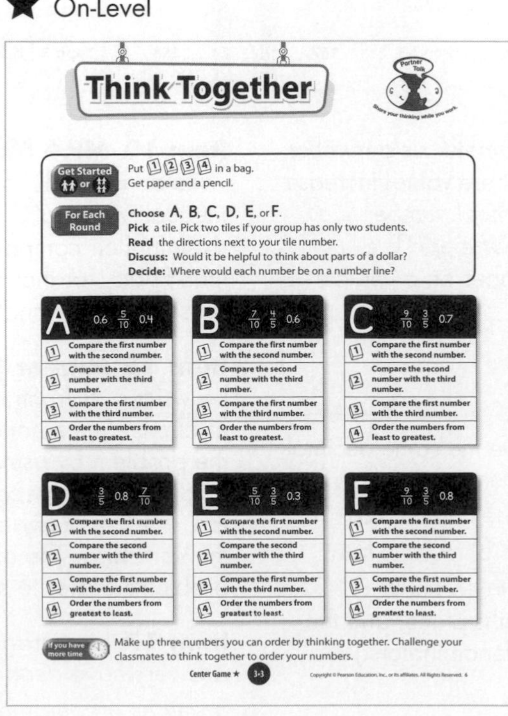

**Think Together**

Partner Talk — Share your thinking while you work.

**Get Started** Put 1 2 3 4 in a bag.
Get paper and a pencil.

**For Each Round** Choose A, B, C, D, E, or F.
**Pick** a tile. Pick two tiles if your group has only two students.
**Read** the directions next to your tile number.
**Discuss:** Would it be helpful to think about parts of a dollar?
**Decide:** Where would each number be on a number line?

**A** 0.6 $\frac{5}{10}$ 0.4
1. Compare the first number with the second number.
2. Compare the second number with the third number.
3. Compare the first number with the third number.
4. Order the numbers from least to greatest.

**B** $\frac{7}{10}$ $\frac{4}{5}$ 0.6
1. Compare the first number with the second number.
2. Compare the second number with the third number.
3. Compare the first number with the third number.
4. Order the numbers from least to greatest.

**C** $\frac{9}{10}$ $\frac{3}{5}$ 0.7
1. Compare the first number with the second number.
2. Compare the second number with the third number.
3. Compare the first number with the third number.
4. Order the numbers from least to greatest.

**D** $\frac{3}{5}$ 0.8 $\frac{7}{10}$
1. Compare the first number with the second number.
2. Compare the second number with the third number.
3. Compare the first number with the third number.
4. Order the numbers from greatest to least.

**E** $\frac{5}{10}$ $\frac{3}{5}$ 0.3
1. Compare the first number with the second number.
2. Compare the second number with the third number.
3. Compare the first number with the third number.
4. Order the numbers from greatest to least.

**F** $\frac{9}{10}$ $\frac{3}{5}$ 0.8
1. Compare the first number with the second number.
2. Compare the second number with the third number.
3. Compare the first number with the third number.
4. Order the numbers from greatest to least.

**If you have more time** Make up three numbers you can order by thinking together. Challenge your classmates to think together to order your numbers.

Center Game ★ 3-3



★★ Advanced

**Think Together**

Partner Talk — Share your thinking while you work.

**Get Started** Put 1 2 3 4 in a bag.
Get paper and a pencil.

**For Each Round** Choose A, B, C, D, E, or F.
**Pick** a tile. Pick two tiles if your group has only two students.
**Say** the two numbers next to your tile number.
**Discuss:** How do you know if a number is between two other numbers?
**Decide:** Where is each one of your numbers on a number line?

**A** Explain why $\frac{1}{2}$ is or is not between the two numbers.
1. 0.3 and $\frac{2}{5}$
2. $\frac{3}{10}$ and 0.4
3. 0.4 and $\frac{7}{10}$
4. 0.4 and 0.6

**B** Explain why $\frac{7}{10}$ is or is not between the two numbers.
1. $\frac{1}{2}$ and 0.6
2. 0.8 and $\frac{9}{10}$
3. 0.6 and $\frac{4}{5}$
4. 0.5 and $\frac{8}{10}$

**C** Explain why 0.5 is or is not between the two numbers.
1. 0.2 and $\frac{2}{5}$
2. 0.6 and $\frac{4}{5}$
3. $\frac{2}{5}$ and 0.7
4. 0.4 and $\frac{3}{5}$

**D** Explain why $\frac{3}{5}$ is or is not between the two numbers.
1. $\frac{2}{5}$ and 0.5
2. 0.8 and $\frac{9}{10}$
3. 0.5 and $\frac{7}{10}$
4. $\frac{4}{10}$ and 0.8

**E** Explain why 0.4 is or is not between the two numbers.
1. $\frac{1}{5}$ and $\frac{3}{10}$
2. 0.3 and $\frac{1}{2}$
3. $\frac{1}{2}$ and 0.6
4. $\frac{1}{10}$ and 0.5

**F** Explain why 0.8 is or is not between the two numbers.
1. $\frac{9}{10}$ and 1.0
2. 0.5 and $\frac{7}{10}$
3. $\frac{3}{5}$ and 0.7
4. $\frac{3}{5}$ and 0.9

**If you have more time** Make up a "Think Together" question with four other pairs of numbers. Challenge your classmates to think together to answer your question.

Center Game ★★ 3-3

15–30 min

Help Practice Buddy Tools Games

**TIMING**

The time allocated to Step 3 will depend on the teacher's instructional decisions and differentiation routines.

## Technology Center    

Tools Games

### Math Tools and Math Games

A link to a specific math tools activity or math game to use with this lesson is provided at PearsonRealize.com.

## Leveled Assignment  Items 1–4, 9–15, 19, 21–22  Items 5–16, 19–22  Items 9–22

Name ____________________

Help Practice Buddy Tools Games

### Homework & Practice 3-3

**Compare and Order Rational Numbers**

**Another Look!**

Order $\frac{3}{5}$, 1.25, and −1.75 from least to greatest. When ordering rational numbers on a number line, the number that is farthest to the right is greatest. The number farthest to the left is least.

- −1.75 is negative, so it is farthest to the left.
- $\frac{3}{5}$ is between 0 and 1.
- 1.25 is greater than 1.

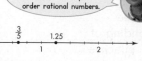

Use number sense and the number line to compare and order rational numbers.

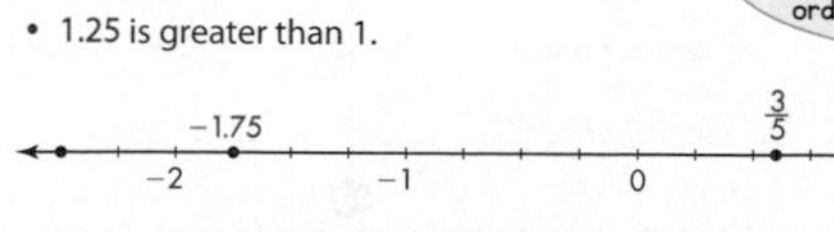



The numbers, in order from least to greatest, are: −1.75, $\frac{3}{5}$, 1.25.

In **1–8**, use <, >, or = to compare.

1. $-12$ **>** $-15$
2. $-\frac{1}{3}$ **>** $-1$
3. $-2$ **>** $-2.1$
4. $\frac{1}{5}$ **<** $\frac{1}{4}$
5. $\frac{7}{10}$ **>** $-0.85$
6. $-0.66$ **>** $-\frac{3}{4}$
7. $-4\frac{1}{2}$ **<** $-3.9$
8. $7\frac{1}{2}$ **<** $7.75$

In **9–11**, order the numbers from least to greatest.

9. 7, −8, −4, 5
   **−8, −4, 5, 7**
10. $-\frac{3}{8}$, $1\frac{1}{2}$, −0.5, −0.9
   **−0.9, −0.5, $-\frac{3}{8}$, $1\frac{1}{2}$**
11. −3.05, $-3\frac{1}{2}$, $-\frac{10}{3}$, 3
   **$-3\frac{1}{2}$, $-\frac{10}{3}$, −3.05, 3**

You can write rational numbers in the same form to help you compare and order.

In **12–14**, order the numbers from greatest to least.

12. −14, −25, 7, −1
   **7, −1, −14, −25**
13. −0.33, $-\frac{1}{4}$, 0.35, $\frac{3}{5}$
   **$\frac{3}{5}$, 0.35, $-\frac{1}{4}$, −0.33**
14. $-\frac{8}{5}$, −2, 1.5, $\frac{4}{3}$
   **1.5, $\frac{4}{3}$, $-\frac{8}{5}$, −2**



In **15–17**, use the map at the right.

15. The map shows how deep archaeologists have dug at several excavation sites. Order the archaeological excavation sites from the least depth to the greatest depth.
   **Site C, Site B, Site A, Site D**

16. **Number Sense** Archaeologists are excavating a new Site E. On a number line, the depth of Site E is in between the depths of Site A and Site B. What is a possible depth of Site E?
   **Sample answer: −2.5 m**

17. **MP.3 Critique Reasoning** Alex says that the sites should be ordered Site C, Site B, Site A, and Site D because $-2.27 > -\frac{21}{9} > -2.7 > -\frac{20}{7}$. Explain the error in Alex's reasoning.
   **Sample answer: Alex's comparisons are backward. Least depth means closest to the surface, which is 0. So, $-2.27 < -\frac{21}{9} < -2.7 < -\frac{20}{7}$.**

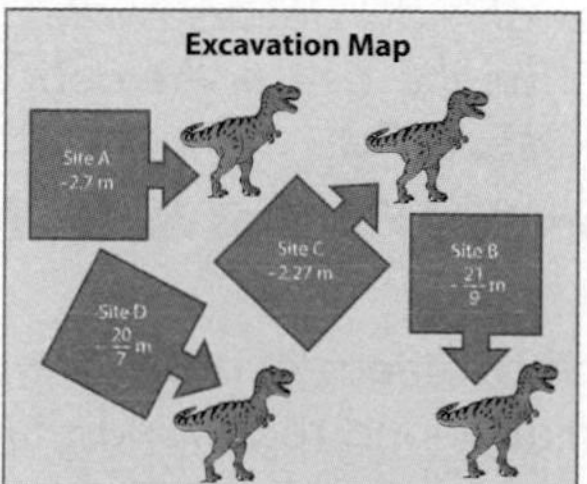



18. **MP.1 Make Sense and Persevere** Order $-6\frac{1}{4}$, −6.35, $-6\frac{1}{5}$, and −6.1 from greatest to least. Explain how you decided.
   **−6.1, $-6\frac{1}{5}$, $-6\frac{1}{4}$, −6.35; Sample answer: I wrote the fractions as decimals and used place value to compare and order.**

19. **Math and Science** Olinquitos are small raccoonlike animals that live in cloud forest habitats in the Andes Mountains, at altitudes of between about 1,500 meters and 2,750 meters. Write two inequalities that describe the altitude, $A$, at which olinquitos can be found.
   **$A \geq 1{,}500$; $A \leq 2{,}750$**

20. **Higher Order Thinking** Tyler says there are infinitely many rational numbers between 0 and 1. Do you agree? Explain.
   **Sample answer: Yes; You can use the unit fractions as an example: $\frac{1}{2}, \frac{1}{3}, \frac{1}{4}, \frac{1}{5}$, and so on. You can keep increasing the denominator by 1 forever.**

### Common Core Assessment

21. Which inequality is true?
   - **(A) $6.5 > \frac{25}{4}$** (filled)
   - (B) $-6.5 > -\frac{25}{4}$
   - (C) $-6 > -5$
   - (D) $5 > \frac{25}{4}$

22. The numbers below are listed in order from least to greatest. Which could be a value for $m$?
   −0.75, $m$, $-\frac{1}{2}$, 0
   - (A) $\frac{2}{3}$
   - (B) $\frac{1}{3}$
   - **(C) $-\frac{2}{3}$** (filled)
   - (D) $-\frac{1}{3}$

# LESSON 3-4

# ABSOLUTE VALUE

## DIGITAL RESOURCES PearsonRealize.com

eText: Student and Teacher eTexts

PD: Listen and Look For Lesson Video

Think: Today's Challenge

Solve: Solve and Share

Learn: Visual Learning Animation Plus

Glossary: Animated Glossary

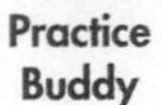
Practice Buddy: Online Personalized Practice

Tools: Math Tools

Assessment: Quick Check

Help: Another Look Homework Video

Games: Math Games

## LESSON OVERVIEW

FCR FOCUS • COHERENCE • RIGOR

### FOCUS

**Domain 6.NS** The Number System

**Cluster 6.NS.C** Apply and extend previous understandings of numbers to the system of rational numbers.

**Content Standard 6.NS.C.7c** Understand the absolute value of a rational number as its distance from 0 on the number line; interpret absolute value as magnitude for a positive or negative quantity in a real-world situation. *For example, for an account balance of −30 dollars, write* $|-30| = 30$ *to describe the size of the debt in dollars.* Also **6.NS.C.7d**.

**Mathematical Practices MP.1, MP.2, MP.3, MP.8**

**Objective** Interpret absolute value in mathematics and real-world situations.

**Essential Understanding** Absolute value is the magnitude of a positive or negative quantity. It can be described as a number's distance from 0 on the number line.

**Vocabulary** Absolute value

**Materials** Number lines (Teaching Tool 13) (optional)

### COHERENCE

In the first three lessons of Topic 3, students developed an understanding of positive and negative rational numbers. In this lesson, they extend their understanding to include absolute value comparisons and ordering of absolute values. Students will interpret the meaning of absolute values in real-world contexts, and distinguish comparisons of absolute value from statements about order. Later, in Lesson 4-3, students will use absolute value when they find distances between points on a coordinate plane.

### RIGOR

This lesson emphasizes **conceptual understanding** and **procedural skill**. Students use their prior knowledge that opposites are equidistant from 0 on the number line to develop an understanding of absolute value. A number line is an effective tool for illustrating absolute value. Students find and interpret absolute values to solve real-world and mathematical problems.

PD Watch the Listen and Look For Lesson Video.

## MATH ANYTIME

### Daily Common Core Review

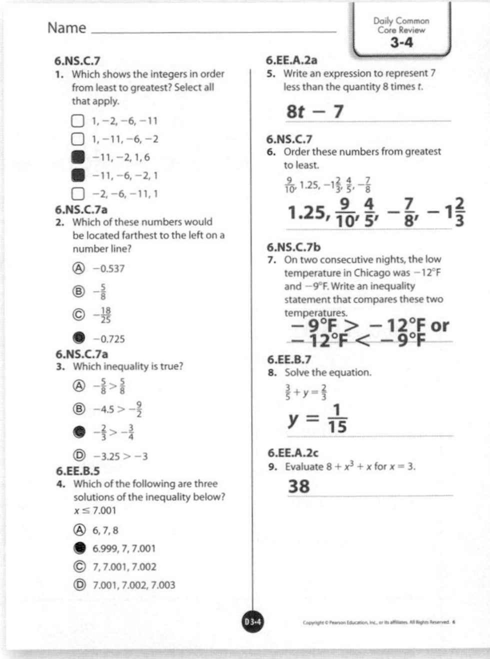

Name ______

Daily Common Core Review 3-4

6.NS.C.7

1. Which shows the integers in order from least to greatest? Select all that apply.
   - ☐ 1, −2, −6, −11
   - ☐ 1, −11, −6, −2
   - ■ −11, −2, 1, 6
   - ■ −11, −6, −2, 1
   - ☐ −2, −6, −11, 1

6.NS.C.7a

2. Which of these numbers would be located farthest to the left on a number line?
   - Ⓐ −0.537
   - Ⓑ $-\frac{5}{8}$
   - Ⓒ $-\frac{18}{25}$
   - ● −0.725

6.NS.C.7a

3. Which inequality is true?
   - Ⓐ $-\frac{5}{8} > \frac{5}{8}$
   - Ⓑ $-4.5 > -\frac{9}{2}$
   - ● $-\frac{2}{3} > -\frac{3}{4}$
   - Ⓓ $-3.25 > -3$

6.EE.B.5

4. Which of the following are three solutions of the inequality below? $x \leq 7.001$
   - Ⓐ 6, 7, 8
   - ● 6.999, 7, 7.001
   - Ⓒ 7, 7.001, 7.002
   - Ⓓ 7.001, 7.002, 7.003

6.EE.A.2a

5. Write an expression to represent 7 less than the quantity 8 times *t*.
   **$8t - 7$**

6.NS.C.7

6. Order these numbers from greatest to least.
   $\frac{9}{10}, 1.25, -1\frac{2}{3}, \frac{4}{5}, -\frac{7}{8}$
   **$1.25, \frac{9}{10}, \frac{4}{5}, -\frac{7}{8}, -1\frac{2}{3}$**

6.NS.C.7b

7. On two consecutive nights, the low temperature in Chicago was −12°F and −9°F. Write an inequality statement that compares these two temperatures.
   **−9°F > −12°F or −12°F < −9°F**

6.EE.B.7

8. Solve the equation.
   $\frac{3}{5} + y = \frac{2}{3}$
   **$y = \frac{1}{15}$**

6.EE.A.2c

9. Evaluate $8 + x^3 + x$ for $x = 3$.
   **38**

D3-4



### Today's Challenge

Think Use the Topic 3 problems any time during this topic.

## ENGLISH LANGUAGE LEARNERS

**Reading** Use contextual support to develop vocabulary.

*Use with the Visual Learning Bridge on Student's Edition p. 162.*

Read Box A. Point to the table. *You may see a table like this in newspapers or on the Internet.* Ask students to predict meanings of positive and negative values. Read Box B.

**Beginning** *The distance of a number from 0 is its absolute value.* Point to the 5 on the number line. Count from 0 to 5. Write $|5| = 5$ on the board. Repeat the process with −5. Read Box C. Point to the 11 on the table and number line. Ask students to write the absolute value of 11 using the sentence stem: "The _____ _____ of 11 is written ____." Ask students to read the sentence. Continue the process with the remaining numbers.

**Intermediate** *The distance of a number from 0 is its absolute value.* Count from 0 to 5 on the number line. Write $|5| = 5$. Ask students to find and write the absolute value of −5. Read Box C. Point to the 11 on the table and number line. Ask students to write the absolute value of 11 using the sentence stem: "The _____ _____ of 11 is written ____." Instruct students to tell partners how they found the absolute value of 11. Continue the process with the remaining numbers.

**Advanced** Explain to students the distance from 0 is absolute value. *The absolute value of 5 is 5.* Write $|5|$. Ask students to find the absolute value of −5. Read Box C. Instruct students to work with partners to find the absolute values of the changes recorded in the table.

**Summarize** What is *absolute value*?

# DEVELOP: PROBLEM-BASED LEARNING

**COHERENCE: Engage learners by connecting prior knowledge to new ideas.**
Students extend their knowledge of distance from 0 on a number line to understand the concept of absolute value.

10–15 min

Solve

## BEFORE

1. **Pose the Solve-and-Share Problem**
**MP.2 Reason Quantitatively** Listen and look for students who apply their personal financial literacy and problem context clues to interpret a negative account balance.

2. **Build Understanding**
*What information are you given?* [A −$30 ending balance for a credit card account] *What are you asked to do?* [To interpret the value of the ending balance]

## DURING

3. **Ask Guiding Questions As Needed**
*When you save more money than you spend, do you have a positive or negative balance?* [Positive] *When you pay with a credit card, why is the balance negative?* [It's money you owe.]

## AFTER

4. **Share and Discuss Solutions**
Start with students' solutions. If needed, project Dylon's work to discuss how to interpret negative balances.

5. **Transition to the Visual Learning Bridge**
*Some real-world situations use negative numbers that may describe related positive measurements. In mathematics, a concept called* absolute value *is used to calculate distances from zero on a number line.*

6. **Extension for Early Finishers**
*Write −30 in as many equivalent ways as you can.*
[Sample answers: $-\frac{30}{1}$, $-\frac{60}{2}$, −30.0]

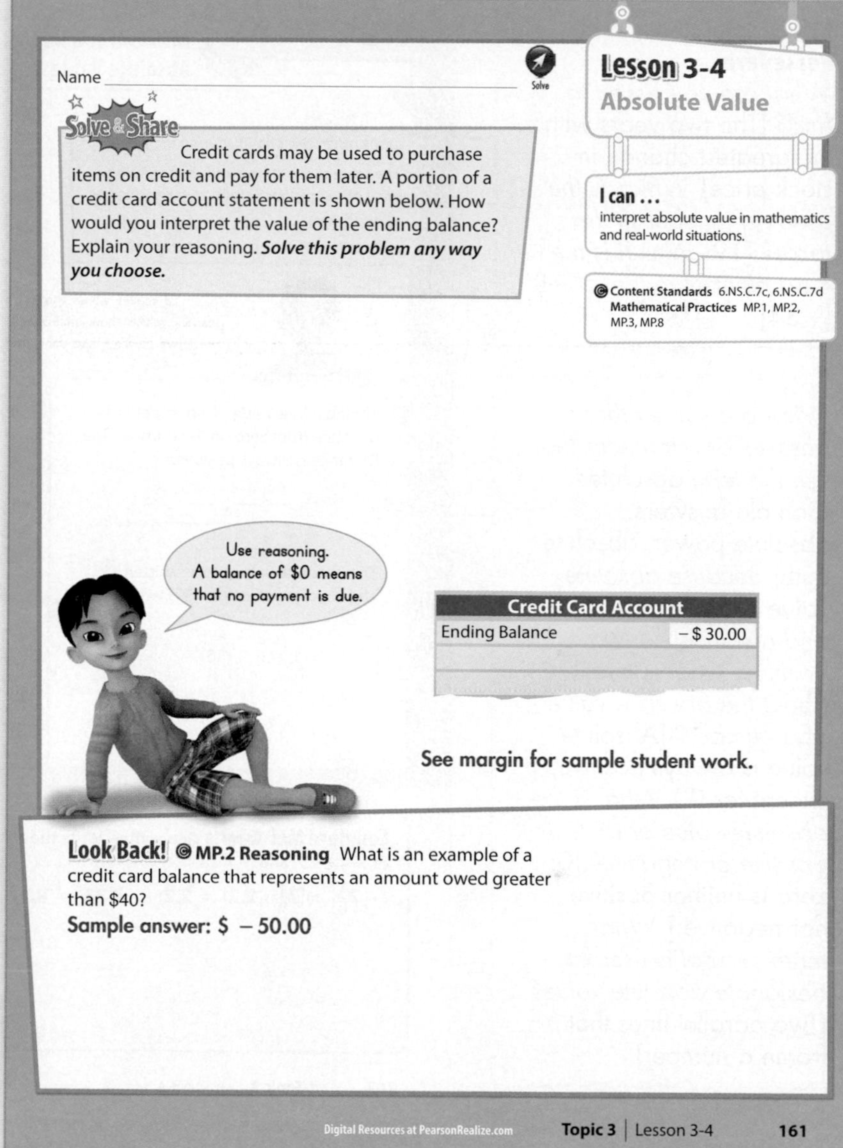

Name
Solve & Share
Credit cards may be used to purchase items on credit and pay for them later. A portion of a credit card account statement is shown below. How would you interpret the value of the ending balance? Explain your reasoning. *Solve this problem any way you choose.*
Lesson 3-4
Absolute Value
I can ...
interpret absolute value in mathematics and real-world situations.
Content Standards 6.NS.C.7c, 6.NS.C.7d
Mathematical Practices MP.1, MP.2, MP.3, MP.8
Use reasoning. A balance of $0 means that no payment is due.
Credit Card Account
Ending Balance − $ 30.00
See margin for sample student work.
Look Back! MP.2 Reasoning What is an example of a credit card balance that represents an amount owed greater than $40?
Sample answer: $ − 50.00
Digital Resources at PearsonRealize.com
Topic 3 | Lesson 3-4 161


### Analyze Student Work

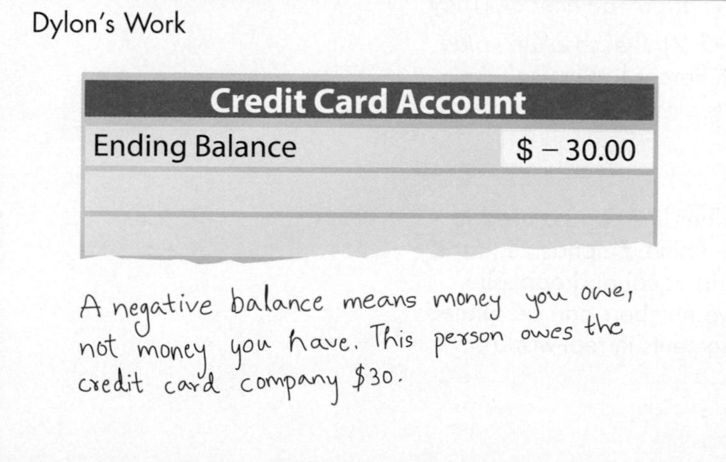

Dylon's Work
Credit Card Account
Ending Balance $ − 30.00
A negative balance means money you owe, not money you have. This person owes the credit card company $30.


Dylon interprets the negative balance as a debt of $30 and explains his reasoning.

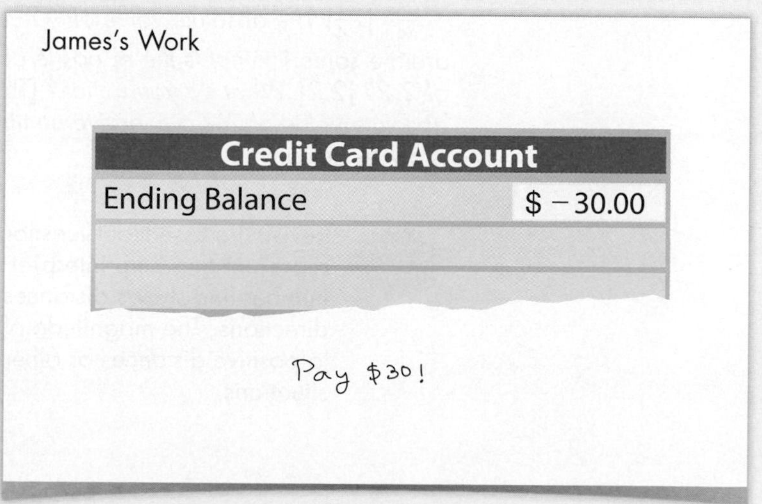


James also interprets the negative balance as a debt of $30 but does not explain his reasoning.

The *Visual Learning Bridge* connects students' thinking in Solve & Share to important math ideas in the lesson. Use the *Visual Learning Bridge* to make these ideas explicit. Also available as a *Visual Learning Animation Plus* at PearsonRealize.com

Visual Learning

PEARSON realize. PearsonRealize.com

Learn Glossary

**MP.1 Make Sense and Persevere**
*What are you asked to find?* [The two years with the greatest change in stock price] *Which is the greatest number in the table?* [19] *Which is the least number in the table?* [−34]

*What are some other phrases or references that use the term absolute?* [Sample answers: absolute power, absolute truth] *Because absolute value is a distance and distance is always positive, what is true about the absolute value of a number?* [Absolute value is always positive, except for 0.] *What is the absolute value of 0? Is it positive or negative?* [0; zero is neither positive nor negative.] *What math symbol is used to designate absolute value?* [Two parallel lines that frame a number]

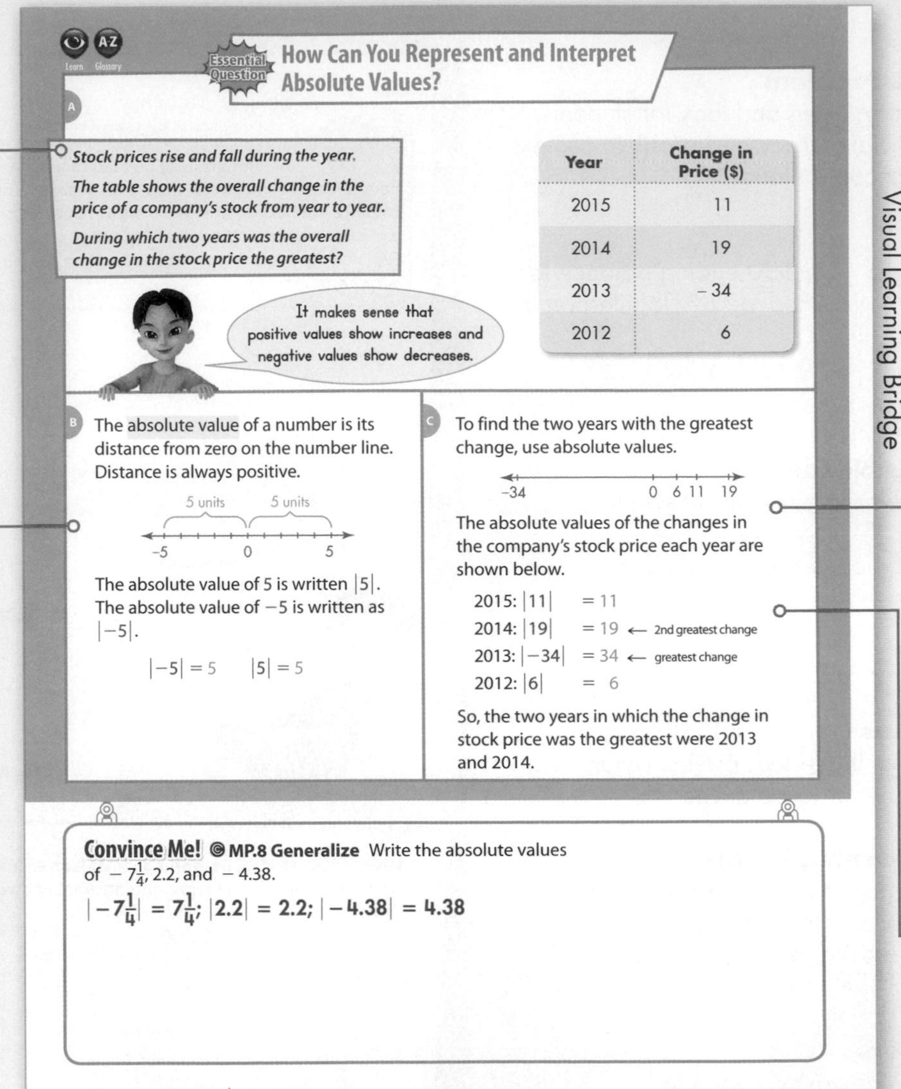

Essential Question **How Can You Represent and Interpret Absolute Values?**

A

*Stock prices rise and fall during the year.*

*The table shows the overall change in the price of a company's stock from year to year.*

*During which two years was the overall change in the stock price the greatest?*

| Year | Change in Price ($) |
|---|---|
| 2015 | 11 |
| 2014 | 19 |
| 2013 | − 34 |
| 2012 | 6 |

It makes sense that positive values show increases and negative values show decreases.

B The absolute value of a number is its distance from zero on the number line. Distance is always positive.

5 units
5 units
−5
0
5

The absolute value of 5 is written $|5|$. The absolute value of −5 is written as $|-5|$.

$|-5| = 5$  $|5| = 5$

C To find the two years with the greatest change, use absolute values.

−34
0 6 11 19

The absolute values of the changes in the company's stock price each year are shown below.

2015: $|11| = 11$
2014: $|19| = 19$ ← 2nd greatest change
2013: $|-34| = 34$ ← greatest change
2012: $|6| = 6$

So, the two years in which the change in stock price was the greatest were 2013 and 2014.

Visual Learning Bridge

**Convince Me!** MP.8 Generalize Write the absolute values of $-7\frac{1}{4}$, 2.2, and − 4.38.

$|-7\frac{1}{4}| = 7\frac{1}{4}$; $|2.2| = 2.2$; $|-4.38| = 4.38$

162 Topic 3 | Lesson 3-4 © Pearson Education, Inc. 6

**MP.2 Reason Quantitatively**
*When you want to find the greatest change in value, does it matter whether the change is positive or negative? Explain your reasoning.* [No; you are only considering the magnitude of the change, not the direction it is in.]

**Prevent Misconceptions**

Explain that numbers that are not preceded by a sign are presumed to be positive. For example, the number 5 is +5, or positive 5.

**Convince Me! MP.8 Generalize** Help students to understand the difference between *opposites* and *absolute value*. *What is the opposite of $-7\frac{1}{4}$?* [$7\frac{1}{4}$] *The absolute value of $-7\frac{1}{4}$?* [$7\frac{1}{4}$] *What do you notice?* [They are the same.] *What is the opposite of 2.2?* [−2.2] *The absolute value of 2.2?* [2.2] *What do you notice?* [They are different.] *Why isn't the absolute value of 2.2 a negative number like its opposite?* [Absolute value is always positive.]

Revisit the Essential Question. A number line can be used to represent and help interpret absolute value. Emphasize that a number line shows distances from 0 in equal and opposite directions. The magnitude of negative numbers can be related to positive distances or other measurements in real-world situations.

PEARSON realize.
PearsonRealize.com

## QUICK CHECK

Check mark indicates items for prescribing differentiation on the next page. Item 8 is worth 1 point. Items 21 and 23 are worth up to 2 points.

20–30 min

Practice Buddy

Tools

Assessment

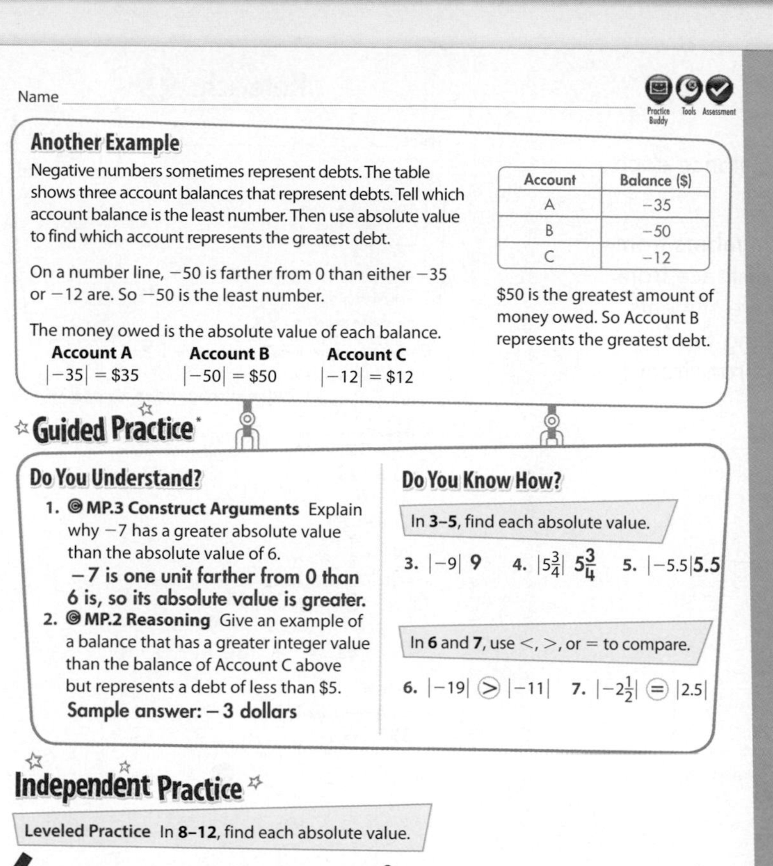

Name ____________

**Another Example**

Negative numbers sometimes represent debts. The table shows three account balances that represent debts. Tell which account balance is the least number. Then use absolute value to find which account represents the greatest debt.

| Account | Balance ($) |
|---|---|
| A | −35 |
| B | −50 |
| C | −12 |

On a number line, −50 is farther from 0 than either −35 or −12 are. So −50 is the least number.

The money owed is the absolute value of each balance.

**Account A** |−35| = $35 **Account B** |−50| = $50 **Account C** |−12| = $12

$50 is the greatest amount of money owed. So Account B represents the greatest debt.

**Guided Practice***

**Do You Understand?**

1. **MP.3 Construct Arguments** Explain why −7 has a greater absolute value than the absolute value of 6. **−7 is one unit farther from 0 than 6 is, so its absolute value is greater.**
2. **MP.2 Reasoning** Give an example of a balance that has a greater integer value than the balance of Account C above but represents a debt of less than $5. **Sample answer: −3 dollars**

**Do You Know How?**

In **3–5**, find each absolute value.

3. |−9| **9** 4. $|5\frac{3}{4}|$ $\mathbf{5\frac{3}{4}}$ 5. |−5.5| **5.5**

In **6** and **7**, use <, >, or = to compare.

6. |−19| (>) |−11| 7. $|-2\frac{1}{2}|$ (=) |2.5|

**Independent Practice***

**Leveled Practice** In **8–12**, find each absolute value.

8. |−46| **46** 9. |0.7| **0.7** 10. $|-\frac{2}{3}|$ $\mathbf{\frac{2}{3}}$ 11. |−7.35| **7.35** 12. $|-4\frac{3}{4}|$ $\mathbf{4\frac{3}{4}}$

In **13–16**, use <, >, or = to compare.

13. |14| (<) |−21| 14. |−11.5| (<) $|11\frac{3}{4}|$ 15. |−6.3| (>) |5.2| 16. |3.75| (=) $|-3\frac{3}{4}|$

17. Order |−6|, |−4|, |11|, |0| from greatest to least. **|11|, |−6|, |−4|, |0|**

18. Order |4|, |−3|, |−18|, |−3.18| from least to greatest. **|−3|, |−3.18|, |4|, |−18|**

*For another example, see Set C on page 176.

Topic 3 | Lesson 3-4 163

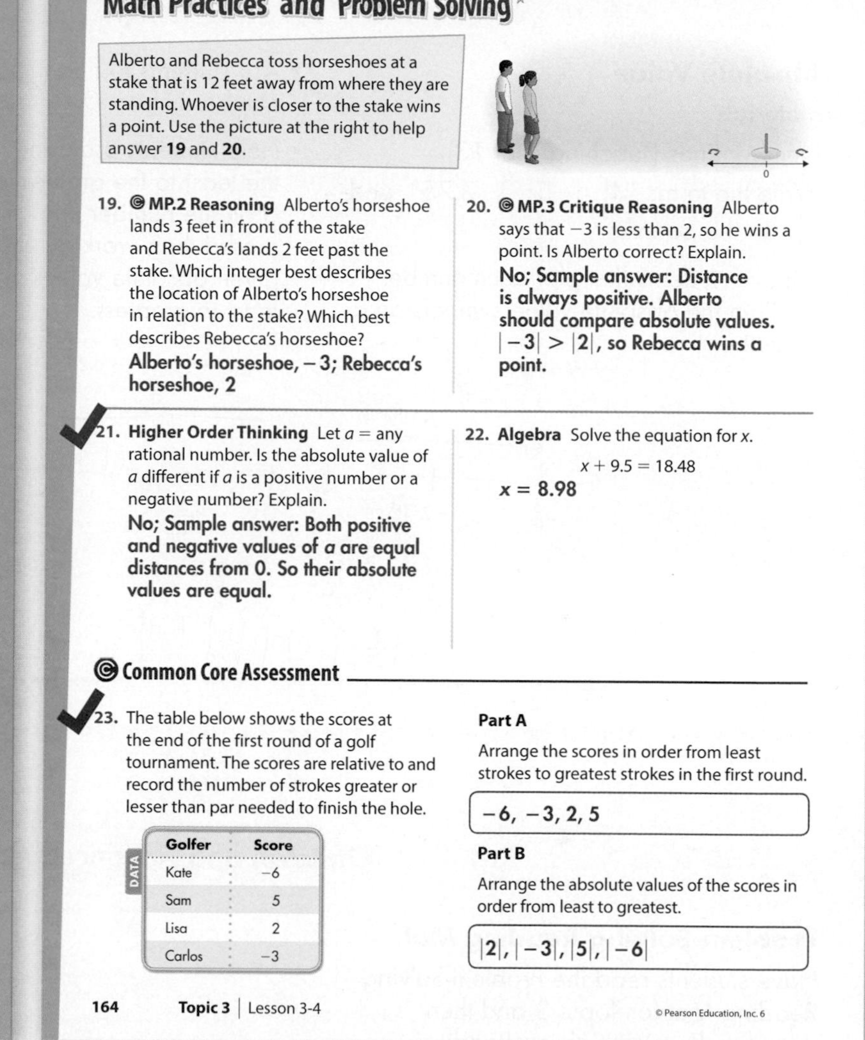

**Math Practices and Problem Solving**

Alberto and Rebecca toss horseshoes at a stake that is 12 feet away from where they are standing. Whoever is closer to the stake wins a point. Use the picture at the right to help answer **19** and **20**.

19. **MP.2 Reasoning** Alberto's horseshoe lands 3 feet in front of the stake and Rebecca's lands 2 feet past the stake. Which integer best describes the location of Alberto's horseshoe in relation to the stake? Which best describes Rebecca's horseshoe? **Alberto's horseshoe, −3; Rebecca's horseshoe, 2**

20. **MP.3 Critique Reasoning** Alberto says that −3 is less than 2, so he wins a point. Is Alberto correct? Explain. **No; Sample answer: Distance is always positive. Alberto should compare absolute values. |−3| > |2|, so Rebecca wins a point.**

21. **Higher Order Thinking** Let *a* = any rational number. Is the absolute value of *a* different if *a* is a positive number or a negative number? Explain. **No; Sample answer: Both positive and negative values of *a* are equal distances from 0. So their absolute values are equal.**

22. **Algebra** Solve the equation for *x*.
$x + 9.5 = 18.48$
$\mathbf{x = 8.98}$

**Common Core Assessment**

23. The table below shows the scores at the end of the first round of a golf tournament. The scores are relative to and record the number of strokes greater or lesser than par needed to finish the hole.

| Golfer | Score |
|---|---|
| Kate | −6 |
| Sam | 5 |
| Lisa | 2 |
| Carlos | −3 |

**Part A**

Arrange the scores in order from least strokes to greatest strokes in the first round.

**−6, −3, 2, 5**

**Part B**

Arrange the absolute values of the scores in order from least to greatest.

**|2|, |−3|, |5|, |−6|**

164 Topic 3 | Lesson 3-4



**Another Example** *What does the negative sign mean in front of the numbers in the "Balance" column?* [Money owed] *On a number line, where is −50 located in relation to the other numbers?* [Farthest to the left]

**Error Intervention: Item 2**

**If** students have difficulty interpreting the words in the problem,

**then** have them draw a number line and locate the integers on the line. *What number will you plot for the balance of Account C?* [−12] *Is a greater integer value to the left or right of −12?* [To the right] *Where is a debt of $5 located on the number line?* [−5] *Is a debt less than $5 to the left or right of −5?* [To the right]

**Reteaching** Assign Reteaching Set C on p. 176.

**Item 20 MP.3 Critique Reasoning** If students agree with Alberto, remind them that although −3 is less than 2, the distance from the stake is what determines the winner. So, they should use the absolute value of −3 to represent the distance from the stake.

**Item 21 Higher Order Thinking** If students have difficulty solving this problem because it involves a variable, suggest they they substitute numerical values for *a*. They should choose both a positive number and a negative number to test in the situation.

**Item 23** Be sure students distinguish between the meanings of the absolute values of scores and the scores themselves. Have them discuss and interpret the ordering of the scores in Part A and Part B. Elicit that the ordering of the scores from least to greatest in Part A shows the winning score first followed by each runner-up. The absolute value of each score shows how close it was to par. So, the ordering of the absolute values of the scores from least to greatest in Part B gives the score closest to par first and the score furthest from par last.

**Multi-Step Problems** *Page 164 Item 23; Page 166 Items 18 and 19*

## STEP 3 ASSESS AND DIFFERENTIATE

Use the **QUICK CHECK** on the previous page to prescribe differentiated instruction.

**(I) Intervention** 0–3 points on the Quick Check

**(O) On-Level** 4 points on the Quick Check

**(A) Advanced** 5 points on the Quick Check

### Intervention Activity 

**Absolute Value**

**Materials**

Number lines (Teaching Tool 13)

Write the terms $|4|$, $|-5|$, $|-2.75|$, and $|\frac{3}{2}|$ on the board.

- Have students first plot each number within the absolute value symbols on a number line.
- Ask students to find the distance each number is from 0.
- Help students order the numbers from the least to the greatest distance from 0 on the number line. Have students record their work by writing the four given absolute values in order from least to greatest.

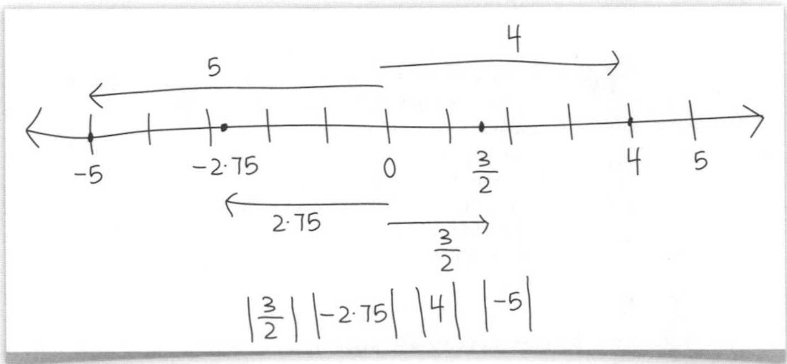


### Reteach (I)

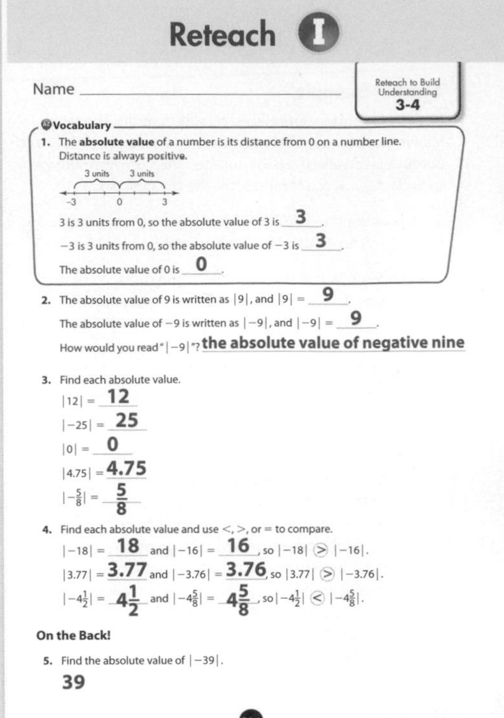

Name ______________________

Reteach to Build Understanding 3-4

**Vocabulary**

1. The **absolute value** of a number is its distance from 0 on a number line. Distance is always positive.

3 is 3 units from 0, so the absolute value of 3 is **3**.

−3 is 3 units from 0, so the absolute value of −3 is **3**.

The absolute value of 0 is **0**.

2. The absolute value of 9 is written as $|9|$, and $|9|$ = **9**.

The absolute value of −9 is written as $|-9|$, and $|-9|$ = **9**.

How would you read "$|-9|$"? **the absolute value of negative nine**

3. Find each absolute value.

$|12|$ = **12**

$|-25|$ = **25**

$|0|$ = **0**

$|4.75|$ = **4.75**

$|-\frac{5}{8}|$ = $\mathbf{\frac{5}{8}}$

4. Find each absolute value and use <, >, or = to compare.

$|-18|$ = **18** and $|-16|$ = **16**, so $|-18| > |-16|$.

$|3.77|$ = **3.77** and $|-3.76|$ = **3.76**, so $|3.77| > |-3.76|$.

$|-4\frac{1}{2}|$ = $\mathbf{4\frac{1}{2}}$ and $|-4\frac{5}{8}|$ = $\mathbf{4\frac{5}{8}}$, so $|-4\frac{1}{2}| < |-4\frac{5}{8}|$.

**On the Back!**

5. Find the absolute value of $|-39|$.

**39**

R 3-4



### On-Level and Advanced Activity Centers  (A)

**Problem-Solving Reading Mat**

Have students read the Problem-Solving Reading Mat for Topic 3 and then complete Problem-Solving Reading Activity 3-4.

See the Problem-Solving Reading Activity Guide for other suggestions on how to use this mat.

## TIMING

The time allocated to Step 3 will depend on the teacher's instructional decisions and differentiation routines.

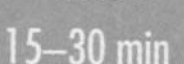
15–30 min

PEARSON realize.
PearsonRealize.com

Help

Practice Buddy

Tools

Games

## Technology Center

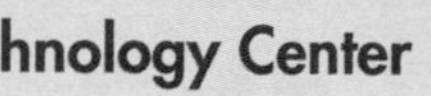

Tools Games

### Math Tools and Math Games

A link to a specific math tools activity or math game to use with this lesson is provided at PearsonRealize.com.

## Leveled Assignment

 Items 1–7, 12–15, 17–19  Items 4, 5, 10–19  Items 8–19

Name ______________________ Help Practice Buddy Tools Games

**Homework & Practice 3-4**
**Absolute Value**

### Another Look!

The **absolute value** of a number is its distance from 0 on a number line. Distance is always positive. The absolute value of 0 is 0.

Except for 0, absolute values are always positive.

The absolute value of any number, $n$, is written $|n|$.

Order the absolute values from least to greatest.
$|-4|, |-1|, |3|$

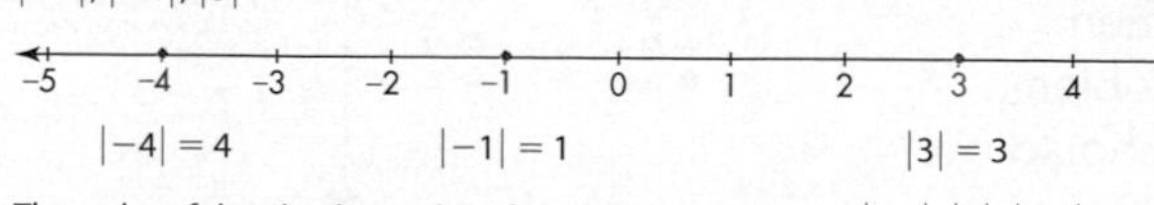


$|-4| = 4$ $|-1| = 1$ $|3| = 3$

The order of the absolute values from least to greatest is $|-1|, |3|, |-4|$.

In **1–5**, find each absolute value.

**1.** $|-21|$ **21** **2.** $|7|$ **7** **3.** $|-\frac{3}{5}|$ $\mathbf{\frac{3}{5}}$ **4.** $|-5.5|$ **5.5** **5.** $|8\frac{3}{4}|$ $\mathbf{8\frac{3}{4}}$

In **6–11**, use <, >, or = to compare.

**6.** $|-22|$ (>) $|-12|$ **7.** $|45|$ (<) $|-46|$ **8.** $|13|$ (>) $|-2|$

**9.** $|48|$ (>) $|-39|$ **10.** $|-55.5|$ (>) $|55|$ **11.** $|21\frac{1}{3}|$ (<) $|-21\frac{1}{2}|$

**12.** Order $|-20|, |16|, |-2|, |37|$ from greatest to least. $\mathbf{|-37|, |-20|, |16|, |-2|}$

**13.** Order $|\frac{1}{4}|, |-\frac{1}{3}|, |-\frac{1}{8}|, |0|$ from least to greatest. $\mathbf{|0|, |-\frac{1}{8}|, |\frac{1}{4}|, |-\frac{1}{3}|}$

**14.** Which account balance represents a debt greater than $50?
**Account A**

| Account | Balance ($) |
|---|---|
| A | –60 |
| B | –25 |
| C | –35 |

You can use absolute values to compare the account balances.



**15.** The table at the right shows the changes in the number of items answered correctly from a first math test to a second math test for five students. Order the students based on the least change to the greatest change.
**Beth, Micah, Antoine, Pat, and Lauren**

| Student | Change in Number of Correct Answers |
|---|---|
| Antoine | 4 |
| Lauren | –6 |
| Micah | 3 |
| Beth | 0 |
| Pat | –5 |

**16. Higher Order Thinking** Is it possible that Lauren answered more questions correctly on the second math test than Antoine did? Explain your reasoning.
**Yes; Sample answer: $|-6| + |4| = 6 + 4 = 10$; If Lauren answered 11 more questions correctly than Antoine on the first math test, she would have a higher score than Antoine on the second test as well.**

**17. Vocabulary** Write an inequality using the *absolute values* of –.3 and $\frac{1}{4}$. Explain how you know the inequality is correct.
**$|-.3| > |\frac{1}{4}|$; Sample answer: $\frac{1}{4} = .25$. When –.3 and .25 are plotted on a number line, .25 is closer to zero, so it has a lesser absolute value.**

**18. Algebra** Evaluate the expression $\frac{1}{5}(3x + 4)$ for $x = 2$.
**2**

### Common Core Assessment

**19.** The table below shows the daily low temperatures for four days.

| Day | Low Temperature |
|---|---|
| Monday | 3°F |
| Tuesday | –4°F |
| Wednesday | –1°F |
| Thursday | 2°F |

**Part A**

Arrange the temperatures in order from coldest to warmest.

**–4, –1, 2, 3**

**Part B**

Arrange the absolute values of the temperatures in order from least to greatest.

$\mathbf{|-1|, |+2|, |+3|, |-4|}$

# REASONING

## DIGITAL RESOURCES PearsonRealize.com

eText — Student and Teacher eTexts

PD — Listen and Look For Lesson Video

Think — Today's Challenge

Solve — Solve and Share

Learn — Visual Learning Animation Plus

Glossary — Animated Glossary

Practice Buddy — Online Personalized Practice

Tools — Math Tools

Assessment — Quick Check

Help — Another Look Homework Video

Games — Math Games

MP — Math Practices Animations

## LESSON OVERVIEW FCR FOCUS • COHERENCE • RIGOR

### FOCUS

**Mathematical Practices MP.2** Reason abstractly and quantitatively. Also **MP.1, MP.4, MP.6**

**Domain 6.NS** The Number System

**Cluster 6.NS.C** Apply and extend previous understandings of numbers to the system of rational numbers.

**Content Standard 6.NS.C.5** Understand that positive and negative numbers are used together to describe quantities having opposite directions or values (e.g., temperature above/below zero, elevation above/below sea level, credits/debits, positive/negative electric charge); use positive and negative numbers to represent quantities in real-world contexts, explaining the meaning of 0 in each situation. Also **6.NS.C.6**.

**Objective** Make sense of quantities and relationships in problem situations.

**Essential Understanding** Good math thinkers know how to think about words and numbers to solve problems.

**Materials** Number lines (Teaching Tool 13) (optional)

### COHERENCE

Throughout this topic, students have needed to reason abstractly and quantitatively while building a greater understanding of rational numbers and solving a variety of problems requiring negative numbers. As students continue to solve problems, focus on helping them develop good thinking habits, such as determining the meanings of numbers and symbols, and identifying relationships between quantities in real-world contexts.

### RIGOR

This lesson emphasizes **application**. Rigorous mathematics instruction calls for the engagement of multiple mathematical practices. For example, modeling with math, MP.4, is a practice students engage when they use an equation to represent a problem. However, the classroom conversation should focus the meaning and use of the Thinking Habits shown for MP.2.

PD Watch the Listen and Look For Lesson Video.

## MATH ANYTIME

### Daily Common Core Review

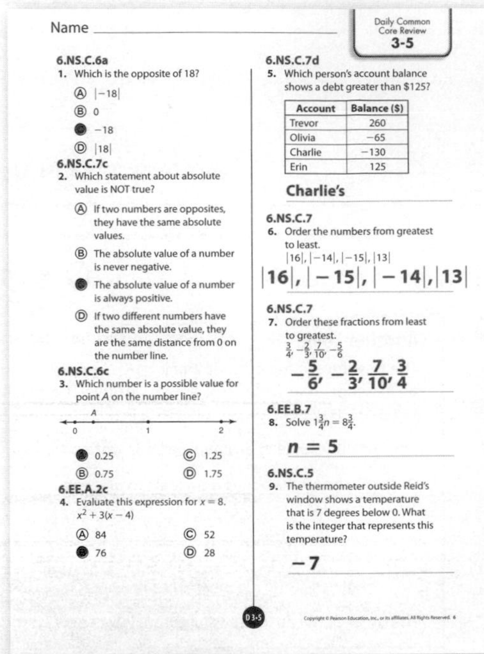
Name ____________

Daily Common Core Review 3-5

**6.NS.C.6a**
1. Which is the opposite of 18?
   Ⓐ $|-18|$
   Ⓑ 0
   ● $-18$
   Ⓓ $|18|$

**6.NS.C.7c**
2. Which statement about absolute value is NOT true?
   Ⓐ If two numbers are opposites, they have the same absolute values.
   Ⓑ The absolute value of a number is never negative.
   ● The absolute value of a number is always positive.
   Ⓓ If two different numbers have the same absolute value, they are the same distance from 0 on the number line.

**6.NS.C.6c**
3. Which number is a possible value for point $A$ on the number line?
   ● 0.25 Ⓒ 1.25
   Ⓑ 0.75 Ⓓ 1.75

**6.EE.A.2c**
4. Evaluate this expression for $x = 8$.
   $x^2 + 3(x - 4)$
   Ⓐ 84 Ⓒ 52
   ● 76 Ⓓ 28

**6.NS.C.7d**
5. Which person's account balance shows a debt greater than $125?

| Account | Balance ($) |
|---|---|
| Trevor | 260 |
| Olivia | −65 |
| Charlie | −130 |
| Erin | 125 |

**Charlie's**

**6.NS.C.7**
6. Order the numbers from greatest to least.
   $|16|, |-14|, |-15|, |13|$
   $|16|, |-15|, |-14|, |13|$

**6.NS.C.7**
7. Order these fractions from least to greatest.
   $\frac{3}{4}, -\frac{2}{3}, \frac{7}{10}, -\frac{5}{6}$
   $-\frac{5}{6}, -\frac{2}{3}, \frac{7}{10}, \frac{3}{4}$

**6.EE.B.7**
8. Solve $1\frac{3}{4}n = 8\frac{3}{4}$.
   $n = 5$

**6.NS.C.5**
9. The thermometer outside Reid's window shows a temperature that is 7 degrees below 0. What is the integer that represents this temperature?
   $-7$

D 3-5

### Today's Challenge

Think Use the Topic 3 problems any time during this topic.

## ENGLISH LANGUAGE LEARNERS ELL

**Speaking** Describe information.

*Use with the Solve & Share on Student's Edition p. 167.*

Read the Solve & Share. Draw [number line −10, −5, 0, 5, 10]. *We'll use pictures and equations to see if the team gains a total of 10 yards.*

**Beginning** *Suppose the football is on the scrimmage line, represented by 0 on the number line. The team loses 6 yards.* Ask students to indicate if the ball moved 6 or −6 yards. Write 0 − 6 = ___. Draw an arrow from 0 to −6 on top of the number line, to represent a loss of 6 yards. *The team gains 2 yards.* Ask students if the ball moved 2 or −2 yards. Write −6 + 2 = ___. Draw an arrow from −6 to −4 on top of the number line to represent a gain of 2 yards. Continue the process with −2 and +14. Ask students to describe how they used the number line with the sentence stem: "We used the number line to ___." [Answers will vary.]

**Intermediate** Instruct students to draw the number line in their notes. Ask students to put their erasers on 0. *The team loses 6 yards.* Ask students to put their erasers where the football is. Write 0 − 6 = ___. Continue the process with +2, −2, and +14. Ask students to describe how the number line was used.

**Advanced** Instruct students to draw the number line in their notes. Read the Solve & Share with students, pausing after each play to give them time to mark the position of the football on the number line. Ask students to write equations to represent each play. Instruct students to describe to partners how the number line was used and how they determined the equations.

**Summarize** How can number lines be used to represent gains and losses?

# DEVELOP: PROBLEM-BASED LEARNING

**COHERENCE: Engage learners by connecting prior knowledge to new ideas.**
Students extend their understanding of positive and negative rational numbers to help them reason about the quantities of a real-world problem and solve it.

10–15 min

Solve

## BEFORE

1. **Pose the Solve-and-Share Problem**
**MP.2 Reason Quantitatively** Listen and look for students who use a number line with positive and negative integers to represent the problem situation and reason about whether the team moved the football 10 yards toward the end zone.

2. **Build Understanding**
*Because the line of scrimmage represents neither a gain nor a loss, what number on a number line could represent the initial position of the football?* [0]

## DURING

3. **Ask Guiding Questions As Needed**
*What integer represents a loss of 6 yards?* [−6] *How can you use the number line to represent a loss of 6 yards?* [From 0, move six units to the left to −6.] *What integer represents a gain of 2 yards?* [2] *How can you use the number line to represent a gain of 2 yards?* [From −6, move two units to the right to −4.]

## AFTER

4. **Share and Discuss Solutions**
Solve Start with students' solutions. If needed, project Leah's work to discuss the reasoning used to find the solution.

5. **Transition to the Visual Learning Bridge**
*You can use positive and negative integers to describe quantities that have opposite directions or values on a number line.*

6. **Extension for Early Finishers**
*How many more yards are needed for a "first down," or a 10-yard gain?* [2 yards]

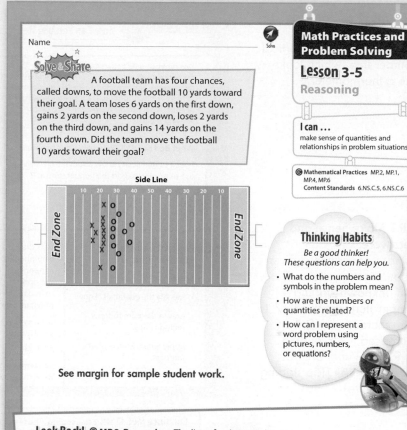

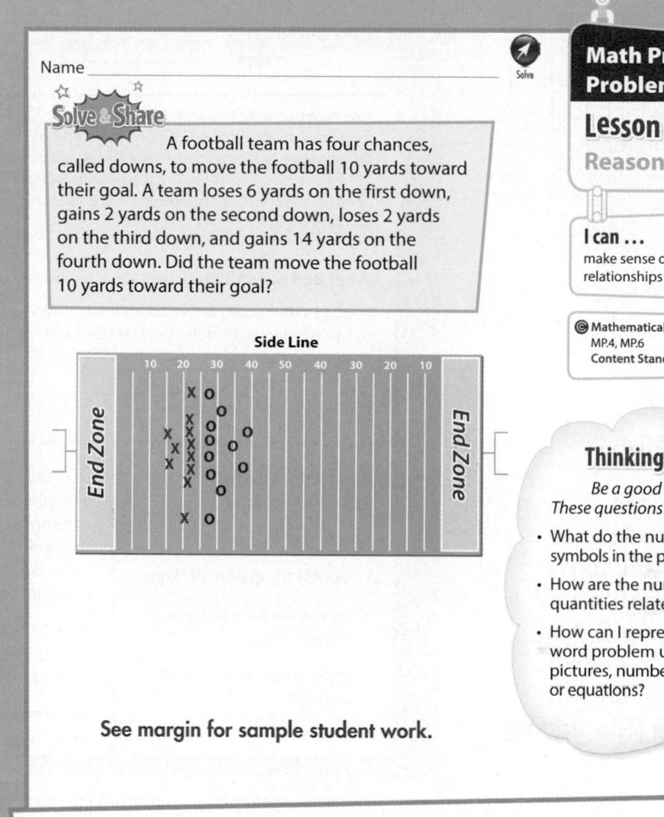
Name

Solve & Share

A football team has four chances, called downs, to move the football 10 yards toward their goal. A team loses 6 yards on the first down, gains 2 yards on the second down, loses 2 yards on the third down, and gains 14 yards on the fourth down. Did the team move the football 10 yards toward their goal?



See margin for sample student work.

**Math Practices and Problem Solving**

**Lesson 3-5**
Reasoning

**I can ...**
make sense of quantities and relationships in problem situations.

Mathematical Practices MP.2, MP.1, MP.4, MP.6
Content Standards 6.NS.C.5, 6.NS.C.6

**Thinking Habits**
*Be a good thinker! These questions can help you.*
- What do the numbers and symbols in the problem mean?
- How are the numbers or quantities related?
- How can I represent a word problem using pictures, numbers, or equations?

**Look Back!** **MP.2 Reasoning** The line of scrimmage is the vertical line that separates the two teams in the diagram. The team represented by the red circles has the ball. The team gains 8 yards, loses 3 yards, and gains 0 yards in its three downs. How many yards must they gain on the next down to score a touchdown? Explain how you know.
**20 yards; Sample answer: They started at the 25 yard line and have gained a total of 5 yards in the first three downs. So they need to gain 20 yards to get a touchdown.**

Digital Resources at PearsonRealize.com

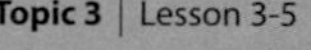
Topic 3 | Lesson 3-5

167

## Analyze Student Work

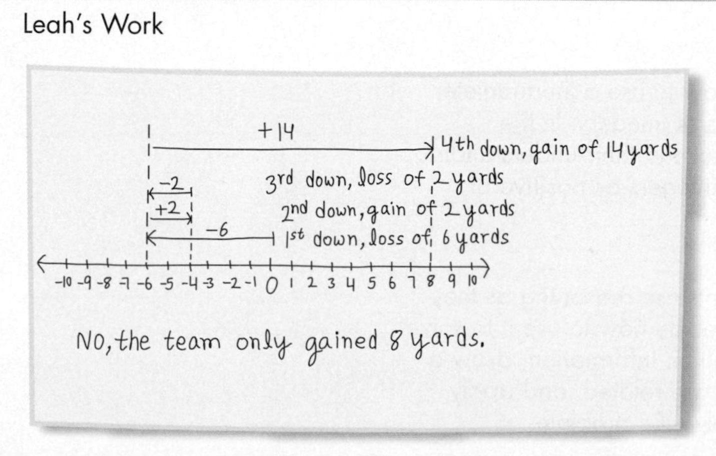


Leah correctly uses the number line to find the net number of yards that the team advanced the football.

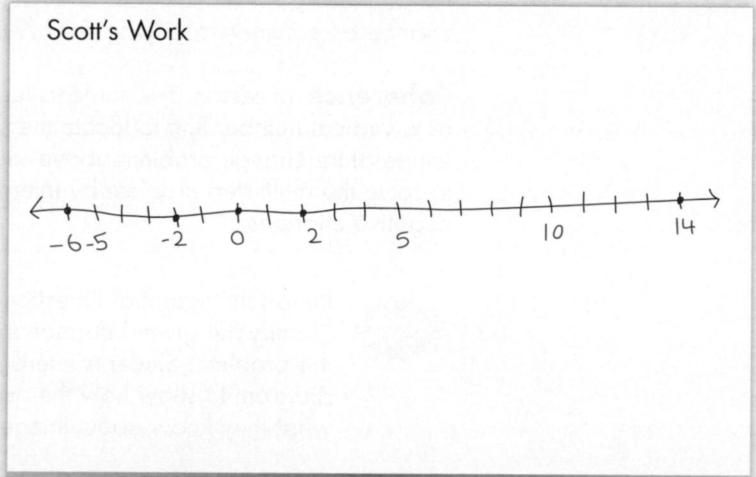


Scott plots the different number of yards gained or lost, but does not determine the net gain or loss.

# DEVELOP: VISUAL LEARNING

The *Visual Learning Bridge* connects students' thinking in Solve & Share to important math ideas in the lesson. Use the *Visual Learning Bridge* to make these ideas explicit. Also available as a *Visual Learning Animation Plus* at PearsonRealize.com

PEARSON realize. PearsonRealize.com

Learn Glossary

*What tool can be used to solve this problem?* [Sample answer: A vertical number line, which looks like a thermometer]

**MP.1 Make Sense and Persevere**
*What information is given about the temperature?* [An unknown starting temperature dropped 17°F, then increased 6°F, then increased 12°F, ending at 92°F.] *What are you asked to find?* [The starting temperature]

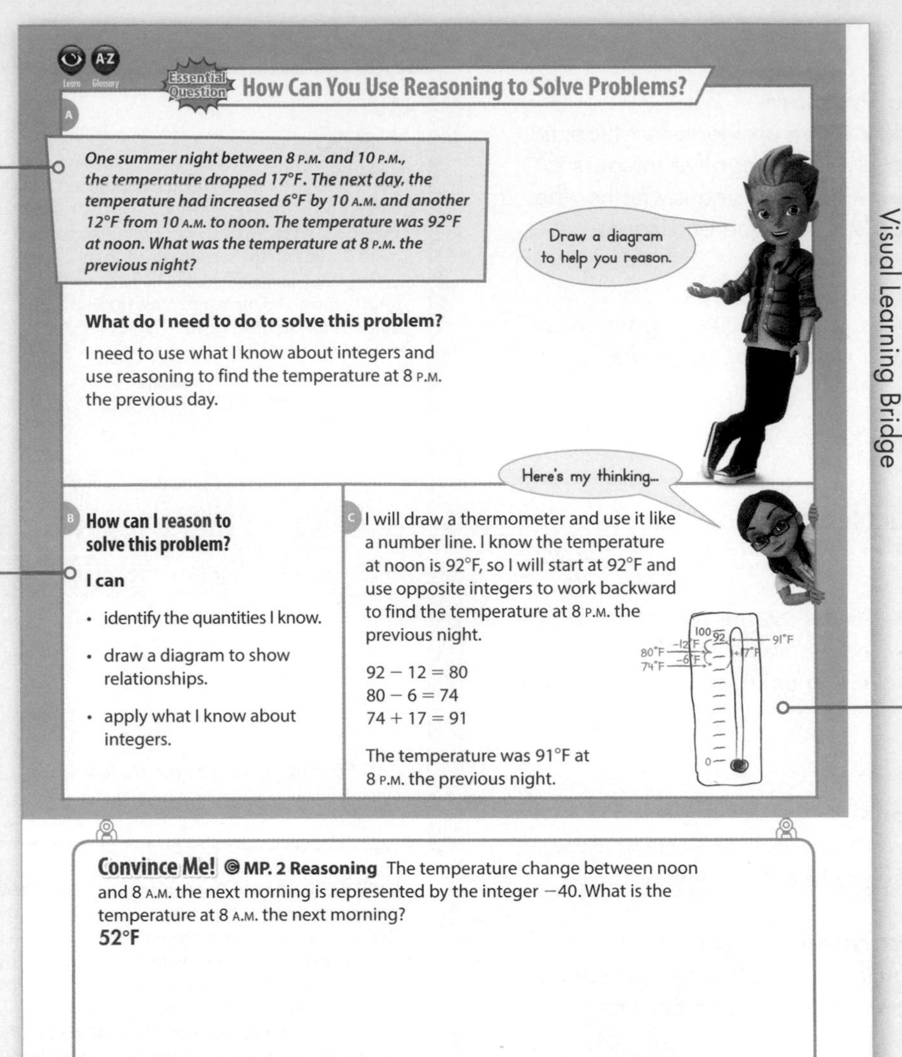

Essential Question **How Can You Use Reasoning to Solve Problems?**

A *One summer night between 8 P.M. and 10 P.M., the temperature dropped 17°F. The next day, the temperature had increased 6°F by 10 A.M. and another 12°F from 10 A.M. to noon. The temperature was 92°F at noon. What was the temperature at 8 P.M. the previous night?*



**What do I need to do to solve this problem?**

I need to use what I know about integers and use reasoning to find the temperature at 8 P.M. the previous day.



B **How can I reason to solve this problem?**

**I can**

- identify the quantities I know.
- draw a diagram to show relationships.
- apply what I know about integers.

C I will draw a thermometer and use it like a number line. I know the temperature at noon is 92°F, so I will start at 92°F and use opposite integers to work backward to find the temperature at 8 P.M. the previous night.

$92 - 12 = 80$
$80 - 6 = 74$
$74 + 17 = 91$

The temperature was 91°F at 8 P.M. the previous night.



**Convince Me!** MP. 2 Reasoning The temperature change between noon and 8 A.M. the next morning is represented by the integer −40. What is the temperature at 8 A.M. the next morning?
**52°F**

Visual Learning Bridge

168 Topic 3 | Lesson 3-5 © Pearson Education, Inc. 6

*What technique is used to find the starting temperature?* [Working backwards using a vertical number line] *Why is 12 subtracted from 92?* [The opposite of an increase of 12 is −12.] *Why is 17 added to 74?* [The opposite of a drop of 17 degrees is an increase of 17 degrees.]

**Convince Me! MP.2 Reason Quantitatively** *Does the temperature increase or decrease between noon and 8 A.M.?* [It decreases.] *Will the temperature be warmer or colder?* [Colder] *How would you write this change as a numerical expression?* [92 − 40]

**Coherence** In Lesson 3-1, students learned how to use a thermometer as a vertical number line to locate the positions of integers. In the temperature change problem above, students extend their understanding to solve the multi-step problem by interpreting integers as positive or negative changes.

Revisit the Essential Question. Students use reasoning as they identify the given information and decide how to use it to solve the problem. Students interpret the given information, draw a diagram to show how the quantities are related, and apply what they know about integers to solve the problem.

## QUICK CHECK

Check mark indicates items for prescribing differentiation on the next page.
Items 3 and 5 are worth 1 point. Items 6–8 are worth up to 3 points.

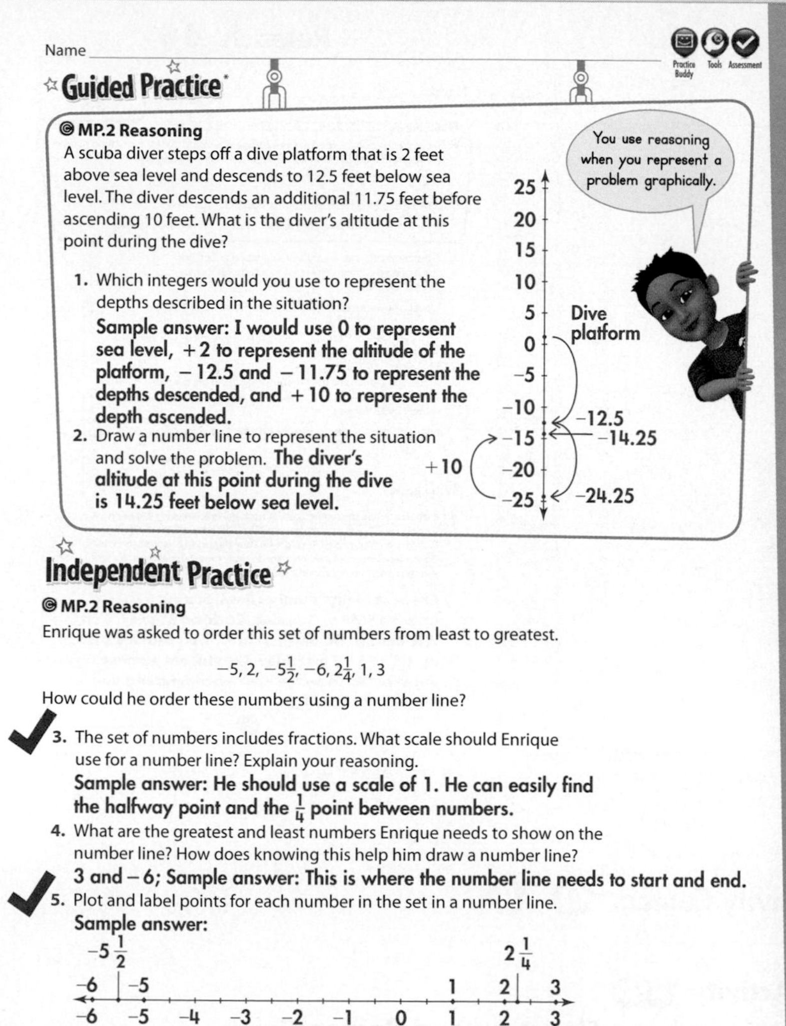

Name

### Guided Practice*

**MP.2 Reasoning**

A scuba diver steps off a dive platform that is 2 feet above sea level and descends to 12.5 feet below sea level. The diver descends an additional 11.75 feet before ascending 10 feet. What is the diver's altitude at this point during the dive?



1. Which integers would you use to represent the depths described in the situation?
**Sample answer: I would use 0 to represent sea level, +2 to represent the altitude of the platform, −12.5 and −11.75 to represent the depths descended, and +10 to represent the depth ascended.**
2. Draw a number line to represent the situation and solve the problem. **The diver's altitude at this point during the dive is 14.25 feet below sea level.**

### Independent Practice

**MP.2 Reasoning**

Enrique was asked to order this set of numbers from least to greatest.

$-5, 2, -5\frac{1}{2}, -6, 2\frac{1}{4}, 1, 3$

How could he order these numbers using a number line?

3. The set of numbers includes fractions. What scale should Enrique use for a number line? Explain your reasoning.
**Sample answer: He should use a scale of 1. He can easily find the halfway point and the $\frac{1}{4}$ point between numbers.**
4. What are the greatest and least numbers Enrique needs to show on the number line? How does knowing this help him draw a number line?
**3 and −6; Sample answer: This is where the number line needs to start and end.**
5. Plot and label points for each number in the set in a number line.
**Sample answer:**



*For another example, see Set D on page 176.

Topic 3 | Lesson 3-5 169

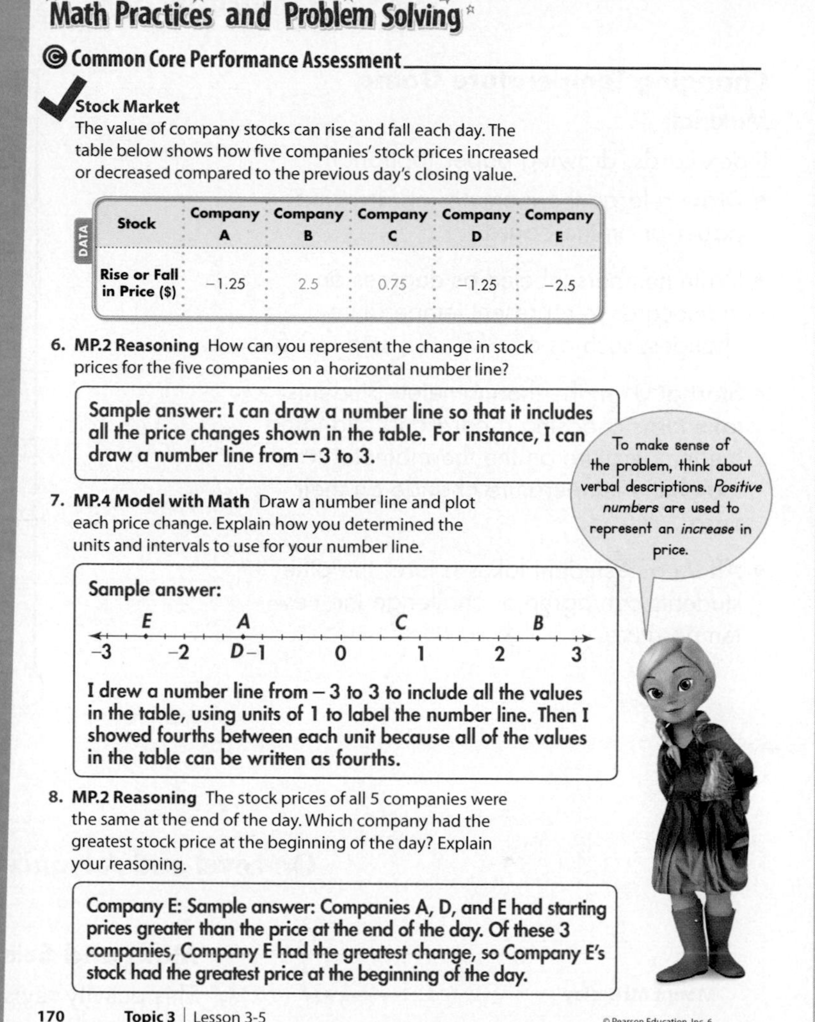

### Math Practices and Problem Solving

**Common Core Performance Assessment**

**Stock Market**

The value of company stocks can rise and fall each day. The table below shows how five companies' stock prices increased or decreased compared to the previous day's closing value.

| Stock | Company A | Company B | Company C | Company D | Company E |
|---|---|---|---|---|---|
| Rise or Fall in Price ($) | −1.25 | 2.5 | 0.75 | −1.25 | −2.5 |

6. **MP.2 Reasoning** How can you represent the change in stock prices for the five companies on a horizontal number line?
**Sample answer: I can draw a number line so that it includes all the price changes shown in the table. For instance, I can draw a number line from −3 to 3.**
7. **MP.4 Model with Math** Draw a number line and plot each price change. Explain how you determined the units and intervals to use for your number line.
**Sample answer:**

**I drew a number line from −3 to 3 to include all the values in the table, using units of 1 to label the number line. Then I showed fourths between each unit because all of the values in the table can be written as fourths.**
8. **MP.2 Reasoning** The stock prices of all 5 companies were the same at the end of the day. Which company had the greatest stock price at the beginning of the day? Explain your reasoning.
**Company E: Sample answer: Companies A, D, and E had starting prices greater than the price at the end of the day. Of these 3 companies, Company E had the greatest change, so Company E's stock had the greatest price at the beginning of the day.**

To make sense of the problem, think about verbal descriptions. *Positive numbers* are used to represent an *increase* in price.



170 Topic 3 | Lesson 3-5 © Pearson Education, Inc. 6

**MP.2 Reason Quantitatively** Listen and look for these behaviors as evidence that students are exhibiting proficiency with MP.2.

- Identifies and understands the quantities in a problem
- Shows and explains how the quantities are related
- Translates real-world contexts correctly to numbers, expressions, equations, or concrete or pictorial representations
- Connects numbers, expressions, equations, or concrete or pictorial representations back to real-world contexts

**Item 1 MP.2 Reason Quantitatively** If students have difficulty using integers to represent the quantities in the problem, remind them that 0 represents sea level. Then ask them to identify directional words in the problem.

**Reteaching** Assign Reteaching Set D on p. 176.

**Item 6 MP.2 Reason Quantitatively** Students should understand that the integers in the table represent the change in stock prices. They reason about the magnitudes of the given integers as they decide how to represent them on a number line.

**Item 7 MP.4 Model with Math** Students should examine all of the price changes and divide each whole unit into fourths on their number line because the price changes are either fourths or halves.

**Item 8 MP.2 Reason Quantitatively** Students use the given information and reason about the quantities as they work backward to find which company started with the greatest stock price.

STEP 3

# ASSESS AND DIFFERENTIATE

Use the **QUICK CHECK** on the previous page to prescribe differentiated instruction.

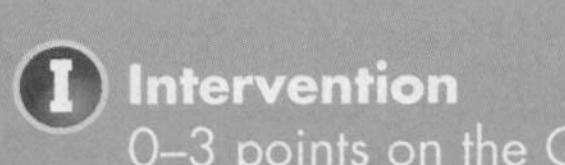


**Intervention**
0–3 points on the Quick Check

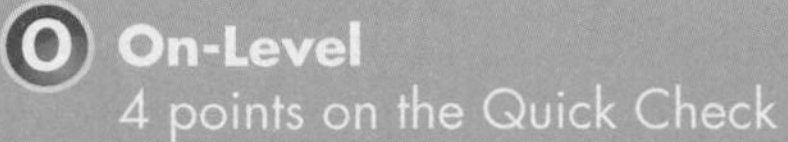


**On-Level**
4 points on the Quick Check

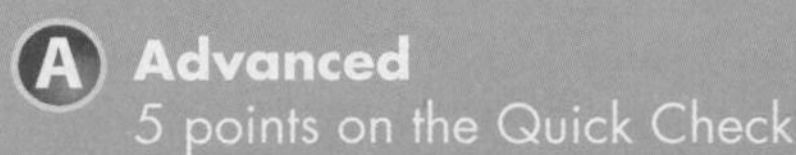


**Advanced**
5 points on the Quick Check

## Intervention Activity

### Changing Temperature Game

**Materials**

Index cards, drawing paper (optional)

- Draw a large thermometer on drawing paper or on the board.
- Write numbers labeled as degrees on index cards to represent temperature changes, such as 6°, −5°, 2°, and −0.5°.
- Start at 0° on the thermometer. Students take turns choosing a card and changing the temperature on the thermometer to match the temperature change on their card.
- After each student takes a turn, the other students can agree or challenge the new temperature.

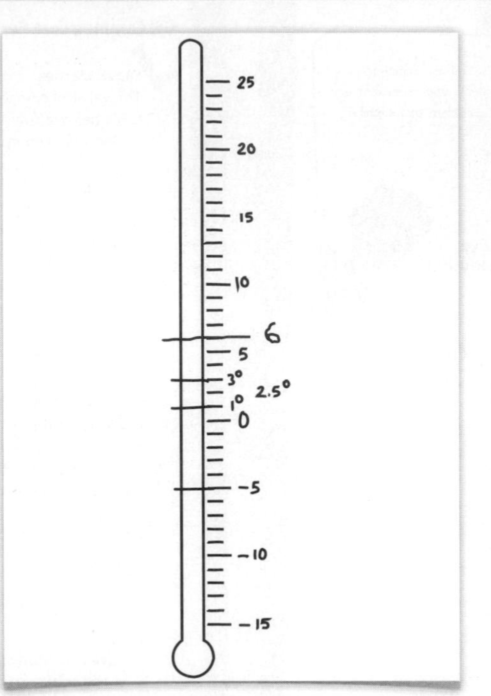


## Reteach I

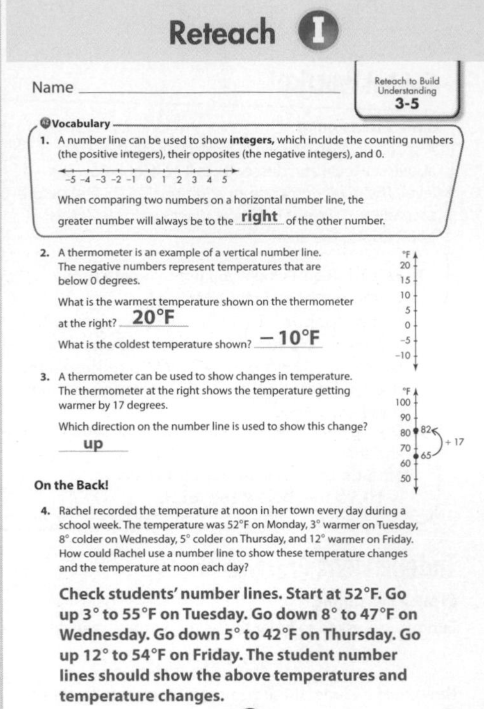

Name ____________________

Reteach to Build Understanding
3-5

**Vocabulary**

1. A number line can be used to show **integers,** which include the counting numbers (the positive integers), their opposites (the negative integers), and 0.

   −5 −4 −3 −2 −1 0 1 2 3 4 5

   When comparing two numbers on a horizontal number line, the greater number will always be to the **right** of the other number.

2. A thermometer is an example of a vertical number line. The negative numbers represent temperatures that are below 0 degrees.

   What is the warmest temperature shown on the thermometer at the right? **20°F**

   What is the coldest temperature shown? **− 10°F**

3. A thermometer can be used to show changes in temperature. The thermometer at the right shows the temperature getting warmer by 17 degrees.

   Which direction on the number line is used to show this change? **up**

**On the Back!**

4. Rachel recorded the temperature at noon in her town every day during a school week. The temperature was 52°F on Monday, 3° warmer on Tuesday, 8° colder on Wednesday, 5° colder on Thursday, and 12° warmer on Friday. How could Rachel use a number line to show these temperatures changes and the temperature at noon each day?

   **Check students' number lines. Start at 52°F. Go up 3° to 55°F on Tuesday. Go down 8° to 47°F on Wednesday. Go down 5° to 42°F on Thursday. Go up 12° to 54°F on Friday. The student number lines should show the above temperatures and temperature changes.**

R 3-5

## On-Level and Advanced Activity Centers

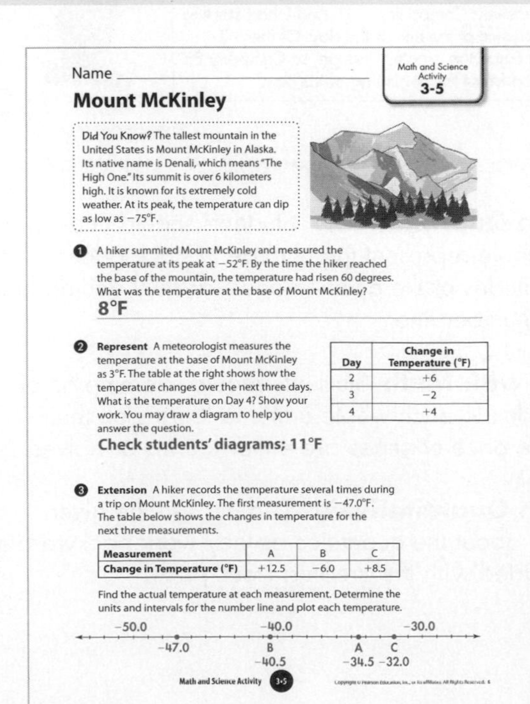

Name ____________________

Math and Science Activity
3-5

**Mount McKinley**

*Did You Know?* The tallest mountain in the United States is Mount McKinley in Alaska. Its native name is Denali, which means "The High One." Its summit is over 6 kilometers high. It is known for its extremely cold weather. At its peak, the temperature can dip as low as −75°F.

1. A hiker summited Mount McKinley and measured the temperature at its peak at −52°F. By the time the hiker reached the base of the mountain, the temperature had risen 60 degrees. What was the temperature at the base of Mount McKinley?

   **8°F**

2. **Represent** A meteorologist measures the temperature at the base of Mount McKinley as 3°F. The table at the right shows how the temperature changes over the next three days. What is the temperature on Day 4? Show your work. You may draw a diagram to help you answer the question.

   | Day | Change in Temperature (°F) |
   |---|---|
   | 2 | +6 |
   | 3 | −2 |
   | 4 | +4 |

   **Check students' diagrams; 11°F**

3. **Extension** A hiker records the temperature several times during a trip on Mount McKinley. The first measurement is −47.0°F. The table below shows the changes in temperature for the next three measurements.

   | Measurement | A | B | C |
   |---|---|---|---|
   | Change in Temperature (°F) | +12.5 | −6.0 | +8.5 |

   Find the actual temperature at each measurement. Determine the units and intervals for the number line and plot each temperature.

   −50.0 −40.0 −30.0
   −47.0 B −40.5 A −34.5 C −32.0

Math and Science Activity 3-5

### Math and Science Activity STEM

This activity revisits the science theme, **Elevation and Boiling Point**, introduced on page 139 in the Student's Edition.

### Sample Student Work

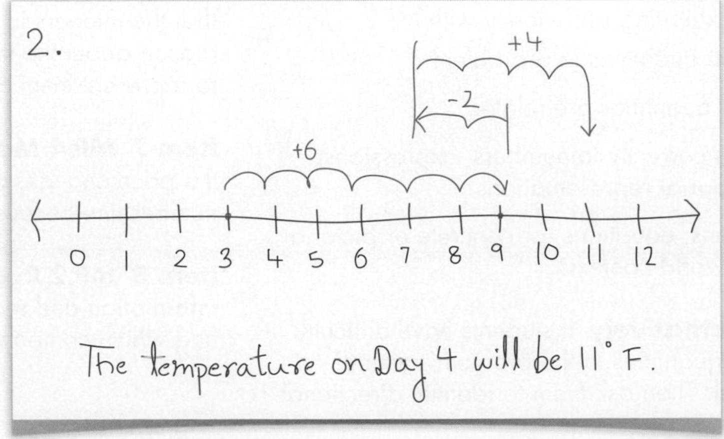

**TIMING**

The time allocated to Step 3 will depend on the teacher's instructional decisions and differentiation routines.

15–30 min

PEARSON realize. PearsonRealize.com

Help | Practice Buddy | Tools | Games

## Technology Center   

Tools Games

### Math Tools and Math Games

A link to a specific math tools activity or math game to use with this lesson is provided at PearsonRealize.com.

## Leveled Assignment  Items 1–6  Items 1–6  Items 1–6

Name ______________

Help Practice Buddy Tools Games

**Homework & Practice 3-5**
**Reasoning**

### Another Look!

Two hikers climb a mountain that begins at sea level and rises to an altitude of 4,010 feet. They stop at 2,540 feet for a break and then continue climbing until they reach the peak. They descend 3,085 feet before stopping for another break. What is their altitude when they stop for the second break?

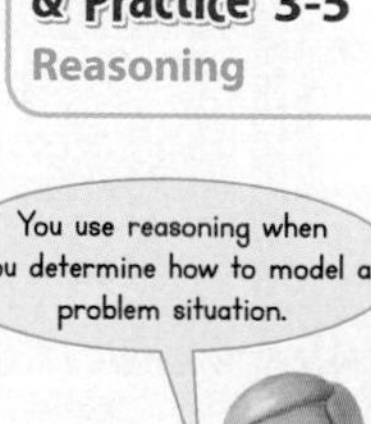

You use reasoning when you determine how to model a problem situation.


**Use reasoning to describe the hikers' locations and plot them on a number line.**

- The mountain begins at sea level. So the base of the mountain can be represented by 0.
- They stop for a break at an altitude of 2,540 feet, so the integer 2,540 represents their location during their first break.
- The peak is 4,010 feet high, so the integer 4,010 represents their location when they reach the peak.
- They stop for another break after descending 3,085 feet, so the integer −3,085 represents the decrease in altitude before their second break.

The hiker's altitude at their second break is 925 feet above sea level.

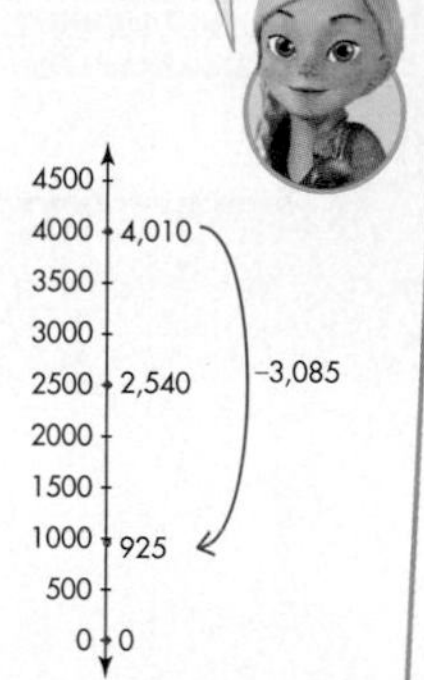


**MP.2 Reasoning**

The Lopez family is on a road trip to visit an amusement park. They entered the highway at mile marker 27. The amusement park is at mile marker 216. They stop at mile marker 146 for gas. How could you use a number line to represent their trip?

To represent a situation graphically, remember to consider the meaning of the given values.

1. What information from the problem can you use to describe the Lopez's locations?
**Sample answer: They started at mile marker 27, they stop for gas at mile marker 146, and the amusement park is at mile marker 216. The mile markers can be used to describe their locations.**
2. Draw a number line and plot the points for the Lopez's locations.
**Sample answer:**

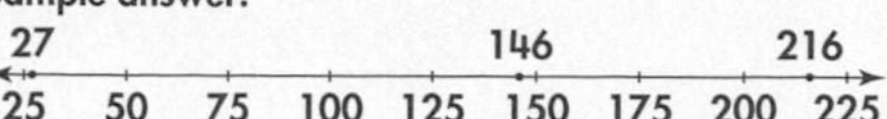




### Common Core Performance Assessment

**Water Animals**

Fish and other aquatic animals sometimes jump out of or dive under the water to avoid predators or to capture prey. The altitude, or height, of five sea animals in relation to sea level are recorded in the table below.

| Animal | Dolphin (D) | Albatross (A) | Shark (S) | Tuna (T) | Marlin (M) |
|---|---|---|---|---|---|
| Altitude (yd) | 1.5 | −1.25 | $-1\frac{1}{2}$ | −1 | $1\frac{3}{4}$ |

3. **MP.4 Model with Math** Use the number line at the right to represent the altitude of each animal. Explain how you determined the units and intervals to use for your number line.
**Sample answer: I labeled the number line from −2 to 2 to include all of the values in the table. I used 0 to represent sea level. I divided each unit into fourths because all the values can be written as fourths. Then I plotted points for each animal's altitude.**
4. **MP.6 Be Precise** Order the animals' altitudes from least to greatest. Explain your reasoning.
**Shark, Albatross, Tuna, Dolphin, Marlin; Sample answer: Altitude means height above or below sea level. I used the number line I made to order the animals from lowest to highest altitude.**
5. **MP.2 Reasoning** Which animal is farthest from the ocean's surface? Which animal is nearest to the ocean surface? Explain.
**The marlin is farthest from the ocean's surface because the ocean's surface is at sea level, or 0, and $1\frac{3}{4}$ yards is the farthest positive distance from 0. The tuna is nearest to the ocean's surface because 1 yard is the closest distance to 0.**
6. **MP.1 Make Sense and Persevere** Dalton saw a loon dive 1.5 yards below sea level to catch a fish. What is the difference between how far the loon and the albatross dove? How do you know?
**.25 yd; Sample answer: −1.5 is 0.25 units farther from 0 (the surface of the water) than −1.25, so the loon dove 0.25 yards farther than the albatross.**

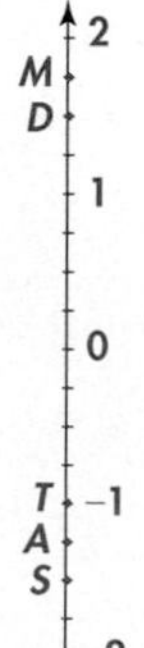

# FLUENCY PRACTICE ACTIVITY

PEARSON realize. PearsonRealize.com

Games

Practice Buddy

## FLUENCY PRACTICE ACTIVITY

Students review the Grade 5 fluency standard about multiplying multi-digit whole numbers during a partner activity that reinforces mathematical practices.

### Common Core Standards

**Content Standard 5.NBT.B.5** Fluently multiply multi-digit whole numbers using the standard algorithm.

**Mathematical Practices MP.3, MP.6, MP.7, MP.8**

**Getting Started** Ask partners to share one page. Tell them that the other partner's page will be used to record tally marks when they repeat the activity. Go over the directions. Note that for any product, only one partner will get a tally mark.

When partners simultaneously point to two numbers, they may point to two numbers that they have already multiplied. In that case, students can point again to find two other numbers to multiply.

**As Students Do the Activity** Remind students to compare and discuss their answers.

**Another Activity** Students can repeat the activity and record tally marks on the other partner's page.

**Extra Challenge** *Take turns with a partner. Point to a product in one of the blue spaces. Ask your partner to get that product by multiplying a number in the column at the right by a number in the column at the left.*

Games

**Online Game** The Game Center at PearsonRealize.com provides opportunities for fluency practice.

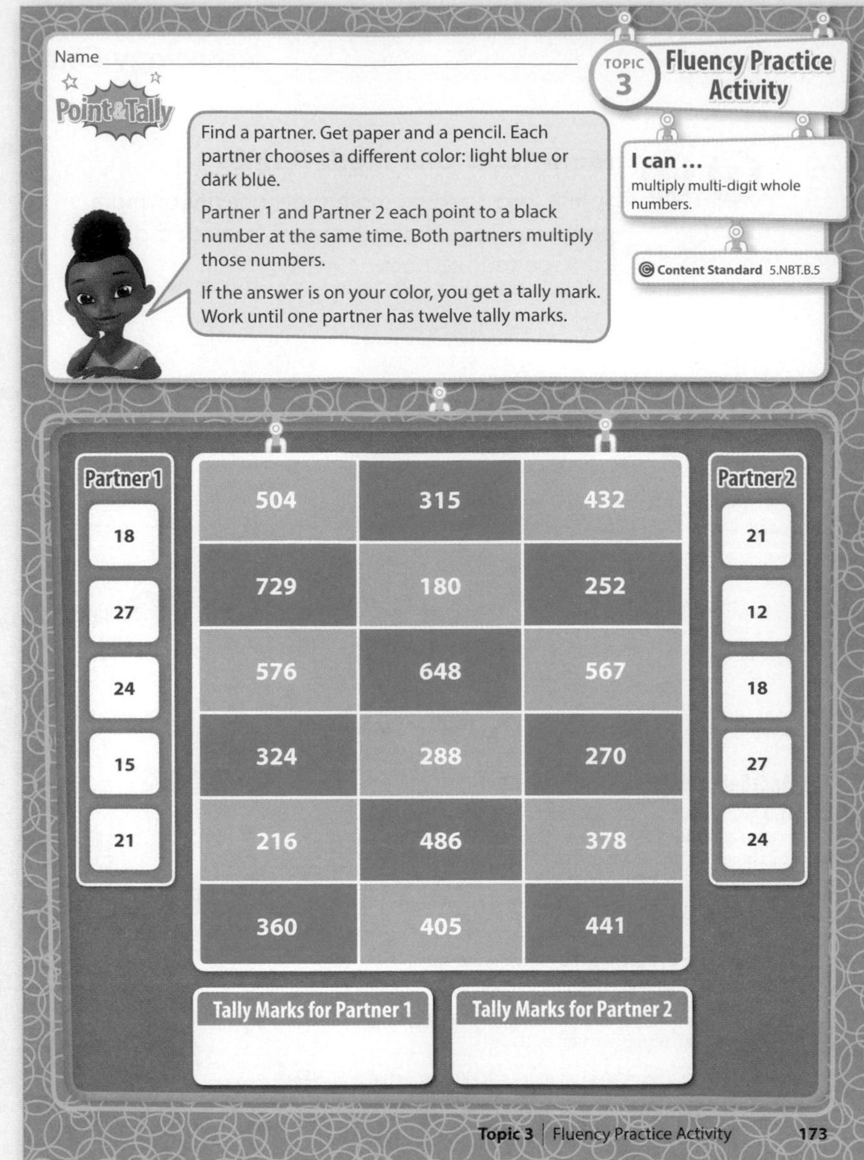

Name

Point & Tally

TOPIC 3 Fluency Practice Activity

Find a partner. Get paper and a pencil. Each partner chooses a different color: light blue or dark blue.

Partner 1 and Partner 2 each point to a black number at the same time. Both partners multiply those numbers.

If the answer is on your color, you get a tally mark. Work until one partner has twelve tally marks.

I can ... multiply multi-digit whole numbers.

Content Standard 5.NBT.B.5

| Partner 1 | | | | Partner 2 |
|---|---|---|---|---|
| 18 | 504 | 315 | 432 | 21 |
| 27 | 729 | 180 | 252 | 12 |
| 24 | 576 | 648 | 567 | 18 |
| 15 | 324 | 288 | 270 | 27 |
| 21 | 216 | 486 | 378 | 24 |
| | 360 | 405 | 441 | |

Tally Marks for Partner 1

Tally Marks for Partner 2

Topic 3 | Fluency Practice Activity 173

# VOCABULARY REVIEW

Glossary

Games

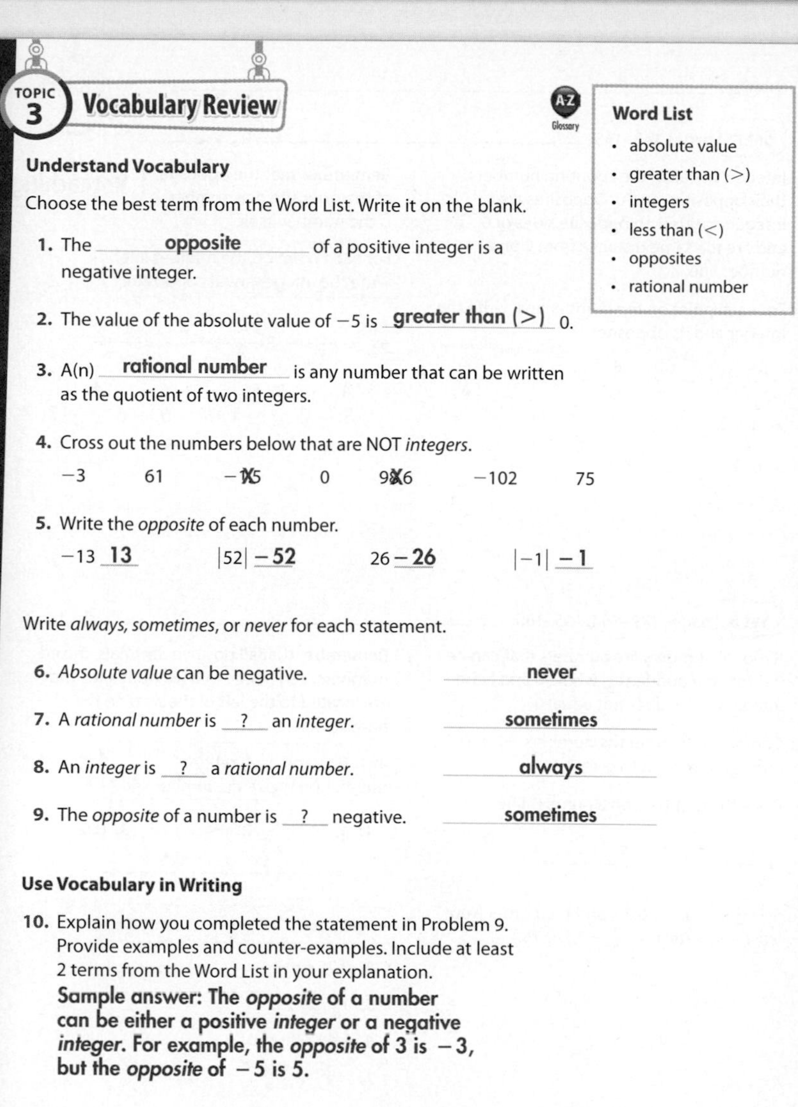

TOPIC 3 **Vocabulary Review**

**Word List**
- absolute value
- greater than (>)
- integers
- less than (<)
- opposites
- rational number

**Understand Vocabulary**

Choose the best term from the Word List. Write it on the blank.

1. The **opposite** of a positive integer is a negative integer.
2. The value of the absolute value of −5 is **greater than (>)** 0.
3. A(n) **rational number** is any number that can be written as the quotient of two integers.
4. Cross out the numbers below that are NOT *integers*.
   −3 61 ~~−1.5~~ 0 ~~9.6~~ −102 75
5. Write the *opposite* of each number.
   −13 **13** |52| **−52** 26 **−26** |−1| **−1**

Write *always, sometimes,* or *never* for each statement.

6. *Absolute value* can be negative. **never**
7. A *rational number* is __?__ an *integer*. **sometimes**
8. An *integer* is __?__ a *rational number*. **always**
9. The *opposite* of a number is __?__ negative. **sometimes**

**Use Vocabulary in Writing**

10. Explain how you completed the statement in Problem 9. Provide examples and counter-examples. Include at least 2 terms from the Word List in your explanation.
    **Sample answer: The *opposite* of a number can be either a positive *integer* or a negative *integer*. For example, the *opposite* of 3 is −3, but the *opposite* of −5 is 5.**

174 Topic 3 | Vocabulary Review

© Pearson Education, Inc. 6

## VOCABULARY REVIEW

Students review vocabulary words used in the topic.

**Oral Language** Before students complete the page, you might reinforce oral language through a class discussion involving one or more of the following activities.

- Have students define the vocabulary terms in their own words and use the terms in math sentences.
- Have student pairs ask and answer math questions that use the words.
- Conduct a math relay. Write the vocabulary terms on index cards, and tape them to the board or wall. Divide the class into relay teams, and have each team stand in a line facing the word wall. Then give a clue. The student at the front of the line of each relay team goes to the word wall, grabs the vocabulary card, and goes to the end of his or her team's relay line.
- Play a "Right or Wrong?" game in which you or a student says a sentence that uses one of the words correctly or incorrectly. Then, others say "right" or "wrong."

**Writing in Math** After students complete the page, you might further reinforce writing in math by doing one or more of the following activities.

- Tell students to close their books. Then, say the words and have students write them. Students trade papers to check if the words are spelled correctly.
- Have students work in pairs to create a word search using the terms in the Word List. Provide grid paper or allow students to use an online word search activity maker. Encourage students to use definitions, examples, or models, rather than the terms themselves, for the word search clues.

Games

**Online Game** The Game Center at PearsonRealize.com includes a vocabulary game that students can access any time.

# TOPIC 3 RETEACHING

## RATIONAL NUMBERS

### RtI Item Analysis for Diagnosis and Intervention

| Reteaching Sets | Standard | MDIS |
|---|---|---|
| Set A | 6.NS.C.5, 6.NS.C.6a, 6.NS.C.6c | F18 |
| Set B | 6.NS.C.6c, 6.NS.C.7a, 6.NS.C.7b | F20 |
| Set C | 6.NS.C.7c, 6.NS.C.7d | F64, F19 |
| Set D | MP.2, MP.1, MP.4, MP.6 | J5, J20 |

Name ______

TOPIC 3

**Set A** pages 143–148

Integers are all of the counting numbers, their opposites, and 0. Opposites are integers located on opposite sides of 0 and are the same distance from 0 on a number line.

For each point on the number line, write the integer and its opposite.

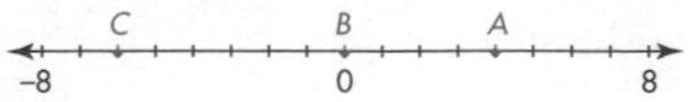

*A*: 4, −4

*B*: 0, 0

*C*: −6, 6

**Remember** that the opposite of the opposite of a number is the number itself.

Reteaching

For each point on the number line, write the integer and its opposite.

1. *A* 3, −3
2. *B* −1, 1
3. *C* 6, −6
4. *D* −7, 7

**Set B** pages 149–154, 155–160

Rational numbers are numbers that can be written as a quotient $\frac{a}{b}$, where *a* and *b* are integers and *b* does not equal 0.

Compare and order the numbers −0.1, 0.75, and $-\frac{1}{4}$ from least to greatest.

Place the numbers on a number line.

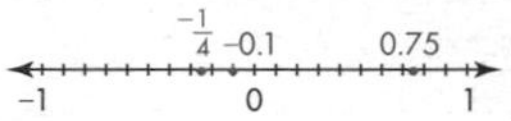

So $-\frac{1}{4} < -0.1 < 0.75$, and their order from least to greatest is $-\frac{1}{4}$, −0.1, 0.75.

**Remember** that all positive decimals, mixed numbers, and fractions have opposites that are located to the left of the zero on the number line.

In **1–3**, graph each rational number on the same number line.

1. $\frac{3}{4}$
2. $-\frac{2}{5}$
3. 0.5

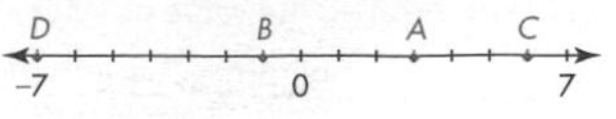

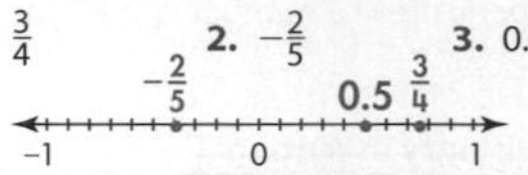

In **4–7**, use <, >, or = to compare.

4. 0.25 (=) $\frac{1}{4}$
5. $1\frac{5}{8}$ (>) 1.6
6. 3.65 (<) $3\frac{3}{4}$
7. $-\frac{2}{3}$ (>) $-\frac{3}{4}$

**Set C** pages 161–166

The absolute value of a number is its distance from zero on the number line. Distance is always positive.

Find the absolute values and order $|3|$, $|4|$, $|-2|$, $|-5|$ from *least* to *greatest*.

$|-5| = 5$
$|-2| = 2$
$|3| = 3$
$|4| = 4$

Ordered from least to greatest:
$|-2|, |3|, |4|, |-5|$

**Remember** that absolute values are always positive.

In **1–4**, find each value.

**1.** $|-9|$ **9**

**2.** $|-2|$ **2**

**3.** $|4|$ **4**

**4.** $-|-10|$ **−10**

In **5–7**, order the values from least to greatest.

**5.** $|-3|, |-2|, |10|$
**$|-2|, |-3|, |10|$**

**6.** $|-7|, |0|, |-5|$
**$|0|, |-5|, |-7|$**

**Set D** pages 167–172

Think about these questions to help you **reason abstractly and quantitatively**.

**Thinking Habits**

- What do the numbers and symbols in the problem mean?
- How are the numbers or quantities related?
- How can I represent a word problem using pictures, numbers, or equations?

**Remember** to use reasoning and what you know about rational numbers to solve problems.

Sarah spent $15.75 at the movies on a ticket and snacks. Then she earned $40 babysitting, and bought a book for $9.50. Sarah has $34.75 left. How much money did she start with?

1. Which integers would you use to represent the dollar amounts described in the situation?
**Sample answer: You would use the integer −15.75 to represent the amount Sarah spent at the movies, +40 to represent the amount earned babysitting, −9.5 to represent the amount spent on a book, and +34.75 to represent the amount she has left.**
2. Draw a number line to represent the situation and solve the problem.
**Sarah started with $20. Check students' number lines.**




## Response to Intervention

**Ongoing Intervention**
- Lessons with guiding questions to assess understanding
- Support to prevent misconceptions and to reteach

**Strategic Intervention**
- Targeted to small groups that need more support
- Easy to implement

**Intensive Intervention**
- Instruction to accelerate progress
- Instruction focused on foundational skills

# TOPIC ASSESSMENT

## RATIONAL NUMBERS

Name ______________________________

TOPIC 3 | Assessment

**1.** Three friends competed in a golf tournament. The table shows their resulting scores compared to a par score of 0. What is the opposite value of Emma's score? **1 point**

DATA

| Name | Score |
|---|---|
| Cassie | −4 |
| Emma | −12 |
| Juanita | 6 |

Ⓐ −12
Ⓑ −4
Ⓒ 4
● 12

**2.** For questions **2a–2d**, choose Yes or No to indicate which of the comparisons is true. **1 point**

**2a.** $-12.5 > 11\frac{3}{4}$ ○ Yes ● No
**2b.** $0 > -12.5$ ● Yes ○ No
**2c.** $20.8 < 20\frac{5}{6}$ ● Yes ○ No
**2d.** $1.1 = -(-1.1)$ ● Yes ○ No

**3.** Order these absolute values from least to greatest. **1 point**
$|-7|, |5|, |-4|, |6|, |-15|$

**$|-4|, |5|, |6|, |-7|, |-15|$**

**4.** Jeremy listed five rational numbers. Then he drew a number line to display and compare them.

**Part A** **3 points**

Fill in the blanks to plot the numbers on the number line.
$\frac{6}{3}, -\frac{3}{4}, 1.5, 0.25, -\frac{5}{4}$

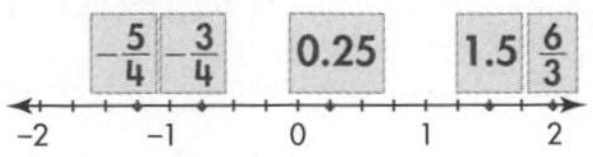


**Part B**

Write an inequality that compares one of the fractions to one of the decimals. Then explain how the number line helps you decide which number is greater.

**Sample answer: $-\frac{3}{4} < 0.25$. Because 0.25 is located to the right of $-\frac{3}{4}$ on the number line, it is the greater number.**

**5.** Which of the following have a value equal to $|37|$? **1 point**

☐ −37
☐ 0
■ 37
■ $|-37|$
■ $-(-37)$



**6.** A swimmer dives to 65 feet below the surface of the ocean. Write the integer that represents the depth of the dive. **1 point**

**−65**

**7.** The table shows the elevations of some places in the United States. The integers represent their distances in feet above or below sea level. **2 points**

DATA

| Place | Elevation |
|---|---|
| Potomac River | 1 |
| New Orleans | −8 |
| Lake Champlain | 95 |
| Death Valley | −282 |

Is the place that has the greatest elevation also located the greatest distance from sea level? Explain your reasoning using an inequality.

**No; Sample answer: Lake Champlain, located at 95 feet above sea level, has the greatest elevation, but Death Valley is located 282 feet below sea level. Since, 282 > 95, it is located a greater distance from sea level.**

**8.** List the following numbers in order from greatest to least. **1 point**
$-11, 1\frac{1}{2}, -1\frac{1}{5}, -(-8), 7.5$

**$-(-8), 7.5, 1\frac{1}{2}, -1\frac{1}{5}, -11$**

**9.** Circle the point that represents −1.4 on the number line. Then identify a point that represents a lesser value and explain how you know. **2 points**

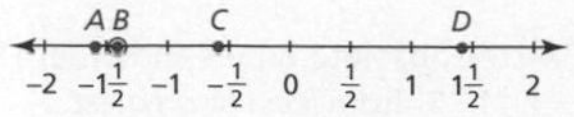


**Point *A* < Point *B* because it is plotted farther left on the number line.**

**10.** Draw lines to match each number on the right to its opposite value on the left. **1 point**

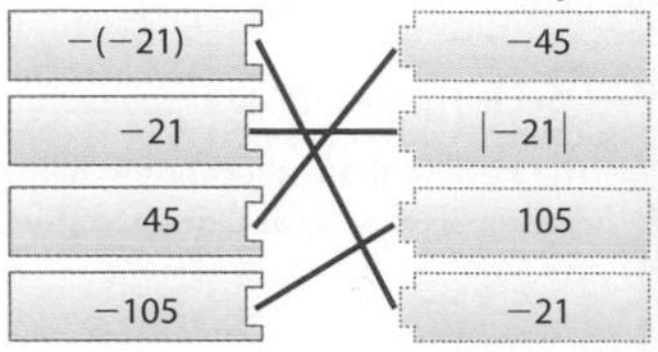


**11.** Nathan lives on the *n*th floor of his building. He got on the elevator on his floor and rode up 10 floors, down 16 floors, and then up 25 floors to arrive at the 36th floor of the building. On what floor of the building does Nathan live? **1 point**

**Nathan lives on the 17th floor of the building.**





## ANSWERING THE TOPIC ESSENTIAL QUESTION

Restate the Topic Essential Questions from the Topic Opener or project them from the Student's Edition eText.

Ask students to answer the Essential Questions (verbally or in writing) and give examples that support their answers. The following are key elements of the answers to the Essential Questions. Be sure these are made explicit when discussing students' answers.

### What are integers and rational numbers?

- Integers are the counting numbers, their opposites, and zero. Rational numbers are numbers that can be written as fractions; each one has a unique point on the number line. The set of rational numbers includes integers (which can be written as fractions with a denominator of 1).

  **Example:** The set of integers includes …−4, −3, −2, −1, 0, 1, 2, 3, 4… Some examples of rational numbers are: −8.5, −5, 0, and $\frac{1}{4}$.

### How can you compare and order rational numbers?

- To compare and order rational numbers, locate them on the number line in relation to zero. A number located to the right of another number is the greater number.

  **Example:** To order the numbers $\frac{4}{2}$, −1.75, $|1.5|$, $-\frac{5}{4}$, locate them on the number line. From left to right (or from least to greatest), the numbers are ordered −1.75, $-\frac{5}{4}$, $|1.5|$, $\frac{4}{2}$

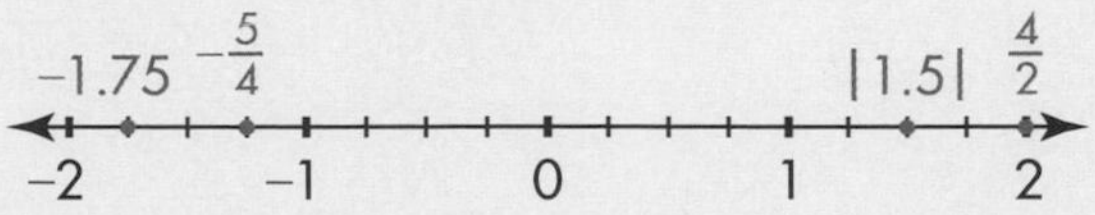


- Another way to compare and order rational numbers is to write them in a common form.

  **Example:** To compare the numbers $|-1\frac{3}{5}|$ and 1.4, write them both as decimals (1.6, 1.4) or as fractions $\left(\frac{8}{5}, \frac{7}{5}\right)$. Then use number sense to write an inequality: $|-1\frac{3}{5}| > 1.4$.

Assessment

## ONLINE TOPIC ASSESSMENT

An auto-scored Topic Assessment is provided at PearsonRealize.com.

## EXAMVIEW® TEST GENERATOR

ExamView can be used to create a blackline-master Topic Assessment with multiple-choice and free-response items.

## Topic Assessment Masters

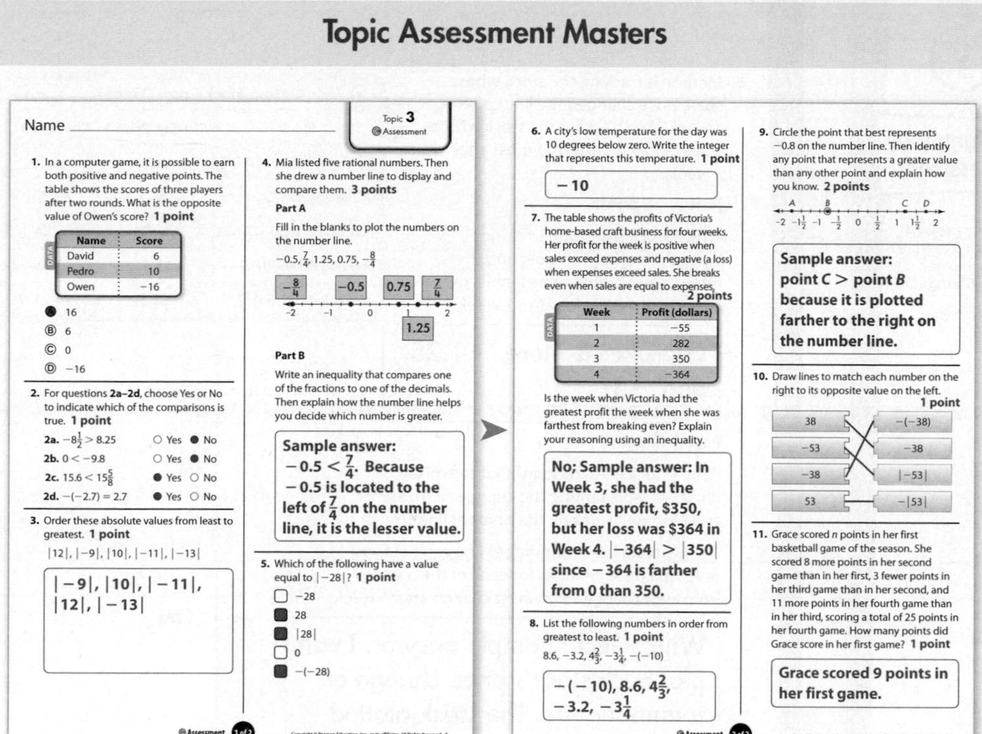

Name ________

Topic 3 Assessment

1. In a computer game, it is possible to earn both positive and negative points. The table shows the scores of three players after two rounds. What is the opposite value of Owen's score? **1 point**

| Name | Score |
|---|---|
| David | 6 |
| Pedro | 10 |
| Owen | −16 |

Ⓐ 16
Ⓑ 6
Ⓒ 0
Ⓓ −16

2. For questions **2a–2d**, choose Yes or No to indicate which of the comparisons is true. **1 point**

**2a.** $-8\frac{1}{2} > 8.25$ ○ Yes ● No
**2b.** $0 < -9.8$ ○ Yes ● No
**2c.** $15.6 < 15\frac{5}{8}$ ● Yes ○ No
**2d.** $-(-2.7) = 2.7$ ● Yes ○ No

3. Order these absolute values from least to greatest. **1 point**

$|12|, |-9|, |10|, |-11|, |-13|$

**$|-9|, |10|, |-11|, |12|, |-13|$**

4. Mia listed five rational numbers. Then she drew a number line to display and compare them. **3 points**

**Part A**

Fill in the blanks to plot the numbers on the number line.

$-0.5, \frac{7}{4}, 1.25, 0.75, -\frac{8}{4}$

$-\frac{8}{4}$, $-0.5$, $0.75$, $\frac{7}{4}$, $1.25$

**Part B**

Write an inequality that compares one of the fractions to one of the decimals. Then explain how the number line helps you decide which number is greater.

**Sample answer: $-0.5 < \frac{7}{4}$. Because $-0.5$ is located to the left of $\frac{7}{4}$ on the number line, it is the lesser value.**

5. Which of the following have a value equal to $|-28|$? **1 point**

☐ −28
■ 28
■ |28|
☐ 0
■ −(−28)

Assessment 1 of 2



6. A city's low temperature for the day was 10 degrees below zero. Write the integer that represents this temperature. **1 point**

**−10**

7. The table shows the profits of Victoria's home-based craft business for four weeks. Her profit for the week is positive when sales exceed expenses and negative (a loss) when expenses exceed sales. She breaks even when sales are equal to expenses. **2 points**

| Week | Profit (dollars) |
|---|---|
| 1 | −55 |
| 2 | 282 |
| 3 | 350 |
| 4 | −364 |

Is the week when Victoria had the greatest profit the week when she was farthest from breaking even? Explain your reasoning using an inequality.

**No; Sample answer: In Week 3, she had the greatest profit, $350, but her loss was $364 in Week 4. $|-364| > |350|$ since −364 is farther from 0 than 350.**

8. List the following numbers in order from greatest to least. **1 point**

$8.6, -3.2, 4\frac{2}{3}, -3\frac{1}{4}, -(-10)$

**$-(-10), 8.6, 4\frac{2}{3}, -3.2, -3\frac{1}{4}$**

9. Circle the point that best represents −0.8 on the number line. Then identify any point that represents a greater value than any other point and explain how you know. **2 points**

A B C D
$-2\ -1\frac{1}{2}\ -1\ -\frac{1}{2}\ 0\ \frac{1}{2}\ 1\ 1\frac{1}{2}\ 2$

**Sample answer: point C > point B because it is plotted farther to the right on the number line.**

10. Draw lines to match each number on the right to its opposite value on the left. **1 point**

| | |
|---|---|
| 38 | −(−38) |
| −53 | −38 |
| −38 | \|−53\| |
| 53 | −\|53\| |

11. Grace scored *n* points in her first basketball game of the season. She scored 8 more points in her second game than in her first, 3 fewer points in her third game than in her second, and 11 more points in her fourth game than in her third, scoring a total of 25 points in her fourth game. How many points did Grace score in her first game? **1 point**

**Grace scored 9 points in her first game.**

Assessment 2 of 2



## Item Analysis for Diagnosis and Intervention

RtI

| Item | Standard | DOK | MDIS |
|---|---|---|---|
| 1 | 6.NS.C.6a | 1 | F18 |
| 2 | 6.NS.C.7a | 1 | F20 |
| 3 | 6.NS.C.7c | 1 | F64, F19 |
| 4 | 6.NS.C.6c, 6.NS.C.7a | 2 | F20 |
| 5 | 6.NS.C.7c, 6.NS.C.6a | 1 | F64 |
| 6 | 6.NS.C.5 | 1 | F18 |
| 7 | 6.NS.C.5, 6.NS.C.7d | 3 | F19 |
| 8 | 6.NS.C.7 | 1 | F20 |
| 9 | 6.NS.C.6c, 6.NS.C.7a | 2 | F20 |
| 10 | 6.NS.C.6a, 6.NS.C.7c | 1 | F18, F64 |
| 11 | 6.NS.C.5, MP.2 | 2 | J5, F18 |

The Topic Assessment Masters assess the same content item for item as the Topic Assessment in the Student's Edition.

## Scoring Guide

| Item | Points | Topic Assessment (Student's Edition and Masters) |
|---|---|---|
| 1 | 1 | Correct choice |
| 2 | 1 | All correct choices |
| 3 | 1 | Correct answer |
| 4 | 3 | Correct answers for Part A and Part B |
| | 2 | Correct answer for Part A or Part B |
| | 1 | Incomplete answers for Part A and Part B |
| 5 | 1 | All correct choices |
| 6 | 1 | Correct answer |
| 7 | 2 | Correct inequality and explanation |
| | 1 | Correct inequality or explanation |
| 8 | 1 | Correct answer |
| 9 | 2 | Correct answer and explanation |
| | 1 | Correct answer or explanation |
| 10 | 1 | All matches correct |
| 11 | 1 | Correct answer |

# TOPIC 3 TOPIC PERFORMANCE ASSESSMENT

## RATIONAL NUMBERS

Name ______________________________

TOPIC 3 Performance Assessment

**Tracking Stocks**

Groups of students in Ms. Kim's 6th-grade class chose 5 stocks to track for a class project. The share price of a stock can go up or down each day as the result of trading on the stock market. A student in each group tracked the change in share price of one stock for a week.

**Closing Stock Prices (Day 1)**

| Stock | Closing Price $ | Change $ |
|---|---|---|
| Trends 'n' Threadz (TRDZ) | 45.34 | +3 |
| U.S. Toy Maker (USTY) | 52.27 | −2 |
| Cupcakes & More (CCML) | 44.17 | +5 |
| Ling Ling Purses (LLPC) | 48.87 | −3 |
| Whirly Tech (WHRL) | 177.26 | −7 |

1. Bonita is tracking the stock that had the least change in share price after 1 day. What stock is she tracking and what integer represents its change in price? **1 point**

**U.S. Toy Maker, −2**

2. **Part A 1 point**

Sidney made a number line to compare the changes in price of the stocks after Day 1. Use the following list of acronyms to name and plot each stock on the number line.

TRDZ USTY CCML LLPC WHRL

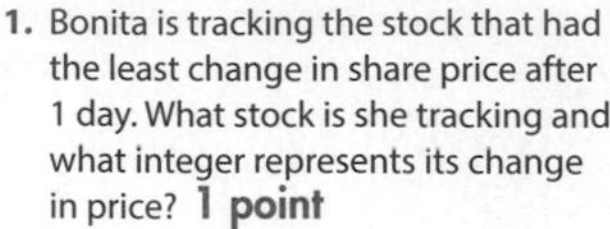


**Part B 1 point**

Jalen and Kyra are tracking stocks whose price changes after Day 1 are opposites. Which two stocks are they tracking and what are the integers that represent the price change for each stock?

**Trends 'n' Threadz (+3) and Ling Ling Purses (−3)**



3. Monroe is tracking the stock whose share price changed the least after 1 week. Yu is tracking the stock whose share price changed the most after 1 week.

**Closing Stock Prices (Week)**

| Stock | Closing Price $ | Change $ |
|---|---|---|
| Trends 'n' Threadz (TRDZ) | 44.84 | +2.5 |
| U.S. Toy Maker (USTY) | 55.77 | +1.5 |
| Cupcakes & More (CCML) | 37.92 | −1.25 |
| Ling Ling Purses (LLPC) | 48.62 | −3.25 |
| Whirly Tech (WHRL) | 188.51 | +4.25 |

**Part A 1 point**

Which stock is Monroe tracking? Write the decimal number and the mixed number that represent its overall change in share price after 1 week.

**Cupcakes & More, −1.25 and $-1\frac{1}{4}$**

**Part B 3 points**

Which stock is Yu tracking? Plot the mixed numbers representing the change for Yu's stock and Monroe's stock on the number line.

Then explain how the number line can help you order the price changes for each of the 5 stocks from least change to greatest change after 1 week.

5, $4\frac{1}{4}$ WHRL, 0, $-1\frac{1}{4}$ CCML, −5

**Whirly Tech; Sample answer: I can plot each stock's price change on a number line. The stock plotted closest to zero on the number line, $-1\frac{1}{4}$, has the least change. The stock plotted farthest from zero, $+4\frac{1}{4}$, has the greatest change. Compare distances from zero to order the other three stocks. So, $-1\frac{1}{4}, +1\frac{1}{2}, +2\frac{1}{2}, -3\frac{1}{4}, +4\frac{1}{4}$.**





## Scoring Guide

| Item | Points | Topic Performance Assessment in the Student's Edition |
|---|---|---|
| 1 | 1 | Correct answer |
| 2A | 1 | Correct number line |
| 2B | 1 | Correct answer |
| 3A | 1 | Correct answer |
| 3B | 3 | Correct number line and explanation |
| | 2 | Correct number line, but incomplete explanation |
| | 1 | Incorrect number line, but explanation shows some understanding |

## RtI Item Analysis for Diagnosis and Intervention

| Item | Standard | DOK | MDIS |
|---|---|---|---|
| 1 | 6.NS.C.5, 6.NS.C.7d, MP.2 | 1 | F18, F64 |
| 2A | 6.NS.C.6c, MP.5 | 2 | F19 |
| 2B | 6.NS.C.6a, MP.2 | 2 | F18 |
| 3A | 6.NS.C.5, 6.NS.C.7d, MP.1 | 2 | F64, F20 |
| 3B | 6.NS.C.6c, 6.NS.C.7d, MP.6 | 3 | F64, F20 |

## Topic Performance Assessment Masters

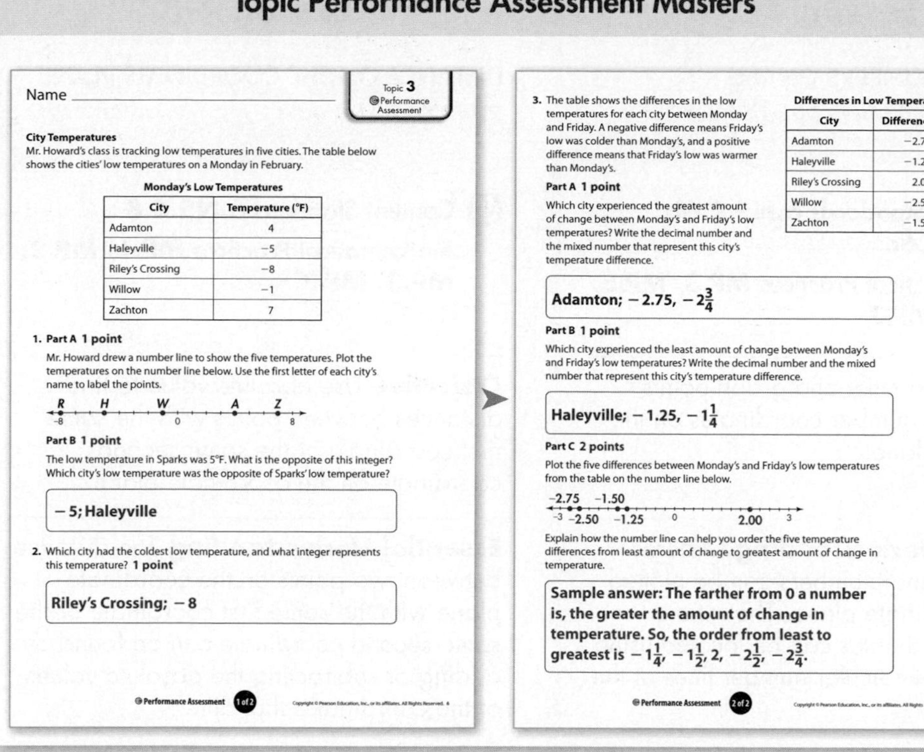

Name ______________________

Topic 3 Performance Assessment

**City Temperatures**
Mr. Howard's class is tracking low temperatures in five cities. The table below shows the cities' low temperatures on a Monday in February.

**Monday's Low Temperatures**

| City | Temperature (°F) |
|---|---|
| Adamton | 4 |
| Haleyville | −5 |
| Riley's Crossing | −8 |
| Willow | −1 |
| Zachton | 7 |

1. **Part A 1 point**
Mr. Howard drew a number line to show the five temperatures. Plot the temperatures on the number line below. Use the first letter of each city's name to label the points.



**Part B 1 point**
The low temperature in Sparks was 5°F. What is the opposite of this integer? Which city's low temperature was the opposite of Sparks' low temperature?

**− 5; Haleyville**

2. Which city had the coldest low temperature, and what integer represents this temperature? **1 point**

**Riley's Crossing; − 8**




3. The table shows the differences in the low temperatures for each city between Monday and Friday. A negative difference means Friday's low was colder than Monday's, and a positive difference means that Friday's low was warmer than Monday's.

**Differences in Low Temperatures**

| City | Difference (°F) |
|---|---|
| Adamton | −2.75 |
| Haleyville | −1.25 |
| Riley's Crossing | 2.00 |
| Willow | −2.50 |
| Zachton | −1.50 |

**Part A 1 point**
Which city experienced the greatest amount of change between Monday's and Friday's low temperatures? Write the decimal number and the mixed number that represent this city's temperature difference.

**Adamton; − 2.75, $-2\frac{3}{4}$**

**Part B 1 point**
Which city experienced the least amount of change between Monday's and Friday's low temperatures? Write the decimal number and the mixed number that represent this city's temperature difference.

**Haleyville; − 1.25, $-1\frac{1}{4}$**

**Part C 2 points**
Plot the five differences between Monday's and Friday's low temperatures from the table on the number line below.



Explain how the number line can help you order the five temperature differences from least amount of change to greatest amount of change in temperature.

**Sample answer: The farther from 0 a number is, the greater the amount of change in temperature. So, the order from least to greatest is $-1\frac{1}{4}$, $-1\frac{1}{2}$, 2, $-2\frac{1}{2}$, $-2\frac{3}{4}$.**




## RtI Item Analysis for Diagnosis and Intervention

| Item | Standard | DOK | MDIS |
|---|---|---|---|
| 1A | 6.NS.C.6c, MP.5 | 2 | F19 |
| 1B | 6.NS.C.5, 6.NS.C.6a, MP.2 | 2 | F18 |
| 2 | 6.NS.C.5, 6.NS.C.7d, MP.2 | 1 | F19 |
| 3A | 6.NS.C.5, 6.NS.C.7d, MP.1 | 2 | F64, F20 |
| 3B | 6.NS.C.5, 6.NS.C.7d, MP.1 | 2 | F64, F20 |
| 3C | 6.NS.C.6c, 6.NS.C.7d, MP.6 | 3 | F64, F20 |

## Scoring Guide

| Item | Points | Topic Performance Assessment Masters |
|---|---|---|
| 1A | 1 | Correct number line |
| 1B | 1 | Correct answer |
| 2 | 1 | Correct answer |
| 3A | 1 | Correct answer |
| 3B | 1 | Correct answer |
| 3C | 2 | Correct number line and explanation |
| | 1 | Correct number line or explanation |

TOPIC 4

# TOPIC PLANNER

## ALGEBRA: COORDINATE GEOMETRY

| Lesson 4-1 | Lesson 4-2 | Lesson 4-3 |
|---|---|---|
| INTEGERS ON THE COORDINATE PLANE pp. 185–190 | RATIONAL NUMBERS ON THE COORDINATE PLANE pp. 191–196 | DISTANCE ON THE COORDINATE PLANE pp. 197–202 |
| Content Standards **6.NS.C.6b, 6.NS.C.6c**<br>Mathematical Practices **MP.1, MP.7, MP.8** | Content Standards **6.NS.C.6b, 6.NS.C.6c**<br>Mathematical Practices **MP.3, MP.5, MP.6, MP.7** | Content Standard **6.NS.C.8**<br>Mathematical Practices **MP.1, MP.2, MP.3, MP.7** |
| **Objective** Identify and graph points with integer coordinates on the coordinate plane. | **Objective** Identify and graph points with rational number coordinates on the coordinate plane. | **Objective** Use absolute value to find distances between points with the same first coordinate or the same second coordinate on the coordinate plane. |
| **Essential Understanding** The coordinate plane is formed by a horizontal number line, called the *x*-axis, and a vertical number line, called the *y*-axis, that intersect at a point called the origin. An ordered pair (*x*, *y*) locates a point on the coordinate plane. | **Essential Understanding** Ordered pairs of rational numbers can be plotted on the coordinate plane. The rational number coordinates can be located using the two perpendicular number lines of the plane. | **Essential Understanding** The distance between two points on the coordinate plane with the same first coordinate or the same second coordinate can be found by adding or subtracting the absolute values of the coordinates that differ. |
| **Vocabulary** Coordinate plane, *x*-axis, *y*-axis, Quadrant, Ordered pair, Origin | **Vocabulary** None | **Vocabulary** None |
| **ELL Reading:** Develop basic (math) sight vocabulary. | **ELL Speaking:** Give information using key words and expressions. | **ELL Listening:** Learn new (math) language structures. |
| **Materials** Four-quadrant coordinate grids (TT 19), index cards | **Materials** Four-quadrant coordinate grids (TT 19) | **Materials** Four-quadrant coordinate grids (TT 19) |
| **On-Level and Advanced Activity Centers**<br>• Problem-Solving Reading Mat | **On-Level and Advanced Activity Centers**<br>• Math and Science Activity | **On-Level and Advanced Activity Centers**<br>• Problem-Solving Reading Mat |

## LESSON RESOURCES

Digital

Print

- Student's Edition
- Daily Common Core Review
- Reteach to Build Understanding
- Center Games
- Math and Science Activity
- Problem-Solving Reading Mat
- Problem-Solving Reading Activity

Digital

- Listen and Look For PD Lesson Video
- Student's Edition eText
- Today's Challenge
- Solve & Share
- Visual Learning Animation Plus
- Animated Glossary
- Math Tools
- Practice Buddy Online Practice
- Quick Check
- Another Look Homework Video
- Math Games

Digital

## Lesson 4-4

**POLYGONS ON THE COORDINATE PLANE** pp. 203–208

**Content Standards 6.NS.C.8, 6.G.A.3**
**Mathematical Practices MP.2, MP.3, MP.7, MP.8**

**Objective** Solve problems that involve finding side lengths of polygons on the coordinate plane.

**Essential Understanding** The coordinates of the vertices of a polygon on the coordinate plane can be used to find the lengths of the sides of the polygon.

**Vocabulary** None

**ELL Reading:** Use visual support to develop vocabulary.

**Materials** Four-quadrant coordinate grids (TT 19), sticky notes

**On-Level and Advanced Activity Centers**
- Center Games

## Lesson 4-5

**MATH PRACTICES AND PROBLEM SOLVING: CONSTRUCT ARGUMENTS** pp. 209–214

**Mathematical Practices MP.3 Also MP.1, MP.4, MP.6**
**Content Standards 6.NS.C.8, 6.G.A.3**

**Objective** Construct arguments using previously learned concepts and skills, such as finding distances on the coordinate plane.

**Essential Understanding** Good math thinkers use math to explain why they are right. They can talk about the math that others do, too.

**Vocabulary** None

**ELL Learning Strategies:** Use academic language in meaningful ways when speaking.

**Materials** Four-quadrant coordinate grids (TT 19), sticky notes

**On-Level and Advanced Activity Centers**
- Math and Science Activity

## TOPIC RESOURCES

Digital

Print

**Start of Topic**
- Math and Science Project
- Home-School Connection
- Review What You Know
- My Word Cards

**End of Topic**
- Fluency Practice Activity
- Vocabulary Review
- Reteaching
- Topic Assessment
- Topic Performance Assessment
- Cumulative/Benchmark Assessment

Digital

**Start of Topic**
- Topic Overview PD Video

**End of Topic**
- Math Practices Animations
- Online Topic Assessment
- ExamView® Test Generator
- Practice Buddy Fluency Practice/Assessment
- Online Cumulative/Benchmark Assessment

PearsonRealize.com

TOPIC 4

# TOPIC OPENER

# ALGEBRA: COORDINATE GEOMETRY

## TOPIC ESSENTIAL QUESTION

**How are points graphed on a coordinate plane?**

Revisit the Topic Essential Question throughout the topic, and see a note about answering the question in the Teacher's Edition for the Topic Assessment.

## MATH AND SCIENCE PROJECT STEM

**Science Theme** The science theme for this project is **Map to Predict and Plan**. This theme will be revisited in the Math and Science Activities in Lessons 4-2 and 4-5 and in some lesson exercises.

Earthquakes are caused by movements between tectonic plates. The plates can slide past each other, or a plate can push over or slide under a neighboring plate.

Knowing the boundaries between tectonic plates can help scientists prepare for future earthquakes in those areas.

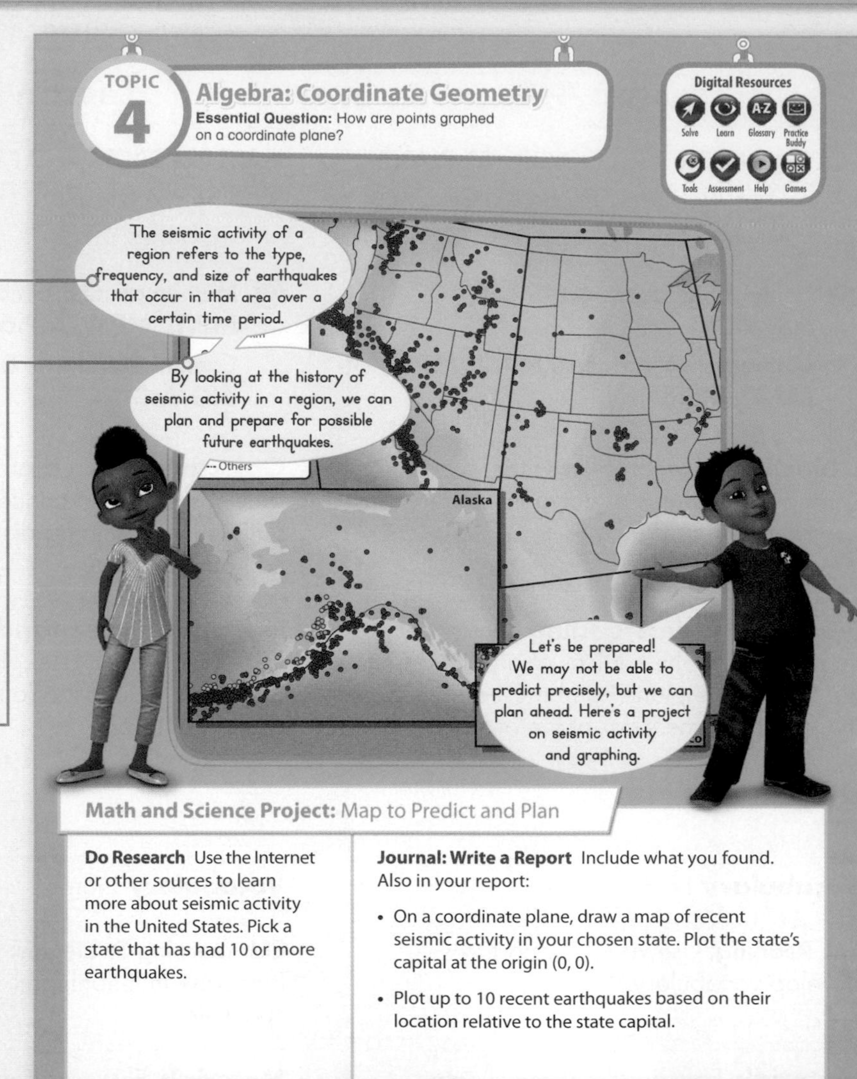


**Project-Based Learning** Have students work on the **Math and Science Project** over the course of several days.

## EXTENSION

Have students research the boundaries of tectonic plates in the United States based on frequent earthquake activity.

### Sample Student Work for Math and Science Project

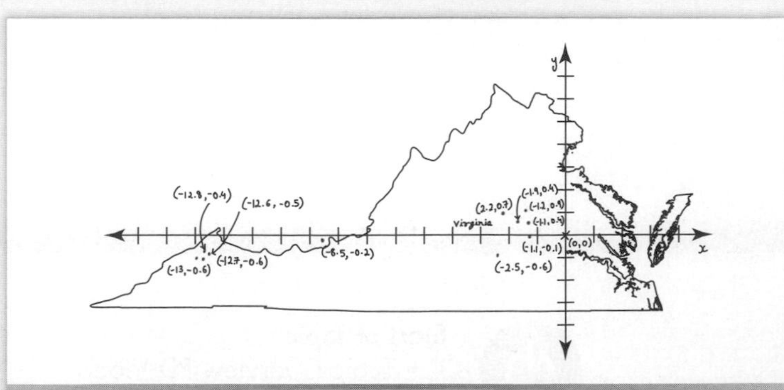


## Home-School Connection

Name ______________________

**Algebra: Coordinate Geometry**

Home-School Connection Topic 4

**Topic 4 Standards**

6.NS.C.6b, 6.NS.C.6c, 6.NS.C.8, 6.G.A.3

*See the front of the Student's Edition for complete standards.*

Dear Family,

In this topic, your child will learn about integers and rational numbers and their positions on a coordinate plane. He or she will graph shapes and use absolute value to find distances between the shape's vertices with the same first coordinate or the same second coordinate.

You can help your child understand the concept of a coordinate plane by playing the game below.

**Where Am I?**

**Materials** Two sheets of blank paper, pencil

**Step 1** Draw a coordinate plane on one sheet of paper with labels. The ordered pairs, such as (−, +), represent the signs of the $x$ and $y$-coordinates in the quadrant.

**Step 2** On a second sheet of paper, draw a coordinate plane, but do not include quadrants and ordered pairs. Use this to play the game.

**Step 3** Ask your child to identify and locate the quadrant of an ordered pair that you state. Continue until your child correctly identifies the quadrant, and then switch roles.

**Step 4** Vary the game by naming a quadrant and asking your child to locate the quadrant and give a possible ordered pair in that quadrant.

Quadrant II (−, +) | Quadrant I (+, +) | Quadrant III (−, −) | Quadrant IV (+, −) | 5 | −5 | 0 | $x$ | $y$

**Observe Your Child**

**Focus on Mathematical Practice 6**
Attend to precision

Help your child become proficient with Mathematical Practice 6. Have your child explain the reasoning used to identify the quadrant of each ordered pair using precise mathematical terminology. Clarify misunderstandings or inaccurate use of mathematical language as you play the game.



Send this page home at the start of Topic 4 to give families an overview of the content in the topic.

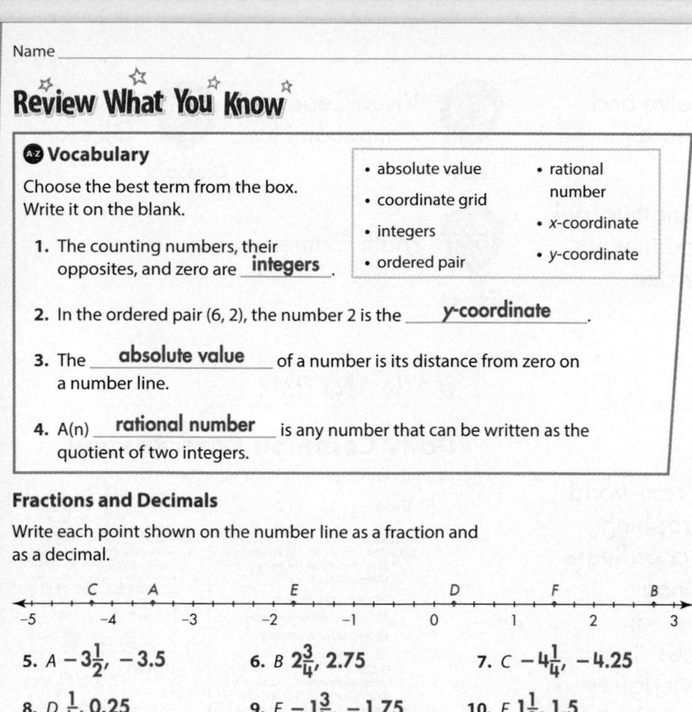

Name ____________________

## Review What You Know

**Vocabulary**

Choose the best term from the box. Write it on the blank.

- absolute value
- coordinate grid
- integers
- ordered pair
- rational number
- x-coordinate
- y-coordinate

1. The counting numbers, their opposites, and zero are **integers**.
2. In the ordered pair (6, 2), the number 2 is the **y-coordinate**.
3. The **absolute value** of a number is its distance from zero on a number line.
4. A(n) **rational number** is any number that can be written as the quotient of two integers.

**Fractions and Decimals**

Write each point shown on the number line as a fraction and as a decimal.

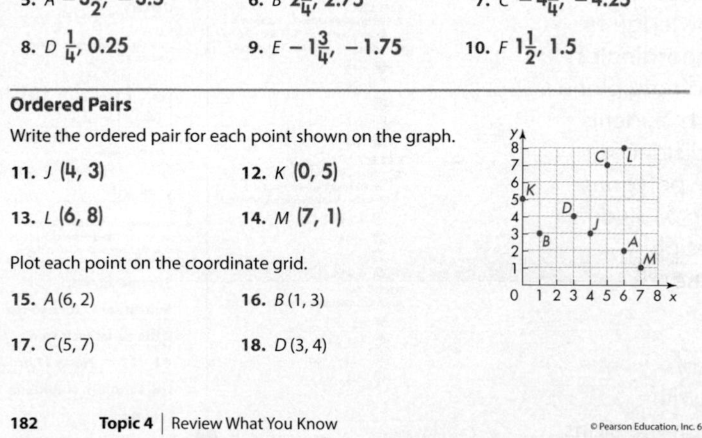



5. $A$ $-3\frac{1}{2}$, $-3.5$
6. $B$ $2\frac{3}{4}$, $2.75$
7. $C$ $-4\frac{1}{4}$, $-4.25$
8. $D$ $\frac{1}{4}$, $0.25$
9. $E$ $-1\frac{3}{4}$, $-1.75$
10. $F$ $1\frac{1}{2}$, $1.5$

**Ordered Pairs**

Write the ordered pair for each point shown on the graph.

11. $J$ (4, 3)
12. $K$ (0, 5)
13. $L$ (6, 8)
14. $M$ (7, 1)

Plot each point on the coordinate grid.

15. $A$ (6, 2)
16. $B$ (1, 3)
17. $C$ (5, 7)
18. $D$ (3, 4)







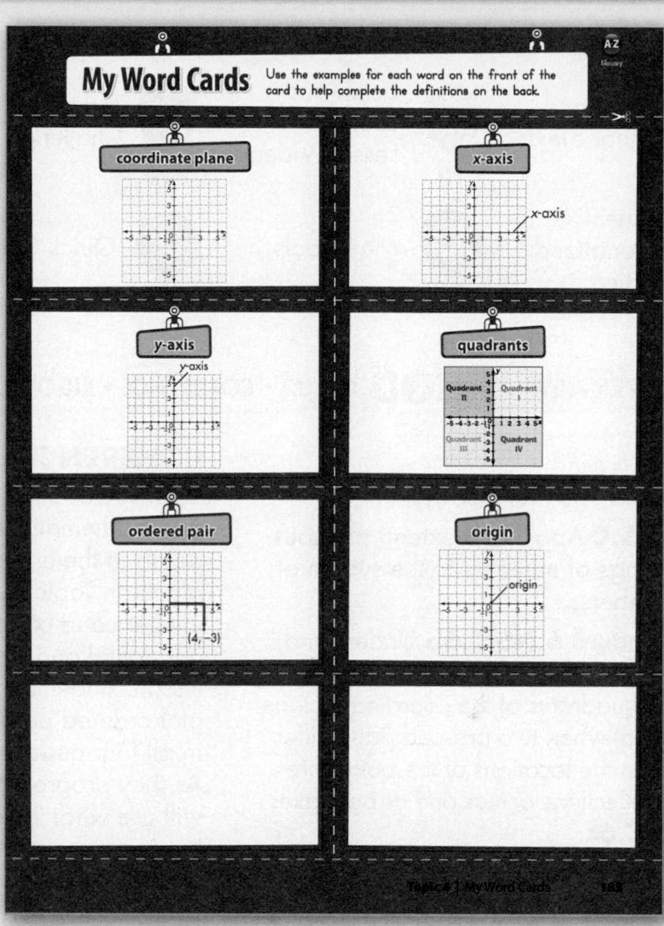

## My Word Cards

Use the examples for each word on the front of the card to help complete the definitions on the back.





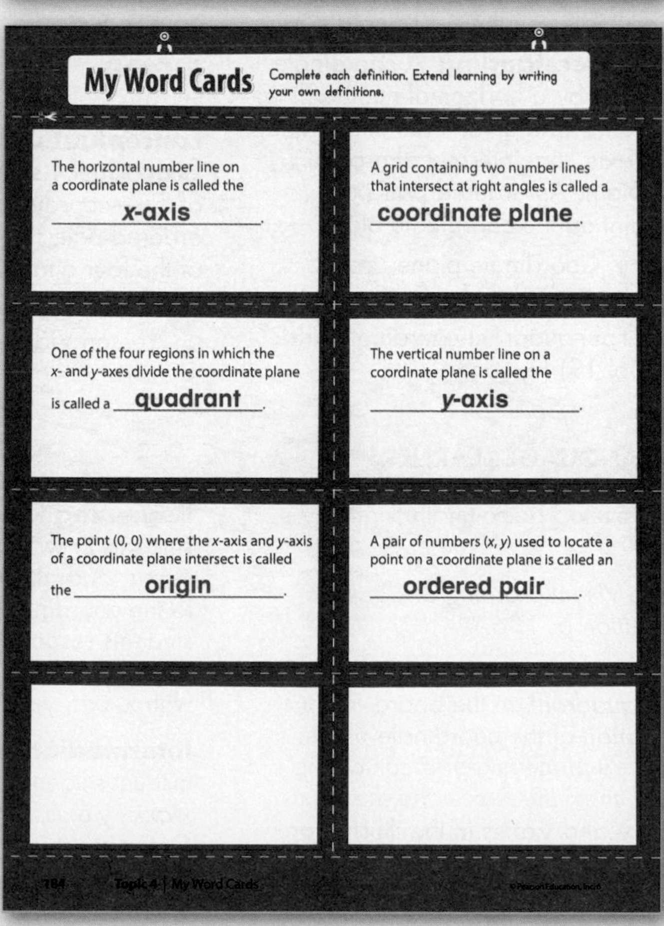

## My Word Cards

Complete each definition. Extend learning by writing your own definitions.

The horizontal number line on a coordinate plane is called the **x-axis**.

A grid containing two number lines that intersect at right angles is called a **coordinate plane**.

One of the four regions in which the x- and y-axes divide the coordinate plane is called a **quadrant**.

The vertical number line on a coordinate plane is called the **y-axis**.

The point (0, 0) where the x-axis and y-axis of a coordinate plane intersect is called the **origin**.

A pair of numbers (x, y) used to locate a point on a coordinate plane is called an **ordered pair**.



## RtI Item Analysis for Diagnosis and Intervention

| Item | Standard | MDIS |
|---|---|---|
| 1–4 | 6.NS.C.6c, 6.NS.C.7 | F18, F20, F32 |
| 5–10 | 6.NS.C.6c | F20 |
| 11–18 | 6.NS.C.6c | F32 |

## Topic 4 Vocabulary Words Activity

Use the Topic 1 activity on p. 3–4 with the Topic 4 words at the right.

LESSON **4-1**

# INTEGERS ON THE COORDINATE PLANE

## DIGITAL RESOURCES PearsonRealize.com

eText — Student and Teacher eTexts

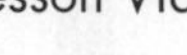

PD — Listen and Look For Lesson Video

Think — Today's Challenge
Solve — Solve and Share

Learn — Visual Learning Animation Plus
Glossary — Animated Glossary

Practice Buddy — Online Personalized Practice
Tools — Math Tools
Assessment — Quick Check
Help — Another Look Homework Video

Games — Math Games

## LESSON OVERVIEW — FCR FOCUS • COHERENCE • RIGOR

### FOCUS

**Domain 6.NS** The Number System

**Cluster 6.NS.C** Apply and extend previous understandings of numbers to the system of rational numbers.

**Content Standard 6.NS.C.6b** Understand signs of numbers in ordered pairs as indicating locations in quadrants of the coordinate plane; recognize that when two ordered pairs differ only by signs, the locations of the points are related by reflections across one or both axes. Also **6.NS.C.6c**.

**Mathematical Practices MP.1, MP.7, MP.8**

**Objective** Identify and graph points with integer coordinates on the coordinate plane.

**Essential Understanding** A coordinate plane is formed by a horizontal number line, called the *x*-axis, and a vertical number line, called the *y*-axis, that intersect at a point called the origin. An ordered pair $(x, y)$ locates a point on the coordinate plane.

**Vocabulary** Coordinate plane, *x*-axis, *y*-axis, Quadrant, Ordered pair, Origin

**Materials** Four-quadrant coordinate grids (Teaching Tool 19) (optional)

### COHERENCE

In Grade 5, students represented real-world and mathematical problems by graphing points in the first quadrant of the coordinate plane. In Topic 3, students positioned integers and other rational numbers on horizontal and vertical number lines. In this lesson, students extend their knowledge to plot ordered pairs with integer coordinates in all four quadrants of the coordinate plane. As they progress through Topic 4, students will use what they learn to find distances between two points and to draw polygons on the coordinate plane. In Topic 5, students will use ordered pairs as they graph equations on the coordinate plane.

### RIGOR

This lesson emphasizes a blend of **conceptual understanding** with **procedural skill**. Depending on the signs of the *x*-coordinate and *y*-coordinate of an ordered pair, the point will be located in one of the four quadrants or on an axis.

PD Watch the Listen and Look For Lesson Video.

## MATH ANYTIME

### Daily Common Core Review

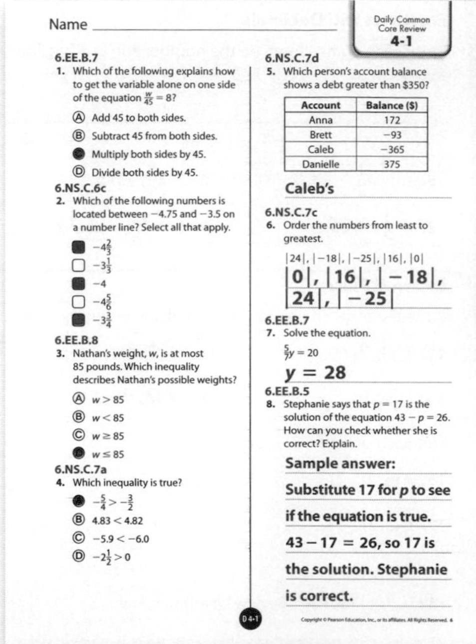
Name ______

Daily Common Core Review **4-1**

**6.EE.B.7**
1. Which of the following explains how to get the variable alone on one side of the equation $\frac{w}{45} = 8$?
   Ⓐ Add 45 to both sides.
   Ⓑ Subtract 45 from both sides.
   ● Multiply both sides by 45.
   Ⓓ Divide both sides by 45.

**6.NS.C.6c**
2. Which of the following numbers is located between −4.75 and −3.5 on a number line? Select all that apply.
   ■ $-4\frac{2}{3}$
   □ $-3\frac{1}{3}$
   ■ $-4$
   □ $-4\frac{5}{6}$
   ■ $-3\frac{3}{4}$

**6.EE.B.8**
3. Nathan's weight, *w*, is at most 85 pounds. Which inequality describes Nathan's possible weights?
   Ⓐ $w > 85$
   Ⓑ $w < 85$
   Ⓒ $w \geq 85$
   ● $w \leq 85$

**6.NS.C.7a**
4. Which inequality is true?
   ● $-\frac{5}{4} > -\frac{3}{2}$
   Ⓑ $4.83 < 4.82$
   Ⓒ $-5.9 < -6.0$
   Ⓓ $-2\frac{1}{2} > 0$

**6.NS.C.7d**
5. Which person's account balance shows a debt greater than $350?

| Account | Balance ($) |
|---|---|
| Anna | 172 |
| Brett | −93 |
| Caleb | −365 |
| Danielle | 375 |

**Caleb's**

**6.NS.C.7c**
6. Order the numbers from least to greatest.
   $|24|, |-18|, |-25|, |16|, |0|$
   **$|0|, |16|, |-18|, |24|, |-25|$**

**6.EE.B.7**
7. Solve the equation.
   $\frac{5}{7}y = 20$
   **$y = 28$**

**6.EE.B.5**
8. Stephanie says that $p = 17$ is the solution of the equation $43 - p = 26$. How can you check whether she is correct? Explain.
   **Sample answer: Substitute 17 for *p* to see if the equation is true. 43 − 17 = 26, so 17 is the solution. Stephanie is correct.**

D 4-1

### Today's Challenge

Think Use the Topic 4 problems any time during this topic.

## ENGLISH LANGUAGE LEARNERS ELL

**Reading** Develop basic (math) sight vocabulary.

*Use with the Visual Learning Bridge on Student's Edition p. 186.*

Read Box A. Write *coordinate plane, x-axis, y-axis,* and *quadrant* on the board. Point to the illustration of the coordinate plane. *The coordinate plane is a grid containing two number lines, the x-axis and the y-axis.* Point to the *x*- and *y*-axes in the illustration. *The coordinate plane is divided into four quadrants.* Point to each quadrant.

**Beginning** Read Box A to students. Instruct students to write *coordinate plane, x-axis, y-axis,* and *quadrant* on index cards. Point to the coordinate plane. *What is this?* Have students respond by reading and holding up the correct index card. Continue the process with *x-axis, y-axis,* and *quadrant.*

**Intermediate** Read Box A with students. Instruct students to write *coordinate plane, x-axis, y-axis,* and *quadrant* on index cards. Organize students into pairs. Student A will hold up an index card, and Student B will read the vocabulary term and identify it in the illustration. Continue the process until each student has identified the parts of the coordinate plane.

**Advanced** Instruct students to read Box A. Have students write *coordinate plane, x-axis, y-axis,* and *quadrant* on index cards. Organize students in pairs. Student A will hold up an index card, and Student B will explain the meaning of the vocabulary term.

**Summarize** What are coordinate planes, *x*- and *y*-axes, and quadrants?

# DEVELOP: PROBLEM-BASED LEARNING

**COHERENCE: Engage learners by connecting prior knowledge to new ideas.**
Students extend their understanding of plotting an integer on a number line to plot an ordered pair with integer coordinates on the coordinate plane.

10–15 min

Solve

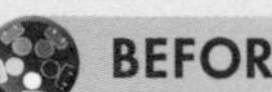

## BEFORE

1. **Pose the Solve-and-Share Problem**
**MP.1 Make Sense and Persevere** Listen and look for students who are able to locate point *B* by making sense of the description of its coordinates in relation to point *A*.

2. **Build Understanding**
*What coordinates describe the location of point A?* [(3, 5)] *How do you find the opposite of a number on a number line?* [Find the number that is the same distance from 0 on the number line, but on the opposite side of 0.]

## DURING

3. **Ask Guiding Questions As Needed**
*For point A, which number is the x-coordinate?* [3] *The y-coordinate?* [5] *What number is the opposite of the y-coordinate?* [−5] *What is the ordered pair for point B?* [(3, −5)] *How can you locate point B on the coordinate plane?* [From zero, go right 3 units and down 5 units.]

## AFTER

4. **Share and Discuss Solutions**
Solve Start with students' solutions. If needed, project Allen's work to discuss how to locate point *B*.

5. **Transition to the Visual Learning Bridge**
*The axes of a coordinate plane divide the plane into four quadrants. An ordered pair (x, y) can locate any point on the coordinate plane.*

6. **Extension for Early Finishers**
*The coordinates of point C are opposites of the coordinates of point B. What is the ordered pair for point C?* [(−3, 5)]

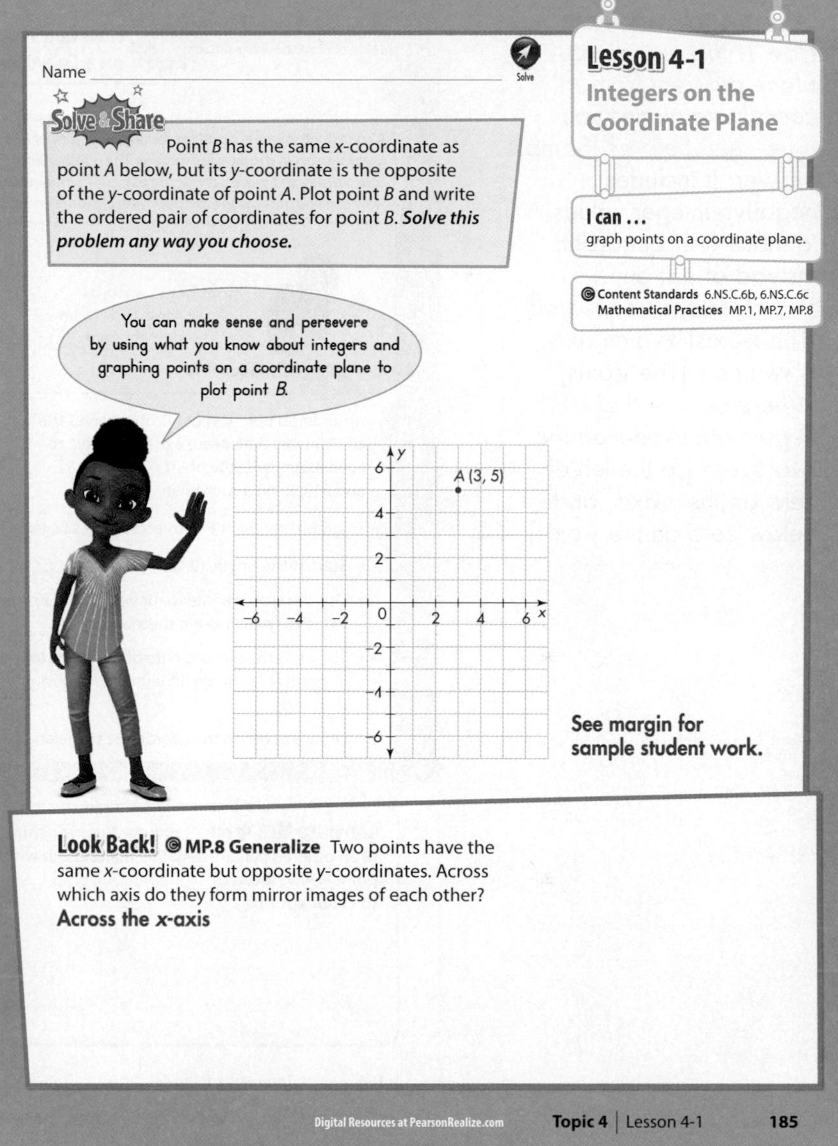

Name
Solve
Solve & Share
Point B has the same x-coordinate as point A below, but its y-coordinate is the opposite of the y-coordinate of point A. Plot point B and write the ordered pair of coordinates for point B. Solve this problem any way you choose.
Lesson 4-1
Integers on the Coordinate Plane
I can ...
graph points on a coordinate plane.
Content Standards 6.NS.C.6b, 6.NS.C.6c
Mathematical Practices MP.1, MP.7, MP.8
You can make sense and persevere by using what you know about integers and graphing points on a coordinate plane to plot point B.
A (3, 5)
See margin for sample student work.
Look Back! MP.8 Generalize Two points have the same x-coordinate but opposite y-coordinates. Across which axis do they form mirror images of each other?
Across the x-axis
Digital Resources at PearsonRealize.com
Topic 4 | Lesson 4-1
185


## Analyze Student Work

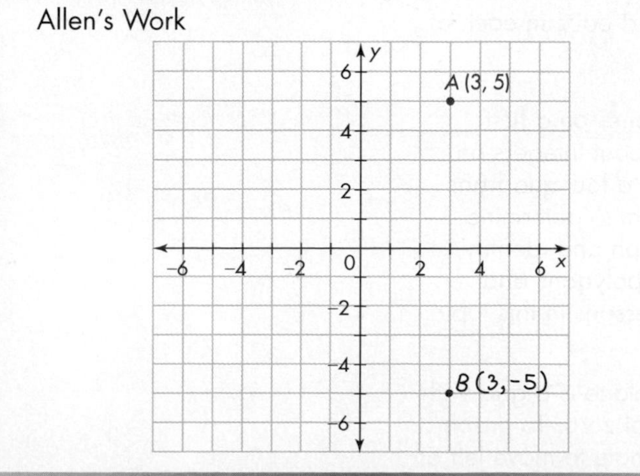


Allen interprets the description of the coordinates for point *B* and correctly plots and labels the ordered pair (3, −5).

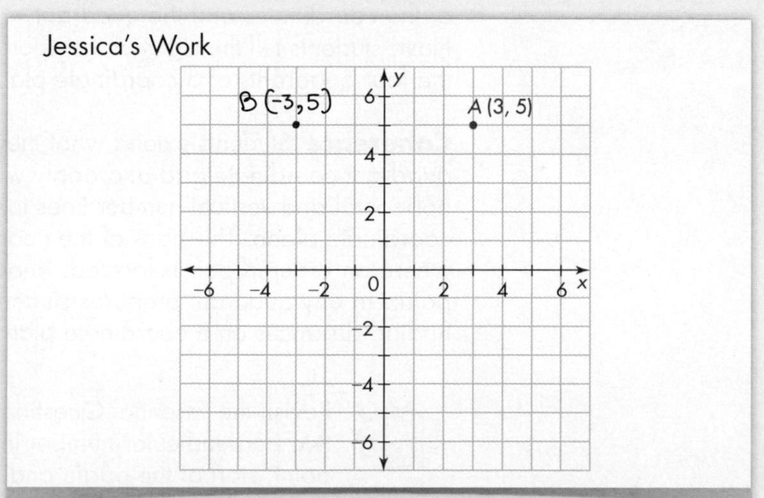


Jessica confuses the opposite coordinates and incorrectly plots point *B* at (−3, 5).

# DEVELOP: VISUAL LEARNING

The *Visual Learning Bridge* connects students' thinking in Solve & Share to important math ideas in the lesson. Use the *Visual Learning Bridge* to make these ideas explicit. Also available as a *Visual Learning Animation Plus* at PearsonRealize.com

Visual Learning

PEARSON realize. PearsonRealize.com

Learn Glossary

**MP.4 Model with Math**
*How is this coordinate plane different from coordinate planes you have seen before?* [Sample answer: It includes negative integer values to make four quadrants instead of just one.] *Which axis is horizontal?* [The *x*-axis] *Which axis is vertical?* [The *y*-axis] *Where do you find negative numbers on the two axes?* [To the left of zero on the *x*-axis, and below zero on the *y*-axis]

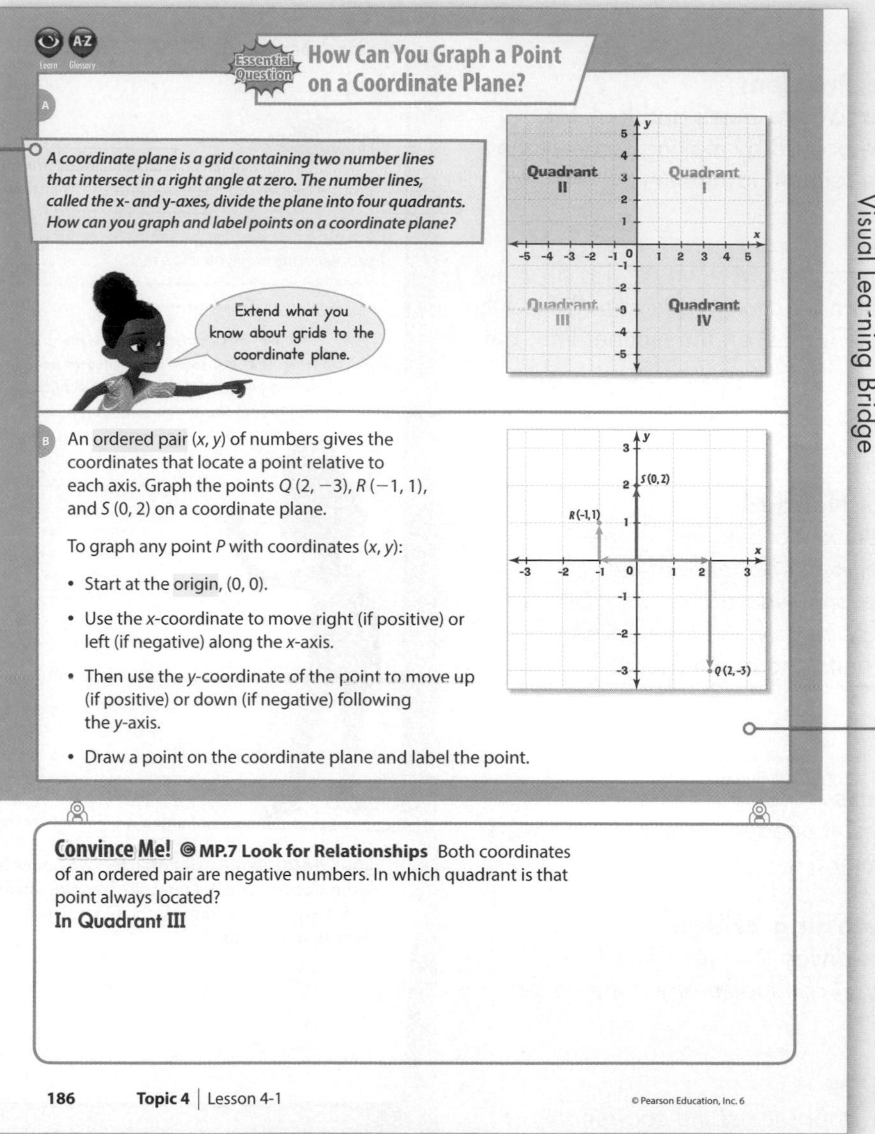

Essential Question
How Can You Graph a Point on a Coordinate Plane?
A coordinate plane is a grid containing two number lines that intersect in a right angle at zero. The number lines, called the x- and y-axes, divide the plane into four quadrants. How can you graph and label points on a coordinate plane?
Extend what you know about grids to the coordinate plane.
Quadrant II
Quadrant I
Quadrant III
Quadrant IV
An ordered pair (x, y) of numbers gives the coordinates that locate a point relative to each axis. Graph the points Q (2, −3), R (−1, 1), and S (0, 2) on a coordinate plane.
To graph any point P with coordinates (x, y):
• Start at the origin, (0, 0).
• Use the x-coordinate to move right (if positive) or left (if negative) along the x-axis.
• Then use the y-coordinate of the point to move up (if positive) or down (if negative) following the y-axis.
• Draw a point on the coordinate plane and label the point.
S(0, 2)
R(−1, 1)
Q(2, −3)
Convince Me! MP.7 Look for Relationships Both coordinates of an ordered pair are negative numbers. In which quadrant is that point always located?
In Quadrant III
186 Topic 4 | Lesson 4-1
© Pearson Education, Inc. 6
Visual Learning Bridge


*What is the x-coordinate of point Q?* [2] *What is the y-coordinate of point Q?* [−3] *Describe how to graph point Q on the coordinate plane.* [Start at the origin. Move 2 units right, and then move 3 units down.] *In which quadrant is point Q located?* [Quadrant IV] *The x-coordinate of point S is 0. How would you plot point S?* [Start at the origin but do not move left or right. Move up 2 units on the *y*-axis.]

**Prevent Misconceptions**

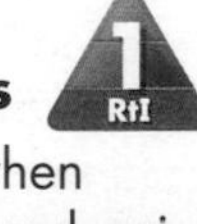

Emphasize that when graphing an ordered pair, the *x*-coordinate tells the number of units to move right or left, even when the *x*-coordinate is 0. The *y*-coordinate tells the number of units to move up or down. For point *S*(0, 2), be sure students move vertically for the *y*-coordinate, instead of horizontally.

**Convince Me! MP.7 Look for Relationships** As students practice graphing ordered pairs, they will notice a relationship between the signs of the coordinates and the quadrant where the ordered pair is located. Have students tell the signs of the coordinates of ordered pairs in each of the four quadrants of a coordinate plane.

**Coherence** Students extend what they know about points on a first-quadrant coordinate grid and apply what they know about integers on horizontal and vertical number lines to graph points on a four-quadrant coordinate plane. The signs of the coordinates help them to determine where an ordered pair is located. Knowing how to graph and identify points in any quadrant prepares students for graphing polygons and finding distances on a coordinate plane in upcoming lessons in this topic.

Revisit the Essential Question. A coordinate plane is a grid with two perpendicular number lines intersecting at zero. To graph a point, start at the origin and use the *x*-coordinate to move left or right, and from there use the *y*-coordinate to move up or down. Then draw and label the point on the coordinate plane.

## QUICK CHECK

Check mark indicates items for prescribing differentiation on the next page. Items 13 and 22 are worth 1 point. Item 19 is worth up to 3 points.

20–30 min

Practice Buddy · Tools · Assessment

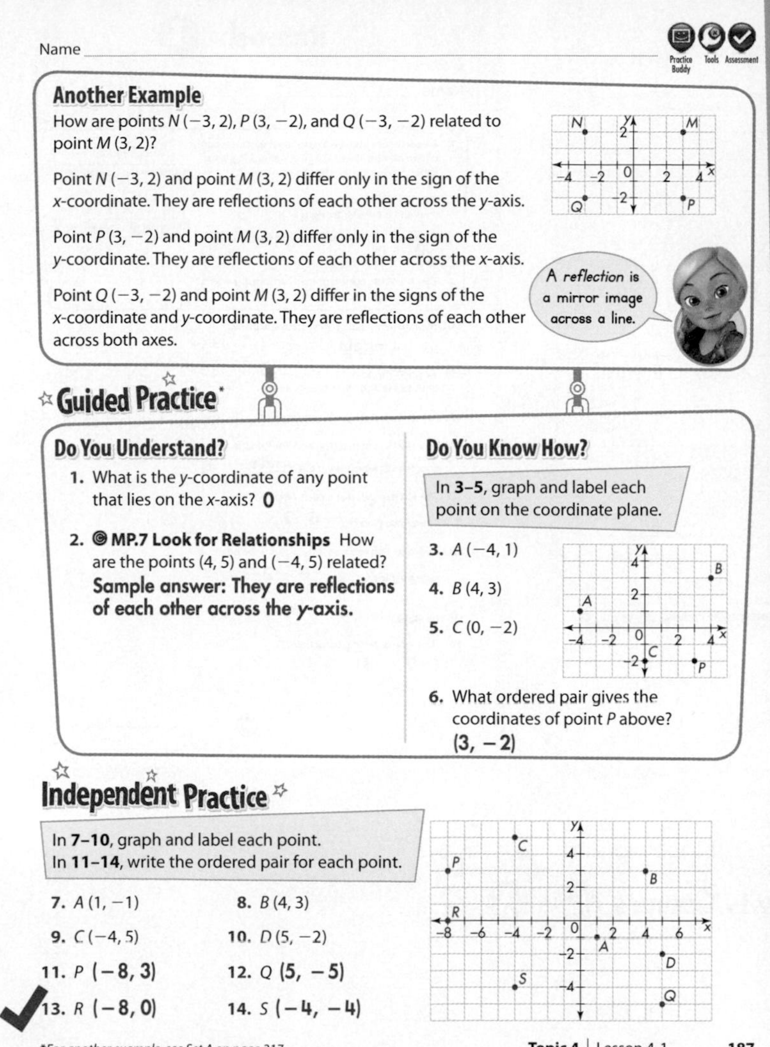

Name

**Another Example**

How are points N (−3, 2), P (3, −2), and Q (−3, −2) related to point M (3, 2)?

Point N (−3, 2) and point M (3, 2) differ only in the sign of the x-coordinate. They are reflections of each other across the y-axis.

Point P (3, −2) and point M (3, 2) differ only in the sign of the y-coordinate. They are reflections of each other across the x-axis.

Point Q (−3, −2) and point M (3, 2) differ in the signs of the x-coordinate and y-coordinate. They are reflections of each other across both axes.



**Guided Practice***

**Do You Understand?**

1. What is the y-coordinate of any point that lies on the x-axis? **0**
2. MP.7 **Look for Relationships** How are the points (4, 5) and (−4, 5) related? **Sample answer: They are reflections of each other across the y-axis.**

**Do You Know How?**

In **3–5**, graph and label each point on the coordinate plane.

3. A (−4, 1)
4. B (4, 3)
5. C (0, −2)
6. What ordered pair gives the coordinates of point P above? **(3, −2)**

**Independent Practice***

In **7–10**, graph and label each point.
In **11–14**, write the ordered pair for each point.

7. A (1, −1)
8. B (4, 3)
9. C (−4, 5)
10. D (5, −2)
11. P **(−8, 3)**
12. Q **(5, −5)**
13. R **(−8, 0)**
14. S **(−4, −4)**

*For another example, see Set A on page 217.

Topic 4 | Lesson 4-1 187

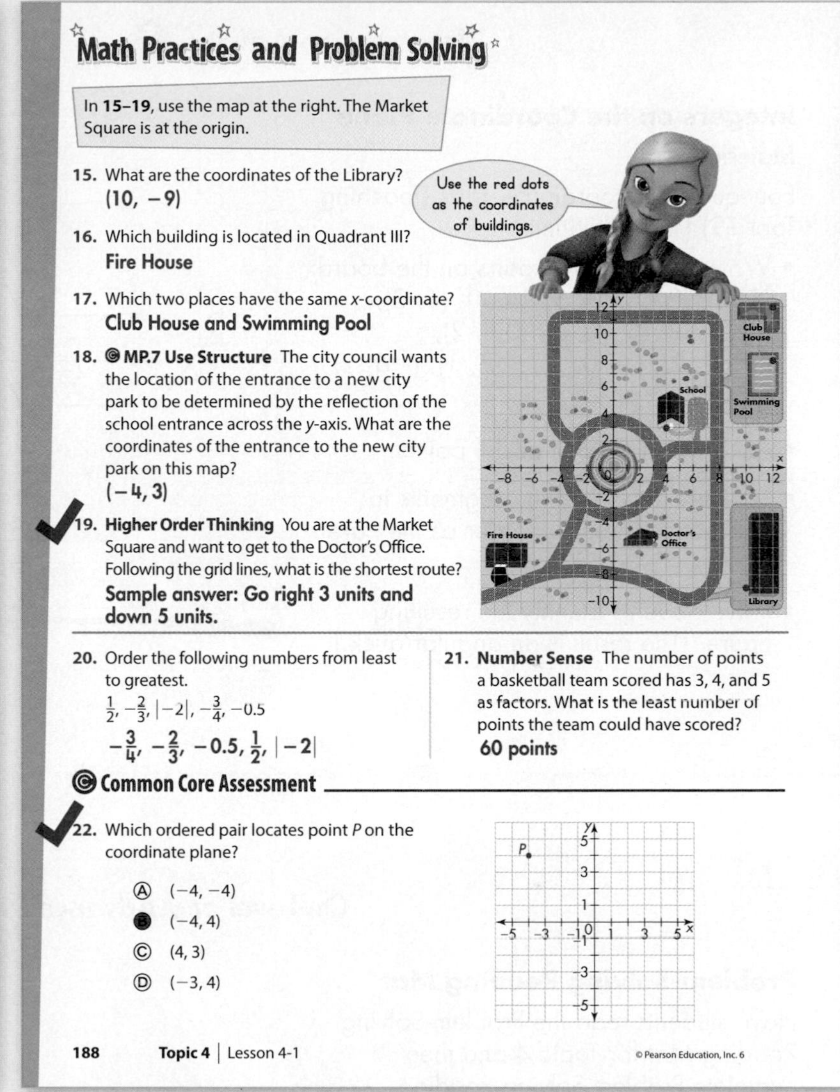

**Math Practices and Problem Solving***

In **15–19**, use the map at the right. The Market Square is at the origin.



15. What are the coordinates of the Library? **(10, −9)**
16. Which building is located in Quadrant III? **Fire House**
17. Which two places have the same x-coordinate? **Club House and Swimming Pool**
18. MP.7 **Use Structure** The city council wants the location of the entrance to a new city park to be determined by the reflection of the school entrance across the y-axis. What are the coordinates of the entrance to the new city park on this map? **(−4, 3)**
19. **Higher Order Thinking** You are at the Market Square and want to get to the Doctor's Office. Following the grid lines, what is the shortest route? **Sample answer: Go right 3 units and down 5 units.**
20. Order the following numbers from least to greatest. $\frac{1}{2}, -\frac{2}{3}, |-2|, -\frac{3}{4}, -0.5$ **$-\frac{3}{4}, -\frac{2}{3}, -0.5, \frac{1}{2}, |-2|$**
21. **Number Sense** The number of points a basketball team scored has 3, 4, and 5 as factors. What is the least number of points the team could have scored? **60 points**

**Common Core Assessment**

22. Which ordered pair locates point P on the coordinate plane?
 Ⓐ (−4, −4)
 ● (−4, 4)
 Ⓒ (4, 3)
 Ⓓ (−3, 4)

188 Topic 4 | Lesson 4-1 © Pearson Education, Inc. 6

**Another Example** *When two points are reflections of each other across the y-axis, which of their coordinates is the same?* [The y-coordinate] *Which is different?* [The x-coordinate] *How do they differ?* [They are opposites.] *What does "mirror image" mean?* [Sample answer: A mirror shows an image of a figure the same distance from, but reflected on the other side of, the mirror.]

**Error Intervention: Item 1**

**If** students have difficulty identifying the y-coordinate,

**then** have them plot any point on the x-axis. *Which number line is the y-axis?* [The vertical number line] *When you place a point anywhere on the x-axis, do you move up or down following the y-axis?* [No] *So, what is the y-coordinate?* [0]

**Reteaching** Assign Reteaching Set A on p. 217.

**Item 18 MP.7 Use Structure** *What is the ordered pair for the school entrance?* [(4, 3)] *When a point is reflected across the y-axis, which coordinate of the ordered pair becomes its opposite?* [The x-coordinate]

**Item 19 Higher Order Thinking** Students apply their knowledge of the coordinate plane to determine the shortest route along grid lines. They can add vertical and horizontal distances to find the shortest route. They may discover there are two possible shortest routes: they can go right 3 units and down 5 units, or down 5 units and right 3 units.

**Item 22 Coherence** Students extend their previous understanding of locating integers on a number line when they identify a point in the coordinate plane using an ordered pair with integer coordinates.

**Multi-Step Problems** *Page 188 Item 18; Page 190 Items 20 and 21*

# ASSESS AND DIFFERENTIATE

Use the **QUICK CHECK** on the previous page to prescribe differentiated instruction.

**I Intervention** 0–3 points on the Quick Check

**O On-Level** 4 points on the Quick Check

**A Advanced** 5 points on the Quick Check

## Intervention Activity I

### Integers on the Coordinate Plane

**Materials**

Four-quadrant coordinate grids (Teaching Tool 19) (1 per student)

- Write these ordered pairs on the board: (1, 4), (2, 5), (3, 5), (4, 4), (6, 3), (4, 3), (3, 2), (2, 2), (0, −2), (−6, −2), (−10, 3), (−7, 1), (−5, 2), (0, 2)
- Ask students to plot all 14 points.
- Tell students to use line segments to connect the points in order as they are listed.
- Have students identify the resulting figure. [The result is an angular duck.]

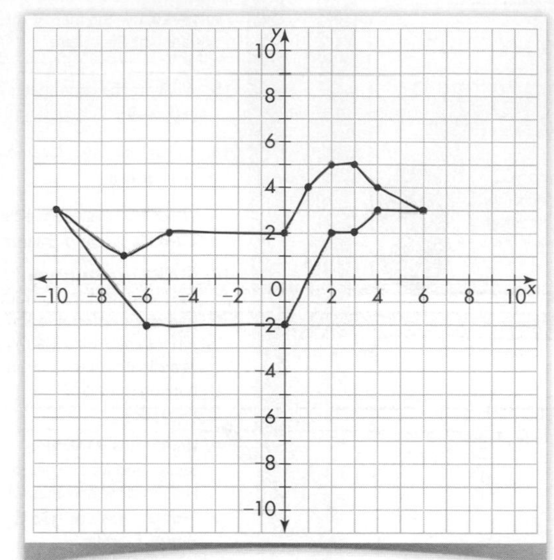

## Reteach I

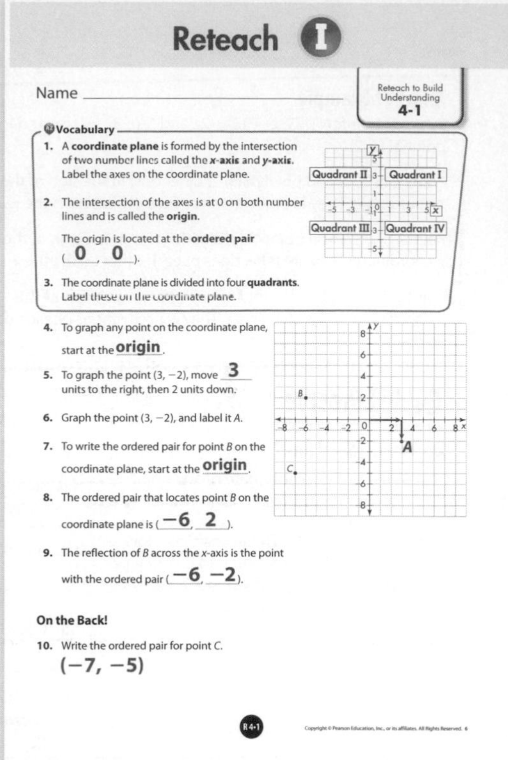

Name ______

Reteach to Build Understanding 4-1

**Vocabulary**

1. A **coordinate plane** is formed by the intersection of two number lines called the ***x*-axis** and ***y*-axis.** Label the axes on the coordinate plane.
2. The intersection of the axes is at 0 on both number lines and is called the **origin**.

   The origin is located at the **ordered pair** (**0**, **0**).
3. The coordinate plane is divided into four **quadrants**. Label these on the coordinate plane.



4. To graph any point on the coordinate plane, start at the **origin**.
5. To graph the point (3, −2), move **3** units to the right, then 2 units down.
6. Graph the point (3, −2), and label it *A*.
7. To write the ordered pair for point *B* on the coordinate plane, start at the **origin**.
8. The ordered pair that locates point *B* on the coordinate plane is (**−6**, **2**).
9. The reflection of *B* across the *x*-axis is the point with the ordered pair (**−6**, **−2**).



**On the Back!**

10. Write the ordered pair for point *C*.

    **(−7, −5)**

R 4-1

## On-Level and Advanced Activity Centers O A

### Problem-Solving Reading Mat

Have students read the Problem-Solving Reading Mat for Topic 4 and then complete Problem-Solving Reading Activity 4-1.

See the Problem-Solving Reading Activity Guide for other suggestions on how to use this mat.

## TIMING

The time allocated to Step 3 will depend on the teacher's instructional decisions and differentiation routines.

15–30 min

Help | Practice Buddy | Tools | Games

## Technology Center   

Tools Games

### Math Tools and Math Games

A link to a specific math tools activity or math game to use with this lesson is provided at PearsonRealize.com.

## Leveled Assignment  Items 1–6, 11–14, 17–19, 21–23  Items 7–23  Items 7–14, 17–23

Name ____________________

Help Practice Buddy Tools Games

## Homework & Practice 4-1

### Integers on the Coordinate Plane

### Another Look!

A **coordinate plane** is a grid that contains number lines that intersect at right angles and divide the plane into four **quadrants**. The horizontal number line is called the ***x*-axis** and the vertical number line is called the ***y*-axis**.

The location of a point on a coordinate plane is written as an **ordered pair** $(x, y)$.

Graph and label the point $K(4, -3)$ on the coordinate plane at the right.

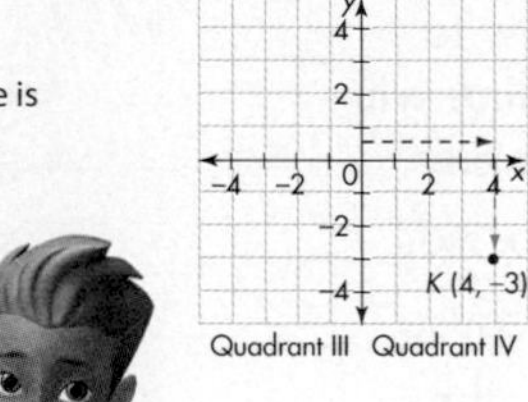

To locate point (4, −3), start at the origin. Move to 4 on the x-axis. Then move to −3 by following the y-axis.

In **1–10**, write the ordered pair for each point.
In **11–16**, graph and label each point.

1. $A$ **(−8, 6)**
2. $B$ **(2, 2)**
3. $C$ **(−3, −6)**
4. $D$ **(8, −8)**
5. $E$ **(−7, −9)**
6. $F$ **(6, 6)**
7. $G$ **(−6, 3)**
8. $H$ **(4, −4)**
9. $I$ **(9, 0)**
10. $J$ **(0, 4)**
11. $U(-5, -3)$
12. $V(-9, 3)$
13. $W(3, 8)$
14. $X(8, 3)$
15. $Y(6, -6)$
16. $Z(-5, 0)$

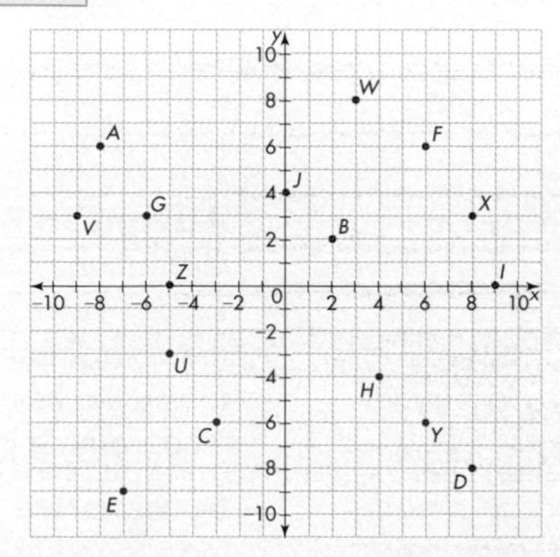



In **17–20**, use the map at the right.

17. What are the coordinates of the Roller Coaster?
**(8, −5)**
18. In which quadrant is the Drinking Fountain located?
**Quadrant III**
19. Which location is a reflection across the $y$-axis from $(-7, 3)$?
**Paddle Boat Rides**
20. **Higher Order Thinking** Follow the grid lines. Is the Shooting Gallery or the Bumper Cars closer to the Hot Dog Stand? Explain.
**Shooting Gallery; Sample answer: The Hot Dog Stand is at the origin. The Shooting Gallery is 11 units away; the Bumper Cars are 12 units away.**

Use the red dots to locate the coordinates of places in the fun park.

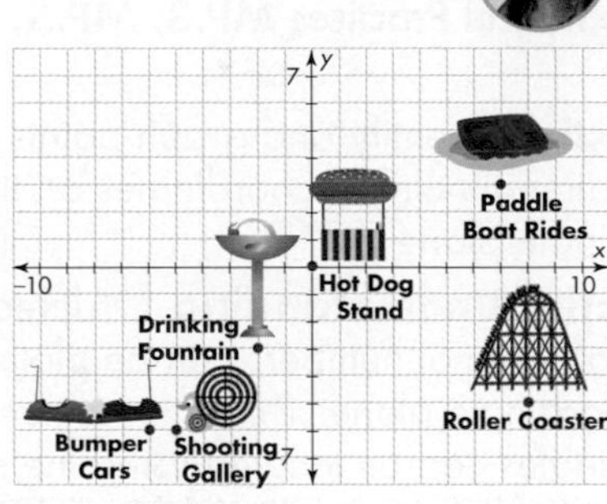


21. **Math and Science** The magnitude of an earthquake is frequently expressed using the Richter scale. Each whole-number increase in the Richter scale represents a 10 times greater magnitude. Use the expression $10^a$, where $a$ is the difference in the magnitude of two earthquakes, to find how much greater a 5.6 magnitude earthquake is than a 2.6 magnitude earthquake. **1,000 times greater**

22. **Vocabulary** Write four examples of ordered pairs, each located in a different quadrant of the coordinate plane.
**Sample answer:**
**Quadrant I: (1, 1);**
**Quadrant II: (−1, 1);**
**Quadrant III: (−1, −1);**
**Quadrant IV: (1, −1)**

### Common Core Assessment

23. Which ordered pair is **NOT** a reflection of point $P$ across the $x$-axis, the $y$-axis, or both axes?

Ⓐ (2, 4)
Ⓑ (2, −4)
Ⓒ (−2, 4)
● (−2, −4)

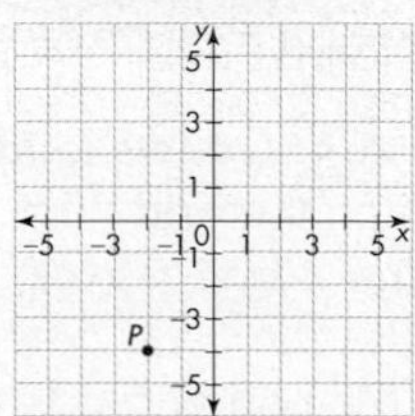

# LESSON 4-2

# RATIONAL NUMBERS ON THE COORDINATE PLANE

## DIGITAL RESOURCES PearsonRealize.com

Student and Teacher eTexts

eText

Listen and Look For Lesson Video
PD

Today's Challenge
Think

Solve and Share
Solve

Visual Learning Animation Plus
Learn

Animated Glossary
Glossary

Online Personalized Practice
Practice Buddy

Math Tools

Tools

Quick Check
Assessment

Another Look Homework Video
Help

Math Games
Games

## LESSON OVERVIEW FCR FOCUS • COHERENCE • RIGOR

### FOCUS

**Domain 6.NS** The Number System

**Cluster 6.NS.C** Apply and extend previous understandings of numbers to the system of rational numbers.

**Content Standard 6.NS.C.6b** Understand signs of numbers in ordered pairs as indicating locations in quadrants of the coordinate plane; recognize that when two ordered pairs differ only by signs, the locations of the points are related by reflections across one or both axes. Also **6.NS.C.6c**.

**Mathematical Practices MP.3, MP.5, MP.6, MP.7**

**Objective** Identify and graph points with rational number coordinates on the coordinate plane.

**Essential Understanding** Ordered pairs of rational numbers can be plotted on the coordinate plane. The rational number coordinates can be located using the two perpendicular number lines of the plane.

**Materials** Four-quadrant coordinate grids (Teaching Tool 19) (optional)

### COHERENCE

In the previous lesson, students used their understanding of horizontal and vertical number lines to locate and graph ordered pairs of integers on the coordinate plane. In this lesson, students employ the same technique to plot points that have rational number coordinates. In Lessons 4-3 and 4-4, students will use this skill to find distances between points and graph polygons on the coordinate plane.

### RIGOR

This lesson emphasizes a blend of **conceptual understanding** with **procedural skill**. Understanding how to locate rational numbers on a number line will help students to graph rational coordinates. For example, to graph $\left(-5\frac{1}{2}, 0\right)$, the *x*-axis can be labeled in increments of $\frac{1}{2}$. Because $-5\frac{1}{2}$ is halfway between $-5$ and $-6$, the *x*-coordinate is $5\frac{1}{2}$ units to the left of the origin. Because the *y*-coordinate is 0, the point is located on the *x*-axis.

PD Watch the Listen and Look For Lesson Video.

## MATH ANYTIME

### Daily Common Core Review

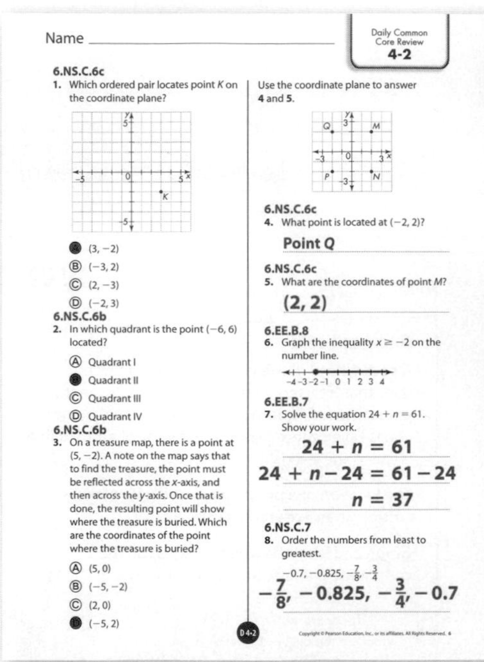
Name ______

Daily Common Core Review 4-2

6.NS.C.6c
1. Which ordered pair locates point *K* on the coordinate plane?
● (3, −2)
Ⓑ (−3, 2)
Ⓒ (2, −3)
Ⓓ (−2, 3)

6.NS.C.6b
2. In which quadrant is the point (−6, 6) located?
Ⓐ Quadrant I
● Quadrant II
Ⓒ Quadrant III
Ⓓ Quadrant IV

6.NS.C.6b
3. On a treasure map, there is a point at (5, −2). A note on the map says that to find the treasure, the point must be reflected across the *x*-axis, and then across the *y*-axis. Once that is done, the resulting point will show where the treasure is buried. Which are the coordinates of the point where the treasure is buried?
Ⓐ (5, 0)
Ⓑ (−5, −2)
Ⓒ (2, 0)
● (−5, 2)

Use the coordinate plane to answer 4 and 5.

6.NS.C.6c
4. What point is located at (−2, 2)?
**Point Q**

6.NS.C.6c
5. What are the coordinates of point *M*?
**(2, 2)**

6.EE.B.8
6. Graph the inequality $x \geq -2$ on the number line.

6.EE.B.7
7. Solve the equation $24 + n = 61$. Show your work.
$24 + n = 61$
$24 + n - 24 = 61 - 24$
$n = 37$

6.NS.C.7
8. Order the numbers from least to greatest.
$-0.7, -0.825, -\frac{7}{8}, -\frac{3}{4}$
$-\frac{7}{8}, -0.825, -\frac{3}{4}, -0.7$

D 4-2



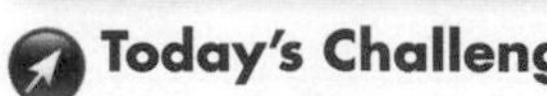

### Today's Challenge

Think Use the Topic 4 problems any time during this topic.

## ENGLISH LANGUAGE LEARNERS 

**Speaking** Give information using key words and expressions.

*Use with the Visual Learning Bridge on Student's Edition p. 192.*

Read Box A. Ask students to identify the *x*- and *y*-axes on the grid map. Point to the numbers on the *x*- and *y*-axes. *These numbers are coordinates for the x- and y-axes.* Point to the Jefferson Memorial. *Find the coordinates using decimals.* Read Box B. Demonstrate how coordinates are used to find the location of the Jefferson Memorial.

**Beginning** Point to the White House in the illustration. *Find the x-coordinate.* Have students respond using the sentence stem: The *x*-coordinate of the White House is ___. Continue the process for the *y*-coordinate.

**Intermediate** Point to the White House in the illustration. *How is the x-coordinate found?* Have students respond using the sentence stem: The *x*-coordinate is found by ______. Continue the process for the *y*-coordinate.

**Advanced** Point to the White House in the illustration. *How are the x- and y-coordinates found?* Have students explain to partners how the coordinates are found. Instruct students to use the key words *x-coordinate* and *y-coordinate* in their explanations.

**Summarize** How are locations on a grid map found using *x*- and *y*-coordinates?

# DEVELOP: PROBLEM-BASED LEARNING

**COHERENCE: Engage learners by connecting prior knowledge to new ideas.**
Students extend their understanding of graphing ordered pairs of integers on a coordinate plane to graph ordered pairs of rational numbers.

10–15 min

Solve

## BEFORE

**1. Pose the Solve-and-Share Problem**
**MP.5 Use Appropriate Tools Strategically** Listen and look for students who notice that the coordinate plane has a scale in increments of $\frac{1}{4}$ and apply what they know about rational numbers to graph point *B*.

**2. Build Understanding**
*What is the ordered pair for point B?* $\left[\left(-1\frac{3}{4}, 2\frac{1}{2}\right)\right]$ *What tool are you given to graph the point?* [A coordinate plane] *How many grid squares separate each integer label on the axes?* [4] *What fractional part does each grid square represent?* $\left[\frac{1}{4}\right]$

## DURING

**3. Ask Guiding Questions As Needed**
*To locate* $-1\frac{3}{4}$*, how many grid squares should you count beyond* $-1$*?* [3 squares to the left] *To locate* $2\frac{1}{2}$*, how many grid squares should you count beyond 2?* [2 squares up]

## AFTER

**4. Share and Discuss Solutions**
Start with students' solutions. If needed, project Lisa's Solve work to discuss how to locate point *B*.

**5. Transition to the Visual Learning Bridge**
*An ordered pair of rational numbers can be used to plot or describe any location on a coordinate plane. Use the scales on the axes to determine the precise location of the coordinates.*

**6. Extension for Early Finishers**
*Graph and label a point D that is a reflection of point B across the y-axis.* [Check that students' graphs show point *D* at $\left(1\frac{3}{4}, 2\frac{1}{2}\right)$.]

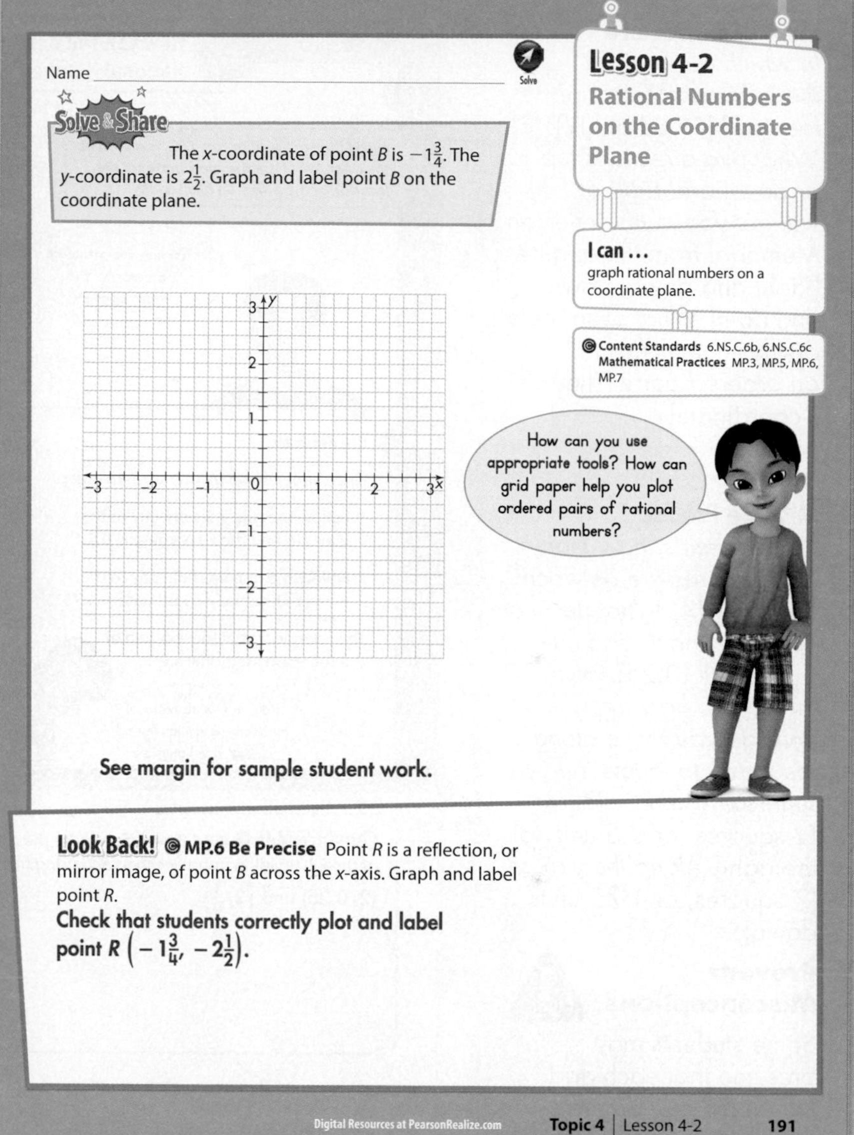

Name
Solve & Share
The x-coordinate of point B is $-1\frac{3}{4}$. The y-coordinate is $2\frac{1}{2}$. Graph and label point B on the coordinate plane.
Lesson 4-2
Rational Numbers on the Coordinate Plane
I can ...
graph rational numbers on a coordinate plane.
Content Standards 6.NS.C.6b, 6.NS.C.6c
Mathematical Practices MP.3, MP.5, MP.6, MP.7
How can you use appropriate tools? How can grid paper help you plot ordered pairs of rational numbers?
See margin for sample student work.
Look Back! MP.6 Be Precise Point R is a reflection, or mirror image, of point B across the x-axis. Graph and label point R.
Check that students correctly plot and label point R $\left(-1\frac{3}{4}, -2\frac{1}{2}\right)$.
Digital Resources at PearsonRealize.com
Topic 4 | Lesson 4-2
191


## Analyze Student Work

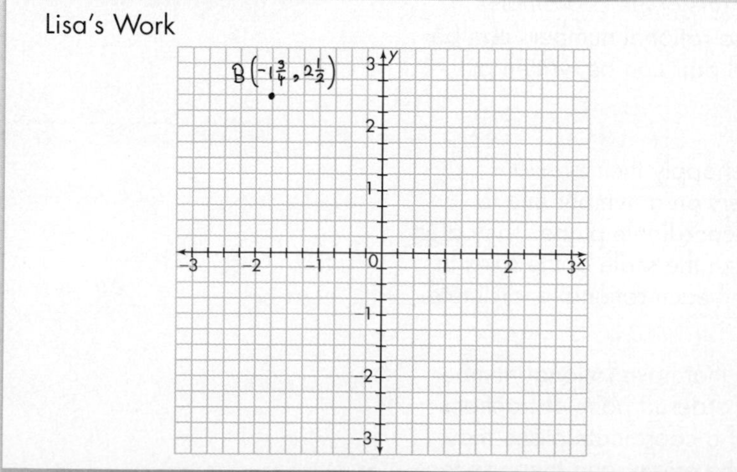


Lisa correctly graphs and labels point *B*.

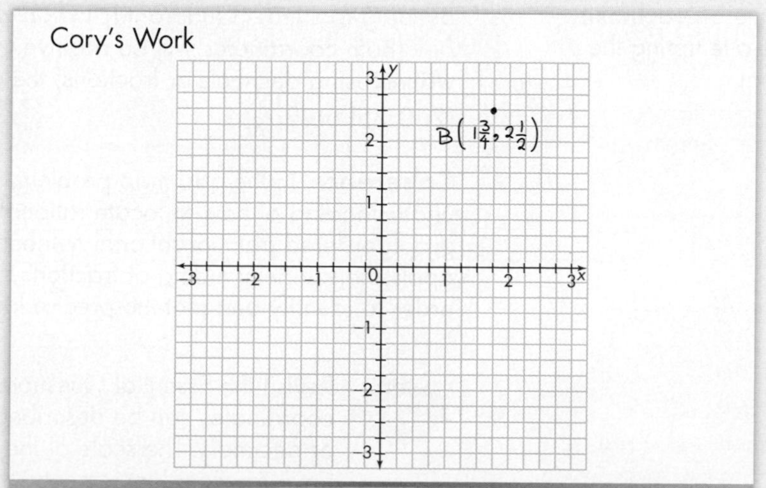


Cory mistakenly overlooks the signs and plots positive rational numbers.

# DEVELOP: VISUAL LEARNING

The *Visual Learning Bridge* connects students' thinking in Solve & Share to important math ideas in the lesson. Use the *Visual Learning Bridge* to make these ideas explicit. Also available as a *Visual Learning Animation Plus* at PearsonRealize.com

Visual Learning

PEARSON realize. PearsonRealize.com

Learn Glossary

**MP.7 Use Structure**
*In which quadrant is the Jefferson Memorial located?* [Quadrant IV] *What two directions (up or down and right or left) will get you to the Jefferson Memorial from the origin?* [Right and down; down and right] *What coordinate always comes first in an ordered pair?* [The x-coordinate]

**MP.6 Be Precise**
*On the x-axis, how many grid squares are between 0 and 1?* [4] *What decimal part does each grid line represent?* [0.25] *From the origin, how many units do you move along the x-axis to locate the Jefferson Memorial?* [2 squares, or 0.5 unit, to the right] *Along the y-axis?* [7 squares, or 1.75 units, down]

**Prevent Misconceptions**
Some students may presume that each grid line in the coordinate plane represents 1 unit. Emphasize to students the importance of determining the scale on each axis before attempting the problem.

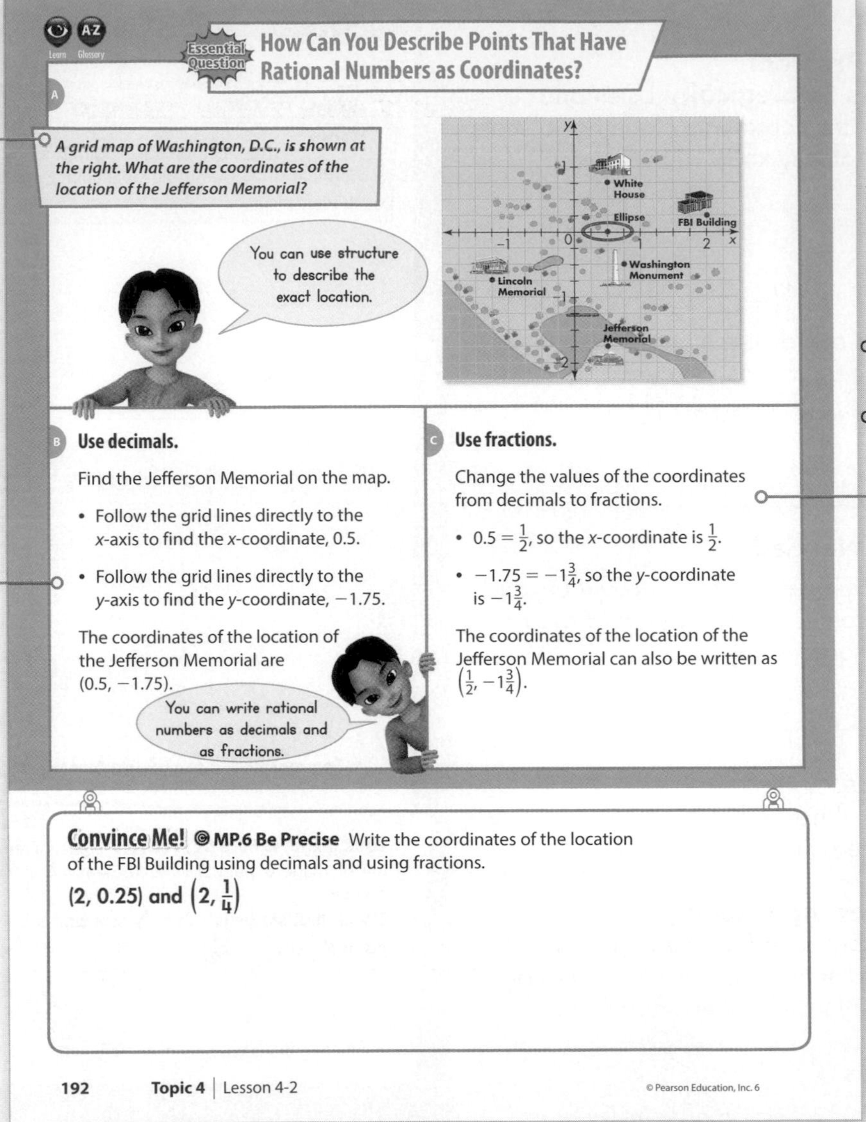

How Can You Describe Points That Have Rational Numbers as Coordinates?
A grid map of Washington, D.C., is shown at the right. What are the coordinates of the location of the Jefferson Memorial?
You can use structure to describe the exact location.
White House
Ellipse
FBI Building
Lincoln Memorial
Washington Monument
Jefferson Memorial
Use decimals.
Find the Jefferson Memorial on the map.
Follow the grid lines directly to the x-axis to find the x-coordinate, 0.5.
Follow the grid lines directly to the y-axis to find the y-coordinate, −1.75.
The coordinates of the location of the Jefferson Memorial are (0.5, −1.75).
You can write rational numbers as decimals and as fractions.
Use fractions.
Change the values of the coordinates from decimals to fractions.
$0.5 = \frac{1}{2}$, so the x-coordinate is $\frac{1}{2}$.
$-1.75 = -1\frac{3}{4}$, so the y-coordinate is $-1\frac{3}{4}$.
The coordinates of the location of the Jefferson Memorial can also be written as $\left(\frac{1}{2}, -1\frac{3}{4}\right)$.
Convince Me! MP.6 Be Precise Write the coordinates of the location of the FBI Building using decimals and using fractions.
(2, 0.25) and $\left(2, \frac{1}{4}\right)$
192 Topic 4 | Lesson 4-2
© Pearson Education, Inc. 6
Visual Learning Bridge


*How do you change a decimal with tenths, like 0.5, to a fraction?* [Write the number of tenths over 10. $0.5 = \frac{5}{10}$, which is equivalent to $\frac{1}{2}$.]
*How do you change a decimal with hundredths, like −1.75, to a fraction?* [Write the number of hundredths over 100. $-1.75 = -1\frac{75}{100}$, which is equivalent to $-1\frac{3}{4}$.]

**Convince Me! MP.6 Be Precise** Every location on the coordinate plane can be described by a unique ordered pair. *In which quadrant is the FBI Building located?* [Quadrant I] *What will the signs of the coordinates be?* [Both coordinates will be positive.] Because rational numbers can be written using decimals or fractions, the ordered pair can be written as (2, 0.25) or $\left(2, \frac{1}{4}\right)$.

**Coherence** In the grid map problem, students apply their previous understanding of how to locate rational numbers on a number line to graph ordered pairs of rational numbers on a coordinate plane. They also apply their understanding of fractions to analyze the scale of the axes in order to identify and plot the precise location of each rational coordinate.

Revisit the Essential Question. Points that have rational number coordinates can be described using ordered pairs of fractions or decimals. The scale of the axes of a coordinate plane may have fractional increments. Start at the origin, and then use the x-coordinate to move horizontally and the y-coordinate to move vertically in order to locate a point.

## QUICK CHECK

Check mark indicates items for prescribing differentiation on the next page.
Item 9 is worth 1 point. Items 22 and 25 are worth up to 2 points.

20–30 min

Practice Buddy | Tools | Assessment

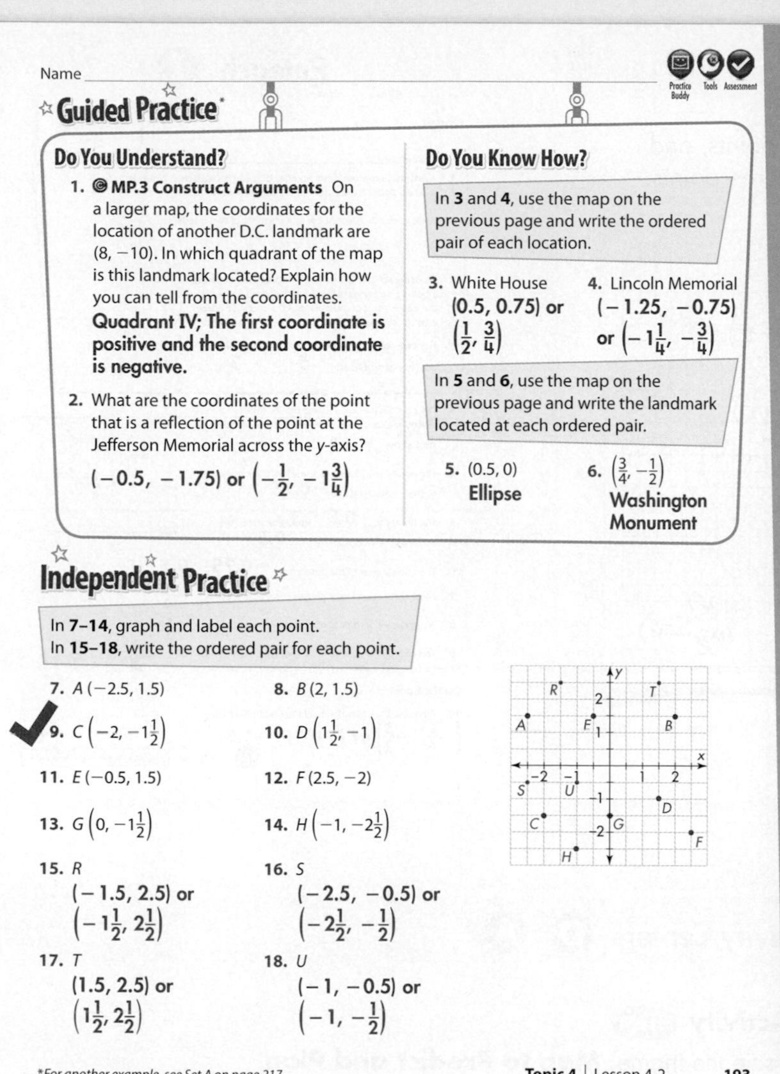

Name ______

## Guided Practice*

### Do You Understand?

1. MP.3 Construct Arguments On a larger map, the coordinates for the location of another D.C. landmark are (8, −10). In which quadrant of the map is this landmark located? Explain how you can tell from the coordinates.
**Quadrant IV; The first coordinate is positive and the second coordinate is negative.**

2. What are the coordinates of the point that is a reflection of the point at the Jefferson Memorial across the y-axis?
**$(-0.5, -1.75)$ or $\left(-\frac{1}{2}, -1\frac{3}{4}\right)$**

### Do You Know How?

In **3** and **4**, use the map on the previous page and write the ordered pair of each location.

3. White House **$(0.5, 0.75)$ or $\left(\frac{1}{2}, \frac{3}{4}\right)$**

4. Lincoln Memorial **$(-1.25, -0.75)$ or $\left(-1\frac{1}{4}, -\frac{3}{4}\right)$**

In **5** and **6**, use the map on the previous page and write the landmark located at each ordered pair.

5. $(0.5, 0)$ **Ellipse**

6. $\left(\frac{3}{4}, -\frac{1}{2}\right)$ **Washington Monument**

## Independent Practice

In **7–14**, graph and label each point.
In **15–18**, write the ordered pair for each point.

7. $A(-2.5, 1.5)$
8. $B(2, 1.5)$
9. $C\left(-2, -1\frac{1}{2}\right)$
10. $D\left(1\frac{1}{2}, -1\right)$
11. $E(-0.5, 1.5)$
12. $F(2.5, -2)$
13. $G\left(0, -1\frac{1}{2}\right)$
14. $H\left(-1, -2\frac{1}{2}\right)$
15. $R$ **$(-1.5, 2.5)$ or $\left(-1\frac{1}{2}, 2\frac{1}{2}\right)$**
16. $S$ **$(-2.5, -0.5)$ or $\left(-2\frac{1}{2}, -\frac{1}{2}\right)$**
17. $T$ **$(1.5, 2.5)$ or $\left(1\frac{1}{2}, 2\frac{1}{2}\right)$**
18. $U$ **$(-1, -0.5)$ or $\left(-1, -\frac{1}{2}\right)$**

*For another example, see Set A on page 217.

Topic 4 | Lesson 4-2 193

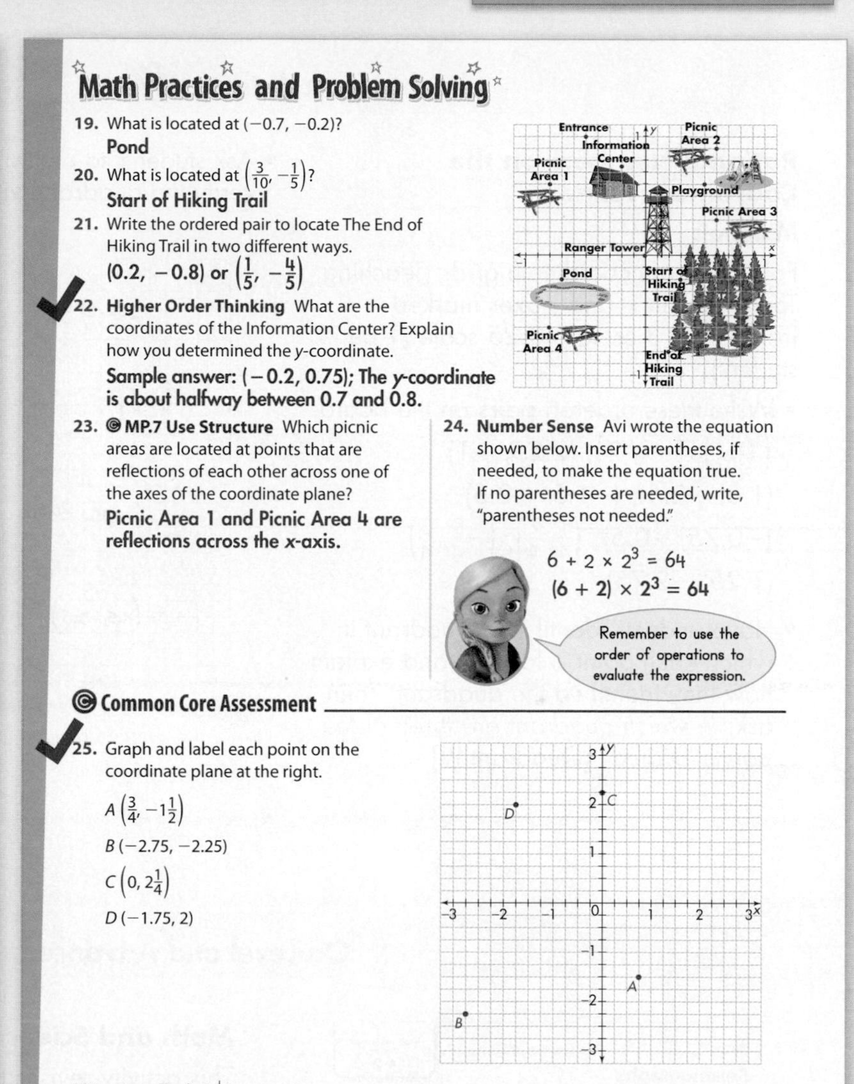

## Math Practices and Problem Solving

19. What is located at $(-0.7, -0.2)$?
**Pond**

20. What is located at $\left(\frac{3}{10}, -\frac{1}{5}\right)$?
**Start of Hiking Trail**

21. Write the ordered pair to locate The End of Hiking Trail in two different ways.
**$(0.2, -0.8)$ or $\left(\frac{1}{5}, -\frac{4}{5}\right)$**

22. **Higher Order Thinking** What are the coordinates of the Information Center? Explain how you determined the y-coordinate.
**Sample answer: $(-0.2, 0.75)$; The y-coordinate is about halfway between 0.7 and 0.8.**



23. MP.7 Use Structure Which picnic areas are located at points that are reflections of each other across one of the axes of the coordinate plane?
**Picnic Area 1 and Picnic Area 4 are reflections across the x-axis.**

24. **Number Sense** Avi wrote the equation shown below. Insert parentheses, if needed, to make the equation true. If no parentheses are needed, write, "parentheses not needed."

$6 + 2 \times 2^3 = 64$
**$(6 + 2) \times 2^3 = 64$**

Remember to use the order of operations to evaluate the expression.

### Common Core Assessment

25. Graph and label each point on the coordinate plane at the right.
$A\left(\frac{3}{4}, -1\frac{1}{2}\right)$
$B(-2.75, -2.25)$
$C\left(0, 2\frac{1}{4}\right)$
$D(-1.75, 2)$

194 Topic 4 | Lesson 4-2

© Pearson Education, Inc. 6

**Error Intervention: Item 2**

**If** students have difficulty identifying the coordinates of the reflection, **then** ask: *What do you know about the distances from the Jefferson Memorial to the y-axis and from the reflection point to the y-axis?* [They are the same.] Have students refer to the grid map on the previous page to help them visualize the reflection of the point across the y-axis.

**Items 19–20 Coherence** Students build on their previous work locating ordered pairs of integers on the coordinate plane as they locate ordered pairs with rational number coordinates. *What do the negative signs in front of the x-coordinate and y-coordinate tell you about the location of (−0.7, −0.2)? Explain.* [The point is in Quadrant III, since the negative coordinates indicate a location to the left and down from the origin.]

**Reteaching** Assign Reteaching Set A on p. 217.

**Item 22 Higher Order Thinking** *What does each grid line represent?* [0.1] *Is the Information Center located directly on two grid lines?* [No] *What is the x-coordinate?* [−0.2] *Describe the location of the y-coordinate.* [About halfway between 0.7 and 0.8, or 0.75] Students may find it helpful to think of 0.7 as 0.70 and 0.8 as 0.80, so they can determine that 0.75 is halfway between 0.7 and 0.8.

**Item 23 MP.7 Use Structure** Students should recognize that points that are reflections of each other have opposite x-coordinates or opposite y-coordinates. Help them use the structure of the coordinate plane to identify the picnic areas.

**Item 24 Number Sense** *How can you determine whether parentheses are needed to make the equation true?* [Evaluate the expression on the left side of the equation to determine whether it is equal to 64.] *If parentheses are needed, how will you determine where to insert them?* [Sample answer: You can reason that because $2^3$ is 8 and $8 \times 8$ is 64, the parentheses must go around $6 + 2$.]

**Multi-Step Problems** *Page 194 Items 21, 23, and 24; Page 196 Items 21 and 22*

STEP 3

# ASSESS AND DIFFERENTIATE

Use the **QUICK CHECK** on the previous page to prescribe differentiated instruction.

**I Intervention** 0–3 points on the Quick Check

**O On-Level** 4 points on the Quick Check

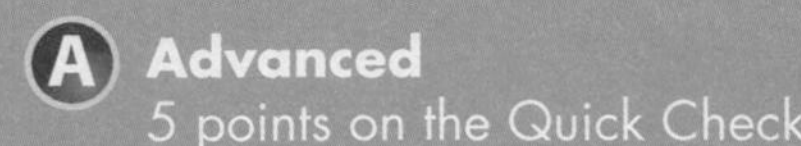

**A Advanced** 5 points on the Quick Check

## Intervention Activity 

### Rational Numbers on the Coordinate Plane

**Materials**

Four-quadrant coordinate grids (Teaching Tool 19) with *x*- and *y*-axes marked from −3 to 3 using a 0.25 scale (1 per student)

- Write these ordered pairs on the board: $\left(1, \frac{1}{2}\right)$, $\left(-\frac{3}{2}, 2\right)$, (2.25, −1), (1.5, −2.5), (−1.5, −2.5), (−0.75, −0.5), $\left(\frac{1}{4}, \frac{7}{4}\right)$, $\left(-\frac{9}{4}, \frac{3}{4}\right)$, (1.25, −2.75)
- Have students identify the quadrant in which each point is located and explain how they identified the quadrant. Then ask: *In which quadrant are three of the points located?* [Quadrant IV]
- Ask students to plot all 9 points, and verify the quadrant with three points.

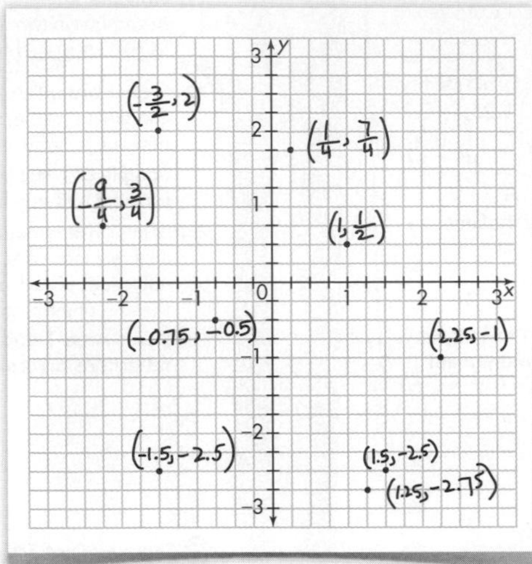

## Reteach I

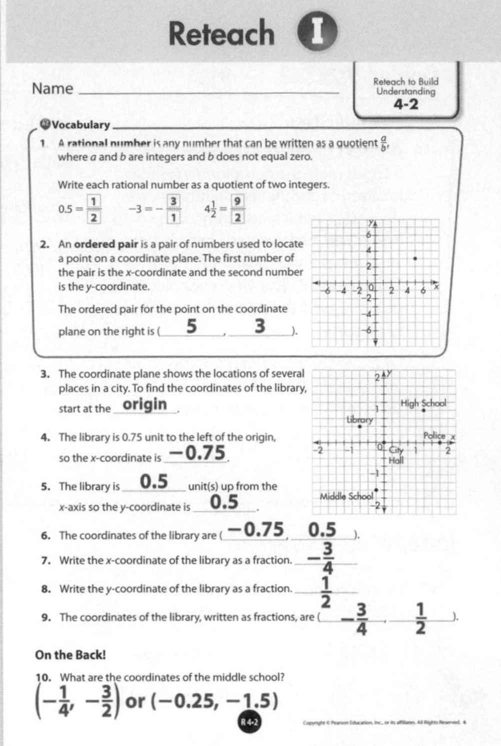

Name ______ Reteach to Build Understanding 4-2

Vocabulary

1. A **rational number** is any number that can be written as a quotient $\frac{a}{b}$, where *a* and *b* are integers and *b* does not equal zero.

Write each rational number as a quotient of two integers.

$0.5 = \frac{1}{2}$ $-3 = -\frac{3}{1}$ $4\frac{1}{2} = \frac{9}{2}$

2. An **ordered pair** is a pair of numbers used to locate a point on a coordinate plane. The first number of the pair is the *x*-coordinate and the second number is the *y*-coordinate.

The ordered pair for the point on the coordinate plane on the right is ( 5 , 3 ).

3. The coordinate plane shows the locations of several places in a city. To find the coordinates of the library, start at the **origin**.
4. The library is 0.75 unit to the left of the origin, so the *x*-coordinate is **−0.75**.
5. The library is **0.5** unit(s) up from the *x*-axis so the *y*-coordinate is **0.5**.
6. The coordinates of the library are ( **−0.75**, **0.5** ).
7. Write the *x*-coordinate of the library as a fraction. $-\frac{3}{4}$
8. Write the *y*-coordinate of the library as a fraction. $\frac{1}{2}$
9. The coordinates of the library, written as fractions, are ( $-\frac{3}{4}$, $\frac{1}{2}$ ).



On the Back!

10. What are the coordinates of the middle school? $\left(-\frac{1}{4}, -\frac{3}{2}\right)$ or (−0.25, −1.5)

R 4-2



## On-Level and Advanced Activity Centers  

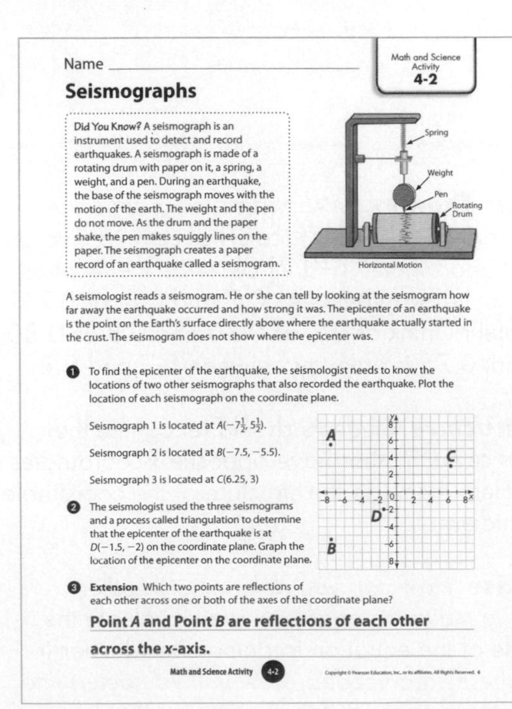

Name ______ Math and Science Activity 4-2

**Seismographs**

*Did You Know?* A seismograph is an instrument used to detect and record earthquakes. A seismograph is made of a rotating drum with paper on it, a spring, a weight, and a pen. During an earthquake, the base of the seismograph moves with the motion of the earth. The weight and the pen do not move. As the drum and the paper shake, the pen makes squiggly lines on the paper. The seismograph creates a paper record of an earthquake called a seismogram.



A seismologist reads a seismogram. He or she can tell by looking at the seismogram how far away the earthquake occurred and how strong it was. The epicenter of an earthquake is the point on the Earth's surface directly above where the earthquake actually started in the crust. The seismogram does not show where the epicenter was.

1. To find the epicenter of the earthquake, the seismologist needs to know the locations of two other seismographs that also recorded the earthquake. Plot the location of each seismograph on the coordinate plane.

Seismograph 1 is located at $A(-7\frac{1}{2}, 5\frac{1}{2})$.

Seismograph 2 is located at $B(-7.5, -5.5)$.

Seismograph 3 is located at $C(6.25, 3)$.

2. The seismologist used the three seismograms and a process called triangulation to determine that the epicenter of the earthquake is at $D(-1.5, -2)$ on the coordinate plane. Graph the location of the epicenter on the coordinate plane.

3. **Extension** Which two points are reflections of each other across one or both of the axes of the coordinate plane?

**Point A and Point B are reflections of each other across the *x*-axis.**

Math and Science Activity 4-2



### Math and Science Activity STEM

This activity revisits the science theme, **Map to Predict and Plan**, introduced on page 181 in the Student's Edition.

### Sample Student Work

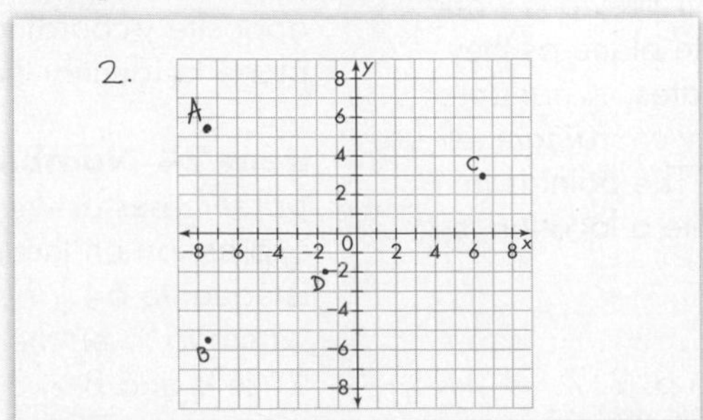

PearsonRealize.com

**TIMING**

The time allocated to Step 3 will depend on the teacher's instructional decisions and differentiation routines.

15–30 min

 Help  Practice Buddy  Tools Games

## Technology Center I O A

Tools Games

### Math Tools and Math Games

A link to a specific math tools activity or math game to use with this lesson is provided at PearsonRealize.com.

## Leveled Assignment

 Items 1–6, 13–19, 22, 23  Items 7–20, 22, 23  Items 7–10, 13–23

Name ______

**Homework & Practice 4-2**
**Rational Numbers on the Coordinate Plane**

### Another Look!

The coordinate plane has two units between each integer value. So the length of each unit is $\frac{1}{2}$. Graph and label the point $\left(-2, -1\frac{1}{2}\right)$.

To locate point $\left(-2, -1\frac{1}{2}\right)$, start at the origin. Move 2 units to the left on the x-axis. Then move down $1\frac{1}{2}$ units on the y-axis.

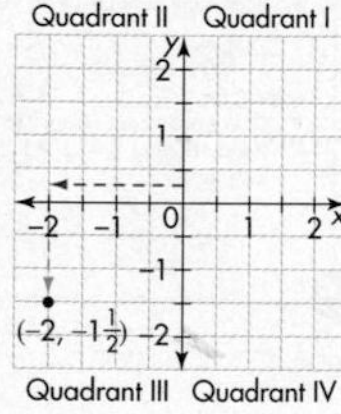

In **1–10**, write the ordered pair for each point.
In **11–16**, plot and label each point.

1. A $(-1.5, -1)$ or $\left(-1\frac{1}{2}, -1\right)$
2. B $(1.25, 0.5)$ or $\left(1\frac{1}{4}, \frac{1}{2}\right)$
3. C $(-1.5, 1.25)$ or $\left(-1\frac{1}{2}, 1\frac{1}{4}\right)$
4. D $(0, 1.5)$ or $\left(0, 1\frac{1}{2}\right)$
5. E $(0.5, -0.5)$ or $\left(\frac{1}{2}, -\frac{1}{2}\right)$
6. F $(1.5, -1.75)$ or $\left(1\frac{1}{2}, -1\frac{3}{4}\right)$
7. G $(-0.75, 0.5)$ or $\left(-\frac{3}{4}, \frac{1}{2}\right)$
8. H $(-1.25, 0)$ or $\left(-1\frac{1}{4}, 0\right)$
9. I $(1.75, 1.75)$ or $\left(1\frac{3}{4}, 1\frac{3}{4}\right)$
10. J $(-0.25, -0.25)$ or $\left(-\frac{1}{4}, -\frac{1}{4}\right)$
11. $U(1, -1.5)$
12. $V\left(-\frac{1}{2}, 1\right)$
13. $W\left(-1\frac{3}{4}, -1\frac{3}{4}\right)$
14. $X(1.75, -0.75)$
15. $Y\left(0, -1\frac{3}{4}\right)$
16. $Z\left(\frac{3}{4}, 1\right)$

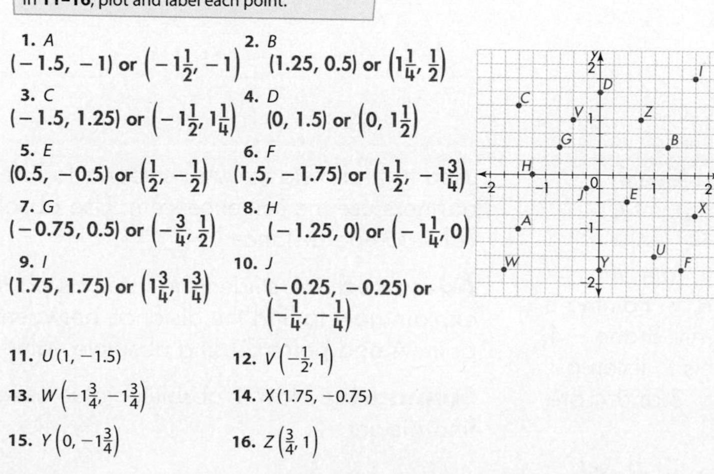



17. What is located at (0.5, −0.5)?
**Red Rock Canyon**

18. What is located at $\left(-\frac{1}{2}, \frac{2}{5}\right)$?
**Mystery Mountain**

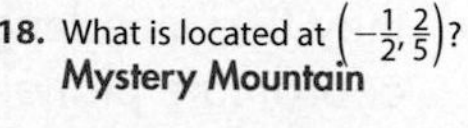


19. Write the ordered pair to locate Brown Bat Cave.
**(0.8, −0.7) or $\left(\frac{4}{5}, -\frac{7}{10}\right)$**

20. **Higher Order Thinking** Suppose ✠ marks the spot where the treasure is buried. Explain the shortest route, using grid lines as units, from Pirate's Cove to the treasure.
**Sample answer: Go right 7 units, then up 6 units.**

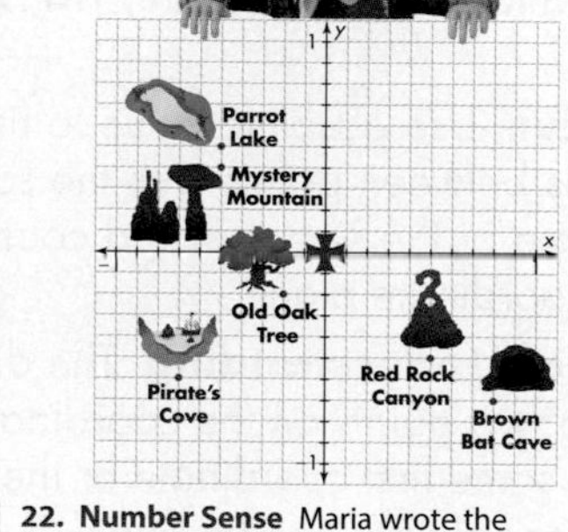


21. Which two locations are reflections of each other across one or both of the axes of the coordinate plane?
**Red Rock Canyon and Parrot Lake are reflections across both axes.**

22. **Number Sense** Maria wrote the equation shown below. Insert parentheses, if needed, to make the equation true. If no parentheses are needed, write, "parentheses not needed."

$3^3 - 2^2 \times 5 = 7$

**Parentheses not needed**

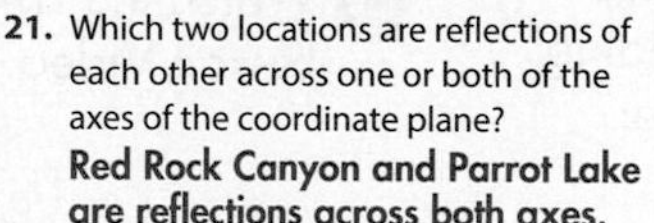

### Common Core Assessment

23. Graph and label each point on the coordinate plane at the right.

$E\left(-2\frac{1}{4}, -1\frac{3}{4}\right)$

$F(1.5, -2.75)$

$G(-0.75, 0)$

$H(3, 1.5)$

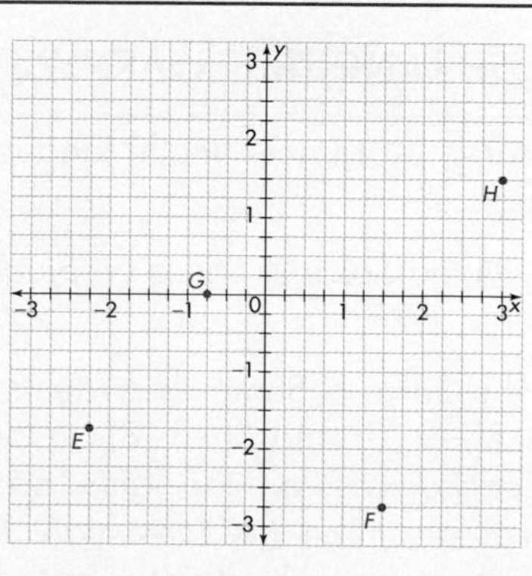

# LESSON 4-3

# DISTANCE ON THE COORDINATE PLANE

## DIGITAL RESOURCES PearsonRealize.com

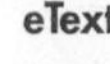
eText — Student and Teacher eTexts

PD — Listen and Look For Lesson Video

Think — Today's Challenge

Solve — Solve and Share

Learn — Visual Learning Animation Plus

Glossary — Animated Glossary

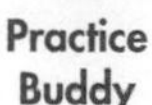
Practice Buddy — Online Personalized Practice

Tools — Math Tools

Assessment — Quick Check

Help — Another Look Homework Video

Games — Math Games

## LESSON OVERVIEW FCR FOCUS • COHERENCE • RIGOR

### FOCUS

**Domain 6.NS** The Number System

**Cluster 6.NS.C** Apply and extend previous understandings of numbers to the system of rational numbers.

**Content Standard 6.NS.C.8** Solve real-world and mathematical problems by graphing points in all four quadrants of the coordinate plane. Include use of coordinates and absolute value to find distances between points with the same first coordinate or the same second coordinate.

**Mathematical Practices MP.1, MP.2, MP.3, MP.7**

**Objective** Use absolute value to find distances between points with the same first coordinate or the same second coordinate on the coordinate plane.

**Essential Understanding** The distance between two points on the coordinate plane with the same first coordinate or the same second coordinate can be found by adding or subtracting the absolute values of the coordinates that differ.

**Materials** Four-quadrant coordinate grids (Teaching Tool 19) (optional)

### COHERENCE

In Topic 3, students learned that the absolute value of a number is its distance from 0 on the number line. In this lesson, students use absolute value to calculate the distance between two points that lie on the same horizontal or vertical line on a coordinate plane. Development of this skill prepares students for the next lesson in which they find side lengths of polygons on the coordinate plane.

### RIGOR

This lesson emphasizes a blend of **procedural skill** with **application**. Students learn a procedure for finding vertical and horizontal distances on the coordinate plane and use this skill to solve real-world and mathematical problems.

PD Watch the Listen and Look For Lesson Video.

## MATH ANYTIME

### Daily Common Core Review

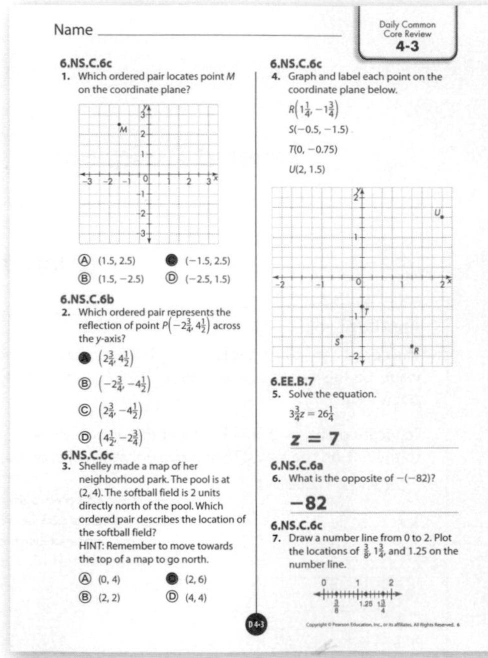
Name ____________

Daily Common Core Review 4-3

**6.NS.C.6c**
1. Which ordered pair locates point $M$ on the coordinate plane?

Ⓐ (1.5, 2.5) ● (−1.5, 2.5)
Ⓑ (1.5, −2.5) Ⓓ (−2.5, 1.5)

**6.NS.C.6b**
2. Which ordered pair represents the reflection of point $P\left(-2\frac{3}{4}, 4\frac{1}{2}\right)$ across the $y$-axis?

● $\left(2\frac{3}{4}, 4\frac{1}{2}\right)$
Ⓑ $\left(-2\frac{3}{4}, -4\frac{1}{2}\right)$
Ⓒ $\left(2\frac{3}{4}, -4\frac{1}{2}\right)$
Ⓓ $\left(4\frac{1}{2}, -2\frac{3}{4}\right)$

**6.NS.C.6c**
3. Shelley made a map of her neighborhood park. The pool is at (2, 4). The softball field is 2 units directly north of the pool. Which ordered pair describes the location of the softball field?
HINT: Remember to move towards the top of a map to go north.

Ⓐ (0, 4) ● (2, 6)
Ⓑ (2, 2) Ⓓ (4, 4)

**6.NS.C.6c**
4. Graph and label each point on the coordinate plane below.

$R\left(1\frac{1}{4}, -1\frac{3}{4}\right)$
$S(-0.5, -1.5)$
$T(0, -0.75)$
$U(2, 1.5)$

**6.EE.B.7**
5. Solve the equation.

$3\frac{3}{4}z = 26\frac{1}{4}$

**z = 7**

**6.NS.C.6a**
6. What is the opposite of −(−82)?

**−82**

**6.NS.C.6c**
7. Draw a number line from 0 to 2. Plot the locations of $\frac{3}{8}$, $1\frac{3}{4}$, and 1.25 on the number line.

D 4-3

Copyright © Pearson Education, Inc., or its affiliates. All Rights Reserved. 6

### Today's Challenge

Think Use the Topic 4 problems any time during this topic.

## ENGLISH LANGUAGE LEARNERS 

**Listening** Learn new (math) language structures.

*Use with the Solve & Share on Student's Edition p. 197.*

Read the Solve & Share as students listen. Write $A(-9, 8)$ and $B(-3, 8)$ on the board. *The y-coordinates are the same, and the x-coordinates have the same sign. To find the distance between point A and point B, subtract the absolute values of the x-coordinates.* Write $|-9| - |-3|$.

**Beginning** Instruct students to identify the coordinates of point $A$ and point $C$. Then write $A(-9, 8)$ and $C(-9, -4)$. *The x-coordinates are the same, and the y-coordinates have different signs.* Point to 8 and −4. Instruct students to write 8 and −4 as absolute values. Ask students to listen as partners use the sentence stem: 8 and 4 are the ____ ____ of $|8|$ and $|-4|$.

**Intermediate** Instruct students to identify the coordinates of point $A$ and point $C$. Have students write 8 and −4 as absolute values and explain how absolute value is used to find distance. Ask students to listen as partners use the sentence stem: Use absolute value to find distance by ____.

**Advanced** Ask students to listen as partners explain how to find the distance between point $A$ and point $C$ using absolute value.

**Summarize** How is absolute value used to find distance?

# DEVELOP: PROBLEM-BASED LEARNING

PEARSON realize. PearsonRealize.com

**COHERENCE: Engage learners by connecting prior knowledge to new ideas.**
Students apply what they know about absolute value to find the distance between two points that lie on the same horizontal or vertical line on a coordinate plane.

10–15 min

Solve

## BEFORE

1. **Pose the Solve-and-Share Problem**
**MP.7 Use Structure** Listen and look for students who count grid lines or squares to find the distance between two points.

2. **Build Understanding**
*What do you notice about how the locations of points A and B are related?* [Sample answer: They are on the same horizontal grid line. They are both in Quadrant II.] *What do you notice about how the locations of points A and C are related?* [Sample answer: They are on the same vertical grid line, but in different quadrants.]

## DURING

3. **Ask Guiding Questions As Needed**
*What are the coordinates of points A and B?* [$A(-9, 8)$, $B(-3, 8)$] *Which coordinates are the same?* [The *y*-coordinates] *Which are different?* [The *x*-coordinates] *What are the absolute values of the x-coordinates?* [9 and 3] Use similar questions to compare points *A* and *C*.

## AFTER

4. **Share and Discuss Solutions**
Start with students' solutions. If needed, project Ben's work to discuss how to calculate the distances.

5. **Transition to the Visual Learning Bridge**
*You can use absolute value to find the distance between two points that lie on a horizontal or vertical line on a coordinate plane.*

6. **Extension for Early Finishers**
*Could you find the exact distance between points B and C by counting grid lines or squares? Explain.* [No. The distance is a diagonal line, which does not follow grid lines.]

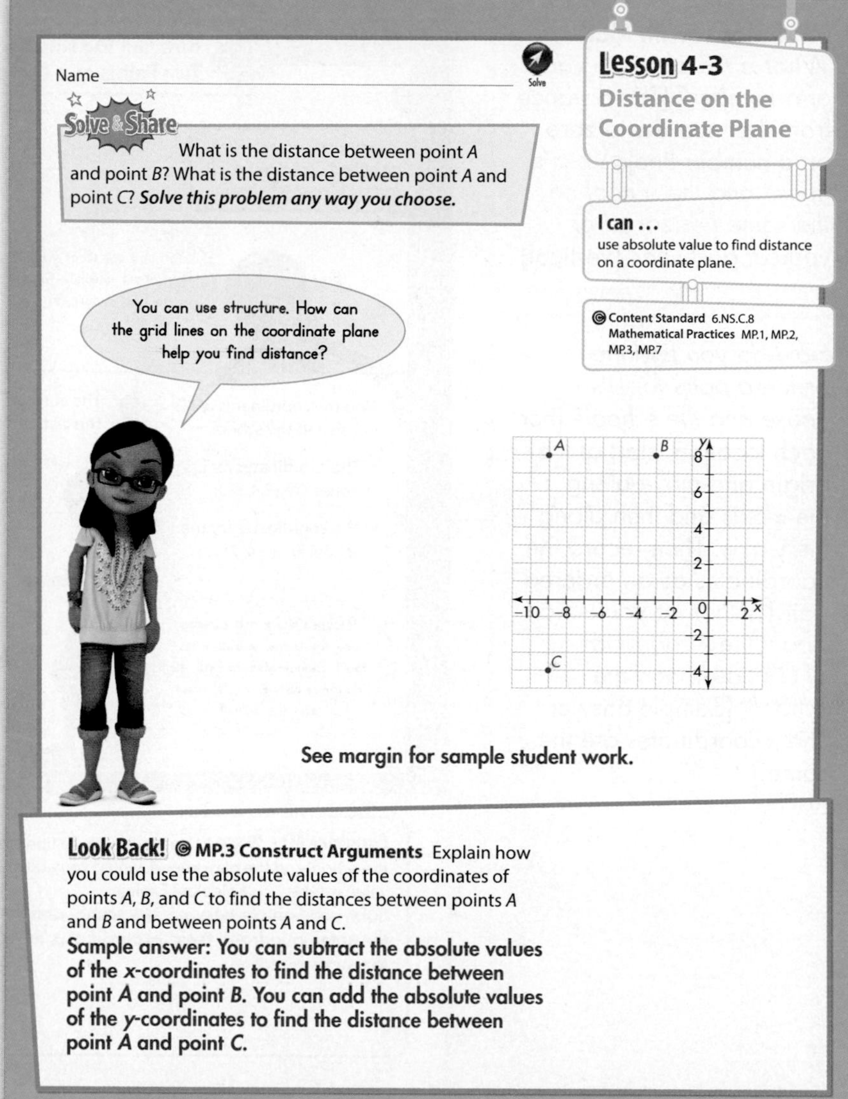

Name
Solve & Share
What is the distance between point A and point B? What is the distance between point A and point C? Solve this problem any way you choose.
Lesson 4-3
Distance on the Coordinate Plane
I can ...
use absolute value to find distance on a coordinate plane.
Content Standard 6.NS.C.8
Mathematical Practices MP.1, MP.2, MP.3, MP.7
You can use structure. How can the grid lines on the coordinate plane help you find distance?
A
B
C
See margin for sample student work.
Look Back! MP.3 Construct Arguments Explain how you could use the absolute values of the coordinates of points A, B, and C to find the distances between points A and B and between points A and C.
Sample answer: You can subtract the absolute values of the x-coordinates to find the distance between point A and point B. You can add the absolute values of the y-coordinates to find the distance between point A and point C.
Digital Resources at PearsonRealize.com
Topic 4 | Lesson 4-3
197


### Analyze Student Work

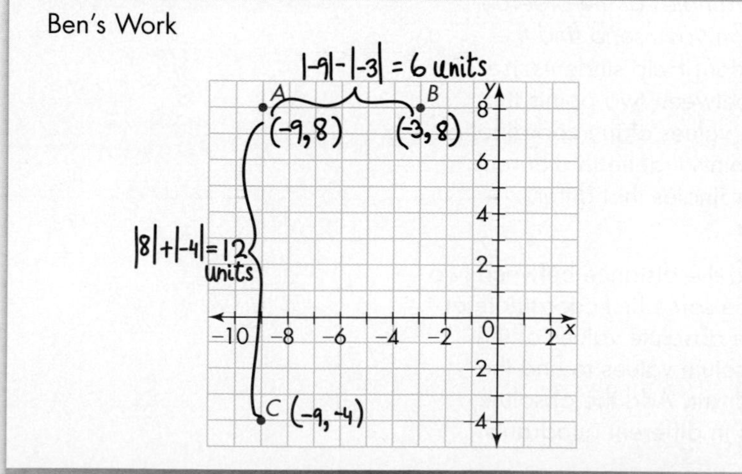


Ben subtracts the absolute values of the *x*-coordinates of points *A* and *B*, and adds the absolute values of the *y*-coordinates of points *A* and *C*.

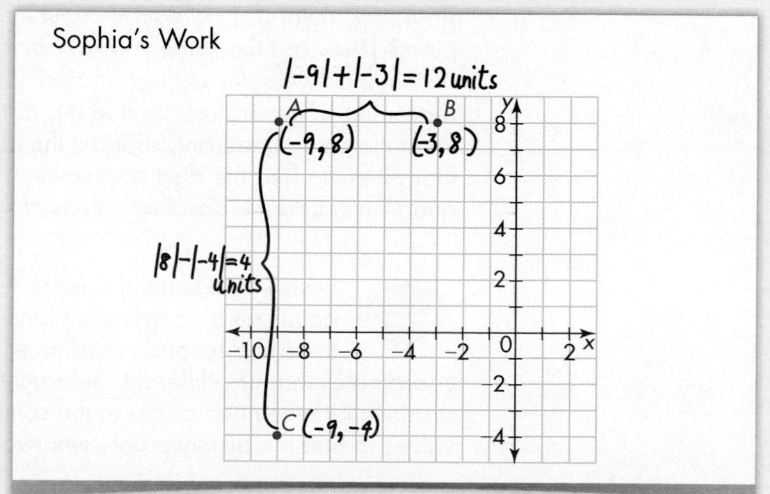


Sophia also uses the absolute values of the coordinates, but confuses when to add and when to subtract to find the distance.

# DEVELOP: VISUAL LEARNING

The *Visual Learning Bridge* connects students' thinking in Solve & Share to important math ideas in the lesson. Use the *Visual Learning Bridge* to make these ideas explicit. Also available as a *Visual Learning Animation Plus* at PearsonRealize.com

ELL Visual Learning

PEARSON realize. PearsonRealize.com

Learn

Glossary

**MP.4 Model with Math** *What is the absolute value of a number?* [The distance from that number to zero on a number line] *Are Li's house and the school on the same horizontal or vertical grid line?* [Vertical]

*How do you find the ordered pairs for Li's house and the school?* [For each location, start at the origin and move along the *x*-axis and then along the *y*-axis. Then record the coordinates as an ordered pair.] *What do you notice about the x-coordinates of Li's house and the school?* [Sample answer: The *x*-coordinates are the same.]

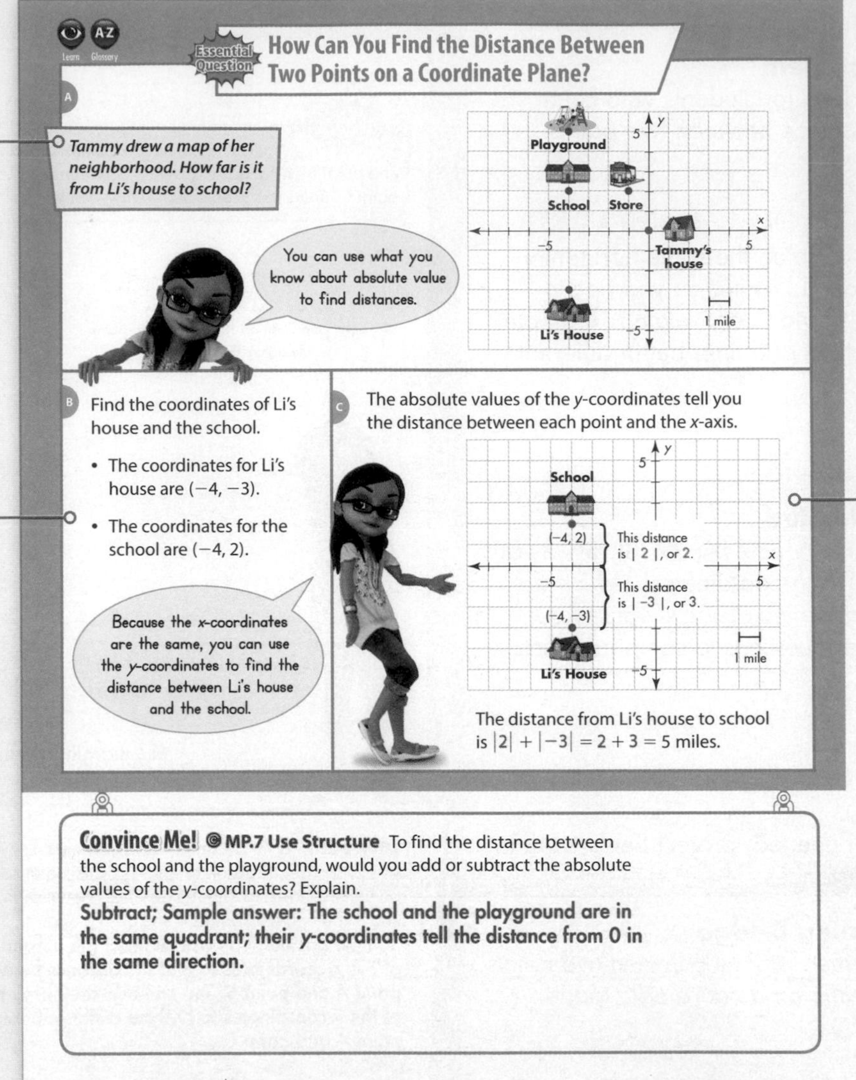

Essential Question
How Can You Find the Distance Between Two Points on a Coordinate Plane?
A
Tammy drew a map of her neighborhood. How far is it from Li's house to school?
You can use what you know about absolute value to find distances.
Playground
School
Store
Tammy's house
Li's House
1 mile
B
Find the coordinates of Li's house and the school.
• The coordinates for Li's house are (−4, −3).
• The coordinates for the school are (−4, 2).
Because the x-coordinates are the same, you can use the y-coordinates to find the distance between Li's house and the school.
C
The absolute values of the y-coordinates tell you the distance between each point and the x-axis.
School
(−4, 2)
This distance is | 2 |, or 2.
This distance is | −3 |, or 3.
(−4, −3)
Li's House
1 mile
The distance from Li's house to school is |2| + |−3| = 2 + 3 = 5 miles.
Convince Me! MP.7 Use Structure To find the distance between the school and the playground, would you add or subtract the absolute values of the y-coordinates? Explain.
Subtract; Sample answer: The school and the playground are in the same quadrant; their y-coordinates tell the distance from 0 in the same direction.
198 Topic 4 | Lesson 4-3
© Pearson Education, Inc. 6


Visual Learning Bridge

*Why do you add the distances between each point and the x-axis to find the total distance from Li's house to the school?* [Because the two distances combined result in the total distance between Li's house and the school]

**Prevent Misconceptions** RtI 1

Emphasize to students that they should always use the absolute values of coordinates when calculating distances. The distance from one point to another point is always positive.

**Convince Me! MP.7 Use Structure** *What is the ordered pair that describes the location of the school?* [(−4, 2)] *The playground?* [(−4, 5)] *What do you notice about the x-coordinates of the ordered pairs?* [They are the same.] *What operation can you use to find the distance between those coordinates?* [Subtraction] Help students use reasoning to generalize. To find the distance between two points that lie in the same quadrant, subtract the absolute values of the coordinates that differ. To find the distance between two points that lie in different quadrants, add the absolute values of the coordinates that differ.

Essential Question Revisit the Essential Question. To find the distance between two points on a coordinate plane with the same first coordinate or the same second coordinate, use the absolute values of the coordinates that are different. Subtract the absolute values to find the distance between two points in the same quadrant. Add the absolute values to find the distance between two points in different quadrants.

Check mark indicates items for prescribing differentiation on the next page.
Item 12 is worth 1 point. Items 18 and 21 are worth up to 2 points.

20–30 min

Practice Buddy

Tools

Assessment

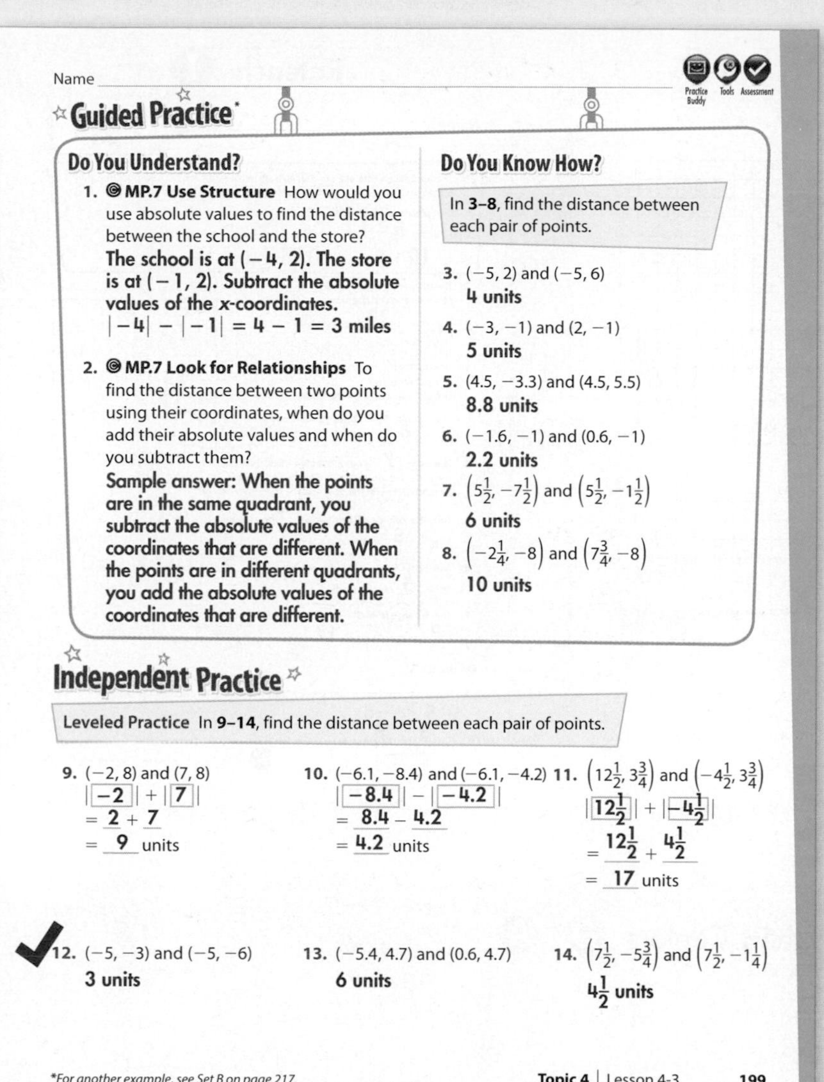

Name

## Guided Practice*

### Do You Understand?

1. MP.7 Use Structure How would you use absolute values to find the distance between the school and the store?
**The school is at (−4, 2). The store is at (−1, 2). Subtract the absolute values of the x-coordinates.**
$|-4| - |-1| = 4 - 1 = 3$ **miles**

2. MP.7 Look for Relationships To find the distance between two points using their coordinates, when do you add their absolute values and when do you subtract them?
**Sample answer: When the points are in the same quadrant, you subtract the absolute values of the coordinates that are different. When the points are in different quadrants, you add the absolute values of the coordinates that are different.**

### Do You Know How?

In **3–8**, find the distance between each pair of points.

3. (−5, 2) and (−5, 6)
**4 units**
4. (−3, −1) and (2, −1)
**5 units**
5. (4.5, −3.3) and (4.5, 5.5)
**8.8 units**
6. (−1.6, −1) and (0.6, −1)
**2.2 units**
7. $\left(5\frac{1}{2}, -7\frac{1}{2}\right)$ and $\left(5\frac{1}{2}, -1\frac{1}{2}\right)$
**6 units**
8. $\left(-2\frac{1}{4}, -8\right)$ and $\left(7\frac{3}{4}, -8\right)$
**10 units**

## Independent Practice

Leveled Practice In **9–14**, find the distance between each pair of points.

9. (−2, 8) and (7, 8)
$|-2| + |7|$
$= 2 + 7$
$= 9$ units

10. (−6.1, −8.4) and (−6.1, −4.2)
$|-8.4| - |-4.2|$
$= 8.4 - 4.2$
$= 4.2$ units

11. $\left(12\frac{1}{2}, 3\frac{3}{4}\right)$ and $\left(-4\frac{1}{2}, 3\frac{3}{4}\right)$
$\left|12\frac{1}{2}\right| + \left|-4\frac{1}{2}\right|$
$= 12\frac{1}{2} + 4\frac{1}{2}$
$= 17$ units

12. (−5, −3) and (−5, −6)
**3 units**

13. (−5.4, 4.7) and (0.6, 4.7)
**6 units**

14. $\left(7\frac{1}{2}, -5\frac{3}{4}\right)$ and $\left(7\frac{1}{2}, -1\frac{1}{4}\right)$
$4\frac{1}{2}$ **units**

*For another example, see Set B on page 217.

Topic 4 | Lesson 4-3 199

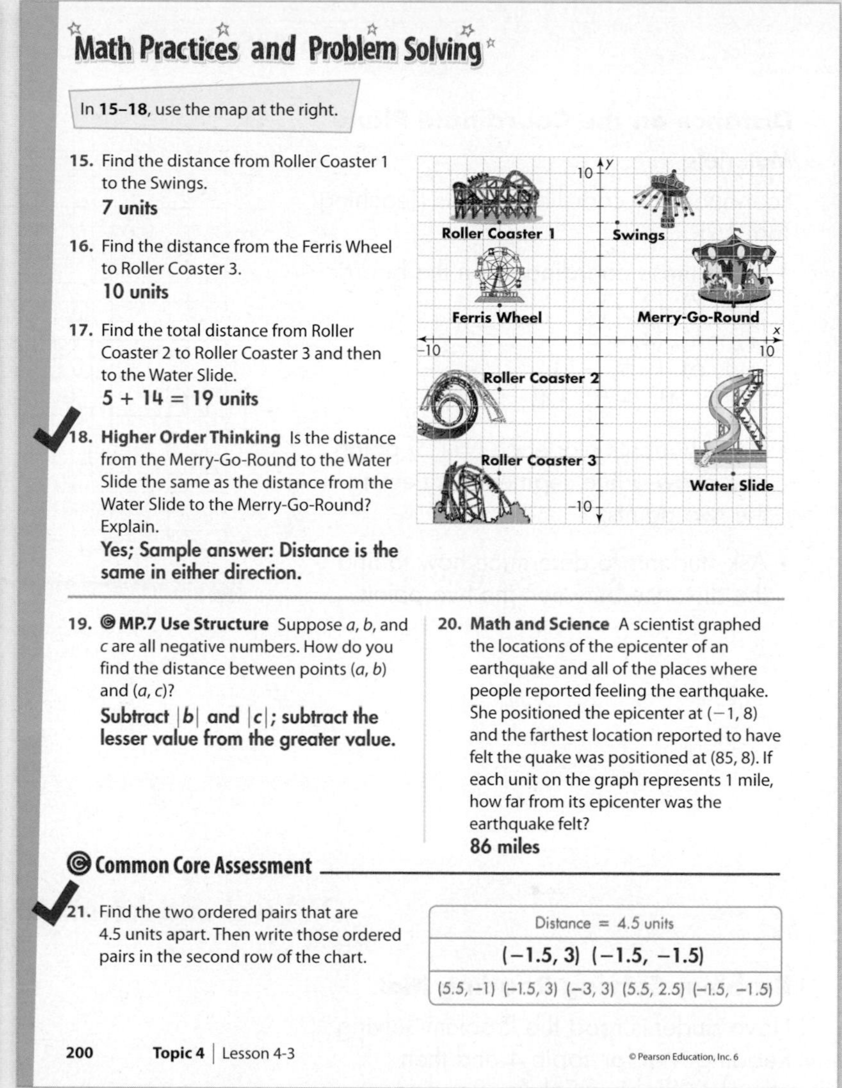

## Math Practices and Problem Solving

In **15–18**, use the map at the right.

15. Find the distance from Roller Coaster 1 to the Swings.
**7 units**

16. Find the distance from the Ferris Wheel to Roller Coaster 3.
**10 units**

17. Find the total distance from Roller Coaster 2 to Roller Coaster 3 and then to the Water Slide.
$5 + 14 = 19$ **units**

18. Higher Order Thinking Is the distance from the Merry-Go-Round to the Water Slide the same as the distance from the Water Slide to the Merry-Go-Round? Explain.
**Yes; Sample answer: Distance is the same in either direction.**



19. MP.7 Use Structure Suppose a, b, and c are all negative numbers. How do you find the distance between points (a, b) and (a, c)?
**Subtract $|b|$ and $|c|$; subtract the lesser value from the greater value.**

20. Math and Science A scientist graphed the locations of the epicenter of an earthquake and all of the places where people reported feeling the earthquake. She positioned the epicenter at (−1, 8) and the farthest location reported to have felt the quake was positioned at (85, 8). If each unit on the graph represents 1 mile, how far from its epicenter was the earthquake felt?
**86 miles**

### Common Core Assessment

21. Find the two ordered pairs that are 4.5 units apart. Then write those ordered pairs in the second row of the chart.

| Distance = 4.5 units | |
|---|---|
| **(−1.5, 3)** | **(−1.5, −1.5)** |

(5.5, −1) (−1.5, 3) (−3, 3) (5.5, 2.5) (−1.5, −1.5)

200 Topic 4 | Lesson 4-3 © Pearson Education, Inc. 6

### Error Intervention: Items 3–8

**If** students do not know whether to add or subtract the absolute values,

**then** ask: *Look at the coordinates that differ. Are the signs the same or different?* [Answers will vary.] *If the signs are the same (different), are the points located in the same quadrant or different quadrants?* [Same (different)] *How do you find the distance between two points in the same (different) quadrant?* [Subtract (add) the absolute values of the coordinates that differ.]

**Reteaching** Assign Reteaching Set B on p. 217.

**Items 9–11 Coherence** Students have learned that the absolute value of a number is its distance from zero on a number line. They use this understanding and reasoning to determine how to find the distance between two points on a coordinate plane.

**Item 18 Higher Order Thinking** Help students reason that the distance between two points is the same regardless of which point is the starting point.

**Item 19 MP.7 Use Structure** Students should recognize that if the coordinates are all negative, then the two points must be located in Quadrant III. They must subtract $|b|$ and $|c|$ because those variables represent the coordinates that differ. Be sure students specify that the lesser value should be subtracted from the greater value.

**Multi-Step Problems** *Page 200 Items 17, 18, and 21; Page 202 Items 13–17*

# ASSESS AND DIFFERENTIATE

Use the **QUICK CHECK** on the previous page to prescribe differentiated instruction.

**I Intervention** 0–3 points on the Quick Check

**O On-Level** 4 points on the Quick Check

**A Advanced** 5 points on the Quick Check

## Intervention Activity I

### Distance on the Coordinate Plane

**Materials**

Four-quadrant coordinate grids (Teaching Tool 19)

- Write these coordinates on the board:
  (−9, 7), (2, 7)
  (2, −1), (2, −3)
  (−5, 6), (−5, −5)
  (−8, −4), (−5, −4)
- Have students plot each pair of points and draw a line segment connecting the two points.
- Ask students to determine how to find the distance between the two points.

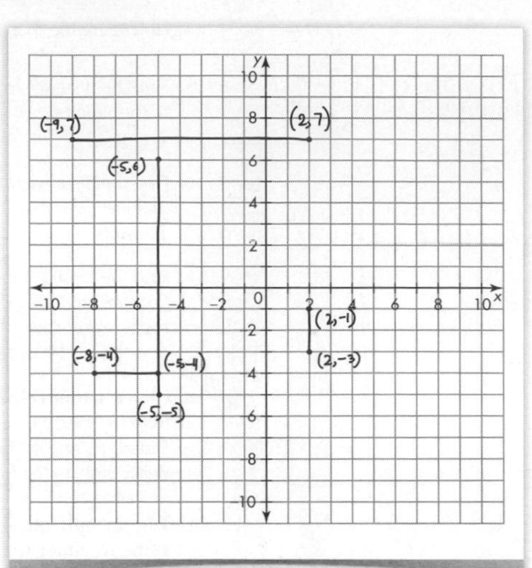

## Reteach I

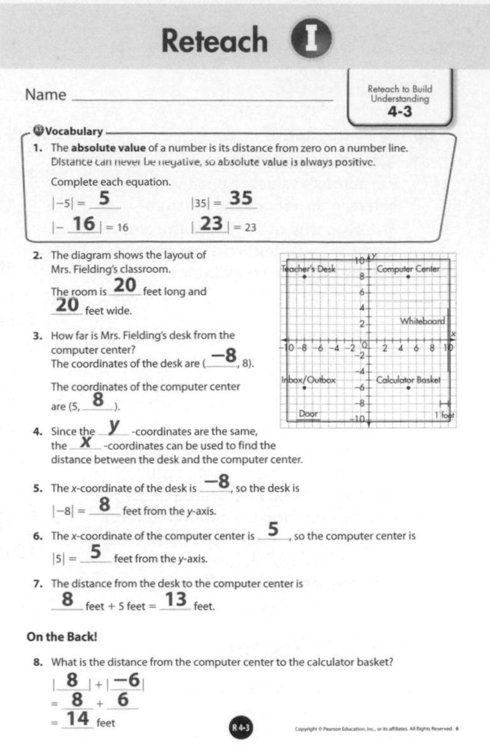

Name ______________

Reteach to Build Understanding
**4-3**

**Vocabulary**

1. The **absolute value** of a number is its distance from zero on a number line. Distance can never be negative, so absolute value is always positive.

   Complete each equation.

   |−5| = **5**  |35| = **35**

   |− **16** | = 16  | **23** | = 23

2. The diagram shows the layout of Mrs. Fielding's classroom.

   The room is **20** feet long and **20** feet wide.

3. How far is Mrs. Fielding's desk from the computer center?
   The coordinates of the desk are (**−8**, 8).

   The coordinates of the computer center are (5, **8**).

4. Since the **y** -coordinates are the same, the **x** -coordinates can be used to find the distance between the desk and the computer center.

5. The *x*-coordinate of the desk is **−8**, so the desk is |−8| = **8** feet from the *y*-axis.

6. The *x*-coordinate of the computer center is **5**, so the computer center is |5| = **5** feet from the *y*-axis.

7. The distance from the desk to the computer center is **8** feet + 5 feet = **13** feet.

**On the Back!**

8. What is the distance from the computer center to the calculator basket?
   | **8** | + | **−6** |
   = **8** + **6**
   = **14** feet



R 4-3



## On-Level and Advanced Activity Centers O A

### Problem-Solving Reading Mat

Have students read the Problem-Solving Reading Mat for Topic 4 and then complete Problem-Solving Reading Activity 4-3.

See the Problem-Solving Reading Activity Guide for other suggestions on how to use this mat.

## TIMING

The time allocated to Step 3 will depend on the teacher's instructional decisions and differentiation routines.

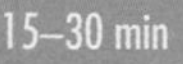
15–30 min

 Help  Practice Buddy Tools  Games

PearsonRealize.com

## Technology Center   

Tools Games

### Math Tools and Math Games

A link to a specific math tools activity or math game to use with this lesson is provided at PearsonRealize.com.

## Leveled Assignment  Items 1–6, 11–13, 16, 17  Items 5–14, 16–17  Items 7–17

Name ____________

Help Practice Buddy Tools Games

### Homework & Practice 4-3
### Distance on the Coordinate Plane

**Another Look!**

What is the distance between the dentist and the museum? Between the park and the gym?

You can use absolute values to find distances.


**Dentist to Museum:** (−3, 5) to (4, 5)
The *y*-coordinates are the same so use the *x*-coordinates. Since the points are in different quadrants, add the absolute values: $|-3| + |4| = 3 + 4 = 7$ units.

**Park to Gym:** (−4, −5) to (−4, −1)
The *x*-coordinates are the same so use the *y*-coordinates. Since the points are in the same quadrants, subtract the absolute values: $|-5| - |-1| = 5 - 1 = 4$ units.

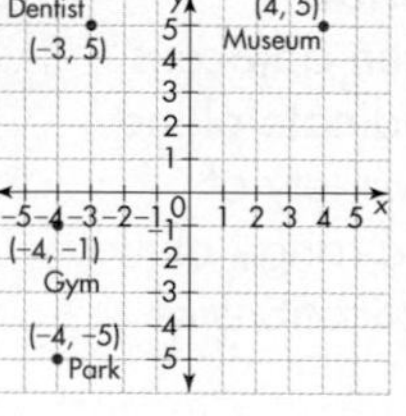


In **1–9**, find the distance between each pair of points.

**1.** (5, −6) and (2, −6)
$|5| + |2|$
$= 5 - 2$
$= 3$ units

**2.** (−6, −4.7) and (−6, 4.1)
$|-4.7| + |4.1|$
$= 4.7 + 4.1$
$= 8.8$ units

**3.** $\left(-2\frac{1}{2}, 1\frac{3}{4}\right)$ and $\left(-1\frac{1}{4}, 1\frac{3}{4}\right)$
$\left|-2\frac{1}{2}\right| - \left|-1\frac{1}{4}\right|$
$= 2\frac{1}{2} - 1\frac{1}{4}$
$= 1\frac{1}{4}$ units

**4.** (−7, −4) and (−7, 9)
**13 units**

**5.** (2.4, 1.8) and (−0.6, 1.8)
**3 units**

**6.** $\left(7\frac{1}{2}, -6\right)$ and $\left(7\frac{1}{2}, -2\frac{1}{2}\right)$
**$3\frac{1}{2}$ units**

**7.** (0, −6) and (−10, −6)
**10 units**

**8.** (−3, 8.5) and (−3, 7.7)
**0.8 unit**

**9.** $\left(\frac{1}{2}, 3\frac{3}{4}\right)$ and $\left(\frac{1}{2}, -1\frac{1}{4}\right)$
**5 units**

**10.** On a map, a museum is located at (15, −2). A library is located at (15, −17). If each unit on the map is a city block, how many city blocks is the museum from the library?
**15 city blocks**

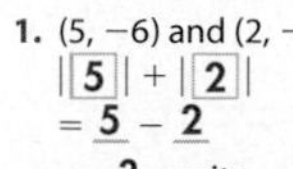

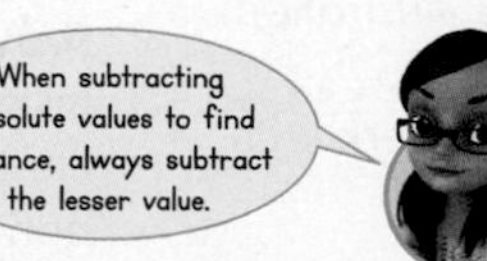

When subtracting absolute values to find distance, always subtract the lesser value.




In **11–14**, use the map at the right.

**11.** Find the distance from the Fishing area to the Canoes.
**6 units**

**12.** What is the distance from the Swimming area to the Water Slide?
**4 units**

**13.** Find the total distance from the Waterfalls to the Canoes and then to the Fishing area.
**6 + 6 = 12 units**

**14. Higher Order Thinking** What are the coordinates of the reflection of the Water Slide across both axes?
**$\left(2\frac{1}{2}, -3\right)$**

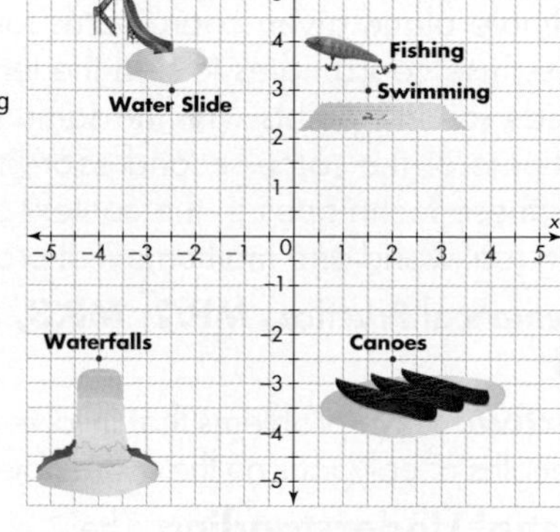


**15. MP.2 Reasoning** On a map, Jorge is standing at (11, −11). His friend Leslie is standing at (1, −11). If Jorge walks 10 units to the right, will he be standing with Leslie? Explain.
**No; Sample answer: If Jorge walks 10 units to the right, he will be at (21, −11), not (1, −11).**

**16. MP.1 Make Sense and Persevere** Helena is thinking of a number. That number raised to the third power is 100 greater than when it is raised to the second power. What number is Helena thinking about?
**5**

### Common Core Assessment

**17.** Find the two ordered pairs that are $3\frac{1}{2}$ units apart. Then write those ordered pairs in the second row of the chart.

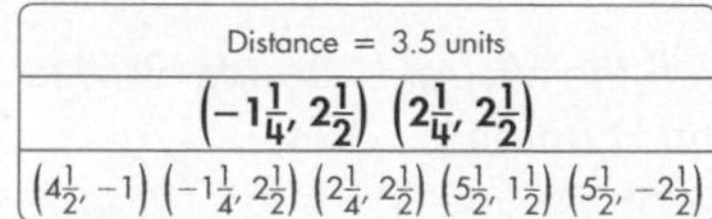

| Distance = 3.5 units | | | | |
|---|---|---|---|---|
| $\left(-1\frac{1}{4}, 2\frac{1}{2}\right)$ | $\left(2\frac{1}{4}, 2\frac{1}{2}\right)$ | | | |
| $\left(4\frac{1}{2}, -1\right)$ | $\left(-1\frac{1}{4}, 2\frac{1}{2}\right)$ | $\left(2\frac{1}{4}, 2\frac{1}{2}\right)$ | $\left(5\frac{1}{2}, 1\frac{1}{2}\right)$ | $\left(5\frac{1}{2}, -2\frac{1}{2}\right)$ |

# LESSON 4-4

# POLYGONS ON THE COORDINATE PLANE

## DIGITAL RESOURCES PearsonRealize.com

eText — Student and Teacher eTexts

PD — Listen and Look For Lesson Video

Think — Today's Challenge

Solve — Solve and Share

Learn — Visual Learning Animation Plus

Glossary — Animated Glossary

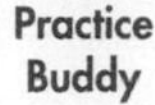
Practice Buddy — Online Personalized Practice

Tools — Math Tools

Assessment — Quick Check

Help — Another Look Homework Video

Games — Math Games

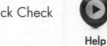

## LESSON OVERVIEW FCR FOCUS • COHERENCE • RIGOR

### FOCUS

**Domain 6.NS** The Number System

**Cluster 6.NS.C** Apply and extend previous understandings of numbers to the system of rational numbers.

**Content Standard 6.NS.C.8** Solve real-world and mathematical problems by graphing points in all four quadrants of the coordinate plane. Include use of coordinates and absolute value to find distances between points with the same first coordinate or the same second coordinate. **6.G.A.3** Draw polygons in the coordinate plane given coordinates for the vertices; use coordinates to find the length of a side joining points with the same first coordinate or the same second coordinate. Apply these techniques in the context of solving real-world and mathematical problems.

**Mathematical Practices MP.2, MP.3, MP.7, MP.8**

**Objective** Solve problems that involve finding side lengths of polygons on the coordinate plane.

**Essential Understanding** The coordinates of the vertices of a polygon on the coordinate plane can be used to find the lengths of the sides of the polygon.

**Materials** Four-quadrant coordinate grids (Teaching Tool 19) (optional)

### COHERENCE

In the previous lesson, students learned how to calculate the distance between two points that lie on a horizontal or vertical line on the coordinate plane. In this lesson, students apply this skill in order to find the side lengths of polygons on the coordinate plane and to solve problems. This skill will help students in Topic 14 when they draw two-dimensional nets of three-dimensional figures.

### RIGOR

This lesson emphasizes a blend of **procedural skill** with **application**. Students find the distances between adjacent vertices of a polygon on the coordinate plane and use the distances to solve a variety of problems that demonstrate a wide range of real-world and mathematical applications of perimeter.

PD Watch the Listen and Look For Lesson Video.

## MATH ANYTIME

### Daily Common Core Review

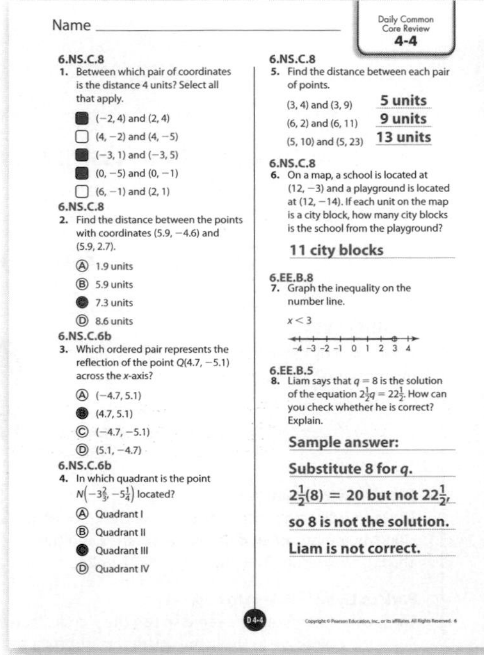

Name ______

Daily Common Core Review 4-4

6.NS.C.8
1. Between which pair of coordinates is the distance 4 units? Select all that apply.
   - ■ (−2, 4) and (2, 4)
   - □ (4, −2) and (4, −5)
   - ■ (−3, 1) and (−3, 5)
   - ■ (0, −5) and (0, −1)
   - □ (6, −1) and (2, 1)

6.NS.C.8
2. Find the distance between the points with coordinates (5.9, −4.6) and (5.9, 2.7).
   - Ⓐ 1.9 units
   - Ⓑ 5.9 units
   - ● 7.3 units
   - Ⓓ 8.6 units

6.NS.C.6b
3. Which ordered pair represents the reflection of the point $Q(4.7, -5.1)$ across the $x$-axis?
   - Ⓐ (−4.7, 5.1)
   - ● (4.7, 5.1)
   - Ⓒ (−4.7, −5.1)
   - Ⓓ (5.1, −4.7)

6.NS.C.6b
4. In which quadrant is the point $N\left(-3\frac{2}{3}, -5\frac{1}{4}\right)$ located?
   - Ⓐ Quadrant I
   - Ⓑ Quadrant II
   - ● Quadrant III
   - Ⓓ Quadrant IV

6.NS.C.8
5. Find the distance between each pair of points.
   (3, 4) and (3, 9) **5 units**
   (6, 2) and (6, 11) **9 units**
   (5, 10) and (5, 23) **13 units**

6.NS.C.8
6. On a map, a school is located at (12, −3) and a playground is located at (12, −14). If each unit on the map is a city block, how many city blocks is the school from the playground?
   **11 city blocks**

6.EE.B.8
7. Graph the inequality on the number line.
   $x < 3$
   −4 −3 −2 −1 0 1 2 3 4

6.EE.B.5
8. Liam says that $q = 8$ is the solution of the equation $2\frac{1}{2}q = 22\frac{1}{2}$. How can you check whether he is correct? Explain.
   **Sample answer: Substitute 8 for $q$. $2\frac{1}{2}(8) = 20$ but not $22\frac{1}{2}$, so 8 is not the solution. Liam is not correct.**

D4-4



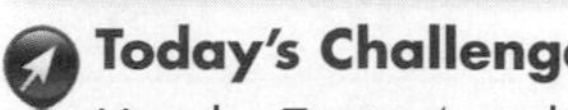

### Today's Challenge

Think Use the Topic 4 problems any time during this topic.

## ENGLISH LANGUAGE LEARNERS ELL

**Reading** Use visual support to develop vocabulary.

*Use with the Visual Learning Bridge on Student's Edition p. 204.*

Read Box A. Write *polygon* and *perimeter* on the board. Ask students to remind partners how to find the perimeter of a polygon. Point to the flags in the illustration. *These flags represent the corners, or vertices, of a polygon.*

**Beginning** Write (−4, 6), (2, 6), (2, 1), and (−4, 1) on sticky notes. Ask students to identify the corner indicated by the ordered pair on each sticky note. Read Box B to students. Trace your finger from *A* to *B*. *This distance is 6 m.* Write *6 m* on the illustration. Continue the process for the remaining bullets in Box B. Instruct students to work with partners to find the perimeter.

**Intermediate** Instruct students to identify the coordinates of each corner. Read Box B with students. Instruct students to write the distance from *A* to *B* on the illustration. Then have them write the distances from the remaining bullets in Box B on the illustration. Instruct students to work with partners to find the perimeter.

**Advanced** Read Box B with students. Instruct them to write the distances on the illustration and then explain how to find the perimeter of the polygon.

**Summarize** How is the perimeter of a polygon found using a coordinate plane?

# DEVELOP: PROBLEM-BASED LEARNING

**COHERENCE: Engage learners by connecting prior knowledge to new ideas.**
Students extend their knowledge of plotting points on a coordinate plane and finding distances between the points to solve problems involving polygons.

10–15 min

Solve

## BEFORE

**1. Pose the Solve-and-Share Problem**
**MP.7 Use Structure** Listen and look for students who use the structure of the coordinate plane to plot the vertices of the polygon and then find its perimeter.

**2. Build Understanding**
*How many sides does the polygon have?* [Four] *How can you find the perimeter of a polygon?* [Add the lengths of its sides.]

## DURING

**3. Ask Guiding Questions As Needed**
*How do you determine the four side lengths?* [Find the distances between the following points: *A* and *B*, *B* and *C*, *C* and *D*, and *D* and *A*.] *What are two ways to find the distance from point A to point B?* [Count the number of grid lines from point *A* to point *B*, or subtract the absolute values of the *x*-coordinates.] *The distance from point B to point C?* [Count the number of grid lines from point *B* to point *C*, or add the absolute values of the *y*-coordinates.]

## AFTER

**4. Share and Discuss Solutions**
Start with students' solutions. If needed, project Luis's and Caitlyn's work to discuss two methods of finding the perimeter.

**5. Transition to the Visual Learning Bridge**
*You can use what you know about finding the distance between two points in the coordinate plane in order to find the side lengths and perimeter of a polygon.*

**6. Extension for Early Finishers**
*What is the area of the polygon ABCD?* [54 square units]

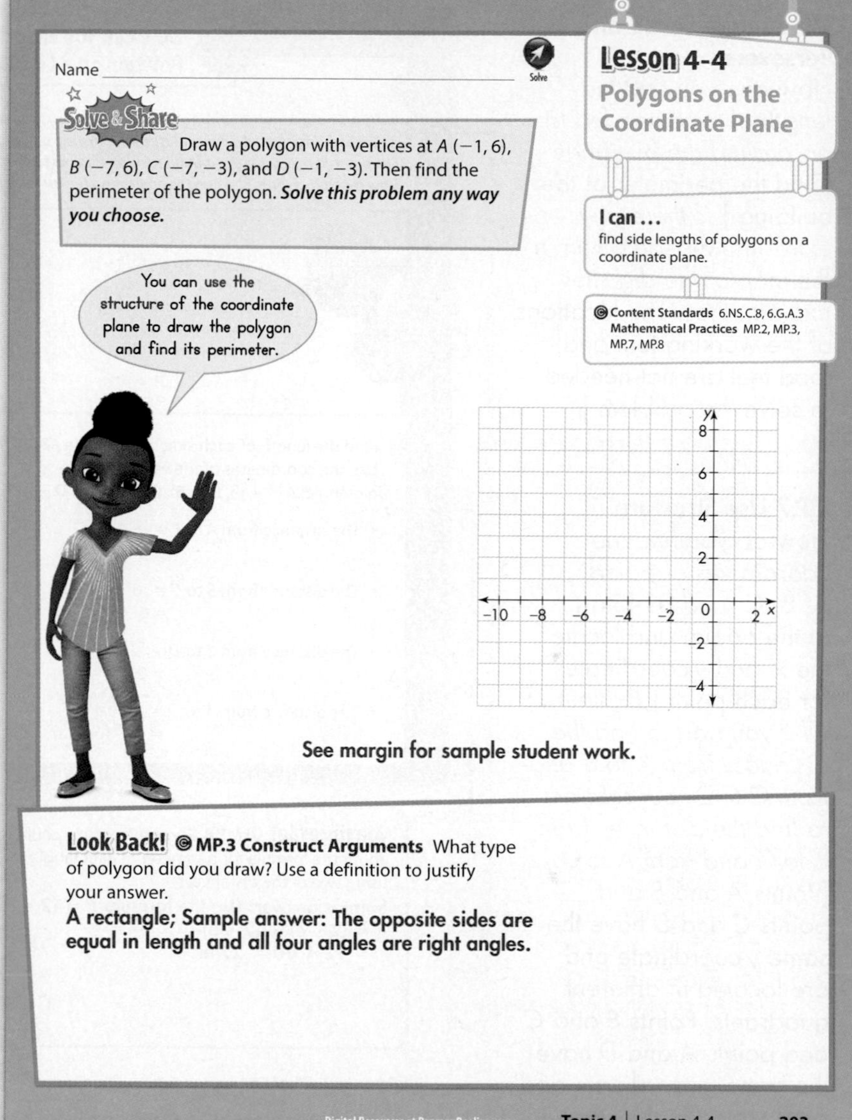

Name
Solve & Share
Draw a polygon with vertices at A (−1, 6), B (−7, 6), C (−7, −3), and D (−1, −3). Then find the perimeter of the polygon. Solve this problem any way you choose.
Lesson 4-4
Polygons on the Coordinate Plane
I can ...
find side lengths of polygons on a coordinate plane.
Content Standards 6.NS.C.8, 6.G.A.3
Mathematical Practices MP.2, MP.3, MP.7, MP.8
You can use the structure of the coordinate plane to draw the polygon and find its perimeter.
See margin for sample student work.
Look Back! MP.3 Construct Arguments What type of polygon did you draw? Use a definition to justify your answer.
A rectangle; Sample answer: The opposite sides are equal in length and all four angles are right angles.
Digital Resources at PearsonRealize.com
Topic 4 | Lesson 4-4
203


## Analyze Student Work

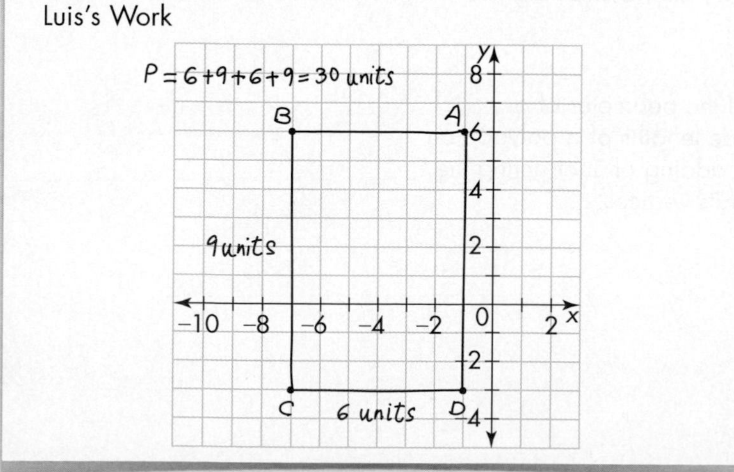


Luis counts the units between the vertices to find side lengths and adds them to find the perimeter.

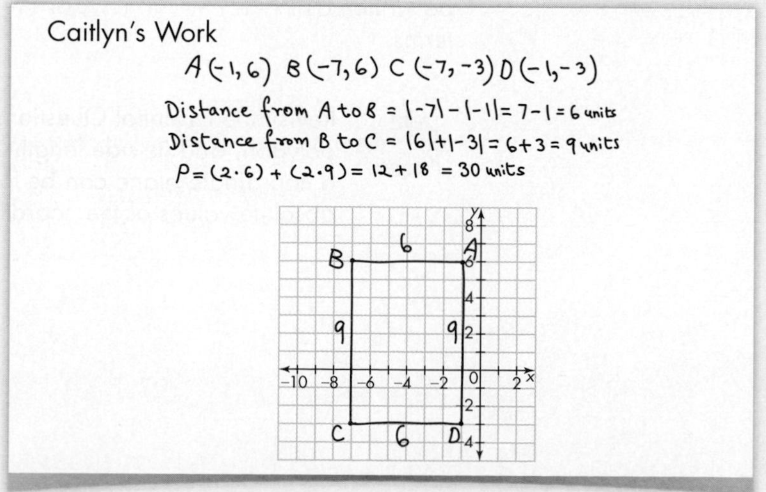


Caitlyn finds the side lengths by calculating the distances between the vertices. Then she adds the side lengths to find the perimeter.

# DEVELOP: VISUAL LEARNING

The *Visual Learning Bridge* connects students' thinking in Solve & Share to important math ideas in the lesson. Use the *Visual Learning Bridge* to make these ideas explicit. Also available as a *Visual Learning Animation Plus* at PearsonRealize.com

Learn Glossary

**MP.1 Make Sense and Persevere**
*How can you find the length of rope needed to go around the building?* [Find the perimeter of the building.] *Is there any extra information given in the map of the dig site? Explain.* [Yes. The locations of the working tent and food tent are not needed to solve the problem.]

**MP.7 Use Structure**
*How do you find the coordinates of points A, B, C, and D?* [Start at the origin, and locate the *x*- and *y*-coordinates for each point.] *Explain why you add to find the distances from A to B and from C to D, but subtract to find the distances from B to C and from A to D.* [Points *A* and *B* and points *C* and *D* have the same *y*-coordinate and are located in different quadrants. Points *B* and *C* and points *A* and *D* have the same *x*-coordinate and are located in the same quadrant.]

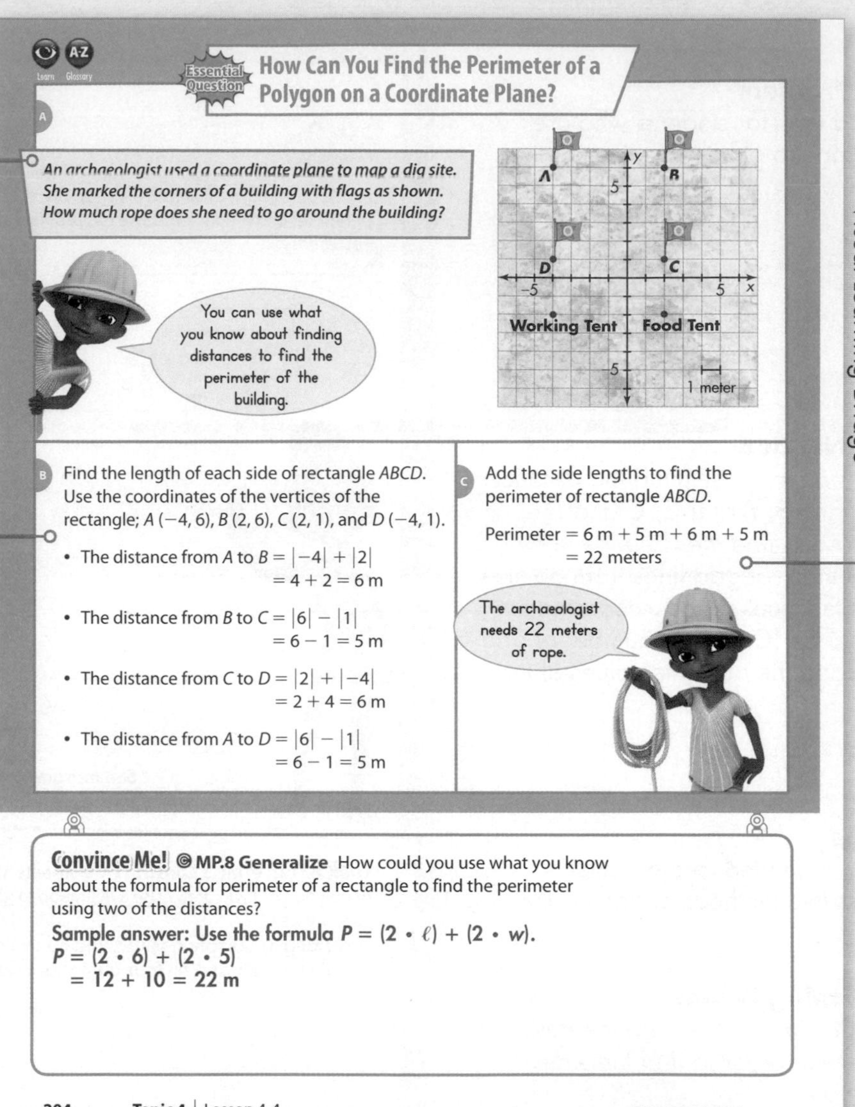

Essential Question
How Can You Find the Perimeter of a Polygon on a Coordinate Plane?
A
An archaeologist used a coordinate plane to map a dig site. She marked the corners of a building with flags as shown. How much rope does she need to go around the building?
You can use what you know about finding distances to find the perimeter of the building.
A
B
C
D
y
x
5
-5
Working Tent
Food Tent
1 meter
B
Find the length of each side of rectangle ABCD. Use the coordinates of the vertices of the rectangle; A (−4, 6), B (2, 6), C (2, 1), and D (−4, 1).
• The distance from A to B = |−4| + |2| = 4 + 2 = 6 m
• The distance from B to C = |6| − |1| = 6 − 1 = 5 m
• The distance from C to D = |2| + |−4| = 2 + 4 = 6 m
• The distance from A to D = |6| − |1| = 6 − 1 = 5 m
C
Add the side lengths to find the perimeter of rectangle ABCD.
Perimeter = 6 m + 5 m + 6 m + 5 m = 22 meters
The archaeologist needs 22 meters of rope.
Visual Learning Bridge
Convince Me! MP.8 Generalize How could you use what you know about the formula for perimeter of a rectangle to find the perimeter using two of the distances?
Sample answer: Use the formula P = (2 • ℓ) + (2 • w).
P = (2 • 6) + (2 • 5)
= 12 + 10 = 22 m
204 Topic 4 | Lesson 4-4
© Pearson Education, Inc. 6


**MP.2 Reason Quantitatively**
*Could you have solved this problem if you had only calculated the distances from point A to point B and from point B to point C? Explain.* [Yes. A rectangle has two pairs of sides of equal length, so the distance from *A* to *B* is the same as the distance from *C* to *D*, and the distance from *B* to *C* is the same as the distance from *A* to *D*.]

**Convince Me! MP.8 Generalize** Since a rectangle has two pairs of sides of equal length, the formula for the perimeter of a rectangle could be written as $P = \ell + w + \ell + w$, or $P = 2\ell + 2w$, after combining like terms.

Revisit the Essential Question. To find the perimeter of a polygon, add its side lengths. The side lengths of a polygon on a coordinate plane can be found by adding or subtracting the absolute values of the coordinates of its vertices.

# QUICK CHECK

Check mark indicates items for prescribing differentiation on the next page. Item 7 is worth 1 point. Items 9 and 13 are worth up to 2 points.

20–30 min

PEARSON realize. PearsonRealize.com

Practice Buddy

Tools

Assessment

Name ______

## Guided Practice*

### Do You Understand?

1. MP.2 Reasoning In the problem on the previous page, why do you add absolute values to find the distance from *A* to *B*, but subtract absolute values to find the distance from *B* to *C*?
**Sample answer: Points *A* and *B* are in different quadrants. Points *B* and *C* are in the same quadrant.**

2. MP.3 Construct Arguments Could you use the method of adding or subtracting the absolute values of coordinates to find the length of the diagonal *AC* of rectangle *ABCD*? Explain.
**No; Sample answer: Points *A* (−4, 6) and *C* (2, 1) do not have an *x*-coordinate or a *y*-coordinate that is the same. So you cannot add or subtract the absolute values of coordinates to find the length of the diagonal *AC*.**

### Do You Know How?

3. Use the map of the archaeological dig site on the previous page. What is the perimeter of the rectangle with vertices at point *D*, point *C*, the food tent, and the working tent?
**18 m**

4. Find the perimeter of rectangle *MNOP* with vertices *M* (−2, 5), *N* (−2, −4), *O* (3, −4), and *P* (3, 5).
**28 units**

## Independent Practice

**Leveled Practice** In **5** and **6**, find the perimeter of each rectangle.

5. Rectangle *JKLM*: *J* (−3, 8), *K* (−3, −1), *L* (4, −1), *M* (4, 8)
$JK = |\boxed{8}| + |\boxed{-1}|$
$= \underline{8} + \underline{1} = \underline{9}$
$KL = |\boxed{-3}| + |\boxed{4}|$
$= \underline{3} + \underline{4} = \underline{7}$
Perimeter = *JK* + *KL* + *LM* + *MJ*
$= \underline{9} + \underline{7} + \underline{9} + \underline{7} = \underline{32}$ units

6. Rectangle *WXYZ*: *W* (−3, −2), *X* (4, −2), *Y* (4, −5), *Z* (−3, −5)
$WX = |\boxed{-3}| + |\boxed{4}|$
$= \underline{3} + \underline{4} = \underline{7}$
$XY = |\boxed{-5}| - |\boxed{-2}|$
$= \underline{5} - \underline{2} = \underline{3}$
Perimeter = *WX* + *XY* + *YZ* + *ZW*
$= \underline{7} + \underline{3} + \underline{7} + \underline{3} = \underline{20}$ units

✓ 7. Rectangle *EFGH* has vertices *E* (−9, 10), *F* (−9, 2), *G* (6, 2), and *H* (6, 10). What is the perimeter of rectangle *EFGH*? **46 units**

*For another example, see Set B on page 217.



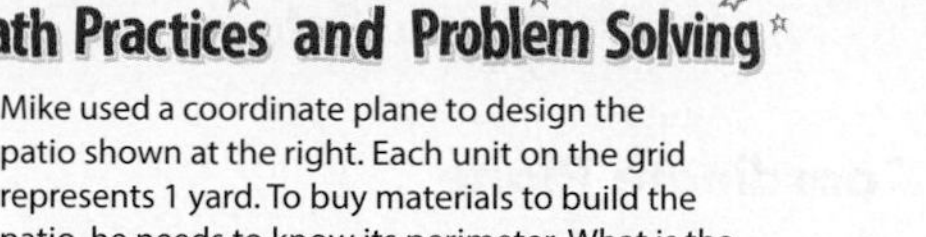

## Math Practices and Problem Solving

8. Mike used a coordinate plane to design the patio shown at the right. Each unit on the grid represents 1 yard. To buy materials to build the patio, he needs to know its perimeter. What is the perimeter of the patio?
**22 yards**

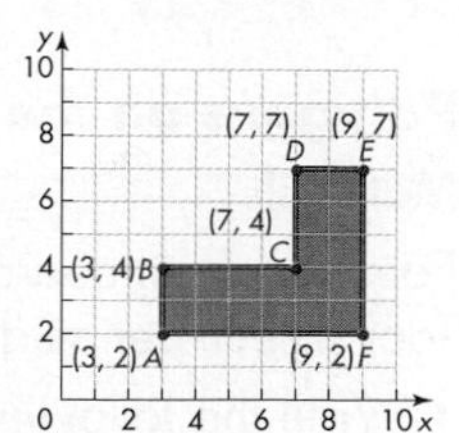


✓ 9. Higher Order Thinking A square on a coordinate plane has one vertex at (−0.5, −2) and a perimeter of 10 units. If all of the vertices are located in Quadrant III, what are the coordinates of the other 3 vertices?
**(−3, −2), (−3, −4.5), (−0.5, −4.5)**

10. MP.7 Use Structure Ana drew a plan for a rectangular piece of material that she will use for a quilt. Three of the vertices are (−1.2, −3.5), (−1.2, 4.4), and (5.5, 4.4). What are the coordinates of the fourth vertex?
**(5.5, −3.5)**

11. Vocabulary Why is absolute value used to find distances on a coordinate plane?
**Sample answer: Absolute value is the distance from zero to a point on a number line, so it tells you the distance relative to zero on the coordinate plane.**

12. Number Sense Suzanne is dividing 439 prizes among 14 booths set up for a fair. She wants to share the prizes equally. About how many prizes will each booth get?
**Sample answer: About 30 prizes**

### Common Core Assessment

✓ 13. The coordinates of triangle *ABC* are $A\left(-1\frac{1}{2}, -\frac{1}{2}\right)$, $B\left(-1\frac{1}{2}, -3\right)$, and *C* (4, −3).

**Part A**

What is the distance between points *A* and *B*?

$|-3| - \left|-\frac{1}{2}\right| = 3 - \frac{1}{2} = 2\frac{1}{2}$ **units**

**Part B**

Give the coordinates for two points that are 8 units from point *C*.

**Students should list two of the following points. (12, −3), (−4, −3), (4, 5), (4, −11)**





### Error Intervention: Item 4

**If** students have difficulty finding the perimeter of rectangle *MNOP*, **then** have them plot the vertices on a coordinate plane. *What are the sides of the rectangle?* [Sides *MN*, *NO*, *OP*, and *MP*] *How do you find the lengths of the sides of the rectangle?* [Find the distances between each of the points that form the sides of the rectangle.]

**Reteaching** Assign Reteaching Set B on p. 217.

**Item 8** Have students share how they solved this problem. *How many sides does this L-shaped polygon have?* [6] *How can you find the perimeter of a polygon that has more than four sides?* [The perimeter of any polygon can be found by adding the lengths of all its sides.]

**Item 10 MP.7 Use Structure** Students may find it helpful to graph the three given vertices in order to use the structure of the coordinate plane and the definition of a rectangle to determine the coordinates of the fourth vertex.

**Item 13** Encourage students to plot triangle *ABC* on a coordinate plane and to apply what they know about absolute value to find the distance between points *A* and *B*. Then help students use the coordinate plane to recognize that there are four possible points that are 8 units from point *C*.

**Multi-Step Problems** *Page 206 Items 8, 9, and 13; Page 208 Items 4, 5, 7, and 9*

# ASSESS AND DIFFERENTIATE

Use the **QUICK CHECK** on the previous page to prescribe differentiated instruction.

**Intervention** 0–3 points on the Quick Check

**On-Level** 4 points on the Quick Check

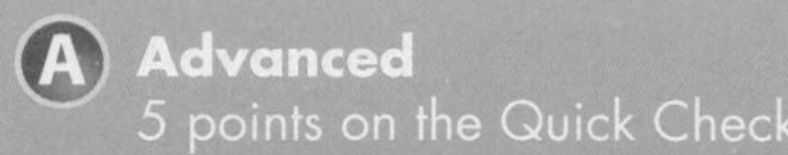

**Advanced** 5 points on the Quick Check

## Intervention Activity 

### Polygons on the Coordinate Plane

**Materials**

Four-quadrant coordinate grids (Teaching Tool 19) (1 per student)

- Write the following set of ordered pairs on the board:
  (1, 5), (−2, 5), (−2, −4), (1, −4)
- Ask volunteers to explain the steps they take to plot the points, connect them with line segments to draw a polygon, identify the type of polygon, and find the perimeter.
- Repeat the steps for two more sets of ordered pairs.
  (5, 3), (10, 3), (10, −2), (5, −2)
  (−8, −1), (−6, −1), (−6, −8), (−8, −8)

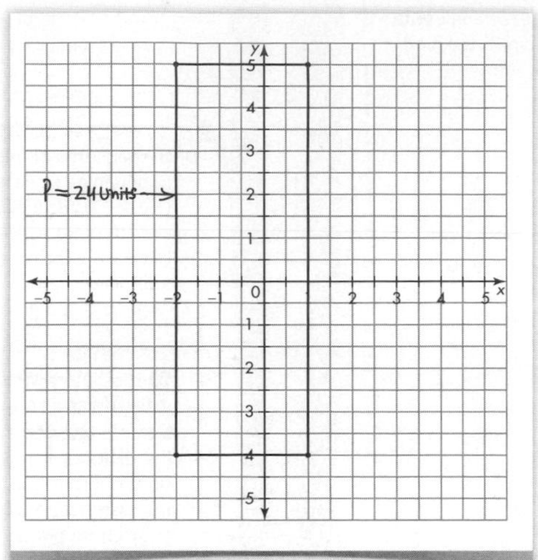


## Reteach

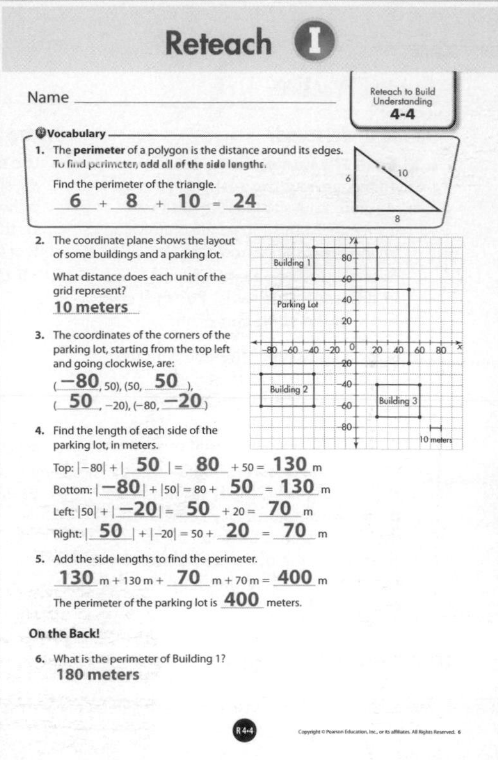

Name ________________

Reteach to Build Understanding 4-4

Vocabulary

1. The **perimeter** of a polygon is the distance around its edges. To find perimeter, add all of the side lengths.
   Find the perimeter of the triangle.
   6 + 8 + 10 = 24
2. The coordinate plane shows the layout of some buildings and a parking lot.
   What distance does each unit of the grid represent?
   10 meters
3. The coordinates of the corners of the parking lot, starting from the top left and going clockwise, are:
   (−80, 50), (50, 50),
   (50, −20), (−80, −20)
4. Find the length of each side of the parking lot, in meters.
   Top: |−80| + |50| = 80 + 50 = 130 m
   Bottom: |−80| + |50| = 80 + 50 = 130 m
   Left: |50| + |−20| = 50 + 20 = 70 m
   Right: |50| + |−20| = 50 + 20 = 70 m
5. Add the side lengths to find the perimeter.
   130 m + 130 m + 70 m + 70 m = 400 m
   The perimeter of the parking lot is 400 meters.

**On the Back!**

6. What is the perimeter of Building 1?
   180 meters

R 4-4



## On-Level and Advanced Activity Centers

### Center Games

Students work in pairs or small groups to plot points and draw polygons on the coordinate plane. Have students record their work and share their thinking as they play the game.

★ On-Level

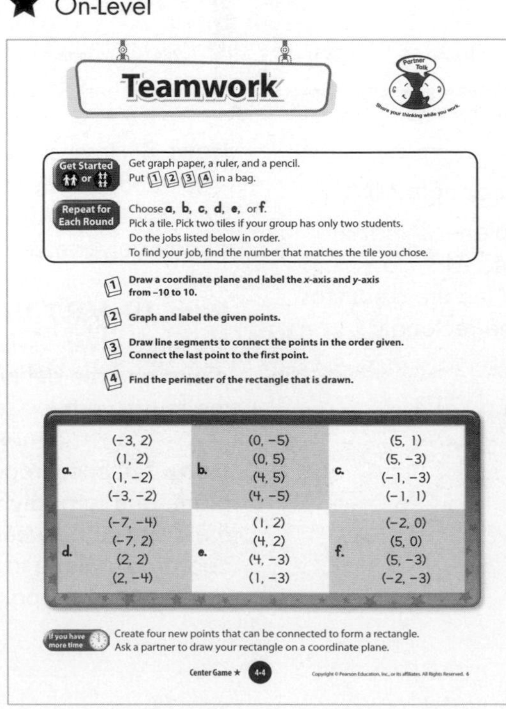

**Teamwork**

Partner Talk — Share your thinking while you work.

**Get Started** Get graph paper, a ruler, and a pencil.
Put 1 2 3 4 in a bag.

**Repeat for Each Round** Choose a, b, c, d, e, or f.
Pick a tile. Pick two tiles if your group has only two students.
Do the jobs listed below in order.
To find your job, find the number that matches the tile you chose.

1. **Draw a coordinate plane and label the *x*-axis and *y*-axis from −10 to 10.**
2. **Graph and label the given points.**
3. **Draw line segments to connect the points in the order given. Connect the last point to the first point.**
4. **Find the perimeter of the rectangle that is drawn.**

| | | | | | |
|---|---|---|---|---|---|
| a. | (−3, 2)<br>(1, 2)<br>(1, −2)<br>(−3, −2) | b. | (0, −5)<br>(0, 5)<br>(4, 5)<br>(4, −5) | c. | (5, 1)<br>(5, −3)<br>(−1, −3)<br>(−1, 1) |
| d. | (−7, −4)<br>(−7, 2)<br>(2, 2)<br>(2, −4) | e. | (1, 2)<br>(4, 2)<br>(4, −3)<br>(1, −3) | f. | (−2, 0)<br>(5, 0)<br>(5, −3)<br>(−2, −3) |

If you have more time: Create four new points that can be connected to form a rectangle. Ask a partner to draw your rectangle on a coordinate plane.

Center Game ★ 4-4



★★ Advanced

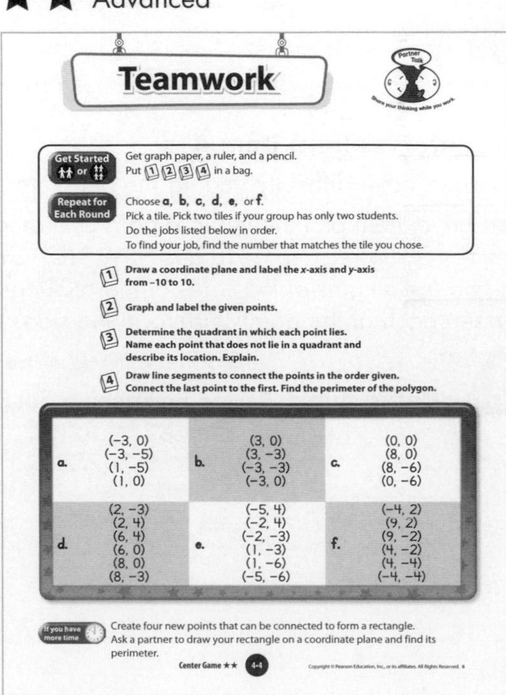

**Teamwork**

Partner Talk — Share your thinking while you work.

**Get Started** Get graph paper, a ruler, and a pencil.
Put 1 2 3 4 in a bag.

**Repeat for Each Round** Choose a, b, c, d, e, or f.
Pick a tile. Pick two tiles if your group has only two students.
Do the jobs listed below in order.
To find your job, find the number that matches the tile you chose.

1. **Draw a coordinate plane and label the *x*-axis and *y*-axis from −10 to 10.**
2. **Graph and label the given points.**
3. **Determine the quadrant in which each point lies. Name each point that does not lie in a quadrant and describe its location. Explain.**
4. **Draw line segments to connect the points in the order given. Connect the last point to the first. Find the perimeter of the polygon.**

| | | | | | |
|---|---|---|---|---|---|
| a. | (−3, 0)<br>(−3, −5)<br>(1, −5)<br>(1, 0) | b. | (3, 0)<br>(3, −3)<br>(−3, −3)<br>(−3, 0) | c. | (0, 0)<br>(8, 0)<br>(8, −6)<br>(0, −6) |
| d. | (2, −3)<br>(2, 4)<br>(6, 4)<br>(6, 0)<br>(8, 0)<br>(8, −3) | e. | (−5, 4)<br>(−2, 4)<br>(−2, −3)<br>(1, −3)<br>(1, −6)<br>(−5, −6) | f. | (−4, 2)<br>(9, 2)<br>(9, −2)<br>(4, −2)<br>(4, −4)<br>(−4, −4) |

If you have more time: Create four new points that can be connected to form a rectangle. Ask a partner to draw your rectangle on a coordinate plane and find its perimeter.

Center Game ★★ 4-4

**TIMING**
The time allocated to Step 3 will depend on the teacher's instructional decisions and differentiation routines.

15–30 min

PEARSON realize.
PearsonRealize.com

 Help  Practice Buddy  Tools  Games

## Technology Center I O A

 Tools  Games

**Math Tools and Math Games**

A link to a specific math tools activity or math game to use with this lesson is provided at PearsonRealize.com.

## Leveled Assignment

 Items 1–4, 8, 9  Items 2–7, 9  Items 3–9

Name ______

Help Practice Buddy Tools Games

**Homework & Practice 4-4**
**Polygons on the Coordinate Plane**

**Another Look!**

Remember, perimeter is the distance around a figure.

Find the perimeter of rectangle *ABCD*.
Add or subtract absolute values to find the length of each side.

*AB*: $|-3| + |2| = 3 + 2 = 5$ units

*BC*: $|4| - |2| = 4 - 2 = 2$ units

*CD*: $|-3| + |2| = 3 + 2 = 5$ units

*DA*: $|4| - |2| = 4 - 2 = 2$ units

The perimeter is $5 + 2 + 5 + 2 = 14$ units.

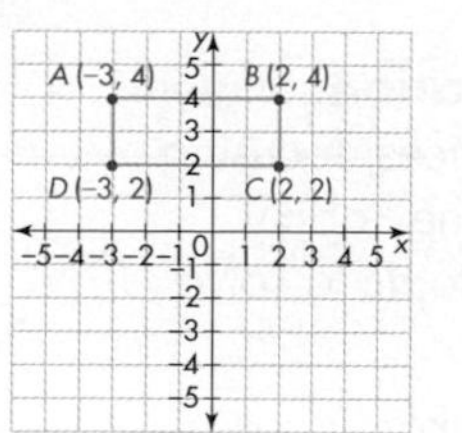


In **1** and **2**, use the coordinate plane below.

**1.** What is the perimeter of rectangle *ABCD*?
**18 units**

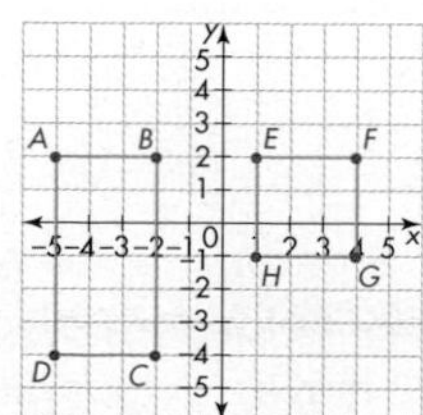


**2.** What is the perimeter of square *EFGH*?
**12 units**

**3.** Rectangle *QRST* has vertices $Q\left(4\frac{1}{2}, 2\right)$, $R\left(8\frac{1}{2}, 2\right)$, $S\left(8\frac{1}{2}, -3\frac{1}{2}\right)$, $T\left(4\frac{1}{2}, -3\frac{1}{2}\right)$. What is the perimeter of rectangle *QRST*?
**19 units**

You can draw a picture to show the rectangle.

**4.** Madison used a coordinate plane to map out an herb garden, shown at the right. To buy a fence for the garden, she needs to know its perimeter. What is the perimeter of the garden?
**14 yards**

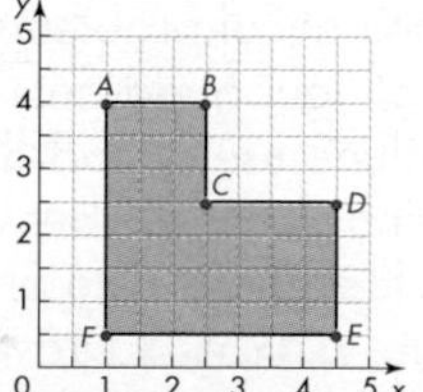


**5. Higher Order Thinking** A rectangle on a coordinate plane has one vertex at $(-5, -6)$ and a perimeter of 30 units. What could be the coordinates of the other 3 vertices?
**Sample answer: $(-5, 2)$, $(2, 2)$, $(2, -6)$**

**6. MP.7 Use Structure** Mr. Wells drew a plan for a rectangular dog run. Three of the vertices are $\left(2\frac{1}{3}, 7\frac{1}{2}\right)$, $\left(12, 7\frac{1}{2}\right)$, and $(12, 1)$. What are the coordinates of the fourth vertex?
**$\left(2\frac{1}{3}, 1\right)$**

**7. Algebra** Mai gave half of the coins in her coin collection to her younger brother. Then, she sold 18 coins to a friend. Now Mai has 35 coins left in her collection. Let $c$ = the number of coins Mai had in her collection to start. Solve the equation $\frac{1}{2}c - 18 = 35$ to find the number of coins Mai had in her collection.
**$c = 106$ coins**

**8.** Joaquín has 513 stamps in his collection. He organizes them in a 26-page album. About how many stamps will be on each page?
**Sample answer: About 20 stamps**

**Common Core Assessment**

**9.** The coordinates of triangle *XYZ* are $X(-3, 3.3)$, $Y(-3, -5.2)$, and $Z(4.5, -5.2)$.

**Part A**

What is the distance between points *X* and *Y*?

**$|3.3| + |-5.2| = 3.3 + 5.2 = 8.5$ units**

**Part B**

Give the coordinates for two points that are 5 units from point *Z*.

**Students should list two of the following points. $(9.5, -5.2)$, $(-0.5, -5.2)$, $(4.5, -0.2)$, $(4.5, -10.2)$**

# CONSTRUCT ARGUMENTS

## DIGITAL RESOURCES PearsonRealize.com

**eText** Student and Teacher eTexts

**PD** Listen and Look For Lesson Video

**Think** Today's Challenge

**Solve** Solve and Share

**Learn** Visual Learning Animation Plus

**Glossary** Animated Glossary

**Practice Buddy** Online Personalized Practice

**Tools** Math Tools

**Assessment** Quick Check

**Help** Another Look Homework Video

**Games** Math Games

**MP** Math Practices Animations

## LESSON OVERVIEW FCR FOCUS • COHERENCE • RIGOR

### FOCUS

**Mathematical Practices MP.3** Construct viable arguments and critique the reasoning of others. Also **MP.1, MP.4, MP.6.**

**Domain 6.NS** The Number System

**Cluster 6.NS.C** Apply and extend previous understandings of numbers to the system of rational numbers.

**Content Standard 6.NS.C.8** Solve real-world and mathematical problems by graphing points in all four quadrants of the coordinate plane. Include use of coordinates and absolute value to find distances between points with the same first coordinate or the same second coordinate. **6.G.A.3** Draw polygons in the coordinate plane given coordinates for the vertices; use coordinates to find the length of a side joining points with the same first coordinate or the same second coordinate. Apply these techniques in the context of solving real-world and mathematical problems.

**Objective** Construct arguments using previously learned concepts and skills, such as finding distances on the coordinate plane.

**Essential Understanding** Good math thinkers use math to explain why they are right. They can talk about the math that others do, too.

**Materials** Four-quadrant coordinate grids (Teaching Tool 19) (optional)

### COHERENCE

Students have engaged in this mathematical practice throughout this program. This lesson provides an opportunity to focus on the thinking habits good problem solvers use when they *construct arguments*. Although the content used in this lesson was developed in this topic, instruction should focus on MP.3.

### RIGOR

This lesson emphasizes **application**. Students engage the mathematical practices, focusing on *constructing arguments*, as they apply what they have learned in this topic to solve problems.

**PD** Watch the Listen and Look For Lesson Video.

## MATH ANYTIME

### Daily Common Core Review

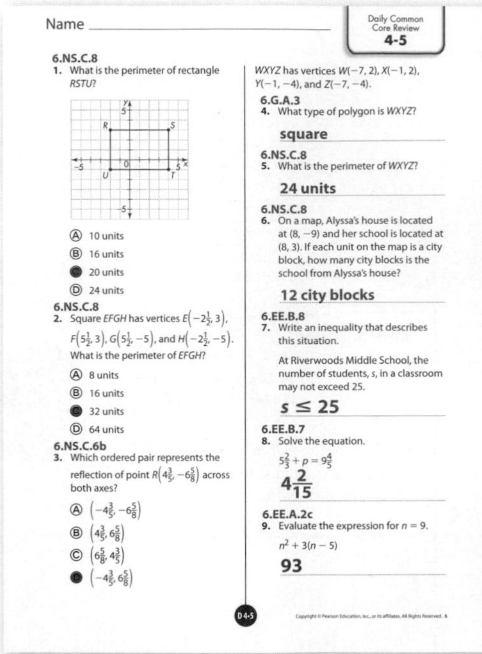
Name ______

Daily Common Core Review 4-5

6.NS.C.8
1. What is the perimeter of rectangle *RSTU*?



Ⓐ 10 units
Ⓑ 16 units
● 20 units
Ⓓ 24 units

6.NS.C.8
2. Square *EFGH* has vertices $E\left(-2\frac{1}{2}, 3\right)$, $F\left(5\frac{1}{2}, 3\right)$, $G\left(5\frac{1}{2}, -5\right)$, and $H\left(-2\frac{1}{2}, -5\right)$. What is the perimeter of *EFGH*?

Ⓐ 8 units
Ⓑ 16 units
● 32 units
Ⓓ 64 units

6.NS.C.6b
3. Which ordered pair represents the reflection of point $R\left(4\frac{3}{5}, -6\frac{5}{8}\right)$ across both axes?

Ⓐ $\left(-4\frac{3}{5}, -6\frac{5}{8}\right)$
Ⓑ $\left(4\frac{3}{5}, 6\frac{5}{8}\right)$
Ⓒ $\left(6\frac{5}{8}, 4\frac{3}{5}\right)$
● $\left(-4\frac{3}{5}, 6\frac{5}{8}\right)$

*WXYZ* has vertices $W(-7, 2)$, $X(-1, 2)$, $Y(-1, -4)$, and $Z(-7, -4)$.

6.G.A.3
4. What type of polygon is *WXYZ*?

**square**

6.NS.C.8
5. What is the perimeter of *WXYZ*?

**24 units**

6.NS.C.8
6. On a map, Alyssa's house is located at (8, −9) and her school is located at (8, 3). If each unit on the map is a city block, how many city blocks is the school from Alyssa's house?

**12 city blocks**

6.EE.B.8
7. Write an inequality that describes this situation.

At Riverwoods Middle School, the number of students, *s*, in a classroom may not exceed 25.

$s \leq 25$

6.EE.B.7
8. Solve the equation.

$5\frac{2}{3} + p = 9\frac{4}{5}$

$4\frac{2}{15}$

6.EE.A.2c
9. Evaluate the expression for $n = 9$.

$n^2 + 3(n - 5)$

**93**

D 4-5



### Today's Challenge

**Think** Use the Topic 4 problems any time during this topic.

## ENGLISH LANGUAGE LEARNERS

**Learning Strategies** Use academic language in meaningful ways when speaking.

*Use with the Visual Learning Bridge on Student's Edition p. 210.*

Read Box A. Point to the coordinate plane. *Is polygon* ABCD *a square?* Instruct students to use as many math terms as possible to construct an argument to justify their answer.

**Beginning** Ask students to write *polygons, coordinate plane, vertices, right angles, x-axis, y-axis, x-coordinates,* and *y-coordinates* on sticky notes. Instruct students to work with partners to identify each term on the coordinate plane by using the sticky notes as labels. *Is polygon* ABCD *a square?* Have students respond using the sentence stem: Polygon *ABCD* _____ a ____.

**Intermediate** Ask students to write *polygons, coordinate plane, vertices, right angles, x-axis, y-axis, x-coordinates,* and *y-coordinates* next to corresponding parts of the coordinate plane. *Is polygon* ABCD *a square?* Have students respond using the sentence stem: Polygon *ABCD* ___ a square because ____.

**Advanced** Ask students to write *polygons, coordinate plane, vertices, right angles, x-axis, y-axis, x-coordinates,* and *y-coordinates* next to corresponding parts of the coordinate plane. Instruct students to use these terms to construct an argument to support whether polygon *ABCD* is or is not a square.

**Summarize** How does an understanding of math terms help in constructing mathematical arguments?

# DEVELOP: PROBLEM-BASED LEARNING

PearsonRealize.com

**COHERENCE: Engage learners by connecting prior knowledge to new ideas.**
Students use what they know about polygons and finding distances on the coordinate plane to construct viable arguments and justify their reasoning.

10–15 min

Solve

## BEFORE

**1. Pose the Solve-and-Share Problem**
**MP.3 Construct Arguments** Listen and look for students who use the math they know to construct an accurate and complete argument.

**2. Build Understanding**
*Is there more than one way that Nathan could draw the square? Explain.* [Yes. The given vertex could be any corner of the square. The side lengths are not given, so the square could be any size.]

## DURING

**3. Ask Guiding Questions As Needed**
*What is the definition of a square?* [A square has four equal sides and four right angles.] *How can you use the definition of a square to construct your argument?* [Sample answer: I can use math and reasoning to show that the figure I draw has four equal sides and four right angles, so it is a square.]

## AFTER

**4. Share and Discuss Solutions**
Solve Start with students' solutions. If needed, project Kelly's work to discuss how to use math to construct an argument.

**5. Transition to the Visual Learning Bridge**
*You can use the Thinking Habits to help you use the math you know to construct an argument.*

**6. Extension for Early Finishers**
*Change two of the vertices so that Nathan draws a rectangle that is not a square. Construct an argument that explains why it is a rectangle.* [Check students' work.]

---

Name ______________ Solve

**Solve & Share**

Nathan uses a coordinate plane to draw a plan for his new garden. For one section, he draws a square with one vertex at (−4, 3). Show one way that Nathan could draw the square.

Construct an argument that explains how you know that the figure is a square.

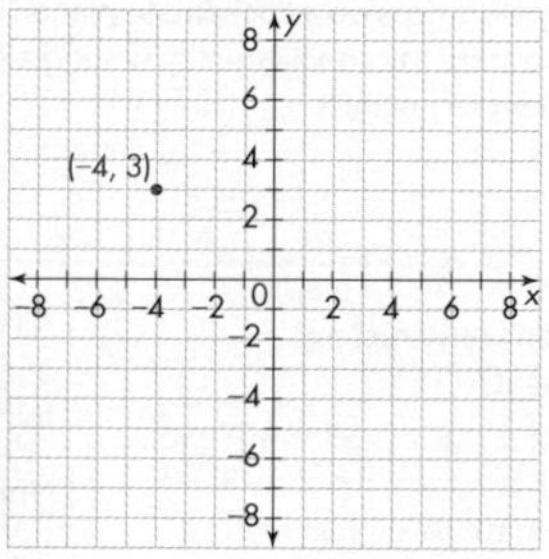

(Coordinate grid from −8 to 8 on each axis, with the point (−4, 3) plotted.)

**See margin for sample student work.**

**Math Practices and Problem Solving**

**Lesson 4-5**
**Construct Arguments**

**I can ...**
construct arguments using what I know about finding distances on the coordinate plane.

**Mathematical Practices** MP.3, MP.1, MP.4, MP.6
**Content Standards** 6.NS.C.8, 6.G.A.3

**Thinking Habits**
*Be a good thinker! These questions can help you.*
- How can I use numbers, objects, drawings, or actions to justify my argument?
- Am I using numbers and symbols correctly?
- Is my explanation clear and complete?
- Can I use a counterexample in my argument?

**Look Back!** **MP.3 Construct Arguments** Suppose that Nathan plotted another vertex of the garden area at (0, 3). Could this represent the corner of a square section of the garden? Construct an argument to justify your answer.
**Sample answer: Yes, it could as long as the other three sides were the same length and formed right angles.**



## Analyze Student Work

Kelly's Work

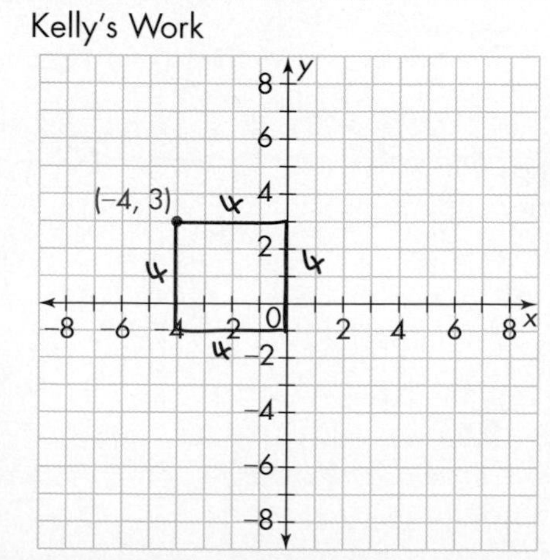


This is a square because all four sides are the same length, and since all the sides are on grid lines, all four angles are 90°.

Kelly draws one possible square on the coordinate plane and explains why the shape is a square.

Vaughn's Work

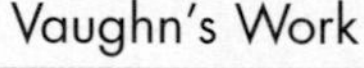

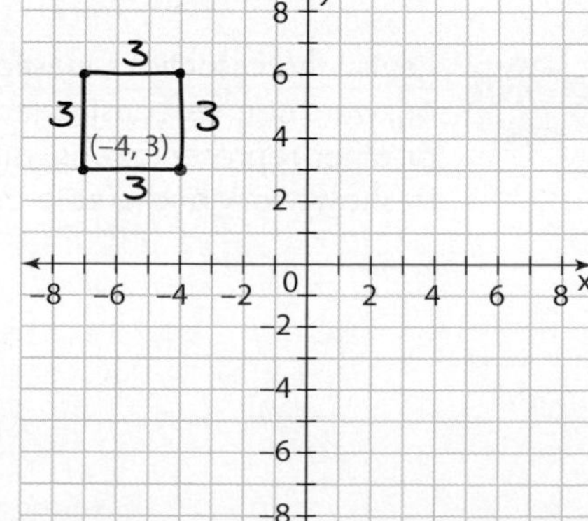


The four sides are all 3 units long, and the four angles are right angles.

Vaughn draws another possible square on the coordinate plane and provides an incomplete explanation.

# DEVELOP: VISUAL LEARNING

The *Visual Learning Bridge* connects students' thinking in Solve & Share to important math ideas in the lesson. Use the *Visual Learning Bridge* to make these ideas explicit. Also available as a *Visual Learning Animation Plus* at PearsonRealize.com

PEARSON realize. PearsonRealize.com

*How can you tell whether polygon ABCD is a square?* [Check whether the four side lengths are equal and the four angles are right angles.] *How do you find the side lengths?* [Find the distances from points *A* to *B*, *B* to *C*, *C* to *D*, and *D* to *A*.]

**MP.3 Construct Arguments** *How do you construct an argument to justify whether the polygon is a square?* [Show that all four sides are the same length using precise calculations with numbers and symbols, and explain why the four angles are right angles.]

**Prevent Misconceptions** (RtI 1)

Some students may only argue that the side lengths are equal. Remind students that a rhombus is a polygon that has four equal sides but is not a square. Emphasize that a complete argument must also include an explanation about the four right angles of the polygon.

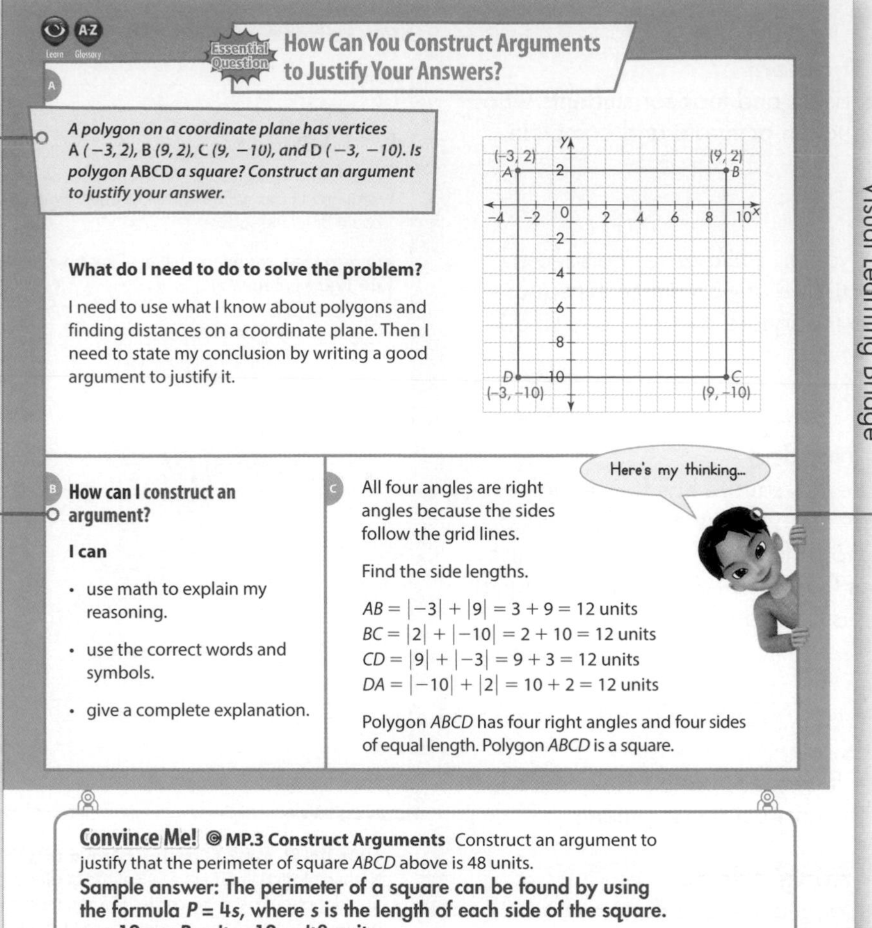

Essential Question **How Can You Construct Arguments to Justify Your Answers?**

A

*A polygon on a coordinate plane has vertices A (−3, 2), B (9, 2), C (9, −10), and D (−3, −10). Is polygon ABCD a square? Construct an argument to justify your answer.*

**What do I need to do to solve the problem?**

I need to use what I know about polygons and finding distances on a coordinate plane. Then I need to state my conclusion by writing a good argument to justify it.



B **How can I construct an argument?**

**I can**

- use math to explain my reasoning.
- use the correct words and symbols.
- give a complete explanation.

C



All four angles are right angles because the sides follow the grid lines.

Find the side lengths.

$AB = |-3| + |9| = 3 + 9 = 12$ units
$BC = |2| + |-10| = 2 + 10 = 12$ units
$CD = |9| + |-3| = 9 + 3 = 12$ units
$DA = |-10| + |2| = 10 + 2 = 12$ units

Polygon *ABCD* has four right angles and four sides of equal length. Polygon *ABCD* is a square.

**Convince Me!** **MP.3 Construct Arguments** Construct an argument to justify that the perimeter of square *ABCD* above is 48 units.
**Sample answer: The perimeter of a square can be found by using the formula $P = 4s$, where $s$ is the length of each side of the square. $s = 12$, so $P = 4 \cdot 12 = 48$ units.**

210 Topic 4 | Lesson 4-5 © Pearson Education, Inc. 6

Visual Learning Bridge

*Why is it important that the argument shows that the polygon has four equal sides and four right angles?* [You have to show that the polygon meets all of the criteria of the definition of a square.]

**Convince Me! MP.3 Construct Arguments** *How can you use the argument in Box C to justify that the perimeter of square ABCD is 48 units?* [I can use the side lengths found in Box C to calculate the perimeter.]

Revisit the Essential Question. Viable arguments that justify answers can be constructed using numbers, symbols, drawings or other representations, and precise mathematical vocabulary to show work and create a clear and complete explanation.

## QUICK CHECK

Check mark indicates items for prescribing differentiation on the next page.
Items 3 and 5 are worth 1 point. Items 6–9 are worth up to 3 points.

Name ____________

### Guided Practice*

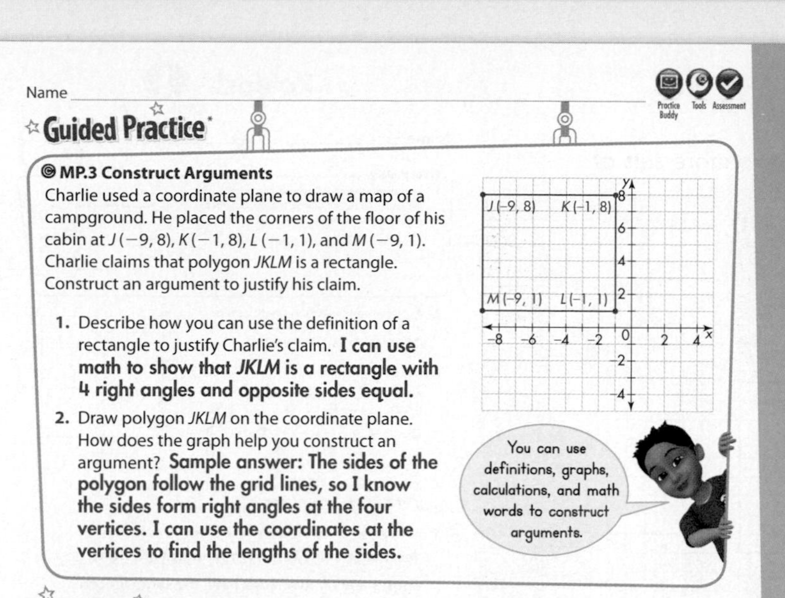

**MP.3 Construct Arguments**
Charlie used a coordinate plane to draw a map of a campground. He placed the corners of the floor of his cabin at $J(-9, 8)$, $K(-1, 8)$, $L(-1, 1)$, and $M(-9, 1)$. Charlie claims that polygon $JKLM$ is a rectangle. Construct an argument to justify his claim.



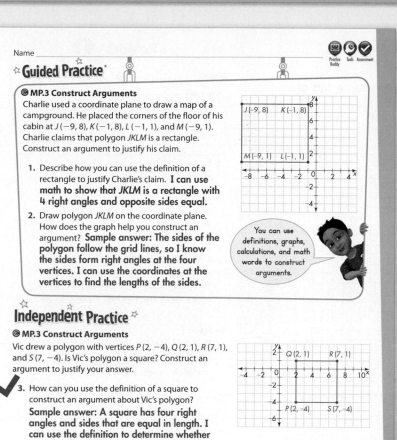

1. Describe how you can use the definition of a rectangle to justify Charlie's claim. **I can use math to show that *JKLM* is a rectangle with 4 right angles and opposite sides equal.**
2. Draw polygon $JKLM$ on the coordinate plane. How does the graph help you construct an argument? **Sample answer: The sides of the polygon follow the grid lines, so I know the sides form right angles at the four vertices. I can use the coordinates at the vertices to find the lengths of the sides.**

### Independent Practice*

**MP.3 Construct Arguments**
Vic drew a polygon with vertices $P(2, -4)$, $Q(2, 1)$, $R(7, 1)$, and $S(7, -4)$. Is Vic's polygon a square? Construct an argument to justify your answer.

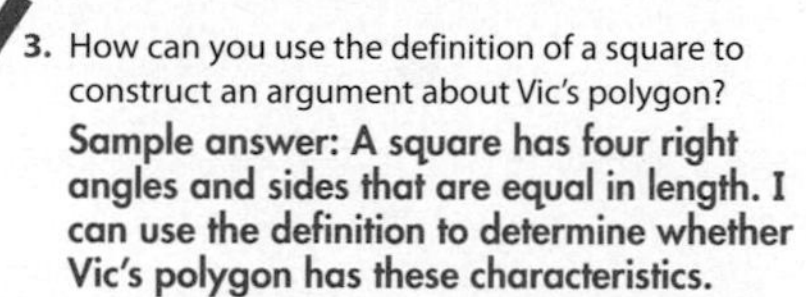

3. How can you use the definition of a square to construct an argument about Vic's polygon? **Sample answer: A square has four right angles and sides that are equal in length. I can use the definition to determine whether Vic's polygon has these characteristics.**

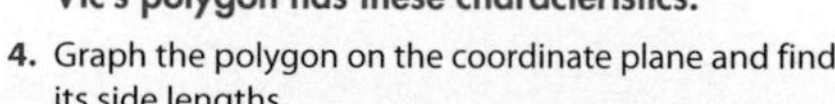

4. Graph the polygon on the coordinate plane and find its side lengths. **$PQ$: $|-4| + |1| = 4 + 1 = 5$ units; $QR$: $|7| - |2| = 7 - 2 = 5$ units; $RS$: $|1| + |-4| = 1 + 4 = 5$ units; $SP$: $|7| - |2| = 7 - 2 = 5$ units**
5. Construct an argument to justify whether Vic's polygon is a square. **Sample answer: Polygon $PQRS$ is a square because $PQRS$ has four right angles and four sides of equal length.**

*For another example, see Set C on page 218.



### Math Practices and Problem Solving*

**Common Core Performance Assessment**

**Floor Plan**
Sophia drew a floor plan of her classroom on a coordinate plane. She placed the corners of a closet floor at $A(-4, 4)$, $B(2, 4)$, $C(2, 1)$, and $D(-4, 1)$. Sophia says that the closet floor is a rectangle with an area of 18 square feet. Each unit on the grid represents 1 foot. Do you agree with Sophia's claims? Construct an argument to justify your answer.

6. **MP.1 Make Sense and Persevere** What do you need to know about the definitions of a rectangle and area to check Sophia's claim?
   **Sample answer: A rectangle is a polygon that has four right angles and opposite sides of equal length. The formula for the area of a rectangle is $A = \ell \cdot w$, where $\ell$ represents length and $w$ represents width.**
7. **MP.4 Model with Math** Graph and label the polygon that represents the closet floor on the coordinate plane. What do you know about the angles of polygon $ABCD$?

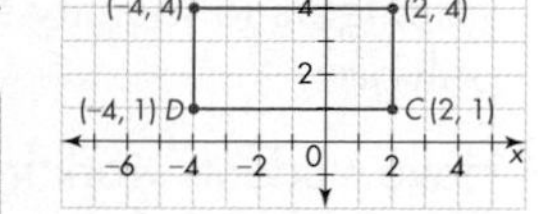


   **Sample answer: All four angles are right angles because the sides of the polygon follow the grid lines.**
8. **MP.6 Be Precise** Find the side lengths and the area of polygon $ABCD$.
   **$AB = |-4| + |2| = 4 + 2 = 6$ units**
   **$BC = |4| - |1| = 4 - 1 = 3$ units**
   **$CD = |-4| + |2| = 4 + 2 = 6$ units**
   **$DA = |4| - |1| = 4 - 1 = 3$ units**
   **$A = \ell w = 6 \cdot 3 = 18$ square feet**
9. **MP.3 Construct Arguments** Do you agree with Sophia's claims? Construct an argument to justify your answer.
   **I agree with Sophia's claims. Polygon $ABCD$ has four right angles and opposite sides of equal length, so the polygon is a rectangle. Each unit on the coordinate plane represents 1 foot, so $\ell = 6$ feet and $w = 3$ feet. The area of the closet floor is $A = 6 \cdot 3 = 18$ square feet.**

**MP.3 Construct Arguments** Listen and look for these behaviors as evidence that students are exhibiting proficiency with MP.3.

- Uses numbers, objects, drawings, or actions to justify arguments
- Provides clear and complete explanations of one's thinking and work
- Uses counterexamples in arguments, when appropriate
- Decides if other students' explanations make sense; clarifies or improves other students' arguments

**Items 1–2 MP.3 Construct Arguments** *What is the definition of a rectangle?* [A figure with four right angles and four sides, with opposite sides of equal length] A complete argument should support all aspects of the definition of a rectangle.

**Items 3–5 MP.3 Construct Arguments** Be sure that students include justifications about the number of sides and lengths of the sides of the polygon, as well as the number of angles and sizes of angles, in order to create a complete argument.

**Reteaching** Assign Reteaching Set C on p. 218.

**Item 6 MP.1 Make Sense and Persevere** Students first must make sense of the problem before they begin graphing a representation of the closet floor. They decide what information is needed or not, and determine how to solve the problem.

**Item 7 MP.4 Model with Math** Students use the coordinate plane to draw the floor plan of the closet floor. The problem context gives the scale as 1 unit representing 1 foot.

**Item 8 MP.6 Be Precise** Students must be precise as they determine side lengths of the polygon.

**Item 9 MP.3 Construct Arguments** Students' arguments must include support for all of the criteria required by the definition of a rectangle as well as the calculation of the area of rectangle $ABCD$ to be complete.

# ASSESS AND DIFFERENTIATE

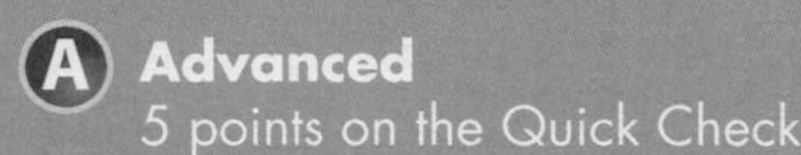

Use the **QUICK CHECK** on the previous page to prescribe differentiated instruction.

**Ⓘ Intervention** 0–3 points on the Quick Check

**Ⓞ On-Level** 4 points on the Quick Check

**Ⓐ Advanced** 5 points on the Quick Check

## Intervention Activity Ⓘ

**Math Practices and Problem Solving: Construct Arguments**

**Materials**

Four-quadrant coordinate grids (Teaching Tool 19) (1 per student)

- Write the following set of ordered pairs on the board:
  (4, −1), (−6, −1), (−6, 8), (4, 8)
- Have students plot and connect the points with line segments. Ask volunteers to identify the type of polygon.
- Have students work in pairs to provide a complete explanation to justify the type of polygon created by the set of ordered pairs. You may wish to review the definitions of rectangles, squares, and triangles.
- Repeat the activity with two more sets of ordered pairs.
  (5, 4), (10, 4), (5, −1), (10, −1)
  (−2, 5), (−4, −5), (0, −5)

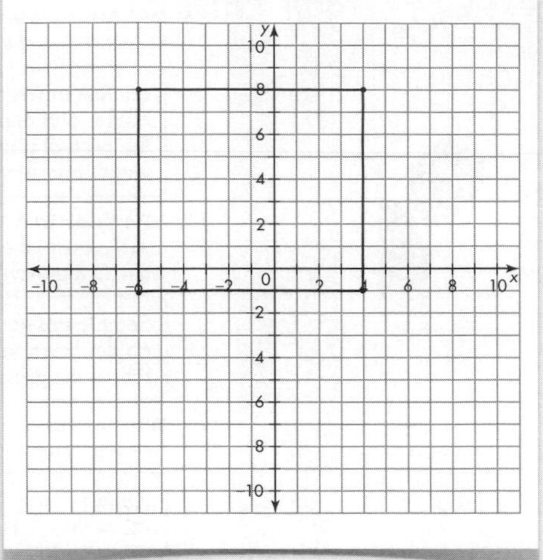

## Reteach Ⓘ

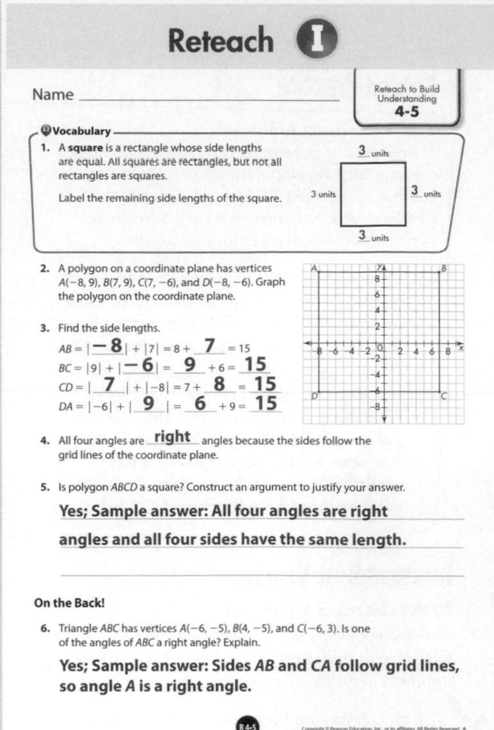

Name ______ Reteach to Build Understanding 4-5

Vocabulary

1. A **square** is a rectangle whose side lengths are equal. All squares are rectangles, but not all rectangles are squares.
   Label the remaining side lengths of the square. 3 units, 3 units, 3 units, 3 units
2. A polygon on a coordinate plane has vertices $A(-8, 9)$, $B(7, 9)$, $C(7, -6)$, and $D(-8, -6)$. Graph the polygon on the coordinate plane.
3. Find the side lengths.
   $AB = |-8| + |7| = 8 + 7 = 15$
   $BC = |9| + |-6| = 9 + 6 = 15$
   $CD = |7| + |-8| = 7 + 8 = 15$
   $DA = |-6| + |9| = 6 + 9 = 15$
4. All four angles are **right** angles because the sides follow the grid lines of the coordinate plane.
5. Is polygon $ABCD$ a square? Construct an argument to justify your answer.
   **Yes; Sample answer: All four angles are right angles and all four sides have the same length.**

On the Back!

6. Triangle $ABC$ has vertices $A(-6, -5)$, $B(4, -5)$, and $C(-6, 3)$. Is one of the angles of $ABC$ a right angle? Explain.
   **Yes; Sample answer: Sides $AB$ and $CA$ follow grid lines, so angle $A$ is a right angle.**

R 4-5

## On-Level and Advanced Activity Centers Ⓞ Ⓐ

Name ______ Math and Science Activity 4-5

**Plate Tectonics**

Did You Know? The earth's crust is made up of many pieces that slowly move around and even bump into each other. These pieces are called tectonic plates. The edges of these plates are rough and jagged. Because the edges are rough, they sometimes get stuck together while the rest of the plate continues to move. When the plate has moved far enough, the edges get unstuck and there is an earthquake.

**A geologist uses a coordinate plane to map a model of a tectonic plate.**

1. A geologist graphs a model of a tectonic plate on a coordinate plane using the points $A(-2, 3.5)$, $B(1.5, 3.5)$, $C(1.5, 1)$, and $D(-2, 1)$. Graph the four points. Then draw polygon $ABCD$.
2. What is the perimeter of the tectonic plate $ABCD$?
   **12,000 km**
3. Is polygon $ABCD$ a rectangle? Construct an argument to justify your answer.
   **Yes; Sample answer: $ABCD$ is a rectangle because all the angles are right angles. The opposite sides are the same length.**
   $AB = |-2| + |1.5| = 2 + 1.5 = 3.5$
   $CD = |1.5| + |-2| = 1.5 + 2 = 3.5$
   $AD = |3.5| - |1| = 3.5 - 1 = 2.5$
   $BC = |3.5| - |1| = 3.5 - 1 = 2.5$

Math and Science Activity 4-5

### Math and Science Activity STEM

This activity revisits the science theme, **Map to Predict and Plan**, introduced on page 181 in the Student's Edition.

### Sample Student Work

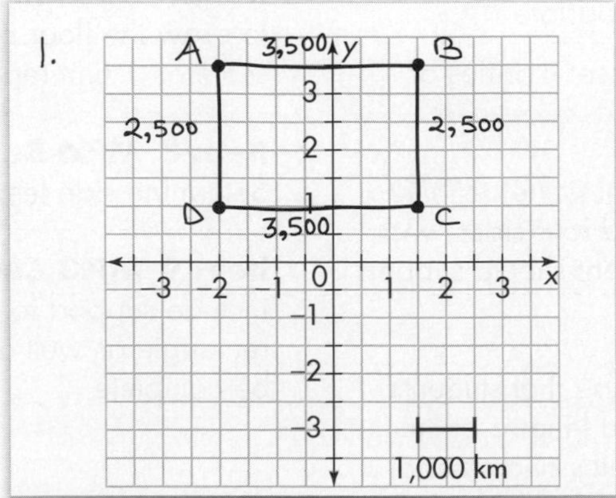

**TIMING**

The time allocated to Step 3 will depend on the teacher's instructional decisions and differentiation routines.

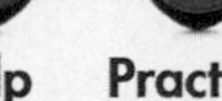

Help | Practice Buddy | Tools | Games

## Technology Center    

Tools Games

### Math Tools and Math Games

A link to a specific math tools activity or math game to use with this lesson is provided at PearsonRealize.com.

## Leveled Assignment  Items 1–7  Items 1–7  Items 1–7

Name ______________________

**Homework & Practice 4-5**

**Construct Arguments**

### Another Look!

The vertices of triangle $RST$ are $R(-6, 8)$, $S(-6, 1)$, and $T(1, 1)$. Is triangle $RST$ an isosceles right triangle?

**How can you construct an argument to justify your answer?**

**I can Draw**

triangle $RST$ on a coordinate plane.

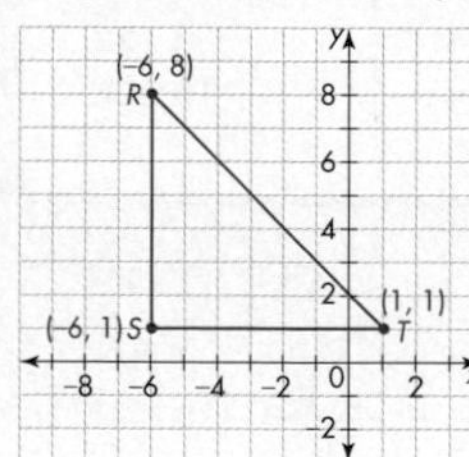

Angle $S$ is a right angle because its sides follow the grid lines.

Find the lengths of the two shorter sides.

$RS = |8| - |1| = 8 - 1 = 7$ units
$ST = |-6| + |1| = 6 + 1 = 7$ units

Triangle $RST$ has a right angle and two sides of equal length, so it is an isosceles right triangle.

**MP.3 Construct Arguments**

Cynthia drew a plan for a triangular pennant on a coordinate plane using vertices $U(2, -4)$, $V(8, -4)$, and $W(2, 2)$. Cynthia claims that the pennant is in the shape of an isosceles right triangle. Is she correct? Construct an argument to justify your answer.

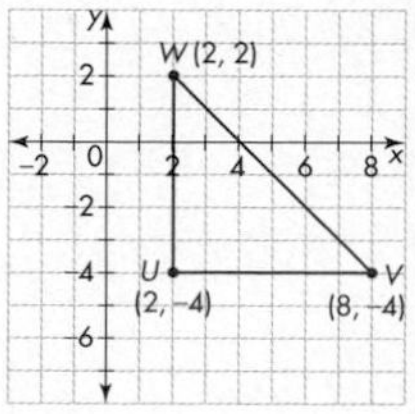

1. Graph triangle $UVW$ on the coordinate plane. Is one of the angles a right angle? Explain.
   **Sample answer: Angle $U$ is a right angle because the sides follow the perpendicular lines on the grid.**

2. Does triangle $UVW$ have two sides that are the same length? Explain.
   **Yes; Sample answer: $UV$: $|8| - |2| = 8 - 2 = 6$ units**
   **$WU$: $|2| + |-4| = 2 + 4 = 6$ units**

3. Is Cynthia's claim correct? Construct an argument to justify your answer.
   **Yes; Sample answer: $UVW$ is an isosceles right triangle because it has a right angle and two sides of equal length.**

(Graph: $W(2, 2)$, $U(2, -4)$, $V(8, -4)$ plotted on a coordinate plane.)



### Common Core Performance Assessment

**Downtown Map**

Rolando drew a map of downtown on a coordinate plane. He placed the bank at $B(0, -7)$, City Hall at $C(0, 0)$, the library at $L(5, 0)$, and the post office at $P(5, -7)$. Each unit on the grid represents 5 yards. Rolando claims that the path that joins the landmarks is a rectangle with a perimeter of 120 yards.

Is Rolando's claim correct? Construct an argument to justify your answer.

4. **MP.1 Make Sense and Persevere** What do you need to know about the definitions of a rectangle and perimeter to check Rolando's claim?
   **Sample answer: A rectangle is a polygon that has four right angles and opposite sides of equal length. The formula for perimeter of a rectangle is $P = 2\ell + 2w$, where $\ell$ represents length and $w$ represents width.**

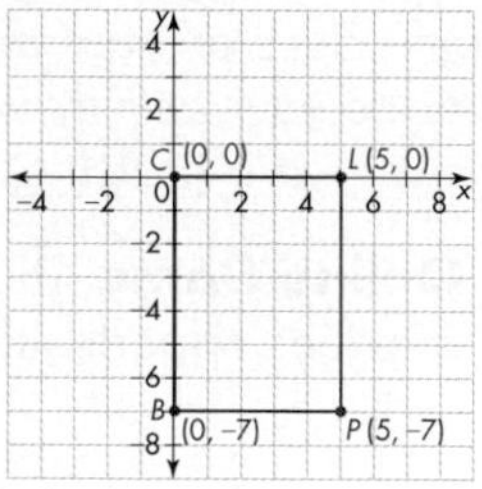

(Graph: $C(0, 0)$, $L(5, 0)$, $B(0, -7)$, $P(5, -7)$ plotted on a coordinate plane.)

5. **MP.4 Model with Math** Graph and label the polygon on the coordinate plane. What do you know about the angles of the polygon?

   **Sample answer: All four angles are right angles because the sides of the polygon follow the grid lines.**

6. **MP.6 Be Precise** Find the side lengths and perimeter of the polygon.

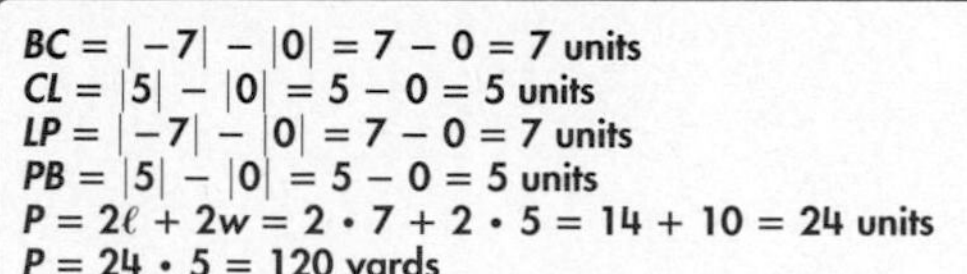

   **$BC = |-7| - |0| = 7 - 0 = 7$ units**
   **$CL = |5| - |0| = 5 - 0 = 5$ units**
   **$LP = |-7| - |0| = 7 - 0 = 7$ units**
   **$PB = |5| - |0| = 5 - 0 = 5$ units**
   **$P = 2\ell + 2w = 2 \cdot 7 + 2 \cdot 5 = 14 + 10 = 24$ units**
   **$P = 24 \cdot 5 = 120$ yards**

Remember to be precise. Each unit represents 5 yards.

7. **MP.3 Construct Arguments** Is Rolando's claim correct? Construct an argument to justify your answer.
   **Sample answer: Rolando's claim is correct. $BCLP$ has four right angles and opposite sides that are equal in length, so the path is a rectangle with a perimeter of 120 yards.**

# FLUENCY PRACTICE ACTIVITY

PEARSON realize.
PearsonRealize.com

Games

Practice Buddy

## FLUENCY PRACTICE ACTIVITY

Students review the Grade 5 fluency standard about multiplying multi-digit whole numbers during a partner activity that reinforces mathematical practices.

### Common Core Standards

**Content Standard 5.NBT.B.5** Fluently multiply multi-digit whole numbers using the standard algorithm.

**Mathematical Practices MP.3, MP.6, MP.7, MP.8**

**Getting Started** Ask students to work with a partner. Tell them to record their matches on their own page. Go over the directions.

Both students should solve each problem and record their work. Tell students to take turns identifying the match.

**As Students Do the Activity** Remind students that each clue can be matched with only one problem.

Encourage students to use estimation to help choose the matches efficiently. Some students may find all of the answers first and then match the clues. Allow this strategy as it provides the same fluency practice.

**Another Activity** Have students work together to write a new set of clues for the problems on the page. Ask them to record the new rules on a separate sheet of paper.

**Extra Challenge** *Create your own Find a Match activity. Use the same clues on your page. Write a new problem for each clue. Then trade your activity with your partner and complete your partner's Find a Match activity.*

Games

**Online Game** The Game Center at PearsonRealize.com provides opportunities for fluency practice.

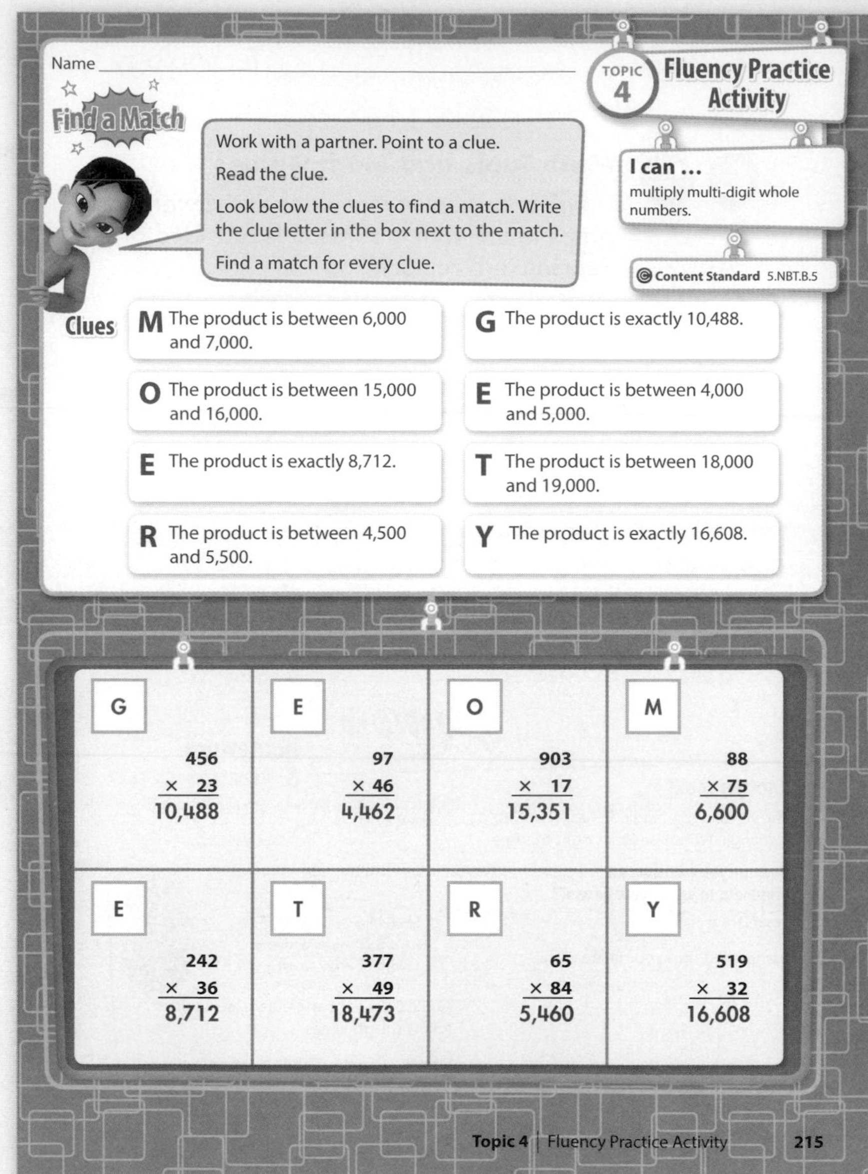

Name ______

Find a Match

TOPIC 4 Fluency Practice Activity

Work with a partner. Point to a clue.

Read the clue.

Look below the clues to find a match. Write the clue letter in the box next to the match.

Find a match for every clue.

I can ...
multiply multi-digit whole numbers.

Content Standard 5.NBT.B.5

Clues

**M** The product is between 6,000 and 7,000.

**O** The product is between 15,000 and 16,000.

**E** The product is exactly 8,712.

**R** The product is between 4,500 and 5,500.

**G** The product is exactly 10,488.

**E** The product is between 4,000 and 5,000.

**T** The product is between 18,000 and 19,000.

**Y** The product is exactly 16,608.

| G | E | O | M |
|---|---|---|---|
| 456 × 23 = 10,488 | 97 × 46 = 4,462 | 903 × 17 = 15,351 | 88 × 75 = 6,600 |
| **E** | **T** | **R** | **Y** |
| 242 × 36 = 8,712 | 377 × 49 = 18,473 | 65 × 84 = 5,460 | 519 × 32 = 16,608 |

Topic 4 | Fluency Practice Activity 215

Glossary

Games

**Word List**
- coordinate plane
- ordered pair
- origin
- quadrant
- *x*-axis
- *x*-coordinate
- *y*-axis
- *y*-coordinate

**Understand Vocabulary**

Choose the best term from the Word List. Write it on the blank.

1. A point on a coordinate plane is represented by a(n) **ordered pair**.
2. The **x-axis** is a horizontal number line on the coordinate plane.
3. One of the the four regions into which the *x*- and *y*-axes divide the coordinate plane is called a **quadrant**.
4. Circle the *ordered pair* that represents the *origin* on a coordinate plane.

   (0, 3) (0, 0) (3, 0) (3, 3)

5. Circle the *ordered pair* that lies on the *y-axis.*

   (0, 6) (6, 0) (−6, 6) (6, −6)

Draw a line from each ordered pair in Column A to the *quadrant* in which it is located in Column B.

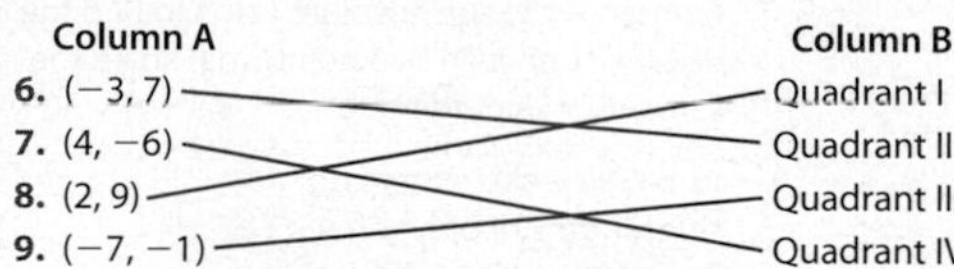

| Column A | Column B |
|---|---|
| 6. (−3, 7) | Quadrant I |
| 7. (4, −6) | Quadrant II |
| 8. (2, 9) | Quadrant III |
| 9. (−7, −1) | Quadrant IV |

**Use Vocabulary in Writing**

10. Explain how the points *A* (9, −2) and *B* (9, 2) are related. Use at least 4 words from the Word List in your explanation.
**Sample answer: The *x-coordinate* for each *ordered pair* is located at 9 on the *x-axis*. The *y-coordinates* for the *ordered pairs* are opposites. Point *A* is located in *Quadrant* IV. Point *B* is located in *Quadrant* I.**

216 Topic 4 | Vocabulary Review



## VOCABULARY REVIEW

Students review vocabulary words used in the topic.

**Oral Language** Before students complete the page, you might reinforce oral language through a class discussion involving one or more of the following activities.

- Draw or project a blank four-quadrant coordinate plane on the board. As you read each term from the Word List, ask student volunteers to label the coordinate plane with the term and describe or define the term.
- Draw or project blank grid paper on the board. Ask student volunteers to use the terms in the Word List to create a clearly labeled coordinate plane. Read the list in a logical order: *x*-axis, *y*-axis, origin, quadrant, *x*-coordinate, *y*-coordinate, ordered pair, and coordinate plane.

**Writing in Math** After students complete the page, you might further reinforce writing in math by doing one or more of the following activities.

- Have students work independently to create a crossword puzzle using the terms in the Word List. Provide grid paper or allow students to use an online crossword puzzle maker. Encourage students to use words, pictures, and examples for clues.
- Have students define the terms in their own words. Students should draw a coordinate plane to illustrate and label each of the vocabulary terms in the Word List.

Games

**Online Game** The Game Center at PearsonRealize.com includes a vocabulary game that students can access any time.

# RETEACHING

## ALGEBRA: COORDINATE GEOMETRY

### Item Analysis for Diagnosis and Intervention

| Reteaching Sets | Standard | MDIS |
|---|---|---|
| Set A | 6.NS.C.6b, 6.NS.C.6c | F32, F35 |
| Set B | 6.NS.C.8, 6.G.A.3 | F33 |
| Set C | MP.3, MP.1, MP.4, MP.6 | I4, J37 |

Name ____________

TOPIC 4

**Reteaching**

**Set A** pages 185–190, 191–196

An ordered pair (*x*, *y*) of numbers gives the coordinates that locate a point on a coordinate plane.

To graph any point *P* with coordinates (*x*, *y*):

- Start at the origin, (0, 0).
- Use the *x*-coordinate to move right (if positive) or left (if negative) along the *x*-axis.
- Then use the *y*-coordinate of the point to move up (if positive) or down (if negative) following the *y*-axis.
- Draw and label the point on the coordinate plane.

To give the location of a point on a coordinate plane, follow the grid line from the point to the *x*-axis to name the *x*-coordinate, and follow the grid line from the point to the *y*-axis to name the *y*-coordinate.

**Remember** that coordinates can be whole numbers, fractions, mixed numbers, or decimals.

In **1–6**, give the ordered pair for each point.

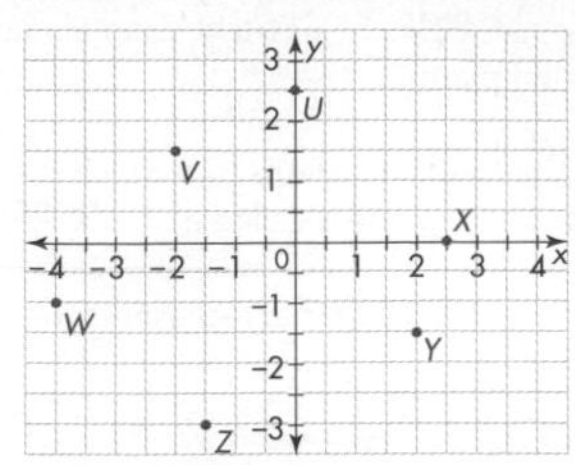

1. *U* $\left(0, 2\frac{1}{2}\right)$
2. *V* (−2, 1.5)
3. *W* (−4, −1)
4. *X* $\left(2\frac{1}{2}, 0\right)$
5. *Y* (2, −1.5)
6. *Z* $\left(-1\frac{1}{2}, -3\right)$

**Set B** pages 197–202, 203–208

Find the the length of side *AB*.

You can use what you know about finding the distance between two points to find the lengths of the sides of a polygon on a coordinate plane.

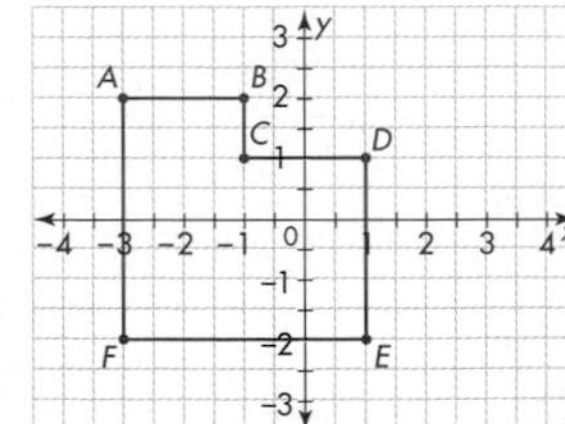

Find the distance from *A* (−3, 2) to *B* (−1, 2).

$|-3| - |-1| = 3 - 1 = 2$ units

**Remember** to use absolute value to find the distance between two points that share the same *x*- or *y*-coordinate.

In **1–6**, find the remaining side lengths of polygon *ABCDEF*. Then find its perimeter.

1. Length of *BC* **1 unit**
2. Length of *CD* **2 units**
3. Length of *DE* **3 units**
4. Length of *EF* **4 units**
5. Length of *FA* **4 units**
6. Perimeter of *ABCDEF* **16 units**
7. Find the perimeter of rectangle *WXYZ* with vertices *W* (−2, 8), *X* (2.5, 8), *Y* (2.5, −2), and *Z* (−2, −2). **29 units**

**Set C** pages 209–214

Think about these questions to help you **construct arguments.**

**Thinking Habits**

- How can I use numbers, objects, drawings, or actions to justify my argument?
- Am I using numbers and symbols correctly?
- Is my explanation clear and complete?
- Can I use a counterexample in my argument?

**Remember** that you can use definitions, reasoning, and math words to make a good argument.

Elise draws a polygon on a coordinate plane. It has vertices $Q(-4, -1)$, $R(-4, 5)$, $S(2, 5)$, and $T(2, -1)$. Is polygon *QRST* a square? Construct a math argument to justify your answer.

1. How can you use the definition of a square to determine whether the polygon *QRST* is a square?
**Sample answer: A square has 4 right angles and equal sides. I have to show that polygon *QRST* has four right angles and equal sides.**

2. Draw and label polygon *QRST* on the coordinate plane.

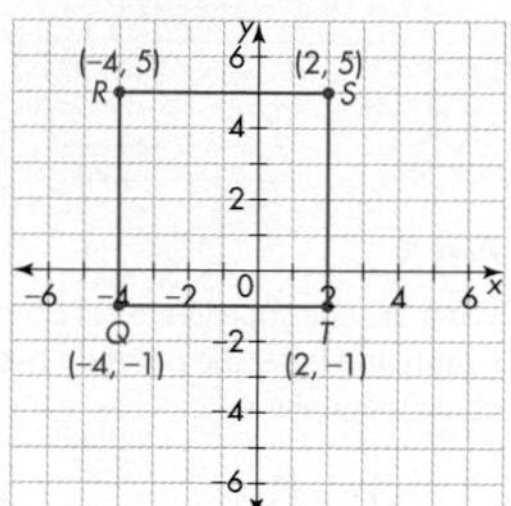


3. Construct an argument to justify whether polygon *QRST* is a square.
**Sample answer: Polygon *QRST* is a square because it has four right angles and four sides of equal length.**

$QR = |-1| + |5| = 1 + 5 = 6$

$RS = |-4| + |2| = 4 + 2 = 6$

$ST = |5| + |-1| = 5 + 1 = 6$

$TQ = |2| + |-4| = 2 + 4 = 6$





## Response to Intervention

**Ongoing Intervention**

- Lessons with guiding questions to assess understanding
- Support to prevent misconceptions and to reteach

**Strategic Intervention**

- Targeted to small groups that need more support
- Easy to implement

**Intensive Intervention**

- Instruction to accelerate progress
- Instruction focused on foundational skills

# TOPIC ASSESSMENT

## ALGEBRA: COORDINATE GEOMETRY

Name ______

**1.** Which ordered pair locates point *P* on the coordinate plane below? **1 point**

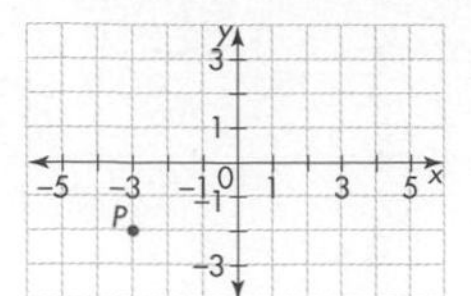

Ⓐ (−3, −2) Ⓑ (−3, 2)
Ⓒ (−2, −3) Ⓓ (−3, −3)

**2.** Write the ordered pair that locates point *Q* on the coordinate plane. **1 point**

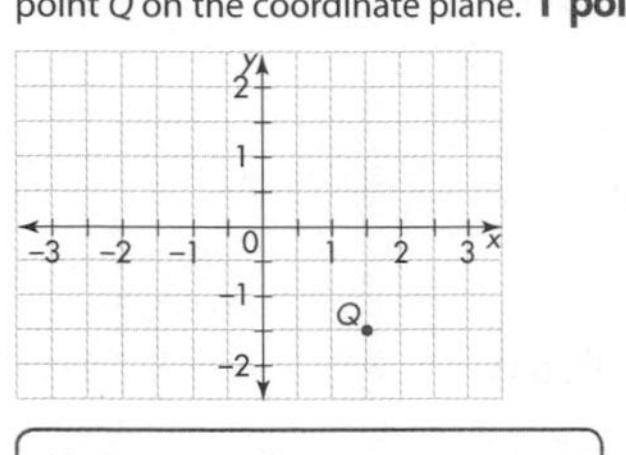

**(1.5, −1.5)**

**3.** For questions 3a–3d, choose Yes or No to tell if the statement is correct. **1 point**

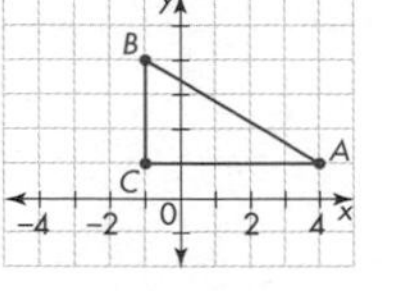

**3a.** *BC* is 2 units long. ○ Yes ● No
**3b.** *CA* is 5 units long. ● Yes ○ No
**3c.** *BC* is shorter than *BA*. ● Yes ○ No
**3d.** *AC* is 2 units longer than *BC*. ● Yes ○ No

**4.** What is the distance from point *P* (−4, 4) to point *R* (−4, −3)? **1 point**

**7 units**

**5.** Carlos drew a plan for his garden on a coordinate plane. Rose bushes are located at *A* (−5, 4), *B* (3, 4), and *C* (3, −5). **3 points**

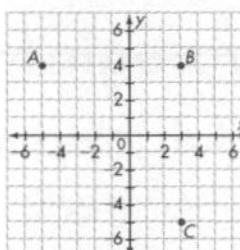

**Part A**

Graph and label the points to show the locations of the rose bushes.

**Part B**

Where should Carlos place a fourth rose bush if he wants to have the bushes form a rectangle? Explain.

**(−5, −5); Sample answer: *A* and *B* are 8 units apart; *B* and *C* are 9 units apart. A rectangle has opposite sides parallel and equal, so the fourth rose bush should be 8 units from *C* and 9 units from *A*.**



**6.** Choose all of the ordered pairs that are 3 units apart. **1 point**

☐ (2, 2) and (−2, 1)
■ (2, −1) and (2, −4)
■ (2, 2) and (2, 5)
■ (−1, 2) and (2, 2)

**7.** Liana graphs a point *B* in Quadrant II on the coordinate plane below, so that point *B* is $2\frac{1}{2}$ units away from point *A*. **3 points**

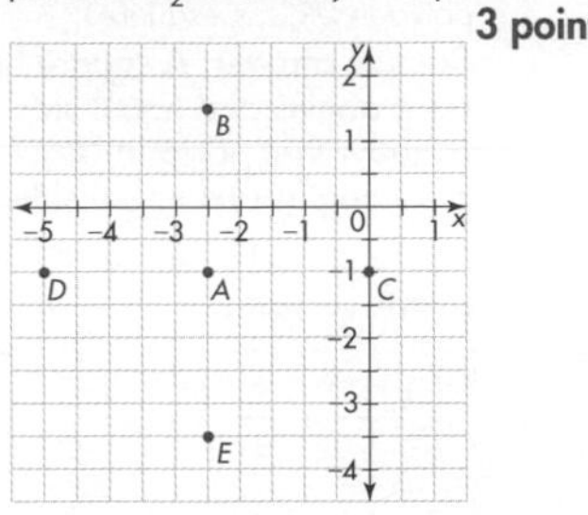

**Part A**

What are the coordinates of point *B*? Graph and label the point on the coordinate plane.

$\left(-2\frac{1}{2}, 1\frac{1}{2}\right)$

**Part B**

Are there other points on the coordinate plane that are $2\frac{1}{2}$ units from point *A*? If so, graph them on the coordinate plane and write their coordinates.

**C (0, −1), D (−5, −1), E** $\left(-2\frac{1}{2}, -3\frac{1}{2}\right)$

**8.** Draw lines to match the coordinates of each point with the coordinates of that point's reflection across the *y*-axis. **1 point**

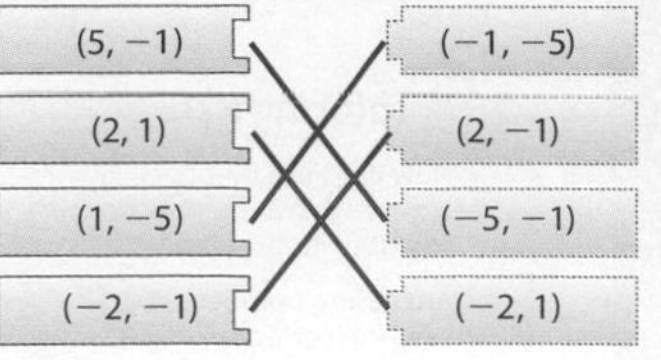


**9.** Choose all of the points that are reflections of each other across both axes. **1 point**

☐ $\left(-4\frac{1}{2}, 1\right)$ and $\left(-1, 4\frac{1}{2}\right)$
■ (2.5, −1) and $\left(-2\frac{1}{2}, 1\right)$
☐ (4.2, −1) and (2.4, −1)
■ (1, −2.25) and $\left(-1, 2\frac{1}{4}\right)$

**10.** What is the perimeter, in units, of polygon *PQRSTU*? **2 points**

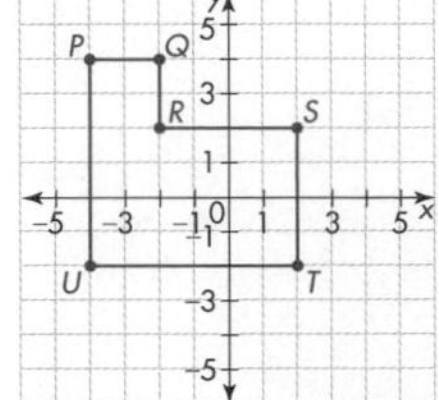

**24 units; *PQ* = 2 units, *QR* = 2 units, *RS* = 4 units, *ST* = 4 units, *TU* = 6 units, and *UP* = 6 units. 2 + 2 + 4 + 4 + 6 + 6 = 24 units**





## ANSWERING THE TOPIC ESSENTIAL QUESTION

**How are points graphed on a coordinate plane?**

Restate the Topic Essential Question from the Topic Opener or project it from the Student's Edition eText.

Ask students to answer the Essential Question (verbally or in writing) and give examples that support their answers. The following are key elements of the answer to the Essential Question. Be sure these are made explicit when discussing students' answers.

- A coordinate plane is a grid that contains two number lines that intersect at right angles at zero and divide the plane into four quadrants. The horizontal number line is called the *x*-axis, and the vertical number line is called the *y*-axis.

  **Example:** The coordinate plane shown to the right is labeled with its four quadrants.

- The location of a point on a coordinate plane is written as an ordered pair (*x*, *y*). The *x*-coordinate tells how many units to move horizontally from the origin, and the *y*-coordinate tells how many units to move vertically. Any location on a coordinate plane can be identified using an ordered pair. The point where the horizontal and vertical axes intersect is (0, 0), which is called the origin.

**Example:** To graph point *K* at (4, −3) on the coordinate plane, start at the origin and move 4 units to the right and 3 units down.

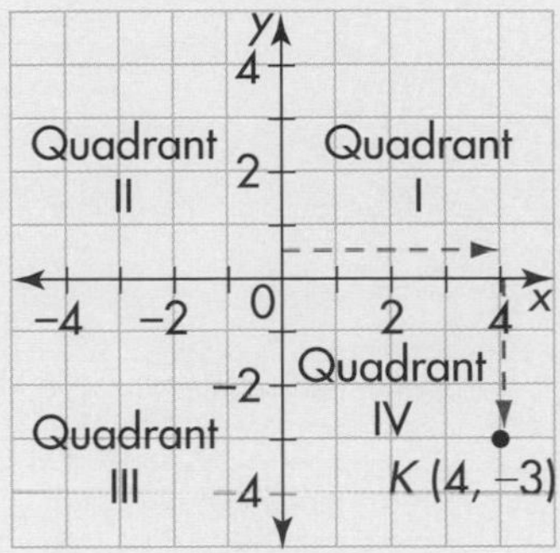

Assessment

**ONLINE TOPIC ASSESSMENT**
An auto-scored Topic Assessment is provided at PearsonRealize.com.

**EXAMVIEW® TEST GENERATOR**
ExamView can be used to create a blackline-master Topic Assessment with multiple-choice and free-response items.

## Topic Assessment Masters

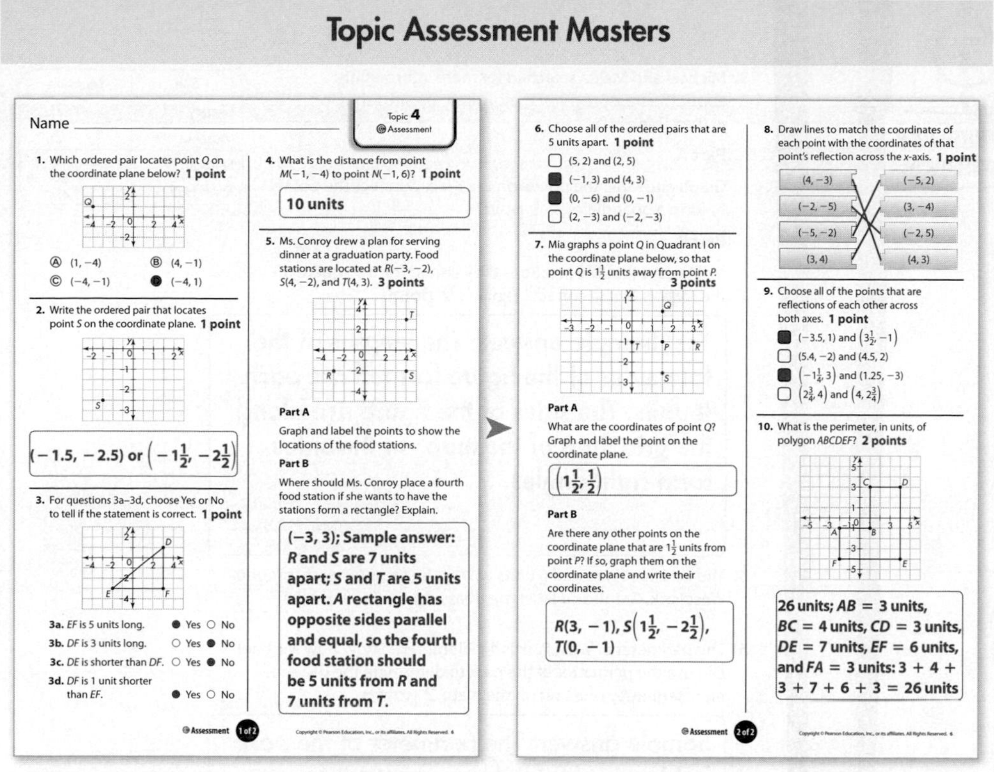

Name ______________________

Topic 4
Assessment

1. Which ordered pair locates point *Q* on the coordinate plane below? **1 point**

Ⓐ (1, −4) Ⓑ (4, −1)
Ⓒ (−4, −1) ● (−4, 1)

2. Write the ordered pair that locates point *S* on the coordinate plane. **1 point**

**(−1.5, −2.5) or $\left(-1\frac{1}{2}, -2\frac{1}{2}\right)$**

3. For questions 3a–3d, choose Yes or No to tell if the statement is correct. **1 point**

3a. *EF* is 5 units long. ● Yes ○ No
3b. *DF* is 3 units long. ○ Yes ● No
3c. *DE* is shorter than *DF*. ○ Yes ● No
3d. *DF* is 1 unit shorter than *EF*. ● Yes ○ No

4. What is the distance from point *M*(−1, −4) to point *N*(−1, 6)? **1 point**

**10 units**

5. Ms. Conroy drew a plan for serving dinner at a graduation party. Food stations are located at *R*(−3, −2), *S*(4, −2), and *T*(4, 3). **3 points**

**Part A**
Graph and label the points to show the locations of the food stations.

**Part B**
Where should Ms. Conroy place a fourth food station if she wants to have the stations form a rectangle? Explain.

**(−3, 3); Sample answer: *R* and *S* are 7 units apart; *S* and *T* are 5 units apart. *A* rectangle has opposite sides parallel and equal, so the fourth food station should be 5 units from *R* and 7 units from *T*.**

Assessment 1 of 2



6. Choose all of the ordered pairs that are 5 units apart. **1 point**

☐ (5, 2) and (2, 5)
■ (−1, 3) and (4, 3)
■ (0, −6) and (0, −1)
☐ (2, −3) and (−2, −3)

7. Mia graphs a point *Q* in Quadrant I on the coordinate plane below, so that point *Q* is $1\frac{1}{2}$ units away from point *P*. **3 points**

**Part A**
What are the coordinates of point *Q*? Graph and label the point on the coordinate plane.

**$\left(1\frac{1}{2}, \frac{1}{2}\right)$**

**Part B**
Are there any other points on the coordinate plane that are $1\frac{1}{2}$ units from point *P*? If so, graph them on the coordinate plane and write their coordinates.

**$R(3, -1), S\left(1\frac{1}{2}, -2\frac{1}{2}\right), T(0, -1)$**

8. Draw lines to match the coordinates of each point with the coordinates of that point's reflection across the *x*-axis. **1 point**

(4, −3) (−5, 2)
(−2, −5) (3, −4)
(−5, −2) (−2, 5)
(3, 4) (4, 3)

9. Choose all of the points that are reflections of each other across both axes. **1 point**

■ (−3.5, 1) and $\left(3\frac{1}{2}, -1\right)$
☐ (5.4, −2) and (4.5, 2)
■ $\left(-1\frac{1}{4}, 3\right)$ and (1.25, −3)
☐ $\left(2\frac{3}{4}, 4\right)$ and $\left(4, 2\frac{3}{4}\right)$

10. What is the perimeter, in units, of polygon *ABCDEF*? **2 points**

**26 units; *AB* = 3 units, *BC* = 4 units, *CD* = 3 units, *DE* = 7 units, *EF* = 6 units, and *FA* = 3 units: 3 + 4 + 3 + 7 + 6 + 3 = 26 units**

Assessment 2 of 2



## Scoring Guide

| Item | Points | Topic Assessment (Student's Edition and Masters) |
|---|---|---|
| 1 | 1 | Correct choice selected |
| 2 | 1 | Correct answer |
| 3 | 1 | All correct choices selected |
| 4 | 1 | Correct answer |
| 5A | 1 | Correct graph and labels |
| 5B | 2<br>1 | Correct answer and explanation<br>Correct answer with incomplete or missing explanation |
| 6 | 1 | All correct choices selected |
| 7A | 1 | Correct ordered pair and graph |
| 7B | 2<br>1 | Correct ordered pairs and graph<br>Correct ordered pairs, but no graph |
| 8 | 1 | All matches correct |
| 9 | 1 | All correct choices selected |
| 10 | 2<br>1 | Correct perimeter<br>Correct side length calculations, but incorrect perimeter |

## RtI Item Analysis for Diagnosis and Intervention

| Item | Standard | DOK | MDIS |
|---|---|---|---|
| 1 | 6.NS.C.6c | 1 | F35 |
| 2 | 6.NS.C.6c | 1 | F35 |
| 3 | 6.NS.C.8 | 1 | F33 |
| 4 | 6.NS.C.8 | 2 | F33 |
| 5A | 6.NS.C.6c | 1 | F35 |
| 5B | 6.NS.C.8, 6.G.A.3, MP.3 | 3 | F33, I6 |
| 6 | 6.NS.C.8 | 2 | F33 |
| 7A | 6.NS.C.6b, 6.NS.C.6c | 2 | F33 |
| 7B | 6.NS.C.8 | 3 | F33 |
| 8 | 6.NS.C.6b | 2 | F35 |
| 9 | 6.NS.C.6b | 2 | F35 |
| 10 | 6.NS.C.8, 6.G.A.3 | 1 | I41 |

The Topic Assessment Masters assess the same content item for item as the Topic Assessment in the Student's Edition.

# TOPIC 4 TOPIC PERFORMANCE ASSESSMENT

## ALGEBRA: COORDINATE GEOMETRY

Name ____________________

TOPIC 4 Performance Assessment

**Find the Treasure**

Michael and Melita are making a treasure map on a coordinate plane. Answer the questions to help them complete the treasure map.

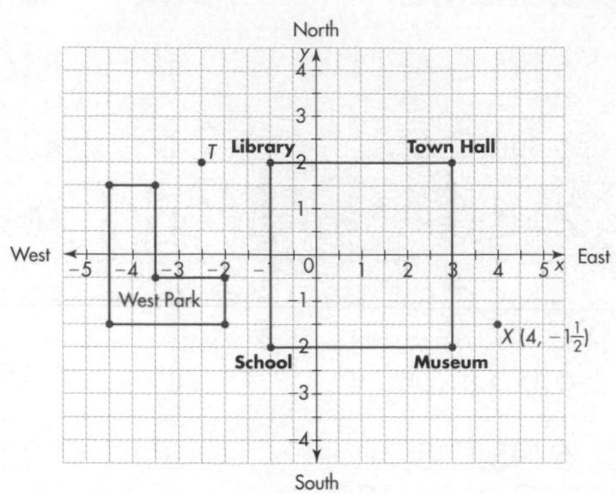


**1.** A tall palm tree is located at $\left(-2\frac{1}{2}, 2\right)$. Graph and label the tree point $T$ on the map. **1 point**

**2.** West Park is L-shaped. Its 6 corners are located at $\left(-4\frac{1}{2}, 1\frac{1}{2}\right)$, $\left(-4\frac{1}{2}, -1\frac{1}{2}\right)$, $\left(-2, -1\frac{1}{2}\right)$, $\left(-2, -\frac{1}{2}\right)$, $\left(-3\frac{1}{2}, -\frac{1}{2}\right)$, and $\left(-3\frac{1}{2}, 1\frac{1}{2}\right)$.

**Part A**

Graph the 6 corners and connect the points to show the borders. **1 point**

**Part B**

What is the perimeter of West Park? **1 point**

**11 units**



**3.** Michael and Melita searched for more information about the treasure map. They visited the sites shown in the table.

| Site | Location |
|---|---|
| Library | (−1, 2) |
| Museum | (3, −2) |
| School | (−1, −2) |
| Town Hall | (3, 2) |

**Part A**

Graph and label the points on the map. Connect the points to form a quadrilateral. **1 point**

**Part B**

Melita says that the locations they visited form a square on the map. Is Melita correct? Explain. **2 points**

**Yes; Sample answer: The lengths of the four sides of the figure formed are each 4 units. The sides of the figure are along the grid lines of the map, so the sides form right angles.**

**4.** The treasure is located 6 units east of the far southeast corner of West Park. Graph and label the treasure point $X$. **1 point**

**5.** The perimeter of West Park is 44 kilometers. Show how Michael can use the perimeter of the park to determine the distance represented by one unit on the map. **2 points**

**Sample answer: The perimeter of the park is 11 units. Michael can divide 44 km by 11 units to determine that one unit on the map represents 4 km.**




### Scoring Guide

| Item | Points | Topic Performance Assessment in the Student's Edition |
|---|---|---|
| 1 | 1 | Correct graph and label |
| 2A | 1 | Correct graph |
| 2B | 1 | Correct answer |
| 3A | 1 | Correct graph and labels |
| 3B | 2<br>1 | Correct answer and explanation<br>Correct answer with incomplete or missing explanation |
| 4 | 1 | Correct graph and label |
| 5 | 2<br>1 | Correct answer and explanation<br>Correct answer or explanation |

### RtI Item Analysis for Diagnosis and Intervention

| Item | Standard | DOK | MDIS |
|---|---|---|---|
| 1 | 6.NS.C.6c, MP.4 | 1 | F35 |
| 2A | 6.NS.C.6c, 6.G.A.3, MP.7 | 2 | F35 |
| 2B | 6.NS.C.8, 6.G.A.3, MP.6 | 1 | F33, I41 |
| 3A | 6.NS.C.6c, 6.G.A.3, MP.7 | 2 | F35 |
| 3B | 6.NS.C.8, 6.G.A.3, MP.3 | 3 | I6 |
| 4 | 6.NS.C.6c, 6.NS.C.8, MP.4 | 2 | F35 |
| 5 | 6.NS.C.8, 6.G.A.3, MP.2 | 3 | I41 |

## Topic Performance Assessment Masters

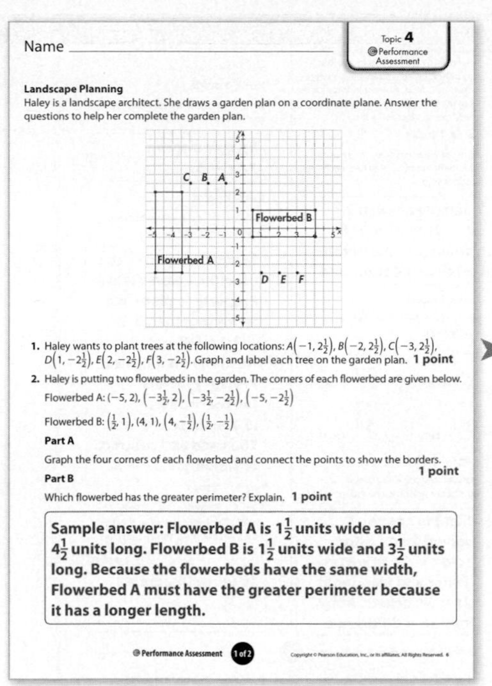

Name ____________________

Topic **4**
Performance Assessment

**Landscape Planning**
Haley is a landscape architect. She draws a garden plan on a coordinate plane. Answer the questions to help her complete the garden plan.



1. Haley wants to plant trees at the following locations: $A\left(-1, 2\frac{1}{2}\right)$, $B\left(-2, 2\frac{1}{2}\right)$, $C\left(-3, 2\frac{1}{2}\right)$, $D\left(1, -2\frac{1}{2}\right)$, $E\left(2, -2\frac{1}{2}\right)$, $F\left(3, -2\frac{1}{2}\right)$. Graph and label each tree on the garden plan. **1 point**
2. Haley is putting two flowerbeds in the garden. The corners of each flowerbed are given below.
   Flowerbed A: $(-5, 2)$, $\left(-3\frac{1}{2}, 2\right)$, $\left(-3\frac{1}{2}, -2\frac{1}{2}\right)$, $\left(-5, -2\frac{1}{2}\right)$
   Flowerbed B: $\left(\frac{1}{2}, 1\right)$, $(4, 1)$, $\left(4, -\frac{1}{2}\right)$, $\left(\frac{1}{2}, -\frac{1}{2}\right)$

   **Part A**
   Graph the four corners of each flowerbed and connect the points to show the borders. **1 point**

   **Part B**
   Which flowerbed has the greater perimeter? Explain. **1 point**

   **Sample answer: Flowerbed A is $1\frac{1}{2}$ units wide and $4\frac{1}{2}$ units long. Flowerbed B is $1\frac{1}{2}$ units wide and $3\frac{1}{2}$ units long. Because the flowerbeds have the same width, Flowerbed A must have the greater perimeter because it has a longer length.**

Performance Assessment 1 of 2



3. Is Flowerbed A a rectangle? Construct an argument to justify your answer. **2 points**

   **Yes; Sample answer: The sides of the flowerbed follow the grid lines so the angles formed by the sides are right angles. Pairs of opposite sides are equal in length, so Flowerbed A is a rectangle.**

4. If one unit on the garden plan represents 3 meters, what is the actual perimeter of Flowerbed A? Show your work. **2 points**

   **36 meters; Sample answer: Flowerbed A has a width of $1\frac{1}{2} \times 3$, or $4\frac{1}{2}$ meters and a length of $4\frac{1}{2} \times 3$, or $13\frac{1}{2}$ meters. So, the actual perimeter is $2\left(4\frac{1}{2}\right) + 2\left(13\frac{1}{2}\right) = 9 + 27 = 36$ meters.**

5. Haley decides to make Flowerbed B a square instead of a rectangle by changing the locations of two of its corners. One of the corners of the new flowerbed is $(2\frac{1}{2}, 1)$.

   **Part A**
   Write the coordinates of the other three corners that Haley chose to make Flowerbed B a square with a perimeter of 6 units. **1 point**

   **$(4, 1)$, $\left(4, -\frac{1}{2}\right)$, $\left(2\frac{1}{2}, -\frac{1}{2}\right)$**

   **Part B**
   Explain how you know that the new Flowerbed B is a square. **1 point**

   **Flowerbed B is a square because the sides of the figure follow the grid lines so the angles formed by the sides are right angles. All sides are the same length, or $1\frac{1}{2}$ units.**

6. Haley wants to add an L-shaped water feature to the garden plan. Draw an L-shaped figure on the plan. Then write the coordinates for the 6 corners. **1 point**

   **Check students' work.**

Performance Assessment 2 of 2



## Scoring Guide

| Item | Points | Topic Performance Assessment Masters |
|---|---|---|
| 1 | 1 | Correct graph and labels |
| 2A | 1 | Correct graph |
| 2B | 1 | Correct answer and explanation |
| 3 | 2 | Correct answer and explanation |
| | 1 | Correct answer with incomplete or missing explanation |
| 4 | 2 | Correct perimeter and work shown |
| | 1 | Correct perimeter with incomplete or missing work |
| 5A | 1 | Correct coordinates |
| 5B | 1 | Correct explanation |
| 6 | 1 | Correct graph and coordinates |

## Item Analysis for Diagnosis and Intervention

| Item | Standard | DOK | MDIS |
|---|---|---|---|
| 1 | 6.NS.C.6c, MP.7 | 1 | F35 |
| 2A | 6.NS.C.6c, MP.4 | 2 | F35 |
| 2B | 6.NS.C.8, 6.G.A.3, MP.2 | 2 | F33, I41 |
| 3 | 6.NS.C.8, 6.G.A.3, MP.3 | 3 | I6 |
| 4 | 6.NS.C.8, 6.G.A.3, MP.2 | 2 | F33, I41 |
| 5A | 6.NS.C.6c, 6.NS.C.8, 6.G.A.3, MP.1 | 2 | F35, I41 |
| 5B | 6.NS.C.8, 6.G.A.3, MP.3 | 3 | I6 |
| 6 | 6.NS.C.6c, 6.G.A.3, MP.4 | 3 | F35 |

# CUMULATIVE/BENCHMARK ASSESSMENT

## Topics 1–4 Cumulative/Benchmark Assessment

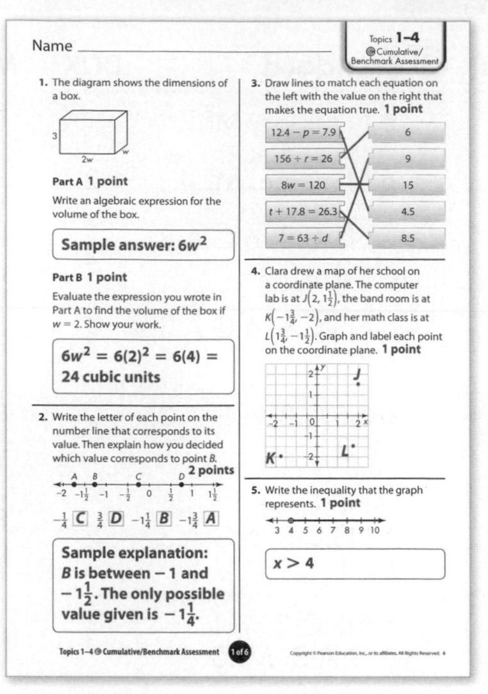

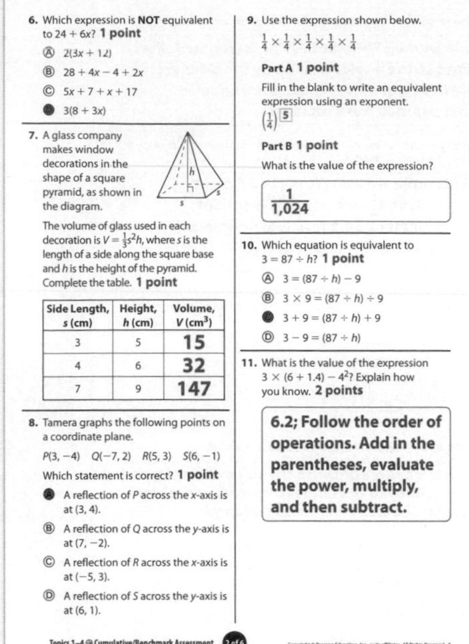

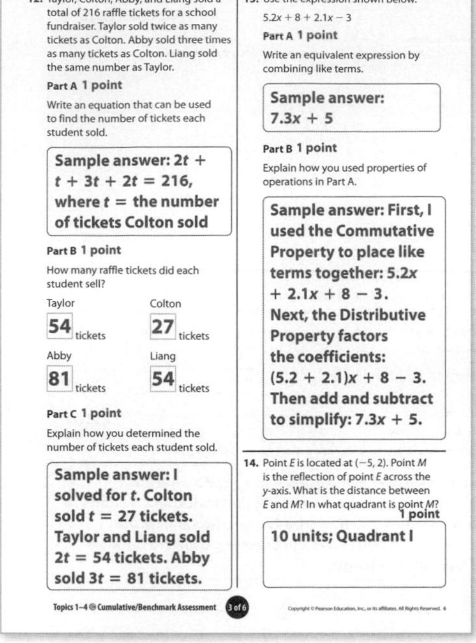

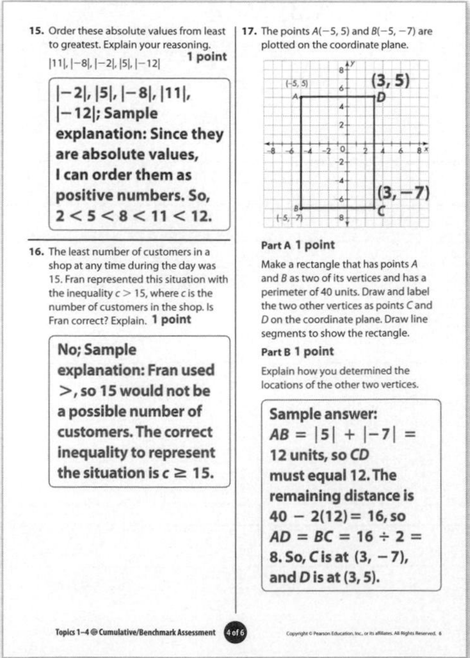

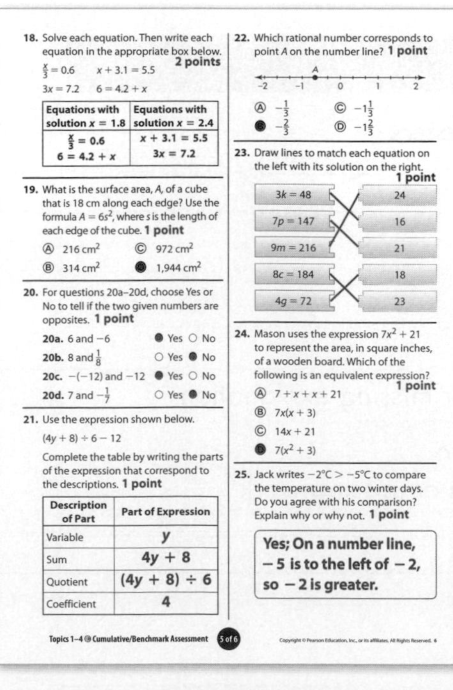

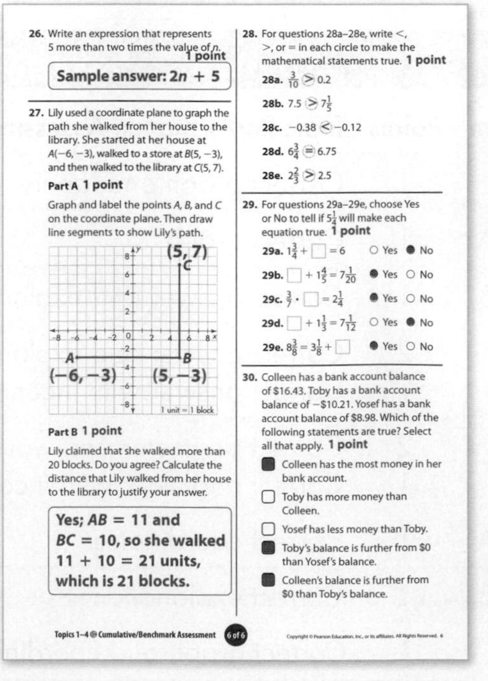

All items assess content taught in Topics 1–4.

## ONLINE CUMULATIVE/BENCHMARK ASSESSMENT

An auto-scored Cumulative/Benchmark Assessment is provided at PearsonRealize.com.

Assessment

### Item Analysis for Diagnosis and Intervention

| Item | Standard | DOK | MDIS |
|---|---|---|---|
| 1A | 6.EE.B.6, MP.4 | 1 | F46 |
| 1B | 6.EE.A.2c | 1 | F45 |
| 2 | 6.NS.C.6c, MP.2 | 2 | F20 |
| 3 | 6.EE.B.5 | 1 | F49, F50 |
| 4 | 6.NS.C.6c | 1 | F35 |
| 5 | 6.EE.B.8 | 1 | F61 |
| 6 | 6.EE.A.4 | 1 | F59 |
| 7 | 6.EE.A.2c, MP.7 | 2 | F47 |
| 8 | 6.NS.C.6b, MP.6 | 2 | F35 |
| 9A | 6.EE.A.1 | 1 | G60 |
| 9B | 6.EE.A.1 | 1 | G60 |
| 10 | 6.EE.A.4 | 1 | F48 |
| 11 | 6.EE.A.1 | 2 | F40, F41 |
| 12A | 6.EE.B.6 | 2 | F53, F54 |
| 12B | 6.EE.B.7, MP.1 | 2 | F50 |
| 12C | 6.EE.B.7 | 3 | F50, F60 |
| 13A | 6.EE.A.3 | 1 | F60 |
| 13B | 6.EE.A.3, MP.3 | 3 | F43, F60 |
| 14 | 6.NS.C.6b, 6.NS.C.8, 6.G.A.3 | 2 | F33 |
| 15 | 6.NS.C.7, MP.2 | 2 | F64, F19 |
| 16 | 6.EE.B.8, MP.6 | 2 | F61 |
| 17A | 6.NS.C.8, 6.G.A.3 | 3 | I41, F33 |
| 17B | 6.NS.C.8, 6.G.A.3 | 3 | F33, I73 |
| 18 | 6.EE.B.7 | 2 | F52 |
| 19 | 6.EE.A.2c | 1 | F47 |
| 20 | 6.NS.C.6a, MP.7 | 1 | F18 |
| 21 | 6.EE.A.2b | 2 | F58 |
| 22 | 6.NS.C.6c | 1 | H23 |
| 23 | 6.EE.B.7 | 1 | F50 |
| 24 | 6.EE.A.4 | 1 | F59 |
| 25 | 6.NS.C.7b | 2 | F19 |
| 26 | 6.EE.A.2a | 1 | F37 |
| 27A | 6.NS.C.6c, MP.4 | 2 | F35 |
| 27B | 6.NS.C.8, MP.3 | 3 | F33 |
| 28 | 6.NS.C.7a | 1 | F20, H22 |
| 29 | 6.EE.B.5 | 1 | F55 |
| 30 | 6.NS.C.7d | 2 | F18 |

For items worth 1 point, responses should be completely correct to get a score of 1 point. For other items, use the Scoring Guide below.

### Scoring Guide

| Item | Points | Topics 1–4 Cumulative/Benchmark Assessment |
|---|---|---|
| 2 | 2 | Four correct letter labels and reasonable explanation |
| | 1 | Two correct letter labels and reasonable explanation, OR four correct letter labels with incomplete or missing explanation |
| 11 | 2 | Correct solution and explanation |
| | 1 | Correct solution or explanation |
| 18 | 2 | Correct chart |
| | 1 | Partially correct or partially completed chart |

# MAJOR CLUSTER 6.EE.C

## MATH BACKGROUND: FOCUS

FCR FOCUS | COHERENCE | RIGOR

MAJOR CLUSTER

SUPPORTING CLUSTER

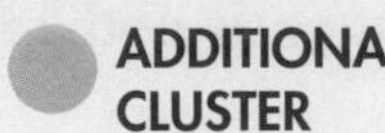
ADDITIONAL CLUSTER

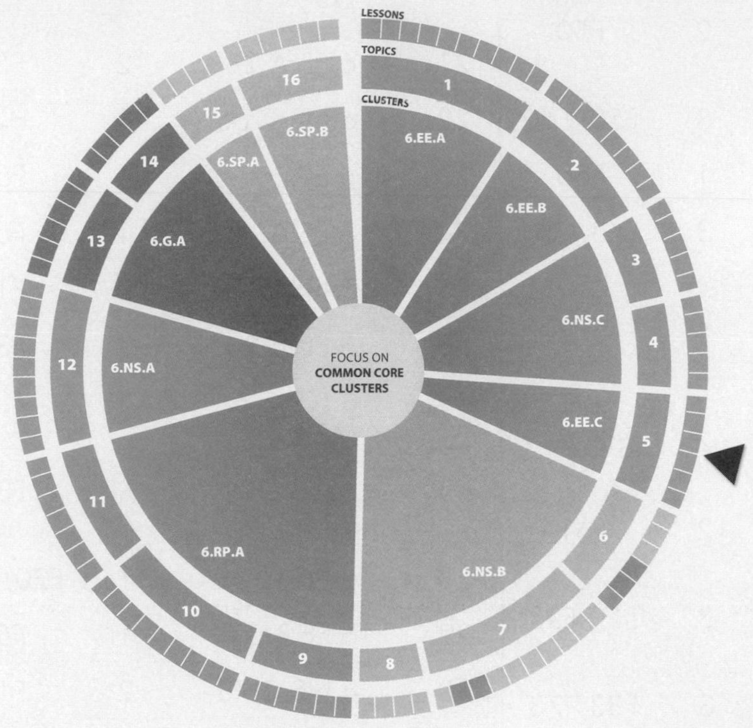


**TOPIC 5** **Algebra: Patterns and Equations**

TOPIC 5 FOCUSES ON

**MAJOR CLUSTER 6.EE.C**

Represent and analyze quantitative relationships between dependent and independent variables.

**Content Focus in enVisionmath2.0**

Topic 5 focuses on deep understanding of the relationship between two quantities when one quantity, the dependent variable, changes in relationship to the other quantity, the independent variable. The relationship can be represented in an equation, table, or graph.

### INDEPENDENT AND DEPENDENT VARIABLES

- **Identify Independent and Dependent Variables** In Lesson 5-1, students identify the dependent and the independent variable in different situations. They learn that the dependent variable changes in response to the independent variable. (6.EE.C.9)

  The amount of money taken in by an orchard in a day, *m*, depends on the number of pounds of apples sold that day, *p*.

  *m* is the dependent variable.

  *p* is the independent variable.

- **Write Equations to Represent Relationships** In Lesson 5-2, students are given a table of ordered pairs which have a constant relationship between the independent and dependent variables. They look for the pattern between the variables and write an equation to represent the relationship. Students can evaluate the equation for a given value of the independent variable. (6.EE.C.9)

| Number, *n* | Cost, *c* |
|---|---|
| 3 | $16.50 |
| 4 | $22.00 |
| 5 | $27.50 |
| 6 | |

The table shows the relationship between the number of tickets to a water park and the total cost of the tickets. The number of tickets *n* is the independent variable and the cost *c* is the dependent variable.

State the rule:
The total cost, *c*, is $5.50 times the number of tickets, *n*.

Write an equation:
$c = 5.50 \times n$, or $c = 5.5n$

Find the cost of 6 tickets.

$c = 5.5(6)$

$c = 33$

The cost of 6 tickets is $33.00.

PD



In Lesson 5-3, students continue to work with patterns and equations that have two operations. Students write equations to represent values in a table, and also complete a table for a given equation.

## GRAPH EQUATIONS

- **Graph Linear Equations** Relationships between a dependent and independent variable can be represented with graphs as well as with tables and equations. In Lesson 5-4, students use a given equation to make a table of ordered pairs and then use the table to draw the graph. The graph through the points is a straight line, so the equation is called a linear equation. In Lesson 5-5, students continue to graph equations and then they use the graphs to solve problems. (6.EE.C.9)

By convention, the independent variable is usually shown on the horizontal *x*-axis and the dependent variable on the vertical *y*-axis.

> ***The temperature was 6°C and increased 2°C each hour for 6 hours.***
>
> ***Let x = the number of hours.***
>
> ***Let y = the temperature in °C.***
>
> ***The equation y = 6 + 2x shows the relationship between the number of hours and the increase in temperature. After how many hours was the temperature 12°C?***

| x | y |
|---|---|
| 0 | 6 |
| 2 | 10 |
| 4 | 14 |

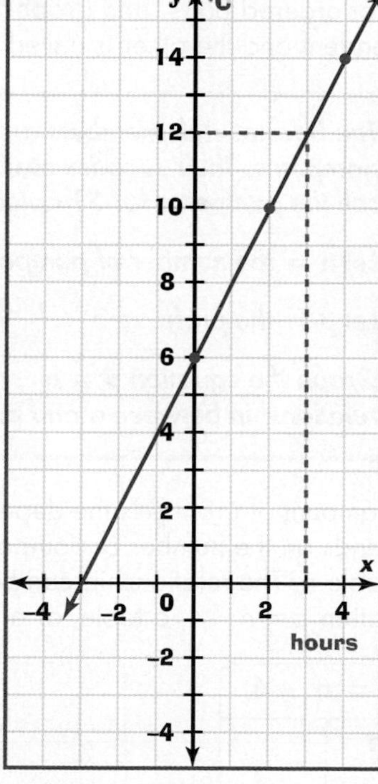

**Professional Development Videos** Topic Overview Videos and Listen and Look For Lesson Videos present additional important information about the content of this cluster.

# MAJOR CLUSTER 6.EE.C

## MATH BACKGROUND: COHERENCE



### Content Coherence in enVisionmath2.0

Students learn best when ideas are connected in a coherent curriculum. This coherence is achieved through various types of connections including connections within clusters, across clusters, across domains, and across grades.

### BIG IDEAS IN GRADES K–6

Big Ideas are the conceptual underpinnings of **enVisionmath2.0** and provide conceptual cohesion of the content. Big Ideas connect Essential Understandings throughout the program.

A Big Idea that connects most of the work in this cluster is that relationships sometimes exist where the members of one set change in a predictable way in relationship to the members of a second set. Relationships in which the value of the variable representing one set depends on the value of the variable representing the other set can be represented with equations, tables of ordered pairs, and graphs. One variable is called independent and the other is called dependent.

> ***The booster club members are making school pompoms. Their supplies cost \$4, and they plan to sell the pompoms for \$1 apiece.***
>
> ***Let*** **n** ***= the number of pompoms sold.***
>
> ***Let*** **p** ***= the profit.***
>
> ***Graph the equation*** **p = n − 4** ***to show the relationship between*** **n** ***and*** **p*****.***

The amount of profit $p$ is the dependent variable because it depends on the number of pompoms sold, the independent variable $n$. The relationship can be represented with the equation $p = n - 4$, a table, or a graph.

| $p = n - 4$ | |
|---|---|
| $n$ | $p$ |
| 4 | 0 |
| 5 | 1 |
| 6 | 2 |

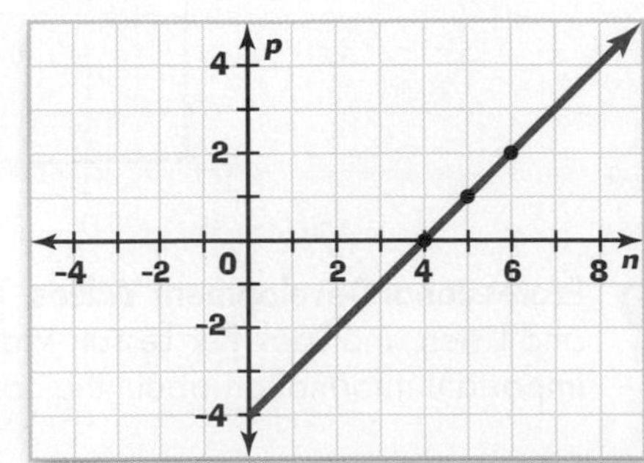


For a complete list of Big Ideas, see pages 110–111 in the *Teacher's Edition Program Overview.*

### LOOK BACK

*How does Topic 5 connect to what students learned earlier?*

#### GRADE 5

- **Graph Points on the Coordinate Plane** Students first learned about graphing points on the coordinate plane in Topic 14. They learned new vocabulary, including ordered pair, *x*-axis, *y*-axis, origin, *x*-coordinate, and *y*-coordinate. They used a table of ordered pairs to graph a line and used the line to solve a problem. (5.G.A.1, 5.G.A.2)

DATA

| Week | Start | 1 | 2 | 3 | 4 | 5 |
|---|---|---|---|---|---|---|
| Ann's earnings in \$ | 0 | 3 | 6 | 9 | 12 | 15 |
| Bill's earnings in \$ | 5 | 8 | 11 | 14 | 17 | 20 |

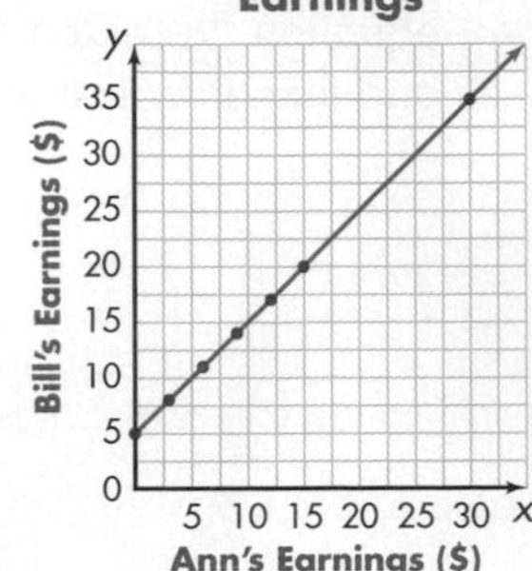


#### EARLIER IN GRADE 6

- **Evaluate Formulas and Algebraic Expressions** In Topic 1, students evaluated algebraic expressions and formulas for given values of one or more variables. These skills are used to solve problems and to create a table of ordered pairs for a given equation. (6.EE.A.2c)
- **Solve Equations** In Topic 2, students used properties of equality to solve equations. (6.EE.B.7)
- **Graph Integers on the Coordinate Plane** In Topic 4, students graphed integers on a coordinate plane. (6.NS.C.6b, 6.NS.C.6c)

## TOPIC 5

*How is content connected within Topic 5?*

- **Independent and Dependent Variables** In Lesson 5-1, students learn to identify the dependent and independent variables in various situations. This understanding is used throughout Topic 5 to represent linear relationships with equations, to create tables of ordered pairs, and to graph relationships. (6.EE.C.9)
- **Different Representations for Linear Relationships** In Lesson 5-3, students expand their work on linear relationships from equations that are described with one operation to equations that are described with two operations. They use a table to graph an equation in Lessons 5-4 and 5-5. (6.EE.C.9)
- **Solve Linear Equations** Topic 5 also develops content from Major Cluster 6.EE.B on reasoning about and solving one-variable equations. (6.EE.B.5)

## LOOK AHEAD

*How does Topic 5 connect to what students will learn later?*

### LATER IN GRADE 6

- **Different Representations for Equivalent Ratios** In Lesson 9-3, students will find equivalent ratios and represent them in a table. They will use a table to graph ratios in Lesson 9-5. (6.RP.A.3a)

| Number of Balloons ($x$) | 3 | 6 | 9 | 12 |
|---|---|---|---|---|
| Cost in Dollars ($y$) | 2 | 4 | 6 | 8 |

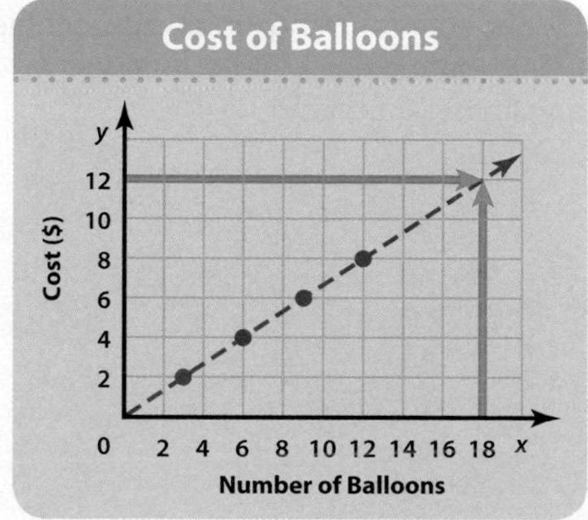


### GRADE 7

- **Solve Simple Equations and Inequalities** In Grade 7, students will fluently solve algebraic word problems with relationships in the form $px + q = r$. Students will also represent relationships that can be expressed as inequalities rather than equations, such as $px + q < r$ or $px + q > r$. (7.EE.B.4)
- **Proportional Relationships** In Grade 7, students will use tables and equations to represent proportional relationships, and graph proportional relationships on a coordinate plane. (7.RP.A.2)

# MATH BACKGROUND: RIGOR



**Content Rigor in enVisionmath2.0**

A rigorous curriculum emphasizes conceptual understanding, procedural skill and fluency, and applications.

## CONCEPTUAL UNDERSTANDING

- **Independent and Dependent Variables** The concepts of independent and dependent variables are the foundation for understanding linear relationships, proportional relationships, and functions. By convention, the dependent variable is usually alone on one side of an equation, the second row or column in a table, or the vertical axis on a graph. (6.EE.C.9)
- **Different Representations for a Linear Relationship** Just as a fraction and decimal can name the same number, so can a table, equation, and graph represent the same relationship. This topic helps build a foundation for the concept of functions. (6.EE.C.9)

## PROCEDURAL SKILL AND FLUENCY

There are no standards in this cluster that call for fluency.

- **Tables, Equations, and Graphs** In Lessons 5-2, 5-3, 5-4, and 5-5, students learn procedures for writing an equation to represent a table of ordered pairs, creating a table of ordered pairs for a given equation, and graphing a relationship given an equation or a table of ordered pairs. (6.EE.C.9)

## APPLICATIONS

- **Real-World Relationships** Throughout Topic 5, students work with relationships which have a real-world context. (6.EE.C.9)

| Tickets, $t$ | $3 + 2t$ | Cost, $c$ |
|---|---|---|
| 0 | 3 + 2(0) | $3 |
| 2 | 3 + 2(2) | $7 |
| 4 | 3 + 2(4) | $11 |
| 6 | 3 + 2(6) | $15 |

The entry fee to a carnival is $3 and it costs $2 for each ride ticket. The table represents the cost $c$ of going to a carnival and buying $t$ tickets.

The relationship between the dependent variable $c$ and the independent variable $t$ can be represented with the equation $c = 3 + 2t$.

# MAJOR CLUSTER 6.EE.C

## MATH PRACTICES

MP

Connecting Math Practices and Content Standards in enVisionmath2.0

Math practices and content standards are connected within all lessons including the lessons that focus on math practices.

### MATH PRACTICES WITHIN LESSONS

- **MP.1 Make sense of problems and persevere in solving them.**
  Students make sense of a set of ordered pairs, and persevere in checking that a relationship satisfies all the given values. (e.g., p. 235, Item 3)
- **MP.2 Reason abstractly and quantitatively.**
  Students use reasoning as they determine dependent and independent variables, identify patterns, and solve and graph equations. (e.g., p. 228, Convince Me!)
- **MP.3 Construct viable arguments.**
  Students use equations to construct arguments about graphs. (e.g., p. 247, Item 2)
- **MP.4 Model with mathematics.**
  Students use independent and dependent variables to represent and solve problems. (e.g., p. 248, Item 7)
- **MP.5 Use appropriate tools strategically.**
  Students use tools, such as tables and grids, to identify patterns and solve and represent equations. (e.g., p. 260, Item 8)
- **MP.6 Attend to precision.**
  Students attend to precision when they compute variables accurately to solve a problem. (e.g., p. 262, Item 6)
- **MP.7 Look for and make use of structure.**
  Students look for structure when they solve and graph equations. (e.g., p. 233, Look Back!)
- **MP.8 Look for and express regularity in repeated reasoning.**
  Students use repeated reasoning when they use an equation as a shortcut for finding values for a table. (e.g., p. 240, Convince Me!)

### LESSON THAT FOCUSES ON MATH PRACTICES

- **Lesson 5-6** This lesson focuses on MP.4. Students model with math to solve problems in real-world contexts involving equations, tables, and the coordinate plane. They use these representations to solve problems involving relationships between dependent and independent variables.

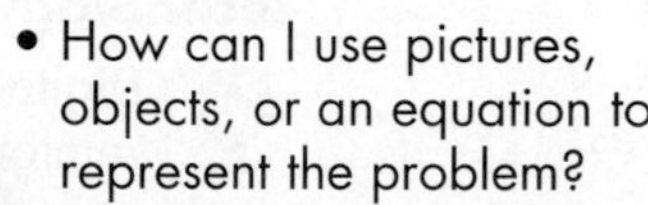


*Be a good thinker! These questions can help you.*

- How can I use math I know to help solve the problem?
- How can I use pictures, objects, or an equation to represent the problem?
- How can I use numbers, words, and symbols to solve the problem?

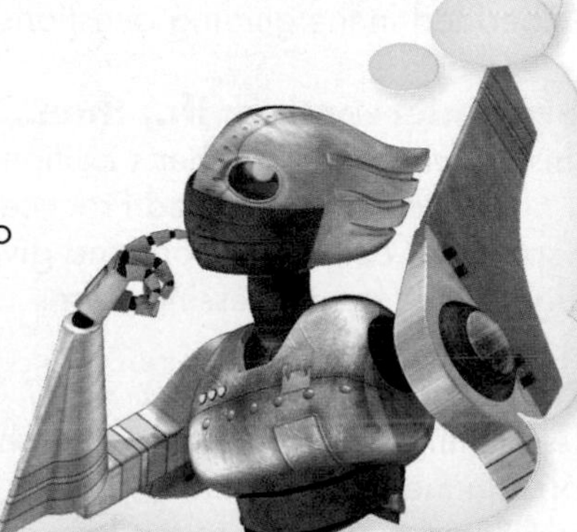

Revisit the information about MP.4 in these other resources:

- **Math Practices and Problem Solving Handbook** before Topic 1; includes Math Practices Proficiency Rubrics.
- **Math Practices Posters** to display in your classroom
- MP **Math Practices Animations,** one for each math practice, available at PearsonRealize.com.

# MAJOR CLUSTER 6.EE.C

## DIFFERENTIATED INSTRUCTION

 Intervention  On-Level  Advanced

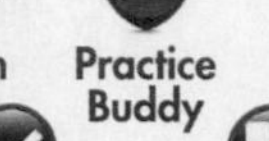

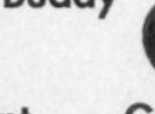


### Ongoing Intervention

**During the core lesson,** monitor progress, reteach as needed, and extend students' thinking.

**Guiding Questions**

- **In the Teacher's Edition** Guiding questions are used to monitor understanding during instruction.

**Online Guiding Questions** Guiding questions are also in the online Visual Learning Animation Plus.

**Prevent Misconceptions**
This feature in the Teacher's Edition is embedded in the guiding questions.

**Error Intervention: If... then...**
This feature in the Teacher's Edition is provided during Guided Practice. It spotlights common errors and gives suggestions for addressing them.

**Reteaching**
Reteaching sets are at the end of the topic in the Student's Edition. They provide additional examples, reminders, and practice. Use these sets as needed before students do the Independent Practice.

**Higher Order Thinking**
These problems require students to think more deeply about the rich, conceptual knowledge developed in the lesson.

**Practice Buddy Online**

Online auto-scored practice is provided for each lesson. On-screen learning aids include Help Me Solve This and View an Example.

### Strategic Intervention

**At the end of the lesson,** assess to identify students' strengths and needs and then provide appropriate support.

**Quick Check**

**In the Student's Edition** Assess the lesson using 3 items checked in the Teacher's Edition.

**Online Quick Check** You can also assess the lesson using 5 online, machine-scored items.

**Intervention Activity** I
Teachers work with struggling students.

**Reteach to Build Understanding** I
This is a page of guided reteaching.

**Technology Center** I O A

**Digital Math Tools Activities** reinforce the lesson content or previously taught content using a suite of digital math tools.

**Online Games** provide practice on the lesson content or previously taught content.

**Homework and Practice** I O A
Use the leveled assignment to provide differentiated homework and practice.

*Additional resources to support differentiated instruction for on-level and advanced students include:*

**On-Level and Advanced Activity Centers** O A

- **Center Games** are provided in on-level and advanced versions.
- **Math and Science Activity** is related to the topic science theme introduced at the start of the topic.
- **Problem-Solving Reading Mat** is used with a lesson-specific activity.

### Intensive Intervention

**As needed,** provide more instruction that is on or below grade level for students who are struggling.

**Math Diagnosis and Intervention System 2.0**

- **Diagnosis** Use the diagnostic tests in the system. Also, use the item analysis charts given with program assessments at the start of a grade or topic, or at the end of a topic, group of topics, or the year.
- **Intervention Lessons** These two-page lessons include guided instruction followed by practice. The system includes lessons below, on, and above grade level.
- **Teacher Support** Teacher Notes provide the support needed to conduct a short lesson. The lesson focuses on vocabulary, concept development, and practice. The Teacher's Guide contains individual and class record forms and correlations to Student's Edition lessons.

**Resources for Fluency Success**

- A variety of print and digital resources are provided to ensure success on Common Core fluency standards. See Steps to Fluency Success on pages 271K–271N and 317E–317H.

# THE LANGUAGE OF MATH

PEARSON
realize
PearsonRealize.com

Glossary

Games

## English Language Learners

**Provide ELL support** through visual learning throughout the program, ELL instruction in every lesson, and additional ideas in an ELL Toolkit.

### Visual Learning

The visual learning that is infused in **enVision**math**2.0** provides support for English language learners. This support includes a Visual Learning Animation Plus and a Visual Learning Bridge for each lesson.

### English Language Learners Instruction

E L L

Lessons provide instruction for English language learners at Beginning, Intermediate, and Advanced levels of English proficiency.

### English Language Learners Toolkit

This resource provides professional development and resources for supporting English language learners.

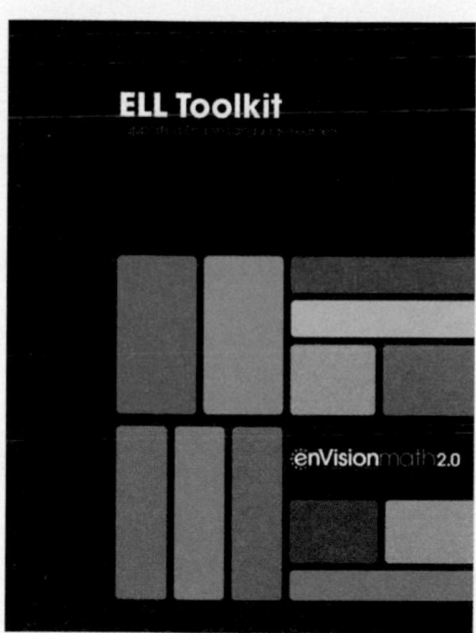
ELL Toolkit
enVisionmath2.0

## Math Vocabulary

**Build math vocabulary** using the vocabulary cards, vocabulary activities, vocabulary review, and glossary plus the online glossary and vocabulary game.

### My Word Cards

Vocabulary cards for a topic are provided in the Student's Edition. Students use the example on the front of the card to complete the definition on the back.

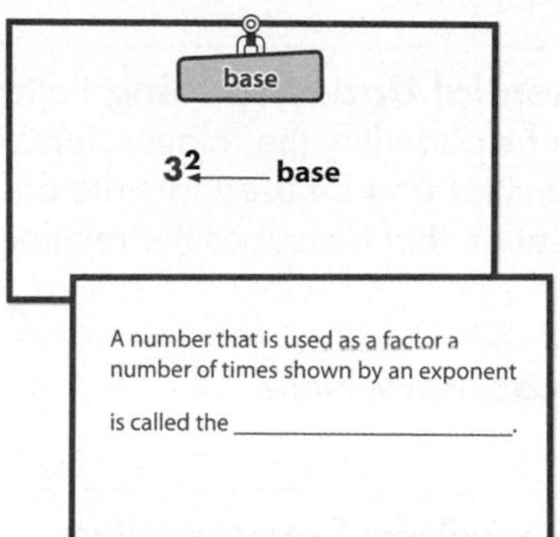
base
3² base
A number that is used as a factor a number of times shown by an exponent is called the ________.

### Vocabulary Activities

The Teacher's Edition provides vocabulary activities at the start of topics. These include activities for vocabulary in My Word Cards and/or activities for vocabulary in Review What You Know.

### Vocabulary Review

A page of vocabulary review is provided at the end of each topic. It reviews vocabulary used in the topic.

### Glossary

A glossary is provided at the back of the Student's Edition.

### Animated Glossary

Glossary

An online, bilingual, animated glossary uses motion and sound to build understanding of math vocabulary.

### Online Vocabulary Game

Games

An online vocabulary game is available in the Game Center.

## Math and Reading

**Connect reading and math** using a data-filled reading mat for the topic with accompanying activity masters and guide.

### Problem-Solving Reading Mats

There is a large, beautiful mat for each topic. At the start of the topic, help students become familiar with the mat and the vocabulary used by reading the mat aloud as students follow along. Use the Problem-Solving Reading Activity Guide for suggestions about how to use the mat.

### Problem-Solving Reading Activity

At the end of some lessons, a Problem-Solving Reading Activity provides a page of math problems to solve by using the data on the mat.

TOPIC 5

# TOPIC PLANNER

## ALGEBRA: PATTERNS AND EQUATIONS

### Lesson 5-1

**DEPENDENT AND INDEPENDENT VARIABLES** pp. 227–232

Content Standard **6.EE.C.9**
Mathematical Practices **MP.2, MP.3, MP.6, MP.7**

**Objective** Identify dependent and independent variables.

**Essential Understanding** Variables can be used to represent two quantities that change in relationship to one another. The dependent variable changes in response to the independent variable.

**Vocabulary** Dependent variable, Independent variable

**ELL Learning Strategies:** Use familiar language to learn new and essential language in the process.

**Materials** Timer, counters

**On-Level and Advanced Activity Centers**
- Problem-Solving Reading Mat

### Lesson 5-2

**PATTERNS AND EQUATIONS** pp. 233–238

Content Standard **6.EE.C.9**
Mathematical Practices **MP.1, MP.2, MP.7**

**Objective** Analyze the relationships between variables by using tables and write equations to represent the relationships.

**Essential Understanding** Patterns can help identify the relationship between quantities and be used to write an equation that describes the relationship.

**Vocabulary** None

**ELL Speaking:** Express opinions.

**Materials** None

**On-Level and Advanced Activity Centers**
- Center Games

### Lesson 5-3

**MORE PATTERNS AND EQUATIONS** pp. 239–244

Content Standard **6.EE.C.9**
Mathematical Practices **MP.2, MP.4, MP.7, MP.8**

**Objective** Analyze the relationships between variables by using tables and write equations to represent the relationships.

**Essential Understanding** Patterns can help identify the relationship between quantities and be used to write an equation that describes the relationship.

**Vocabulary** None

**ELL Reading:** Use reading supports such as illustrations.

**Materials** None

**On-Level and Advanced Activity Centers**
- Math and Science Activity

## LESSON RESOURCES

Digital

Print

- Student's Edition
- Daily Common Core Review
- Reteach to Build Understanding
- Center Games
- Math and Science Activity
- Problem-Solving Reading Mat
- Problem-Solving Reading Activity

Digital

- Listen and Look For PD Lesson Video
- Student's Edition eText
- Today's Challenge
- Solve & Share
- Visual Learning Animation Plus
- Animated Glossary
- Math Tools
- Practice Buddy Online Practice
- Quick Check
- Another Look Homework Video
- Math Games

Digital

## Lesson 5-4

**GRAPH EQUATIONS** pp. 245–250

**Content Standard 6.EE.C.9**
**Mathematical Practices MP.2, MP.3, MP.4**

**Objective** Graph linear equations on a coordinate plane.

**Essential Understanding** Graphs of relationships in the form of $y = ax$ and $y = x + a$, where $a$ is a real number, are straight lines.

**Vocabulary** Linear equation

**ELL Speaking:** Share information in cooperative learning interactions.

**Materials** First quadrant coordinate grids (TT 18), index cards

**On-Level and Advanced Activity Centers**
- Problem-Solving Reading Mat

## Lesson 5-5

**CONTINUE TO GRAPH EQUATIONS** pp. 251–256

**Content Standard 6.EE.C.9**
**Mathematical Practices MP.2, MP.3, MP.4, MP.8**

**Objective** Graph linear equations involving more than one operation.

**Essential Understanding** Graphs of relationships in the form of $y = ax + b$, where $a$ and $b$ are real numbers, are straight lines.

**Vocabulary** None

**ELL Listening:** Demonstrate listening comprehension by summarizing.

**Materials** First quadrant coordinate grids (TT 18)

**On-Level and Advanced Activity Centers**
- Center Games

## Lesson 5-6

**MATH PRACTICES AND PROBLEM SOLVING: MODEL WITH MATH** pp. 257–262

**Mathematical Practices MP.4 Also MP.1, MP.5, MP.6, MP.7**
**Content Standards 6.EE.C.9, 6.EE.B.5**

**Objective** Use math models to represent and solve problems involving previously learned concepts and skills.

**Essential Understanding** Good math thinkers choose and apply math they know to show and solve problems from everyday life.

**Vocabulary** None

**ELL Learning Strategies:** Use prior knowledge to understand meanings.

**Materials** First quadrant coordinate grids (TT 18) (optional)

**On-Level and Advanced Activity Centers**
- Math and Science Activity

## TOPIC RESOURCES

Digital

Print

**Start of Topic**
- Math and Science Project
- Home-School Connection
- Review What You Know
- My Word Cards

**End of Topic**
- Fluency Practice Activity
- Vocabulary Review
- Reteaching
- Topic Assessment
- Topic Performance Assessment

Digital

**Start of Topic**
- Topic Overview PD Video

**End of Topic**
- Math Practices Animations
- Online Topic Assessment
- ExamView® Test Generator
- Practice Buddy Fluency Practice/Assessment

PearsonRealize.com

TOPIC 5

# TOPIC OPENER

# ALGEBRA: PATTERNS AND EQUATIONS

## TOPIC ESSENTIAL QUESTIONS

**How can equations be written? What patterns can be found in tables of values? How are equations that can relate real-world quantities graphed?**

Revisit the Topic Essential Questions throughout the topic, and see a note about answering the questions in the Teacher's Edition for the Topic Assessment.

## MATH AND SCIENCE PROJECT STEM

**Science Theme** The science theme for this project is **Ocean Currents and Weather Patterns**. This theme will be revisited in the Math and Science Activities in Lessons 5-3 and 5-6 and in some lesson exercises.

Over half the heat energy from the sun is absorbed by the ocean. Water is able to hold a temperature for a long time.

Massive ocean currents act as conveyer belts, transporting warm water and air from the equator toward the North Pole and South Pole, and circulating cold water and air back to the tropics. These currents help distribute the uneven amounts of solar radiation that reach Earth. Otherwise, the tropics would be too hot to live in and the poles would be even colder.

**Project-Based Learning** Have students work on the **Math and Science Project** over the course of several days.

### EXTENSION

Draw arrows that indicate the directions of ocean currents on a world map. Name about 10 of these currents. Indicate which currents transport warm water and which currents transport cold water. Write one interesting fact about each of three different ocean currents. For example, because of the Gulf Stream, the Atlantic Ocean near Canada is locked in ice every winter, but it is free-flowing near England. The temperature difference between these locations is 30°F–40°F during the month of January.

### Sample Student Work for Math and Science Project

| Month | Average °F Ocean City, NJ | Average °F Kansas City, KS | Difference °F |
|---|---|---|---|
| Jan. | 36 | 29 | 36 − 29 = 7 |
| Feb. | 37 | 34 | 37 − 34 = 3 |
| Mar. | 43 | 44 | 44 − 43 = 1 |
| April | 52 | 55 | 55 − 52 = 3 |
| May | 61 | 65 | 65 − 61 = 4 |

**Math and Science Project:** Ocean Currents and Weather Patterns

**Do Research** Use the Internet or other sources to learn more about how ocean currents affect weather patterns. How does an ocean current cool or warm a city? Compare weather data for two cities, one coastal and one far inland, which are at the same latitude.

**Journal: Write a Report** Include what you found. Also in your report:

- Find and record each city's average monthly daytime temperature for all twelve months of a year in a data table.
- For each month, write an equation that shows the difference between the two cities' monthly average temperatures.

Topic 5 223

## Home-School Connection

Name ________________

Home-School Connection Topic 5

### Algebra: Patterns and Equations

**Topic 5 Standards**
6.EE.B.5, 6.EE.C.9
*See the front of the Student's Edition for complete standards.*

Dear Family,

In this topic, your child will learn how to use variables to represent related quantities in real-world situations. He or she will look for and use patterns to write rules and equations with these variables to describe and extend the patterns. He or she will also represent the patterns using math models, such as tables and graphs on the coordinate plane.

You can help your child understand the concepts of patterns and equations by playing the game below.

**What's My Equation?**

**Materials:** Sheets of blank paper, pencil

Help your child relate patterns and equations by playing the game below.

**Step 1** Create a table like the one shown. Think of a situation involving money or other quantities that can change by a consistent amount. For example, Chris had $100 in his savings account. Each week, he deposits $40.

**Step 2** Complete the table and write an equation that matches the situation. Think of variables to use in writing the equation. In this case, you might write $S = 40w + 100$, where $S$ is the total amount saved after $w$ weeks.

**Step 3** Ask your child to identify how much money Chris has saved in all after various numbers of weeks.

**Step 4** Think of a new situation that involves more than one operation. Create a table and write an equation for your new scenario.

| Week | Total Amount Saved |
|---|---|
| Start | $100 |
| 1 | $140 |
| 2 | $180 |
| 3 | |
| 4 | |
| 5 | |
| 6 | |

**Observe Your Child**

**Focus on Mathematical Practice 6**
Attend to precision.

Help your child become proficient with Mathematical Practice 6. Have him or her write out the equation for the table above and solve it using different values for the variable $w$. Then double check that the answers are correct. Remind him or her of the importance of accuracy when dealing with money.

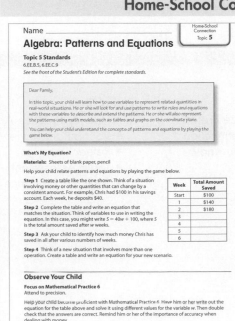

Send this page home at the start of Topic 5 to give families an overview of the content in the topic.

Name ____________________

## Review What You Know

### Vocabulary

Choose the best term from the box. Write it on the blank.

- equation
- variable
- ordered pair
- *x*-axis
- solution
- *y*-axis

1. The horizontal number line on the coordinate plane is called the **x-axis**.
2. The value of the variable that makes an equation true is the **solution**.
3. A(n) **ordered pair** contains the coordinates of a point located on the coordinate plane.
4. The expressions on each side of the equal sign in a(n) **equation** are equal.

### Using Variables

Solve each equation by finding the value of the variable.

5. $52 - x = 17$ $x =$ **35**
6. $61 = g + 13$ $g =$ **48**
7. $8 = t \div 9$ $t =$ **72**
8. $m - 3.7 = 8.6$ $m =$ **12.3**
9. $12n = 84$ $n =$ **7**
10. $54 \div c = 9$ $c =$ **6**

### Equations

Solve each equation.

11. $y \div 20 = 3$ **$y = 60$**
12. $52 = 4a$ **$a = 13$**
13. $z - 67 = 141$ **$z = 208$**
14. $489 = b + 313$ **$b = 176$**
15. $s \div 8 = 11$ **$s = 88$**
16. $15d = 45$ **$d = 3$**

### Graphing in the Coordinate Plane

17. Describe how to plot point $A(-6, 2)$ on a coordinate plane.
**Start at the origin (0, 0), and move left six units along the *x*-axis to −6. Next, move up two units following the *y*-axis. Draw a point at that location and label it *A*.**

## Item Analysis for Diagnosis and Intervention

| Item | Standard | MDIS |
|---|---|---|
| 1–4 | 5.G.A.2, 6.EE.B.5 | F32, F48 |
| 5–10 | 6.EE.B.7 | F49, F50 |
| 11–16 | 6.EE.B.7 | F51 |
| 17 | 6.NS.C.8 | F32 |

## Topic 5 Vocabulary Words Activity

Use the Topic 1 activity on p. 3–4 with the Topic 5 words at the right.

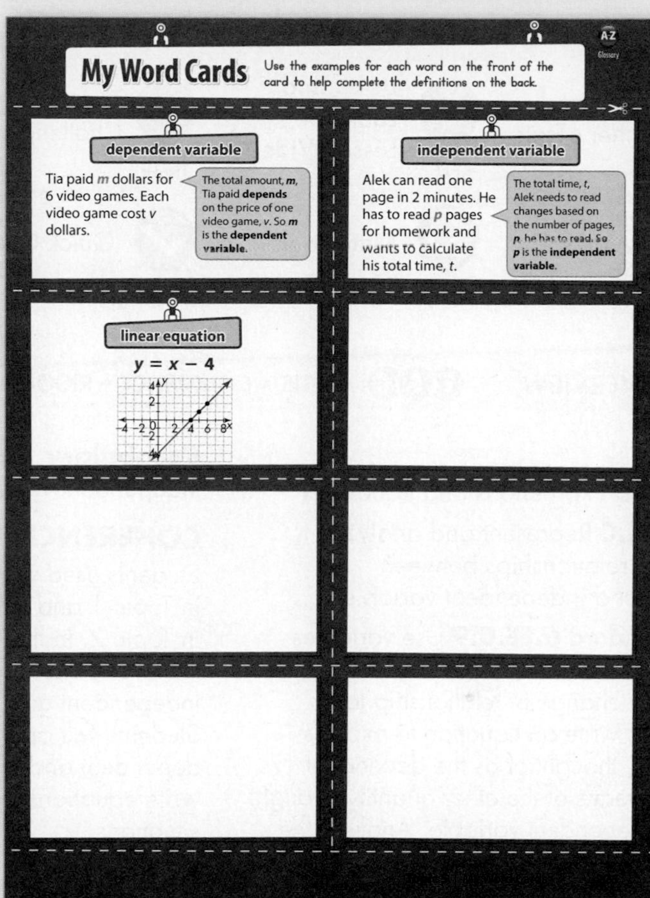

**My Word Cards** Use the examples for each word on the front of the card to help complete the definitions on the back.

**dependent variable**

Tia paid *m* dollars for 6 video games. Each video game cost *v* dollars.

The total amount, *m*, Tia paid **depends** on the price of one video game, *v*. So *m* is the **dependent variable.**

**independent variable**

Alek can read one page in 2 minutes. He has to read *p* pages for homework and wants to calculate his total time, *t*.

The total time, *t*, Alek needs to read changes based on the number of pages, *p*, he has to read. So *p* is the **independent variable.**

**linear equation**

$y = x - 4$

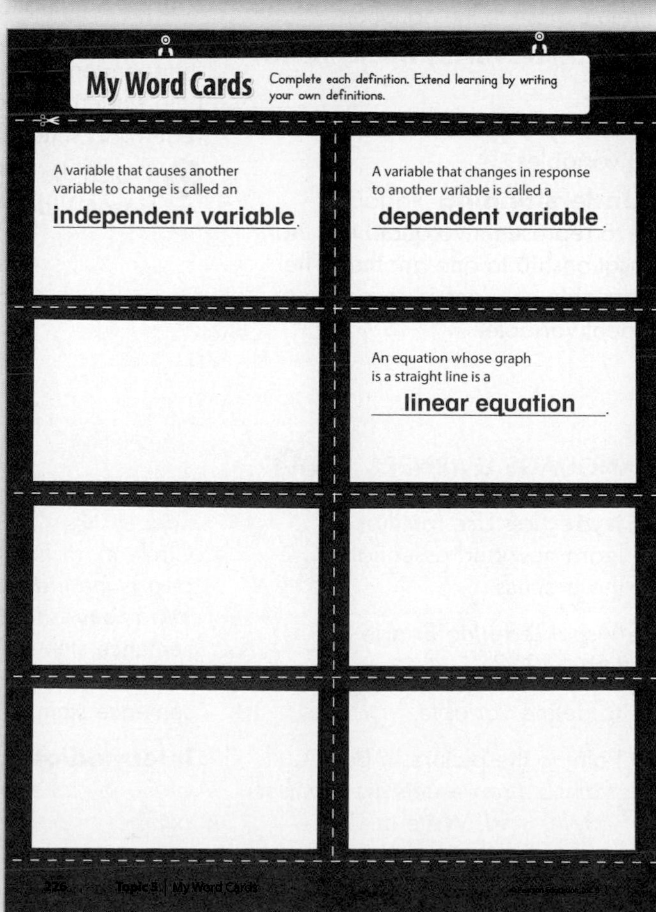

**My Word Cards** Complete each definition. Extend learning by writing your own definitions.

A variable that causes another variable to change is called an **independent variable**.

A variable that changes in response to another variable is called a **dependent variable**.

An equation whose graph is a straight line is a **linear equation**.

# LESSON 5-1

# DEPENDENT AND INDEPENDENT VARIABLES

## DIGITAL RESOURCES PearsonRealize.com

eText — Student and Teacher eTexts

PD — Listen and Look For Lesson Video

Think — Today's Challenge

Solve — Solve and Share

Learn — Visual Learning Animation Plus

Glossary — Animated Glossary

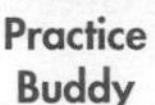
Practice Buddy — Online Personalized Practice

Tools — Math Tools

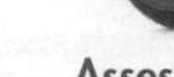
Assessment — Quick Check

Help — Another Look Homework Video

Games — Math Games

## LESSON OVERVIEW FCR FOCUS • COHERENCE • RIGOR

### FOCUS

**Domain 6.EE** Expressions and Equations

**Cluster 6.EE.C** Represent and analyze quantitative relationships between dependent and independent variables.

**Content Standard 6.EE.C.9** Use variables to represent two quantities in a real-world problem that change in relationship to one another; write an equation to express one quantity, thought of as the dependent variable, in terms of the other quantity, thought of as the independent variable. Analyze the relationship between the dependent and independent variables using graphs and tables, and relate these to the equation.

**Mathematical Practices MP.2, MP.3, MP.6, MP.7**

**Objective** Identify dependent and independent variables.

**Essential Understanding** Variables can be used to represent two quantities that change in relationship to one another. The dependent variable changes in response to the independent variable.

**Vocabulary** Dependent variable, Independent variable

### COHERENCE

Students used variables to write expressions in Topic 1 and solved one-variable equations in Topic 2. In this lesson, students analyze real-world situations and identify the independent and dependent variables. Students will apply this understanding of dependent and independent variables to write equations to represent real-world situations.

### RIGOR

This lesson emphasizes **conceptual understanding**. Understanding independent and dependent variables will help students write equations to represent real-world situations.

PD Watch the Listen and Look For Lesson Video.

## MATH ANYTIME

### Daily Common Core Review

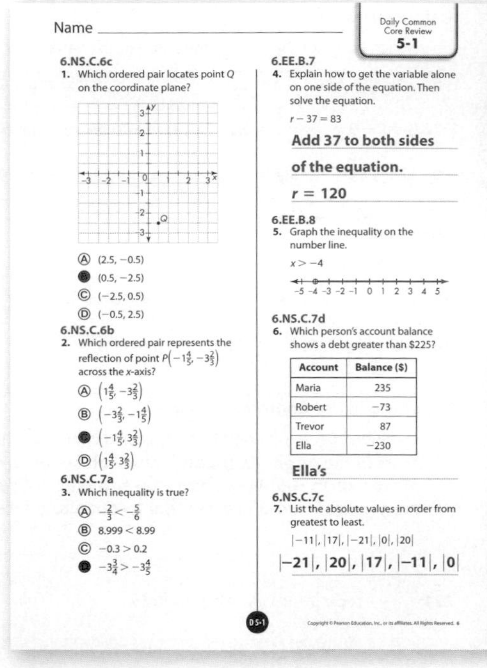
Name ______

Daily Common Core Review 5-1

6.NS.C.6c

1. Which ordered pair locates point $Q$ on the coordinate plane?

Ⓐ (2.5, −0.5)
● (0.5, −2.5)
Ⓒ (−2.5, 0.5)
Ⓓ (−0.5, 2.5)

6.NS.C.6b

2. Which ordered pair represents the reflection of point $P\left(-1\frac{4}{5}, -3\frac{2}{3}\right)$ across the $x$-axis?

Ⓐ $\left(1\frac{4}{5}, -3\frac{2}{3}\right)$
Ⓑ $\left(-3\frac{2}{3}, -1\frac{4}{5}\right)$
● $\left(-1\frac{4}{5}, 3\frac{2}{3}\right)$
Ⓓ $\left(1\frac{4}{5}, 3\frac{2}{3}\right)$

6.NS.C.7a

3. Which inequality is true?

Ⓐ $-\frac{2}{3} < -\frac{5}{6}$
Ⓑ $8.999 < 8.99$
Ⓒ $-0.3 > 0.2$
● $-3\frac{3}{4} > -3\frac{4}{5}$

6.EE.B.7

4. Explain how to get the variable alone on one side of the equation. Then solve the equation.

$r - 37 = 83$

**Add 37 to both sides of the equation.**

$r = 120$

6.EE.B.8

5. Graph the inequality on the number line.

$x > -4$

6.NS.C.7d

6. Which person's account balance shows a debt greater than $225?

| Account | Balance ($) |
|---|---|
| Maria | 235 |
| Robert | −73 |
| Trevor | 87 |
| Ella | −230 |

**Ella's**

6.NS.C.7c

7. List the absolute values in order from greatest to least.

$|-11|, |17|, |-21|, |0|, |20|$

$|-21|, |20|, |17|, |-11|, |0|$

D 5-1



### Today's Challenge

Think Use the Topic 5 problems any time during this topic.

## ENGLISH LANGUAGE LEARNERS ELL

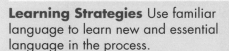

**Learning Strategies** Use familiar language to learn new and essential language in the process.

*Use with the Visual Learning Bridge on Student's Edition p. 228.*

Ask students to define *variable*.

**Beginning** Point to the picture in Box A. Write *p*. *This variable represents the number of pounds of apples sold.* Write *m*. *This variable represents money taken in.* Draw an arrow from *m* to *p*. *The amount of money "depends on" the number of pounds sold.* Circle *m*. *m is the dependent variable.* Circle *p*. *p is the independent variable.* Point to *m*. *What is m?* Have students respond using the sentence stem: *m* is the ___ ___. Point to *p*. *What is p?* Have students respond using the sentence stem: *p* is the ___ ___.

**Intermediate** Write *m* and *p*. *The amount of money taken in, m, "depends on" the number of pounds sold, p.* Point to *m* and *p*. *m is the dependent variable, and p is the independent variable.* Instruct students to complete the sentence stems: *m* is the ___ ___ because ___. *p* is the ___ ___ because ___.

**Advanced** Write *m* and *p*. *The amount of money taken in, m, "depends on" the number of pounds sold, p.* Point to *m* and *p*. *m is the dependent variable, and p is the independent variable.* Instruct students to explain to partners why *m* is the dependent variable and *p* is the independent variable.

**Summarize** What are dependent and independent variables?

# DEVELOP: PROBLEM-BASED LEARNING

**COHERENCE: Engage learners by connecting prior knowledge to new ideas.**
Students extend their understanding of variables as they reason about how dependent and independent variables are related within a real-world context.

10–15 min

Solve

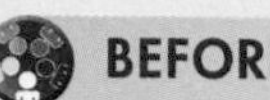

## BEFORE

**1. Pose the Solve-and-Share Problem**
**MP.2 Reason Abstractly** Listen and look for students who identify characteristics of the box that do and do not relate to its weight. Encourage creativity, but remind them that solutions must be relevant to the weight of the box.

**2. Build Understanding**
*In general, what is meant by the phrase "think outside the box?"* [To think in unexpected ways or to have a creative approach]
*Why might you want to know what things determine the weight of the box?* [Sample answers: To select an appropriate box, to decide whether you can carry it yourself]

## DURING

**3. Ask Guiding Questions As Needed**
*How could two boxes be the same size, but have different weights?* [Sample answer: One box might hold heavier objects or be made of a thicker, heavier material.]

## AFTER

**4. Share and Discuss Solutions**
Start with students' solutions. If needed, project Erica's work to discuss how to determine what affects the weight of a box.

**5. Transition to the Visual Learning Bridge**
*When you know which quantity has an effect on another quantity, you can identify the dependent and independent variables.*

**6. Extension for Early Finishers**
*Think of something that you do every day that varies, like the number of hours you sleep each night. Describe at least three things that are related to it.* [Sample answer: Amount of homework, sports events, time spent watching television]

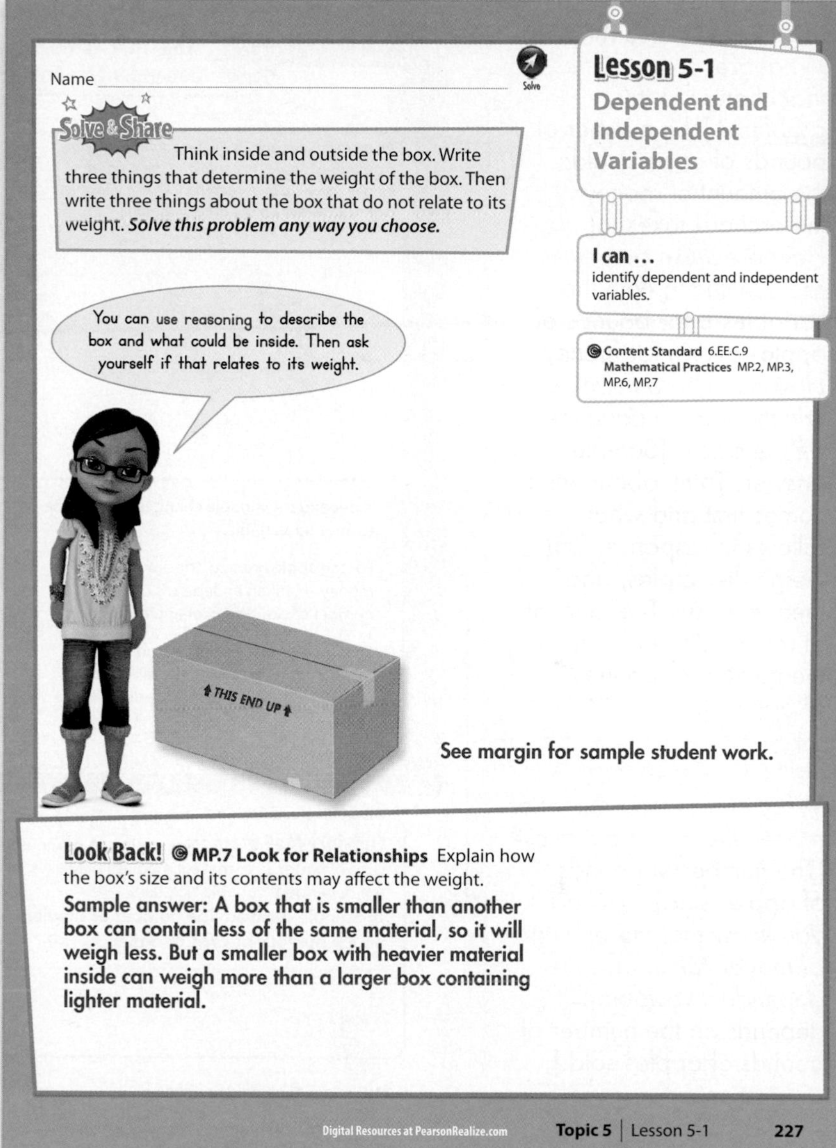

Name
Solve & Share
Think inside and outside the box. Write three things that determine the weight of the box. Then write three things about the box that do not relate to its weight. Solve this problem any way you choose.
Lesson 5-1
Dependent and Independent Variables
I can ...
identify dependent and independent variables.
Content Standard 6.EE.C.9
Mathematical Practices MP.2, MP.3, MP.6, MP.7
You can use reasoning to describe the box and what could be inside. Then ask yourself if that relates to its weight.
THIS END UP
See margin for sample student work.
Look Back! MP.7 Look for Relationships Explain how the box's size and its contents may affect the weight.
Sample answer: A box that is smaller than another box can contain less of the same material, so it will weigh less. But a smaller box with heavier material inside can weigh more than a larger box containing lighter material.
Digital Resources at PearsonRealize.com
Topic 5 | Lesson 5-1 227


## Analyze Student Work

**Erica's Work**

Three things that determine the total weight of the box:
1. Size of the box
2. Box materials
3. Items in the box

Three things that are not related to the weight of the box:
1. Color of the box
2. Day the box was made
3. Name of the box manufacturer

Erica correctly lists three distinct items in each category.

**Demi's Work**

Things that determine weight:
1. Width of box
2. Height of box
3. What box is made of

Things that don't affect weight:
1. when the box was made
2. where the box was made
3. How the box was made

Demi also lists three distinct items in each category.

# DEVELOP: VISUAL LEARNING

The *Visual Learning Bridge* connects students' thinking in Solve & Share to important math ideas in the lesson. Use the *Visual Learning Bridge* to make these ideas explicit. Also available as a *Visual Learning Animation Plus* at PearsonRealize.com

PEARSON realize. PearsonRealize.com

**MP.2 Reason Quantitatively** *What are the quantities that change in this problem?* [The number of pounds of apples sold; the amount of money the orchard takes in] *How are these quantities represented?* [With the variables *p* for pounds of apples and *m* for money] *How can you determine which variable depends on the other?* [Sample answer: Think about what comes first and what follows in response. You weigh the apples, and then you pay. The amount of money depends on the number of pounds of apples.]

*What affects the amount of money the orchard makes?* [The number of pounds of apples sold] *How do you know that the amount of money taken in is the dependent variable?* [It depends on the number of pounds of apples sold.]

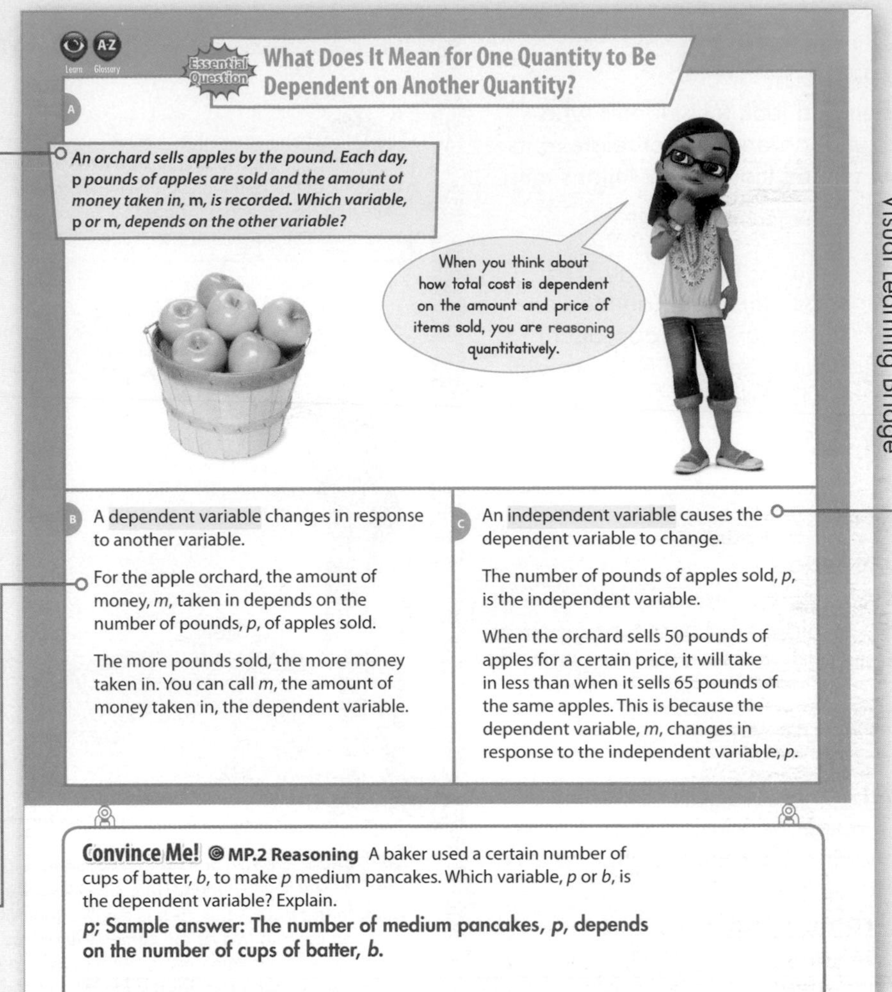

Essential Question **What Does It Mean for One Quantity to Be Dependent on Another Quantity?**

A

*An orchard sells apples by the pound. Each day, p pounds of apples are sold and the amount of money taken in, m, is recorded. Which variable, p or m, depends on the other variable?*

When you think about how total cost is dependent on the amount and price of items sold, you are reasoning quantitatively.



B

A dependent variable changes in response to another variable.

For the apple orchard, the amount of money, *m*, taken in depends on the number of pounds, *p*, of apples sold.

The more pounds sold, the more money taken in. You can call *m*, the amount of money taken in, the dependent variable.

C

An independent variable causes the dependent variable to change.

The number of pounds of apples sold, *p*, is the independent variable.

When the orchard sells 50 pounds of apples for a certain price, it will take in less than when it sells 65 pounds of the same apples. This is because the dependent variable, *m*, changes in response to the independent variable, *p*.

Visual Learning Bridge

**Convince Me!** **MP.2 Reasoning** A baker used a certain number of cups of batter, *b*, to make *p* medium pancakes. Which variable, *p* or *b*, is the dependent variable? Explain.

**p; Sample answer: The number of medium pancakes, p, depends on the number of cups of batter, b.**

228 **Topic 5** | Lesson 5-1 © Pearson Education, Inc. 6

*How does the number of pounds of apples sold affect the amount of money the orchard takes in?* [If they sell more apples, they make more money.] *What would happen if they sold no apples?* [They would take in no money.] *Then what is the independent variable?* [The pounds of apples sold]

**Convince Me! MP.2 Reason Quantitatively** *What does the number of pancakes the baker can make depend on?* [The number of cups of batter he has] *In this situation, does the number of cups of batter depend on the number of pancakes the baker can make?* [No, the problem says that the baker used a certain number of cups of batter to make the pancakes.] *Can you think of a different situation where b is dependent on p?* [Sample answer: The baker is making breakfast for 10 people and determines how many pancakes to make. So the amount of batter, *b*, depends on the number of pancakes, *p*, he wants to make.]

Revisit the Essential Question. Remind students that the independent variable affects another variable. A dependent variable "depends on" another variable. In other words, a dependent variable changes when the independent variable changes.

## QUICK CHECK

Check mark indicates items for prescribing differentiation on the next page. Items 8 and 17 are worth 1 point. Item 16 is worth up to 3 points.

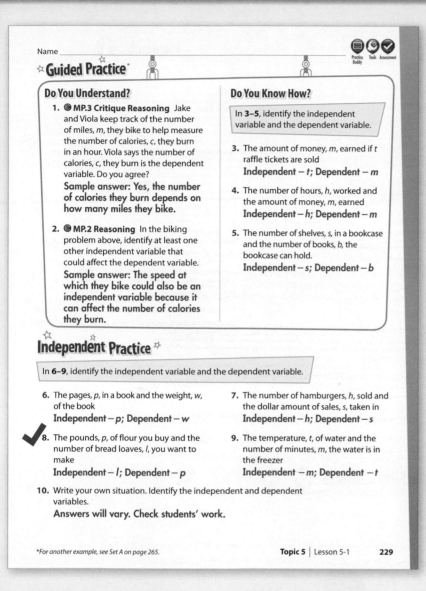

20–30 min

Practice Buddy

Tools

Assessment

Name

### Guided Practice*

#### Do You Understand?

1. MP.3 Critique Reasoning Jake and Viola keep track of the number of miles, *m*, they bike to help measure the number of calories, *c*, they burn in an hour. Viola says the number of calories, *c*, they burn is the dependent variable. Do you agree?
**Sample answer: Yes, the number of calories they burn depends on how many miles they bike.**

2. MP.2 Reasoning In the biking problem above, identify at least one other independent variable that could affect the dependent variable.
**Sample answer: The speed at which they bike could also be an independent variable because it can affect the number of calories they burn.**

#### Do You Know How?

In 3–5, identify the independent variable and the dependent variable.

3. The amount of money, *m*, earned if *t* raffle tickets are sold
**Independent – *t*; Dependent – *m***

4. The number of hours, *h*, worked and the amount of money, *m*, earned
**Independent – *h*; Dependent – *m***

5. The number of shelves, *s*, in a bookcase and the number of books, *b*, the bookcase can hold.
**Independent – *s*; Dependent – *b***

### Independent Practice

In 6–9, identify the independent variable and the dependent variable.

6. The pages, *p*, in a book and the weight, *w*, of the book
**Independent – *p*; Dependent – *w***

7. The number of hamburgers, *h*, sold and the dollar amount of sales, *s*, taken in
**Independent – *h*; Dependent – *s***

✓ 8. The pounds, *p*, of flour you buy and the number of bread loaves, *l*, you want to make
**Independent – *l*; Dependent – *p***

9. The temperature, *t*, of water and the number of minutes, *m*, the water is in the freezer
**Independent – *m*; Dependent – *t***

10. Write your own situation. Identify the independent and dependent variables.
**Answers will vary. Check students' work.**

*For another example, see Set A on page 265.



### Math Practices and Problem Solving

11. The table records distances driven by the Williams family each day of their vacation. What is an independent variable that would affect the total distance they drove each day? **Sample answer: The number of hours driven per day**

DATA — Family Vacation

| Day | Distance |
|---|---|
| 1 | 480 mi |
| 2 | 260 mi |
| 3 | 40 mi |
| 4 | 150 mi |
| 5 | 100 mi |
| 6 | 320 mi |

12. MP.7 Look for Relationships The Williams family drove 50 miles each hour on Day 6. How many hours did they drive to equal the distance shown? **6.4 hr**

13. MP.6 Be Precise On Monday, Jill bought $3\frac{2}{3}$ feet of ribbon for her art project. On Tuesday, she bought another $1\frac{1}{6}$ feet of ribbon. How many inches of ribbon did she buy in all? **58 inches**

14. MP.2 Reasoning Name something that could result in a change in a person's heart rate. Is this a dependent or an independent variable? **Sample answer: Exercising; independent variable**

15. MP.7 Use Structure Darryl put 8 boxes of apples on a cart. Each box contains 6 rows of 5 apples. Use the Associative Property of Multiplication to show two different ways to find the number of apples in all.
$8 \times (6 \times 5) = 240$; $(8 \times 6) \times 5 = 240$

✓ 16. Higher Order Thinking Lidia said that time, *t*, could be either an independent or dependent variable. Write a situation where time, *t*, is an independent variable. Then write a situation where time, *t*, is a dependent variable.
**Sample answer: Time, *t*, could be an independent variable that affects how far someone has walked. Time, *t*, could also be a dependent variable based on the distance and pace walked from one place to another.**

#### Common Core Assessment

✓ 17. The dependent variable *g* represents the growth of a plant. Which of the variables described below can represent an independent variable in this situation?

- ☐ The height of the plant, *h*, when placed in the ground
- ■ The amount of sunlight, *s*
- ☐ How many leaves, *m*, the plant has
- ■ The amount of water, *w*, it receives




**Error Intervention: Item 1**

**If** students are unable to identify the dependent variable,
**then** ask: *Does the number of miles Jake and Viola bike depend on the number of calories they burn?* [No] *What does the number of calories they burn depend on?* [The number of miles they bike]

**Items 6–9** If students have difficulty identifying the variables, have them restate the two quantities in a sentence using the phrase *depends on*. Use Item 6 as an example. *How can you relate these variables in a sentence that uses the phrase* depends on? [The weight of the book *depends on* the number of pages in the book.] *Which variable is the dependent variable?* [The weight of the book, *w*]

**Reteaching** Assign Reteaching Set A on p. 265.

**Item 13 MP.6 Be Precise** In this problem, students will need to pay attention to the units and convert between feet and inches. They use precision when performing the calculations with mixed numbers. *What are the units provided in the problem?* [Feet] *What units are asked for in the question?* [Inches] *How do you convert feet to inches?* [1 foot = 12 inches, so multiply the number of feet by 12.]

**Item 16 Higher Order Thinking** Allow students to work together in pairs and, if needed, provide sentence frames such as:

- *The time it takes to get to school depends on* _____. [Sample answers: The distance from home to the school, the number of other commuters, the number of green lights, your speed]
- _____ *depends on the time it takes to get to school.* [Sample answers: The time you wake up, the amount of homework you can do during your commute]

**Multi-Step Problems** *Page 230 Items 13, 15, and 16; Page 232 Items 11 and 14*

# ASSESS AND DIFFERENTIATE

Use the **QUICK CHECK** on the previous page to prescribe differentiated instruction.

**(I) Intervention**
0–3 points on the Quick Check

**(O) On-Level**
4 points on the Quick Check

**(A) Advanced**
5 points on the Quick Check

## Intervention Activity 

### Dependent and Independent Variables

**Materials**

Timer, Counters (per pair)

- Have students work in pairs.
- Have one student in each pair use the timer. Have the other student make as many stacks of 3 counters as possible in 10 seconds.
- Then repeat the activity, having the same student make as many stacks of 3 counters as possible in 20 seconds.
- Have students switch roles and repeat the activity.
- Ask students to explain whether the number of stacks of counters would be represented by a dependent or independent variable.

*The number of stacks of counters would be represented by the dependent variable because it depends on the amount of time you have to make the stacks.*

## Reteach 

Name ______________________

Reteach to Build Understanding
**5-1**

**Vocabulary**

1. A **dependent variable** is a variable whose value changes in response to another variable.
   The number of eggs, $g$, produced by a farm depends on the number of chickens, $c$, on the farm.
   The variable $g$ represents the **dependent** variable because the number of eggs produced depends on the number of chickens on the farm.
2. An **independent variable** is a variable that causes the value of the dependent variable to change.
   The amount of money, $m$, collected selling popcorn depends on the number of bags of popcorn, $p$, sold.
   The variable $p$ represents the **independent** variable because the number of bags of popcorn sold causes the amount of money collected to change.
3. A restaurant is offering an omelet special for Sunday brunch. The chef can make a number of omelets, $x$, for brunch. There are a number of eggs, $y$, in the restaurant's refrigerator.
   The number of **omelets** depends on the number of **eggs**.
   Identify each variable: independent variable **$y$**, dependent variable **$x$**
4. Jacob earns $5 every time his online ad is viewed, $v$. He earns $d$ dollars from his ad.
   The number of **dollars** depends on the number of **views**.
   Identify each variable: independent variable **$v$**, dependent variable **$d$**
5. Write your own situation where the number of tennis players, $p$, is an independent variable.
   **Sample answer: The number of matches, $m$, scheduled depends on the number of tennis players, $p$, registered for a tournament.**

**On the Back!**

6. Underline the independent variable and circle the dependent variable for the following situation: A book has a number of pages, $p$. It takes Caroline a number of hours, $h$, to read the book.

## On-Level and Advanced Activity Centers (O) (A)

### Problem-Solving Reading Mat

Have students read the Problem-Solving Reading Mat for Topic 5 and then complete Problem-Solving Reading Activity 5-1.

See the Problem-Solving Reading Activity Guide for other suggestions on how to use this mat.

## TIMING

The time allocated to Step 3 will depend on the teacher's instructional decisions and differentiation routines.

15–30 min

PEARSON realize. PearsonRealize.com

Help | Practice Buddy | Tools | Games

## Technology Center   

 Tools  Games

### Math Tools and Math Games

A link to a specific math tools activity or math game to use with this lesson is provided at PearsonRealize.com.

## Leveled Assignment

 Items 1–8, 11, 14, 15  Items 1–6, 9–12, 14, 15  Items 5–15

Name ______________________

## Homework & Practice 5-1

### Dependent and Independent Variables

### Another Look!

A bicycle shop rents bicycles by the hour. Each day, *b* bicycles are rented. The shop collects *d* dollars per day in total rental fees. Identify which variable is the independent variable and which is the dependent variable.

Think about whether a variable causes change or changes in response to other variables.


A **dependent variable** changes in response to another variable, called an independent variable.

An **independent variable** causes the change in a dependent variable. It is *independent* because its value is not affected by other variables and can be used to find the value of the dependent variable.

The number of bikes *b*, that are rented each day affects the total rental fees collected each day, *d*.

So, the number of bikes rented, *b*, is the independent variable that causes the dependent variable, *d*, the total rental fees, to change.

In **1–8**, underline the independent variable and circle the dependent variable in each situation.

1. The number of hours, *h*, spent studying and the score, *s*, on a test
2. The length, *l*, of a pencil and the number of times, *t*, it has been sharpened
3. The length of a story in pages, *p*, and the number of words, *w*, in a story
4. The number of students, *s*, ahead of you in the lunch line and the time, *t*, it takes you to get lunch
5. The amount of time, *t*, to finish a race and the number of laps, *l*, around a track
6. Tickets, *t*, sold for a race and the amount of money, *m*, collected
7. The length, *l*, of a fence and the amount of wood, *w*, to make the fence
8. The height, *h*, of a fence and the time, *t*, it takes to climb the fence
9. Write your own situation where speed, *s*, is an independent variable.
**Sample answer: The time, *t*, it takes me to walk to school and the speed, *s*, I walk.**



10. **MP.2 Reasoning** Two friends hiked the Appalachian Trail from Georgia to Maine. List at least two independent variables that could affect the number of days they took to hike the trail.
**Sample answer: The speed at which they hiked; The number of hours they hiked each day**

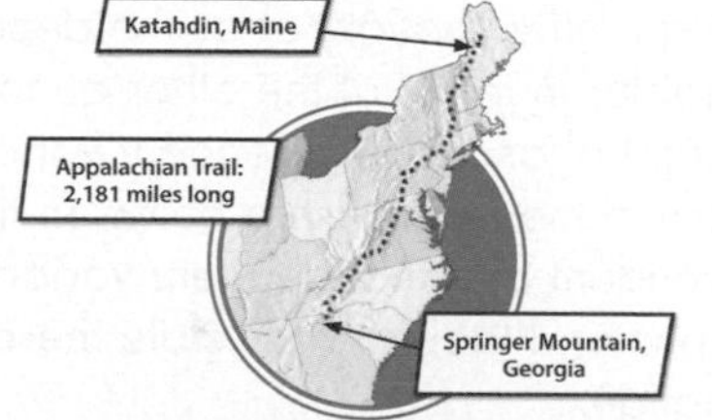


11. **Algebra** Steve had 21 songs on his MP3 player. He bought some new songs. Now he has 30 songs on his player. Write an equation to show how many new songs he put on his player. Let *s* stand for the number of new songs. Solve for *s* and show your work.
**$21 + s = 30$; $30 - 21 = 9$; $s = 9$; Steve put 9 new songs on his player.**

12. **MP.3 Construct Arguments** A baseball team gets 3 outs for each inning it comes up to bat. So far this season, Silvio's team has batted in 45 innings, *n*, and has made 135 outs, *t*. What is the dependent variable? Explain your reasoning.
**Dependent variable: *t*; Sample answer: The number of outs is dependent on the number of innings the team has batted.**

13. **Vocabulary** Underline the *independent variable* and circle the *dependent variable* in the situation below.
The number of laps you swim, *s*, and the time, *t*, you spend swimming.

14. **Higher Order Thinking** Ivan says that length, *l*, can be used as an independent variable and as a dependent variable. Give an example of a case where length, *l*, is a dependent variable. Then describe another situation where it is an independent variable.
**Sample answer: Independent variable, the finishing time, *t*, of a runner and the length, *l* of the race; Dependent variable, the length, *l*, of a song and the number of notes, *n*, played.**

### Common Core Assessment

15. The cost, *c*, of a hamburger at a restaurant depends on other factors at the restaurant. Which of the variables described below can represent an independent variable in this situation?

- [x] The number of hamburgers, *h*, typically sold at the restaurant
- [ ] The distance, *d*, the owner lives from the restaurant
- [x] The cost, *c*, to maintain the restaurant
- [ ] The color of the table cloths, *t*

# LESSON 5-2

# PATTERNS AND EQUATIONS

## DIGITAL RESOURCES PearsonRealize.com

eText — Student and Teacher eTexts

PD — Listen and Look For Lesson Video

Think — Today's Challenge

Solve — Solve and Share

Learn — Visual Learning Animation Plus

Glossary — Animated Glossary

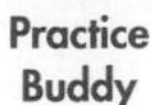
Practice Buddy — Online Personalized Practice

Tools — Math Tools

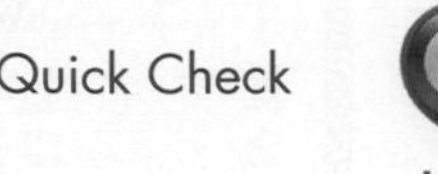
Assessment — Quick Check

Help — Another Look Homework Video

Games — Math Games

## LESSON OVERVIEW FCR FOCUS • COHERENCE • RIGOR

### FOCUS

**Domain 6.EE** Expressions and Equations

**Cluster 6.EE.C** Represent and analyze quantitative relationships between dependent and independent variables.

**Content Standard 6.EE.C.9** Use variables to represent two quantities in a real-world problem that change in relationship to one another; write an equation to express one quantity, thought of as the dependent variable, in terms of the other quantity, thought of as the independent variable. Analyze the relationship between the dependent and independent variables using graphs and tables, and relate these to the equation.

**Mathematical Practices MP.1, MP.2, MP.7**

**Objective** Analyze the relationships between variables by using tables and write equations to represent the relationships.

**Essential Understanding** Patterns can help identify the relationship between quantities and be used to write an equation that describes the relationship.

### COHERENCE

In Topic 1, students learned how to write and evaluate algebraic expressions. In Topic 2, students wrote and solved equations in one variable. They extend this knowledge to use tables to analyze relationships between quantities that vary together and to write equations to represent the relationships. This prepares students for later lessons in this topic and to write and solve more complicated equations in Grade 7.

### RIGOR

This lesson emphasizes a blend of **conceptual understanding** with **procedural skill**. Students analyze simple patterns in tables and write rules and equations to describe the relationship between the dependent and independent variables in real-world contexts.

PD Watch the Listen and Look For Lesson Video.

## MATH ANYTIME

### Daily Common Core Review

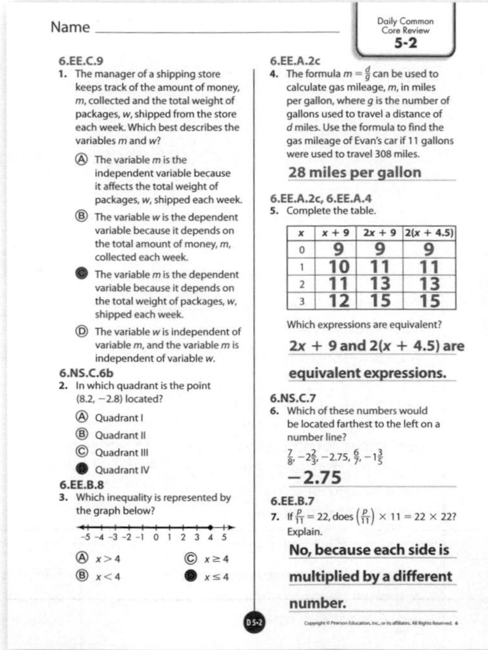
Name ____________

Daily Common Core Review 5-2

6.EE.C.9
1. The manager of a shipping store keeps track of the amount of money, *m*, collected and the total weight of packages, *w*, shipped from the store each week. Which best describes the variables *m* and *w*?
   - Ⓐ The variable *m* is the independent variable because it affects the total weight of packages, *w*, shipped each week.
   - Ⓑ The variable *w* is the dependent variable because it depends on the total amount of money, *m*, collected each week.
   - ● The variable *m* is the dependent variable because it depends on the total weight of packages, *w*, shipped each week.
   - Ⓓ The variable *w* is independent of variable *m*, and the variable *m* is independent of variable *w*.

6.NS.C.6b
2. In which quadrant is the point (8.2, −2.8) located?
   - Ⓐ Quadrant I
   - Ⓑ Quadrant II
   - Ⓒ Quadrant III
   - ● Quadrant IV

6.EE.B.8
3. Which inequality is represented by the graph below?

   −5 −4 −3 −2 −1 0 1 2 3 4 5

   - Ⓐ $x > 4$
   - Ⓑ $x < 4$
   - Ⓒ $x \geq 4$
   - ● $x \leq 4$

6.EE.A.2c
4. The formula $m = \frac{d}{g}$ can be used to calculate gas mileage, *m*, in miles per gallon, where *g* is the number of gallons used to travel a distance of *d* miles. Use the formula to find the gas mileage of Evan's car if 11 gallons were used to travel 308 miles.

   **28 miles per gallon**

6.EE.A.2c, 6.EE.A.4
5. Complete the table.

| $x$ | $x + 9$ | $2x + 9$ | $2(x + 4.5)$ |
|---|---|---|---|
| 0 | 9 | 9 | 9 |
| 1 | 10 | 11 | 11 |
| 2 | 11 | 13 | 13 |
| 3 | 12 | 15 | 15 |

   Which expressions are equivalent?

   **$2x + 9$ and $2(x + 4.5)$ are equivalent expressions.**

6.NS.C.7
6. Which of these numbers would be located farthest to the left on a number line?

   $\frac{7}{8}, -2\frac{2}{3}, -2.75, \frac{6}{7}, -1\frac{3}{5}$

   **−2.75**

6.EE.B.7
7. If $\frac{p}{11} = 22$, does $\left(\frac{p}{11}\right) \times 11 = 22 \times 22$? Explain.

   **No, because each side is multiplied by a different number.**

D 5•2



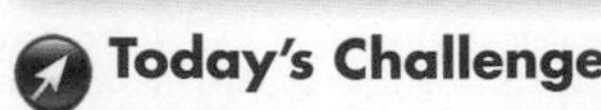
### Today's Challenge

Think Use the Topic 5 problems any time during this topic.

## ENGLISH LANGUAGE LEARNERS 

**Speaking** Express opinions.

*Use with the Visual Learning Bridge on Student's Edition p. 234.*

Read Box A. Write *n* and *c*. Ask students to tell partners the meanings of the variables *n* and *c*. Point to the table and read the information to students. *What information do you need to identify first in order to find out the cost of 6 tickets?* Instruct students to respond by expressing opinions.

**Beginning** Have students express opinions using the sentence stem: First find the ____. Instruct students to work with partners to complete the table. *Is there a pattern?* Students will respond using one- to two-word answers.

**Intermediate** Have students express opinions using the sentence stem: First find the ___ because ___. Instruct students to work with partners to complete the table. *Is there a pattern?* Students will respond using complete sentences.

**Advanced** Instruct students to express opinions to partners about the information that needs to be identified first. *Why is that information important for completing the table?* Then ask students to complete the table. *What is the pattern?* Have students explain the pattern to partners.

**Summarize** What information is needed to find a pattern on the table?

# DEVELOP: PROBLEM-BASED LEARNING

**COHERENCE: Engage learners by connecting prior knowledge to new ideas.**
Students extend their understanding of independent and dependent variables to analyze relationships between quantities and write equations to represent the relationships.

10–15 min

Solve

## BEFORE

**1. Pose the Solve-and-Share Problem**
**MP.7 Look for Relationships** Listen and look for students who analyze and describe the pattern in the table, and use the pattern to answer the question.

**2. Build Understanding**
*How can you find a pattern that explains the relationship between c and b?* [Sample answer: Find which operations you can use with each value of *c* to result in the corresponding value of *b*.]

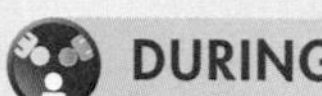

## DURING

**3. Ask Guiding Questions As Needed**
*Start by considering the first row. What rules can you use with 8 that result in 2?* [Subtract 6, divide by 4, multiply by $\frac{1}{4}$] *Look at the second row. Which of these rules do not apply to the values of c and b in the second row of the table?* [Subtract 6] *What should you do next?* [Check the pattern using the values in the third row.] *What is the pattern?* [$\frac{c}{4} = b$ or $\frac{1}{4}c = b$.]

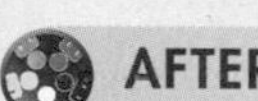

## AFTER

**4. Share and Discuss Solutions**
Start with students' solutions. If needed, project both Jay's work and Dan's work to discuss two possible solutions.

**5. Transition to the Visual Learning Bridge**
*By finding patterns in tables, you can write equations that represent the relationship between the variables.*

**6. Extension for Early Finishers**
*Create a table with a pattern in it. Trade papers with a partner and write a rule and an equation for the pattern.* [Check students' work.]

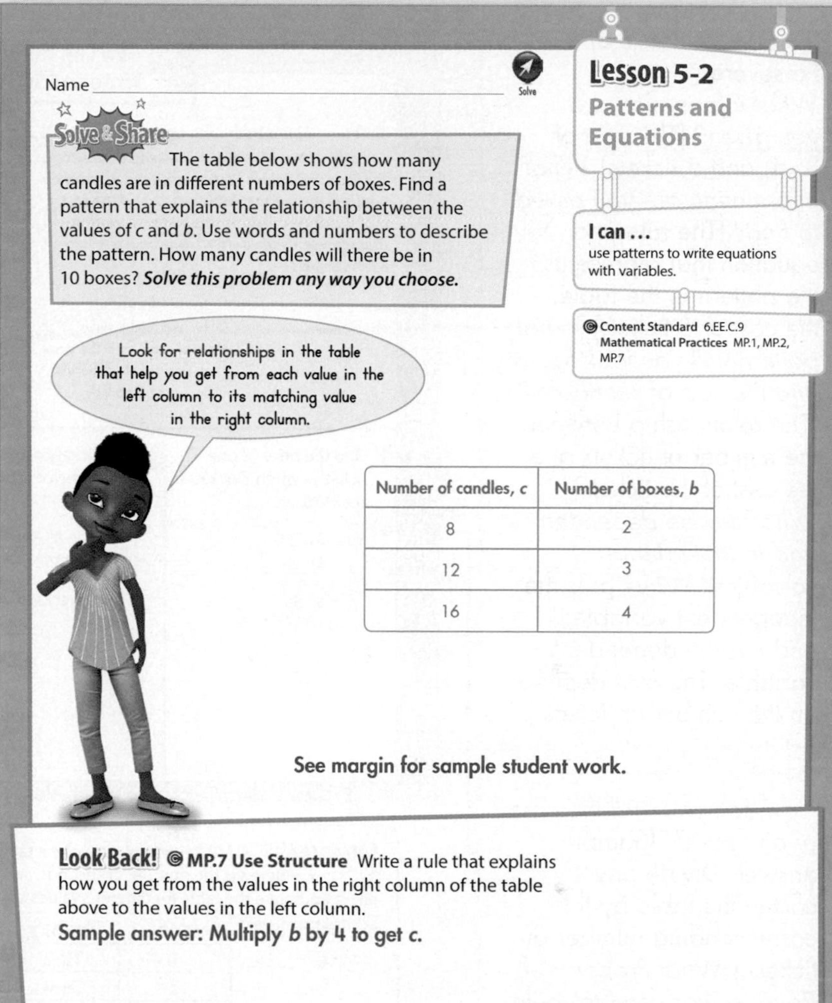

Name

**Solve & Share** The table below shows how many candles are in different numbers of boxes. Find a pattern that explains the relationship between the values of *c* and *b*. Use words and numbers to describe the pattern. How many candles will there be in 10 boxes? ***Solve this problem any way you choose.***

**Lesson 5-2**
**Patterns and Equations**

**I can ...**
use patterns to write equations with variables.

Content Standard 6.EE.C.9
Mathematical Practices MP.1, MP.2, MP.7

Look for relationships in the table that help you get from each value in the left column to its matching value in the right column.

| Number of candles, *c* | Number of boxes, *b* |
|---|---|
| 8 | 2 |
| 12 | 3 |
| 16 | 4 |

**See margin for sample student work.**

**Look Back!** **MP.7 Use Structure** Write a rule that explains how you get from the values in the right column of the table above to the values in the left column.
**Sample answer: Multiply *b* by 4 to get *c*.**

Digital Resources at PearsonRealize.com   Topic 5 | Lesson 5-2   233

## Analyze Student Work

**Jay's Work**

Each value for $c$ is four times as much as each value for $b$.
So, each value for $b$ is one fourth as much as each value for $c$.

$$\frac{1}{4}c = b$$

Let $b = 10$. $\frac{1}{4}c = 10$, so $c = 40$.

There will be 40 candles in 10 boxes.

Jay correctly explains how to use multiplication to relate the variables.

**Dan's Work**

Divide each value of $c$ by 4 to get $b$.

$$c \div 4 = b$$

For $b = 10$: $c \div 4 = 10$, so $c = 40$.

In 10 boxes, there will be 40 candles.

Dan correctly explains how to use division to relate the variables.

# DEVELOP: VISUAL LEARNING

The *Visual Learning Bridge* connects students' thinking in Solve & Share to important math ideas in the lesson. Use the *Visual Learning Bridge* to make these ideas explicit. Also available as a *Visual Learning Animation Plus* at PearsonRealize.com

Learn Glossary

**MP.1 Make Sense and Persevere**
*What information are you given?* [The cost of 3, 4, and 5 tickets] *What information are you asked to find?* [The rule and equation that represents the pattern in the table, the cost of 6 tickets] *What pattern will you look for to find the cost of six tickets?* [The relationship between the number of tickets and the cost of the tickets] *What are the dependent and independent variables? Why?* [*n* is the independent variable, and *c* is the dependent variable. The cost depends on the number of tickets.]

*How can you find the cost of one ticket?* [Sample answer: Divide any cost in the table by the corresponding number of tickets.] *What Property of Equality was used to solve the equation?* [The Division Property of Equality]

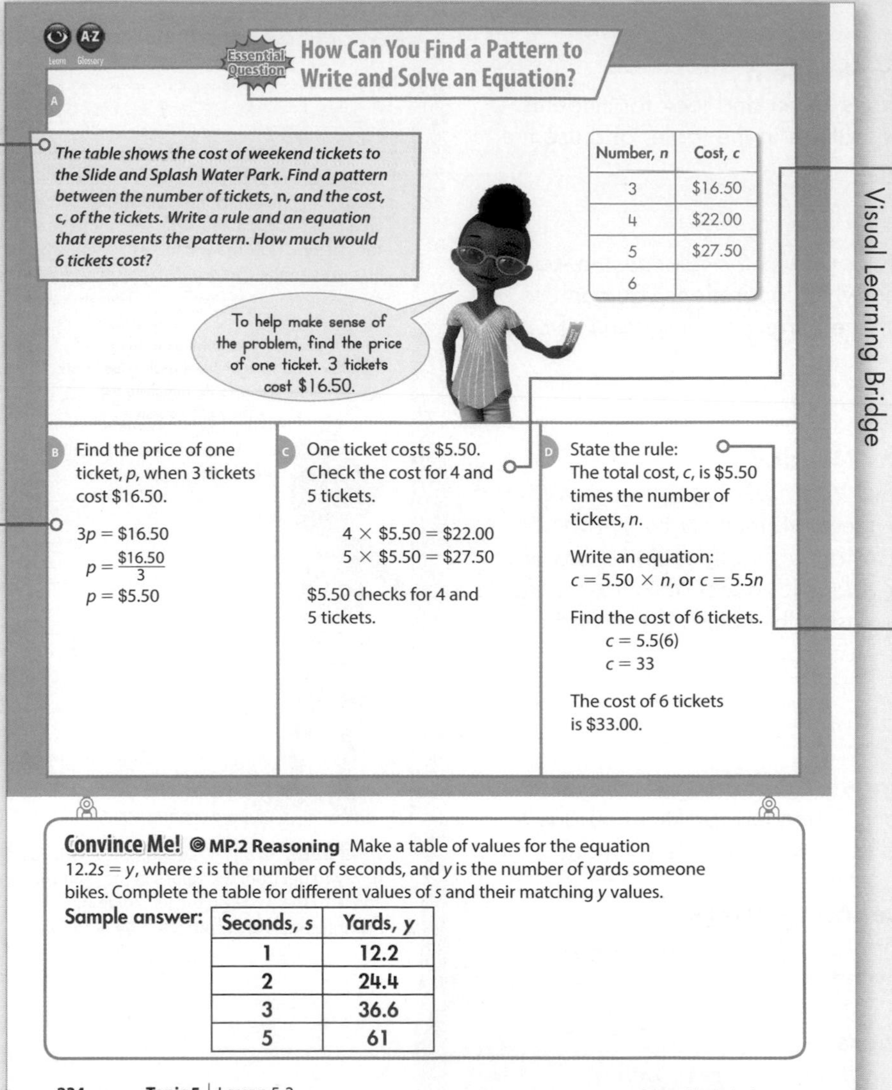

Learn Glossary

Essential Question **How Can You Find a Pattern to Write and Solve an Equation?**

A

*The table shows the cost of weekend tickets to the Slide and Splash Water Park. Find a pattern between the number of tickets, n, and the cost, c, of the tickets. Write a rule and an equation that represents the pattern. How much would 6 tickets cost?*

| Number, *n* | Cost, *c* |
|---|---|
| 3 | $16.50 |
| 4 | $22.00 |
| 5 | $27.50 |
| 6 | |

To help make sense of the problem, find the price of one ticket. 3 tickets cost $16.50.

Visual Learning Bridge

B Find the price of one ticket, *p*, when 3 tickets cost $16.50.

$3p = \$16.50$

$p = \frac{\$16.50}{3}$

$p = \$5.50$

C One ticket costs $5.50. Check the cost for 4 and 5 tickets.

$4 \times \$5.50 = \$22.00$

$5 \times \$5.50 = \$27.50$

$5.50 checks for 4 and 5 tickets.

D State the rule: The total cost, *c*, is $5.50 times the number of tickets, *n*.

Write an equation: $c = 5.50 \times n$, or $c = 5.5n$

Find the cost of 6 tickets.

$c = 5.5(6)$

$c = 33$

The cost of 6 tickets is $33.00.

**Convince Me!** MP.2 Reasoning Make a table of values for the equation $12.2s = y$, where *s* is the number of seconds, and *y* is the number of yards someone bikes. Complete the table for different values of *s* and their matching *y* values.

**Sample answer:**

| Seconds, *s* | Yards, *y* |
|---|---|
| 1 | 12.2 |
| 2 | 24.4 |
| 3 | 36.6 |
| 5 | 61 |

234 Topic 5 | Lesson 5-2 © Pearson Education, Inc. 6

*Why is it important to check the costs for 4 and 5 tickets?* [You must make sure the rule works for all the related numbers in the table.]

**MP.7 Use Structure**
*Why can you write $5.50 as 5.5 in the equation?* [Dropping the zero at the end of a decimal does not change the value of the decimal.] *How was the equation used to find the cost of 6 tickets?* [Substitute 6 for *n* and then multiply $5.5 \times 6$. Write the answer in dollars.]

**Convince Me! MP.2 Reason Quantitatively** Students use reasoning to understand the relationship between quantities in a real-world context, represented as an equation. They use the given equation to create a table of values showing corresponding values of the two related variables.

Essential Question Revisit the Essential Question. Finding patterns in a table can be a trial-and-error process. Start by identifying possible rules for the relationship between one pair of related values. Then test the possible rules against the other pairs of values to find the rule that works for all pairs. Then write an equation to express this relationship between the two quantities.

## QUICK CHECK

Check mark indicates items for prescribing differentiation on the next page.
Item 6 is worth 1 point. Items 12 and 13 are each worth up to 2 points.

20–30 min

Practice Buddy

Tools

Assessment

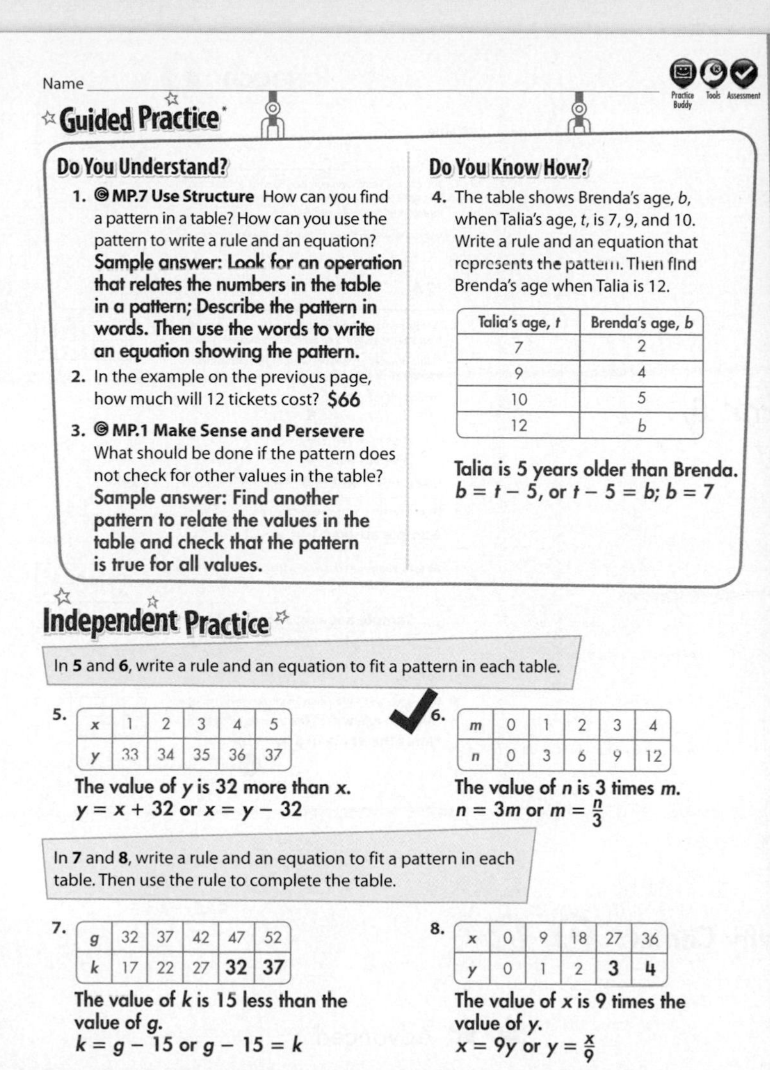

Name

### Guided Practice*

**Do You Understand?**

1. **MP.7 Use Structure** How can you find a pattern in a table? How can you use the pattern to write a rule and an equation? **Sample answer: Look for an operation that relates the numbers in the table in a pattern; Describe the pattern in words. Then use the words to write an equation showing the pattern.**
2. In the example on the previous page, how much will 12 tickets cost? **$66**
3. **MP.1 Make Sense and Persevere** What should be done if the pattern does not check for other values in the table? **Sample answer: Find another pattern to relate the values in the table and check that the pattern is true for all values.**

**Do You Know How?**

4. The table shows Brenda's age, $b$, when Talia's age, $t$, is 7, 9, and 10. Write a rule and an equation that represents the pattern. Then find Brenda's age when Talia is 12.

| Talia's age, $t$ | Brenda's age, $b$ |
|---|---|
| 7 | 2 |
| 9 | 4 |
| 10 | 5 |
| 12 | $b$ |

**Talia is 5 years older than Brenda. $b = t - 5$, or $t - 5 = b$; $b = 7$**

### Independent Practice*

In **5** and **6**, write a rule and an equation to fit a pattern in each table.

5.

| $x$ | 1 | 2 | 3 | 4 | 5 |
|---|---|---|---|---|---|
| $y$ | 33 | 34 | 35 | 36 | 37 |

**The value of $y$ is 32 more than $x$. $y = x + 32$ or $x = y - 32$**

6.

| $m$ | 0 | 1 | 2 | 3 | 4 |
|---|---|---|---|---|---|
| $n$ | 0 | 3 | 6 | 9 | 12 |

**The value of $n$ is 3 times $m$. $n = 3m$ or $m = \frac{n}{3}$**

In **7** and **8**, write a rule and an equation to fit a pattern in each table. Then use the rule to complete the table.

7.

| $g$ | 32 | 37 | 42 | 47 | 52 |
|---|---|---|---|---|---|
| $k$ | 17 | 22 | 27 | **32** | **37** |

**The value of $k$ is 15 less than the value of $g$. $k = g - 15$ or $g - 15 = k$**

8.

| $x$ | 0 | 9 | 18 | 27 | 36 |
|---|---|---|---|---|---|
| $y$ | 0 | 1 | 2 | **3** | **4** |

**The value of $x$ is 9 times the value of $y$. $x = 9y$ or $y = \frac{x}{9}$**

*For another example, see Set B on page 265.



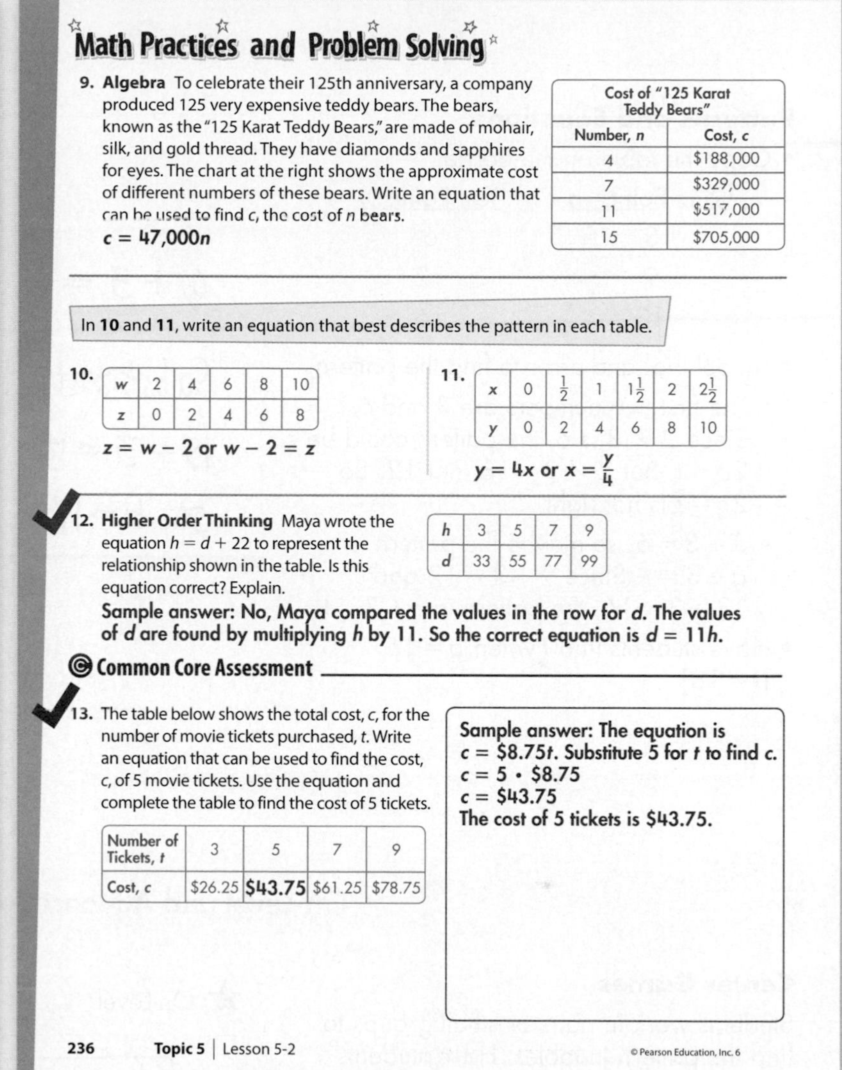

### Math Practices and Problem Solving

9. **Algebra** To celebrate their 125th anniversary, a company produced 125 very expensive teddy bears. The bears, known as the "125 Karat Teddy Bears," are made of mohair, silk, and gold thread. They have diamonds and sapphires for eyes. The chart at the right shows the approximate cost of different numbers of these bears. Write an equation that can be used to find $c$, the cost of $n$ bears. **$c = 47{,}000n$**

| Cost of "125 Karat Teddy Bears" | |
|---|---|
| Number, $n$ | Cost, $c$ |
| 4 | $188,000 |
| 7 | $329,000 |
| 11 | $517,000 |
| 15 | $705,000 |

In **10** and **11**, write an equation that best describes the pattern in each table.

10.

| $w$ | 2 | 4 | 6 | 8 | 10 |
|---|---|---|---|---|---|
| $z$ | 0 | 2 | 4 | 6 | 8 |

**$z = w - 2$ or $w - 2 = z$**

11.

| $x$ | 0 | $\frac{1}{2}$ | 1 | $1\frac{1}{2}$ | 2 | $2\frac{1}{2}$ |
|---|---|---|---|---|---|---|
| $y$ | 0 | 2 | 4 | 6 | 8 | 10 |

**$y = 4x$ or $x = \frac{y}{4}$**

12. **Higher Order Thinking** Maya wrote the equation $h = d + 22$ to represent the relationship shown in the table. Is this equation correct? Explain.

| $h$ | 3 | 5 | 7 | 9 |
|---|---|---|---|---|
| $d$ | 33 | 55 | 77 | 99 |

**Sample answer: No, Maya compared the values in the row for $d$. The values of $d$ are found by multiplying $h$ by 11. So the correct equation is $d = 11h$.**

**Common Core Assessment**

13. The table below shows the total cost, $c$, for the number of movie tickets purchased, $t$. Write an equation that can be used to find the cost, $c$, of 5 movie tickets. Use the equation and complete the table to find the cost of 5 tickets.

| Number of Tickets, $t$ | 3 | 5 | 7 | 9 |
|---|---|---|---|---|
| Cost, $c$ | $26.25 | **$43.75** | $61.25 | $78.75 |

**Sample answer: The equation is $c = \$8.75t$. Substitute 5 for $t$ to find $c$. $c = 5 \cdot \$8.75$ $c = \$43.75$ The cost of 5 tickets is $43.75.**





**Error Intervention: Item 2**

**If** students have difficulty finding the cost of 12 tickets,

**then** ask: *How can you use the equation you found in Box D to find the cost of 12 tickets?* [Substitute 12 for $n$ in the equation and evaluate to find the cost, $c$.]

**Item 3 MP.1 Make Sense and Persevere** Students gain critical experience with the mathematical practice of perseverance as they find patterns in tables. If their initial rules for patterns do not check for all related values in a table, they must find another possible rule and check all related values again.

**Reteaching** Assign Reteaching Set B on p. 265.

**Item 5** As students look for patterns, they may note that the values of $x$ and $y$ each increase by one as they look across the table. Remind students that they are not looking for patterns as they move from one $x$-value or $y$-value to the next. They are looking for an operation that relates the $x$-value to the $y$-value in each column.

**Items 6–8** It may be helpful for some students to use a process as they look for patterns. Suggest that they begin by adding a number to value of one variable to get the value of the other variable. Then have them test the whether the pattern is true for each subsequent pairs of values. If it does not work for one of the pairs, have students repeat the process using another operation such as multiplication.

**Item 12 Higher Order Thinking** Some students may recognize that Maya's error is that she wrote a rule that represents the pattern generated by the values for $d$, instead of analyzing how the values of $h$ and $d$ are related.

**Multi-Step Problems** *Page 236 Item 13; Page 238 Items 12 and 13*

# ASSESS AND DIFFERENTIATE

Use the **QUICK CHECK** on the previous page to prescribe differentiated instruction.

**I Intervention** 0–3 points on the Quick Check

**O On-Level** 4 points on the Quick Check

**A Advanced** 5 points on the Quick Check

## Intervention Activity 

### Patterns and Equations

- Copy the table on the board.

| Quiz Points, $q$ | Test Points, $t$ |
|---|---|
| 3 | 6 |
| 9 | 12 |
| 13 | 16 |

- Model trial and error to find the pattern.
  - The first two numbers are 3 and 6, Since $2 \times 3$ is 6, the pattern could be $2q = t$. But $2 \times 9 = 18$, not 12. So $2q = t$ is not right.
  - $3 + 3 = 6$, so maybe the pattern is $q + 3 = t$. Since $9 + 3 = 12$ and $13 + 3 = 16$, the pattern is $q + 3 = t$.
- Have students find $t$ when $q = 15$. [$t = 18$]

$q + 3 = t$

Substitute 15 for $q$.

$15 + 3 = t$

so, $t = 18$.

## Reteach I

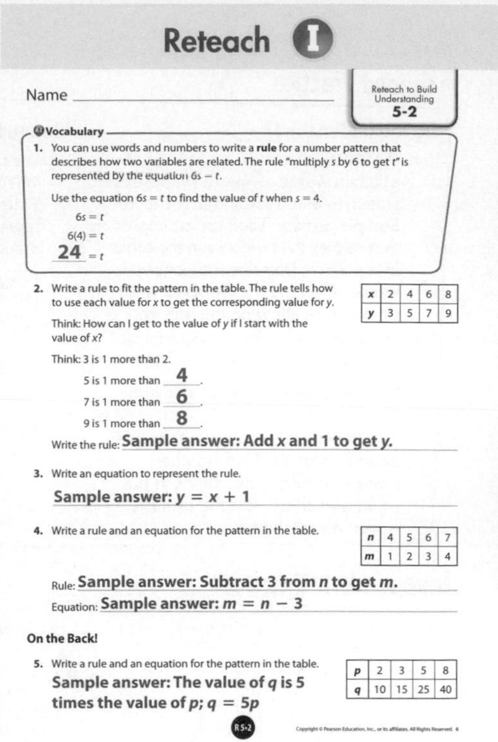

Name ____________

Reteach to Build Understanding 5-2

**Vocabulary**

1. You can use words and numbers to write a **rule** for a number pattern that describes how two variables are related. The rule "multiply $s$ by 6 to get $t$" is represented by the equation $6s = t$.

   Use the equation $6s = t$ to find the value of $t$ when $s = 4$.

   $6s = t$

   $6(4) = t$

   **24** $= t$

2. Write a rule to fit the pattern in the table. The rule tells how to use each value for $x$ to get the corresponding value for $y$.

| x | 2 | 4 | 6 | 8 |
|---|---|---|---|---|
| y | 3 | 5 | 7 | 9 |

   Think: How can I get to the value of $y$ if I start with the value of $x$?

   Think: 3 is 1 more than 2.

   5 is 1 more than **4**.

   7 is 1 more than **6**.

   9 is 1 more than **8**.

   Write the rule: **Sample answer: Add $x$ and 1 to get $y$.**

3. Write an equation to represent the rule.

   **Sample answer: $y = x + 1$**

4. Write a rule and an equation for the pattern in the table.

| n | 4 | 5 | 6 | 7 |
|---|---|---|---|---|
| m | 1 | 2 | 3 | 4 |

   Rule: **Sample answer: Subtract 3 from $n$ to get $m$.**

   Equation: **Sample answer: $m = n - 3$**

**On the Back!**

5. Write a rule and an equation for the pattern in the table.

| p | 2 | 3 | 5 | 8 |
|---|---|---|---|---|
| q | 10 | 15 | 25 | 40 |

   **Sample answer: The value of $q$ is 5 times the value of $p$; $q = 5p$**

R 5-2



## On-Level and Advanced Activity Centers  A

### Center Games

Students work in pairs or small groups to find the pattern in tables. Have students record the patterns they try as they play the game.

★ On-Level

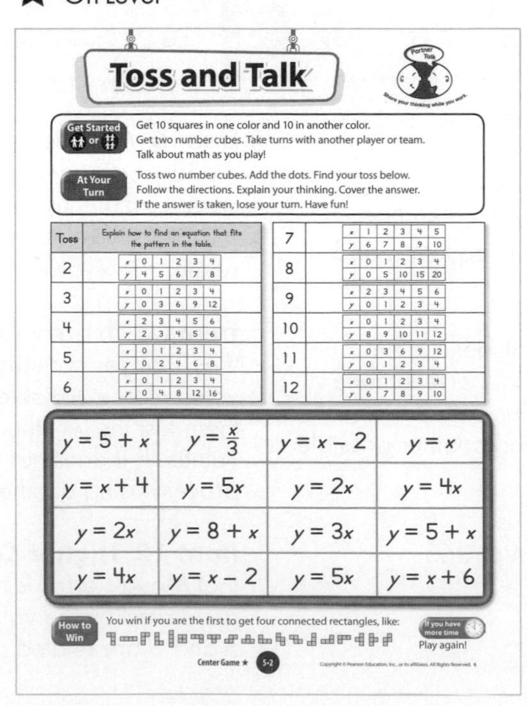

**Toss and Talk**

Share your thinking while you work.

**Get Started** Get 10 squares in one color and 10 in another color. Get two number cubes. Take turns with another player or team. Talk about math as you play!

**At Your Turn** Toss two number cubes. Add the dots. Find your toss below. Follow the directions. Explain your thinking. Cover the answer. If the answer is taken, lose your turn. Have fun!

Explain how to find an equation that fits the pattern in the table.

| Toss | | | | | | |
|---|---|---|---|---|---|---|
| 2 | x | 0 | 1 | 2 | 3 | 4 |
| | y | 4 | 5 | 6 | 7 | 8 |
| 3 | x | 0 | 1 | 2 | 3 | 4 |
| | y | 0 | 3 | 6 | 9 | 12 |
| 4 | x | 2 | 3 | 4 | 5 | 6 |
| | y | 2 | 3 | 4 | 5 | 6 |
| 5 | x | 0 | 1 | 2 | 3 | 4 |
| | y | 0 | 2 | 4 | 6 | 8 |
| 6 | x | 0 | 1 | 2 | 3 | 4 |
| | y | 0 | 4 | 8 | 12 | 16 |
| 7 | x | 1 | 2 | 3 | 4 | 5 |
| | y | 6 | 7 | 8 | 9 | 10 |
| 8 | x | 0 | 1 | 2 | 3 | 4 |
| | y | 0 | 5 | 10 | 15 | 20 |
| 9 | x | 2 | 3 | 4 | 5 | 6 |
| | y | 0 | 1 | 2 | 3 | 4 |
| 10 | x | 0 | 1 | 2 | 3 | 4 |
| | y | 8 | 9 | 10 | 11 | 12 |
| 11 | x | 0 | 3 | 6 | 9 | 12 |
| | y | 0 | 1 | 2 | 3 | 4 |
| 12 | x | 0 | 1 | 2 | 3 | 4 |
| | y | 6 | 7 | 8 | 9 | 10 |

| | | | |
|---|---|---|---|
| $y = 5 + x$ | $y = \frac{x}{3}$ | $y = x - 2$ | $y = x$ |
| $y = x + 4$ | $y = 5x$ | $y = 2x$ | $y = 4x$ |
| $y = 2x$ | $y = 8 + x$ | $y = 3x$ | $y = 5 + x$ |
| $y = 4x$ | $y = x - 2$ | $y = 5x$ | $y = x + 6$ |

**How to Win** You win if you are the first to get four connected rectangles, like:

If you have more time: Play again!

Center Game ★ 5-2

★★ Advanced

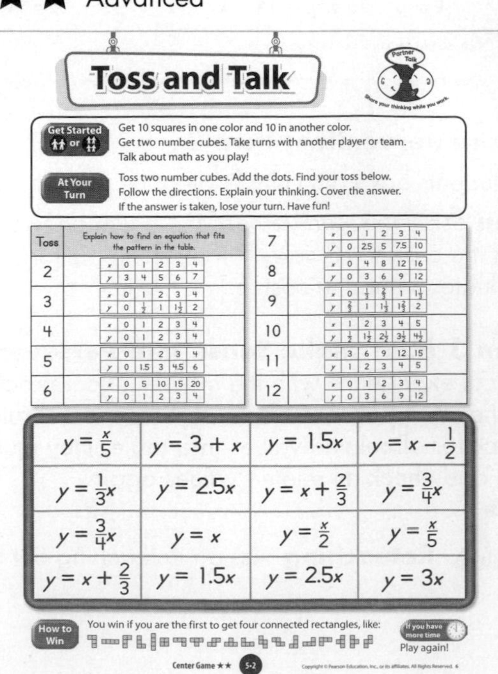

**Toss and Talk**

Share your thinking while you work.

**Get Started** Get 10 squares in one color and 10 in another color. Get two number cubes. Take turns with another player or team. Talk about math as you play!

**At Your Turn** Toss two number cubes. Add the dots. Find your toss below. Follow the directions. Explain your thinking. Cover the answer. If the answer is taken, lose your turn. Have fun!

Explain how to find an equation that fits the pattern in the table.

| Toss | | | | | | |
|---|---|---|---|---|---|---|
| 2 | x | 0 | 1 | 2 | 3 | 4 |
| | y | 3 | 4 | 5 | 6 | 7 |
| 3 | x | 0 | 1 | 2 | 3 | 4 |
| | y | 0 | $\frac{1}{2}$ | 1 | $1\frac{1}{2}$ | 2 |
| 4 | x | 0 | 1 | 2 | 3 | 4 |
| | y | 0 | 1 | 2 | 3 | 4 |
| 5 | x | 0 | 1 | 2 | 3 | 4 |
| | y | 0 | 1.5 | 3 | 4.5 | 6 |
| 6 | x | 0 | 5 | 10 | 15 | 20 |
| | y | 0 | 1 | 2 | 3 | 4 |
| 7 | x | 0 | 1 | 2 | 3 | 4 |
| | y | 0 | 2.5 | 5 | 7.5 | 10 |
| 8 | x | 0 | 4 | 8 | 12 | 16 |
| | y | 0 | 3 | 6 | 9 | 12 |
| 9 | x | 0 | $\frac{1}{3}$ | $\frac{2}{3}$ | 1 | $1\frac{1}{3}$ |
| | y | $\frac{2}{3}$ | 1 | $1\frac{1}{3}$ | $1\frac{2}{3}$ | 2 |
| 10 | x | 1 | 2 | 3 | 4 | 5 |
| | y | $\frac{1}{2}$ | $1\frac{1}{2}$ | $2\frac{1}{2}$ | $3\frac{1}{2}$ | $4\frac{1}{2}$ |
| 11 | x | 3 | 6 | 9 | 12 | 15 |
| | y | 1 | 2 | 3 | 4 | 5 |
| 12 | x | 0 | 1 | 2 | 3 | 4 |
| | y | 0 | 3 | 6 | 9 | 12 |

| | | | |
|---|---|---|---|
| $y = \frac{x}{5}$ | $y = 3 + x$ | $y = 1.5x$ | $y = x - \frac{1}{2}$ |
| $y = \frac{1}{3}x$ | $y = 2.5x$ | $y = x + \frac{2}{3}$ | $y = \frac{3}{4}x$ |
| $y = \frac{3}{4}x$ | $y = x$ | $y = \frac{x}{2}$ | $y = \frac{x}{5}$ |
| $y = x + \frac{2}{3}$ | $y = 1.5x$ | $y = 2.5x$ | $y = 3x$ |

**How to Win** You win if you are the first to get four connected rectangles, like:

If you have more time: Play again!

Center Game ★★ 5-2

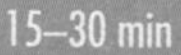


**TIMING**

The time allocated to Step 3 will depend on the teacher's instructional decisions and differentiation routines.

15–30 min

 Help  Practice Buddy  Tools Games

## Technology Center    

 Tools  Games

### Math Tools and Math Games

A link to a specific math tools activity or math game to use with this lesson is provided at PearsonRealize.com.

## Leveled Assignment  Items 1–8, 11, 13  Items 3–9, 11–13  Items 4–13

Name ______________

### Homework & Practice 5-2

**Patterns and Equations**

**Another Look!**

Write a rule and an equation for the pattern in the table.

| $j$ | 1 | 4 | 7 | 8 | 9 |
|---|---|---|---|---|---|
| $m$ | 3 | 12 | 21 | 24 | 27 |

**Think:** 3 is $1 \times 3$ 12 is $4 \times 3$

State a theory: It seems that $3j = m$.

Test the other pairs: $7 \times 3 = 21$ ✔ $8 \times 3 = 24$ ✔ $9 \times 3 = 27$ ✔

Write a rule: The value of $m$ is the value of $j$ times 3.

Write an equation: $m = j \cdot 3$, or $m = 3j$

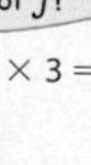

In **1–4**, write a rule and an equation for the pattern in each table.

**1.**

| $x$ | 3 | 6 | 11 | 13 | 15 |
|---|---|---|---|---|---|
| $y$ | 5 | 8 | 13 | 15 | 17 |

**The value of $y$ is 2 more than the value of $x$; $y = x + 2$ or $x = y - 2$**

**2.**

| $x$ | 2 | 5 | 6 | 8 | 9 |
|---|---|---|---|---|---|
| $y$ | 6 | 15 | 18 | 24 | 27 |

**The value of $y$ is the value of $x$ times 3; $y = 3x$ or $x = \frac{y}{3}$**

**3.**

| $x$ | 4 | 12 | 20 | 36 | 40 |
|---|---|---|---|---|---|
| $y$ | 1 | 3 | 5 | 9 | 10 |

**The value of $y$ is the value of $x$ divided by 4; $y = x \div 4$ or $x = 4y$**

**4.**

| $x$ | 5 | 7 | 9 | 10 | 12 |
|---|---|---|---|---|---|
| $y$ | 0 | 2 | 4 | 5 | 7 |

**The value of $y$ is 5 less than the value of $x$; $y = x - 5$ or $x = y + 5$**

**5.** Complete the table to show a pattern. Then write a rule and an equation for the pattern.
**Answers will vary. Check student's work.**

| $x$ | | | | | |
|---|---|---|---|---|---|
| $y$ | | | | | |

**6.** Explain how you would find the pattern in this table, and how you would write a rule and an equation for the pattern.

| $x$ | 4 | 5 | 7 | 10 | 12 |
|---|---|---|---|---|---|
| $y$ | 0 | 1 | 3 | 6 | 8 |

**Sample answer: For every pair of numbers, you could subtract 4 from $x$ to get $y$. The rule is *The value of* y *is 4 less than the value of* x. The equation is $y = x - 4$.**



**7. MP.2 Reasoning** The Gadget Factory sells winkydiddles. The table shows the cost, $c$, of $w$ winkydiddles. If each winkydiddle costs the same amount, what is the price of each winkydiddle?
**\$3.50**

| Number of Winkydiddles, $w$ | 7 | 12 | 26 | 31 |
|---|---|---|---|---|
| Cost, $c$ | \$24.50 | \$42.00 | \$91.00 | \$108.50 |

**8.** Write an equation that can be used to find $c$, the cost of $w$ winkydiddles.
**$c = 3.5w$**

For **9** and **10**, write an equation that best describes the pattern in each table.

**9.**

| $n$ | 4 | 6 | 8 | 10 | 12 |
|---|---|---|---|---|---|
| $v$ | 11 | 13 | 15 | 17 | 19 |

**$v = n + 7$ or $n = v - 7$**

**10.**

| $x$ | 5 | 6 | 7 | 10 | 11 | 12 |
|---|---|---|---|---|---|---|
| $y$ | 2.5 | 3 | 3.5 | 5 | 5.5 | 6 |

**$y = \frac{x}{2}$ or $x = 2y$**

**11.** Write a real-world problem that could be represented in the table below.

| $x$ | 1 | 2 | 3 | 4 |
|---|---|---|---|---|
| $y$ | 2.5 | 5 | 7.5 | 10 |

**Sample answer: The cost, $y$, of hot dogs is \$2.50 times the number of hot dogs, $x$.**

**12. Higher Order Thinking** All the values of $x$ in a table are greater than the corresponding values of $y$. Write a rule that fits this situation. Then write an equation to go along with the rule.
**Sample answer: Rule, the value of $x$ is 4 times the value of $y$; $x = 4y$ or $\frac{1}{4}x = y$**

### Common Core Assessment

**13.** The table below shows the total cost, $c$, for the number of raffle tickets purchased, $t$. Write an equation that can be used to find the cost, $c$, of 10 raffle tickets. Use the equation and complete the table to find the cost of 10 tickets.

| Number of Tickets, $t$ | 5 | 8 | 10 | 11 |
|---|---|---|---|---|
| Cost, $c$ | \$417.50 | \$668 | **\$835** | \$918.50 |

**Sample answer: The equation is: $c = 83.50t$; $c = 10 \cdot 83.50 = 835$. So, the cost of 10 tickets is \$835.**

# LESSON 5-3

# MORE PATTERNS AND EQUATIONS

## DIGITAL RESOURCES PearsonRealize.com

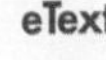
eText — Student and Teacher eTexts

PD — Listen and Look For Lesson Video

Think — Today's Challenge

Solve — Solve and Share

Learn — Visual Learning Animation Plus

Glossary — Animated Glossary

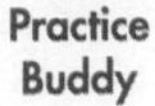
Practice Buddy — Online Personalized Practice

Tools — Math Tools

Assessment — Quick Check

Help — Another Look Homework Video

Games — Math Games

## LESSON OVERVIEW  FOCUS • COHERENCE • RIGOR

### FOCUS

**Domain 6.EE** Expressions and Equations

**Cluster 6.EE.C** Represent and analyze quantitative relationships between dependent and independent variables.

**Content Standard 6.EE.C.9** Use variables to represent two quantities in a real-world problem that change in relationship to one another; write an equation to express one quantity, thought of as the dependent variable, in terms of the other quantity, thought of as the independent variable. Analyze the relationship between the dependent and independent variables using graphs and tables, and relate these to the equation.

**Mathematical Practices MP.2, MP.4, MP.7, MP.8**

**Objective** Analyze the relationships between variables by using tables and write equations to represent the relationships.

**Essential Understanding** Patterns can help identify the relationship between quantities and be used to write an equation that describes the relationship.

### COHERENCE

In the previous lesson, students identified patterns in tables and wrote corresponding rules and one-step equations to describe the related quantities. In this lesson, they continue looking for patterns in tables and write equations involving two operations to describe the relationship between the dependent and independent variables. They then use the equations they write to solve problems in a real-world context. In Lessons 5-4 and 5-5, students will graph linear equations with two variables, connecting a table, equation, and graph as multiple representations of the same relationship between two quantities.

### RIGOR

This lesson emphasizes a blend of **conceptual understanding** and **procedural skill**. Students will apply what they know about patterns and equations to analyze more complex patterns and reason quantitatively to represent them with two-step equations.

 PD Watch the Listen and Look For Lesson Video.

## MATH ANYTIME

### Daily Common Core Review

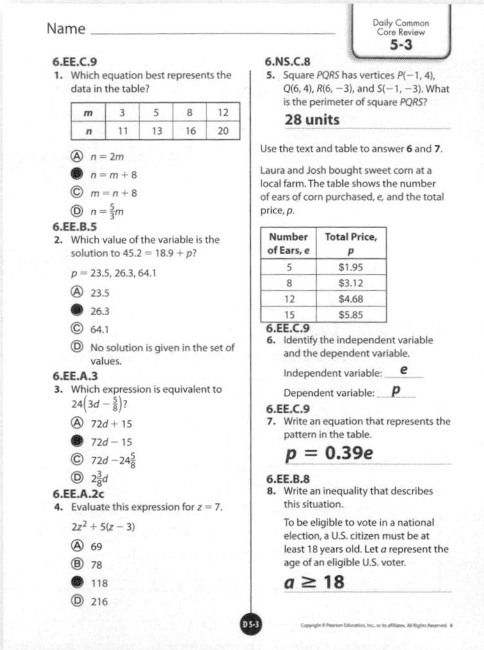
Name ______

Daily Common Core Review 5-3

6.EE.C.9

1. Which equation best represents the data in the table?

| m | 3 | 5 | 8 | 12 |
|---|---|---|---|---|
| n | 11 | 13 | 16 | 20 |

Ⓐ $n = 2m$
● $n = m + 8$
Ⓒ $m = n + 8$
Ⓓ $n = \frac{5}{3}m$

6.EE.B.5

2. Which value of the variable is the solution to $45.2 = 18.9 + p$?

$p = 23.5, 26.3, 64.1$

Ⓐ 23.5
● 26.3
Ⓒ 64.1
Ⓓ No solution is given in the set of values.

6.EE.A.3

3. Which expression is equivalent to $24\left(3d - \frac{5}{8}\right)$?

Ⓐ $72d + 15$
● $72d - 15$
Ⓒ $72d - 24\frac{5}{8}$
Ⓓ $2\frac{3}{8}d$

6.EE.A.2c

4. Evaluate this expression for $z = 7$.

$2z^2 + 5(z - 3)$

Ⓐ 69
Ⓑ 78
● 118
Ⓓ 216

6.NS.C.8

5. Square $PQRS$ has vertices $P(-1, 4)$, $Q(6, 4)$, $R(6, -3)$, and $S(-1, -3)$. What is the perimeter of square $PQRS$?

**28 units**

Use the text and table to answer **6** and **7**.

Laura and Josh bought sweet corn at a local farm. The table shows the number of ears of corn purchased, $e$, and the total price, $p$.

| Number of Ears, $e$ | Total Price, $p$ |
|---|---|
| 5 | $1.95 |
| 8 | $3.12 |
| 12 | $4.68 |
| 15 | $5.85 |

6.EE.C.9

6. Identify the independent variable and the dependent variable.

Independent variable: $e$

Dependent variable: $p$

6.EE.C.9

7. Write an equation that represents the pattern in the table.

$p = 0.39e$

6.EE.B.8

8. Write an inequality that describes this situation.

To be eligible to vote in a national election, a U.S. citizen must be at least 18 years old. Let $a$ represent the age of an eligible U.S. voter.

$a \geq 18$

D5-3

### Today's Challenge

Think Use the Topic 5 problems any time during this topic.

## ENGLISH LANGUAGE LEARNERS 

**Reading** Use reading supports such as illustrations.

*Use with the Visual Learning Bridge on Student's Edition p. 240.*

Read Box A. Point to the illustration. *How does this illustration explain the problem?* [Ethan repays $5 each week.] *A table is another way to represent the problem situation.*

**Beginning** Read Box B to students. Point to the first row. *Ethan owes $75. He pays $5 each week.* Point to the second row. *After week 1, he owes $70.* Continue the process to find how much Ethan owes after 12 weeks. *What pattern do you see in the table?* Students will respond with one or two words.

**Intermediate** Read Box B with students. Point to the first row. *Ethan owes $75. He pays $5 each week.* Ask students to look at the remaining information in the table. *What pattern do you see?* Students will respond using complete sentences. Instruct students to work with partners to complete the table through Week 12.

**Advanced** Read Box B with students. Ask students to analyze the table. *What pattern do you see?* Have students explain patterns in the table. Instruct students to complete the table through Week 12.

**Summarize** Patterns in tables can be extended to solve problems.

# DEVELOP: PROBLEM-BASED LEARNING

**COHERENCE: Engage learners by connecting prior knowledge to new ideas.**
Students extend their work with patterns, tables, and equations as they investigate more complex relationships between two variables.

10–15 min

Solve

## BEFORE

**1. Pose the Solve-and-Share Problem**
**MP.2 Reason Quantitatively** Listen and look for students who create a table to show related values and describe the relationship between the two quantities, *c* and *g*.

**2. Build Understanding**
*What does $c = 3 + 2g$ represent?* [The total cost for bowling is $3 for shoes plus $2 for each game played.] *Which variable depends on the other?* [The cost, *c*, depends on the number of games, *g*, that are played.]

## DURING

**3. Ask Guiding Questions As Needed**
*How can you complete the table?* [Write the number of games, 1, 2, 3, and 4, in the first column. Then use each value for *g* in the equation to find the value for *c*.] *What patterns do you see in each column? Explain why.* [The *g*-values increase by 1 because the number of games increases by 1. The *c*-values increase by 2 because each additional game costs $2.]

## AFTER

**4. Share and Discuss Solutions**
Start with students' solutions. If needed, project Sylvia's work to discuss how to describe the pattern in the table.

**5. Transition to the Visual Learning Bridge**
*You can use tables and equations to find values of related quantities in a pattern.*

**6. Extension for Early Finishers**
*What is the pattern if the shoe rental is $5 and each game is $2.50?* [Each value of *c* is 5 more than 2.5 times the value of *g*.]

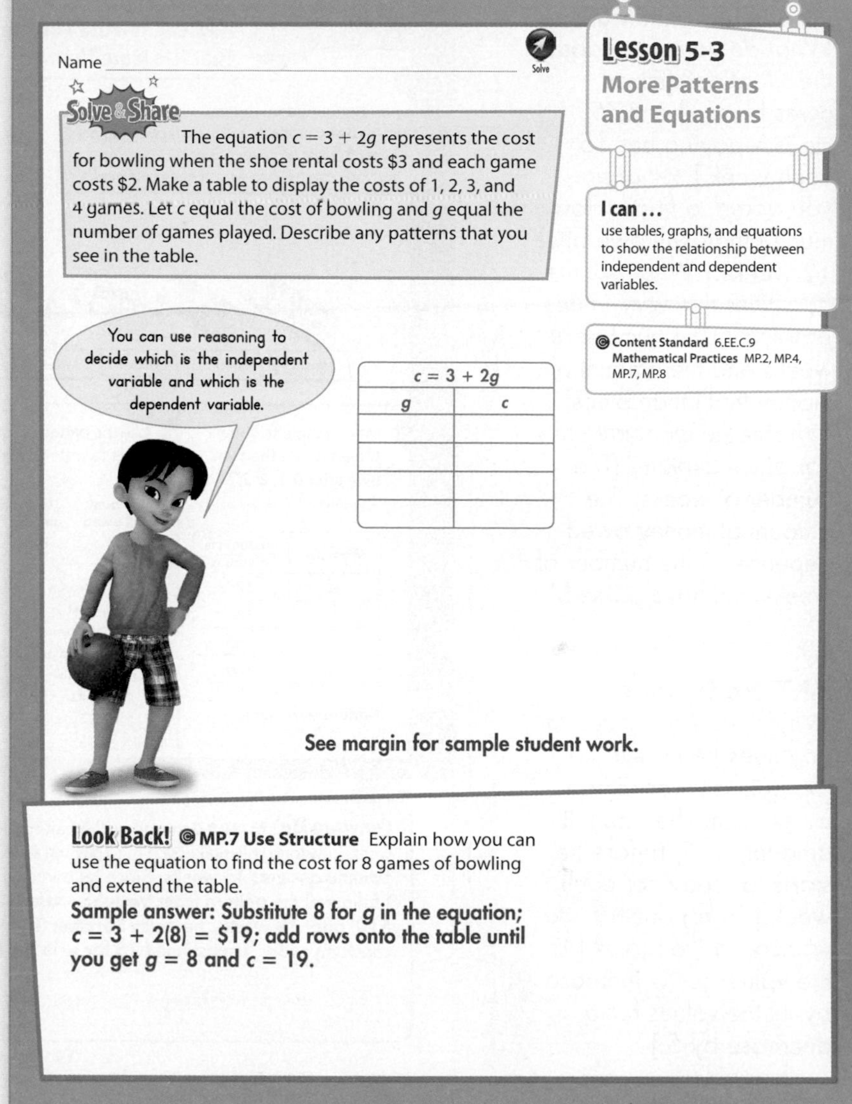

Name

Lesson 5-3
More Patterns and Equations

Solve & Share

The equation $c = 3 + 2g$ represents the cost for bowling when the shoe rental costs $3 and each game costs $2. Make a table to display the costs of 1, 2, 3, and 4 games. Let *c* equal the cost of bowling and *g* equal the number of games played. Describe any patterns that you see in the table.

I can … use tables, graphs, and equations to show the relationship between independent and dependent variables.

Content Standard 6.EE.C.9
Mathematical Practices MP.2, MP.4, MP.7, MP.8



| $c = 3 + 2g$ | |
|---|---|
| *g* | *c* |
| | |
| | |
| | |
| | |

See margin for sample student work.

**Look Back!** **MP.7 Use Structure** Explain how you can use the equation to find the cost for 8 games of bowling and extend the table.
**Sample answer: Substitute 8 for *g* in the equation; $c = 3 + 2(8) = \$19$; add rows onto the table until you get $g = 8$ and $c = 19$.**

Digital Resources at PearsonRealize.com Topic 5 | Lesson 5-3 239

## Analyze Student Work

Sylvia's Work

| $c = 3 + 2g$ | |
|---|---|
| g | c |
| 1 | 5 |
| 2 | 7 |
| 3 | 9 |
| 4 | 11 |

*Each value of c is 3 more than 2 times the value of g.*

Sylvia completes the table and describes a pattern that relates the dependent variable to the independent variable.

Ann-Marie's Work

| $c = 3 + 2g$ | |
|---|---|
| g | c |
| 1 | 5 |
| 2 | 7 |
| 3 | 9 |
| 4 | 11 |

Values for g increase by 1.
Values for c increase by 2.

Ann-Marie describes the pattern for the dependent variable when values of the independent variable increase by 1.

# DEVELOP: VISUAL LEARNING

The *Visual Learning Bridge* connects students' thinking in Solve & Share to important math ideas in the lesson. Use the *Visual Learning Bridge* to make these ideas explicit. Also available as a *Visual Learning Animation Plus* at PearsonRealize.com.

ELL Visual Learning

PEARSON realize. PearsonRealize.com

Learn Glossary

**MP.4 Model with Math**
*What do you know about the situation?* [Ethan owes his mother $75. He is repaying her $5 each week.] *What are you asked to find?* [How much Ethan will owe after 12 weeks.] *What are the quantities that vary in this problem?* [The number of weeks and the amount of money that Ethan owes] *What is the independent variable? Explain.* [The number of weeks; The amount of money owed depends on the number of weeks that have passed.]

**MP.7 Use Structure**
*Why does the first column of values begin with 0?* [Sample answer: Ethan owes his mother the full amount, $75, before he starts to repay her each week.] *What patterns do you see in the table?* [As the values for $w$ increase by 1, the values for $a$ decrease by 5.]

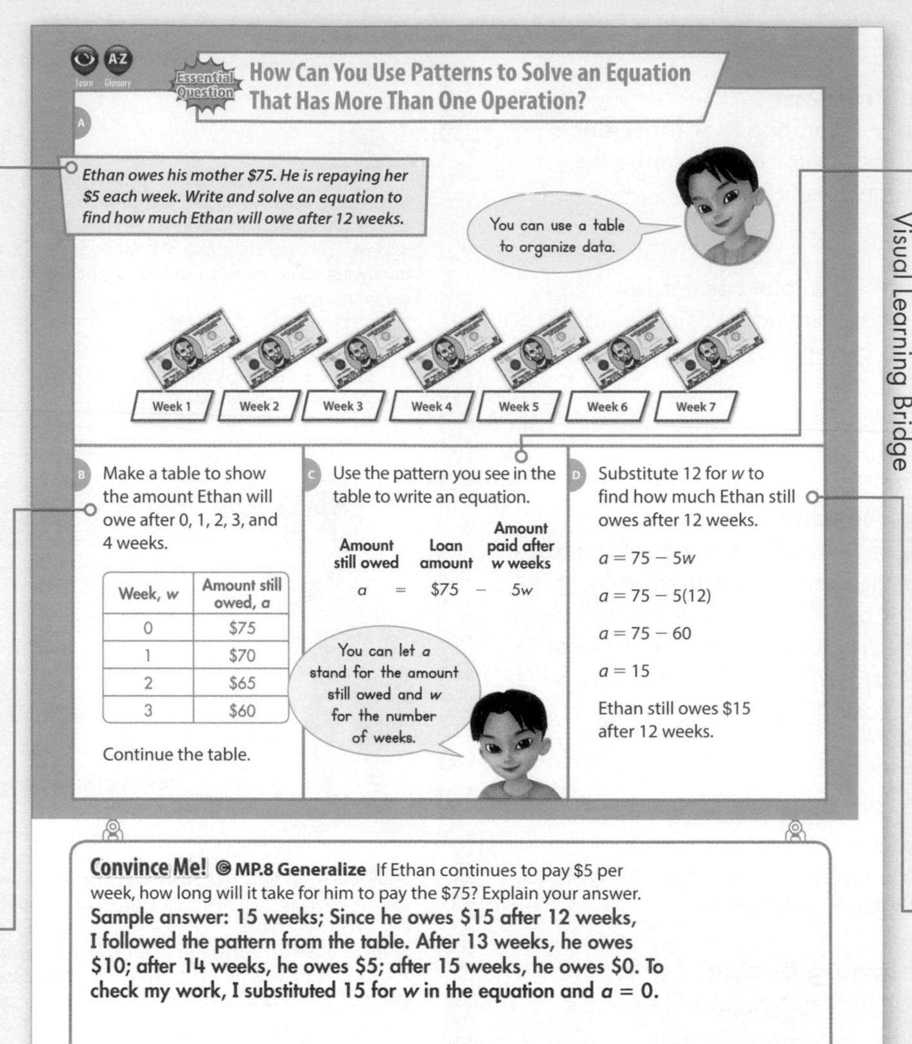

Essential Question **How Can You Use Patterns to Solve an Equation That Has More Than One Operation?**

A *Ethan owes his mother $75. He is repaying her $5 each week. Write and solve an equation to find how much Ethan will owe after 12 weeks.*

You can use a table to organize data.
Week 1
Week 2
Week 3
Week 4
Week 5
Week 6
Week 7

B Make a table to show the amount Ethan will owe after 0, 1, 2, 3, and 4 weeks.

| Week, $w$ | Amount still owed, $a$ |
|---|---|
| 0 | $75 |
| 1 | $70 |
| 2 | $65 |
| 3 | $60 |

Continue the table.

C Use the pattern you see in the table to write an equation.

| Amount still owed | | Loan amount | | Amount paid after $w$ weeks |
|---|---|---|---|---|
| $a$ | $=$ | $75 | $-$ | $5w$ |

You can let $a$ stand for the amount still owed and $w$ for the number of weeks.

D Substitute 12 for $w$ to find how much Ethan still owes after 12 weeks.

$a = 75 - 5w$

$a = 75 - 5(12)$

$a = 75 - 60$

$a = 15$

Ethan still owes $15 after 12 weeks.

**Convince Me!** MP.8 Generalize If Ethan continues to pay $5 per week, how long will it take for him to pay the $75? Explain your answer.
**Sample answer: 15 weeks; Since he owes $15 after 12 weeks, I followed the pattern from the table. After 13 weeks, he owes $10; after 14 weeks, he owes $5; after 15 weeks, he owes $0. To check my work, I substituted 15 for $w$ in the equation and $a = 0$.**

240 Topic 5 | Lesson 5-3 © Pearson Education, Inc. 6

Visual Learning Bridge

*What operations are used to find the values of a? In what order are they used?* [Multiplication, and then subtraction] *What does the 5 in front of the w represent?* [$5 that Ethan repays his mother each week]

**Prevent Misconceptions** 1 RtI
When values in the column for the dependent variable increase or decrease by a constant amount, students might write the operation with a constant and forget to write the variable.

*How much will Ethan still owe after 8 weeks? Explain how you determined your answer.* [$35; I substituted 8 for $w$ in the equation and did the math.] *How much has he already paid back? Explain.* [$40; $75 − $35 = $40, or $5 × 8 = $40]

**Convince Me! MP.8 Generalize** *You used an equation to find the amount owed after a given number of weeks. Can you use the same equation to find the number of weeks needed to pay off the loan? Explain.* [Yes. The equation relates both variables, so you can substitute for either one. When the loan is paid off, the amount owed is 0. So, let $a = 0$ and solve for $w$, the number of weeks.]

Revisit the Essential Question. A table can be used to organize data and look for a pattern that relates dependent and independent variables. Both tables and equations can be used to describe patterns involving more than one operation.

## ✓ QUICK CHECK

Check mark indicates items for prescribing differentiation on the next page.
Item 5 is worth 1 point. Items 15 and 17 are worth up to 2 points.

20–30 min

PEARSON realize. PearsonRealize.com

Practice Buddy

Tools

Assessment

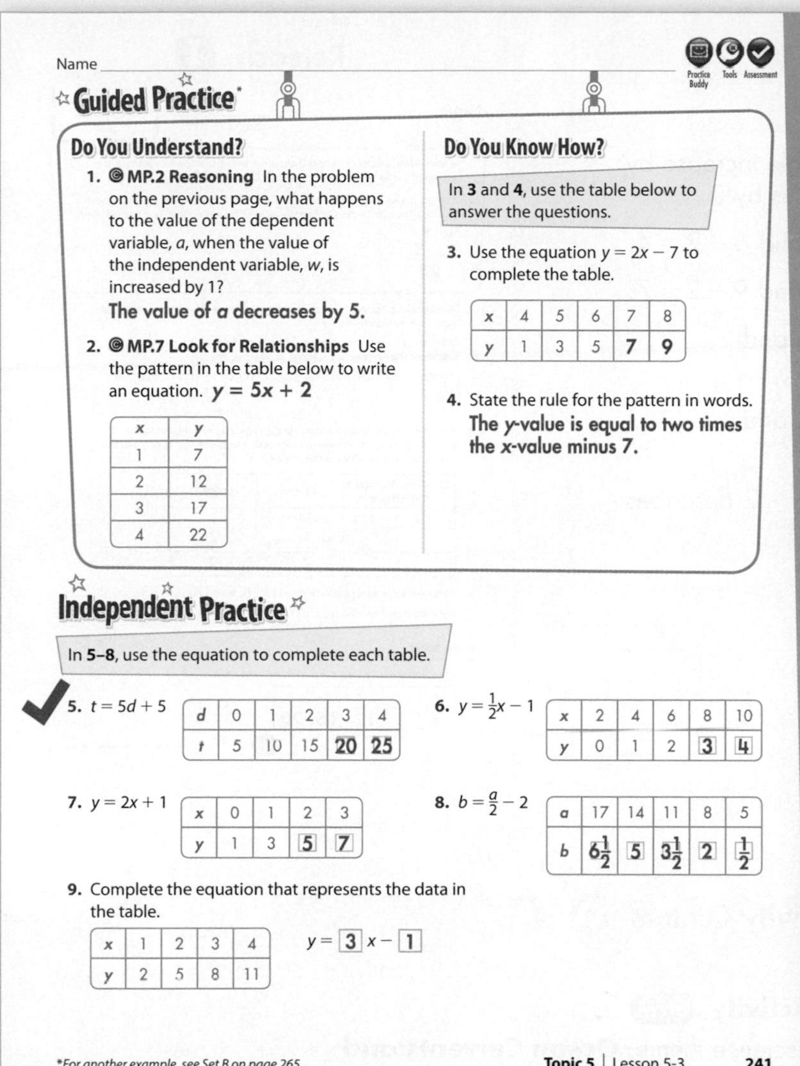

Name

### Guided Practice*

**Do You Understand?**

1. MP.2 Reasoning In the problem on the previous page, what happens to the value of the dependent variable, *a*, when the value of the independent variable, *w*, is increased by 1?
**The value of *a* decreases by 5.**

2. MP.7 Look for Relationships Use the pattern in the table below to write an equation. **$y = 5x + 2$**

| x | y |
|---|---|
| 1 | 7 |
| 2 | 12 |
| 3 | 17 |
| 4 | 22 |

**Do You Know How?**

In **3** and **4**, use the table below to answer the questions.

3. Use the equation $y = 2x - 7$ to complete the table.

| x | 4 | 5 | 6 | 7 | 8 |
|---|---|---|---|---|---|
| y | 1 | 3 | 5 | **7** | **9** |

4. State the rule for the pattern in words.
**The *y*-value is equal to two times the *x*-value minus 7.**

### Independent Practice*

In **5–8**, use the equation to complete each table.

5. $t = 5d + 5$

| d | 0 | 1 | 2 | 3 | 4 |
|---|---|---|---|---|---|
| t | 5 | 10 | 15 | **20** | **25** |

6. $y = \frac{1}{2}x - 1$

| x | 2 | 4 | 6 | 8 | 10 |
|---|---|---|---|---|---|
| y | 0 | 1 | 2 | **3** | **4** |

7. $y = 2x + 1$

| x | 0 | 1 | 2 | 3 |
|---|---|---|---|---|
| y | 1 | 3 | **5** | **7** |

8. $b = \frac{a}{2} - 2$

| a | 17 | 14 | 11 | 8 | 5 |
|---|---|---|---|---|---|
| b | $6\frac{1}{2}$ | **5** | $3\frac{1}{2}$ | **2** | $\frac{1}{2}$ |

9. Complete the equation that represents the data in the table.

| x | 1 | 2 | 3 | 4 |
|---|---|---|---|---|
| y | 2 | 5 | 8 | 11 |

$y =$ **3** $x -$ **1**

*For another example, see Set B on page 265.



### Math Practices and Problem Solving*

10. MP.7 Look for Relationships A county fair charges $8 for general admission and $2.50 for each ride. Use the pattern in the table to the find the cost of 5 rides and 8 rides. Then write an equation for the pattern. **$c = 8 + 2.50r$**

| Rides, r | Cost, c |
|---|---|
| 3 | $15.50 |
| 4 | $18.00 |
| 5 | **$20.50** |
| 6 | $23.00 |
| 8 | **$28.00** |

11. MP.8 Generalize Find the cost, *c*, for 12 rides. **$38.00**

12. Elizabeth is using 1-inch square tiles to decorate a wall. Use the equation $p = 2t + 2$ to make a table to record the perimeter, *p*, of *t* tiles in a single row when *t* is 1, 2, 3, and 6.

| Tiles, t | 1 | 2 | 3 | 6 |
|---|---|---|---|---|
| Perimeter, p | **4** | **6** | **8** | **14** |

13. **Number Sense** Of the 60 students who take art class, 12 are going to display their art at the local art museum. What fraction of the students are **NOT** going to display their art?
**$\frac{48}{60}$ or $\frac{4}{5}$**

In **14–16**, use the pattern.

14. MP.7 Look for Relationships Complete the table and describe any patterns you see.
**Sample answer: The values for *b* are increasing by 2.**

15. **Higher Order Thinking** Write an equation for the pattern. **$b = 2p + 1$**

16. How many blocks are needed to make the 10th figure in the pattern? **21**

| Pattern Number, p | 1 | 2 | 3 | 4 | 5 |
|---|---|---|---|---|---|
| Number of Blocks, b | 3 | **5** | **7** | **9** | **11** |

#### Common Core Assessment

17. Complete each table below by writing the *y*-values in the right column. Use the choices in the box to the right.

$y = 4x - 3$

| x | y |
|---|---|
| 2 | **5** |
| 4 | **13** |
| 5 | **17** |
| 7 | **25** |

$y = 3x + 2$

| x | y |
|---|---|
| 2 | **8** |
| 3 | **11** |
| 6 | **20** |
| 9 | **29** |

| Possible y Values | | | | | |
|---|---|---|---|---|---|
| 3 | 5 | 8 | 11 | 13 | 15 |
| 17 | 20 | 23 | 25 | 29 | 30 |





**Error Intervention: Item 2**

**If** students use $x + 1$ or $y + 5$ in their equation,

**then** they are describing the pattern in the column for the independent variable or the pattern in the column for the dependent variable. Emphasize to students that they should be looking for the connection between *x* and *y*.

**Item 9** Encourage students to first describe the pattern using a rule in their own words. *How can you describe the relationship between x and y?* [Sample answer: *y* is 1 less than 3 times *x*.]

**Reteaching** Assign Reteaching Set B on p. 265.

**Item 10 MP.7 Look for Relationships** When completing the table, some students may add $2.50 to $23.00 to fill in the cost for 8 rides in the right column. They will incorrectly answer that the cost for 8 rides is $25.50. Remind them that it is important to look at how the values in the left column increase. In this case, the number of rides, *r*, skips from 6 to 8. Adding a row for 7 rides will allow them to find the correct answer using that method.

**Item 13 Number Sense** Encourage students to first find the fraction of students that are going to display their art. *If $\frac{1}{5}$ of the students are going to display their art, what fraction are not going to display their art?* [$\frac{4}{5}$]

**Items 14–16 Coherence** In Grade 4, students generated shape patterns that followed a given rule. In this set of items, students extend this understanding by relating a characteristic of each shape to its position in the pattern. Students write a two-step equation to describe this relationship and use it to find the number of blocks in the 10th figure.

**Multi-Step Problems** *Page 242 Items 10, 13, and 17; Page 244 Items 7, 10, and 13*

# ASSESS AND DIFFERENTIATE

Use the **QUICK CHECK** on the previous page to prescribe differentiated instruction.

**I Intervention** 0–3 points on the Quick Check

**O On-Level** 4 points on the Quick Check

**A Advanced** 5 points on the Quick Check

## Intervention Activity I

### More Patterns and Equations

- Write this table on the board.

| $x$ | 2 | 3 | 4 | 5 |
|---|---|---|---|---|
| $y$ | 4 | 7 | 10 | 13 |

- Model how to use trial and error to figure out the pattern.
    - Addition:
      $2 + 2 = 4$, but $3 + 2 \neq 7$.
    - Multiplication:
      $2 \times 2 = 4$, but $2 \times 3 \neq 7$.
- Two-step equation:
  Since $y$-values in the table increase by 3, try multiplying $x$-values by 3.

  For $x = 2$, $2 \times 3 = 6$, and $6 - 2 = 4$.

  For $x = 3$, $3 \times 3 = 9$, and $9 - 2 = 7$.

  For $x = 4$, $3 \times 4 = 12$, and $12 - 2 = 10$.

  For $x = 5$, $3 \times 5 = 15$, and $15 - 2 = 13$.

  So, the equation $y = 3x - 2$ describes the pattern in the table.

## Reteach I

Name ______________

Reteach to Build Understanding
5-3

**Vocabulary**

1. A **variable** is a letter or symbol that represents an unknown quantity. In the equation $y = 7x - 3$, the variables are **x** and **y**.
2. You can use **substitution** to replace a variable in an algebraic expression with a number. Use substitution to find the value of the expression $4x + 1$ when $x = 5$.
   $4x + 1$
   $= 4($**5**$) + 1$
   $=$ **21**
3. Katelyn earns 2 points for each question answered correctly on a math quiz, plus 5 extra credit points.
   Write an expression that describes how to find Katelyn's score. Let $q$ represent the number of questions answered correctly.
   2 points for each question answered correctly, plus 5 extra credit points
   **2** × **q** + **5**
4. Complete the table to show how Katelyn's quiz score is related to the number of questions she answers correctly. Substitute values of $q$ into the expression to find values of the score, $s$.

| Questions Answered Correctly, $q$ | $2q + 5$ | Score, $s$ |
|---|---|---|
| 0 | $2(0) + 5$ | 5 |
| 1 | $2($**1**$) + 5$ | **7** |
| 2 | $2($**2**$) + 5$ | **9** |

5. Write and solve an equation that can be used to find Katelyn's score, $s$, if she answers 9 questions correctly. **$s = 2q + 5$; 23**

**On the Back!**

6. Use the equation $d = 4c + 8$ to complete the table.

| $c$ | 0 | 1 | 2 | 3 |
|---|---|---|---|---|
| $d$ | **8** | **12** | **16** | **20** |

R 5-3



## On-Level and Advanced Activity Centers O A

Name ______________

Math and Science Activity
5-3

### Cool Ocean Breezes

*Did You Know?* Water heats up and cools down relatively slowly because it has a high specific heat value. In contrast, land heats and cools much faster than water. It takes a lot of energy to warm a body of water as large as an ocean. The cool ocean water sucks energy, in the form of heat, from the air over the land. Cool ocean breezes are a result of this temperature difference.

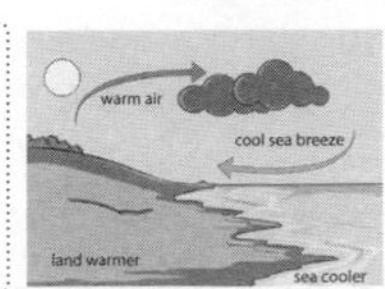


Jerred's class is learning about the specific heat value for water. The class observes and records the temperature of a beaker of water as it is heated over time.

| Time, $t$ (minutes) | 0 | 5 | 10 | 15 | 20 | 25 |
|---|---|---|---|---|---|---|
| Water Temperature, $f$ (°F) | 57 | 60.7 | 64.4 | 68.1 | 71.8 | 75.5 |

1. Let $t$ = the time in minutes and $f$ = the water temperature in °F. Which is the independent variable? Which is the dependent variable? Explain.
   **Independent: $t$; Dependent: $f$. The water temperature depends on how long the water is heated.**
2. Complete the equation and write a rule that represents the data in the table.
   Equation: $f = 0.74t +$ **57**
   Rule: **$f$ is 57 more than 0.74 times $t$.**
3. Use the equation to find the temperature of the water after 30 minutes of heating. Show your work.
   **$f = 0.74t + 57 = 0.74(30) + 57 = 79.2$°F**
4. **Represent** Emily conducted the same experiment but the temperature of the water at $t = 0$ was 68°F. Every minute that the water was heated, the temperature of the water rose 0.62°F. Write a new equation to represent this situation.
   **$f = 0.62t + 68$**
5. **Extension** Make a table using the equation you wrote in Problem 4.
   **Check students' work.**

Math and Science Activity 5-3



### Math and Science Activity STEM

This activity revisits the science theme, **Ocean Currents and Weather Patterns,** introduced on page 223 in the Student's Edition.

### Sample Student Work

5.
$f = 0.62t + 68$

| Time, $t$ (minutes) | 0 | 5 | 10 | 15 | 20 | 25 |
|---|---|---|---|---|---|---|
| Water Temperature, $f$ (°F) | 68 | 71.1 | 74.2 | 77.3 | 80.4 | 83.5 |

PEARSON realize. PearsonRealize.com

Help | Practice Buddy | Tools | Games

**TIMING**

The time allocated to Step 3 will depend on the teacher's instructional decisions and differentiation routines.

15–30 min

## Technology Center   

Tools Games

### Math Tools and Math Games

A link to a specific math tools activity or math game to use with this lesson is provided at PearsonRealize.com.

## Leveled Assignment  Items 1–6, 10, 11, 13  Items 3–8, 10–11, 13  Items 5–13

Name ______________________

Help Practice Buddy Tools Games

# Homework & Practice 5-3

## More Patterns and Equations

### Another Look!

The entry fee to a carnival is \$3. Each ride ticket is \$2. The cost, $c$, of going to the carnival equals the entry fee plus two times the number of tickets, $t$, purchased. Find the cost for going on 10 rides.

| Tickets, $t$ | $3 + 2t$ | Cost, $c$ |
|---|---|---|
| 0 | $3 + 2(0)$ | \$3 |
| 2 | $3 + 2(2)$ | \$7 |
| 4 | $3 + 2(4)$ | \$11 |
| 6 | $3 + 2(6)$ | \$15 |

The table shows the costs if you go on 0, 2, 4, and 6 rides.

Use the table rule to write an equation: $c = 3 + 2t$.

You can substitute numbers into the equation to find the total cost when ten ride tickets are purchased.

$c = 3 + 2(10)$
$c = 23$

When you purchase 10 ride tickets, the total cost is \$23.

In **1–4**, use the equation to complete each table.

**1.** $y = 3x + 7$

| $x$ | 0 | 1 | 2 | 3 |
|---|---|---|---|---|
| $y$ | **7** | **10** | **13** | **16** |

**2.** $y = 4x - 4$

| $x$ | 2 | 4 | 6 | 8 |
|---|---|---|---|---|
| $y$ | **4** | **12** | **20** | **28** |

**3.** $y = 2x + 7$

| $x$ | 1 | 3 | 5 | 7 |
|---|---|---|---|---|
| $y$ | **9** | **13** | **17** | **21** |

**4.** $y = \frac{1}{4}x + 5$

| $x$ | 0 | 4 | 8 | 12 |
|---|---|---|---|---|
| $y$ | **5** | **6** | **7** | **8** |

**5.** Grace has \$100. She is buying charms for her bracelet that cost \$5 each. Write an equation showing the relationship between the number of charms, $c$, she buys and the amount of money she has left, $m$. $\mathbf{m = 100 - 5c}$

**6.** Use the equation you wrote for Exercise 5 to find the number of charms Grace can buy before she runs out of money. **20 charms**



**7.** MP.7 **Look for Relationships** The first ride on a kiddie train at the mall is \$2.50. Each additional ride is \$1.50. Use the equation $c = 2.50 + 1.50(r - 1)$ to complete the table and find the cost of 2, 3, and 6 rides.

| Rides, $r$ | Cost, $c$ |
|---|---|
| 1 | \$2.50 |
| 2 | **\$4.00** |
| 3 | **\$5.50** |
| 4 | \$7.00 |
| 6 | **\$10.00** |

**8.** MP.8 **Generalize** Find the cost, $c$, for 9 rides. **\$14.50**

In **9** and **10**, the equation $\ell = 3w$ represents that the length, $\ell$, of a rectangle is 3 times its width, $w$.

**9.** MP.4 **Model with Math** Create a table to show the length of the rectangle when its width is 1, 2, 3, 5, and 8 units.

| Width, $w$ | 1 | 2 | 3 | 5 | 8 |
|---|---|---|---|---|---|
| Length, $\ell$ | **3** | **6** | **9** | **15** | **24** |

**10. Higher Order Thinking** How could you use the equation $p = 2\ell + 2w$ to find the perimeter, $p$, of the rectangle when the width, $w$, is 15?
**Sample answer: Since $\ell = 3w$, I substituted $3w$ for $\ell$ in the equation and rewrote it as $p = 2(3w) + 2w$. I then substituted 15 for each $w$. This gave me $2(3 \times 15) + 2(15) = 2(45) + 2(15)$. I evaluated this and got 120.**

**11.** MP.7 **Use Structure** A triangular pattern has 21 dots in the 6th pattern. Use the equation $\frac{p(p+1)}{2}$, where $p$ is the pattern number, to find the number of dots in the 7th pattern. **28**

**12.** Use the equation from Exercise 11. How many dots will be in the 10th pattern? **55**

### Common Core Assessment

**13.** Complete each table below by writing the $y$-values in the right column. Use the choices in the box to the right.

$y = \frac{1}{2}x + 5$

| $x$ | $y$ |
|---|---|
| 4 | **7** |
| 6 | **8** |
| 9 | **9.5** |
| 16 | **13** |

$y = 3(x - 2)$

| $x$ | $y$ |
|---|---|
| 3 | **3** |
| 6 | **12** |
| 8 | **18** |
| 11 | **27** |

| Possible $y$ Values | | | | | |
|---|---|---|---|---|---|
| 3 | 4 | 7 | 8 | 9.5 | 12 |
| 13 | 16 | 18 | 22.5 | 27 | 32 |

# LESSON 5-4

# GRAPH EQUATIONS

## DIGITAL RESOURCES PearsonRealize.com

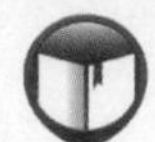
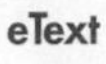
Student and Teacher eTexts — eText

Listen and Look For Lesson Video — PD

Today's Challenge — Think

Solve and Share — Solve

Visual Learning Animation Plus — Learn

Animated Glossary — Glossary

Online Personalized Practice — Practice Buddy

Math Tools — Tools

Quick Check — Assessment

Another Look Homework Video — Help

Math Games — Games

## LESSON OVERVIEW FCR FOCUS • COHERENCE • RIGOR

### FOCUS

**Domain 6.EE** Expressions and Equations

**Cluster 6.EE.C** Represent and analyze quantitative relationships between dependent and independent variables.

**Content Standard 6.EE.C.9** Use variables to represent two quantities in a real-world problem that change in relationship to one another; write an equation to express one quantity, thought of as the dependent variable, in terms of the other quantity, thought of as the independent variable. Analyze the relationship between the dependent and independent variables using graphs and tables, and relate these to the equation.

**Mathematical Practices MP.2, MP.3, MP.4**

**Objective** Graph linear equations on a coordinate plane.

**Essential Understanding** Graphs of relationships in the form of $y = ax$, and $y = x + a$, where $a$ is a real number, are straight lines.

**Vocabulary** Linear equation

**Materials** First quadrant coordinate grids (Teaching Tool 18) (optional)

### COHERENCE

In this topic, students have learned to identify dependent and independent variables and to analyze the relationship between these variables using tables. In Topic 4, students graphed ordered pairs on a coordinate plane. In this lesson, students connect these previously learned skills by applying what they know to create tables of related values and graph linear equations on a coordinate plane. This prepares students for Algebra I, when they will graph linear and quadratic functions on a coordinate plane.

### RIGOR

This lesson emphasizes a blend of **conceptual understanding** with **procedural skill**. Students develop understanding of linear relationships by analyzing them using multiple representations; tables, equations, and graphs.

PD Watch the Listen and Look For Lesson Video.

## MATH ANYTIME

### Daily Common Core Review

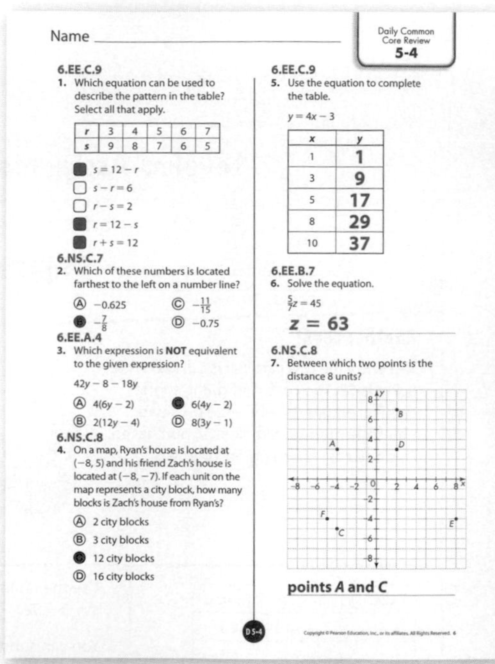
Name ______

Daily Common Core Review 5-4

6.EE.C.9
1. Which equation can be used to describe the pattern in the table? Select all that apply.

| r | 3 | 4 | 5 | 6 | 7 |
|---|---|---|---|---|---|
| s | 9 | 8 | 7 | 6 | 5 |

■ $s = 12 - r$
□ $s - r = 6$
□ $r - s = 2$
■ $r = 12 - s$
■ $r + s = 12$

6.NS.C.7
2. Which of these numbers is located farthest to the left on a number line?

Ⓐ $-0.625$
● $-\frac{7}{8}$
Ⓒ $-\frac{11}{15}$
Ⓓ $-0.75$

6.EE.A.4
3. Which expression is **NOT** equivalent to the given expression?

$42y - 8 - 18y$

Ⓐ $4(6y - 2)$
Ⓑ $2(12y - 4)$
● $6(4y - 2)$
Ⓓ $8(3y - 1)$

6.NS.C.8
4. On a map, Ryan's house is located at (−8, 5) and his friend Zach's house is located at (−8, −7). If each unit on the map represents a city block, how many blocks is Zach's house from Ryan's?

Ⓐ 2 city blocks
Ⓑ 3 city blocks
● 12 city blocks
Ⓓ 16 city blocks

6.EE.C.9
5. Use the equation to complete the table.

$y = 4x - 3$

| x | y |
|---|---|
| 1 | **1** |
| 3 | **9** |
| 5 | **17** |
| 8 | **29** |
| 10 | **37** |

6.EE.B.7
6. Solve the equation.

$\frac{5}{7}z = 45$

$z = 63$

6.NS.C.8
7. Between which two points is the distance 8 units?



**points A and C**

D 5-4



### Today's Challenge

Think Use the Topic 5 problems any time during this topic.

## ENGLISH LANGUAGE LEARNERS 

**Speaking** Share information in cooperative learning interactions.

*Use with the Visual Learning Bridge on Student's Edition p. 246.*

Read Box A. Write the variables $n$ and $p$. Ask students to write, in their notes, the meaning of each variable. Read Box B. Write $p = n - 4$. Organize students into small groups. Have students explain what each term of the equation represents in the problem. Read Box C. Point to the line drawn through the points. Write *linear equation. This straight line is the graph of a linear equation.*

**Beginning** *What if 7 pompoms are sold?* Instruct students to work in groups to extend the table and graph the information for 7 pompoms on the coordinate plane. Continue with 8 and 9 pompoms. *Are these points on the graph of the linear equation?* Have students respond using the sentence stem: Yes, these are points on the graph of the ____ ____.

**Intermediate** Instruct students to work in groups to extend the table and graph for 7, 8, and 9 pompoms. *Are these points on the graph of the linear equation?* Have students respond using the sentence stem: Yes, these are points on the graph of the ___ ___ because ___.

**Advanced** Instruct students to work in groups to extend the table and graph for 7, 8, and 9 pompoms. Ask groups to determine how graphing helps them understand linear equations.

**Summarize** What are *linear equations*?

# DEVELOP: PROBLEM-BASED LEARNING

**COHERENCE: Engage learners by connecting prior knowledge to new ideas.**
Students extend their previous knowledge of dependent and independent variables as they plot and connect points to graph an equation in two variables.

10–15 min

Solve

## BEFORE

**1. Pose the Solve-and-Share Problem**
**MP.4 Model with Math** Listen and look for students who fill in the table with the number of blocks Nancy walks given the number of miles Maria walks, and then model the situation by plotting three points on the coordinate plane.

**2. Build Understanding**
*Which column of the table represents the number of blocks Nancy walks?* [The right column] *Which axis on the coordinate plane represents the number of blocks Nancy walks?* [The $y$-axis]

## DURING

**3. Ask Guiding Questions As Needed**
*How far will Nancy have walked after she and Maria walk 1 block together?* [5 blocks] *Where should you write "5" in the table?* [In the $n$ column, next to $m = 1$.] *What ordered pair do you plot on the coordinate plane?* [(1, 5)]

## AFTER

**4. Share and Discuss Solutions**
Solve: Start with students' solutions. If needed, project Pedro's work to discuss how to determine three points using the table and then graph the linear equation.

**5. Transition to the Visual Learning Bridge**
*Some real-world situations can be represented by equations using dependent and independent variables. The relationship between these variables can be graphed on a coordinate plane.*

**6. Extension for Early Finishers**
*Graph the equation $y = 3$. Explain your thinking.* [Check students' graphs and explanations.]

---

Name ______________________

**Lesson 5-4**
**Graph Equations**

**Solve & Share**

Nancy walks 4 blocks to Maria's house. Together, they continue the walk. Graph the equation $n = m + 4$ on a coordinate plane, where $n$ is the number of blocks Nancy walks and $m$ is the number of blocks Maria walks.

**I can …** graph algebraic expressions.

Content Standard 6.EE.C.9
Mathematical Practices MP.2, MP.3, MP.4

How can you use what you know about making tables and plotting points to model the problem on a graph?

| $n = m + 4$ | |
|---|---|
| $m$ | $n$ |
| 1 | |
| 2 | |
| 3 | |

See margin for sample student work.

**Look Back!** **MP.4 Model with Math** Draw a line through the points you graphed. What ordered pair on the line includes $m = 5$? Explain what that ordered pair represents.
**(5, 9) Sample answer: When Maria has walked 5 blocks, Nancy has walked 9 blocks.**



---

## Analyze Student Work

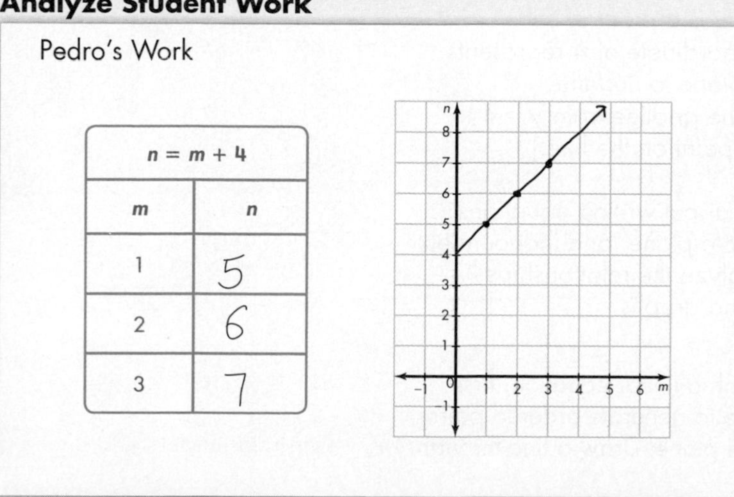


Pedro correctly completes the table and uses the values of $m$ and $n$ to plot ordered pairs on the coordinate plane.

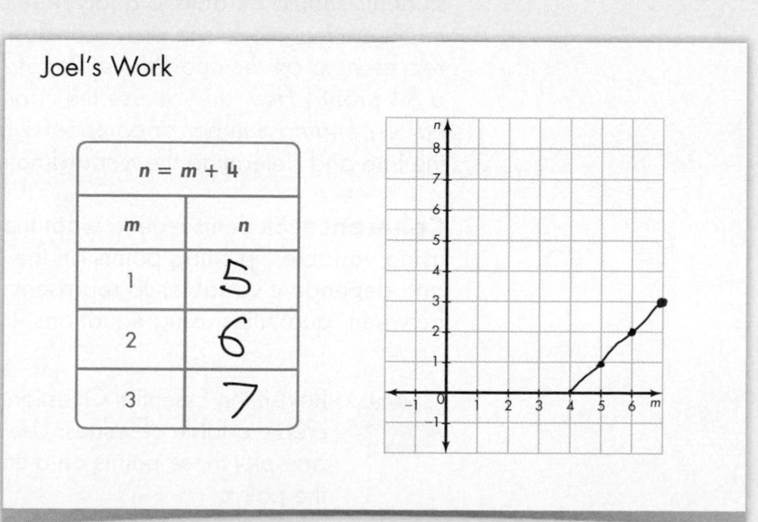

Joel's Work
n = m + 4
m n
1 5
2 6
3 7


Joel correctly completes the table but confuses the columns of the table and the horizontal and vertical axes of the coordinate plane.

STEP 2

# DEVELOP: VISUAL LEARNING

The *Visual Learning Bridge* connects students' thinking in Solve & Share to important math ideas in the lesson. Use the *Visual Learning Bridge* to make these ideas explicit. Also available as a *Visual Learning Animation Plus* at PearsonRealize.com

ELL Visual Learning

PEARSON realize. PearsonRealize.com

Learn Glossary

**MP.4 Model with Math** *How does the equation p = n − 4 show the profit?* [The profit, $p$, is the amount in sales minus the $4 cost of the supplies. Since each pompom costs $1, $1n = n$ represents the amount in sales.] *Where are the dependent and independent variables represented on the coordinate plane?* [The dependent variable is represented on the vertical axis, and the independent variable is represented on the horizontal axis.]

*Why do the values of n in the table start at 4?* [There is no profit when fewer than 4 pompoms are sold.] *Explain how to translate this table into ordered pairs to graph.* [The values for the independent variable $n$ become the $x$-coordinates in the ordered pairs. The corresponding values for the dependent variable $p$ become the $y$-coordinates in the ordered pairs.]

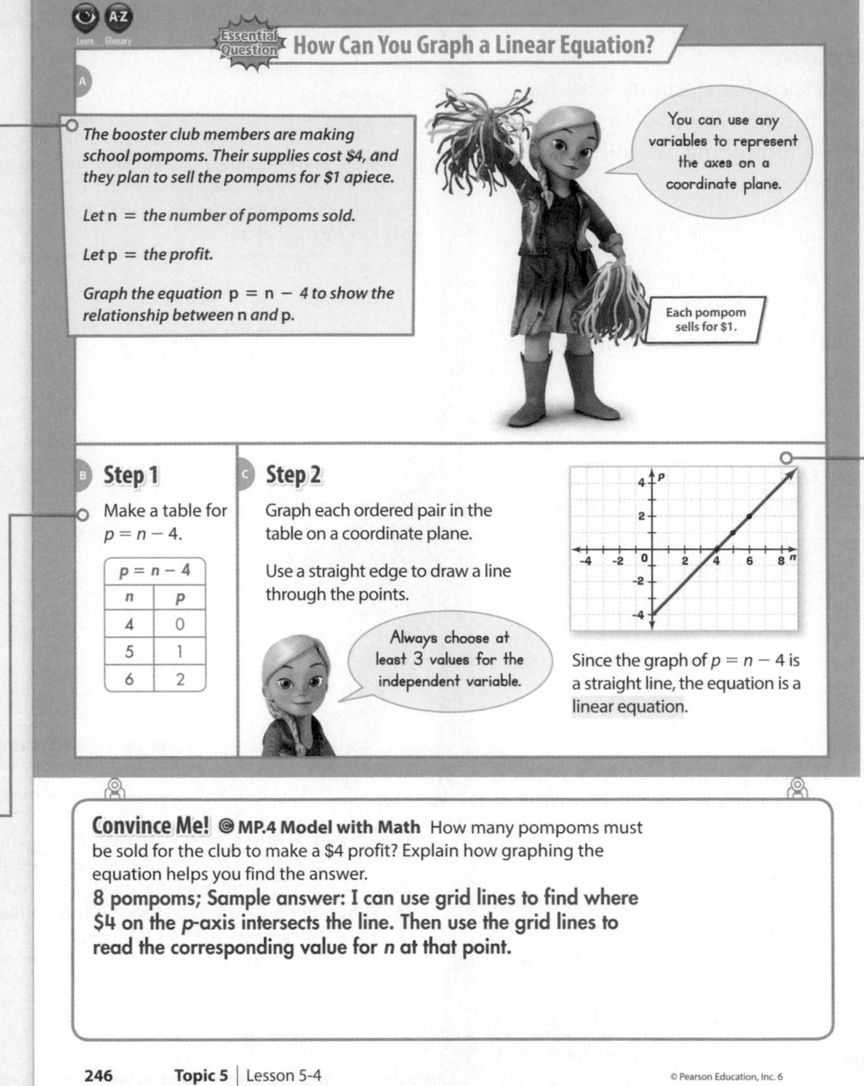

Essential Question **How Can You Graph a Linear Equation?**

A

*The booster club members are making school pompoms. Their supplies cost $4, and they plan to sell the pompoms for $1 apiece.*

*Let n = the number of pompoms sold.*

*Let p = the profit.*

*Graph the equation p = n − 4 to show the relationship between n and p.*



B **Step 1**

Make a table for $p = n - 4$.

| $p = n - 4$ | |
|---|---|
| $n$ | $p$ |
| 4 | 0 |
| 5 | 1 |
| 6 | 2 |

C **Step 2**

Graph each ordered pair in the table on a coordinate plane.

Use a straight edge to draw a line through the points.



Since the graph of $p = n - 4$ is a straight line, the equation is a linear equation.

**Convince Me!** MP.4 Model with Math How many pompoms must be sold for the club to make a $4 profit? Explain how graphing the equation helps you find the answer.
**8 pompoms; Sample answer: I can use grid lines to find where $4 on the $p$-axis intersects the line. Then use the grid lines to read the corresponding value for $n$ at that point.**

246 Topic 5 | Lesson 5-4 © Pearson Education, Inc. 6

Visual Learning Bridge

**MP.2 Reason Quantitatively** *Although the line represents all the solutions of p = n − 4, do all points on this line represent reasonable solutions for this problem situation? Explain.* [No. Only the points with a whole number $n$-value are reasonable because the club can only sell a whole number of pompoms.] *If the club does not sell any pompoms, then p = −4. What does that mean in the context of the problem?* [The club lost $4 because it spent $4 on supplies and did not make any money.]

**Prevent Misconceptions** 1 RtI

Make sure students do not extend the line on the graph to the left of the vertical axis. *What does n represent?* [The number of pompoms sold] *Can n be a negative number? Explain.* [No. The club cannot sell a negative number of pompoms.]

**Convince Me! MP.4 Model with Math** Mathematically proficient students should be able to analyze relationships represented in mathematical models to draw conclusions. *How is a profit of $4 represented on the coordinate plane?* [The $y$-coordinate of 4 represents a $4 profit.] *How do you use the coordinate plane to find the corresponding number of pompoms?* [Follow the gridline from $y = 4$ to the line and determine the $x$-coordinate of the point on the line.]

**Coherence** Students extend what they know about writing equations using variables, plotting points on the coordinate plane, and independent and dependent variables to represent and analyze the relationships between quantities using equations, tables, and graphs.

Revisit the Essential Question. To graph a linear equation, first create a table of values. Use the table to generate ordered pairs and plot those points on a coordinate plane. Draw a line through the points.

PEARSON realize. PearsonRealize.com

## QUICK CHECK

Check mark indicates items for prescribing differentiation on the next page. Items 5 and 13 are worth 1 point. Item 12 is worth up to 3 points.

20–30 min

Practice Buddy

Tools

Assessment

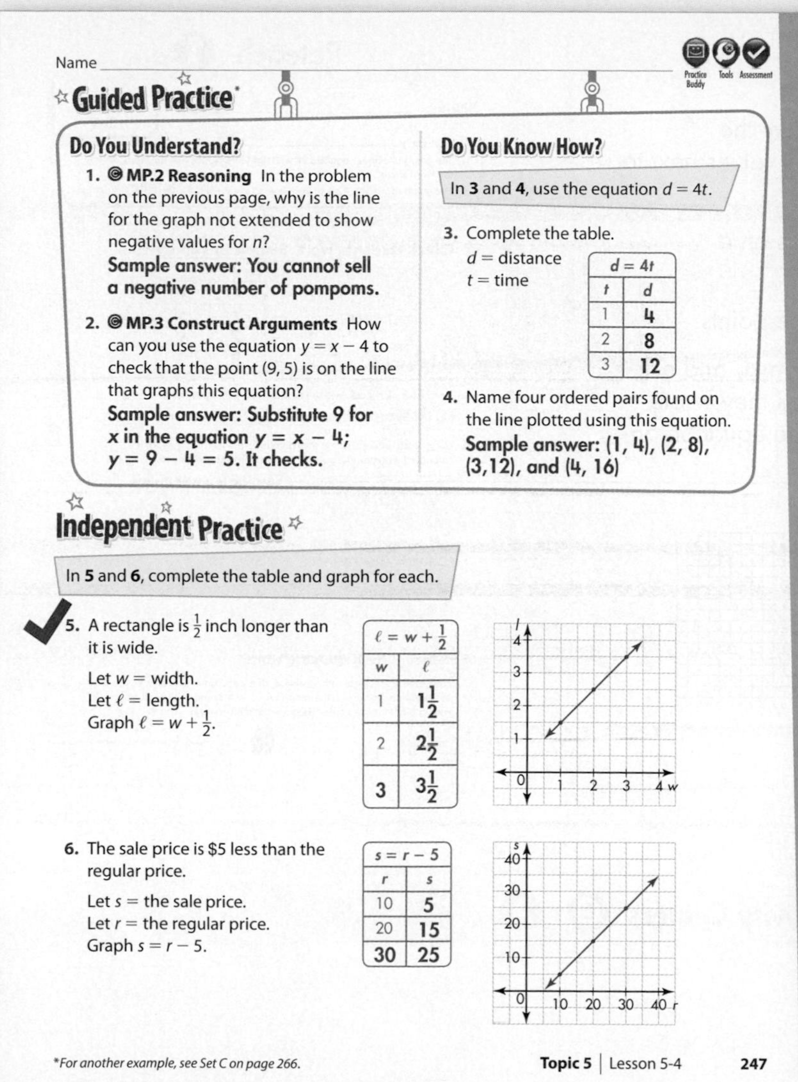

Name

### Guided Practice*

**Do You Understand?**

1. **MP.2 Reasoning** In the problem on the previous page, why is the line for the graph not extended to show negative values for *n*?
   **Sample answer: You cannot sell a negative number of pompoms.**
2. **MP.3 Construct Arguments** How can you use the equation $y = x - 4$ to check that the point (9, 5) is on the line that graphs this equation?
   **Sample answer: Substitute 9 for $x$ in the equation $y = x - 4$; $y = 9 - 4 = 5$. It checks.**

**Do You Know How?**

In **3** and **4**, use the equation $d = 4t$.

3. Complete the table.
   $d$ = distance
   $t$ = time

| $d = 4t$ | |
|---|---|
| $t$ | $d$ |
| 1 | 4 |
| 2 | 8 |
| 3 | 12 |

4. Name four ordered pairs found on the line plotted using this equation.
   **Sample answer: (1, 4), (2, 8), (3,12), and (4, 16)**

### Independent Practice*

In **5** and **6**, complete the table and graph for each.

5. A rectangle is $\frac{1}{2}$ inch longer than it is wide.
   Let $w$ = width.
   Let $\ell$ = length.
   Graph $\ell = w + \frac{1}{2}$.

| $\ell = w + \frac{1}{2}$ | |
|---|---|
| $w$ | $\ell$ |
| 1 | $1\frac{1}{2}$ |
| 2 | $2\frac{1}{2}$ |
| 3 | $3\frac{1}{2}$ |

6. The sale price is $5 less than the regular price.
   Let $s$ = the sale price.
   Let $r$ = the regular price.
   Graph $s = r - 5$.

| $s = r - 5$ | |
|---|---|
| $r$ | $s$ |
| 10 | 5 |
| 20 | 15 |
| 30 | 25 |

*For another example, see Set C on page 266.

Topic 5 | Lesson 5-4 247

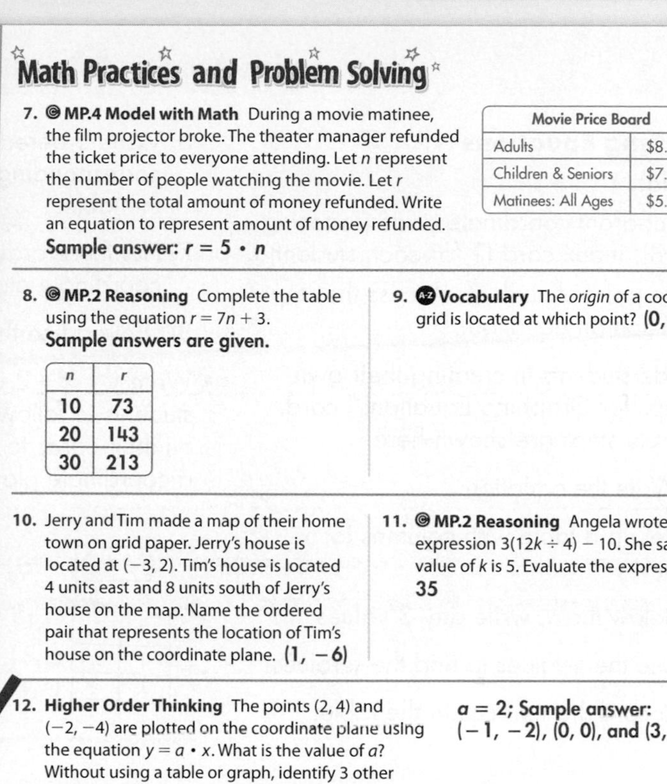

### Math Practices and Problem Solving*

7. **MP.4 Model with Math** During a movie matinee, the film projector broke. The theater manager refunded the ticket price to everyone attending. Let *n* represent the number of people watching the movie. Let *r* represent the total amount of money refunded. Write an equation to represent amount of money refunded.
   **Sample answer: $r = 5 \cdot n$**

| Movie Price Board | |
|---|---|
| Adults | $8.50 |
| Children & Seniors | $7.00 |
| Matinees: All Ages | $5.00 |

8. **MP.2 Reasoning** Complete the table using the equation $r = 7n + 3$.
   **Sample answers are given.**

| $n$ | $r$ |
|---|---|
| 10 | 73 |
| 20 | 143 |
| 30 | 213 |

9. **Vocabulary** The *origin* of a coordinate grid is located at which point? **(0, 0)**

10. Jerry and Tim made a map of their home town on grid paper. Jerry's house is located at (−3, 2). Tim's house is located 4 units east and 8 units south of Jerry's house on the map. Name the ordered pair that represents the location of Tim's house on the coordinate plane. **(1, −6)**

11. **MP.2 Reasoning** Angela wrote the expression $3(12k \div 4) - 10$. She says the value of *k* is 5. Evaluate the expression.
    **35**

12. **Higher Order Thinking** The points (2, 4) and (−2, −4) are plotted on the coordinate plane using the equation $y = a \cdot x$. What is the value of *a*? Without using a table or graph, identify 3 other points a graph of this equation will pass through.
    **$a = 2$; Sample answer: (−1, −2), (0, 0), and (3, 6)**

**Common Core Assessment**

13. Which equation represents the graph on the right?
    Ⓐ $y = 4x$
    Ⓑ $y = \frac{x}{2}$
    ● $y = 2x$
    Ⓓ $y = x + 2$

248 Topic 5 | Lesson 5-4



**Error Intervention: Items 3–4**

**If** students have difficulty finding related values of variables for the table or when writing ordered pairs,

**then** have students write the original equation $d = 4t$ and then substitute one value for $t$, showing their work as they perform calculations to find the related value for $d$. For each pair of related values, ask: *Do the values make the equation true?* Be sure students check their answers.

**Item 5 Coherence** Students use what they know from the previous topic about plotting ordered pairs with rational number coordinates on a coordinate plane as they graph the linear equation for this item. Be sure that students recognize that each gridline along the horizontal and vertical axes represents $\frac{1}{2}$.

**Reteaching** Assign Reteaching Set C on p. 266.

**Item 7 MP.4 Model with Math** Students may generate several equations that look different but represent the same linear relationship between $r$ and $n$, such as $r = 5 \cdot n$, $r = 5 \times n$, $r = 5n$, $n = r \div 5$, and $5 = r \div n$.

**Item 8 MP.2 Reason Quantitatively** Students reason that they can apply the familiar procedure of filling in a table of values for variables of a one-step equation when given a multi-step equation.

**Item 9 Vocabulary** Review the definition of *origin* as the point where the *x*-axis and *y*-axis of a coordinate plane intersect. Students learned about the structure of a coordinate plane, including the axes, quadrants, origin, and ordered pairs, in the previous topic. This provided the necessary foundation for this lesson's work with graphing equations.

**Multi-Step Problems** *Page 248 Items 8, 11, and 12; Page 250 Items 3 and 7*

# ASSESS AND DIFFERENTIATE

Use the **QUICK CHECK** on the previous page to prescribe differentiated instruction.

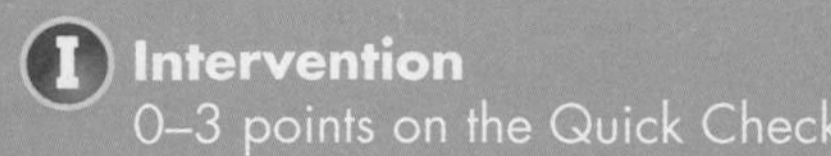

**Intervention**
0–3 points on the Quick Check

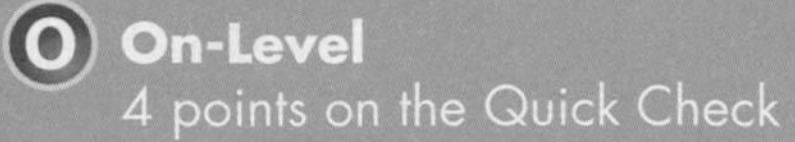

**On-Level**
4 points on the Quick Check

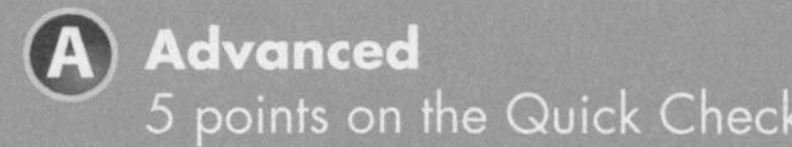

**Advanced**
5 points on the Quick Check

## Intervention Activity 

### Graphing Equations

**Materials**

First quadrant coordinate grids (Teaching Tool 18), index card (1 for each student)

- Have pairs of students discuss the steps to graph an equation.
- Guide students in creating their own "Steps for Graphing Equations" card. Sample steps are shown here.
  1) Write the equation.
  2) Set up a table with columns for $x$ and $y$.
  3) Below the $x$, write any 3 values.
  4) Use the $x$-values to find the $y$-values.
  5) Record the $y$-values in the table.
  6) Write ordered pairs from the corresponding $x$- and $y$-values next to the table.
  7) Plot these ordered pairs on a coordinate plane.
  8) Draw a line through the points.
- Write $y = x + 2$ on the board, and ask students to follow the steps they wrote on their cards to graph the equation on a coordinate plane.

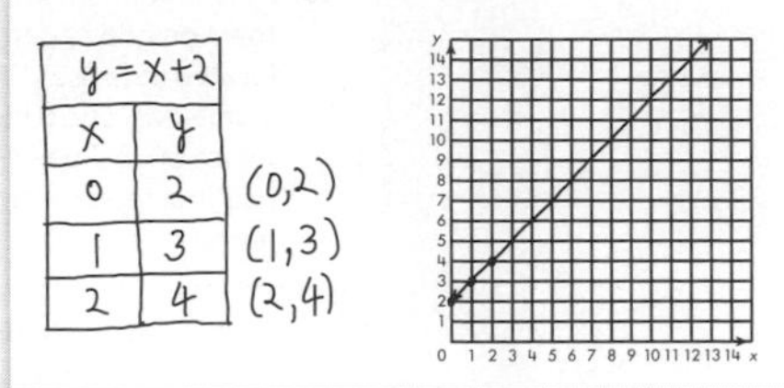


## Reteach

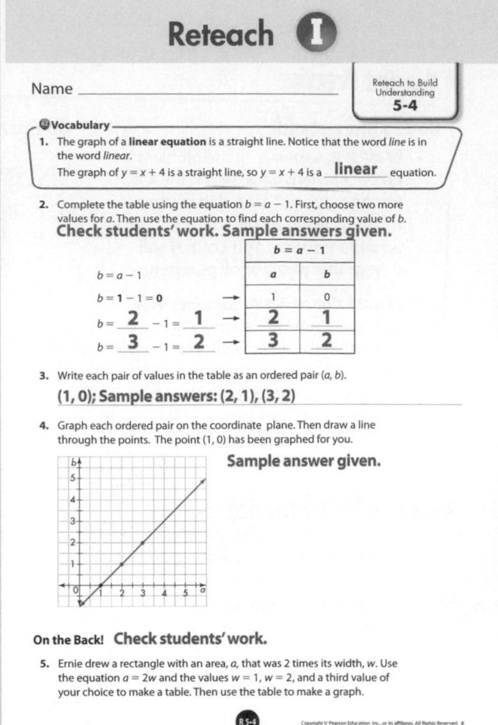

Name ____________ Reteach to Build Understanding 5-4

**Vocabulary**

1. The graph of a **linear equation** is a straight line. Notice that the word *line* is in the word *linear*.
The graph of $y = x + 4$ is a straight line, so $y = x + 4$ is a **linear** equation.

2. Complete the table using the equation $b = a - 1$. First, choose two more values for $a$. Then use the equation to find each corresponding value of $b$.
**Check students' work. Sample answers given.**

$b = a - 1$
$b = 1 - 1 = 0$
$b = 2 - 1 = 1$
$b = 3 - 1 = 2$

| $b = a - 1$ | |
|---|---|
| $a$ | $b$ |
| 1 | 0 |
| 2 | 1 |
| 3 | 2 |

3. Write each pair of values in the table as an ordered pair $(a, b)$.
**(1, 0); Sample answers: (2, 1), (3, 2)**

4. Graph each ordered pair on the coordinate plane. Then draw a line through the points. The point (1, 0) has been graphed for you.
**Sample answer given.**

**On the Back!** **Check students' work.**

5. Ernie drew a rectangle with an area, $a$, that was 2 times its width, $w$. Use the equation $a = 2w$ and the values $w = 1$, $w = 2$, and a third value of your choice to make a table. Then use the table to make a graph.

R 5-4

## On-Level and Advanced Activity Centers  

### Problem-Solving Reading Mat

Have students read the Problem-Solving Reading Mat for Topic 5 and then complete Problem-Solving Reading Activity 5-4.

See the Problem-Solving Reading Activity Guide for other suggestions on how to use this mat.

**TIMING**

The time allocated to Step 3 will depend on the teacher's instructional decisions and differentiation routines.

15–30 min

PEARSON realize. PearsonRealize.com

Help | Practice Buddy | Tools | Games

## Technology Center   

 Tools  Games

### Math Tools and Math Games

A link to a specific math tools activity or math game to use with this lesson is provided at PearsonRealize.com.

## Leveled Assignment  Items 1–4, 7, 8  Items 1, 3–8  Items 2–8

Name ______________________

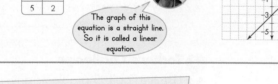

Help | Practice Buddy | Tools | Games

**Homework & Practice 5-4**
**Graph Equations**

**Another Look!**

Graph the equation $y = x - 3$.

First make a table. Use at least 3 values for the independent variable, $x$, in this problem. Find the corresponding values for the dependent variable.

| $y = x - 3$ | |
|---|---|
| $x$ | $y$ |
| 3 | 0 |
| 4 | 1 |
| 5 | 2 |

Graph each ordered pair on the coordinate plane. Then draw a line connecting the points.

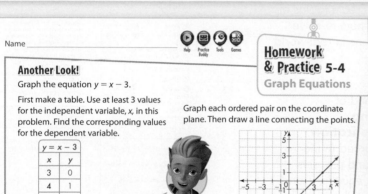

The graph of this equation is a straight line. So it is called a linear equation.

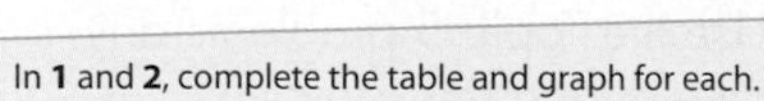

In **1** and **2**, complete the table and graph for each.

**1.** Bodie drew a triangle. The base of his triangle is $\frac{1}{2}$ the height of the triangle.

Let $h$ = height.
Let $b$ = base.
Graph $b = \frac{h}{2}$.

| $b = \frac{h}{2}$ | |
|---|---|
| $h$ | $b$ |
| 1 | $\frac{1}{2}$ |
| 2 | 1 |
| 3 | $1\frac{1}{2}$ |

**2.** Eva's mother will add $5 to all other donations she collects for the school fund drive.

Let $a$ = all other donations.
Let $t$ = total donations.
Graph $t = a + 5$.

| $t = a + 5$ | |
|---|---|
| $a$ | $t$ |
| 10 | 15 |
| 20 | 25 |
| 30 | 35 |



**3. Math and Science** People get energy from the food they eat. This energy is measured in calories. When you exercise, you use up or burn calories. The picture at the right shows about how many calories a 125-pound person burns each minute bowling. How many calories does a 125-pound person burn in 2 hours of bowling?
**About 360 calories**

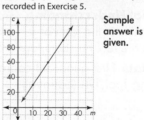

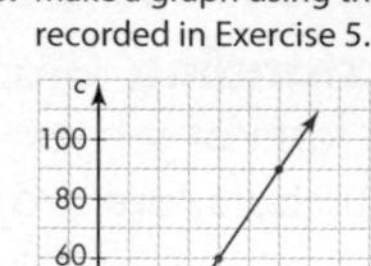


**4.** **MP.4 Model with Math** Use the information from Exercise 3 to write an equation representing the number of calories burned each minute while bowling. Let $m$ represent the number of minutes a 125 pound person bowls. Let $c$ represent the number of calories burned.
**Sample answer: $c = 3 \cdot m$**

**5.** Make a table for the equation you wrote in Exercise 4. **Sample answers given.**

| $m$ | $c$ |
|---|---|
| 10 | 30 |
| 20 | 60 |
| 30 | 90 |

**6.** Make a graph using the table data you recorded in Exercise 5. **Sample answer is given.**

**7. Higher Order Thinking** A 185-pound person burns about 64.5 calories every 15 minutes while bowling. Write an equation to represent how many calories a 185-pound person burns every minute. Will a 185-pound person or a 125-pound person burn more calories in 1 hour of bowling? Explain. **Sample answer: $c = 4.3 \cdot m$; The 185-lb person will burn more calories. A 185-lb person burns about 1.3 more calories each minute than a 125-lb person.**

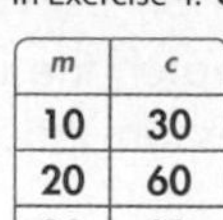

**Common Core Assessment**

**8.** Which equation represents the table on the right?

| $x$ | $y$ |
|---|---|
| 0 | 0 |
| 2 | 5 |
| 4 | 10 |

Ⓐ $y = 2x$
● $y = 2.5x$
Ⓒ $y = x + 3$
Ⓓ $y = x + 6$

# LESSON 5-5

# CONTINUE TO GRAPH EQUATIONS

## DIGITAL RESOURCES PearsonRealize.com

eText — Student and Teacher eTexts

PD — Listen and Look For Lesson Video

Think — Today's Challenge

Solve — Solve and Share

Learn — Visual Learning Animation Plus

Glossary — Animated Glossary

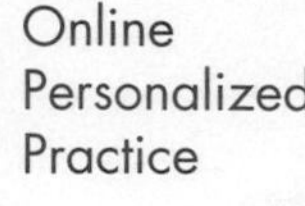
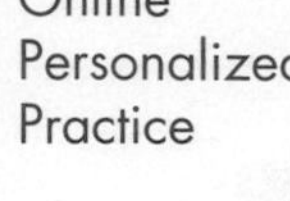
Practice Buddy — Online Personalized Practice

Tools — Math Tools

Assessment — Quick Check

Help — Another Look Homework Video

Games — Math Games

## LESSON OVERVIEW  FOCUS • COHERENCE • RIGOR

### FOCUS

**Domain 6.EE** Expressions and Equations

**Cluster 6.EE.C** Represent and analyze quantitative relationships between dependent and independent variables.

**Content Standard 6.EE.C.9** Use variables to represent two quantities in a real-world problem that change in relationship to one another; write an equation to express one quantity, thought of as the dependent variable, in terms of the other quantity, thought of as the independent variable. Analyze the relationship between the dependent and independent variables using graphs and tables, and relate these to the equation.

**Mathematical Practices MP.2, MP.3, MP.4, MP.8**

**Objective** Graph linear equations involving more than one operation.

**Essential Understanding** Graphs of relationships in the form of $y = ax + b$, where $a$ and $b$ are real numbers, are straight lines.

**Materials** First quadrant coordinate grids (Teaching Tool 18) (optional)

### COHERENCE

In the previous lesson, students learned how to graph relationships in the form of $y = ax$ and $y = x + a$, where $a$ is a real number. In this lesson, they extend this knowledge of graphing one-step linear equations to graph linear equations involving more than one operation. Students will create tables of values and graphs, and use them to solve problems and make predictions in real-world contexts.

### RIGOR

This lesson emphasizes a blend of **conceptual understanding, procedural skill,** and **application**. Students apply what they learned in the previous lesson to generate and plot sets of ordered pairs for two-step equations and analyze the graphs to solve mathematical and real-world problems.

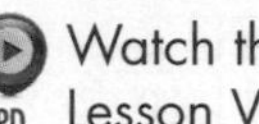
PD Watch the Listen and Look For Lesson Video.

## MATH ANYTIME

### Daily Common Core Review

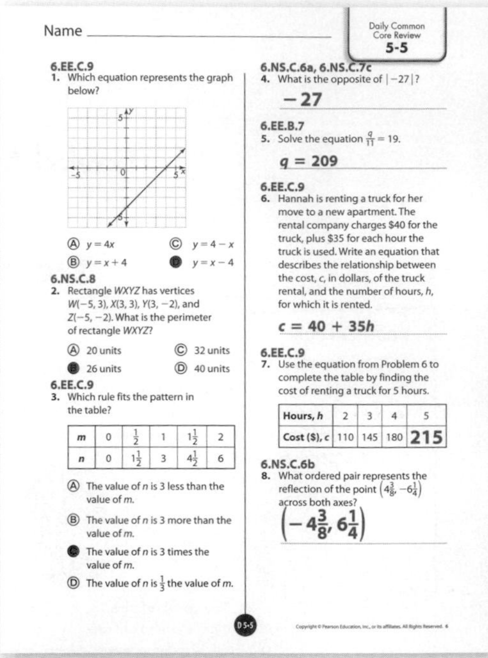

Name ______

Daily Common Core Review 5-5

6.EE.C.9
1. Which equation represents the graph below?



Ⓐ $y = 4x$
Ⓑ $y = x + 4$
Ⓒ $y = 4 - x$
● $y = x - 4$

6.NS.C.8
2. Rectangle $WXYZ$ has vertices $W(-5, 3)$, $X(3, 3)$, $Y(3, -2)$, and $Z(-5, -2)$. What is the perimeter of rectangle $WXYZ$?

Ⓐ 20 units
● 26 units
Ⓒ 32 units
Ⓓ 40 units

6.EE.C.9
3. Which rule fits the pattern in the table?

| $m$ | 0 | $\frac{1}{2}$ | 1 | $1\frac{1}{2}$ | 2 |
|---|---|---|---|---|---|
| $n$ | 0 | $1\frac{1}{2}$ | 3 | $4\frac{1}{2}$ | 6 |

Ⓐ The value of $n$ is 3 less than the value of $m$.
Ⓑ The value of $n$ is 3 more than the value of $m$.
● The value of $n$ is 3 times the value of $m$.
Ⓓ The value of $n$ is $\frac{1}{3}$ the value of $m$.

6.NS.C.6a, 6.NS.C.7c
4. What is the opposite of $|-27|$?

**−27**

6.EE.B.7
5. Solve the equation $\frac{q}{11} = 19$.

**$q = 209$**

6.EE.C.9
6. Hannah is renting a truck for her move to a new apartment. The rental company charges $40 for the truck, plus $35 for each hour the truck is used. Write an equation that describes the relationship between the cost, $c$, in dollars, of the truck rental, and the number of hours, $h$, for which it is rented.

**$c = 40 + 35h$**

6.EE.C.9
7. Use the equation from Problem 6 to complete the table by finding the cost of renting a truck for 5 hours.

| Hours, $h$ | 2 | 3 | 4 | 5 |
|---|---|---|---|---|
| Cost ($), $c$ | 110 | 145 | 180 | **215** |

6.NS.C.6b
8. What ordered pair represents the reflection of the point $\left(4\frac{3}{8}, -6\frac{1}{4}\right)$ across both axes?

**$\left(-4\frac{3}{8}, 6\frac{1}{4}\right)$**

D 5-5



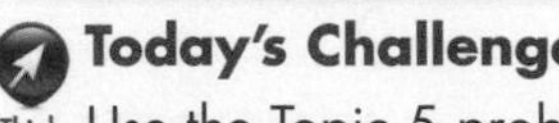

### Today's Challenge

Think Use the Topic 5 problems any time during this topic.

## ENGLISH LANGUAGE LEARNERS 

**Listening** Demonstrate listening comprehension by summarizing.

*Use with the Visual Learning Bridge on Student's Edition p. 252.*

Read Box A and ask students to summarize the information. Read Box B. Point to each row in the table. *After 2 hours, the temperature is 10°C. After 4 hours, the temperature is 14°C.* Read Box C. Point to the coordinate plane. *Can you use the coordinate plane to determine what the temperature is after 1, 3, or 5 hours? How do you know?* Instruct students to summarize information that will help them determine the temperatures.

**Beginning** Have students listen as partners summarize using the sentence stem: After 1 hour, the temperature will be ___. Continue the process for 3 and 5 hours. Instruct students to point to information on the coordinate plane that helped them make their conclusions.

**Intermediate** Have students listen as partners summarize using the sentence stem: After 1 hour, the temperature will be ___ because ___. Continue the process for 3 and 5 hours. Instruct students to identify information on the coordinate plane that helped them make their conclusions.

**Advanced** Have students listen to partners summarize the information. Instruct students to explain how they used the coordinate plane to make their conclusions.

**Summarize** What information can be gathered using the coordinate plane?

STEP
1

# DEVELOP: PROBLEM-BASED LEARNING

PEARSON realize.
PearsonRealize.com

**COHERENCE: Engage learners by connecting prior knowledge to new ideas.**
Students extend their understanding of graphing one-step linear equations to graph linear equations with more than one operation.

10–15 min

Solve

## BEFORE

**1. Pose the Solve-and-Share Problem**
**MP.8 Generalize** Listen and look for students who generalize the process they learned for graphing one-step equations to complete the table and graph the two-step equation.

**2. Build Understanding**
*How can you tell from looking at the coordinate plane that m is the independent variable?* [The horizontal axis is labeled $m$.] *Use the problem context to explain why c is the dependent variable.* [The contribution amount, $c$, depends on the number of miles, $m$, that Greg walks.]

## DURING

**3. Ask Guiding Questions As Needed**
*If Greg walks 1 mile, how much will his grandmother contribute?* [\$3] *So, what ordered pair do you plot on the coordinate plane?* [(1, 3)] *In the table, could you have used values for m other than the ones given? Explain.* [Yes. You can substitute any non-negative value for $m$ to find the corresponding value of $c$.] *Why shouldn't the graph extend to the left of the y-axis?* [Greg cannot walk a negative number of miles, so $m \geq 0$.]

## AFTER

**4. Share and Discuss Solutions**
Start with students' solutions. If needed, project Kent's work to discuss how to complete the table of values and draw a line.

**5. Transition to the Visual Learning Bridge**
*Some real-world situations can be represented by linear equations, which can be graphed as a straight line.*

**6. Extension for Early Finishers**
*Graph the equation* $c = \frac{1}{2}m + 1$. [Check students' graphs.]

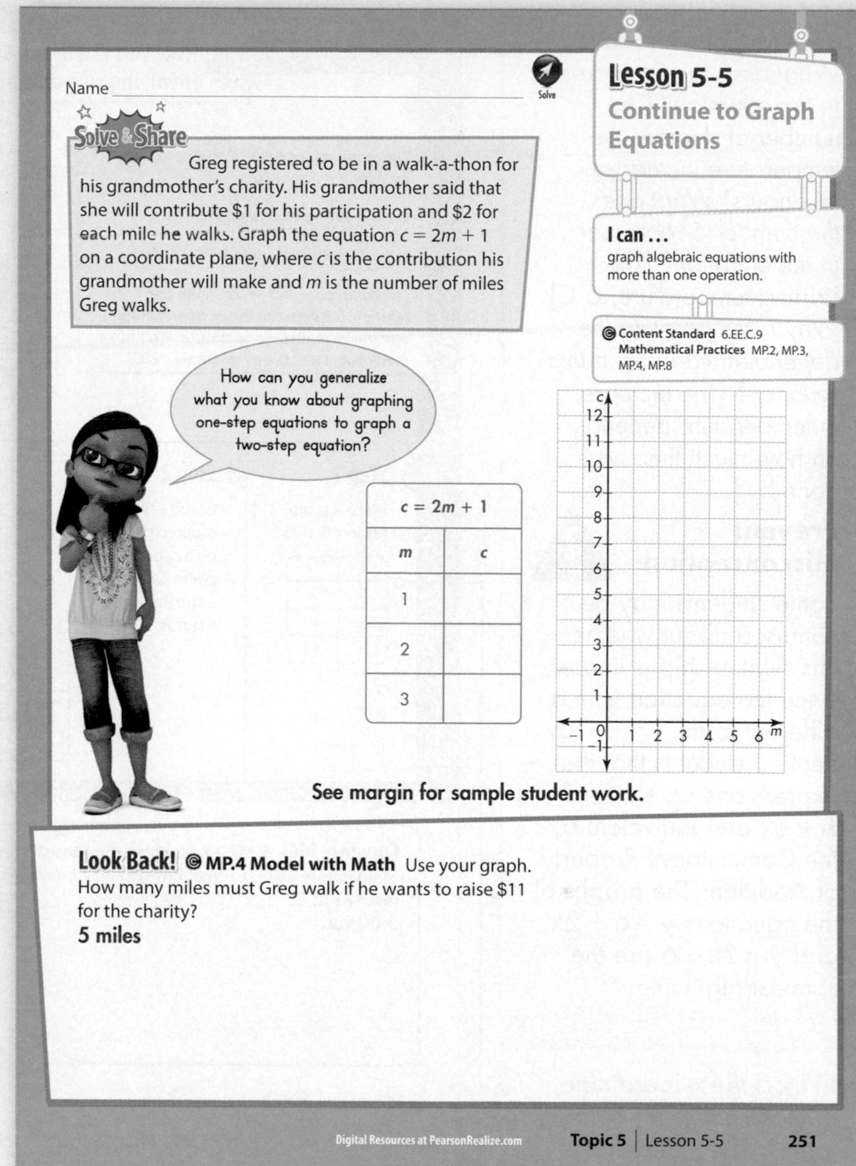

Name

Solve & Share

Greg registered to be in a walk-a-thon for his grandmother's charity. His grandmother said that she will contribute \$1 for his participation and \$2 for each mile he walks. Graph the equation $c = 2m + 1$ on a coordinate plane, where $c$ is the contribution his grandmother will make and $m$ is the number of miles Greg walks.

**Lesson 5-5**
**Continue to Graph Equations**

**I can ...**
graph algebraic equations with more than one operation.

**Content Standard** 6.EE.C.9
**Mathematical Practices** MP.2, MP.3, MP.4, MP.8

How can you generalize what you know about graphing one-step equations to graph a two-step equation?

| $c = 2m + 1$ | |
|---|---|
| $m$ | $c$ |
| 1 | |
| 2 | |
| 3 | |

**See margin for sample student work.**

**Look Back!** **MP.4 Model with Math** Use your graph.
How many miles must Greg walk if he wants to raise \$11 for the charity?
**5 miles**

Digital Resources at PearsonRealize.com    Topic 5 | Lesson 5-5    251

## Analyze Student Work

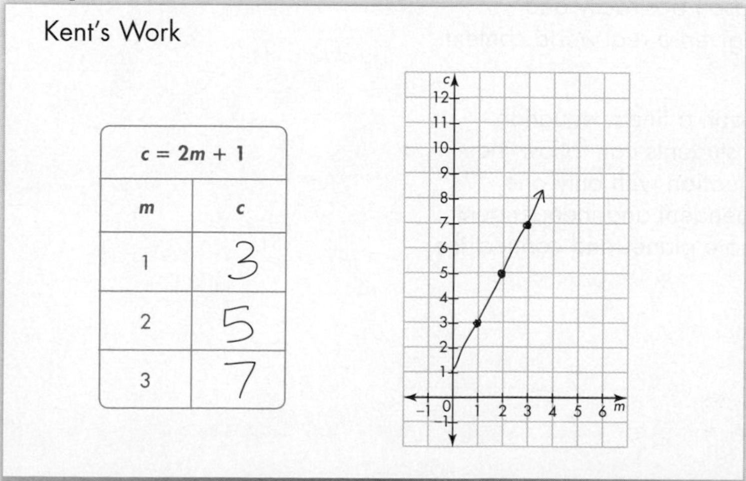

Kent's Work

| $c = 2m + 1$ | |
|---|---|
| $m$ | $c$ |
| 1 | 3 |
| 2 | 5 |
| 3 | 7 |

Kent completes the table, plots the three ordered pairs on the coordinate plane, and draws a line to connect the points. He does not extend the line to the left of $m = 0$.

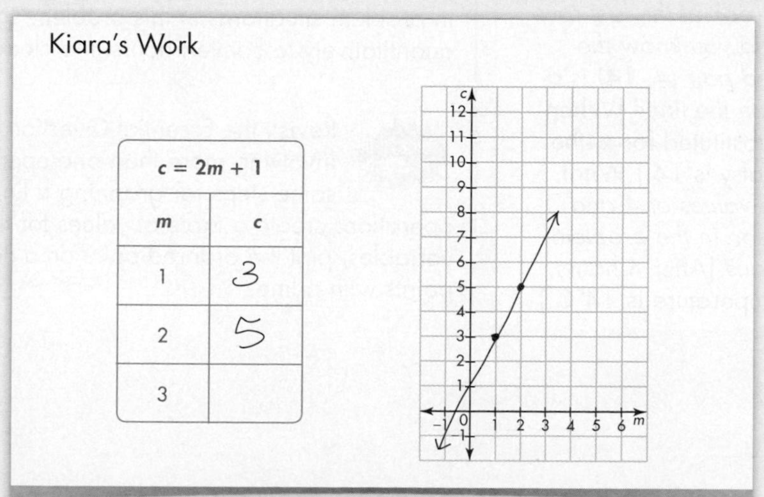

Kiara's Work

| $c = 2m + 1$ | |
|---|---|
| $m$ | $c$ |
| 1 | 3 |
| 2 | 5 |
| 3 | |

Kiara connects two correct points on the coordinate plane, but she does not complete the table nor graph a third point. She does not consider the real-world situation and extends the line beyond the $y$-axis.

## STEP 2 DEVELOP: VISUAL LEARNING

The *Visual Learning Bridge* connects students' thinking in Solve & Share to important math ideas in the lesson. Use the *Visual Learning Bridge* to make these ideas explicit. Also available as a *Visual Learning Animation Plus* at PearsonRealize.com

PEARSON realize. PearsonRealize.com

**MP.4 Model with Math**
*What does the 2x represent in the equation?* [The number of degrees the temperature increased in x hours] *What does the number 6 represent in the equation?* [The starting temperature, 6°C] *Why is temperature the dependent variable in this situation?* [The increase in temperature depends on how much time has gone by.]

**Prevent Misconceptions** (RtI 1)
Some students may be confused about whether this relationship is linear since the equation is in a different form, $y = b + ax$. Remind students that the expressions $ax + b$ and $b + ax$ are equivalent by the Commutative Property of Addition. The graphs of the equations $y = 6 + 2x$ and $y = 2x + 6$ are the same straight line.

*Why is the x-coordinate in the first column of the table?* [The independent variable is the first coordinate in an ordered pair.] *Look at the last row. How do you know the ordered pair (4, 14) is a point on the line?* [When 4 is substituted for x, the value of y is 14.] *What do the values of 4 and 14 mean in the problem situation?* [After 4 hours, the temperature is 14°C.]

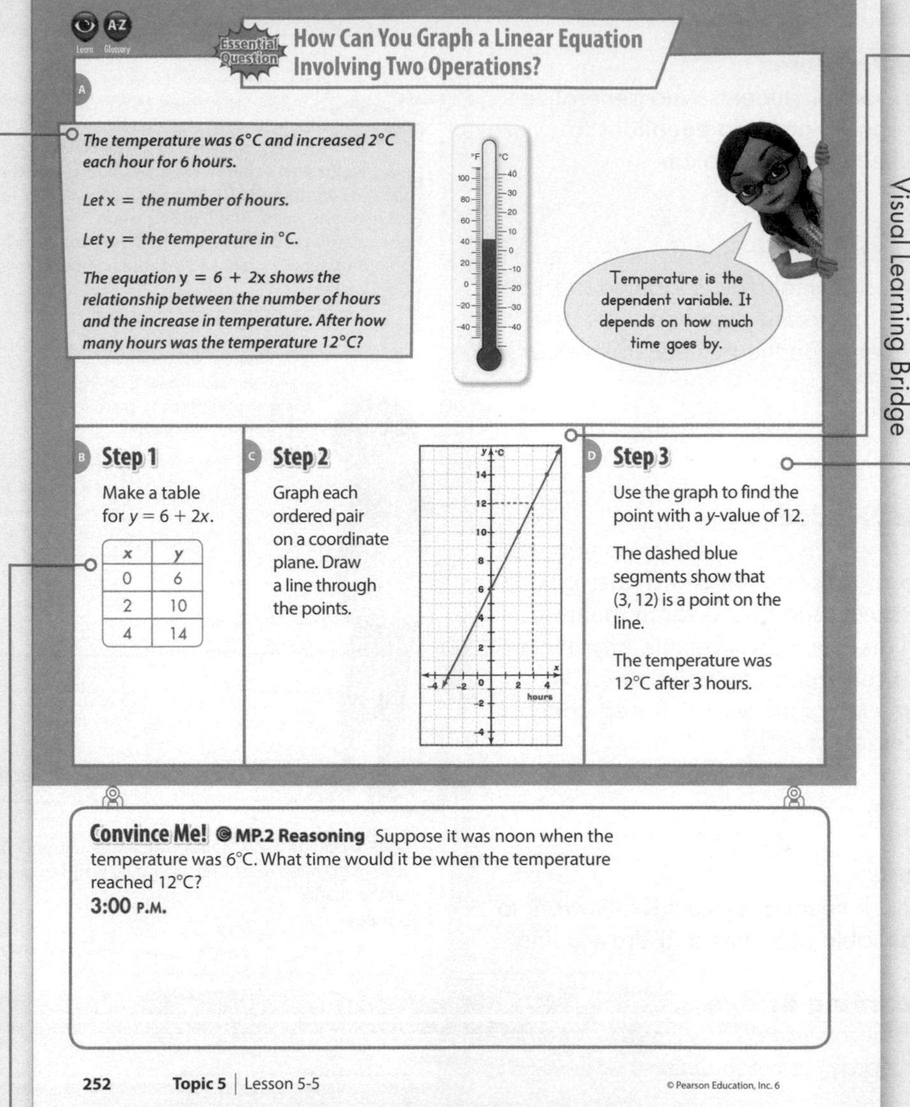


**MP.2 Reason Quantitatively**
*Where is the graph of the point (0, 6)?* [On the y-axis] *What does this point represent?* [The initial temperature, before any hours have passed]

**MP.8 Generalize**
*In this problem, what does a y-value of 12 represent?* [A temperature of 12°C] *Using the graph, after how many hours is the temperature 12°C? Explain how you found your answer.* [3 hours; Sample answer: From 12 on the y-axis, I followed the horizontal blue gridline until it intersected with the line of the equation. From that point, I followed the vertical blue gridline to the x-axis. The value on the x-axis was 3, representing 3 hours.] *How can you use the equation $y = 6 + 2x$ to check that (3, 12) is a point on the line?* [Substitute the x- and y-coordinates into the equation, and evaluate to check if the equation is true.]

**Convince Me! MP.2 Reason Quantitatively** Mathematically proficient students make sense of quantities and their relationships in problem situations. In this problem, they reason abstractly and quantitatively to convert hours into clock time given a real-world context.

**Essential Question** Revisit the Essential Question. To graph a linear equation involving more than one operation, students can follow the same steps for graphing a linear equation with only one operation: create a table of values for the dependent and independent variables, plot the ordered pairs on a coordinate plane, and connect the points with a line.

PEARSON realize. PearsonRealize.com

**QUICK CHECK**

Check mark indicates items for prescribing differentiation on the next page.
Item 4 is worth 1 point. Items 8 and 9 are worth up to 2 points.

20–30 min

Practice Buddy | Tools | Assessment

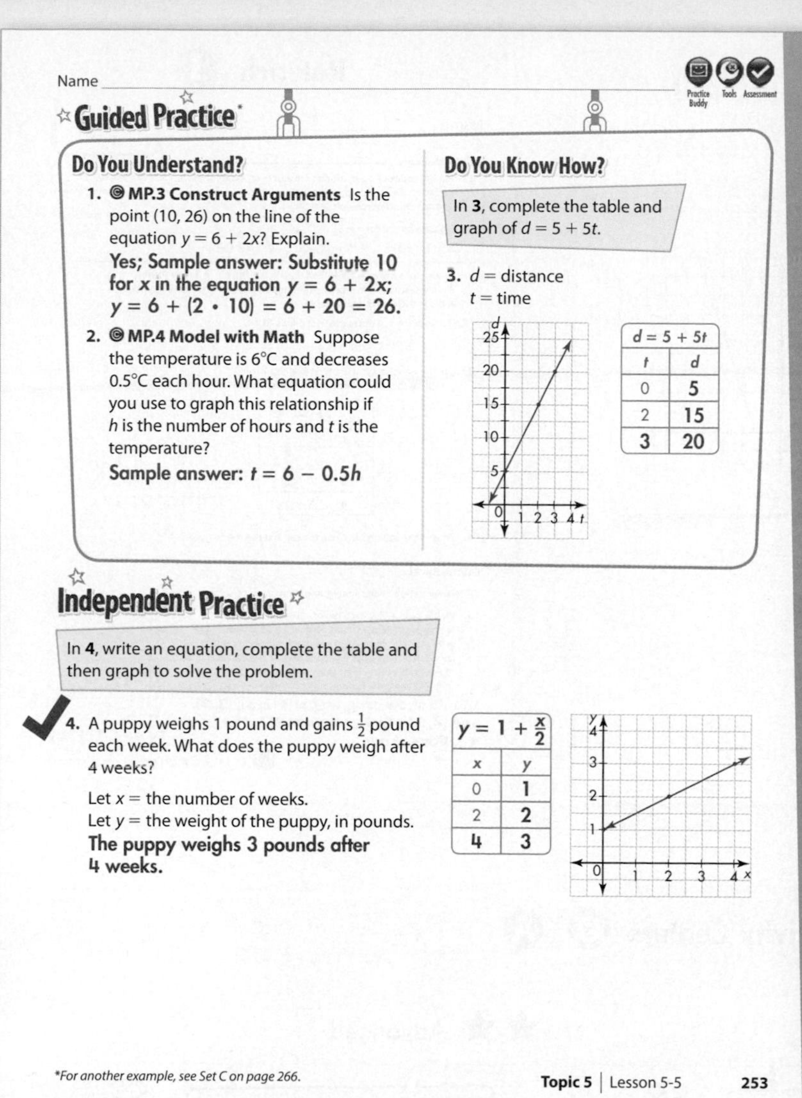

Name

## Guided Practice

**Do You Understand?**

1. **MP.3 Construct Arguments** Is the point (10, 26) on the line of the equation $y = 6 + 2x$? Explain.
**Yes; Sample answer: Substitute 10 for x in the equation $y = 6 + 2x$; $y = 6 + (2 \cdot 10) = 6 + 20 = 26$.**

2. **MP.4 Model with Math** Suppose the temperature is 6°C and decreases 0.5°C each hour. What equation could you use to graph this relationship if *h* is the number of hours and *t* is the temperature?
**Sample answer: $t = 6 - 0.5h$**

**Do You Know How?**

In **3**, complete the table and graph of $d = 5 + 5t$.

3. $d$ = distance
$t$ = time

| $t$ | $d$ |
|---|---|
| 0 | 5 |
| 2 | 15 |
| 3 | 20 |

## Independent Practice

In **4**, write an equation, complete the table and then graph to solve the problem.

4. A puppy weighs 1 pound and gains $\frac{1}{2}$ pound each week. What does the puppy weigh after 4 weeks?
Let $x$ = the number of weeks.
Let $y$ = the weight of the puppy, in pounds.
**The puppy weighs 3 pounds after 4 weeks.**

$y = 1 + \frac{x}{2}$

| $x$ | $y$ |
|---|---|
| 0 | 1 |
| 2 | 2 |
| 4 | 3 |

*For another example, see Set C on page 266.

Topic 5 | Lesson 5-5 253

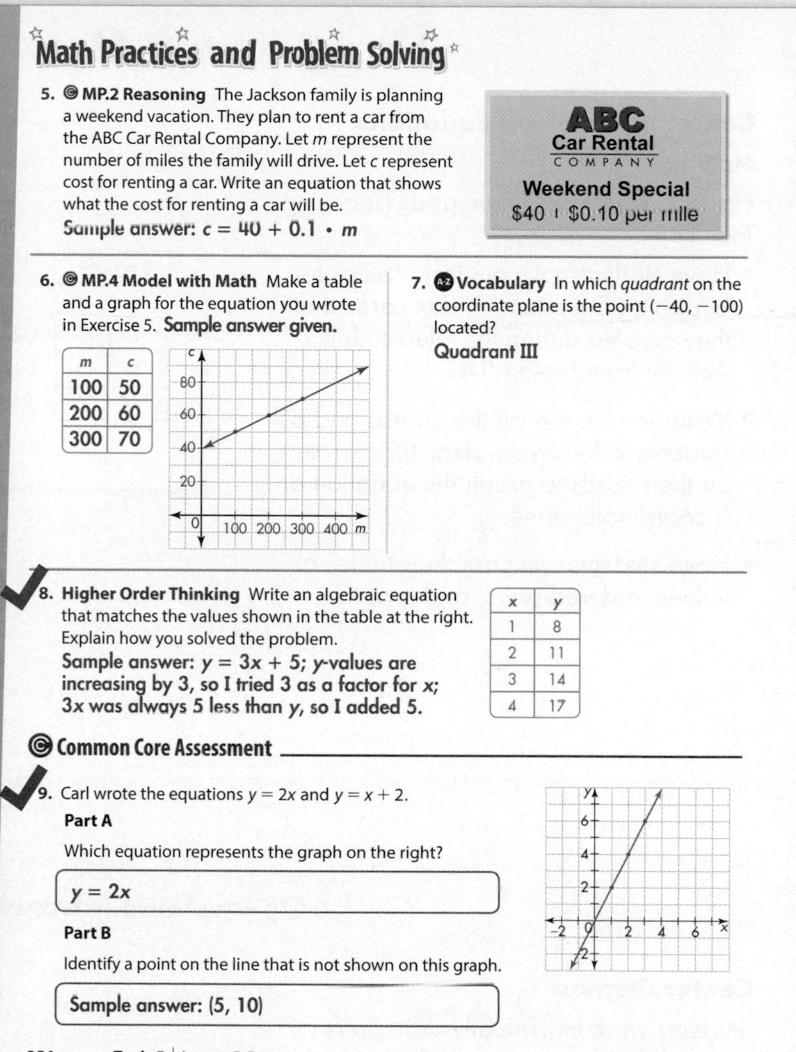

## Math Practices and Problem Solving

5. **MP.2 Reasoning** The Jackson family is planning a weekend vacation. They plan to rent a car from the ABC Car Rental Company. Let *m* represent the number of miles the family will drive. Let *c* represent cost for renting a car. Write an equation that shows what the cost for renting a car will be.
**Sample answer: $c = 40 + 0.1 \cdot m$**

ABC Car Rental COMPANY
Weekend Special
$40 + $0.10 per mile

6. **MP.4 Model with Math** Make a table and a graph for the equation you wrote in Exercise 5. **Sample answer given.**

| $m$ | $c$ |
|---|---|
| 100 | 50 |
| 200 | 60 |
| 300 | 70 |

7. **Vocabulary** In which *quadrant* on the coordinate plane is the point (−40, −100) located?
**Quadrant III**

8. **Higher Order Thinking** Write an algebraic equation that matches the values shown in the table at the right. Explain how you solved the problem.
**Sample answer: $y = 3x + 5$; y-values are increasing by 3, so I tried 3 as a factor for x; 3x was always 5 less than y, so I added 5.**

| $x$ | $y$ |
|---|---|
| 1 | 8 |
| 2 | 11 |
| 3 | 14 |
| 4 | 17 |

**Common Core Assessment**

9. Carl wrote the equations $y = 2x$ and $y = x + 2$.
**Part A**
Which equation represents the graph on the right?
**$y = 2x$**
**Part B**
Identify a point on the line that is not shown on this graph.
**Sample answer: (5, 10)**

254 Topic 5 | Lesson 5-5 © Pearson Education, Inc. 6

### Error Intervention: Item 1

**If** students have difficulty determining whether a point is on a line,
**then** say: *A point is on the line of an equation if its coordinates make the equation true. What does the 10 in the ordered pair (10, 26) represent?* [x-coordinate] *The 26?* [y-coordinate] *How do you know if (10, 26) is a solution to the equation? Explain.* [Sample answer: Substitute 10 for *x* and 26 for *y* in the equation. Both sides of the equal sign have the same value, so (10, 26) is on the line.]

**Item 3** Be sure students examine the labels on the axes of the coordinate plane before they begin graphing points. Students should notice that each horizontal grid line represents 1, but each vertical grid line represents 2.5.

**Reteaching** Assign Reteaching Set C on p. 266.

**Item 6 MP.4 Model with Math** Students may not be sure how to complete a blank table. Tell students that they choose a value of *m* and then use substitution and evaluate to find the corresponding value of *c* to complete the table. It may be helpful to discuss with the class how they can choose reasonable values, as well as how to choose an appropriate scale to label the axes of the graph.

**Item 8 Higher Order Thinking** Students might see that the *y*-values in the table increase by 3 and mistakenly conclude that the equation must contain the operation "+ 3." Point out that multiplication is the same as repeated addition. You may want to have students complete a simpler table of values using the equation $y = 3x$ in order to illustrate how the *y*-values increase by 3 as *x*-values increase by 1. Once they understand that the equation for Item 8 may involve the term "3x," then ask if they can find a pattern in the given table by adding to or subtracting from 3x to get to the *y*-value.

**Multi-Step Problems** *Page 254 Items 5, 6, and 8; Page 256 Items 2–5*

# ASSESS AND DIFFERENTIATE

Use the **QUICK CHECK** on the previous page to prescribe differentiated instruction.

2 RtI

**I Intervention** 0–3 points on the Quick Check

**O On-Level** 4 points on the Quick Check

**A Advanced** 5 points on the Quick Check

## Intervention Activity I

### Continue to Graph Equations

**Materials**

First quadrant coordinate grids (Teaching Tool 18)

- Have students take out their "Steps for Graphing Equations" index cards that they created during the Intervention Activity from Lesson 5-4.
- Write $y = 3x - 4$ on the board, and ask students to follow the steps they wrote on their cards to graph the equation on a coordinate plane.
- Have students compare their tables of values, ordered pairs, and graphs.

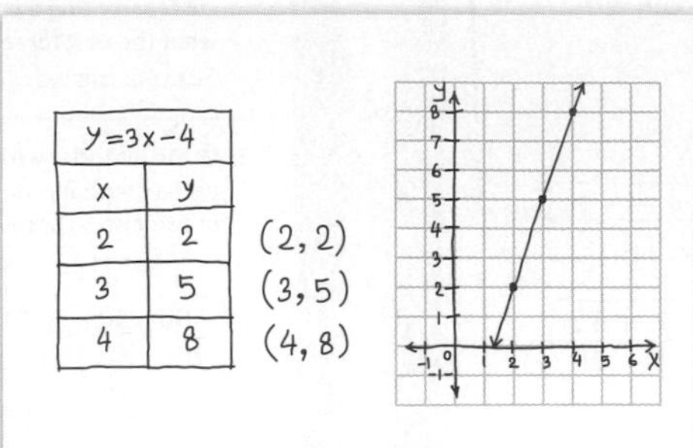


## Reteach I

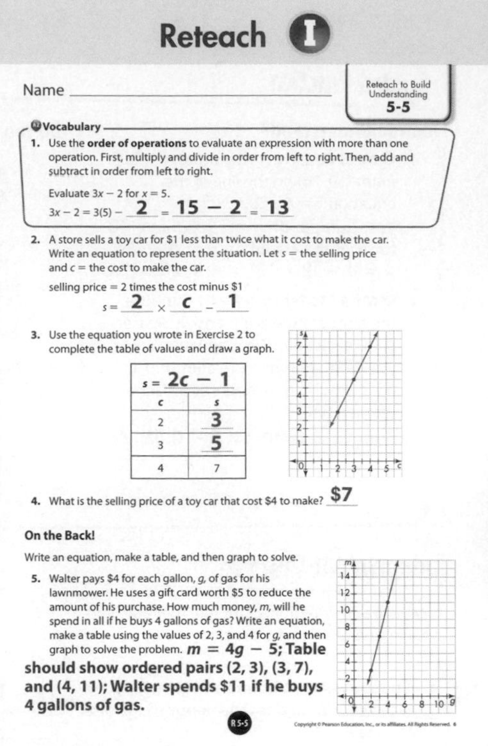

Name ______________________ Reteach to Build Understanding 5-5

**Vocabulary**

1. Use the **order of operations** to evaluate an expression with more than one operation. First, multiply and divide in order from left to right. Then, add and subtract in order from left to right.

   Evaluate $3x - 2$ for $x = 5$.

   $3x - 2 = 3(5) - $ **2** $=$ **15 − 2** $=$ **13**

2. A store sells a toy car for $1 less than twice what it cost to make the car. Write an equation to represent the situation. Let $s$ = the selling price and $c$ = the cost to make the car.

   selling price = 2 times the cost minus $1

   $s =$ **2** $\times$ **c** $-$ **1**

3. Use the equation you wrote in Exercise 2 to complete the table of values and draw a graph.

| $s =$ **2c − 1** | |
|---|---|
| c | s |
| 2 | **3** |
| 3 | **5** |
| 4 | 7 |

4. What is the selling price of a toy car that cost $4 to make? **$7**

**On the Back!**

Write an equation, make a table, and then graph to solve.

5. Walter pays $4 for each gallon, $g$, of gas for his lawnmower. He uses a gift card worth $5 to reduce the amount of his purchase. How much money, $m$, will he spend in all if he buys 4 gallons of gas? Write an equation, make a table using the values of 2, 3, and 4 for $g$, and then graph to solve the problem. **$m = 4g - 5$; Table should show ordered pairs (2, 3), (3, 7), and (4, 11); Walter spends $11 if he buys 4 gallons of gas.**

R 5-5



## On-Level and Advanced Activity Centers O A

### Center Games

Students work individually or in pairs to match linear equations with their corresponding graphs. Have students record their work as they play the game.

★ On-Level

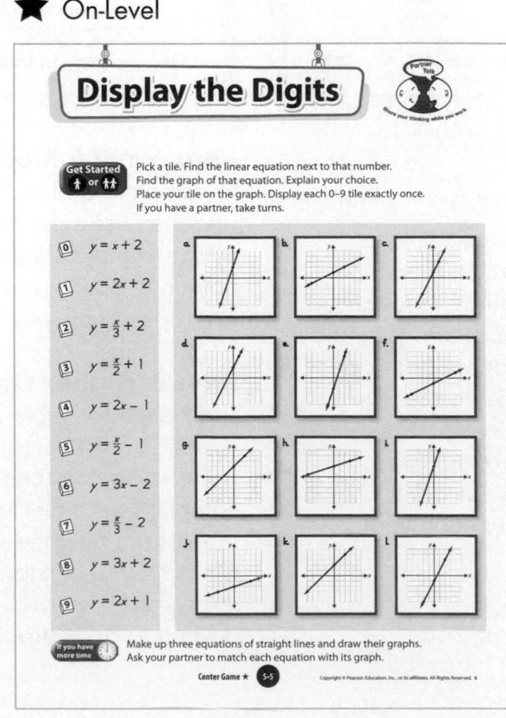

**Display the Digits**

Get Started: Pick a tile. Find the linear equation next to that number. Find the graph of that equation. Explain your choice. Place your tile on the graph. Display each 0–9 tile exactly once. If you have a partner, take turns.

0 $y = x + 2$
1 $y = 2x + 2$
2 $y = \frac{x}{3} + 2$
3 $y = \frac{x}{2} + 1$
4 $y = 2x - 1$
5 $y = \frac{x}{2} - 1$
6 $y = 3x - 2$
7 $y = \frac{x}{3} - 2$
8 $y = 3x + 2$
9 $y = 2x + 1$

If you have more time: Make up three equations of straight lines and draw their graphs. Ask your partner to match each equation with its graph.

Center Game ★ 5-5



★★ Advanced

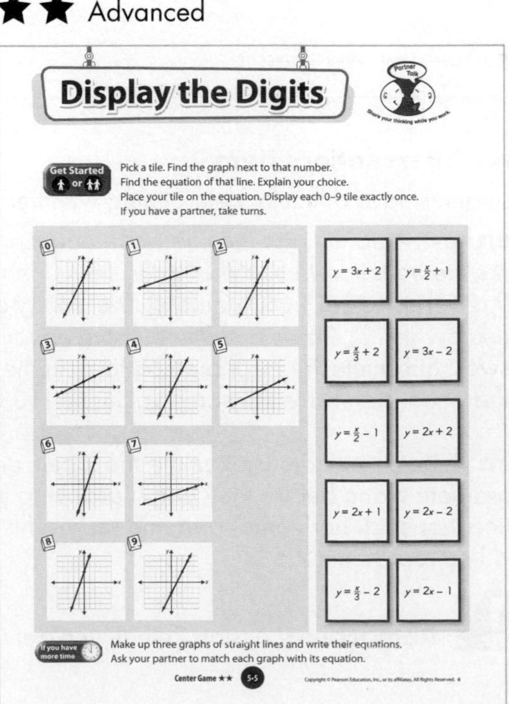

**Display the Digits**

Get Started: Pick a tile. Find the graph next to that number. Find the equation of that line. Explain your choice. Place your tile on the equation. Display each 0–9 tile exactly once. If you have a partner, take turns.

$y = 3x + 2$ | $y = \frac{x}{2} + 1$
$y = \frac{x}{3} + 2$ | $y = 3x - 2$
$y = \frac{x}{2} - 1$ | $y = 2x + 2$
$y = 2x + 1$ | $y = 2x - 2$
$y = \frac{x}{3} - 2$ | $y = 2x - 1$

If you have more time: Make up three graphs of straight lines and write their equations. Ask your partner to match each graph with its equation.

Center Game ★★ 5-5

## TIMING

The time allocated to Step 3 will depend on the teacher's instructional decisions and differentiation routines.

15–30 min

Help

Practice Buddy

Tools

Games

## Technology Center I O A

Tools

Games

### Math Tools and Math Games

A link to a specific math tools activity or math game to use with this lesson is provided at PearsonRealize.com.

## Leveled Assignment I Items 1–5 O Items 1–5 A Items 1–5

Name ______________________

**Homework & Practice 5-5**
**Continue to Graph Equations**

### Another Look!

Graph the equation $y = 2x - 4$.

First make a table. Choose at least 3 values for the independent variable, $x$. Find the corresponding values for the dependent variable, $y$.

| $y = 2x - 4$ | |
|---|---|
| $x$ | $y$ |
| 2 | 0 |
| 3 | 2 |
| 4 | 4 |

Graph each ordered pair on the coordinate plane. Then draw a line to connect the points.

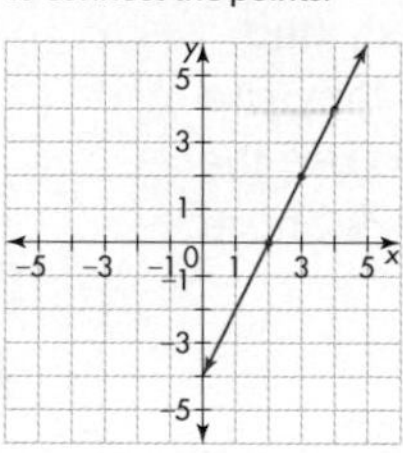

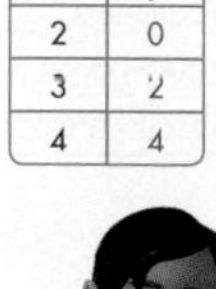

Use the same steps to graph an equation with more than one operation as you would to graph an equation with only one operation.

In **1**, write an equation, make a table and then graph to solve the problem.

1. An artist draws a collage of rectangles. The length of each rectangle is 2 units more than half its width. If the artist paints a rectangle that is 6 units wide, what is its length?

| $\ell = \frac{w}{2} + 2$ | |
|---|---|
| $w$ | $\ell$ |
| 2 | 3 |
| 4 | 4 |
| 6 | 5 |

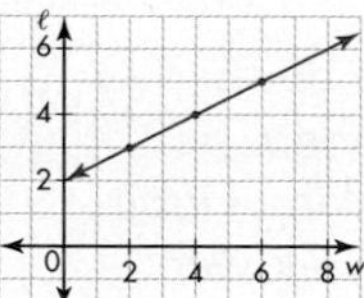

Let $\ell$ = the length of the rectangle.
Let $w$ = the width of the rectangle.
**The rectangle is 5 units in length.**



2. **Math and Science** Forensic anthropologists analyze skeletons to help solve crimes. They can use the length of a femur bone to estimate the height of a skeleton. The height of a skeleton is about 30 inches taller than twice the length of the femur bone. Let $h$ represent the height of a skeleton. Let $f$ represent the length of a femur bone. Write an equation to represent the height of a skeleton.
**Sample answer: $h = 30 + 2 \cdot f$**

Adult femur bones are often between 15 and 20 inches long.

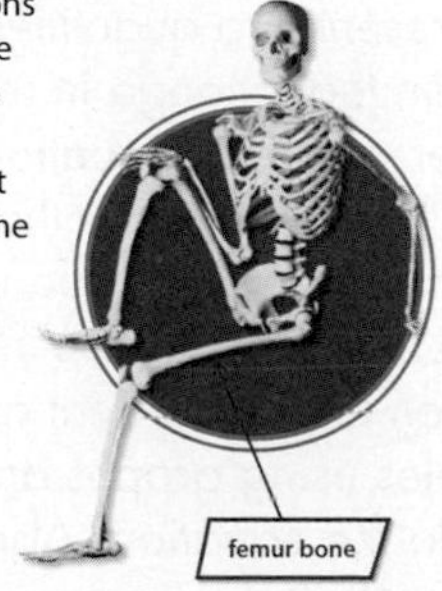


3. **MP.4 Model with Math** Make a table and a graph for the equation you wrote in Exercise 3.

| $f$ | $h$ |
|---|---|
| 10 | 50 |
| 15 | 60 |
| 20 | 70 |

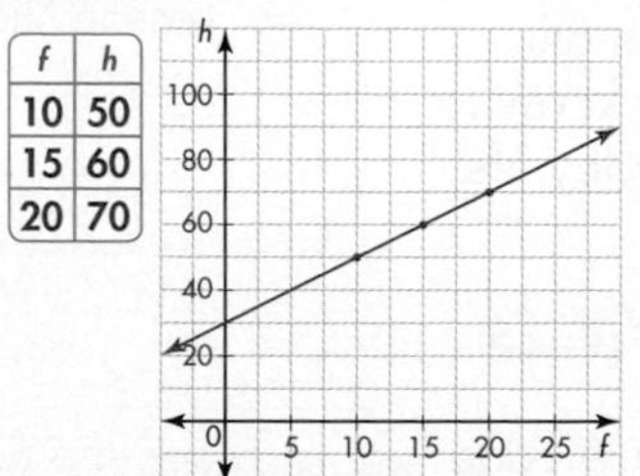

4. **Higher Order Thinking** Rhonda is 5 feet tall. About how long is her femur? Explain how you know.
**About 15 inches; Sample answer: 5 feet are equal to 60 inches. The T-table and graph I made for Exercise 4 show that a person who is 60 inches in height will have a femur that is about 15 inches.**

### Common Core Assessment

5. Ellen wrote the equations $y = 2\frac{1}{2} \cdot x + 1$ and $y = 2\frac{1}{2} \cdot x - 1$.

| $x$ | $y$ |
|---|---|
| 2 | 4 |
| 4 | 9 |
| 6 | 14 |

**Part A**

Which equation represents the table on the right?

$y = 2\frac{1}{2} \cdot x - 1$

**Part B**

If $x = 10$, what is the value of $y$ that would be recorded in the table?

24

MATH PRACTICES AND PROBLEM SOLVING | LESSON **5-6**

# MODEL WITH MATH

## DIGITAL RESOURCES PearsonRealize.com

eText — Student and Teacher eTexts

PD — Listen and Look For Lesson Video

Think — Today's Challenge

Solve — Solve and Share

Learn — Visual Learning Animation Plus

Glossary — Animated Glossary

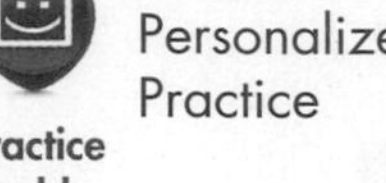
Practice Buddy — Online Personalized Practice

Tools — Math Tools

Assessment — Quick Check

Help — Another Look Homework Video

Games — Math Games

MP — Math Practices Animations

## LESSON OVERVIEW FCR FOCUS • COHERENCE • RIGOR

### FOCUS

**Mathematical Practices MP.4** Model with mathematics. Also **MP.1, MP.5, MP.6, MP.7**

**Domain 6.EE** Expressions and Equations

**Cluster 6.EE.C** Represent and analyze quantitative relationships between dependent and independent variables.

**Content Standard 6.EE.C.9** Use variables to represent two quantities in a real-world problem that change in relationship to one another; write an equation to express one quantity, thought of as the dependent variable, in terms of the other quantity, thought of as the independent variable. Analyze the relationship between the dependent and independent variables using graphs and tables, and relate these to the equation. Also **6.EE.B.5**.

**Objective** Use math models to represent and solve problems involving previously learned concepts and skills.

**Essential Understanding** Good math thinkers choose and apply math they know to show and solve problems from everyday life.

### COHERENCE

Throughout this program, students model with math to solve problems in real-world situations. This lesson focuses on MP.4 to represent and solve problems about linear relationships. To model these relationships, students use the skills they learned in this topic: identifying dependent and independent variables, finding patterns in tables, writing equations, and graphing on a coordinate plane.

### RIGOR

This lesson emphasizes **application** with a focus on MP.4. Students will also engage other mathematical practices such as MP.1, MP.5, MP.6, and MP.7 to make sense of and analyze real-world situations, represent them accurately in a mathematical context, and persevere to correctly answer what they are asked to find. Encourage students to use the Thinking Habits shown in the Solve & Share.

PD Watch the Listen and Look For Lesson Video.

## MATH ANYTIME

### Daily Common Core Review

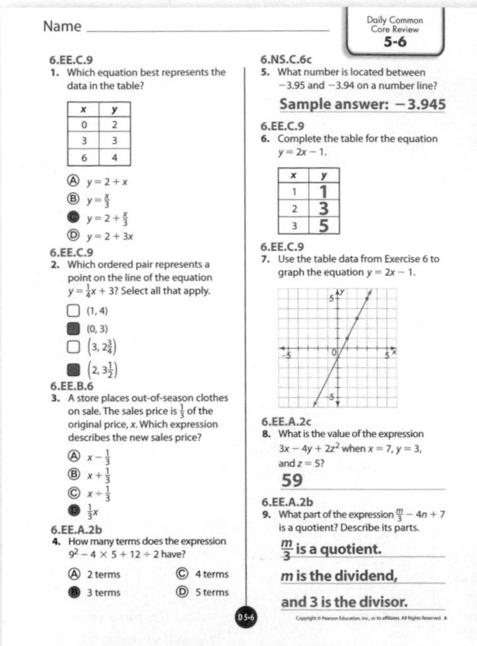
Name ____________  Daily Common Core Review 5-6

6.EE.C.9
1. Which equation best represents the data in the table?

| x | y |
|---|---|
| 0 | 2 |
| 3 | 3 |
| 6 | 4 |

Ⓐ $y = 2 + x$
Ⓑ $y = \frac{x}{3}$
● $y = 2 + \frac{x}{3}$
Ⓓ $y = 2 + 3x$

6.EE.C.9
2. Which ordered pair represents a point on the line of the equation $y = \frac{1}{4}x + 3$? Select all that apply.

☐ (1, 4)
■ (0, 3)
☐ $\left(3, 2\frac{3}{4}\right)$
■ $\left(2, 3\frac{1}{2}\right)$

6.EE.B.6
3. A store places out-of-season clothes on sale. The sales price is $\frac{1}{3}$ of the original price, x. Which expression describes the new sales price?

Ⓐ $x - \frac{1}{3}$
Ⓑ $x + \frac{1}{3}$
Ⓒ $x \div \frac{1}{3}$
● $\frac{1}{3}x$

6.EE.A.2b
4. How many terms does the expression $9^2 - 4 \times 5 + 12 \div 2$ have?

Ⓐ 2 terms
● 3 terms
Ⓒ 4 terms
Ⓓ 5 terms

6.NS.C.6c
5. What number is located between −3.95 and −3.94 on a number line?

**Sample answer: −3.945**

6.EE.C.9
6. Complete the table for the equation $y = 2x - 1$.

| x | y |
|---|---|
| 1 | **1** |
| 2 | **3** |
| 3 | **5** |

6.EE.C.9
7. Use the table data from Exercise 6 to graph the equation $y = 2x - 1$.

6.EE.A.2c
8. What is the value of the expression $3x - 4y + 2z^2$ when $x = 7$, $y = 3$, and $z = 5$?

**59**

6.EE.A.2b
9. What part of the expression $\frac{m}{3} - 4n + 7$ is a quotient? Describe its parts.

**$\frac{m}{3}$ is a quotient.**
***m* is the dividend,**
**and 3 is the divisor.**

D 5-6

### Today's Challenge

Think Use the Topic 5 problems any time during this topic.

## ENGLISH LANGUAGE LEARNERS 

**Learning Strategies** Use prior knowledge to understand meanings.

*Use with the Solve & Share on Student's Edition p. 257.*

Read the Solve & Share. *What have you previously learned that will help you solve this problem?* Have students share with partners. Then read the Thinking Habits for modeling with math.

**Beginning** *What math have you used to solve problems?* Write *words, numbers, table,* and *symbols.* Point to *words. What words in the Solve & Share can be used to solve the problem?* Point to numbers. *What numbers?* Read the second Thinking Habit. *What equation can be used?* Work with students to write an equation to solve the problem.

**Intermediate** *What math have you used to solve problems?* Write *words, numbers, table,* and *symbols. Which of these can you use to solve the problem?* Have students respond using the sentence stem: I will use ___ because ___. Read the second Thinking Habit. *What equation can be used?* Instruct students to work with partners to write an equation to solve the problem. Have student pairs share their equations with other pairs.

**Advanced** Instruct students to work with partners to answer each Thinking Habit question, and then write an equation to solve the problem. Have student pairs explain to other pairs how they wrote the equation.

**Summarize** How can prior knowledge be used to help model with math and solve problems?

# DEVELOP: PROBLEM-BASED LEARNING

**COHERENCE: Engage learners by connecting prior knowledge to new ideas.**
Students use math models, applying what they have learned about patterns, tables, equations, and graphs, to represent and solve real-world problems involving linear relationships.

10–15 min

Solve

## BEFORE

**1. Pose the Solve-and-Share Problem**
**MP.4 Model with Math** Listen and look for students who use a table to organize the data, identify patterns, and then write an equation to represent the situation and solve the problem.

**2. Build Understanding**
*What information is given?* [There is a flat fee of $50 plus $5 per person.] *What are variable quantities in this problem?* [Number of students going the party, total cost] *How are the dependent variable and independent variable related?* [The total cost of the skating party depends on the number of students who go to the party.]

## DURING

**3. Ask Guiding Questions As Needed**
*Would you use a table, a graph, or an equation to solve this problem?* [Sample answer: You could use a table for 20, 60, and 100 students and an equation for *n* students.] *How do you find the cost for 20 students?* [Multiply 20 by $5 and add $50.] *How do you represent the cost of n students?* [Use the equation $c = 5n + 50$]

## AFTER

**4. Share and Discuss Solutions**
Solve Start with students' solutions. If needed, project Teagan's work to discuss how to use mathematical models to represent and solve the problem.

**5. Transition to the Visual Learning Bridge**
*Using math models, such as a table, equation, or graph, can help you understand how quantities are related.*

**6. Extension for Early Finishers**
*Write your own real-world problem. Use two or more different math models to represent and solve it.* [Check students' work.]

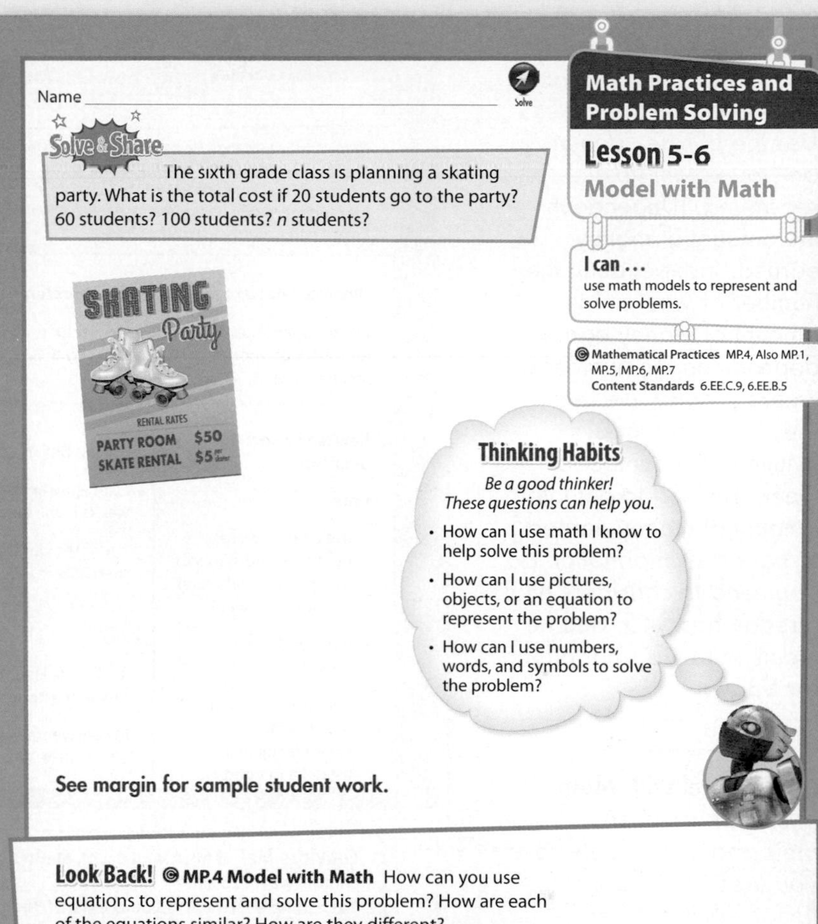

Name
Solve & Share
The sixth grade class is planning a skating party. What is the total cost if 20 students go to the party? 60 students? 100 students? n students?
SKATING Party
RENTAL RATES
PARTY ROOM $50
SKATE RENTAL $5
Math Practices and Problem Solving
Lesson 5-6
Model with Math
I can …
use math models to represent and solve problems.
Mathematical Practices MP.4, Also MP.1, MP.5, MP.6, MP.7
Content Standards 6.EE.C.9, 6.EE.B.5
Thinking Habits
Be a good thinker!
These questions can help you.
How can I use math I know to help solve this problem?
How can I use pictures, objects, or an equation to represent the problem?
How can I use numbers, words, and symbols to solve the problem?
See margin for sample student work.
Look Back! MP.4 Model with Math How can you use equations to represent and solve this problem? How are each of the equations similar? How are they different?
Sample answer: I can use equations to show how the numbers in the problem are related. In each equation, the $50 party room charge and the $5 skate rental are the same. The number of students and the total rental cost are different.
Digital Resources at PearsonRealize.com
Topic 5 | Lesson 5-6
257


## Analyze Student Work

Teagan's Work

| Number of Students | Cost for Skate Rental | Total Cost (including Party Room) |
|---|---|---|
| 10 | $50 | $50 + $50 = $100 |
| 20 | $100 | $100 + $50 = $150 |
| 60 | $300 | $300 + $50 = $350 |
| 100 | $500 | $500 + $50 = $550 |

Let $n$ = the number of students and $c$ = total cost of the party.
The equation $c = 5n + 50$ represents the total cost of the skating party.

Teagan uses both a table and an equation to model the relationship between the dependent and independent variables.

Kevin's Work

20 x $5 = $100, and $100 + $50 = $150 for 20 students
60 x $5 = $300, and $300 + $50 = $350 for 60 students
100 x $5 = $500, and $500 + $50 = $550 for 100 students

$n \times 5 + 50$ for $n$ students

Kevin uses math to solve the problem correctly and writes an expression to represent *n*.

# DEVELOP: VISUAL LEARNING

The *Visual Learning Bridge* connects students' thinking in Solve & Share to important math ideas in the lesson. Use the *Visual Learning Bridge* to make these ideas explicit. Also available as a *Visual Learning Animation Plus* at PearsonRealize.com

Visual Learning

Pearson realize. PearsonRealize.com

Learn Glossary

*What are the dependent and independent variables represented in the table? Use the phrase "depends on" to explain your reasoning.* [Dependent: the amount of money earned. Independent: the number of weeks. The amount of money earned depends on the number of weeks.] *What rule relates these two variables?* [Multiply the number of weeks by $25 to get total amount of money earned.] *What other information do you need to consider?* [Hal already has $45, and he wants to buy a smartphone for $320.]

**MP.4 Model with Math**
*In this topic, what mathematical models have you used to represent linear relationships?* [Tables, equations, graphs] *What other models have you used in math?* [Sample answers: Number lines, bar graphs] *Once you have solved the problem, what should you do?* [Decide if it makes sense, and improve the math model if needed.]

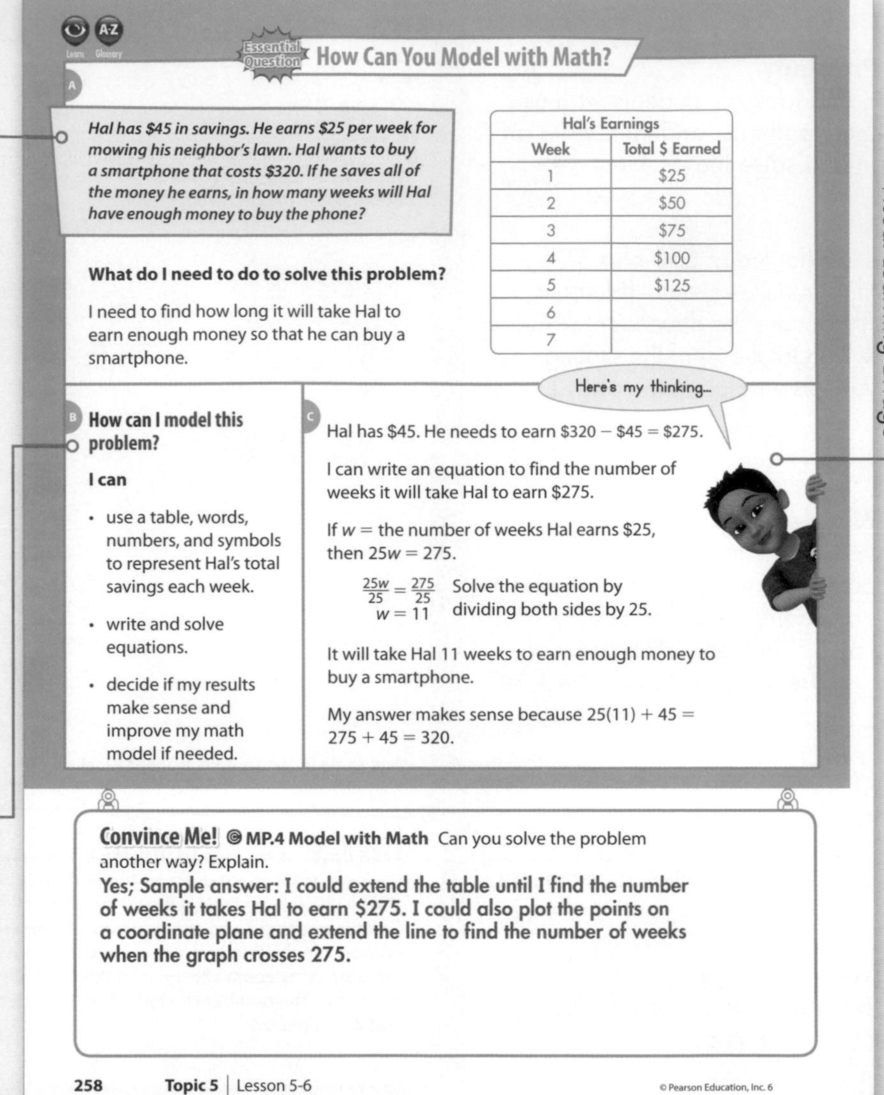

Essential Question How Can You Model with Math?
A
Hal has $45 in savings. He earns $25 per week for mowing his neighbor's lawn. Hal wants to buy a smartphone that costs $320. If he saves all of the money he earns, in how many weeks will Hal have enough money to buy the phone?
What do I need to do to solve this problem?
I need to find how long it will take Hal to earn enough money so that he can buy a smartphone.
Hal's Earnings
Week | Total $ Earned
1 | $25
2 | $50
3 | $75
4 | $100
5 | $125
6
7
Here's my thinking...
B How can I model this problem?
I can
• use a table, words, numbers, and symbols to represent Hal's total savings each week.
• write and solve equations.
• decide if my results make sense and improve my math model if needed.
C Hal has $45. He needs to earn $320 − $45 = $275.
I can write an equation to find the number of weeks it will take Hal to earn $275.
If w = the number of weeks Hal earns $25, then 25w = 275.
25w/25 = 275/25 Solve the equation by dividing both sides by 25.
w = 11
It will take Hal 11 weeks to earn enough money to buy a smartphone.
My answer makes sense because 25(11) + 45 = 275 + 45 = 320.
Convince Me! MP.4 Model with Math Can you solve the problem another way? Explain.
Yes; Sample answer: I could extend the table until I find the number of weeks it takes Hal to earn $275. I could also plot the points on a coordinate plane and extend the line to find the number of weeks when the graph crosses 275.
258 Topic 5 | Lesson 5-6
© Pearson Education, Inc. 6
Visual Learning Bridge


*If a smartphone costs $320, does Hal have to earn that much? Explain.* [No. He already had $45 in savings.] *What property of equality was used to solve the equation? Explain why.* [Division Property of Equality, because multiplication and division have an inverse relationship] *How can you tell that the answer for this problem makes sense?* [Sample answer: Start with the number of weeks (11), multiply it by $25 per week, and then add the $45 of savings to get $320, which was the cost of the smartphone.]

**Convince Me! MP.4 Model with Math** Modeling a real-world problem involves translating a problem situation into mathematics, such as a table or equation. By asking whether they can solve the problem another way, students realize that there is often more than one way to model a problem situation.

**Coherence** In the smartphone problem above and throughout this topic, students examined dependent and independent variables and investigated linear relationships involving one and two operations. They modeled these relationships with tables, equations, and graphs on a coordinate plane. Their familiarity with math models strengthens the conceptual foundation they will need for a more in-depth study of linear relationships (for example, investigating slopes and $x$- and $y$-intercepts) and for the study of non-linear functions in Algebra I and beyond.

Revisit the Essential Question. Tables, equations, and graphs can be used to show how the information in a problem is related. By modeling a real-world situation with mathematics, students can represent and solve problems.

**QUICK CHECK**

Check mark indicates items for prescribing differentiation on the next page.
Items 3 and 4 are worth 1 point. Items 5–8 are worth up to 3 points.

20–30 min

Pearson realize. PearsonRealize.com

Practice Buddy | Tools | Assessment

Name ____

## Guided Practice

**MP.4 Model with Math**

Joanne wants to buy a sweater that costs $72. She earns $12 a week and saves half of it. Joanne started the table below to record her savings after each week. How many weeks will it be until Joanne has enough money to buy the sweater?

1. What equation can you use to represent Joanne's savings each week? Complete the table for the first 4 weeks.
**Sample answer: $\frac{1}{2}e = s$ where $e$ = total earned and $s$ = total saved after each week.**

Joanne's Savings

| Week | Total Earned | Total Saved |
|---|---|---|
| 1 | 12 | 6 |
| 2 | 24 | $\frac{1}{2}(24) = 12$ |
| 3 | **36** | $\frac{1}{2}(36) = 18$ |
| 4 | **48** | $\frac{1}{2}(48) = 24$ |

2. How can you use math you know to solve the problem? Explain.
**Sample answer: Joanne saves $6 each week. I can divide 72 by 6 to find how long it will take her to save $72. It will take Joanne 12 weeks.**

You are modeling with math when you use a table or an equation to describe a problem.

## Independent Practice

**MP.4 Model with Math**

Joe has $372 and spends $12 each week. He made a table to record how much money he has. How long will it be until he spends all of his money?

Joe's Spending

| Week | Dollars Remaining |
|---|---|
| 0 | 372 |
| 1 | 360 |
| 2 | 348 |
| 3 | 336 |

✓ 3. What equation can you use to model the problem? Show how you can use numbers, words, and symbols to represent the given information. **Sample answer: Let $w$ = the number of weeks Joe spends $12 and $r$ = the amount remaining. Then $372 - 12w = r$; $372 - 12(3) = 372 - 36 = 336$. This matches the data recorded in the table, so the equation makes sense.**

✓ 4. How can you use math you know to solve the problem? Explain.
**Sample answer: I can use the equation $372 - 12(31) = 0$ to show that it will take Joe 31 weeks to spend all of his money.**

*For another example, see Set D on page 266.



## Math Practices and Problem Solving

**Common Core Performance Assessment**

✓ **Soccer Cookie Sale**

The soccer team is selling cookies to make money to travel to the state championship. They are hoping to raise $200. Each box of cookies sells for $3.50 and costs the team $1.50. There are 12 boxes of cookies in a carton. How many cartons do they need to sell to meet their goal?

To make sense of a problem, identify what you know and look for relationships.

5. **MP.1 Make Sense and Persevere** What do you know and what do you need to find out?
**Sample answer: I know that the team is trying to raise $200. They make $2 for every box of cookies they sell. There are 12 boxes of cookies in a carton.**

6. **MP.7 Use Structure** What relationship do you see between the profit made on 1 box of cookies and the number of boxes in a carton? Can this pattern help you solve the problem? Explain.
**Sample answer: I can multiply $2 by 12 to find that the team makes $24 for each carton of cookies sold; Yes, I can write the equation $E = 24c$ to represent the earnings, $E$, for selling $c$ cartons of cookies.**

| Number of Cartons Sold | Earnings |
|---|---|
| 1 | **$24** |
| 2 | **$48** |
| 3 | **$72** |
| 4 | **$96** |
| 5 | **$120** |
| 6 | **$144** |

7. **MP.4 Model with Math** Explain how you can use a table, a graph, or an equation to represent the problem.
**Sample answer: I can make a table or a graph to record the team's cookie sales and earnings. I can write an equation to find the earnings, $E$, for selling $c$ cartons of cookies.**

8. **MP.5 Use Appropriate Tools** Complete the table and the graph. Explain how they help you solve the problem.
**Check students' work; Sample answer: The table and the graph show the team's profit as a pattern that can be extended. Using equations and appropriate tools, I can show that the team needs to sell at least 9 cartons to meet the $200 goal.**

**Sample graph:**

Earnings: $30, $60, $90; Number of Cartons $c$: 0, 1, 2, 3, 4, 5





**MP.4 Model with Math** Listen and look for these behaviors as evidence that students are exhibiting proficiency with MP.4.

- Identifies the correct prior knowledge that needs to be applied to solve a problem
- Identifies the hidden question(s) in multiple-step problems
- Uses numbers, symbols, and words to solve problems
- Identifies the operation(s) needed to solve a problem
- Uses estimation as appropriate

**Item 4 MP.4 Model with Math** Help students use math they know to solve the problem. *What is another way to say that Joe has spent all of his money?* [Sample answer: He has no money remaining.] *How can this be represented in the table?* [The amount of dollars remaining will be 0.] Discuss with students how they can use the equation they wrote in Item 3 to solve this problem. Students should realize that they can substitute 0 for the variable $r$, since he will have no dollars remaining.

**Reteaching** Assign Reteaching Set D on p. 266.

**Item 5 MP.1 Make Sense and Persevere** Students must read the problem carefully and decide which pieces of information are necessary to solve the problem. They should understand that the profit per box is $3.50 – $1.50, or $2.00.

**Item 6 MP.7 Use Structure** Students can complete the table and look for patterns. Then they can write an equation to represent the relationship between the number of cartons sold and earnings.

**Item 7 MP.4 Model with Math** Students have used tables, graphs, and equations to represent problem situations. Encourage students to describe how each of these representations can be used to solve problems.

**Item 8 MP.5 Use Appropriate Tools Strategically** Students can use the values they wrote in the table to write ordered pairs and plot them on the coordinate plane. Since the relationship between the number of cartons sold and the earnings is linear, students can connect the points with a line, and then extend the line until they find the desired profit ($200) and corresponding number of cartons (9) to solve the problem.

# ASSESS AND DIFFERENTIATE

Use the **QUICK CHECK** on the previous page to prescribe differentiated instruction.

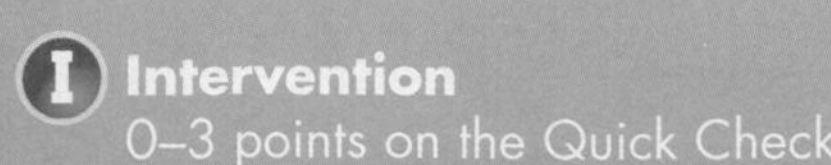

**Intervention**
0–3 points on the Quick Check

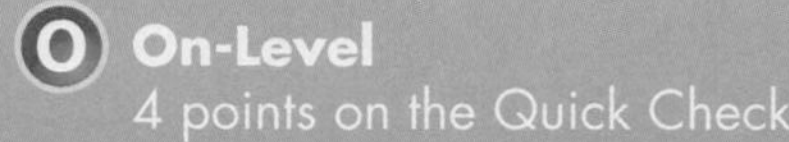

**On-Level**
4 points on the Quick Check

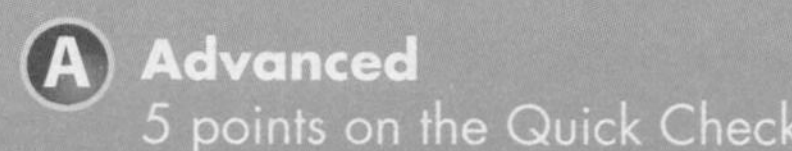

**Advanced**
5 points on the Quick Check

## Intervention Activity 

### Math Practices and Problem Solving: Model with Math

**Materials**

First quadrant coordinate grids (Teaching Tool 18) (optional)

- Write the following on the board: Talik is reading a 452-page novel for class. He has already read 88 pages. He reads 26 pages each day. How much longer will it take Talik to finish reading the novel?
- Have students ask and answer questions until they understand the problem. *What are you asked to find?* [The number of days it will take for Talik to finish reading the novel] *How many pages does he read per day?* [26 pages] *How many pages does he have left to read?* [452 − 88 = 364 pages]
- Ask students to represent the situation with a table, recording Days 1–6.
- Then have them define the dependent and independent variables and write an equation to solve the problem.
- You may choose to have students draw a graph in order to solve the problem.

| Number of Days | Number of Pages |
|---|---|
| 1 | 26 |
| 2 | 52 |
| 3 | 78 |
| 4 | 104 |
| 5 | 130 |
| 6 | 156 |

Let d = the number of days, and p = the number of pages read.

$p = 26d$

$\frac{364}{26} = \frac{26d}{26}$

$14 = d$

It will take Talik 14 more days to finish the novel.

## Reteach 

Name ______________________

Reteach to Build Understanding
**5-6**

**Vocabulary**

1. A **math model,** such as a table, graph, or equation, can be used to represent a problem situation mathematically.

The perimeter, *p*, of a square is 4 times the length of one of its sides, *s*.
Write an equation to model the perimeter of a square. **$p = 4 \times s$**

2. Dion needs 602 square feet of wallpaper. Each roll of wallpaper covers 56 square feet. How many rolls of wallpaper does Dion need?

Model the problem with a table.

| Number of Rolls | Total Square Feet |
|---|---|
| 1 | 56 |
| 2 | 2 × **56** = **112** |
| 4 | **4** × **56** = **224** |
| 8 | **8** × **56** = **448** |
| 10 | **10** × **56** = **560** |

3. What equation can you write to represent the total square feet of wallpaper, *s*, for *r* rolls of wallpaper?
**$s = 56r$**

4. Use the equation you wrote to solve for *r* when $s = 602$. Show your work.
**$602 = 56r; 602 \div 56 = 56r \div 56; 10.75 = r$**

5. If the store only sells whole rolls of wallpaper, how many rolls should Dion buy? Explain.
**11 rolls; 10.75 rolls of wallpaper will cover 602 square feet, but since the store only sells whole rolls, Dion should buy 11 rolls of wallpaper.**

**On the Back!**

6. Cory is filling a large aquarium tank with a hose. The level of the water in the tank rises 4.5 inches each hour. The tank already has 8 inches of water in it. How many hours will it take to fill the tank to a depth of 35 inches? Make a table and write an equation to model and solve the problem.
**6 hours; Check students' tables. Sample answer: $d = 4.5h + 8$, where $d$ = the total number of inches of water in the tank and $h$ = the number of hours. $35 = 4.5h + 8; h = 6$.**

R 5-6



## On-Level and Advanced Activity Centers  

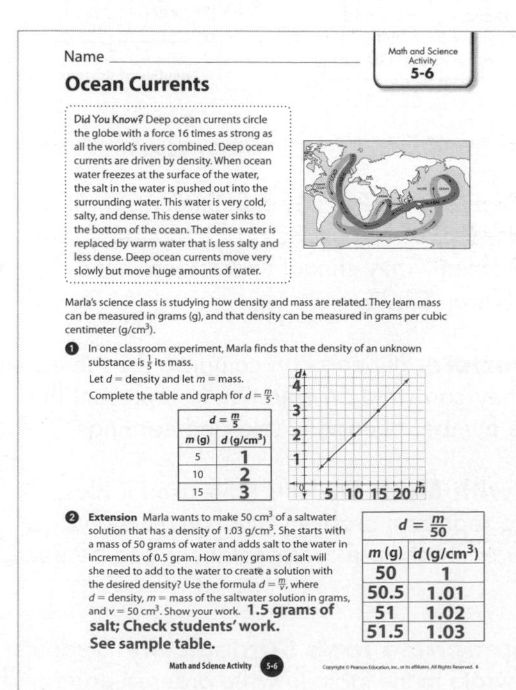

Name ______________________

Math and Science Activity
**5-6**

**Ocean Currents**

*Did You Know?* Deep ocean currents circle the globe with a force 16 times as strong as all the world's rivers combined. Deep ocean currents are driven by density. When ocean water freezes at the surface of the water, the salt in the water is pushed out into the surrounding water. This water is very cold, salty, and dense. This dense water sinks to the bottom of the ocean. The dense water is replaced by warm water that is less salty and less dense. Deep ocean currents move very slowly but move huge amounts of water.

Marla's science class is studying how density and mass are related. They learn mass can be measured in grams (g), and that density can be measured in grams per cubic centimeter (g/cm³).

1. In one classroom experiment, Marla finds that the density of an unknown substance is $\frac{1}{5}$ its mass.
Let $d$ = density and let $m$ = mass.
Complete the table and graph for $d = \frac{m}{5}$.

| $d = \frac{m}{5}$ | |
|---|---|
| $m$ (g) | $d$ (g/cm³) |
| 5 | **1** |
| 10 | **2** |
| 15 | **3** |

2. **Extension** Marla wants to make 50 cm³ of a saltwater solution that has a density of 1.03 g/cm³. She starts with a mass of 50 grams of water and adds salt to the water in increments of 0.5 gram. How many grams of salt will she need to add to the water to create a solution with the desired density? Use the formula $d = \frac{m}{v}$, where $d$ = density, $m$ = mass of the saltwater solution in grams, and $v = 50$ cm³. Show your work. **1.5 grams of salt; Check students' work. See sample table.**

| $d = \frac{m}{50}$ | |
|---|---|
| $m$ (g) | $d$ (g/cm³) |
| **50** | **1** |
| **50.5** | **1.01** |
| **51** | **1.02** |
| **51.5** | **1.03** |

Math and Science Activity 5-6



### Math and Science Activity STEM

This activity revisits the science theme, **Ocean Currents and Weather Patterns,** introduced on page 223 in the Student's Edition.

### Sample Student Work

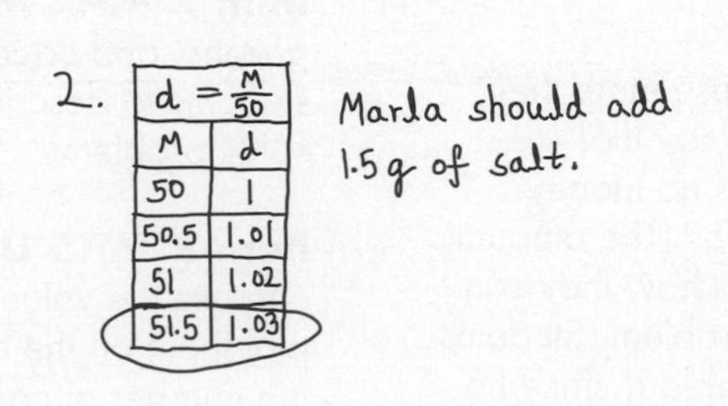

2.
d = M/50
M | d
50 | 1
50.5 | 1.01
51 | 1.02
51.5 | 1.03
Marla should add 1.5 g of salt.

## TIMING

The time allocated to Step 3 will depend on the teacher's instructional decisions and differentiation routines.

15–30 min

## Technology Center   

Tools Games

### Math Tools and Math Games

A link to a specific math tools activity or math game to use with this lesson is provided at PearsonRealize.com.

## Leveled Assignment  Items 1–6  Items 1–6  Items 1–6

Name ______________________

**Homework & Practice 5-6**
**Model with Math**

### Another Look!

Dave is training for a 10-kilometer race. In the next two weeks, he plans to run 100 miles. He runs 8.4 miles every day. How long will it take Dave to run at least 100 miles?

**Explain how you can model and solve this problem.**

- I can use a table or graph to record Dave's daily mileage.
- I can write and solve equations.
- I can represent the problem in different ways to check that my math is correct.

Tables, graphs, and equations are three ways of modeling problems.


**Model and solve the problem.**

Make a table and write an equation.

| Number of Days | Total Miles Run |
|---|---|
| 1 | 8.4 |
| 2 | 16.8 |
| 4 | 33.6 |
| 8 | 67.2 |
| 12 | 100.8 |

Let $d$ = the number of days and $m$ = the total number of miles run: $m = 8.4d$.
Solve the equation:

$$100 = 8.4d$$
$$\frac{100}{8.4} = d$$
$$11.9 = d$$

Dave will have run at least 100 miles by the end of the 12th day.

**MP.4 Model with Math**
Helen's cookie recipe calls for 1.5 packages of chocolate chips for each batch of cookies. She has 1 package of chocolate chips. How many more packages will she need to buy to have enough for 16 batches?

**1.** How does the table represent the problem? Complete the table.
**Sample answer: I can use the table to record how many more packages of chips are needed. I can extend the table to 16 batches. Check students' work.**

| Helen's Cookies | | |
|---|---|---|
| Batches | Number of Packages | Number of Packages Helen Needs |
| 1 | 1.5 | **1.5 − 1 = 0.5** |
| 2 | **3** | **3 − 1 = 2** |
| 3 | **4.5** | **4.5 − 1 = 3.5** |
| 4 | **6** | **6 − 1 = 5** |

**2.** What equation can you write to represent the problem? Use the equation to solve the problem. **Sample answer: Let $b$ = the number of batches and $p$ = the number of packages of chocolate chips needed to make the cookies. $p = 1.5b - 1$. $p = 1.5(16) - 1$; $p = 24 - 1$; $p = 23$ Helen needs 23 more packages.**



### Common Core Performance Assessment

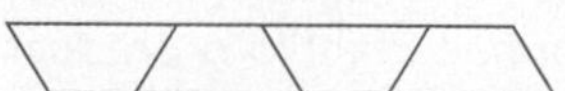

**Trapezoidal Tables**
A cafeteria has trapezoidal tables. There is enough space at one table to seat 5 students. The tables can also be arranged in a row, as shown below. For each table that is added to the row, 3 more students can be seated. How many tables can be assembled in a row to seat 53 students?

**3. MP.1 Make Sense and Persevere** How can you use a table to represent what you know? Complete the table below.

| Number of Tables | 1 | 2 | 3 | 4 | 5 |
|---|---|---|---|---|---|
| Number of Students | 5 | **8** | **11** | **14** | **17** |

**Sample answer: I know that 1 table seats 5 students. For each table added, 3 more students can be seated. I can use the table to record the number of students as more tables are added to the row.**

**4. MP.4 Model with Math** What equation can you write to represent the number of students, $S$, that can sit around $t$ tables?
**Sample answer: $S = 3t + 2$**

**5. MP.7 Use Structure** How can patterns help you solve the problem?

**Sample answer: The pattern in the table shows that I start with 5 students at 1 table and add 3 students for each table that is added to the row. If I start with 53 students and subtract 5, I can divide the difference by 3 to find how many more tables are needed.**

You persevere when you try different strategies until you find one that helps you solve the problem.


**6. MP.6 Be Precise** Use the equation you wrote to solve the problem. How can you check to make sure your calculations are accurate?

**Sample answer: $S = 3t + 2$; $53 = 3t + 2$**
$$53 - 2 = 3t + 2 - 2$$
$$51 = 3t$$
$$\frac{51}{3} = t$$
$$17 = t$$
**They will need 17 tables. $17 \times 3 + 2 = 53$. The math checks.**

# FLUENCY PRACTICE ACTIVITY

realize
PearsonRealize.com
Games
Practice Buddy

## FLUENCY PRACTICE ACTIVITY

Students review the Grade 5 fluency standard about multiplying multi-digit whole numbers during a partner activity that reinforces mathematical practices.

### Common Core Standards

**Content Standard 5.NBT.B.5** Fluently multiply multi-digit whole numbers using the standard algorithm.

**Mathematical Practices MP.3, MP.6, MP.7, MP.8**

**Getting Started** Ask partners to share one page. Tell them that the other partner's page will be used to record tally marks when they repeat the activity. Go over the directions. Note that for any product, only one partner will get a tally mark.

When partners simultaneously point to two numbers, they may point to two numbers that they have already multiplied. In that case, students can point again to find two other numbers to multiply.

**As Students Do the Activity** Remind students to compare and discuss their answers.

**Another Activity** Students can repeat the activity and record their tally marks on the other partner's page.

**Extra Challenge** *Take turns with a partner. Point to a product in one of the blue spaces. Ask your partner to get that product by multiplying a number in the column at the right by a number in the column at the left.*

**Online Game** The Game Center at PearsonRealize.com provides opportunities for fluency practice.

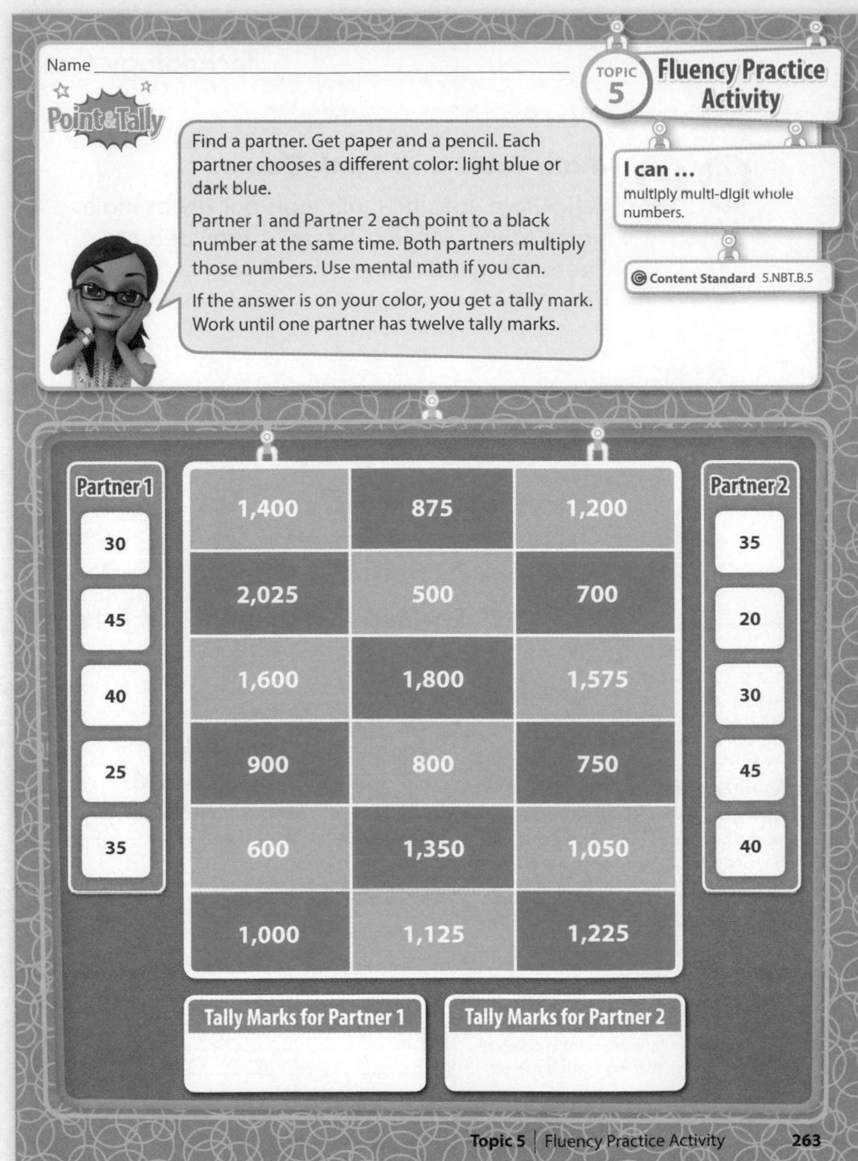

Name
Point & Tally
TOPIC 5 Fluency Practice Activity
Find a partner. Get paper and a pencil. Each partner chooses a different color: light blue or dark blue.
Partner 1 and Partner 2 each point to a black number at the same time. Both partners multiply those numbers. Use mental math if you can.
If the answer is on your color, you get a tally mark. Work until one partner has twelve tally marks.
I can ... multiply multi-digit whole numbers.
Content Standard 5.NBT.B.5
Partner 1
30
45
40
25
35
1,400
875
1,200
2,025
500
700
1,600
1,800
1,575
900
800
750
600
1,350
1,050
1,000
1,125
1,225
Partner 2
35
20
30
45
40
Tally Marks for Partner 1
Tally Marks for Partner 2
Topic 5 | Fluency Practice Activity 263

Glossary

Games

A-Z Glossary

**Word List**

- dependent variable
- independent variable
- linear equation
- ordered pair
- variable

**Understand Vocabulary**

Choose the best term from the box. Write it on the blank.

1. A quantity that can change or vary is a(n) **variable**.
2. A(n) **ordered pair** shows pairs of values $(c, h)$ that are solutions of the equation $c = 2h$.
3. The graph of a(n) **linear equation** is a straight line.
4. In the equation $y = x + 9$, the variable $x$ is the **independent variable**.

Identify the *independent variable* and the *dependent variable* in each situation. Write **I** if the variable is independent. Write **D** if the variable is dependent.

5. The number of hours a canoe is rented, $h$, and the cost in dollars to rent the canoe, $c$ — $h$ **I** $c$ **D**
6. The weight of a box in pounds, $w$, and the number of oranges in the box, $n$ — $w$ **D** $n$ **I**
7. The length of a pool, $l$, and the time it takes to swim the length of the pool, $t$ — $l$ **I** $t$ **D**
8. Look at each *ordered pair*. Write **Y** if the ordered pair $(h, c)$ represents a point on the line $c = h - 2$. Write **N** if it does not.

   (3, 5) **N** (7, 5) **Y** (4, 5) **N**

**Use Vocabulary in Writing**

9. Explain how to graph the equation $d = 5t$ on a coordinate plane. Use at least 5 words from the Word List in your explanation.

   **Sample answer: Make a *table* of values for the *variables*. Use at least three values for $t$, the *independent variable*. Find the corresponding values for $d$, the *dependent variable*. Graph each *ordered pair*. Then draw a line through the points.**




## VOCABULARY REVIEW

Students review vocabulary words used in the topic.

**Oral Language** Before students complete the page, you might reinforce oral language through a class discussion involving one or more of the following activities.

- Create a word web on the classroom wall. First, write all the vocabulary terms on the wall. Then have student volunteers draw lines that connect one term to another and explain how the terms are related.
- Ask one student to give an example of one of the vocabulary terms from this topic. As a class, decide which vocabulary term or terms could describe the student's example. Have students take turns giving examples.
- As a whole class, or in small groups, have students write an acrostic poem in which each line of the poem begins with a letter of the vocabulary word and describes the word in some way. For example, the first two lines of the acrostic-style poem for "ordered pair" could be "Only two coordinates; Represents one point on the coordinate plane."
- Play a "Right or Wrong?" game in which you or a student says a sentence that uses one of the words correctly or incorrectly. Then, others say "right" or "wrong." If the statement is "wrong," ask student volunteers to correct the sentence so that it is "right."

**Writing in Math** After students complete the page, you might further reinforce writing in math by doing one or more of the following activities.

- Have students create a poster that presents one or more of the vocabulary terms and includes a variety of examples. Students can work independently or in pairs, using chart paper or construction paper for their poster.
- Have students work with a partner. Each partner writes a math question that uses one of the words. Then students trade papers and give a written answer that uses the word.

Games

**Online Game** The Game Center at PearsonRealize.com includes a vocabulary game that students can access any time.

# RETEACHING

## ALGEBRA: PATTERNS AND EQUATIONS

### Item Analysis for Diagnosis and Intervention

| Reteaching Sets | Standard | MDIS |
|---|---|---|
| Set A | 6.EE.C.9 | F63 |
| Set B | 6.EE.C.9 | F28–F31 |
| Set C | 6.EE.C.9 | F34, F36 |
| Set D | MP.4, MP.1, MP.5, MP.6, MP.7 | F31, J2, J17 |

Name ____________

TOPIC 5

**Reteaching**

**Set A** pages 227–232

The spirit squad is washing cars. The equation $m = 2c$ represents the money they make, $m$, for washing $c$ cars. Identify the dependent variable and the independent variable and explain.

**Step 1** Identify the dependent variable.

Ask: Which variable depends on the other?

The amount of money the spirit squad makes ***depends*** on the number of cars they wash. The dependent variable is $m$.

**Step 2** Identify the independent variable.

Ask: Which variable causes the change?

The number of cars washed changes the amount of money made. The independent variable is $c$.

**Remember** to think about how the values of the variables affect each other.

Identify the dependent variable and the independent variable in each situation.

1. The distance traveled, $d$, and the speed, $s$ **dependent variable: $d$; independent variable: $s$**
2. The calories, $c$, in a snack and the amount of the snack, $a$ **dependent variable: $c$; independent variable: $a$**
3. The amount of money you have spent, $s$, and how much money you have left, $m$ **dependent variable: $m$; independent variable: $s$**

**Set B** pages 233–238, 239–244

Find the rule that shows the pattern. Then use the rule to complete the table.

| $x$ | 3 | 4 | 6 | 7 | 8 |
|---|---|---|---|---|---|
| $y$ | 12 | 16 | 24 | 28 | 32 |

**Step 1** Find the rule and write an equation.

**Think:** 12 is $3 \times 4$
16 is $4 \times 4$
24 is $6 \times 4$

Rule: The value of $y$ is 4 times the value of $x$.

Equation: $y = 4x$

**Step 2** Evaluate the equation for $x = 7$ and $x = 8$.

$y = 4(7) = 28$

$y = 4(8) = 32$

**Remember** to look for patterns between two related variables to find rules and write equations.

1. Write a rule and an equation to fit the pattern in the table. Then use the rule to complete the table.

| $x$ | 0 | 2 | 10 | 16 | 20 |
|---|---|---|---|---|---|
| $y$ | 0 | 1 | 5 | **8** | **10** |

**The value of $y$ is 0.5 times the value of $x$; $y = 0.5x$ or $y = x \div 2$**

2. Use the equation to complete the table.

$y = 6x + 1$

| $x$ | 1 | 2 | 3 | 4 | 5 |
|---|---|---|---|---|---|
| $y$ | **7** | **13** | **19** | **25** | **31** |

Topic 5 | Reteaching 265

**Set C** pages 245–250, 251–256

Graph the equation $y = x + 1$.

**Step 1** Make a table. Include at least 3 $x$-values.

| $x$ | $y$ |
|---|---|
| 0 | 1 |
| 2 | 3 |
| 3 | 4 |

**Step 2** Graph each ordered pair on a coordinate plane. Then draw a line through the points. Extend the line to show more values that make the equation true.

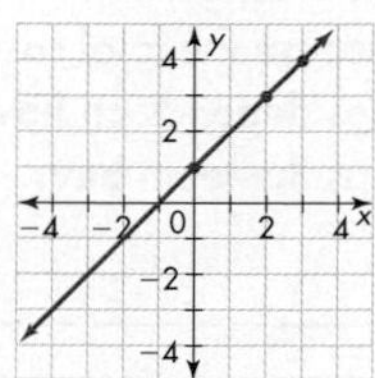

**Remember** that ordered pairs that make an equation true can be used to graph the equation.

Graph each equation on the coordinate plane.

1. $y = x + 3$
2. $y = 3x - 1$

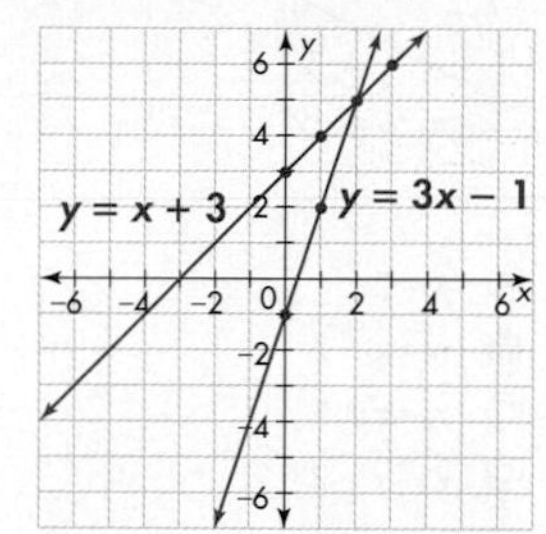


**Set D** pages 257–262

Think about these questions to help you **model with math.**

**Thinking Habits**

- How can I use math I know to help solve this problem?
- How can I use pictures, objects, or an equation to represent the problem?
- How can I use numbers, words, and symbols to solve the problem?

**Remember** that a table, equation, or graph can be used to show the relationship between the quantities in a problem.

Alex is making puppets for a show. He bought string for \$125. It costs \$18 for the remaining materials needed to make each puppet. What is the total cost to make 50 puppets?

1. What equation can you write to represent the problem?
   **Sample answer: $c = 125 + 18p$**
2. Explain how to use the equation to solve the problem. Then solve.
   **Sample answer: I can substitute 50 for $p$ and then solve the equation.**
   **$c = 125 + 18p = 125 + 18(50)$**
   **$= 125 + 900 = 1{,}025$**
   **The total cost is \$1,025.**




## Response to Intervention

**Ongoing Intervention**

- Lessons with guiding questions to assess understanding
- Support to prevent misconceptions and to reteach

**Strategic Intervention**

- Targeted to small groups that need more support
- Easy to implement

**Intensive Intervention**

- Instruction to accelerate progress
- Instruction focused on foundational skills

# TOPIC ASSESSMENT

## ALGEBRA: PATTERNS AND EQUATIONS

Name ____________________

**Assessment**

**1.** The manager of a water park keeps track of the amount of money collected, $m$, and the number of tickets sold, $t$, each day. Which best describes the variables $m$ and $t$? **1 point**

- Ⓐ The variable $m$ is the independent variable because it depends on the number of tickets sold, $t$.
- Ⓑ The variable $t$ is the dependent variable because it depends on the amount of money collected, $m$, each day.
- ● The variable $t$ is the independent variable because it affects the amount of money collected, $m$, each day.
- Ⓓ The variable $m$ is independent of variable $t$, and variable $t$ is independent of variable $m$.

**2.** For questions 2a–2e, choose Yes or No to indicate which of the equations can be used to describe the pattern in the table. **1 point**

| a | 5 | 6 | 7 | 8 | 9 |
|---|---|---|---|---|---|
| b | 0 | 1 | 2 | 3 | 4 |

- **2a.** $b + a = 5$ ○ Yes ● No
- **2b.** $b = a + 5$ ○ Yes ● No
- **2c.** $b = a - 5$ ● Yes ○ No
- **2d.** $a = b - 5$ ○ Yes ● No
- **2e.** $a - b = 5$ ● Yes ○ No

**3.** Which equation can be used to describe the pattern in the table? **1 point**

| x | 8 | 10 | 12 | 14 | 16 |
|---|---|---|---|---|---|
| y | 3 | 4 | 5 | 6 | 7 |

- Ⓐ $y = 2x - 13$
- Ⓑ $y = x \div 2$
- Ⓒ $y = x \div 2 + 1$
- ● $y = x \div 2 - 1$

**4.** April pays a dog-walking service \$30 each week to walk her dog. Complete the table to show how many dollars, $d$, April spends on dog-walking in $w$ weeks. **2 points**

| w | 1 | 2 | **3** | **4** | 5 |
|---|---|---|---|---|---|
| d | 30 | **60** | 90 | 120 | **150** |

**5.** Rhonda graphed the equations listed below. For questions 5a–5d, choose Yes or No to indicate which of the equations include the point (1.25, 2.5). **1 point**

- **5a.** $y = 2x$ ● Yes ○ No
- **5b.** $y = x + 1$ ○ Yes ● No
- **5c.** $y = x + 1.25$ ● Yes ○ No
- **5d.** $y = 1\frac{1}{4} + x$ ● Yes ○ No



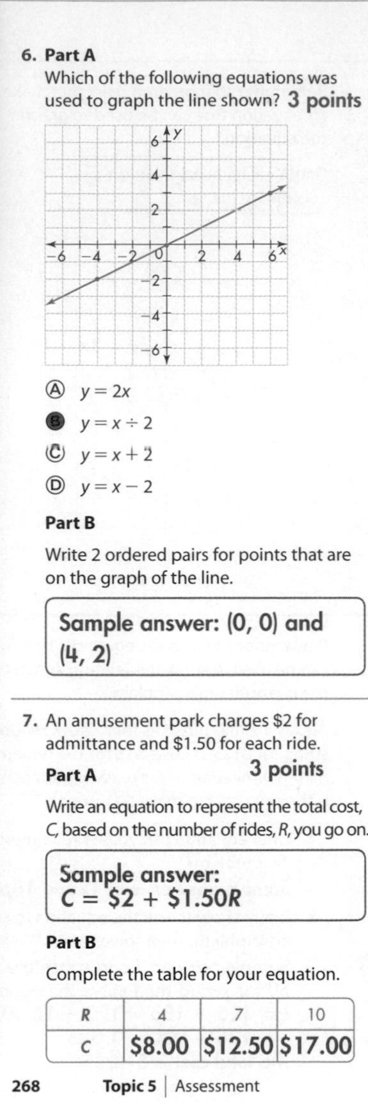

**6. Part A**

Which of the following equations was used to graph the line shown? **3 points**



- Ⓐ $y = 2x$
- ● $y = x \div 2$
- Ⓒ $y = x + 2$
- Ⓓ $y = x - 2$

**Part B**

Write 2 ordered pairs for points that are on the graph of the line.

**Sample answer: (0, 0) and (4, 2)**

**7.** An amusement park charges \$2 for admittance and \$1.50 for each ride. **3 points**

**Part A**

Write an equation to represent the total cost, $C$, based on the number of rides, $R$, you go on.

**Sample answer: $C = \$2 + \$1.50R$**

**Part B**

Complete the table for your equation.

| R | 4 | 7 | 10 |
|---|---|---|---|
| C | **\$8.00** | **\$12.50** | **\$17.00** |

**8.** A softball team plans to buy ball caps for each player. Each cap costs the same amount. The team buys $c$ caps for $d$ dollars. Which variable is the independent variable and which is the dependent variable? Explain how you identified each variable. **1 point**

**Caps, $c$, is the independent variable and dollars, $d$ is the dependent variable; Sample explanation: I know that $d$ is the dependent variable because the total cost of the caps depends on how many caps the team buys.**

**9.** Forensic scientists can use the length of the thighbone, or femur, to estimate the height of a skeleton. One equation that they may use is $h = 2.6f + 65$, where $f$ is the length of the femur in centimeters and $h$ is the height of the skeleton. Complete the table to find the height of a skeleton with a femur that is 37 cm long. **1 point**

| f | 34 | 35 | 36 | 37 |
|---|---|---|---|---|
| h | 153.4 | 156 | 158.6 | **161.2** |





## ANSWERING THE TOPIC ESSENTIAL QUESTIONS

Restate the Topic Essential Questions from the Topic Opener or project them from the Student's Edition eText.

Ask students to answer the Essential Questions (verbally or in writing) and give examples that support their answers. The following are key elements of the answers to the Essential Questions. Be sure these are made explicit when discussing students' answers.

### How can equations be written?

- Equations can be written by using a rule that relates two quantities expressed as variables.

  **Example:** The rule "multiply $c$ by 3 and add 1 to get $d$" can be written as the equation $3c + 1 = d$.

### What patterns can be found in tables of values?

- A pattern is formed by one or more operations that relate the values of the variables in a table. A pattern can be represented by a rule that is true for all the values.

### How are equations that can relate real-world quantities graphed?

- An equation relates real-world quantities using dependent and independent variables and one or more operations. To graph an equation, first find several values of the variables that make the equation true.
- Corresponding values of variables can be written as ordered pairs $(x, y)$, where $x$ is the independent variable and $y$ is the dependent variable.
- Ordered pairs can be graphed as points on a coordinate plane. An equation can be graphed by drawing a line that connects several ordered pairs generated from the equation.

Assessment

## ONLINE TOPIC ASSESSMENT

An auto-scored Topic Assessment is provided at PearsonRealize.com.

## EXAMVIEW® TEST GENERATOR

ExamView can be used to create a blackline-master Topic Assessment with multiple-choice and free-response items.

## Topic Assessment Masters

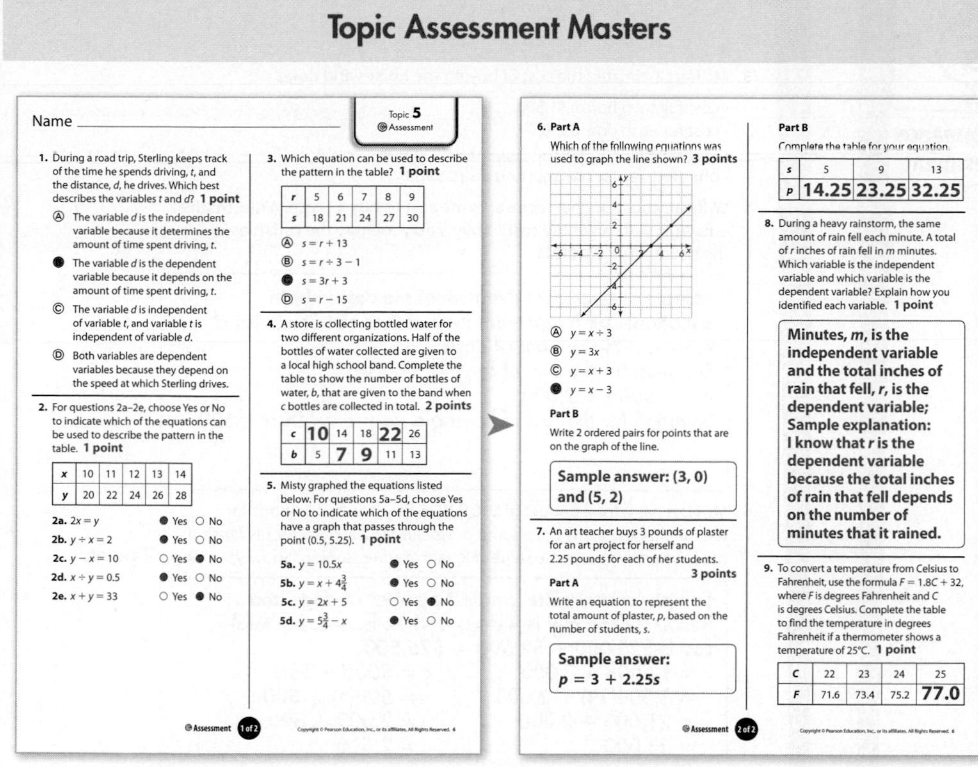

Name ______ Topic 5 Assessment

1. During a road trip, Sterling keeps track of the time he spends driving, $t$, and the distance, $d$, he drives. Which best describes the variables $t$ and $d$? **1 point**
   - Ⓐ The variable $d$ is the independent variable because it determines the amount of time spent driving, $t$.
   - ● The variable $d$ is the dependent variable because it depends on the amount of time spent driving, $t$.
   - Ⓒ The variable $d$ is independent of variable $t$, and variable $t$ is independent of variable $d$.
   - Ⓓ Both variables are dependent variables because they depend on the speed at which Sterling drives.

2. For questions 2a–2e, choose Yes or No to indicate which of the equations can be used to describe the pattern in the table. **1 point**

| x | 10 | 11 | 12 | 13 | 14 |
|---|---|---|---|---|---|
| y | 20 | 22 | 24 | 26 | 28 |

2a. $2x = y$ ● Yes ○ No
2b. $y \div x = 2$ ● Yes ○ No
2c. $y - x = 10$ ○ Yes ● No
2d. $x \div y = 0.5$ ● Yes ○ No
2e. $x + y = 33$ ○ Yes ● No

3. Which equation can be used to describe the pattern in the table? **1 point**

| r | 5 | 6 | 7 | 8 | 9 |
|---|---|---|---|---|---|
| s | 18 | 21 | 24 | 27 | 30 |

- Ⓐ $s = r + 13$
- Ⓑ $s = r + 3 - 1$
- ● $s = 3r + 3$
- Ⓓ $s = r - 15$

4. A store is collecting bottled water for two different organizations. Half of the bottles of water collected are given to a local high school band. Complete the table to show the number of bottles of water, $b$, that are given to the band when $c$ bottles are collected in total. **2 points**

| c | 10 | 14 | 18 | 22 | 26 |
|---|---|---|---|---|---|
| b | 5 | 7 | 9 | 11 | 13 |

5. Misty graphed the equations listed below. For questions 5a–5d, choose Yes or No to indicate which of the equations have a graph that passes through the point (0.5, 5.25). **1 point**

5a. $y = 10.5x$ ● Yes ○ No
5b. $y = x + 4\frac{3}{4}$ ● Yes ○ No
5c. $y = 2x + 5$ ○ Yes ● No
5d. $y = 5\frac{3}{4} - x$ ● Yes ○ No

Assessment 1 of 2

6. **Part A**
Which of the following equations was used to graph the line shown? **3 points**
- Ⓐ $y = x + 3$
- Ⓑ $y = 3x$
- Ⓒ $y = x + 3$
- ● $y = x - 3$

**Part B**
Write 2 ordered pairs for points that are on the graph of the line.

**Sample answer: (3, 0) and (5, 2)**

7. An art teacher buys 3 pounds of plaster for an art project for herself and 2.25 pounds for each of her students. **3 points**

**Part A**
Write an equation to represent the total amount of plaster, $p$, based on the number of students, $s$.

**Sample answer: $p = 3 + 2.25s$**

**Part B**
Complete the table for your equation.

| s | 5 | 9 | 13 |
|---|---|---|---|
| p | 14.25 | 23.25 | 32.25 |

8. During a heavy rainstorm, the same amount of rain fell each minute. A total of $r$ inches of rain fell in $m$ minutes. Which variable is the independent variable and which variable is the dependent variable? Explain how you identified each variable. **1 point**

**Minutes, $m$, is the independent variable and the total inches of rain that fell, $r$, is the dependent variable; Sample explanation: I know that $r$ is the dependent variable because the total inches of rain that fell depends on the number of minutes that it rained.**

9. To convert a temperature from Celsius to Fahrenheit, use the formula $F = 1.8C + 32$, where $F$ is degrees Fahrenheit and $C$ is degrees Celsius. Complete the table to find the temperature in degrees Fahrenheit if a thermometer shows a temperature of 25°C. **1 point**

| C | 22 | 23 | 24 | 25 |
|---|---|---|---|---|
| F | 71.6 | 73.4 | 75.2 | 77.0 |

Assessment 2 of 2

## RtI Item Analysis for Diagnosis and Intervention

| Item | Standard | DOK | MDIS |
|---|---|---|---|
| 1 | 6.EE.C.9 | 2 | F31 |
| 2 | 6.EE.C.9 | 2 | F28 |
| 3 | 6.EE.C.9 | 2 | F30 |
| 4 | 6.EE.C.9 | 1 | F31 |
| 5 | 6.EE.C.9 | 2 | F36 |
| 6A | 6.EE.C.9 | 2 | F34 |
| 6B | 6.EE.C.9 | 1 | F36 |
| 7A | 6.EE.C.9, MP.4 | 3 | F30 |
| 7B | 6.EE.C.9, MP.4 | 1 | F31 |
| 8 | 6.EE.C.9 | 3 | F63 |
| 9 | 6.EE.C.9 | 1 | F31 |

The Topic Assessment Masters assess the same content item for item as the Topic Assessment in the Student's Edition.

## Scoring Guide

| Item | Points | Topic Assessment (Student's Edition and Masters) |
|---|---|---|
| 1 | 1 | Correct choice selected |
| 2 | 1 | All correct choices selected |
| 3 | 1 | Correct choice selected |
| 4 | 2 | All correct answers provided |
| | 1 | Three correct answers provided |
| 5 | 1 | All correct choices selected |
| 6A | 1 | Correct choice selected |
| 6B | 2 | Two correct ordered pairs given |
| | 1 | One correct ordered pair given |
| 7A | 2 | Correct equation |
| | 1 | Partial equation is given |
| 7B | 1 | Table completed correctly |
| 8 | 1 | Correct answer and explanation |
| 9 | 1 | Correct answer |

# TOPIC PERFORMANCE ASSESSMENT

## ALGEBRA: PATTERNS AND EQUATIONS

Name ____________________

TOPIC 5

Performance Assessment

**Life on a Ranch**

Mr. Hart owns a small horse ranch. He also raises dogs on the ranch to help with the horses.

1. Mr. Hart wants to increase the number of horses and dogs on the ranch. **3 points**

**Part A**

He would like to keep the same relationship between horses and dogs shown in the table when he increases their numbers.

Complete the table to show the relationship between the number of horses, *h*, and the numbers of dogs, *d*, on the ranch.

| *d* | *h* |
|---|---|
| 1 | 5 |
| 2 | 8 |
| 3 | **11** |
| 4 | **14** |
| 5 | **17** |

**Part B**

Describe the relationship between the number of dogs and the number of horses on the ranch. Then write an equation that models this relationship.

**Sample answer: The number of horses is three times the number of dogs plus 2.**

Equation: **$h = 3d + 2$**

2. **Part A** **3 points**

Complete and label the graph to show the relationship between horses and dogs.

**Part B**

Mr. Hart would like to increase the number of dogs to 6. Extend the graph. What ordered pair represents the number of horses, *h*, when there are 6 dogs? How many horses will there be?

**(6, 20); 20 horses**

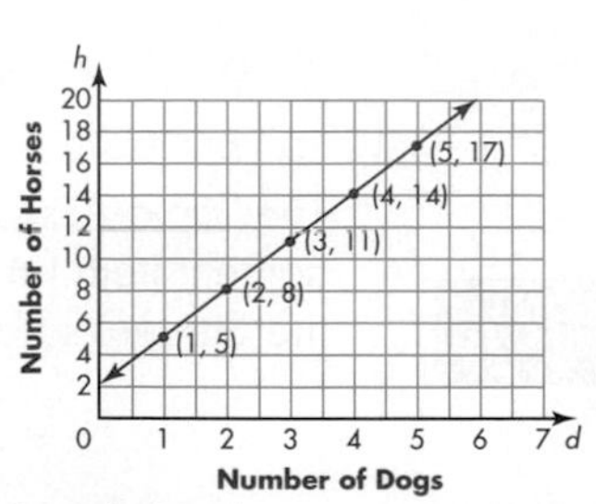

**Sample Graph**



3. Mr. Hart estimated the cost of buying the horses and dogs.

- cost for each horse: $1,500
- cost for each dog: $500
- one-time fee for transporting horses: $2,000
- one-time fee for transporting dogs: $500

Write an equation that represents the cost to buy a horse. Write another equation that shows the cost to buy a dog. Identify the variables in the equations. **2 points**

**Sample answers: Let *c* represent the cost in both equations. Let *h* represent the number of horses. Let *d* represent the number of dogs.**
**Equation for the cost of buying a horse:**
**$c = 1{,}500h + 2{,}000$**
**Equation for the cost of buying a dog: $c = 500d + 500$**

4. Mr. Hart has a total budget of $30,000 to buy horses and dogs for the ranch. How many horses and dogs can Mr. Hart buy for his ranch if the relationship stays the same? Explain your reasoning. Show your work. **2 points**

**Sample answer: The greatest number of dogs and horses he can buy is 4 dogs and 14 horses. The total cost is $23,000 + $2,500 = $25,500.**

$c = 1{,}500h + 2{,}000$
$= 1{,}500(14) + 2{,}000$
$= 21{,}000 + 2{,}000$
$= 23{,}000$

$c = 500d + 500$
$= 500(4) + 500$
$= 2{,}000 + 500$
$= 2{,}500$

**Mr. Hart would have $4,500 left in his budget. The cost to buy 1 more dog and 3 more horses to have 5 dogs and 17 horses would be $500 over budget. $1d + 3h = 500 + 3(1{,}500) = 4{,}500$, and $500 + $4500 = $5,000.**




## Scoring Guide

| Item | Points | Topic Performance Assessment in the Student's Edition |
|---|---|---|
| 1A | 1 | Table completed correctly |
| 1B | 2 | Correct equation and explanation |
| | 1 | Correct equation or explanation |
| 2A | 2 | Correct line graphed and graph labeled correctly |
| | 1 | Correct line graphed but graph not labeled |
| 2B | 1 | Correct answer |
| 3 | 2 | Two correct equations |
| | 1 | One correct equation |
| 4 | 2 | Correct answer and explanation |
| | 1 | Correct answer with no explanation |

## RtI Item Analysis for Diagnosis and Intervention

| Item | Standard | DOK | MDIS |
|---|---|---|---|
| 1A | 6.EE.C.9, MP.4 | 1 | F30 |
| 1B | 6.EE.C.9, MP.4 | 2 | F31 |
| 2A | 6.EE.C.9, MP.4 | 2 | F34 |
| 2B | 6.EE.C.9, MP.2 | 2 | F34 |
| 3 | 6.EE.C.9, MP.2 | 2 | F30, J20 |
| 4 | 6.EE.C.9, MP.1 | 3 | F31, J20 |

## Topic Performance Assessment Masters

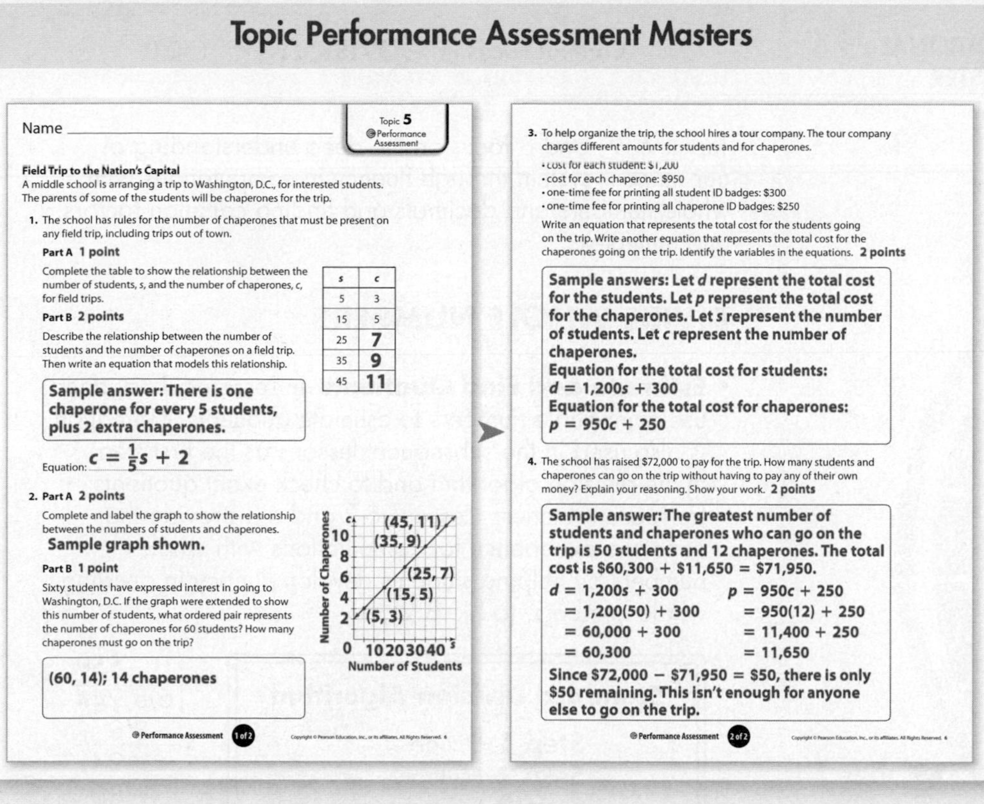

Name ______________________

Topic 5 Performance Assessment

**Field Trip to the Nation's Capital**
A middle school is arranging a trip to Washington, D.C., for interested students. The parents of some of the students will be chaperones for the trip.

1. The school has rules for the number of chaperones that must be present on any field trip, including trips out of town.

**Part A 1 point**

Complete the table to show the relationship between the number of students, $s$, and the number of chaperones, $c$, for field trips.

| $s$ | $c$ |
|---|---|
| 5 | 3 |
| 15 | 5 |
| 25 | **7** |
| 35 | **9** |
| 45 | **11** |

**Part B 2 points**

Describe the relationship between the number of students and the number of chaperones on a field trip. Then write an equation that models this relationship.

**Sample answer: There is one chaperone for every 5 students, plus 2 extra chaperones.**

Equation: $c = \frac{1}{5}s + 2$

2. **Part A 2 points**

Complete and label the graph to show the relationship between the numbers of students and chaperones.

**Sample graph shown.**



**Part B 1 point**

Sixty students have expressed interest in going to Washington, D.C. If the graph were extended to show this number of students, what ordered pair represents the number of chaperones for 60 students? How many chaperones must go on the trip?

**(60, 14); 14 chaperones**

Performance Assessment 1 of 2



3. To help organize the trip, the school hires a tour company. The tour company charges different amounts for students and for chaperones.

- cost for each student: $1,200
- cost for each chaperone: $950
- one-time fee for printing all student ID badges: $300
- one-time fee for printing all chaperone ID badges: $250

Write an equation that represents the total cost for the students going on the trip. Write another equation that represents the total cost for the chaperones going on the trip. Identify the variables in the equations. **2 points**

**Sample answers: Let $d$ represent the total cost for the students. Let $p$ represent the total cost for the chaperones. Let $s$ represent the number of students. Let $c$ represent the number of chaperones.**
**Equation for the total cost for students:**
$d = 1{,}200s + 300$
**Equation for the total cost for chaperones:**
$p = 950c + 250$

4. The school has raised $72,000 to pay for the trip. How many students and chaperones can go on the trip without having to pay any of their own money? Explain your reasoning. Show your work. **2 points**

**Sample answer: The greatest number of students and chaperones who can go on the trip is 50 students and 12 chaperones. The total cost is $60,300 + $11,650 = $71,950.**

$d = 1{,}200s + 300 = 1{,}200(50) + 300 = 60{,}000 + 300 = 60{,}300$

$p = 950c + 250 = 950(12) + 250 = 11{,}400 + 250 = 11{,}650$

**Since $72,000 − $71,950 = $50, there is only $50 remaining. This isn't enough for anyone else to go on the trip.**

Performance Assessment 2 of 2



## RtI Item Analysis for Diagnosis and Intervention

| Item | Standard | DOK | MDIS |
|---|---|---|---|
| 1A | 6.EE.C.9, MP.4 | 1 | F30 |
| 1B | 6.EE.C.9, MP.4 | 2 | F31 |
| 2A | 6.EE.C.9, MP.4 | 2 | F34 |
| 2B | 6.EE.C.9, MP.2 | 2 | F34 |
| 3 | 6.EE.C.9, MP.2 | 2 | F30, J20 |
| 4 | 6.EE.C.9, MP.1 | 3 | F31, J20 |

## Scoring Guide

| Item | Points | Topic Performance Assessment Masters |
|---|---|---|
| 1A | 1 | Table completed correctly |
| 1B | 2 | Correct equation and explanation |
| | 1 | Correct equation or explanation |
| 2A | 2 | Correct line graphed and graph labeled correctly |
| | 1 | Correct line graphed but graph not labeled |
| 2B | 1 | Correct answer |
| 3 | 2 | Two correct equations |
| | 1 | One correct equation |
| 4 | 2 | Correct answer and explanation |
| | 1 | Correct answer with no explanation |

# ADDITIONAL CLUSTER 6.NS.B

## MATH BACKGROUND: FOCUS

 MAJOR CLUSTER

 SUPPORTING CLUSTER

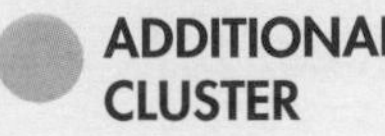 ADDITIONAL CLUSTER

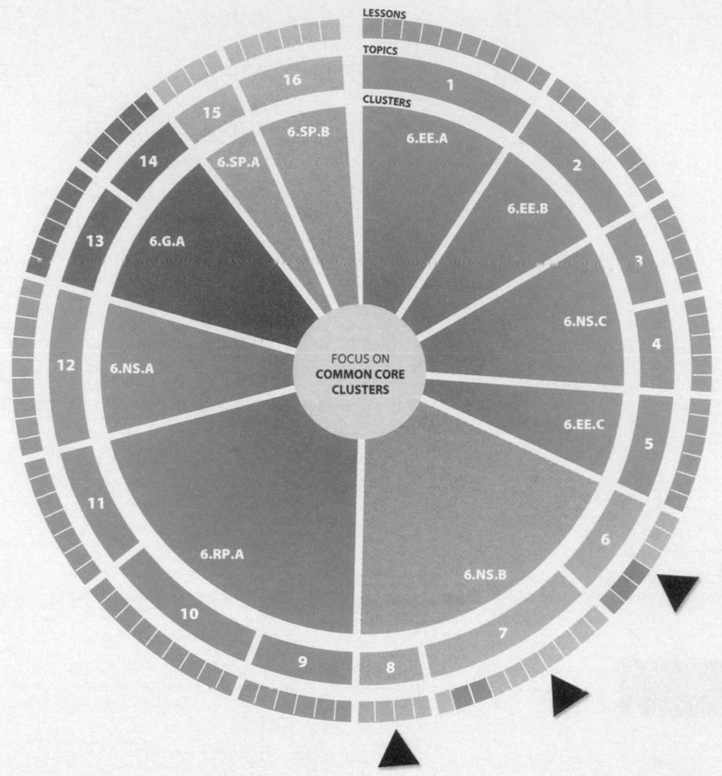


**TOPIC 6** Fluently Divide Whole Numbers

**TOPIC 7** Fluently Add, Subtract, Multiply, and Divide Decimals

**TOPIC 8** Common Factors and Multiples

TOPICS 6, 7, AND 8 FOCUS ON

**ADDITIONAL CLUSTER 6.NS.B**

Compute fluently with multi-digit numbers and find common factors and multiples.

### Content Focus in enVisionmath2.0

Topics 6, 7, and 8 focus on the deep understanding of our number system through fluency in computations with whole numbers and decimals and finding common factors and multiples.

### DIVIDE WHOLE NUMBERS

- **Estimate and Find Quotients** In Lesson 6-1, students use compatible numbers to estimate quotients. Estimation is also used in the subsequent lessons as the first step in the division algorithm and to check exact quotients for reasonableness. Lessons 6-2 and 6-3 provide the capstone experience for computations with whole numbers by helping students develop fluency in dividing whole numbers. (6.NS.B.2)

**Standard Division Algorithm**

**Step 1** Divide
**Step 2** Multiply
**Step 3** Subtract
**Step 4** Bring down the next digit

$$\begin{array}{r} 559 \\ 16\overline{)8{,}944} \\ -8\,0\phantom{44} \\ \hline 94\phantom{4} \\ -80\phantom{4} \\ \hline 144 \\ -144 \\ \hline 0 \end{array}$$

- **Expressions and Equations with Whole Numbers** Lessons 6-4 and 6-5 extend the focus on division to algebra, as students evaluate expressions and formulas, and solve equations involving division. (6.EE.A.2c, 6.EE.B.7, 6.NS.B.2)

PD

Content Focus in enVisionmath2.0 (continued)

## ADD, SUBTRACT, MULTIPLY, AND DIVIDE DECIMALS

- **Add and Subtract Decimals** In Lessons 7-1 and 7-2, students estimate sums and differences and then develop fluency in adding and subtracting multi-digit decimals. (6.NS.B.3)
- **Multiply Decimals** In Lessons 7-3 and 7-4, students estimate products and then develop fluency in multiplying multi-digit decimals. (6.NS.B.3)

$$\begin{array}{r} 3.25 \\ \times\ 2.5 \\ \hline 1{,}625 \\ +\ 6{,}500 \\ \hline 8.125 \end{array}$$

3.25 ← 2 decimal places (hundredths)
× 2.5 ← 1 decimal place (tenths)
8.125 ← 3 decimal places

- **Divide Decimals** In Lessons 7-5, 7-6, and 7-7, students develop fluency in dividing with decimals. (6.NS.B.2, 6.NS.B.3)
- **Expressions and Equations with Decimals** Lessons 7-8 and 7-9 extend the focus on computations with decimals to algebraic concepts as students evaluate expressions and solve equations involving decimals with all four operations. (6.EE.A.2c, 6.EE.B.7, 6.NS.B.2, 6.NS.B.3)

In **3–6**, evaluate each expression.

**3.** $r \div 2.4$; $r = 16.8$

**4.** $9.85 \times s$; $s = 4$

**5.** $4f - 7$; $f = 12.6$

**6.** $6y + (y \div 2)$; $y = 6.1$

## FACTORS AND MULTIPLES

- **Factors** In Lesson 8-1, students identify prime and composite numbers and learn to write the prime factorization of a number. In Lesson 8-2, they find the greatest common factor of two numbers using two methods. In one method, they list all the factors of a number. In the other method, they use the number's prime factorizations. They also factor out the greatest common factor, using the Distributive Property. (6.NS.B.4)

$$18 + 24 = 6 \cdot 3 + 6 \cdot 4 = 6(3 + 4)$$

- **Multiples** In Lesson 8-3, students find the least common multiple of two numbers using two methods. In one method, they list multiples of each number until they find at least one common multiple. In the other method, they use prime factorization. (6.NS.B.4)

| One Way | Another Way |
|---|---|
| 6: 6, 12, 18, 24, 30, 36, 42, 48 . . . | $6 = 2 \times 3$ |
| 8: 8, 16, 24, 32, 40, 48 . . . | $8 = 2 \times 2 \times 2$ |
| | $3 \times 2 \times 2 \times 2 = 24$ |

PD

**Professional Development Videos** Topic Overview Videos and Listen and Look For Lesson Videos present additional important information about the content of this cluster.

# ADDITIONAL CLUSTER 6.NS.B

## MATH BACKGROUND: COHERENCE



### Content Coherence in enVisionmath2.0

Students learn best when ideas are connected in a coherent curriculum. This coherence is achieved through various types of connections including connections within clusters, across clusters, across domains, and across grades.

### BIG IDEAS IN GRADES K–6

Big Ideas are the conceptual underpinnings of **enVision**math**2.0** and provide conceptual cohesion of the content. Big Ideas connect Essential Understandings throughout the program.

A Big Idea that connects most of the work in this cluster is that there are algorithms for performing each of the operations with rational numbers. Strategies and algorithms involving both mental math and paper and pencil use equivalence to transform calculations into simpler ones.

A computation can be transformed into simpler calculations of adding the hundredths, then adding the tenths and regrouping, then adding the ones, then adding the tens.

$$\begin{array}{r} \overset{1}{5}0.90 \\ +\,0.26 \\ \hline 51.16 \end{array}$$

Another prominent Big Idea in this cluster is that calculations can be estimated by replacing numbers with those that are close and easy to compute with mentally.

Estimate $7.83 \times 3.8$.

$$7.83 \times 3.8$$
$$\downarrow \quad \downarrow$$
$$8 \times 4 = 32$$

So, $7.83 \times 3.8 \approx 32$.

For a complete list of Big Ideas, see pages 110–111 in the *Teacher's Edition Program Overview.*

### LOOK BACK

*How do Topics 6–8 connect to what students learned earlier?*

#### GRADE 5

- **Add and Subtract Decimals** In Topic 2, students added and subtracted decimals to the hundredths place. They also estimated the sums and differences and used the estimates to check calculations for reasonableness. (5.NBT.B.7)
- **Multiply Decimals** In Topic 4, students multiplied decimals to the hundredths place. They also estimated products. (5.NBT.B.7)
- **Divide Whole Numbers and Decimals** In Topic 5, students learned how to find quotients of whole numbers with up to 4-digit dividends and up to 2-digit divisors. In Topic 6, they extended this work to divide decimals to the hundredths place using representations, properties, and strategies based on place value. In both topics, they estimated quotients in order to decide where to start dividing and to check calculated quotients for reasonableness. (5.NBT.B.6, 5.NBT.B.7)

***Divide 9.12 by 1.5.***

$$1.5\overline{)9.12} = 15\overline{)91.2} \quad \begin{array}{r} 6.08 \\ 15\overline{)91.20} \\ -\,90 \\ \hline 1\,2 \\ -\;\;0 \\ \hline 1\,20 \\ -\,1\,20 \\ \hline 0 \end{array}$$

#### EARLIER IN GRADE 6

- **Numerical and Algebraic Expressions** In Topic 1, students evaluated algebraic expressions. In Topic 2, they solved equations. (6.EE.A)

## TOPICS 6, 7, AND 8

*How is content connected within Topics 6–8?*

- **Estimate Quotients and Divide Whole Numbers** In Topic 6, students develop fluency in dividing multi-digit whole numbers. The work on estimating quotients in Lesson 6-1 is used as part of the algorithm in Lessons 6-2 and 6-3, and to check quotients for reasonableness. (6.NS.B.2)
- **Fluently Divide Decimals** Students apply their fluency in dividing whole numbers from Topic 6, first to divide a decimal by a whole number in Lesson 7-5, and then to divide a decimal by a decimal in Lessons 7-6 and 7-7. (6.NS.B.3)
- **Common Factors and Multiples** Students use prime factoring of numbers from Lesson 8-1 to find the greatest common factor of two numbers in Lesson 8-2 and to find the least common multiple of two numbers in Lesson 8-3. (6.NS.B.4)
- **Expressions and Equations** Topics 6 and 7 also teach content from Major Clusters 6.EE.A and 6.EE.B on algebraic expressions and solving equations. Lessons 6-4 and 7-8 involve evaluating expressions with quotients and decimals, respectively. Lessons 6-5 and 7-9 involve solving equations with quotients and decimals, respectively. Lesson 6-6 involves being precise when interpreting remainders of expressions arising from real-world situations. (6.EE.A.2c, 6.EE.B.7)

Evaluate $5.1 + 3n$ for $n = 2.6$.

Replace $n$ with 2.6. ⟶ $5.1 + 3(2.6)$

Multiply first. ⟶ $5.1 + 7.8$

Then add. ⟶ $12.9$

The value of the expression is 12.9.

## LOOK AHEAD

*How do Topics 6–8 connect to what students will learn later?*

### LATER IN GRADE 6

- **Fluency in Computations with Whole Numbers and Decimals** Students will use computational fluency throughout the remainder of Grade 6. They will divide whole numbers and add, subtract, multiply, and divide decimals as they solve problems involving rates, including converting units in Topic 10, percents in Topic 11, area in Topic 13, surface area and volume in Topic 14, and statistics in Topics 15 and 16. (6.RP.A.3, 6.G.A.1, 6.G.A.2, 6.G.A.4, 6.SP.B.5c)
- **Evaluate Expressions and Formulas and Solve Equations** Students will use algebraic skills to evaluate expressions and formulas and to solve equations. These skills will be used to solve problems involving percent in Topic 11, to solve area problems in Topic 13, and to solve surface area and volume problems in Topic 14. In Topic 12, students will extend their algebraic skills to evaluate expressions and solve equations containing fractions. (6.EE.A.2c, 6.EE.B.7)

Use an equation to find the total possible points.

90% of *what number* is 135?

Let $p$ = the total number of possible points.

$$90\% \cdot p = 135$$

Write 90% as a decimal. $90\% = \frac{90}{100} = 0.90$

Solve the equation.

$$0.90p = 135$$
$$p = 135 \div 0.90$$
$$p = 150$$

There were 150 total possible points on the test.

### GRADE 7

- **Rational Numbers** Students will use their fluency in computations with whole numbers and positive decimals to evaluate expressions, solve equations, and solve problems with both positive and negative rational numbers. (7.NS.A.3, 7.EE.B.3)

# ADDITIONAL CLUSTER 6.NS.B

## MATH BACKGROUND: RIGOR

FOCUS | COHERENCE |  RIGOR

### Content Rigor in enVisionmath2.0

A rigorous curriculum emphasizes conceptual understanding, procedural skill and fluency, and applications.

### CONCEPTUAL UNDERSTANDING

- **Number Sense and Decimals** Lesson 7-1 focuses on estimating sums and differences of decimals. This lesson lays the foundation for using number sense to judge the reasonableness of sums and differences in Lesson 7-2 (6.NS.B.3)

  Find $20.7 - 0.25$.
  Estimate the difference by rounding.

  $$20.7 - 0.3 = 20.4$$

  $$\begin{array}{r} \scriptstyle 6\,10 \\ 20.\not{7}\not{0} \\ -\ 0.25 \\ \hline 20.45 \end{array}$$

  20.45 is reasonable because it is close to the estimate 20.4.

- **Number Sense and Division** Lesson 6-1 focuses on the use of compatible numbers when estimating quotients. This lesson lays the foundation for using number sense to judge where to start dividing with the algorithm and to judge the reasonableness of quotients in Lessons 6-2, 6-3, 7-5, 7-6, and 7-7. (6.NS.B.2)

### PROCEDURAL SKILL AND FLUENCY

Using standard algorithms with fluency to divide whole numbers and to add, subtract, multiply, and divide decimals is an expectation of this cluster. (6.NS.B.2, 6.NS.B.3)

- **Fluency in Whole Number Algorithms** Lessons 6-2 and 6-3 are the culminating lessons on using whole number algorithms. (6.NS.B.2)

- **Fluency in Decimal Algorithms** Students extend fluency in algorithms for all four operations from whole numbers to multi-digit decimals. This is accomplished by using their conceptual understanding of the base-10 number system. (6.NS.B.3)

### APPLICATIONS

- **Applications Involving Whole Number Division and Decimal Operations** Lessons 6-4 and 6-5 extend understanding of dividing whole numbers to applications involving evaluating expressions and solving equations. Similarly, Lessons 7-8 and 7-9 extend the understanding of operations with decimals to applications involving evaluating expressions and solving equations with decimals. (6.EE.A.2c, 6.EE.B.7, 6.NS.B.2, 6.NS.B.3)

  **18. Higher Order Thinking** You and a friend are paid $38.25 for doing yard work. You worked 2.5 hours and your friend worked 2 hours. You split the money according to the amount of time each of you worked. How much is your share of the money? Explain.

- **Factors and Multiples** In Topic 8, students solve real-world problems by finding the prime factorization of numbers, the greatest common factor of two numbers, and the least common multiple of two numbers. (6.NS.B.4)

  ***Keesha is putting together bags of supplies. She puts an equal number of craft sticks and an equal number of glue bottles in each bag. There are none left over. What is the greatest number of bags of supplies that Keesha can make?***

# MATH PRACTICES

**Connecting Math Practices and Content Standards in enVisionmath2.0**

Math practices and content standards are connected within all lessons including the lessons that focus on math practices.

## MATH PRACTICES WITHIN LESSONS

- **MP.1 Make sense of problems and persevere in solving them.**
  Students make sense of real-world problems involving decimals and work toward a solution. They consider what to expect before jumping into a solution attempt. (e.g., p. 360, Item 13)
- **MP.2 Reason abstractly and quantitatively.**
  Students use reasoning to analyze and identify compatible numbers as they develop fluency with division of whole numbers. (e.g., p. 275, Item 1)
- **MP.3 Construct viable arguments and critique the reasoning of others.**
  Students critique the reasoning and strategies of others as they become fluent in procedures for solving problems involving decimals. (e.g., p. 369, Item 2)
- **MP.4 Model with mathematics.**
  Students apply previously learned concepts, such as evaluating expressions, to model problems involving operations with decimals. (e.g., p. 360, Item 12)
- **MP.5 Use appropriate tools strategically.**
  Students identify, consider, and choose tools strategically to assist them in solving problems related to dividing whole numbers and decimals. (e.g., p. 374, Convince Me!)
- **MP.6 Attend to precision.**
  Students attend to precision by considering definitions when they make computations involving prime numbers. (e.g., p. 393, Item 1)
- **MP.7 Look for and make use of structure.**
  Students use the structure of our number system when they use an algorithm to divide decimals. (e.g., p. 350, Convince Me!)
- **MP.8 Look for and express regularity in repeated reasoning.**
  Students use repeated reasoning when they look for general methods and use shortcuts to determine greatest common factors and least common multiples. (e.g., p. 399, Item 2)

## LESSONS THAT FOCUS ON MATH PRACTICES

- **Lesson 6-6** This lesson focuses on MP.6. Students communicate, calculate accurately and efficiently, and express numerical answers with precision.
- **Lesson 7-10** This lesson focuses on MP.5. Students evaluate which tools can help them solve real-world problems that involve decimal operations.

**Thinking Habits**

*Be a good thinker! These questions can help you.*

- Which tools can I use?
- Why should I use this tool to help me solve the problem?
- Is there a different tool I could use?
- Am I using the tool appropriately?

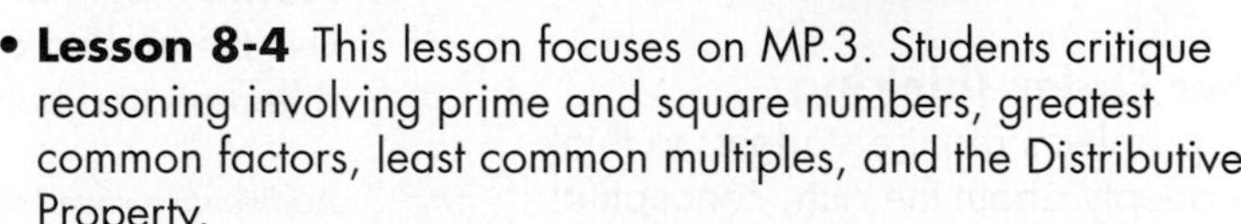

- **Lesson 8-4** This lesson focuses on MP.3. Students critique reasoning involving prime and square numbers, greatest common factors, least common multiples, and the Distributive Property.
  For a list of Thinking Habits for MP.3 and MP.6, see pp. F25 and F28 in Volume 1 of the Math Practices and Problem Solving Handbook.

Revisit the information about MP.3, MP.5, and MP.6 in these other resources:

- **Math Practices and Problem Solving Handbook** before Topic 1; includes Math Practices Proficiency Rubrics.
- **Math Practices Posters** to display in your classroom

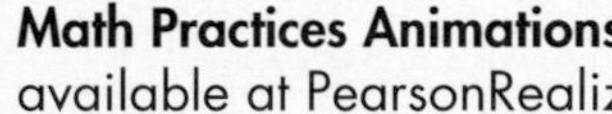

MP **Math Practices Animations,** one for each math practice, available at PearsonRealize.com

# ADDITIONAL CLUSTER 6.NS.B

## DIFFERENTIATED INSTRUCTION

 Intervention  On-Level Ⓐ Advanced

Pearson realize. PearsonRealize.com

 Learn  Practice Buddy  Tools  Assessment  Games

### Ongoing Intervention

**During the core lesson,** monitor progress, reteach as needed, and extend students' thinking.

**Guiding Questions**

- **In the Teacher's Edition** Guiding questions are used to monitor understanding during instruction.

**Online Guiding Questions** Guiding questions are also in the online Visual Learning Animation Plus.

**Prevent Misconceptions**
This feature in the Teacher's Edition is embedded in the guiding questions.

**Error Intervention: If... then...**
This feature in the Teacher's Edition is provided during Guided Practice. It spotlights common errors and gives suggestions for addressing them.

**Reteaching**
Reteaching sets are at the end of the topic in the Student's Edition. They provide additional examples, reminders, and practice. Use these sets as needed before students do the Independent Practice.

**Higher Order Thinking**
These problems require students to think more deeply about the rich, conceptual knowledge developed in the lesson.

**Practice Buddy Online**

Online auto-scored practice is provided for each lesson. On-screen learning aids include Help Me Solve This and View an Example.

### Strategic Intervention

**At the end of the lesson,** assess to identify students' strengths and needs and then provide appropriate support.

**Quick Check**

**In the Student's Edition** Assess the lesson using 3 items checked in the Teacher's Edition.

**Online Quick Check** You can also assess the lesson using 5 online, machine-scored items.

**Intervention Activity** Ⓘ
Teachers work with struggling students.

**Reteach to Build Understanding** Ⓘ
This is a page of guided reteaching.

**Technology Center** ⒾⓄⒶ

**Digital Math Tools Activities** reinforce the lesson content or previously taught content using a suite of digital math tools.

**Online Games** provide practice on the lesson content or previously taught content.

**Homework and Practice** ⒾⓄⒶ
Use the leveled assignment to provide differentiated homework and practice.

*Additional resources to support differentiated instruction for on-level and advanced students include:*

**On-Level and Advanced Activity Centers** ⓄⒶ

- **Center Games** are provided in on-level and advanced versions.
- **Math and Science Activity** is related to the topic science theme introduced at the start of the topic.
- **Problem-Solving Reading Mat** is used with a lesson-specific activity.

### Intensive Intervention

**As needed,** provide more instruction that is on or below grade level for students who are struggling.

**Math Diagnosis and Intervention System 2.0**

- **Diagnosis** Use the diagnostic tests in the system. Also, use the item analysis charts given with program assessments at the start of a grade or topic, or at the end of a topic, group of topics, or the year.
- **Intervention Lessons** These two-page lessons include guided instruction followed by practice. The system includes lessons below, on, and above grade level.
- **Teacher Support** Teacher Notes provide the support needed to conduct a short lesson. The lesson focuses on vocabulary, concept development, and practice. The Teacher's Guide contains individual and class record forms and correlations to Student's Edition lessons.

**Resources for Fluency Success**

- A variety of print and digital resources are provided to ensure success on Common Core fluency standards. See Steps to Fluency Success on pages 271K–271N and 317E–317H.

# THE LANGUAGE OF MATH

PEARSON realize
PearsonRealize.com

A-Z
Glossary

Games

## English Language Learners

**Provide ELL support** through visual learning throughout the program, ELL instruction in every lesson, and additional ideas in an ELL Toolkit.

**Visual Learning**
The visual learning that is infused in **enVision**math**2.0** provides support for English language learners. This support includes a Visual Learning Animation Plus and a Visual Learning Bridge for each lesson.

**English Language Learners Instruction** 
Lessons provide instruction for English language learners at Beginning, Intermediate, and Advanced levels of English proficiency.

**English Language Learners Toolkit**
This resource provides professional development and resources for supporting English language learners.

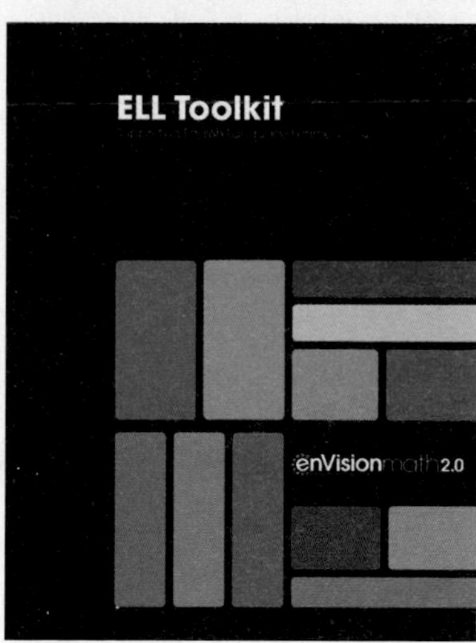
ELL Toolkit
enVisionmath2.0

## Math Vocabulary

**Build math vocabulary** using the vocabulary cards, vocabulary activities, vocabulary review, and glossary plus the online glossary and vocabulary game.

**My Word Cards**
Vocabulary cards for a topic are provided in the Student's Edition. Students use the example on the front of the card to complete the definition on the back.

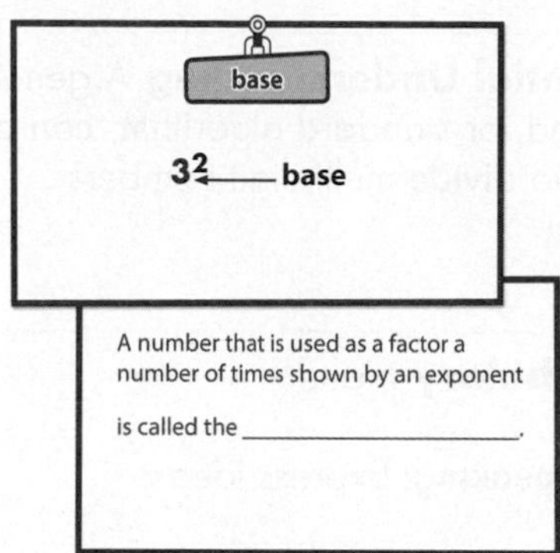
base
3² base
A number that is used as a factor a number of times shown by an exponent
is called the ______.

**Vocabulary Activities**
The Teacher's Edition provides vocabulary activities at the start of topics. These include activities for vocabulary in My Word Cards and/or activities for vocabulary in Review What You Know.

**Vocabulary Review**
A page of vocabulary review is provided at the end of each topic. It reviews vocabulary used in the topic.

**Glossary**
A glossary is provided at the back of the Student's Edition.

**Animated Glossary**
 Glossary
An online, bilingual, animated glossary uses motion and sound to build understanding of math vocabulary.

**Online Vocabulary Game**
 Games
An online vocabulary game is available in the Game Center.

## Math and Reading

**Connect reading and math** using a data-filled reading mat for the topic with accompanying activity masters and guide.

**Problem-Solving Reading Mats**
There is a large, beautiful mat for each topic. At the start of the topic, help students become familiar with the mat and the vocabulary used by reading the mat aloud as students follow along. Use the Problem-Solving Reading Activity Guide for suggestions about how to use the mat.

**Problem-Solving Reading Activity**
At the end of some lessons, a Problem-Solving Reading Activity provides a page of math problems to solve by using the data on the mat.

TOPIC 6

# TOPIC PLANNER

## FLUENTLY DIVIDE WHOLE NUMBERS

| Lesson 6-1 | Lesson 6-2 | Lesson 6-3 |
|---|---|---|
| **ESTIMATE QUOTIENTS INVOLVING WHOLE NUMBERS** pp. 273–278 | **DIVIDE WHOLE NUMBERS** pp. 279–284 | **CONTINUE TO DIVIDE WHOLE NUMBERS** pp. 285–290 |
| Content Standard **6.NS.B.2**<br>Mathematical Practices **MP.2, MP.3, MP.8** | Content Standard **6.NS.B.2**<br>Mathematical Practices **MP.2, MP.3, MP.6, MP.7, MP.8** | Content Standard **6.NS.B.2**<br>Mathematical Practices **MP.1, MP.2, MP.3, MP.4, MP.6, MP.7, MP.8** |
| **Objective** Estimate quotients using compatible numbers. | **Objective** Find the quotient of two whole numbers and solve division problems. | **Objective** Find the quotient of greater whole numbers and interpret the remainder. |
| **Essential Understanding** Compatible numbers and mental math can be used to estimate a quotient. | **Essential Understanding** A general method, or standard algorithm, can be used to divide multi-digit numbers. | **Essential Understanding** A general method, or standard algorithm, can be used to divide multi-digit numbers. |
| **Vocabulary** None | **Vocabulary** None | **Vocabulary** None |
| **ELL Speaking:** Use abstract and content-based vocabulary during speaking assignments. | **ELL Speaking:** Express ideas. | **ELL Reading:** Expand comprehension by predicting. |
| **Materials** Strips of paper, small box | **Materials** Grid paper (or TT 15) (optional), lined paper (optional) | **Materials** Calculators, Grid paper (or TT 15) (optional), lined paper (optional) |
| **On-Level and Advanced Activity Centers**<br>• Problem-Solving Reading Mat | **On-Level and Advanced Activity Centers**<br>• Center Games | **On-Level and Advanced Activity Centers**<br>• Center Games |

### LESSON RESOURCES

Digital

Print

- Student's Edition
- Daily Common Core Review
- Reteach to Build Understanding
- Center Games
- Math and Science Activity
- Problem-Solving Reading Mat
- Problem-Solving Reading Activity

Digital

- Listen and Look For PD Lesson Video
- Student's Edition eText
- Today's Challenge
- Solve & Share
- Visual Learning Animation Plus
- Animated Glossary
- Math Tools
- Practice Buddy Online Practice
- Quick Check
- Another Look Homework Video
- Math Games

Digital

## Lesson 6-4

**EVALUATE EXPRESSIONS** pp. 291–296

**Content Standards 6.EE.A.2c, 6.NS.B.2**
**Mathematical Practices MP.3, MP.4, MP.7**

**Objective** Evaluate expressions involving division by using substitution and order of operations.

**Essential Understanding** Formulas involving division can be evaluated by substituting given values for the variables and then performing the arithmetic operations.

**Vocabulary** None

**ELL Listening:** Listen to ideas and information.

**Materials** None

**On-Level and Advanced Activity Centers**
- Math and Science Activity

## Lesson 6-5

**SOLVE DIVISION EQUATIONS** pp. 297–302

**Content Standards 6.EE.B.7, 6.NS.B.2**
**Mathematical Practices MP.2, MP.3, MP.4, MP.7, MP.8**

**Objective** Solve one-step equations involving division.

**Essential Understanding** Inverse relationships and properties of equality can be used to solve equations that involve division.

**Vocabulary** None

**ELL Listening:** Demonstrate listening comprehension by responding to questions.

**Materials** Index cards

**On-Level and Advanced Activity Centers**
- Problem-Solving Reading Mat

## Lesson 6-6

**MATH PRACTICES AND PROBLEM SOLVING: PRECISION** pp. 303–308

**Mathematical Practices MP.6 Also MP.1, MP.2, MP.3**
**Content Standards 6.EE.A.2c, 6.NS.B.2**

**Objective** Use problem-solving strategies accurately and calculate fluently.

**Essential Understanding** Good math thinkers are careful about what they write and say, so their ideas about math are clear.

**Vocabulary** None

**ELL Speaking:** Describe information.

**Materials** None

**On-Level and Advanced Activity Centers**
- Math and Science Activity

## TOPIC RESOURCES

Digital

Print

**Start of Topic**
- Steps to Fluency Success
- Math and Science Project
- Home-School Connection
- Review What You Know
- My Word Cards

**End of Topic**
- Fluency Practice Activity
- Vocabulary Review
- Reteaching
- Topic Assessment
- Topic Performance Assessment

Digital

**Start of Topic**
- Topic Overview PD Video

**End of Topic**
- Math Practices Animations
- Online Topic Assessment
- ExamView® Test Generator
- Practice Buddy Fluency Practice/Assessment

PearsonRealize.com

TOPIC 6

# STEPS TO FLUENCY SUCCESS

## FLUENTLY DIVIDE MULTI-DIGIT NUMBERS

In Grade 6, students are expected to fluently divide multi-digit numbers using the standard algorithm. (6.NS.B.2) To help all students achieve fluency follow the 6 steps outlined below and use the support materials described on pages 271L, 271M, and 271N.

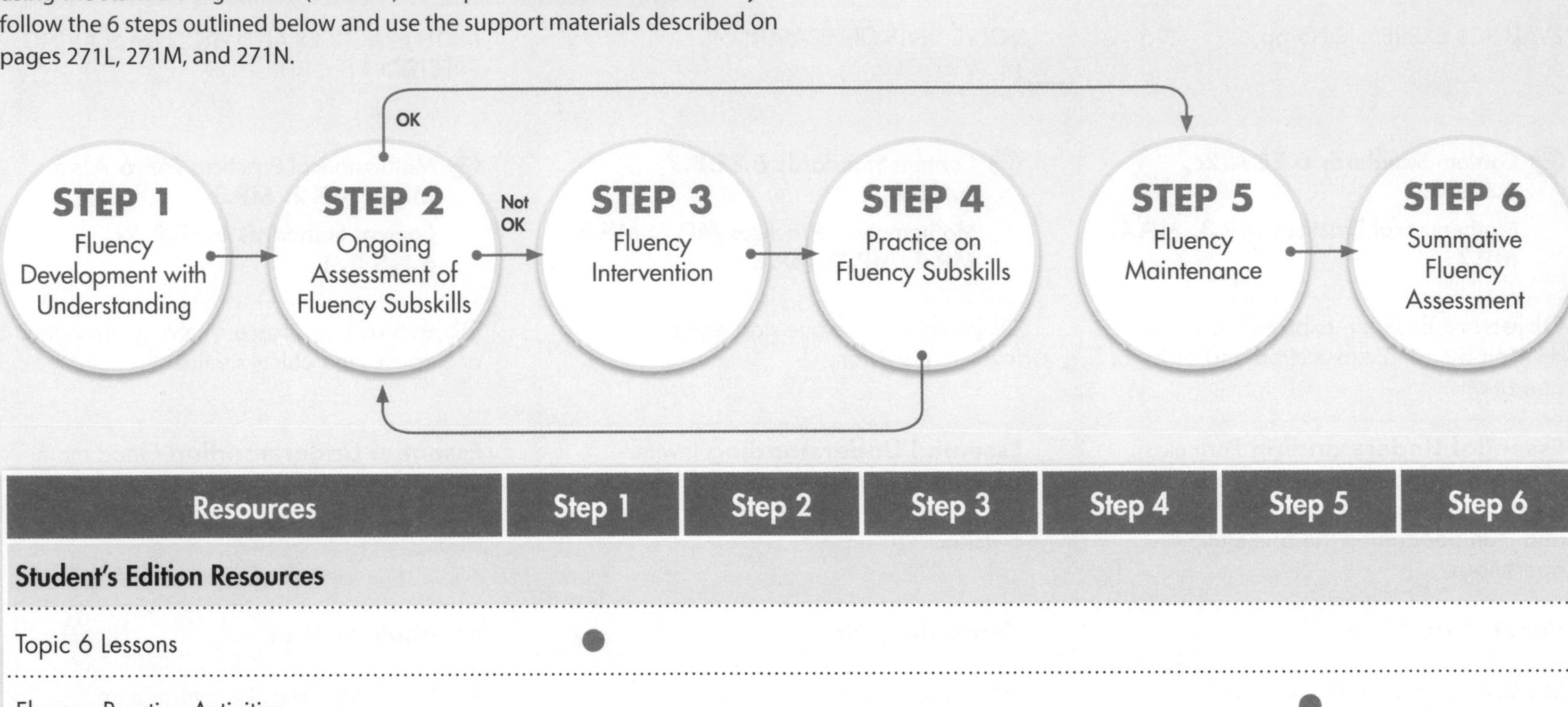


| Resources | Step 1 | Step 2 | Step 3 | Step 4 | Step 5 | Step 6 |
|---|---|---|---|---|---|---|
| **Student's Edition Resources** | | | | | | |
| Topic 6 Lessons | ● | | | | | |
| Fluency Practice Activities | | | | | ● | |
| **Fluency Practice/Assessment Worksheets** | | | | | | |
| Teacher's Resource Masters | | ● | | ● | ● | ● |
| ExamView® CD-ROM | | ● | | ● | ● | ● |
| **Math Diagnosis and Intervention System 2.0** | | | | | | |
| Diagnostic Tests | | | ● | | | |
| Intervention Lessons | | | ● | | | |
| Practice Buddy **Online Practice/Assessment** | | | | | | |
| Auto-Scored Items | | ● | | ● | ● | ● |
| On-Screen Help | | | ● | | | |
| Games **Game Center Online** | | | | | | |
| Games | | | | | ● | |
| **"My Fluency Progress" Form** | | | | | | |
| Teaching Tool 3 | | ● | | | | |

Practice Buddy

Games

## Student's Edition Resources

- **Topic 6 Lessons** Topic 6 provides the development with understanding that students need to fluently divide multi-digit numbers using the standard algorithm. This work builds on foundations for fluency from earlier work.

**Foundations For Fluency**

**Grade 3, Topic 5** Fluently Multiply and Divide within 100

**Grade 4, Topic 5** Use Strategies and Properties to Divide by 1-Digit Numbers

**Grade 4, Topic 6** Use Operations with Whole Numbers to Solve Problems

**Grade 5, Topic 5** Use Models and Strategies to Divide Whole Numbers

- **Fluency Practice Activities** To support fluency for 6.NS.B.2, use the fluency activity found at the end of each of Topics 6, 8, 10, 12, 14, and 16. Students can collaborate on these activities to help each other as needed.

Each Fluency Practice Activity is in one of the following formats: *Point & Tally, Find a Match, or Follow the Path.*

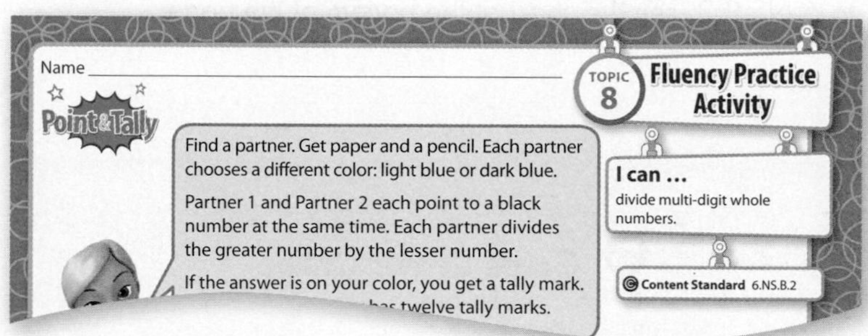


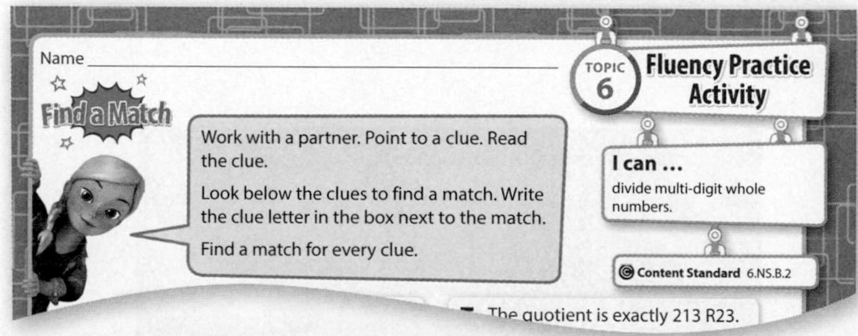


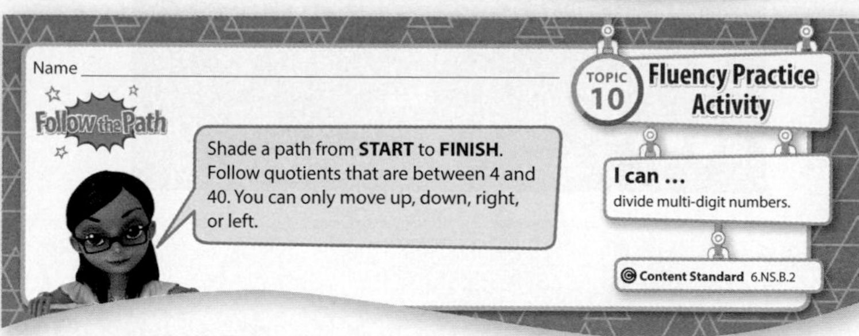


## Fluency Practice/Assessment Worksheets

- **Teacher's Resource Masters** Teacher's Resource Masters for Fluency Practice/Assessment are organized around 3 subskills of 6.NS.B.2. These worksheets can be used for practice on fluency subskills, for maintenance, or for assessment.

- **ExamView® CD-ROM** You can use ExamView to generate worksheets that cover the same content as the items on the Fluency Practice/Assessment Masters.

***Go to pages 271M–271N*** to see the Fluency Practice/Assessment Masters and a list of the subskills for 6.NS.B.2.

# STEPS TO FLUENCY SUCCESS

## FLUENTLY DIVIDE MULTI-DIGIT NUMBERS

### Math Diagnosis and Intervention System 2.0

- **Diagnostic Tests** After covering Topic 6, if a student cannot fluently divide multi-digit numbers, you might want to give a *Math Diagnosis and Intervention System 2.0* Diagnostic Test. These tests can diagnose the need for remediation of on-level content as well as prerequisite content such as multiplication facts and place value.
- **Intervention Lessons** For MDIS intervention lessons related to 6.NS.B.2, see the chart at the bottom of the page.

### Online Practice/Assessment

- **Auto-Scored Items** The online practice/assessment includes items on subskills of 6.NS.B.2. Items are auto-scored to give students instant feedback, and a report is sent to the teacher.
- **On-Screen Help** If students are uncertain how to complete an item, or if they answer incorrectly, intervention is available through on-screen help. This includes "Help Me Solve This," which guides the student through a solution, and "View an Example," which shows a worked-out solution for a similar item.

### Game Center Online

- **Games** The Game Center at PearsonRealize.com includes the Factory Frenzy Game, which involves dividing multi-digit numbers.

### "My Fluency Progress" Form

- **Teaching Tool 3** To help students become personally responsible for monitoring their progress on 6.NS.B.2, have them use the "My Fluency Progress" Form, Teaching Tool 3. This form gives students a place to record progress on fluency subskills.

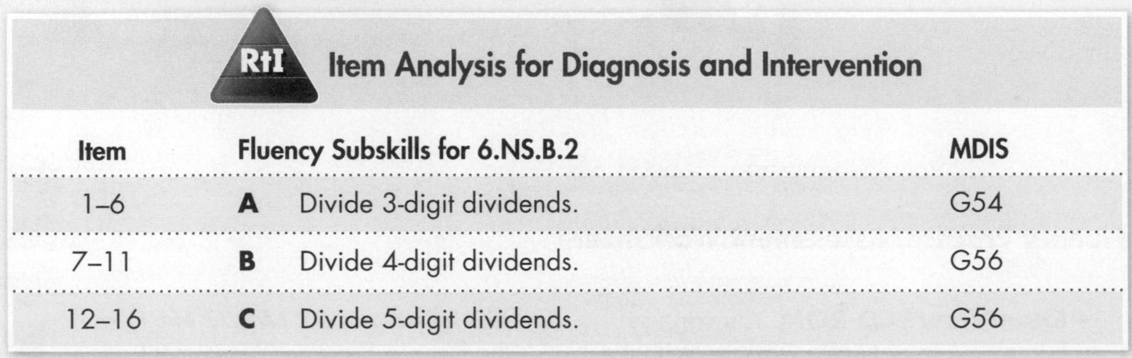

### RtI Item Analysis for Diagnosis and Intervention

| Item | Fluency Subskills for 6.NS.B.2 | | MDIS |
|---|---|---|---|
| 1–6 | **A** | Divide 3-digit dividends. | G54 |
| 7–11 | **B** | Divide 4-digit dividends. | G56 |
| 12–16 | **C** | Divide 5-digit dividends. | G56 |

PEARSON realize. PearsonRealize.com

Practice Buddy

Games

## Fluency Practice/Assessment Worksheets

Name ____________________ Topic 6 Fluency Practice/Assessment

### Divide Multi-Digit Numbers

1. 24)168 **7**
2. 37)333 **9**
3. 82)164 **2**
4. 97)582 **6**
5. 58)470 **8 R6**
6. 71)156 **2 R14**
7. 95)4,180 **44**
8. 49)1,372 **28**
9. 62)4,216 **68**
10. 15)1,065 **71**
11. 98)9,038 **92 R22**
12. 14)11,816 **844**
13. 88)21,208 **241**
14. 53)27,613 **521**
15. 19)18,715 **985**
16. 72)38,990 **541 R38**
17. A school auditorium has 560 seats. Each row in the auditorium has 35 seats. How many rows are in the auditorium? Show how you know.
**16 rows; Check students' work.**




Name ____________________ Topic 6 Fluency Practice/Assessment

### Divide Multi-Digit Numbers

1. 55)495 **9**
2. 63)189 **3**
3. 22)154 **7**
4. 62)124 **2**
5. 75)201 **2 R51**
6. 11)856 **77 R9**
7. 76)5,548 **73**
8. 42)2,562 **61**
9. 44)1,276 **29**
10. 42)1,554 **37**
11. 91)1,095 **12 R3**
12. 96)11,136 **116**
13. 93)18,135 **195**
14. 82)13,366 **163**
15. 89)32,129 **361**
16. 38)25,154 **661 R36**
17. Write one digit in each box to complete the division problem. You will not use the same digit twice.

```
       682
95)64,790
  − 570
     779
   − 760
      190
    − 190
        0
```




Name ____________________ Topic 6 Fluency Practice/Assessment

### Divide Multi-Digit Numbers

1. 77)231 **3**
2. 91)637 **7**
3. 43)215 **5**
4. 73)146 **2**
5. 87)323 **3 R62**
6. 11)239 **21 R8**
7. 68)1,224 **18**
8. 18)1,422 **79**
9. 73)2,263 **31**
10. 48)1,200 **25**
11. 11)1,041 **94 R7**
12. 92)20,056 **218**
13. 86)11,008 **128**
14. 72)60,336 **838**
15. 29)11,426 **394**
16. 69)45,764 **663 R17**
17. One whole number is divided by a second whole number, resulting in a quotient that is also a whole number. The dividend has three digits, and the quotient has one digit. How many digits does the divisor have? Explain.
**Sample answer: The divisor can have 2 or 3 digits. 999 divided by any 4-digit number is less than 1, so the divisor cannot have 4 or more digits. 100 divided by 9 results in a quotient with more than 1 digit. So, the divisor must have more than 1 digit.**




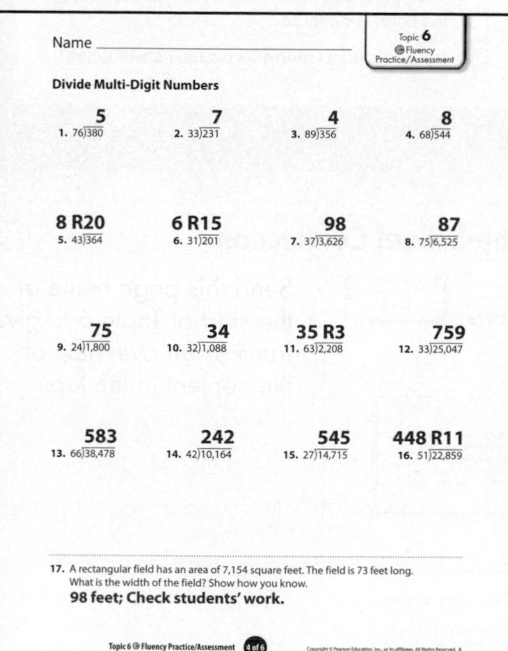
Name ____________________ Topic 6 Fluency Practice/Assessment

### Divide Multi-Digit Numbers

1. 76)380 **5**
2. 33)231 **7**
3. 89)356 **4**
4. 68)544 **8**
5. 43)364 **8 R20**
6. 31)201 **6 R15**
7. 37)3,626 **98**
8. 75)6,525 **87**
9. 24)1,800 **75**
10. 32)1,088 **34**
11. 63)2,208 **35 R3**
12. 33)25,047 **759**
13. 66)38,478 **583**
14. 42)10,164 **242**
15. 27)14,715 **545**
16. 51)22,859 **448 R11**
17. A rectangular field has an area of 7,154 square feet. The field is 73 feet long. What is the width of the field? Show how you know.
**98 feet; Check students' work.**




Name ____________________ Topic 6 Fluency Practice/Assessment

### Divide Multi-Digit Numbers

1. 79)474 **6**
2. 75)300 **4**
3. 82)164 **2**
4. 58)406 **7**
5. 49)382 **7 R39**
6. 22)232 **10 R12**
7. 86)8,428 **98**
8. 31)2,635 **85**
9. 95)5,890 **62**
10. 32)1,184 **37**
11. 55)3,369 **61 R14**
12. 45)16,425 **365**
13. 98)83,594 **853**
14. 36)27,684 **769**
15. 98)40,278 **411**
16. 72)16,796 **233 R20**
17. A four-digit whole number is divided by a two-digit whole number. The digit in the ones place of the dividend is 8. The digit in the ones place of the divisor is 6. The quotient is a whole number with no remainder. What digit(s) could be in the ones place of the quotient? Explain.
**Sample answer: 3 or 8; For the dividend to have 8 in its ones place, the product of the ones digits in the divisor and quotient must have 8 in its ones place. The only products of 6 and another digit that end in 8 are $6 \times 3 = 18$ and $6 \times 8 = 48$.**




Name ____________________ Topic 6 Fluency Practice/Assessment

### Divide Multi-Digit Numbers

1. 23)207 **9**
2. 59)177 **3**
3. 56)280 **5**
4. 91)364 **4**
5. 73)629 **8 R45**
6. 25)876 **35 R1**
7. 99)6,039 **61**
8. 92)8,188 **89**
9. 41)1,353 **33**
10. 42)2,772 **66**
11. 31)2,634 **84 R30**
12. 36)33,228 **923**
13. 48)20,688 **431**
14. 55)28,380 **516**
15. 26)19,942 **767**
16. 89)29,070 **326 R56**
17. For a fundraiser, the students of a middle school raised a total of $22,126. If each student raised $37, how many students are in the middle school? Show how you know.
**598 students; Check students' work.**

# FLUENTLY DIVIDE WHOLE NUMBERS

## TOPIC ESSENTIAL QUESTION

**How are quotients of multi-digit numbers found?**

Revisit the Topic Essential Question throughout the topic, and see a note about answering the question in the Teacher's Edition for the Topic Assessment.

## MATH AND SCIENCE PROJECT STEM

**Science Theme** The science theme for this project is **Water Consumption**. This theme will be revisited in the Math and Science Activities in Lessons 6-4 and 6-6 and in some lesson exercises.

About 20% of the world's energy is generated by hydropower, a clean energy source. Thermoelectric power (steam-generated electricity) accounts for about half of total water withdrawals in the U.S., followed by irrigation, which uses about a third of the total.

Less than 1% of Earth's water is available for human consumption. About 2 billion people currently live in areas where water is scarce. 780 million (1 in 9) people do not have safe drinking water.

**Project-Based Learning** Have students work on the **Math and Science Project** over the course of several days.

### EXTENSION

Make a chart and record your water usage over a 3-day period. Include a portion of the water your family uses for bathing, washing dishes, doing laundry, cooking, and gardening. Then average the results and make a circle graph that indicates your daily household water use.

### Sample Student Work for Math and Science Project

Rates of Household Water Use

| | |
|---|---|
| Drinking Water | about 11 cups/day |
| Outdoor Watering | 2 gal/min |
| Dishwasher | 20 gal/load |
| Bath | 35 gal/bath |
| Kitchen/shower faucets | old: 4 gal/min, new: 2 gal/min |
| Bathroom faucet | old: 2 gal/min, new: 1 gal/min |

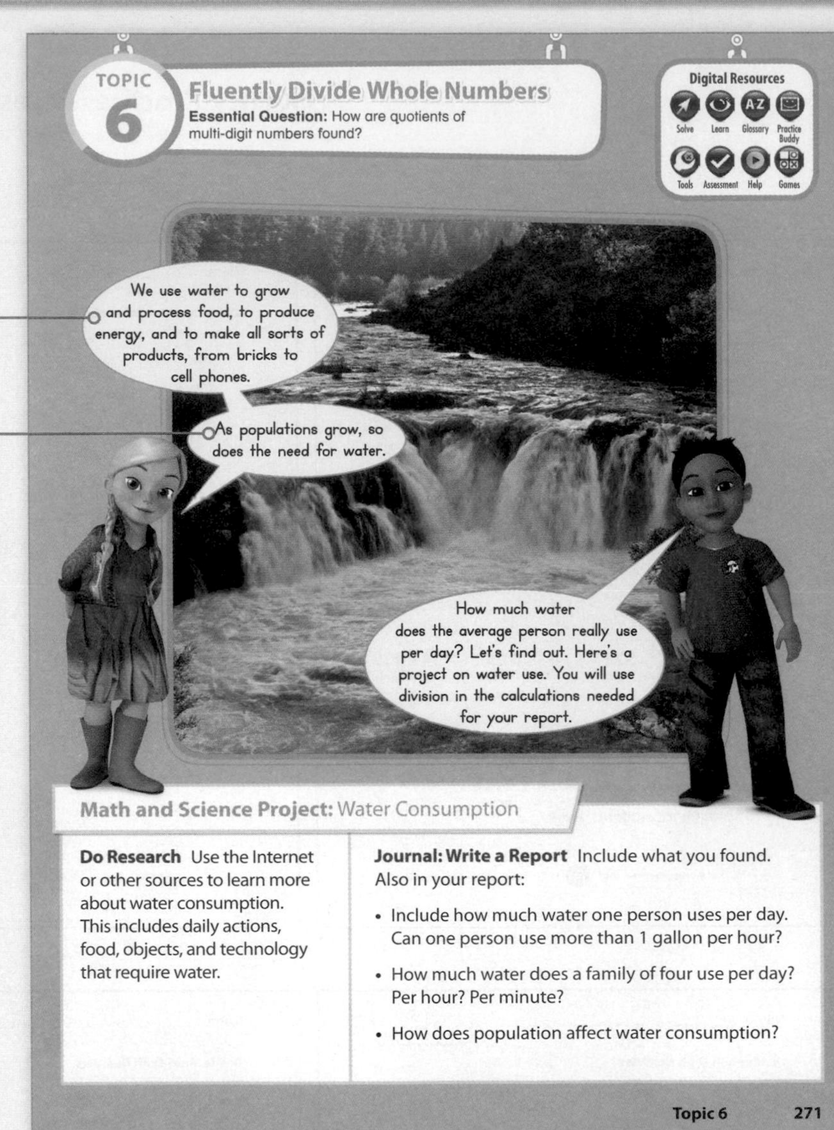

TOPIC 6 **Fluently Divide Whole Numbers**

**Essential Question:** How are quotients of multi-digit numbers found?



**Math and Science Project:** Water Consumption

**Do Research** Use the Internet or other sources to learn more about water consumption. This includes daily actions, food, objects, and technology that require water.

**Journal: Write a Report** Include what you found. Also in your report:

- Include how much water one person uses per day. Can one person use more than 1 gallon per hour?
- How much water does a family of four use per day? Per hour? Per minute?
- How does population affect water consumption?

Topic 6 271

## Home-School Connection

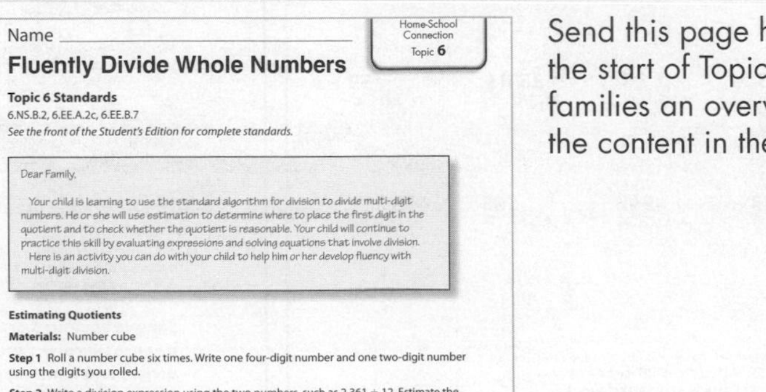

Name ______

Home-School Connection Topic 6

**Fluently Divide Whole Numbers**

**Topic 6 Standards**
6.NS.B.2, 6.EE.A.2c, 6.EE.B.7
*See the front of the Student's Edition for complete standards.*

Dear Family,

Your child is learning to use the standard algorithm for division to divide multi-digit numbers. He or she will use estimation to determine where to place the first digit in the quotient and to check whether the quotient is reasonable. Your child will continue to practice this skill by evaluating expressions and solving equations that involve division.

Here is an activity you can do with your child to help him or her develop fluency with multi-digit division.

**Estimating Quotients**

**Materials:** Number cube

**Step 1** Roll a number cube six times. Write one four-digit number and one two-digit number using the digits you rolled.

**Step 2** Write a division expression using the two numbers, such as 2,361 ÷ 12. Estimate the quotient and then divide.

**Step 3** Choose an estimate, such as 100 or 50. Challenge your child to write a division expression with two- and four-digit numbers that will result in a quotient as close to the estimate as possible.

**Observe Your Child**

**Focus on Mathematical Practice 2**
Reason abstractly and quantitatively.

Help your child become proficient with Mathematical Practice 2. Ask him or her to tell you the division fact that he or she used to determine compatible numbers for the estimate in the activity above.



Send this page home at the start of Topic 6 to give families an overview of the content in the topic.

Name

## Review What You Know

**Vocabulary**

Choose the best term from the box. Write it on the blank.

- compatible numbers
- dividend
- divisor
- estimate
- quotient

1. To find an approximate answer or solution is to **estimate**.
2. The number being divided by another number is the **dividend**.
3. **Compatible numbers** are numbers that are easy to compute mentally.
4. In the equation $20 \div 4 = 5$, the number 5 is the **quotient**.

**Division**

Find each quotient.

5. $4\overline{)432}$ **108**
6. $691 \div 7$ **98 R5**
7. $2\overline{)374}$ **187**
8. $872 \div 8$ **109**
9. $3\overline{)2{,}184}$ **728**
10. $1{,}135 \div 6$ **189 R1**

**Evaluating Expressions**

Evaluate each expression for $x = 5$ and $x = 9$.

11. $7x$ **35; 63**
12. $50 - 5x$ **25; 5**
13. $12x \div 3$ **20; 36**
14. $135 \div x$ **27; 15**
15. $6x + 15 \div 3$ **35; 59**
16. $5 + 4x \div 2$ **15; 23**

**Using Estimation**

17. A small theater has 154 seats in 11 rows. How can Sam estimate the number of seats in each row?
**Sample answer: Sam can use the compatible numbers 150 and 10 and divide to find $150 \div 10 = 15$. There are about 15 seats in each row.**

272 Topic 6 | Review What You Know

## Item Analysis for Diagnosis and Intervention

| Item | Standard | MDIS |
|---|---|---|
| 1–4 | 6.NS.B.2 | G72 |
| 5–10 | 6.NS.B.2 | G56 |
| 11–16 | 6.EE.A.2c | F41, F44 |
| 17 | 6.NS.B.2 | G72 |

## Vocabulary Review Activity

Have students review the vocabulary words with this activity. Each student should write 3 division problems on a sheet of paper. Each problem should be written in a different style: one equation, one with the division house, and one fraction. Use a variable for the "answer." Illustrate this for students on the board.

$472 \div 18 = x$

$82\overline{)885}$ with $y$ above

$\frac{555}{6} = z$

Then have students trade problems with each other.

Activity Directions:

- Circle all the **dividends**.
- Draw a box around the **quotients**.
- Write **compatible numbers** for each number in the problems.
- Use the compatible numbers to **estimate** the quotients, and underline your estimates.

1. (472) ÷ 18 = [x]
$500 \div 20 = 25$
2. $82\overline{)(885)}$ with [y] above
$80\overline{)800}$ with 10 above
3. $\frac{(555)}{6}$ = [w]
$\frac{540}{6} = 90$

# LESSON 6-1

# ESTIMATE QUOTIENTS INVOLVING WHOLE NUMBERS

## DIGITAL RESOURCES PearsonRealize.com

Student and Teacher eTexts
eText

Listen and Look For Lesson Video
PD

Today's Challenge
Think

Solve and Share
Solve

Visual Learning Animation Plus
Learn

Animated Glossary
Glossary

Online Personalized Practice
Practice Buddy

Math Tools
Tools

Quick Check
Assessment

Another Look Homework Video
Help

Math Games
Games

## LESSON OVERVIEW FCR FOCUS • COHERENCE • RIGOR

### FOCUS

**Domain 6.NS** The Number System

**Cluster 6.NS.B** Compute fluently with multi-digit numbers and find common factors and multiples.

**Content Standard 6.NS.B.2** Fluently divide multi-digit numbers using the standard algorithm.

**Mathematical Practices MP.2, MP.3, MP.8**

**Objective** Estimate quotients using compatible numbers.

**Essential Understanding** Compatible numbers and mental math can be used to estimate a quotient.

### COHERENCE

In Grades 4 and 5, students gained familiarity with estimation of whole-number computation to assess the reasonableness of exact answers. In this lesson, students extend this understanding to estimate quotients of whole numbers and two-digit divisors using compatible numbers. This skill is applied throughout the rest of Topic 6, in which students learn and practice the division algorithm and use estimation to determine the reasonableness of their exact answers.

### RIGOR

This lesson emphasizes **conceptual understanding** and **procedural skill**. As students estimate quotients, they develop a sense of the quantities being divided and the relationships between the divisor, dividend, and quotient. Encourage students to round the divisor to the nearest ten, so they can more easily determine a compatible number for the dividend. Students will later use successive estimations as they apply the division algorithm.

Watch the Listen and Look For Lesson Video.

## MATH ANYTIME

### Daily Common Core Review

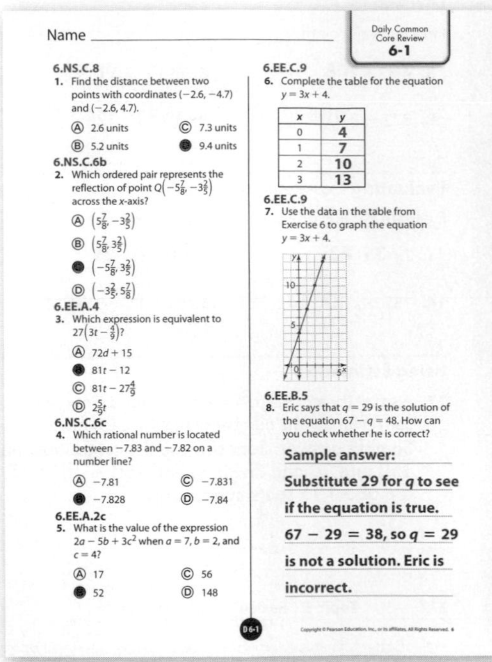

Name ______

Daily Common Core Review 6-1

6.NS.C.8
1. Find the distance between two points with coordinates $(-2.6, -4.7)$ and $(-2.6, 4.7)$.
Ⓐ 2.6 units Ⓒ 7.3 units
Ⓑ 5.2 units ● 9.4 units

6.NS.C.6b
2. Which ordered pair represents the reflection of point $Q\left(-5\frac{7}{8}, -3\frac{2}{5}\right)$ across the $x$-axis?
Ⓐ $\left(5\frac{7}{8}, -3\frac{2}{5}\right)$
Ⓑ $\left(5\frac{7}{8}, 3\frac{2}{5}\right)$
● $\left(-5\frac{7}{8}, 3\frac{2}{5}\right)$
Ⓓ $\left(-3\frac{2}{5}, 5\frac{7}{8}\right)$

6.EE.A.4
3. Which expression is equivalent to $27\left(3t - \frac{4}{9}\right)$?
Ⓐ $72d + 15$
● $81t - 12$
Ⓒ $81t - 27\frac{4}{9}$
Ⓓ $2\frac{5}{9}t$

6.NS.C.6c
4. Which rational number is located between −7.83 and −7.82 on a number line?
Ⓐ −7.81 Ⓒ −7.831
● −7.828 Ⓓ −7.84

6.EE.A.2c
5. What is the value of the expression $2a - 5b + 3c^2$ when $a = 7$, $b = 2$, and $c = 4$?
Ⓐ 17 Ⓒ 56
● 52 Ⓓ 148

6.EE.C.9
6. Complete the table for the equation $y = 3x + 4$.

| $x$ | $y$ |
|---|---|
| 0 | 4 |
| 1 | 7 |
| 2 | 10 |
| 3 | 13 |

6.EE.C.9
7. Use the data in the table from Exercise 6 to graph the equation $y = 3x + 4$.

6.EE.B.5
8. Eric says that $q = 29$ is the solution of the equation $67 - q = 48$. How can you check whether he is correct?
**Sample answer: Substitute 29 for $q$ to see if the equation is true. $67 - 29 = 38$, so $q = 29$ is not a solution. Eric is incorrect.**

D 6-1



### Today's Challenge

Think Use the Topic 6 problems any time during this topic.

## ENGLISH LANGUAGE LEARNERS ELL

**Speaking** Use abstract and content-based vocabulary during speaking assignments.

*Use with the Solve & Share on Student's Edition p. 273.*

Write *estimate* and *compatible numbers* on the board. Have students copy each term on an index card, write a brief definition, and then discuss definitions with partners.

**Beginning** Write 1,489 ÷ 13. Underneath, write 1,500 ÷ 15. *1,500 and 15 are compatible numbers. You can divide them using mental math.* Write the sentence stem: 1,500 and 15 are _____. Have students hold up the index card that completes the sentence as they read it aloud. Write 1,500 ÷ 15 = 100 chairs. *100 chairs is an estimate.* Have students display the correct index card and respond using the sentence stem: 100 chairs is an ____.

**Intermediate** Write 1,489 ÷ 13. Underneath, write 1,500 ÷ 15 = 100 chairs. Ask students to identify *1,500* and *15* by holding up the correct card. Do the same for *100 chairs*. Have students tell how they identified the numbers as compatible numbers or an estimate using sentence stems such as: 1,500 is a(n) _____ because _____.

**Advanced** Write 1,489 ÷ 13. Underneath, write 1,500 ÷ 15 = 100 chairs. Ask students to identify the numbers that are compatible numbers or an estimate, and then explain their reasoning to partners.

**Summarize** What are the meanings of the terms *estimate* and *compatible numbers?*

# DEVELOP: PROBLEM-BASED LEARNING

**COHERENCE: Engage learners by connecting prior knowledge to new ideas.**
Students build upon their understanding of estimation with division as they estimate the quotient of a whole number and a two-digit divisor.

10–15 min

Solve

## BEFORE

**1. Pose the Solve-and-Share Problem**
**MP.2 Reason Quantitatively** Listen and look for students who use compatible numbers and divide mentally to find a reasonable estimate.

**2. Build Understanding**
*What operation can you use to find the number of chairs the school can buy?* [Division] *What phrase in the problem indicates that an estimate, not an exact answer, is expected?* ["About how many"]

## DURING

**3. Ask Guiding Questions As Needed**
*What division expression represents this situation?* [$1,489 ÷ $13] Write this expression on the board. *Can you divide these numbers easily in your head?* [No] *What numbers are close to 1,489 and 13 that would be easy to divide using mental math?* [Sample answers: 1,500 and 15; 1,400 and 14] *What division fact makes the numbers you chose easy to divide using mental math?* [Sample answers: 15 ÷ 15 = 1, so 1,500 ÷ 15 = 100; 14 ÷ 14 = 1, so 1,400 ÷ 14 = 100.]

## AFTER

**4. Share and Discuss Solutions**
Solve Start with students' solutions. If needed, project Ivy's work to discuss how to use reasoning to make better estimates.

**5. Transition to the Visual Learning Bridge**
*You can use compatible numbers and mental math to estimate quotients of whole numbers and two-digit divisors.*

**6. Extension for Early Finishers**
*Estimate 1,563 ÷ 31, 4,818 ÷ 76, and 3,559 ÷ 54.* [Sample answers: 50, 60, and 70]

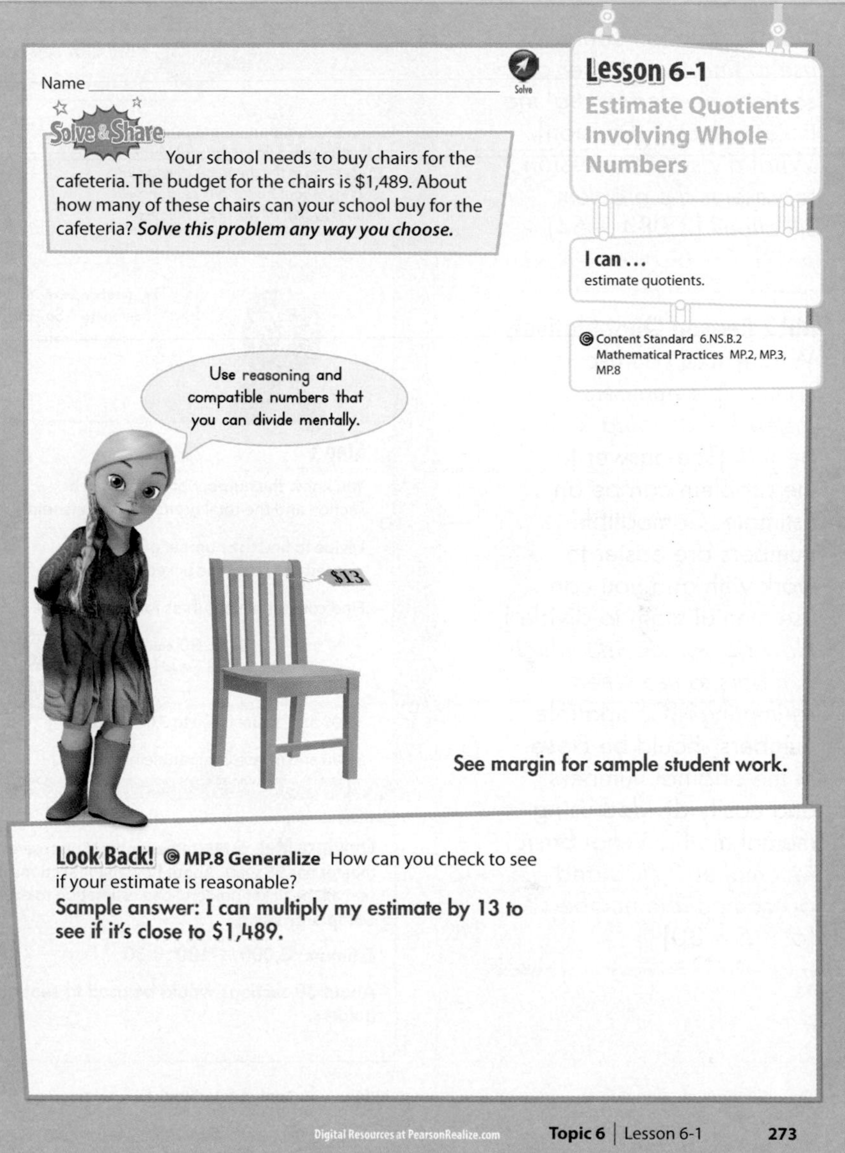

Name

Solve & Share

Your school needs to buy chairs for the cafeteria. The budget for the chairs is $1,489. About how many of these chairs can your school buy for the cafeteria? ***Solve this problem any way you choose.***

**Lesson 6-1**
**Estimate Quotients Involving Whole Numbers**

**I can ...**
estimate quotients.

Content Standard 6.NS.B.2
Mathematical Practices MP.2, MP.3, MP.8

Use reasoning and compatible numbers that you can divide mentally.
$13

**See margin for sample student work.**

**Look Back!** MP.8 Generalize How can you check to see if your estimate is reasonable?
**Sample answer: I can multiply my estimate by 13 to see if it's close to $1,489.**

Digital Resources at PearsonRealize.com Topic 6 | Lesson 6-1 273

## Analyze Student Work

Ivy's Work

$1,500 ÷ 10 = 150
$1,500 ÷ 15 = 100

Since 13 is about halfway between 10 and 15, the quotient will be about halfway between 100 and 150. My estimate is about 125 chairs.

Ivy improves upon her two estimates by reasoning about the quantities in the division problem to find an estimate that is closer to the exact quotient.

Austin's Work

$1,500 ÷ 15 = 100

About 100 chairs

Austin estimates the quotient by using the compatible numbers 1,500 and 15.

# DEVELOP: VISUAL LEARNING

The *Visual Learning Bridge* connects students' thinking in Solve & Share to important math ideas in the lesson. Use the *Visual Learning Bridge* to make these ideas explicit. Also available as a *Visual Learning Animation Plus* at PearsonRealize.com

Visual Learning

*What operation can you use to find the number of sections needed to seat the ticket holders?* [Division] *What division expression represents the problem situation?* [3,084 ÷ 64]

**MP.2 Reason Quantitatively**
*Why would you use compatible numbers instead of dividing 3,084 by 64?* [The answer to the problem can be an estimate. Compatible numbers are easier to work with and you can use mental math to divide.] *How do you decide which numbers to use when estimating?* [Compatible numbers should be close to the original numbers and easily divided using mental math.] *What basic fact makes 3,000 and 60 compatible numbers?* [6 × 5 = 30]

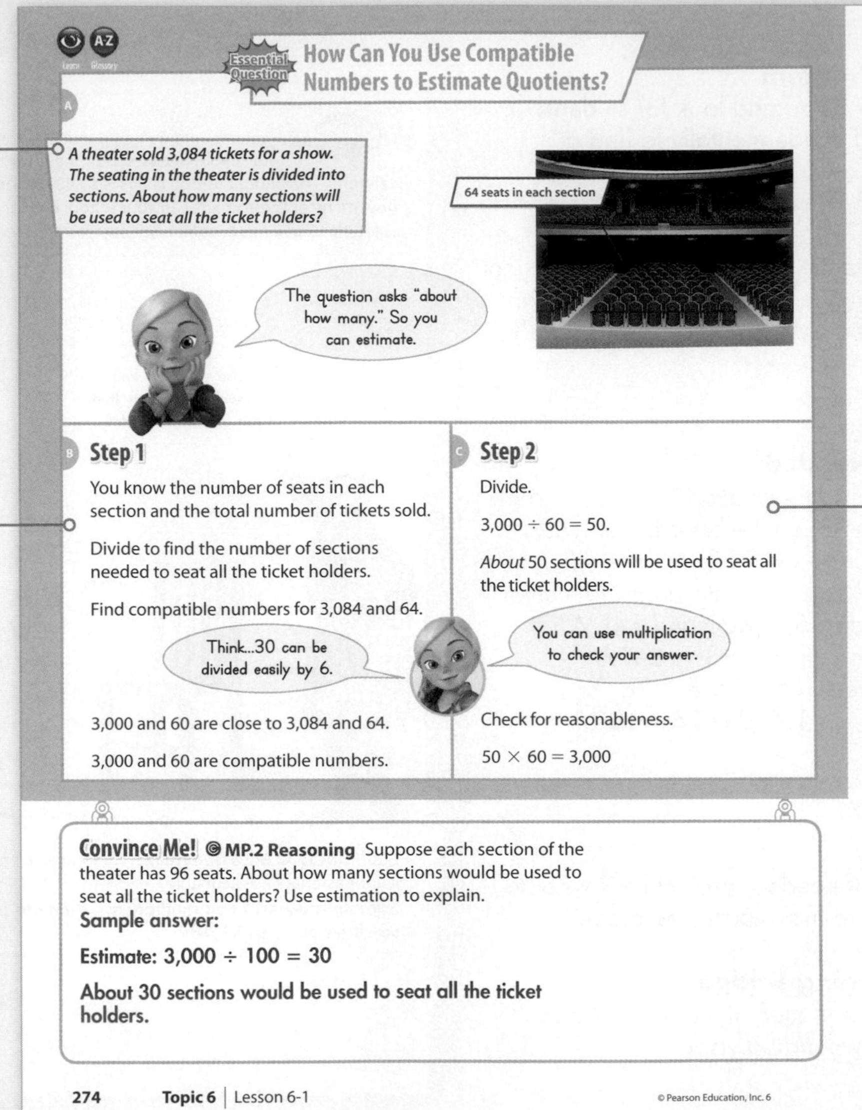

Visual Learning Bridge

Essential Question **How Can You Use Compatible Numbers to Estimate Quotients?**

A theater sold 3,084 tickets for a show. The seating in the theater is divided into sections. About how many sections will be used to seat all the ticket holders?

64 seats in each section
The question asks "about how many." So you can estimate.



**Step 1**

You know the number of seats in each section and the total number of tickets sold.

Divide to find the number of sections needed to seat all the ticket holders.

Find compatible numbers for 3,084 and 64.



Think...30 can be divided easily by 6.

3,000 and 60 are close to 3,084 and 64.

3,000 and 60 are compatible numbers.

**Step 2**

Divide.

3,000 ÷ 60 = 50.

*About* 50 sections will be used to seat all the ticket holders.

You can use multiplication to check your answer.



Check for reasonableness.

50 × 60 = 3,000

**Convince Me!** MP.2 Reasoning Suppose each section of the theater has 96 seats. About how many sections would be used to seat all the ticket holders? Use estimation to explain.

**Sample answer:**

**Estimate: 3,000 ÷ 100 = 30**

**About 30 sections would be used to seat all the ticket holders.**

274 Topic 6 | Lesson 6-1 © Pearson Education, Inc. 6

**MP.8 Generalize**
*Why is the word "About" included in the answer to the problem?* [To stress that the answer is an estimate, not an exact quotient] *How can you check the answer to see if your estimate is reasonable?* [Multiply the divisor and the quotient to check that the product is close to the dividend.]

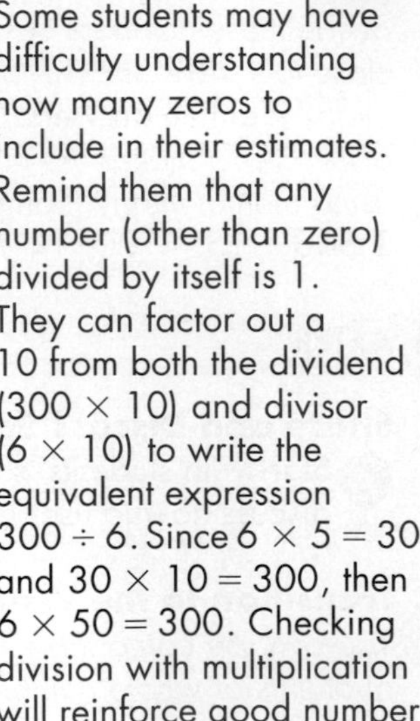

**Prevent Misconceptions** RtI 1

Some students may have difficulty understanding how many zeros to include in their estimates. Remind them that any number (other than zero) divided by itself is 1. They can factor out a 10 from both the dividend (300 × 10) and divisor (6 × 10) to write the equivalent expression 300 ÷ 6. Since 6 × 5 = 30 and 30 × 10 = 300, then 6 × 50 = 300. Checking division with multiplication will reinforce good number sense.

**Convince Me! MP.2 Reason Quantitatively** Mathematically-proficient students will identify and understand the quantities in the problem. They see that the problem situation is the same, but the quantity used as the divisor is different. If students have difficulty choosing compatible numbers to estimate the solution, encourage them to first round the divisor to the nearest ten and then determine a compatible number for the dividend. In this problem, the divisor 96 rounded to the nearest ten is 100.

**Coherence** In the theater problem, students apply mental math skills. They may discuss several choices for compatible numbers as they determine a reasonable estimate. This conceptual development of reasonableness will serve students well in higher-level math courses when they use calculators. Understanding whether a quotient is reasonable will help students identify potential calculator usage error or eliminate incorrect answers.

Revisit the Essential Question. Finding compatible numbers that are close to the given values for the dividend and divisor will result in a reasonable estimate of the quotient.

## QUICK CHECK

Check mark indicates items for prescribing differentiation on the next page.
Item 18 is worth 1 point. Items 28 and 29 are worth up to 2 points.

20–30 min

PearsonRealize.com

Practice Buddy | Tools | Assessment

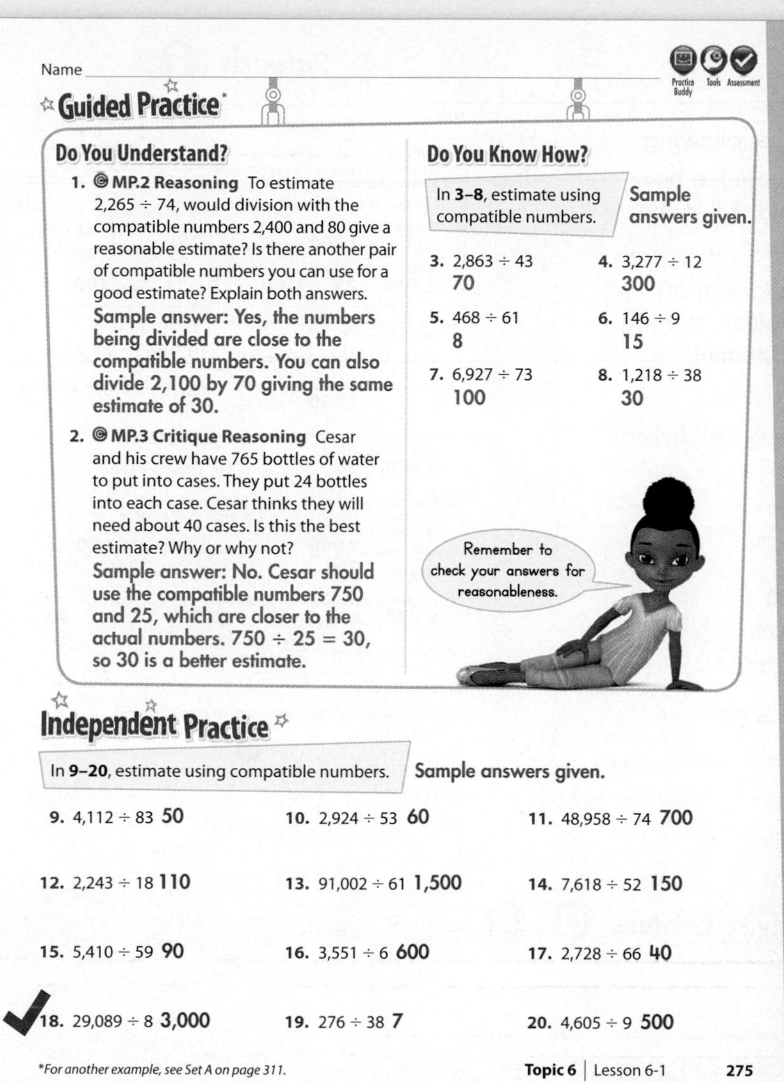

Name

### Guided Practice*

**Do You Understand?**

1. MP.2 Reasoning To estimate 2,265 ÷ 74, would division with the compatible numbers 2,400 and 80 give a reasonable estimate? Is there another pair of compatible numbers you can use for a good estimate? Explain both answers.
**Sample answer: Yes, the numbers being divided are close to the compatible numbers. You can also divide 2,100 by 70 giving the same estimate of 30.**

2. MP.3 Critique Reasoning Cesar and his crew have 765 bottles of water to put into cases. They put 24 bottles into each case. Cesar thinks they will need about 40 cases. Is this the best estimate? Why or why not?
**Sample answer: No. Cesar should use the compatible numbers 750 and 25, which are closer to the actual numbers. 750 ÷ 25 = 30, so 30 is a better estimate.**

**Do You Know How?**

In **3–8**, estimate using compatible numbers. **Sample answers given.**

3. 2,863 ÷ 43 **70**
4. 3,277 ÷ 12 **300**
5. 468 ÷ 61 **8**
6. 146 ÷ 9 **15**
7. 6,927 ÷ 73 **100**
8. 1,218 ÷ 38 **30**

Remember to check your answers for reasonableness.

### Independent Practice*

In **9–20**, estimate using compatible numbers. **Sample answers given.**

9. 4,112 ÷ 83 **50**
10. 2,924 ÷ 53 **60**
11. 48,958 ÷ 74 **700**
12. 2,243 ÷ 18 **110**
13. 91,002 ÷ 61 **1,500**
14. 7,618 ÷ 52 **150**
15. 5,410 ÷ 59 **90**
16. 3,551 ÷ 6 **600**
17. 2,728 ÷ 66 **40**
✔18. 29,089 ÷ 8 **3,000**
19. 276 ÷ 38 **7**
20. 4,605 ÷ 9 **500**

*For another example, see Set A on page 311.

Topic 6 | Lesson 6-1 275

### Math Practices and Problem Solving*

21. A high school volleyball team has made it to the state tournament championship game. There are 965 students who want to go, and 53 students can fit on each bus. About how many buses are needed? **About 20 buses**

22. The school auditorium has 642 seats. Twenty-three of these are reserved for special guests. Adam used the equation $23 + t = 642$ to find the number of tickets, $t$, that could be sold to the school play. How many tickets was it possible to sell? **619 tickets**

23. Leon bought 6 DVDs on sale for $78. At the regular price he would have spent $108. How much did Leon save per DVD at the sale price? **$5 per DVD**

24. MP.8 Generalize Summer needs to estimate the quotient 8,173 ÷ 92. Explain how she can use compatible numbers to make a reasonable estimate. **Sample answer: 8,100 and 90 are compatible numbers. They are close to the actual dividend and divisor. 8,100 ÷ 90 = 90, so 90 is a reasonable estimate for 8,173 ÷ 92.**

25. MP.2 Reasoning The money Percy saved is about how many times as great as the money Bethany has saved? **About 3 times as great**

26. MP.2 Reasoning The money Emily saved is about how many times as great as the money Percy has saved? **About 2 times as great**

Fifth-Grade Trip to Washington, D.C.

| Student | Amount Saved |
|---|---|
| Percy | $1,256 |
| Emily | $2,345 |
| Bethany | $401 |

27. At a department store, a box of 12 water filters costs $55.50. Estimate how much each filter costs. **Sample answer: About $5**

✔28. Higher Order Thinking There are $x$ cages at the zoo for 2,878 birds. Each cage can house between 140 and 160 birds. What would be a reasonable value for $x$? Justify your reasoning. **Sample answer: $x = 20$; 3,000 ÷ 150 = 20**

**Common Core Assessment**

✔29. Which of the following are reasonable estimates for 4,325 ÷ 56?
- ☐ 5,000 ÷ 50 = 100
- ■ 4,200 ÷ 60 = 70
- ■ 4,000 ÷ 50 = 80
- ☐ 3,600 ÷ 60 = 60

30. Which of the following are **NOT** reasonable estimates for 2,432 ÷ 47?
- ☐ 50 = 2,500 ÷ 50
- ■ 30 = 1,500 ÷ 50
- ■ 3,000 ÷ 50 = 60
- ☐ 2,400 ÷ 50 = 48

276 Topic 6 | Lesson 6-1

**Error Intervention: Item 2**

**If** students have difficulty evaluating Cesar's estimate,
**then** have them work backwards by first checking his estimate. *How can you check whether Cesar's estimate is close?* [Multiply 40 × 24 = 960.] *Is this product reasonably close to the original 765 bottles? Explain.* [No. It is an overestimate.] *To find closer compatible numbers, try rounding the divisor to the nearest 10 or nearest 5.* [20 or 25] *For the dividend, think about multiples of 20 or 25 that are close to 76.* [80 or 75] *What compatible numbers would give you the best estimate?* [25 and 750]

**Item 11** *What is the divisor rounded to the nearest ten?* [70] *What is a number close to 48 that can be evenly divided by 7?* [49] *What compatible numbers could you use to estimate?* [49,000 and 70]

**Reteaching** Assign Reteaching Set A on p. 311.

**Item 18 Coherence** Some students may choose to use the compatible numbers 30,000 and 10 to estimate the quotient as 3,000. However, some students may use reasoning based on their basic-fact knowledge that 8 goes into 24 and 32 evenly. Since the dividend, 29,089, is approximately halfway between 24,000 and 32,000, the quotient is approximately halfway between 3,000 and 4,000. Therefore, a better estimate would be 3,500.

**Item 24 MP.8 Generalize** Students have made repeated observations and estimated quotients for numerous division problems with two-digit divisors. Here, they explain the process they have been using to estimate.

**Item 28 Higher Order Thinking** In this division problem, students are not given a specific divisor, but a range of possible values. Students must justify their reasoning for the value they choose as they find a reasonable estimate for the quotient.

**Multi-Step Problems** *Page 276 Items 23, 29, and 30; Page 278 Items 23 and 24*

# ASSESS AND DIFFERENTIATE

Use the **QUICK CHECK** on the previous page to prescribe differentiated instruction.

**Intervention** 0–3 points on the Quick Check

**On-Level** 4 points on the Quick Check

**Advanced** 5 points on the Quick Check

## Intervention Activity

**Division and Mental Math**

**Materials**

Strips of paper, small box

- Write each of the following lines on strips of paper and place them in the box.

| | |
|---|---|
| 45,000 ÷ 90 | ___ × 9 = 45 |
| 56,000 ÷ 70 | ___ × 7 = 56 |
| 4,200 ÷ 60 | ___ × 6 = 42 |
| 36,000 ÷ 60 | ___ × 6 = 36 |
| 480 ÷ 40 | ___ × 4 = 48 |
| 3,200 ÷ 80 | ___ × 8 = 32 |
| 54,000 ÷ 90 | ___ × 9 = 54 |

Have pairs of students do the following:

- Choose a strip of paper from the box, and say the problem aloud. Fill in the blank.
- Write multiplication equations in a pattern based on place values, starting with a basic fact (see the student example).
- Write the answer to the original division problem.

9 × 5 = 45
90 × 5 = 450
90 × 50 = 4,500
90 × 500 = 45,000

So, 45,000 ÷ 90 = 500.

## Reteach

Name ______________ Reteach to Build Understanding 6-1

Vocabulary

1. **Compatible numbers** are numbers that are easy to compute mentally and can be used to estimate solutions to problems.
Estimate 2,529 ÷ 24. **Sample answers given.**
First, find compatible numbers.
2,529 is close to **2,500**, and 24 is close to **25**.
Divide using the compatible numbers you chose.
**2,500** ÷ **25** = **100**. So, 2,529 ÷ 24 is about **100**.

2. How many buses are needed for 1,584 students if each bus can hold 72 students?
Write an expression to represent the problem. **1,584** ÷ **72**

3. Find compatible numbers for the numbers in the expression. **Sample answers given.**
1,584 is close to **1,600**. 72 is close to **80**.

4. Rewrite the expression using the compatible numbers. Then divide to solve the problem.
**1,600** ÷ **80** About **20** buses are needed.

5. There can be more than one reasonable estimate when using compatible numbers. Use two pairs of compatible numbers to find two different estimates for 9,741 ÷ 276.
9,741 is close to **9,000**. 9,741 is close to **10,000**.
276 is close to **300**. 276 is close to **250**.

6. Rewrite each expression using the compatible numbers. Then divide.
**9,000** ÷ **300** = **30** **10,000** ÷ **250** = **40**

7. So, 9,741 ÷ 276 is about **30** or **40**.

On the Back!

8. Estimate using compatible numbers. **Sample answer: 60**
4,673 ÷ 74

R 6-1



## On-Level and Advanced Activity Centers

**Problem-Solving Reading Mat**

Have students read the Problem-Solving Reading Mat for Topic 6 and then complete Problem-Solving Reading Activity 6-1.

See the Problem-Solving Reading Activity Guide for other suggestions on how to use this mat.

**TIMING**

The time allocated to Step 3 will depend on the teacher's instructional decisions and differentiation routines.

15–30 min

PEARSON realize.
PearsonRealize.com

Help · Practice Buddy · Tools · Games

## Technology Center   

Tools Games

### Math Tools and Math Games

A link to a specific math tools activity or math game to use with this lesson is provided at PearsonRealize.com.

## Leveled Assignment  Items 1–12, 18–19, 22–24  Items 7–17, 20–24  Items 10–24

Name ____________________

Help Practice Buddy Tools Games

### Homework & Practice 6-1

**Estimate Quotients Involving Whole Numbers**

**Another Look!**

There are 32 buses in which the same number of people will ride to go to a technology convention. There are 1,759 people signed up to go. About how many people will ride on each bus?

**Step 1**

Find compatible numbers for 1,759 and 32.

32 is close to 30.

1,759 is close to 1,800.

1,800 and 30 are compatible numbers.

**Step 2**

Rewrite the division with the compatible numbers and then divide.

1,800 ÷ 30 = 60

**Step 3**

Use the same compatible numbers to check for reasonableness:

60 × **30** = **1,800**

So, a good estimate of 1,759 ÷ 32 is 60.

About 60 people will ride on each bus.

In **1–15**, estimate using compatible numbers. **Sample answers given.**

**1.** 1,832 ÷ 22
1,800 ÷ **20**
**90**

**2.** 552 ÷ 36
600 ÷ **40**
**15**

**3.** 9,002 ÷ 28
**9,000** ÷ **30**
**300**

**4.** 2,983 ÷ 25 **120**

**5.** 5,491 ÷ 77 **70**

**6.** 29,589 ÷ 15 **2,000**

**7.** 4,622 ÷ 9 **500**

**8.** 1,447 ÷ 48 **30**

**9.** 5,564 ÷ 91 **60**

**10.** 488 ÷ 12 **50**

**11.** 5,879 ÷ 46 **120**

**12.** 89,078 ÷ 93 **1,000**

**13.** 3,579 ÷ 89 **40**

**14.** 63,204 ÷ 8 **8,000**

**15.** 875 ÷ 9 **90**



**16.** A school has 1,030 students. There are 42 teachers. About how times as great as the number of teachers is the number of students?
**About 25 times as great**

**17.** In the 16 years that a college has had a women's basketball team, the athletic department sold 3,140 season tickets. What is a reasonable estimate of how many season tickets they sold each year? Write the compatible numbers you used for your estimate. **Sample answer: About 200 tickets; 3,000 ÷ 15 = 200**

**18.** **MP.2 Reasoning** The number of bikes rented from Shop B is about how many times as great as the number from Shop D? **About 4 times as great**

**19.** **MP.2 Reasoning** The number of bikes rented from Shop C is about how many times as great as the number from Shop A? **About 20 times as great**

**Bicycles rented (May)**

| Rental Shop | Bikes rented |
|---|---|
| Shop A | 68 |
| Shop B | 785 |
| Shop C | 1,410 |
| Shop D | 191 |

**20.** **MP.3 Critique Reasoning** Kyle has 3,104 stamps in his collection. He is placing his stamps in an album with pages that each hold 42 stamps. He estimates he will need about 80 pages. Is his estimate reasonable? Why or why not?
**Sample answer: Yes, his answer is reasonable because he used compatible numbers to give him a good estimate. 3,200 ÷ 40 = 80**

**21.** **Algebra** Delilah is making batches of muffins for a bake sale. Each batch has 12 muffins. Write an inequality to represent the number of batches, *b*, she needs to make in order to have at least 130 muffins for the bake sale.
$12b \geq 130$ or $b \geq \frac{130}{12}$

**22.** **Vocabulary** Find the value for *x* that makes the equation true: $x \div 50 = 300$. Then tell if the variable, *x*, is the divisor, dividend, or quotient in the equation. **$x = 15{,}000$; Dividend**

### Common Core Assessment

**23.** Which of the following are reasonable estimates for 4,739 ÷ 92?

- [x] 4,800 ÷ 100 = 48
- [x] 4,500 ÷ 90 = 50
- [ ] 4,800 ÷ 80 = 60
- [ ] 4,400 ÷ 110 = 40

**24.** Which of the following are **NOT** reasonable estimates for 4,108 ÷ 63?

- [x] 3,800 ÷ 50 = 76
- [x] 4,500 ÷ 50 = 90
- [x] 41 = 4,100 ÷ 100
- [ ] 70 = 4,200 ÷ 60

# LESSON 6-2

# DIVIDE WHOLE NUMBERS

## DIGITAL RESOURCES PearsonRealize.com

 Student and Teacher eTexts

eText

 Listen and Look For Lesson Video
PD

Today's Challenge
Think

 Solve and Share
Solve

 Visual Learning Animation Plus
Learn

 Animated Glossary
Glossary

Online Personalized Practice
Practice Buddy

 Math Tools
Tools

 Quick Check
Assessment

 Another Look Homework Video
Help

 Math Games
Games

## LESSON OVERVIEW

FCR FOCUS • COHERENCE • RIGOR

### FOCUS

**Domain 6.NS** The Number System

**Cluster 6.NS.B** Compute fluently with multi-digit numbers and find common factors and multiples.

**Content Standard 6.NS.B.2** Fluently divide multi-digit numbers using the standard algorithm.

**Mathematical Practices MP.2, MP.3, MP.6, MP.7, MP.8**

**Objective** Find the quotient of two whole numbers and solve division problems.

**Essential Understanding** A general method, or standard algorithm, can be used to divide multi-digit numbers.

**Materials** Grid paper (or Teaching Tool 15) (optional), lined paper (optional)

### COHERENCE

In Grade 5, students found whole-number quotients of four-digit dividends and two-digit divisors, using strategies based on place value, the properties of operations, and the relationship between multiplication and division. In this lesson, they extend these skills to divide a four-digit dividend by a two-digit divisor to find quotients with remainders, using the standard division algorithm. Students are expected to achieve fluency with dividing multi-digit numbers by the end of Grade 6.

### RIGOR

This lesson emphasizes **fluency** with dividing multi-digit numbers. Students learn and practice the standard algorithm for division with greater numbers. They attend to precision as they examine and use place-value structure to divide.

PD Watch the Listen and Look For Lesson Video.

## MATH ANYTIME

### Daily Common Core Review

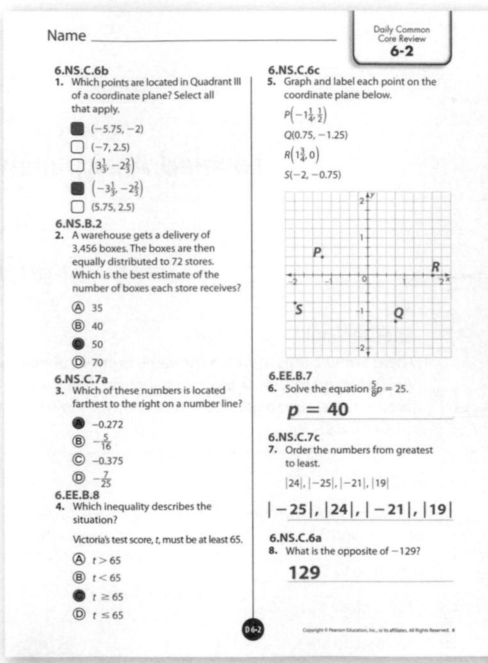
Name ____________

Daily Common Core Review 6-2

6.NS.C.6b
1. Which points are located in Quadrant III of a coordinate plane? Select all that apply.
- ■ (−5.75, −2)
- □ (−7, 2.5)
- □ $\left(3\frac{1}{3}, -2\frac{2}{3}\right)$
- ■ $\left(-3\frac{1}{3}, -2\frac{2}{3}\right)$
- □ (5.75, 2.5)

6.NS.B.2
2. A warehouse gets a delivery of 3,456 boxes. The boxes are then equally distributed to 72 stores. Which is the best estimate of the number of boxes each store receives?
- Ⓐ 35
- Ⓑ 40
- ● 50
- Ⓓ 70

6.NS.C.7a
3. Which of these numbers is located farthest to the right on a number line?
- ● −0.272
- Ⓑ $-\frac{5}{16}$
- Ⓒ −0.375
- Ⓓ $-\frac{7}{25}$

6.EE.B.8
4. Which inequality describes the situation?

Victoria's test score, $t$, must be at least 65.
- Ⓐ $t > 65$
- Ⓑ $t < 65$
- ● $t \geq 65$
- Ⓓ $t \leq 65$

6.NS.C.6c
5. Graph and label each point on the coordinate plane below.

$P\left(-1\frac{1}{4}, \frac{1}{2}\right)$
$Q(0.75, -1.25)$
$R\left(1\frac{3}{4}, 0\right)$
$S(-2, -0.75)$



6.EE.B.7
6. Solve the equation $\frac{5}{8}p = 25$.

**$p = 40$**

6.NS.C.7c
7. Order the numbers from greatest to least.

$|24|, |-25|, |-21|, |19|$

**$|-25|, |24|, |-21|, |19|$**

6.NS.C.6a
8. What is the opposite of −129?

**129**

D 6-2



### Today's Challenge

Think Use the Topic 6 problems any time during this topic.

## ENGLISH LANGUAGE LEARNERS 

**Speaking** Express ideas.

*Use with the Solve & Share on Student's Edition p. 279.*

Read the Solve & Share aloud. Ask students to identify important information for solving the problem. Write the following on a poster: **Step 1:** Divide, **Step 2:** Multiply, **Step 3:** Subtract, **Step 4:** Compare. *Use these steps to divide the numbers in the problem.*

**Beginning** Reread the Solve & Share to students. Write 1,715 ÷ 16. *How would you divide these numbers?* Have students express ideas using the sentence stem: I will ____. Read **Step 1** on the anchor chart. Write the division problem on the board and place a 1 in the quotient. Read **Step 2** and demonstrate multiplying 1 × 16. Continue the process with the remaining steps.

**Intermediate** Reread the Solve & Share with students. Ask students to identify the division problem. Write 1,715 ÷ 16. *How would you divide these numbers?* Have students express ideas using the sentence stem: I will ____ because ____. Read **Steps 1 and 2** of the anchor chart. Ask students to identify what will be divided and multiplied. Continue the process with the remaining steps.

**Advanced** Instruct students to reread the problem and discuss their ideas for solving it with a partner. When all students have shared their ideas, have them solve the problem using the steps listed on the poster.

**Summarize** What are the steps for solving division problems?

# DEVELOP: PROBLEM-BASED LEARNING

**COHERENCE: Engage learners by connecting prior knowledge to new ideas.**
Students extend their knowledge of whole-number division and build on their skills with estimating quotients to find and interpret the exact quotient of two whole numbers that do not divide evenly.

10–15 min

Solve

## BEFORE

**1. Pose the Solve-and-Share Problem**
**MP.2 Reason Quantitatively** Listen and look for students who identify the quantities in the problem and accurately answer the question by interpreting the quotient and remainder.

**2. Build Understanding**
*What division expression represents the problem situation?* [1,715 ÷ 16] *How would you estimate the quotient?* [Sample answer: 1,600 ÷ 16 = 100]

## DURING

**3. Ask Guiding Questions As Needed**
*How can you divide 1,715 by 16?* [Sample answers: Find a related multiplication problem; Draw an area model or rectangular array.] *What is the quotient?* [107 with a remainder of 3] *What does this mean in the problem context?* [107 boxes are full with 3 staplers left over] *How many boxes are needed for the shipment? Explain.* [108 boxes; One more box is needed for the 3 leftover staplers.]

## AFTER

**4. Share and Discuss Solutions**
Solve Start with students' solutions. If needed, project Amara's and Jabari's work to discuss two different ways to solve.

**5. Transition to the Visual Learning Bridge**
*Place-value structure can help you divide with greater numbers. Use estimation with compatible numbers to check if the quotient is reasonable.*

**6. Extension for Early Finishers**
*Write a word problem that can be solved by dividing 2,345 by 12.* [195 R5; Check students' work.]

Name ____________

Solve & Share

An office-supply warehouse is going to ship 1,715 staplers. How many boxes are needed? How many boxes will be filled? ***Solve this problem any way you choose.***

**Lesson 6-2**
**Divide Whole Numbers**

**I can ...**
find the quotient of two whole numbers and solve division problems.

Content Standard 6.NS.B.2
Mathematical Practices MP.2, MP.3, MP.6, MP.7, MP.8

You can use reasoning to decide what operation can be used to find the number of boxes that each have 16 staplers.

16 Staplers

**See margin for sample student work.**

**Look Back!** **MP.6 Be Precise** How many more staplers could be put in the partly filled box so that each box has 16 staplers? Explain your answer.
**13 more; The 108th box only has 3 staplers in it, so adding 13 more staplers to the box would be 16.**

Digital Resources at PearsonRealize.com    **Topic 6** | Lesson 6-2    **279**

## Analyze Student Work

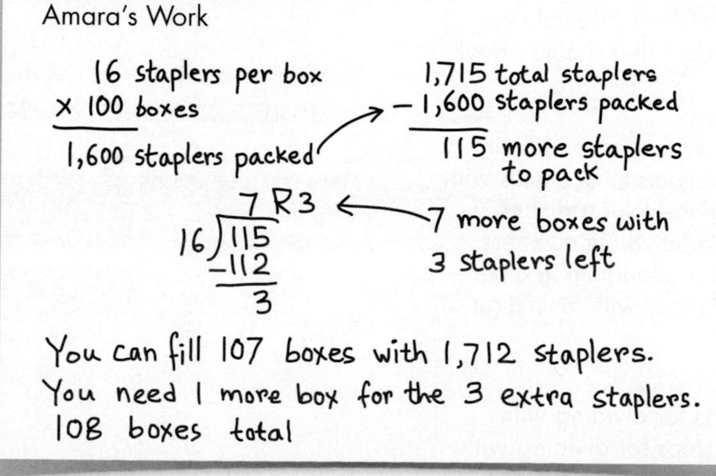

Amara's Work
16 staplers per box
× 100 boxes
1,600 staplers packed
1,715 total staplers
− 1,600 staplers packed
115 more staplers to pack
7 R3
16)115
−112
3
7 more boxes with 3 staplers left
You can fill 107 boxes with 1,712 staplers.
You need 1 more box for the 3 extra staplers.
108 boxes total


Amara uses reasoning to solve the problem. She starts with a multiplication fact that she knows.

Jabari's Work

```
      107 R3
16 ) 1,715
    -16
      11
     - 0
     115
    -112
       3
```

107 boxes are filled. There are 3 staplers left over so one extra box is needed for a total of 108 boxes.

Jabari uses the standard algorithm for division to find the quotient and remainder, and then solve the problem.

# DEVELOP: VISUAL LEARNING

The *Visual Learning Bridge* connects students' thinking in Solve & Share to important math ideas in the lesson. Use the *Visual Learning Bridge* to make these ideas explicit. Also available as a *Visual Learning Animation Plus* at PearsonRealize.com

Visual Learning

PEARSON realize. PearsonRealize.com

Learn

Glossary

**MP.7 Use Structure**
*How do you know that there will be some packages left over?* [Sample answer: 863 is an odd number, but 18 is an even number.] *Will the answer to this problem be in the tens or hundreds? Explain.* [Tens; Sample explanation: $100 \times 18 = 1{,}800$. The dividend, 863, is less than 1,800, so one hundred is too much.]

**MP.2 Reason Quantitatively**
Demonstrate to students that estimating first will help them place the first digit in the quotient. *Since the estimated quotient is 45, place a 4 in the tens place. What is the value of this 4 in the quotient?* [4 tens, or 40] *Why doesn't a 3 or a 5 work?* [3 tens or 30 multiplied by 18 is 54 tens. 86 tens − 54 tens = 32 tens, which is greater than the divisor. 5 tens or 50 multiplied by 18 is 90 tens, which is greater than the dividend. So, the quotient should have 4 tens.]

**Prevent Misconceptions** (RtI 1)
Some students may have difficulty keeping digits of the same place value aligned in the correct columns. Have these students work out division problems on grid paper or lined paper turned sideways. This will help them pay attention to the place-value structure.

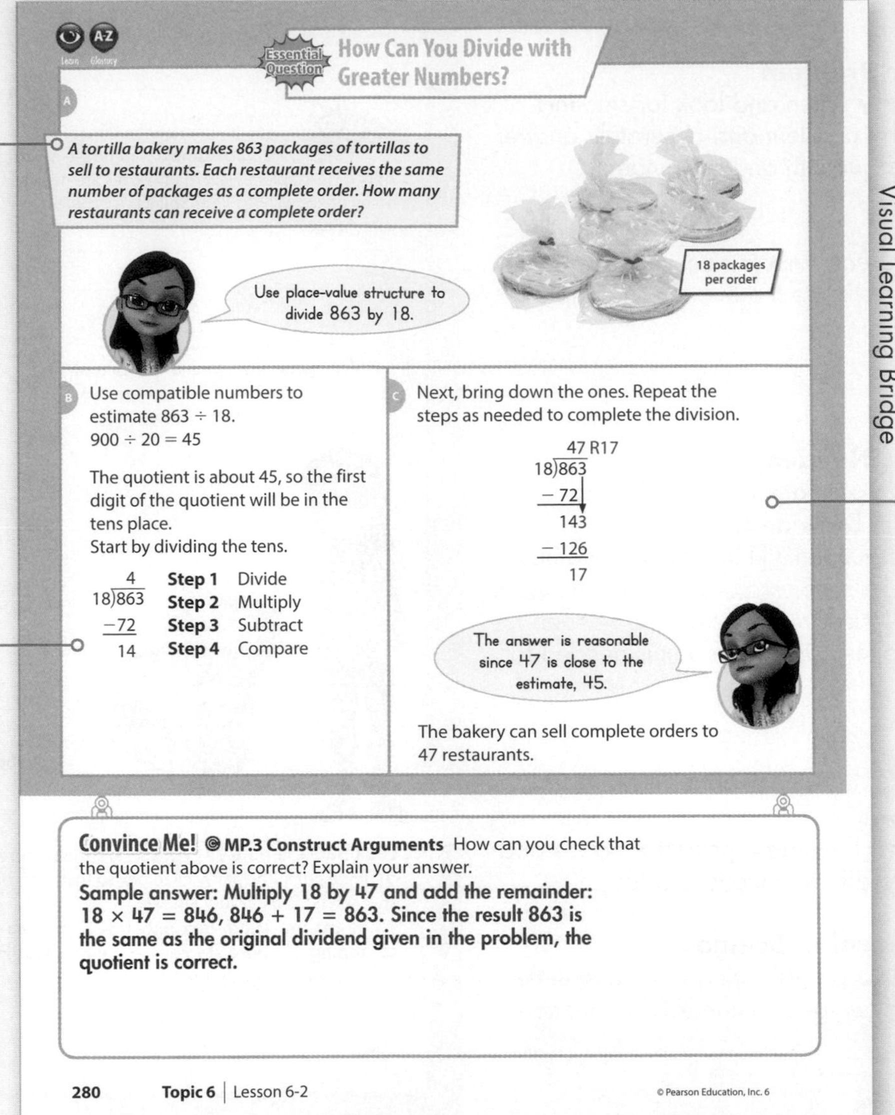

Learn Glossary

Essential Question: **How Can You Divide with Greater Numbers?**

A

*A tortilla bakery makes 863 packages of tortillas to sell to restaurants. Each restaurant receives the same number of packages as a complete order. How many restaurants can receive a complete order?*



B

Use compatible numbers to estimate $863 \div 18$.
$900 \div 20 = 45$

The quotient is about 45, so the first digit of the quotient will be in the tens place.
Start by dividing the tens.

$$\begin{array}{r} 4 \\ 18\overline{)863} \\ -72 \\ \hline 14 \end{array}$$

Step 1 Divide
Step 2 Multiply
Step 3 Subtract
Step 4 Compare

C

Next, bring down the ones. Repeat the steps as needed to complete the division.

$$\begin{array}{r} 47\text{ R}17 \\ 18\overline{)863} \\ -72\downarrow \\ \hline 143 \\ -126 \\ \hline 17 \end{array}$$

The answer is reasonable since 47 is close to the estimate, 45.



The bakery can sell complete orders to 47 restaurants.

**Convince Me!** MP.3 Construct Arguments How can you check that the quotient above is correct? Explain your answer.
**Sample answer: Multiply 18 by 47 and add the remainder: $18 \times 47 = 846$, $846 + 17 = 863$. Since the result 863 is the same as the original dividend given in the problem, the quotient is correct.**

280 Topic 6 | Lesson 6-2 © Pearson Education, Inc. 6

Visual Learning Bridge

**MP.6 Be Precise**
*After you bring down the ones, how many are there?* [14 tens plus 3 ones is 143 ones.] *Next, think of 143 ones divided into 18 groups. How would you estimate the quotient?* [Sample answer: $140 \div 20 = 7$] Remind students that the first estimate may not work and they may need to adjust their answer. *What does the remainder of 17 mean in the context of the problem?* [There are 17 packages left over.]

**Convince Me! MP.3 Construct Arguments** Remind students that division and multiplication have an inverse relationship. Have them generalize their understanding of how to check quotients. *In general, how can you check your answer to a division problem?* [Multiply the quotient by the divisor, and then add the remainder. That should equal the dividend.]

**Coherence** As students solve the tortilla problem, they extend their understanding of division from whole-number quotients to quotients with remainders. They apply their understanding of place-value structure in order to formalize the process for dividing multi-digit whole numbers. Students will continue to practice using the division algorithm in other mathematical and real-world problems to gain fluency with multi-digit division by the end of Grade 6.

Essential Question: Revisit the Essential Question. The steps for dividing with two-digit divisors are the same as the steps for dividing with one-digit divisors. No matter how great the dividends and divisors are, the standard division algorithm can be used to find quotients. Estimation and place-value structure can help determine the placement of digits in the quotient.

## QUICK CHECK

Check mark indicates items for prescribing differentiation on the next page.
Item 9 is worth 1 point. Items 18 and 19 are worth up to 2 points.

20–30 min

PEARSON realize.
PearsonRealize.com

Practice Buddy

Tools

Assessment

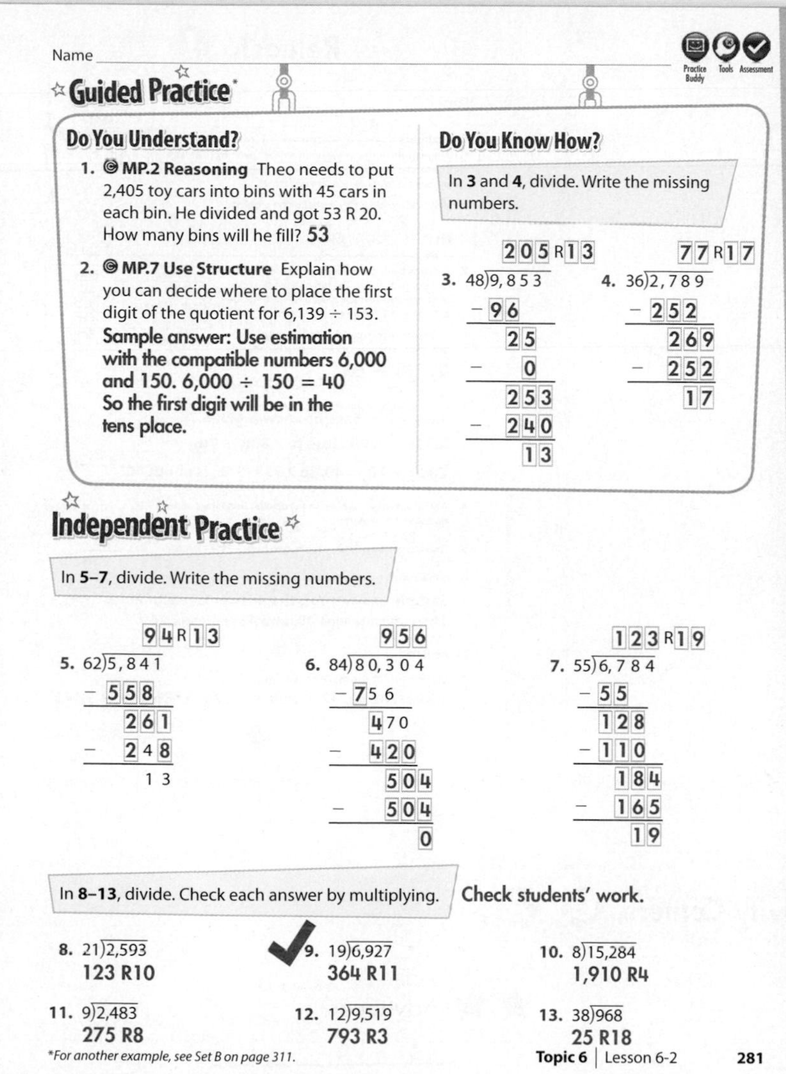

Name

### Guided Practice

**Do You Understand?**

1. MP.2 Reasoning Theo needs to put 2,405 toy cars into bins with 45 cars in each bin. He divided and got 53 R 20. How many bins will he fill? **53**

2. MP.7 Use Structure Explain how you can decide where to place the first digit of the quotient for 6,139 ÷ 153.
**Sample answer: Use estimation with the compatible numbers 6,000 and 150. 6,000 ÷ 150 = 40 So the first digit will be in the tens place.**

**Do You Know How?**

In **3** and **4**, divide. Write the missing numbers.

3. 48)9,853 = 205 R13
− 96 → 25; − 0 → 253; − 240 → 13

4. 36)2,789 = 77 R17
− 252 → 269; − 252 → 17

### Independent Practice

In **5–7**, divide. Write the missing numbers.

5. 62)5,841 = 94 R13
− 558 → 261; − 248 → 13

6. 84)80,304 = 956
− 756 → 470; − 420 → 504; − 504 → 0

7. 55)6,784 = 123 R19
− 55 → 128; − 110 → 184; − 165 → 19

In **8–13**, divide. Check each answer by multiplying. **Check students' work.**

8. 21)2,593 **123 R10**
9. 19)6,927 **364 R11**
10. 8)15,284 **1,910 R4**
11. 9)2,483 **275 R8**
12. 12)9,519 **793 R3**
13. 38)968 **25 R18**

*For another example, see Set B on page 311.

Topic 6 | Lesson 6-2 281

### Math Practices and Problem Solving

14. MP.6 Be Precise Julita bought lunch for herself and a friend. She bought two sandwiches that cost \$3.50 each, two bottles of juice that were \$1.75 each, and a fruit salad for \$4.95. The tax was \$1.35. She paid with a \$20 bill. How much change did she get? **\$3.20**

15. Henri needs to find the quotient 6,273 ÷ 82. Explain how he can use compatible numbers to make a reasonable estimate. **6,400 and 80 are easy to divide and close to the actual dividend and divisor. 6,400 ÷ 80 = 80, so an actual quotient of about 80 is reasonable.**

16. **Number Sense** Ants are one of the Thorny Devil lizard's favorite foods. It can eat up to 45 ants per minute. About how long would it take this lizard to eat 1,080 ants? Express your answer in minutes.
**About 24 minutes**

17. What compatible numbers can you use to estimate 4,134 ÷ 67?
**Sample answer: 4,200 and 70**

18. **Higher Order Thinking** The area of a park is 1,176 square miles. If the park is divided into 58 equal parts, each containing the same whole number of square miles, how large would each part be? How large would the remaining area be? **Each part would be 20 mi$^2$, with a remaining area of 16 mi$^2$.**

#### Common Core Assessment

19. A cereal company has 1,364 boxes of cereal to pack for shipping. Workers can pack 24 boxes of cereal into one shipping box.

**Part A**

How many shipping boxes can be completely filled? Show how you know.

**Sample answer: Divide 1,364 by 24: The quotient is 56 with a remainder of 20. So they will fill 56 shipping boxes.**
24)1,364 = 56 R20; − 1 20 → 164; − 144 → 20

**Part B**

There are left over cereal boxes after the filled boxes are shipped. Explain how many more cereal boxes are needed so the workers can fill another shipping box.

**Sample answer: The remainder tells me there are 20 cereal boxes left over. They will need 4 more boxes in order to fill another shipping box.**

282 Topic 6 | Lesson 6-2



**Error Intervention: Item 1**

**If** students have difficulty interpreting the quotient and remainder in the context of the problem,

**then** say: *2,405 divided into groups of 45 result in 53 groups with 20 left over. In this problem, what items are being divided into groups?* [cars] *What does the remainder of 20 represent?* [The 20 cars left over after filling 53 bins] *Will the remaining cars fill a bin? Explain.* [No; 45 cars are needed, but there are only 20 cars remaining.]

**Reteaching** Assign Reteaching Set B on p. 311.

**Item 6** If students use the compatible numbers 80 and 80,000 to estimate the quotient, they may think that the quotient is in the thousands. If this is the case, have them multiply 84 × 1,000. Help students reason that since 84,000 is greater than the dividend, a quotient of 1,000 is too much. They will need a quotient in the hundreds, with 900 being a reasonable estimate.

**Item 14 MP.6 Be Precise** Students use problem-solving strategies and compute accurately to determine the correct amount of change. Encourage them to read the multi-step problem carefully for the correct number of items at a particular cost (for example, two sandwiches that cost \$3.50 each is translated as 2 × \$3.50 = \$7.00).

**Item 18 Higher Order Thinking** *What operation will determine the size of the equal parts in the park?* [Division] *What will the remainder determine?* [The size of the remaining area, in square miles]

**Multi-Step Problems** *Page 282 Items 14 and 19; Page 284 Items 17, 18, and 20*

# ASSESS AND DIFFERENTIATE

2 RtI

Use the **QUICK CHECK** on the previous page to prescribe differentiated instruction.

**I Intervention** 0–3 points on the Quick Check

**O On-Level** 4 points on the Quick Check

**A Advanced** 5 points on the Quick Check

## Intervention Activity 

### Divide Whole Numbers by Two-Digit Divisors

- On the board, write: 21)6,458
- Remind students to estimate first to decide where to place the first digit in the quotient.
- Point out that compatible numbers can be used to estimate 6,458 ÷ 21 as 6,000 ÷ 20 = 300. The first digit in the quotient is in the hundreds place. Some estimates may need to be adjusted.
- Once students have estimated, they should divide, multiply, subtract, and compare. Use student suggestions to work out the problem on the board.
- Repeat for 8,809 ÷ 42 and 9,786 ÷ 31.

```
     307 R11
21 ) 6,458
    -63
      15
     - 0
      158
     -147
       11
```

## Reteach I

Name ____________________

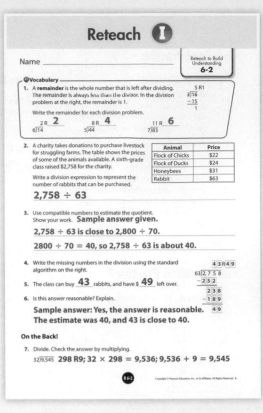

Reteach to Build Understanding 6-2

**Vocabulary**

1. A **remainder** is the whole number that is left after dividing. The remainder is always less than the divisor. In the division problem at the right, the remainder is 1.

   5 R1 / 3)16 / −15 / 1

   Write the remainder for each division problem.

   6)14 = 2 R **2** 5)44 = 8 R **4** 7)83 = 11 R **6**

2. A charity takes donations to purchase livestock for struggling farms. The table shows the prices of some of the animals available. A sixth-grade class raised $2,758 for the charity.

| Animal | Price |
|---|---|
| Flock of Chicks | $22 |
| Flock of Ducks | $24 |
| Honeybees | $31 |
| Rabbit | $63 |

   Write a division expression to represent the number of rabbits that can be purchased.

   **2,758 ÷ 63**

3. Use compatible numbers to estimate the quotient. Show your work. **Sample answer given.**

   **2,758 ÷ 63 is close to 2,800 ÷ 70.**

   **2800 ÷ 70 = 40, so 2,758 ÷ 63 is about 40.**

4. Write the missing numbers in the division using the standard algorithm on the right.

```
    43 R49
63)2,758
  -252
    238
   -189
     49
```

5. The class can buy **43** rabbits, and have $ **49** left over.

6. Is this answer reasonable? Explain.

   **Sample answer: Yes, the answer is reasonable. The estimate was 40, and 43 is close to 40.**

**On the Back!**

7. Divide. Check the answer by multiplying.

   32)9,545 **298 R9; 32 × 298 = 9,536; 9,536 + 9 = 9,545**

R 6-2



## On-Level and Advanced Activity Centers  

### Center Games

Students work in pairs or small groups to find the quotients. Have students record their work as they play the game.

★ On-Level

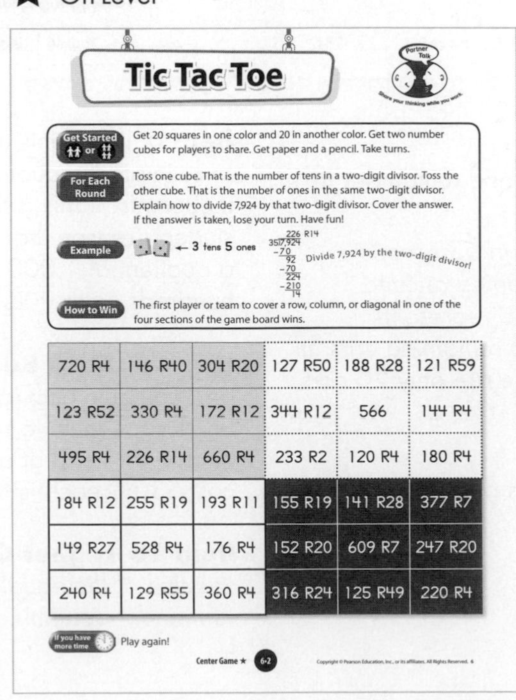

# Tic Tac Toe



**Get Started** Get 20 squares in one color and 20 in another color. Get two number cubes for players to share. Get paper and a pencil. Take turns.

**For Each Round** Toss one cube. That is the number of tens in a two-digit divisor. Toss the other cube. That is the number of ones in the same two-digit divisor. Explain how to divide 7,924 by that two-digit divisor. Cover the answer. If the answer is taken, lose your turn. Have fun!

**Example** ← 3 tens 5 ones

```
    226 R14
35)7,924
  -70
    92
   -70
    224
   -210
     14
```

Divide 7,924 by the two-digit divisor!

**How to Win** The first player or team to cover a row, column, or diagonal in one of the four sections of the game board wins.

| | | | | | |
|---|---|---|---|---|---|
| 720 R4 | 146 R40 | 304 R20 | 127 R50 | 188 R28 | 121 R59 |
| 123 R52 | 330 R4 | 172 R12 | 344 R12 | 566 | 144 R4 |
| 495 R4 | 226 R14 | 660 R4 | 233 R2 | 120 R4 | 180 R4 |
| 184 R12 | 255 R19 | 193 R11 | 155 R19 | 141 R28 | 377 R7 |
| 149 R27 | 528 R4 | 176 R4 | 152 R20 | 609 R7 | 247 R20 |
| 240 R4 | 129 R55 | 360 R4 | 316 R24 | 125 R49 | 220 R4 |

**If you have more time** Play again!

Center Game ★ 6-2

★★ Advanced

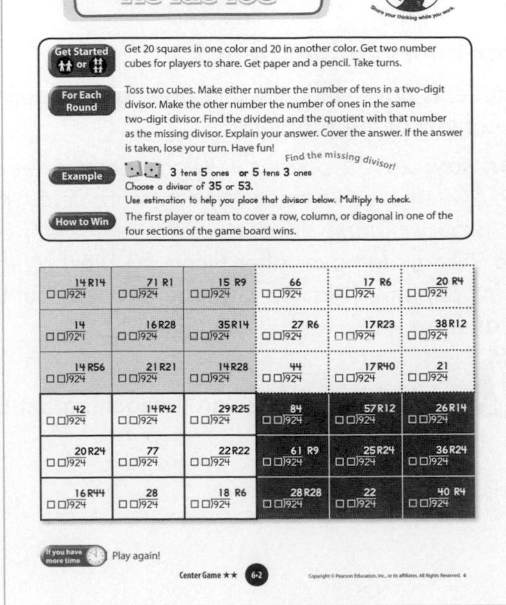

# Tic Tac Toe



**Get Started** Get 20 squares in one color and 20 in another color. Get two number cubes for players to share. Get paper and a pencil. Take turns.

**For Each Round** Toss two cubes. Make either number the number of tens in a two-digit divisor. Make the other number the number of ones in the same two-digit divisor. Find the dividend and the quotient with that number as the missing divisor. Explain your answer. Cover the answer. If the answer is taken, lose your turn. Have fun!

**Example** 3 tens 5 ones or 5 tens 3 ones
Choose a divisor of 35 or 53.
Use estimation to help you place that divisor below. Multiply to check.

Find the missing divisor!

**How to Win** The first player or team to cover a row, column, or diagonal in one of the four sections of the game board wins.

| | | | | | |
|---|---|---|---|---|---|
| 14 R14 □□)924 | 71 R1 □□)924 | 15 R9 □□)924 | 66 □□)924 | 17 R6 □□)924 | 20 R4 □□)924 |
| 14 □□)924 | 16 R28 □□)924 | 35 R14 □□)924 | 27 R6 □□)924 | 17 R23 □□)924 | 38 R12 □□)924 |
| 14 R56 □□)924 | 21 R21 □□)924 | 14 R28 □□)924 | 44 □□)924 | 17 R40 □□)924 | 21 □□)924 |
| 42 □□)924 | 14 R42 □□)924 | 29 R25 □□)924 | 84 □□)924 | 57 R12 □□)924 | 26 R14 □□)924 |
| 20 R24 □□)924 | 77 □□)924 | 22 R22 □□)924 | 61 R9 □□)924 | 25 R24 □□)924 | 36 R24 □□)924 |
| 16 R44 □□)924 | 28 □□)924 | 18 R6 □□)924 | 28 R28 □□)924 | 22 □□)924 | 40 R4 □□)924 |

**If you have more time** Play again!

Center Game ★★ 6-2

**TIMING**

The time allocated to Step 3 will depend on the teacher's instructional decisions and differentiation routines.

15–30 min

Help

Practice Buddy

Tools

Games

## Technology Center

Tools

Games

### Math Tools and Math Games

A link to a specific math tools activity or math game to use with this lesson is provided at PearsonRealize.com.

## Leveled Assignment

 Items 1–9, 16, 19–20  Items 6–12, 16–20  Items 10–20

Name ______________

### Homework & Practice 6-2

**Divide Whole Numbers**

**Another Look!**

Maggie's Orange Grove sells orange gift cartons. They have 3,987 oranges to pack into gift cartons. If 22 oranges can fit into each gift carton, how many cartons can they fill?

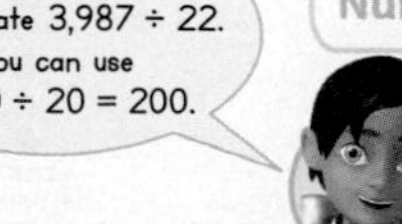

Use compatible numbers to estimate 3,987 ÷ 22.
You can use 4,000 ÷ 20 = 200.

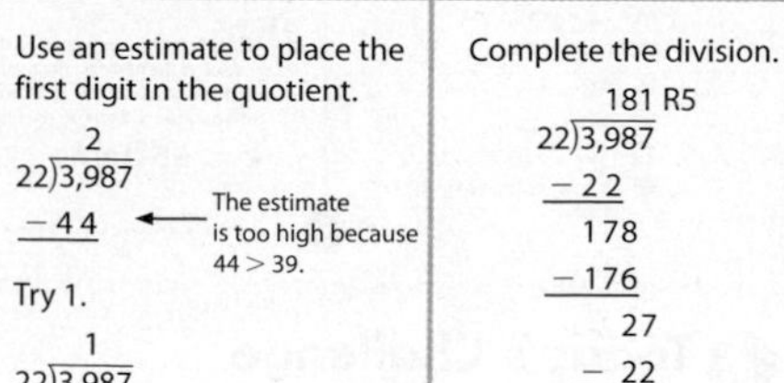

| Use an estimate to place the first digit in the quotient. | Complete the division. | They can fill 181 cartons and have 5 oranges left over. |
|---|---|---|
| 2 <br> 22)3,987 <br> − 4 4 ← The estimate is too high because 44 > 39. <br> Try 1. <br> 1 <br> 22)3,987 <br> − 2 2 | 181 R5 <br> 22)3,987 <br> − 2 2 <br> 178 <br> − 176 <br> 27 <br> − 22 <br> 5 | 181 is close to the estimate. <br> I know the estimate is too high, so the answer is reasonable. |

In **1–3**, divide. Write the missing numbers.

1. 39)4,372 112 R4
2. 24)6,3 1 5 263 R3
3. 26)23,9 0 1 919 R7

In **4–15**, divide. Check each answer by multiplying. **Check students' work.**

4. 13)1,722 **132 R6**
5. 44)6,668 **151 R24**
6. 48)4,896 **102**
7. 65)99,521 **1,531 R6**
8. 99)8,624 **87 R11**
9. 17)1,727 **101 R10**
10. 51)6,001 **117 R34**
11. 87)1,920 **22 R6**
12. 8)64,218 **8,027 R2**
13. 7)1,222 **174 R4**
14. 34)968 **28 R16**
15. 77)7,098 **92 R14**



16. **MP.8 Generalize** Roberto needs to estimate the quotient 59,563 ÷ 57. Explain how he can use compatible numbers to make a reasonable estimate. **60,000 and 60 are easy to divide and close to the actual dividend and divisor. 60,000 ÷ 60 = 1,000, so an actual quotient of about 1,000 is reasonable.**

17. **MP.3 Construct Arguments** April has 905 baseball cards. She wants to organize them on pages that hold 18 cards each. She has 50 pages. Does April have enough pages to organize all her cards? Explain. **No, she has enough pages for only 900 cards. She will have 5 cards left over. 905 ÷ 18 = 50 R5**

18. **Higher Order Thinking** The school student council sponsored a Switch Week where students were able to switch classes every 20 minutes. The students are in school for 7 hours each day, Monday through Friday. If a student switched as often as possible, how many times in all did that student switch classes? **105 times**

19. **MP.6 Be Precise** Use the coordinate plane below to find the distance between the points (−6, 4) and (3, 4). **9 units**

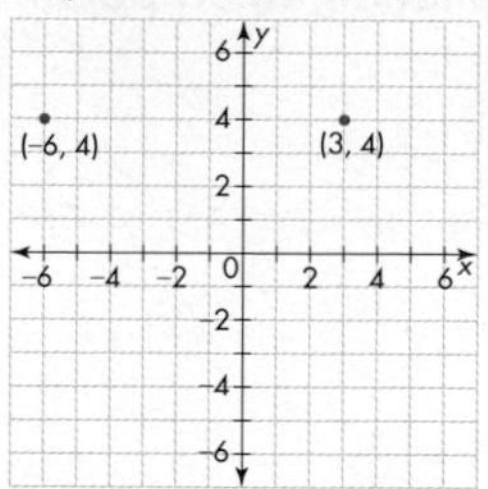


**Common Core Assessment**

20. A pickup truck can haul 75 plants each trip from a nursery to a garden center. There are 1,440 plants to be transported.

**Part A**

How many trips with a full load of plants can the pickup make? Show how you know.

**Sample answer: Divide 1,440 by 75: The quotient is 19 with a remainder of 15. So there are 19 full loads of plants.**

**19 R15**
**75)1,440**
**− 75**
**690**
**67 5**
**1 5**

**Part B**

How many more plants does the nursery need to fill another truck? Explain your reasoning.

**Sample answer: The remainder means there are 15 plants left over. 75 − 15 = 60, so the nursery needs 60 more plants to make a full load.**

# LESSON 6-3

# CONTINUE TO DIVIDE WHOLE NUMBERS

## DIGITAL RESOURCES PearsonRealize.com

eText — Student and Teacher eTexts

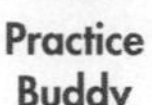
Practice Buddy — Online Personalized Practice

PD — Listen and Look For Lesson Video

Tools — Math Tools

Think — Today's Challenge

Assessment — Quick Check

Solve — Solve and Share

Help — Another Look Homework Video

Learn — Visual Learning Animation Plus

Games — Math Games

Glossary — Animated Glossary

## LESSON OVERVIEW FCR FOCUS • COHERENCE • RIGOR

### FOCUS

**Domain 6.NS** The Number System

**Cluster 6.NS.B** Compute fluently with multi-digit numbers and find common factors and multiples.

**Content Standard 6.NS.B.2** Fluently divide multi-digit numbers using the standard algorithm.

**Mathematical Practices MP.1, MP.2, MP.3, MP.4, MP.6, MP.7, MP.8**

**Objective** Find the quotient of greater whole numbers and interpret the remainder.

**Essential Understanding** A general method, or standard algorithm, can be used to divide multi-digit numbers.

**Materials** Grid paper (or Teaching Tool 15) (optional), lined paper (optional)

### COHERENCE

In Lesson 6-1, students established a conceptual understanding of division by estimating quotients with two-digit divisors. In the previous lesson, they extended their basic understanding of the division algorithm with one-digit divisors to two-digit divisors. In this lesson, students continue to practice dividing whole numbers and interpreting the quotient and remainder in problem contexts. They are expected to achieve fluency with dividing multi-digit numbers using the standard algorithm by the end of Grade 6.

### RIGOR

This lesson emphasizes **procedural skill** and **fluency**. Students continue to develop fluency with dividing multi-digit whole numbers using the standard algorithm. They are expected to fluently divide multi-digit numbers by the end of Grade 6.

PD Watch the Listen and Look For Lesson Video.

## MATH ANYTIME

### Daily Common Core Review

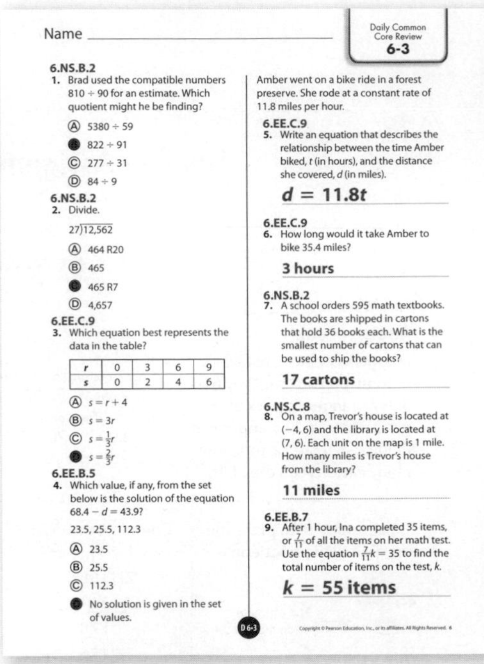
Name ____________

Daily Common Core Review 6-3

6.NS.B.2
1. Brad used the compatible numbers 810 ÷ 90 for an estimate. Which quotient might he be finding?
   - Ⓐ 5380 ÷ 59
   - ● 822 ÷ 91
   - Ⓒ 277 ÷ 31
   - Ⓓ 84 ÷ 9

6.NS.B.2
2. Divide.
   27)12,562
   - Ⓐ 464 R20
   - Ⓑ 465
   - ● 465 R7
   - Ⓓ 4,657

6.EE.C.9
3. Which equation best represents the data in the table?

| r | 0 | 3 | 6 | 9 |
|---|---|---|---|---|
| s | 0 | 2 | 4 | 6 |

   - Ⓐ $s = r + 4$
   - Ⓑ $s = 3r$
   - Ⓒ $s = \frac{1}{3}r$
   - ● $s = \frac{2}{3}r$

6.EE.B.5
4. Which value, if any, from the set below is the solution of the equation $68.4 - d = 43.9$?
   23.5, 25.5, 112.3
   - Ⓐ 23.5
   - Ⓑ 25.5
   - Ⓒ 112.3
   - ● No solution is given in the set of values.

Amber went on a bike ride in a forest preserve. She rode at a constant rate of 11.8 miles per hour.

6.EE.C.9
5. Write an equation that describes the relationship between the time Amber biked, $t$ (in hours), and the distance she covered, $d$ (in miles).
   $d = 11.8t$

6.EE.C.9
6. How long would it take Amber to bike 35.4 miles?
   **3 hours**

6.NS.B.2
7. A school orders 595 math textbooks. The books are shipped in cartons that hold 36 books each. What is the smallest number of cartons that can be used to ship the books?
   **17 cartons**

6.NS.C.8
8. On a map, Trevor's house is located at (−4, 6) and the library is located at (7, 6). Each unit on the map is 1 mile. How many miles is Trevor's house from the library?
   **11 miles**

6.EE.B.7
9. After 1 hour, Ina completed 35 items, or $\frac{7}{11}$ of all the items on her math test. Use the equation $\frac{7}{11}k = 35$ to find the total number of items on the test, $k$.
   $k = 55$ **items**

D 6-3

### Today's Challenge

Think Use the Topic 6 problems any time during this topic.

## ENGLISH LANGUAGE LEARNERS

**Reading** Expand comprehension by predicting.

*Use with the Visual Learning Bridge on Student's Edition p. 286.*

Read aloud Box A of the Visual Learning Bridge. *How many minutes of music do you predict the band records in one day?*

**Beginning** Reread the problem in Box A, and circle 8,944 and 16. *What are compatible numbers for 8,944 and 16? What is your estimate?* Read Box B. *Is your prediction close to 600?* Students may change their predictions, as desired. Read Box C, and point to 559. *The band records 559 minutes in one day.* Ask students to give thumbs up or thumbs down to show whether their predictions were close.

**Intermediate** Reread the problem in Box A. Ask students to identify compatible numbers for 8,944 and 16. *What is your estimate?* Read Box B. *Is your prediction close to 600?* Read Box C, and point to 559. Ask students to tell if their predictions were reasonable using the sentence stem: My prediction was/was not reasonable because _____.

**Advanced** Reread the problem in Box A. Ask students to use compatible numbers to make an estimate before reading Boxes B and C with a partner. Ask students to identify if they could have done anything differently to ensure their predictions were reasonable.

**Summarize** How are compatible numbers used when solving division problems?

# DEVELOP: PROBLEM-BASED LEARNING

**COHERENCE: Engage learners by connecting prior knowledge to new ideas.**
Students continue their study of division by solving problems with multi-digit whole numbers.

10–15 min

Solve

## BEFORE

1. **Pose the Solve-and-Share Problem**
**MP.8 Generalize** Listen and look for students who accurately estimate the quotient, use the division algorithm, and check the reasonableness of their solution.

2. **Build Understanding**
*What division expression can you use to represent this problem?* [1,164 ÷ 24] *What do you know about the number of hours the students worked?* [All students worked the same number of hours.]

## DURING

3. **Ask Guiding Questions As Needed**
*What compatible numbers will help you estimate the quotient?* [Sample answer: 1,000 ÷ 25 = 40] *When you divide, what first digit for the quotient will you try and in which place?* [4 in the tens place] Have students work through the division algorithm. *What does the remainder of 12 tell you?* [12 hours were worked in addition to the 48 hours worked by each student.]

## AFTER

4. **Share and Discuss Solutions**
Solve Start with students' solutions. If needed, project Tara's work to discuss how to use division to solve.

5. **Transition to the Visual Learning Bridge**
*Bar diagrams can be used to make sense of a division problem and write the correct division expression to solve.*

6. **Extension for Early Finishers**
*Write and solve a word problem that can be represented by the division expression 2,345 ÷ 18.* [130 R5; Check students' work.]

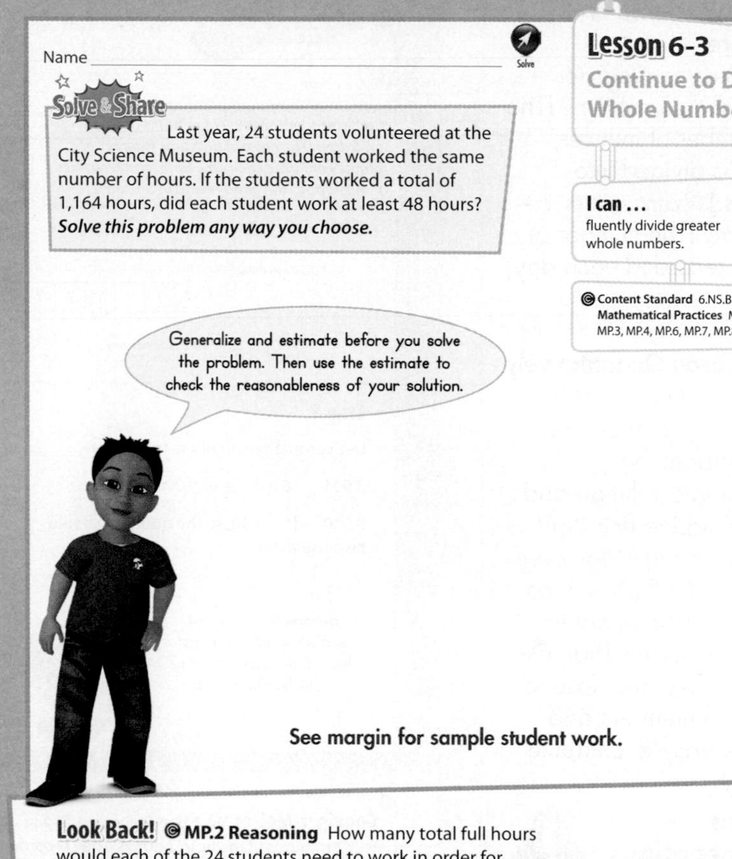

Name
Solve & Share
Last year, 24 students volunteered at the City Science Museum. Each student worked the same number of hours. If the students worked a total of 1,164 hours, did each student work at least 48 hours? *Solve this problem any way you choose.*
Lesson 6-3
Continue to Divide Whole Numbers
I can ... fluently divide greater whole numbers.
Content Standard 6.NS.B.2
Mathematical Practices MP.1, MP.2, MP.3, MP.4, MP.6, MP.7, MP.8
Generalize and estimate before you solve the problem. Then use the estimate to check the reasonableness of your solution.
See margin for sample student work.


**Look Back!** MP.2 Reasoning How many total full hours would each of the 24 students need to work in order for the group to work at least 1,338 total hours? Explain your answer.
**Sample answer: I calculated 1,338 ÷ 24 and got 55 R18. So in order to reach 1,338 hours, the 24 students each need to work 56 full hours.**

Digital Resources at PearsonRealize.com  Topic 6 | Lesson 6-3  285

## Analyze Student Work

**Tara's Work**

Estimate: 1,000 ÷ 25 = 40

$$\begin{array}{r} 48\ R12 \\ 24\overline{)1,164} \\ -96 \\ \hline 204 \\ -192 \\ \hline 12 \end{array}$$

The students each worked at least 48 hours.

Tara uses an estimate and the division algorithm to find the number of hours each student worked. Since there is a remainder, each student worked *at least* 48 hours.

**Jai's Work**

$$\begin{array}{r} 48 \\ \times\ 24 \\ \hline 192 \\ 96\ \\ \hline 1,152 \end{array}$$

The students worked at least 48 hours each, since 1,164 is greater than 1,152.

Jai multiplies to find the total hours worked if each student worked 48 hours. Then he compares the product to the actual number of hours worked.

# DEVELOP: VISUAL LEARNING

The *Visual Learning Bridge* connects students' thinking in Solve & Share to important math ideas in the lesson. Use the *Visual Learning Bridge* to make these ideas explicit. Also available as a *Visual Learning Animation Plus* at PearsonRealize.com

Visual Learning

PEARSON realize. PearsonRealize.com

Learn

Glossary

**MP.1 Make Sense and Persevere**
*How does the diagram represent the problem?* [The total number of minutes, 8,944, is divided into 16 days.] *What is the unknown?* [The number of minutes recorded each day]

**MP.2 Reason Quantitatively**
*Why would you start by estimating the quotient?* [To anticipate the approximate solution and to help find the first digit of the quotient] *Why were 9,000 and 15 chosen as the compatible numbers used to estimate?* [Sample answer: They are close to the actual numbers and they are easy to compute mentally.]

**Prevent Misconceptions**

Some students may have difficulty identifying and placing the first digit of the quotient. Possible estimates are 450 and 600, so they could try 4, 5, or 6. The actual first digit might not be the same as the first digit in their estimate, but it will be close.

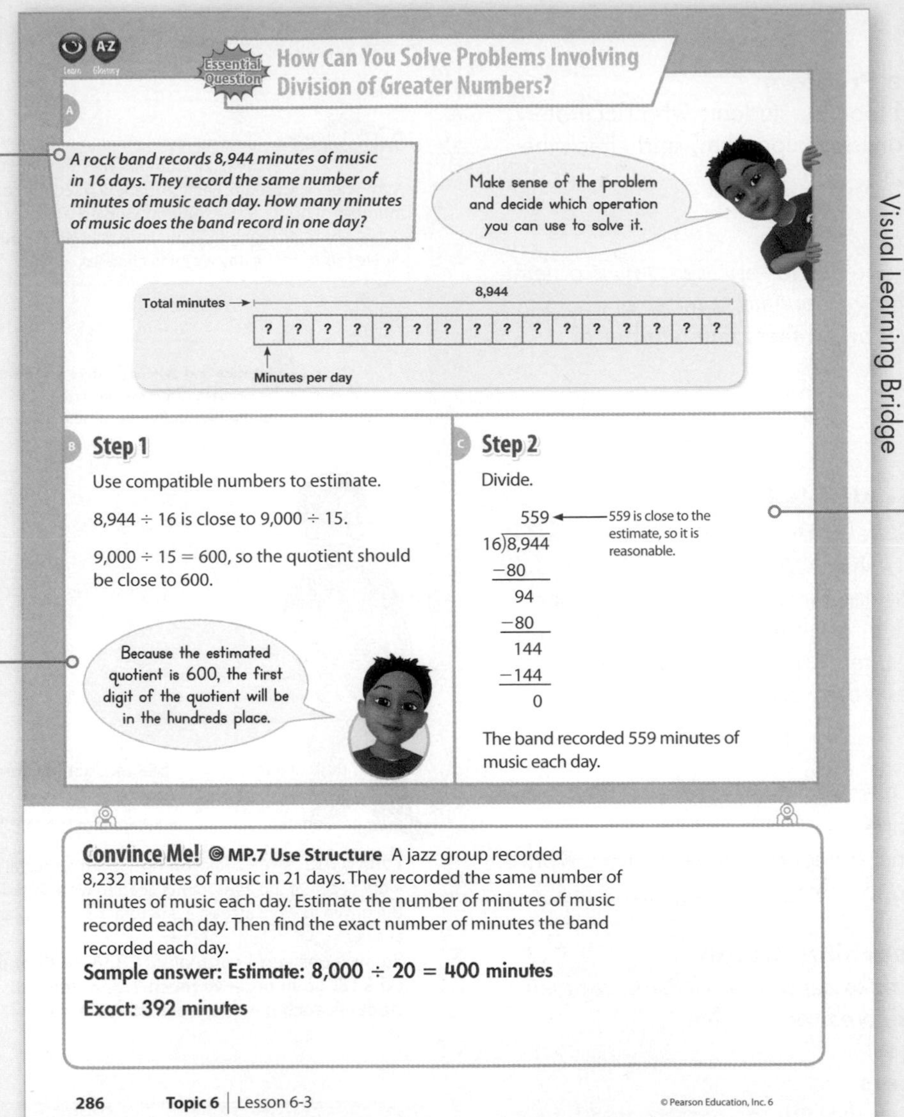

Essential Question **How Can You Solve Problems Involving Division of Greater Numbers?**

A

*A rock band records 8,944 minutes of music in 16 days. They record the same number of minutes of music each day. How many minutes of music does the band record in one day?*

Make sense of the problem and decide which operation you can use to solve it.
Total minutes
8,944
? ? ? ? ? ? ? ? ? ? ? ? ? ? ? ?
Minutes per day

B **Step 1**

Use compatible numbers to estimate.

8,944 ÷ 16 is close to 9,000 ÷ 15.

9,000 ÷ 15 = 600, so the quotient should be close to 600.

Because the estimated quotient is 600, the first digit of the quotient will be in the hundreds place.

C **Step 2**

Divide.

```
   559   ← 559 is close to the estimate, so it is reasonable.
16)8,944
  −80
    94
   −80
   144
  −144
     0
```

The band recorded 559 minutes of music each day.

**Convince Me!** MP.7 Use Structure A jazz group recorded 8,232 minutes of music in 21 days. They recorded the same number of minutes of music each day. Estimate the number of minutes of music recorded each day. Then find the exact number of minutes the band recorded each day.

**Sample answer: Estimate: 8,000 ÷ 20 = 400 minutes**

**Exact: 392 minutes**

286 Topic 6 | Lesson 6-3 © Pearson Education, Inc. 6

Visual Learning Bridge

*Based on the estimate in Box B, what digit would you put in the hundreds place of the quotient?* [6] *Why doesn't the number 6 work in the division algorithm?* [6 × 16 = 96, which is greater than the number of hundreds in the dividend.] *How can you check your solution?* [Multiply the quotient by the divisor, and then add the remainder. The result should be the same as the dividend.]

**Convince Me! MP.7 Use Structure** Students estimate a reasonable quotient. Then they use place-value structure to help them apply the division algorithm to find the exact quotient. Students' estimates may not have the same first digit as the exact quotient. Be sure students understand that an estimate may be reasonable even though it does not have the same first digit as the quotient.

Essential Question Revisit the Essential Question. Mathematical and real-world problems involving the division of greater numbers can be solved using the standard division algorithm. Estimation and place-value structure can help determine the placement of digits in the quotient.

PEARSON realize.
PearsonRealize.com

## QUICK CHECK

Check mark indicates items for prescribing differentiation on the next page.
Item 12 is worth 1 point. Items 27 and 28 are worth up to 2 points.

20–30 min

Practice Buddy

Tools

Assessment

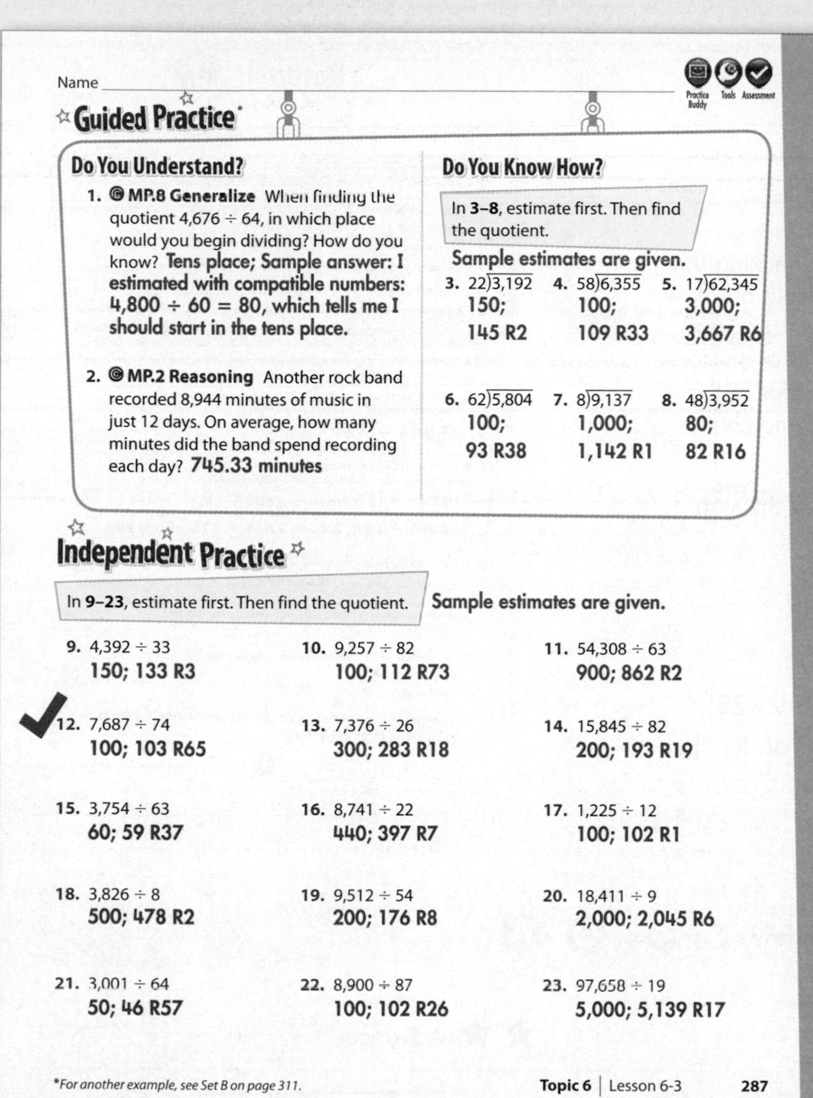

Name

**Guided Practice**

**Do You Understand?**

1. **MP.8 Generalize** When finding the quotient 4,676 ÷ 64, in which place would you begin dividing? How do you know? **Tens place; Sample answer: I estimated with compatible numbers: 4,800 ÷ 60 = 80, which tells me I should start in the tens place.**

2. **MP.2 Reasoning** Another rock band recorded 8,944 minutes of music in just 12 days. On average, how many minutes did the band spend recording each day? **745.33 minutes**

**Do You Know How?**

In **3–8**, estimate first. Then find the quotient.

**Sample estimates are given.**

3. 22)3,192 **150; 145 R2**
4. 58)6,355 **100; 109 R33**
5. 17)62,345 **3,000; 3,667 R6**
6. 62)5,804 **100; 93 R38**
7. 8)9,137 **1,000; 1,142 R1**
8. 48)3,952 **80; 82 R16**

**Independent Practice**

In **9–23**, estimate first. Then find the quotient. **Sample estimates are given.**

9. 4,392 ÷ 33 **150; 133 R3**
10. 9,257 ÷ 82 **100; 112 R73**
11. 54,308 ÷ 63 **900; 862 R2**
12. 7,687 ÷ 74 **100; 103 R65**
13. 7,376 ÷ 26 **300; 283 R18**
14. 15,845 ÷ 82 **200; 193 R19**
15. 3,754 ÷ 63 **60; 59 R37**
16. 8,741 ÷ 22 **440; 397 R7**
17. 1,225 ÷ 12 **100; 102 R1**
18. 3,826 ÷ 8 **500; 478 R2**
19. 9,512 ÷ 54 **200; 176 R8**
20. 18,411 ÷ 9 **2,000; 2,045 R6**
21. 3,001 ÷ 64 **50; 46 R57**
22. 8,900 ÷ 87 **100; 102 R26**
23. 97,658 ÷ 19 **5,000; 5,139 R17**

*For another example, see Set B on page 311.



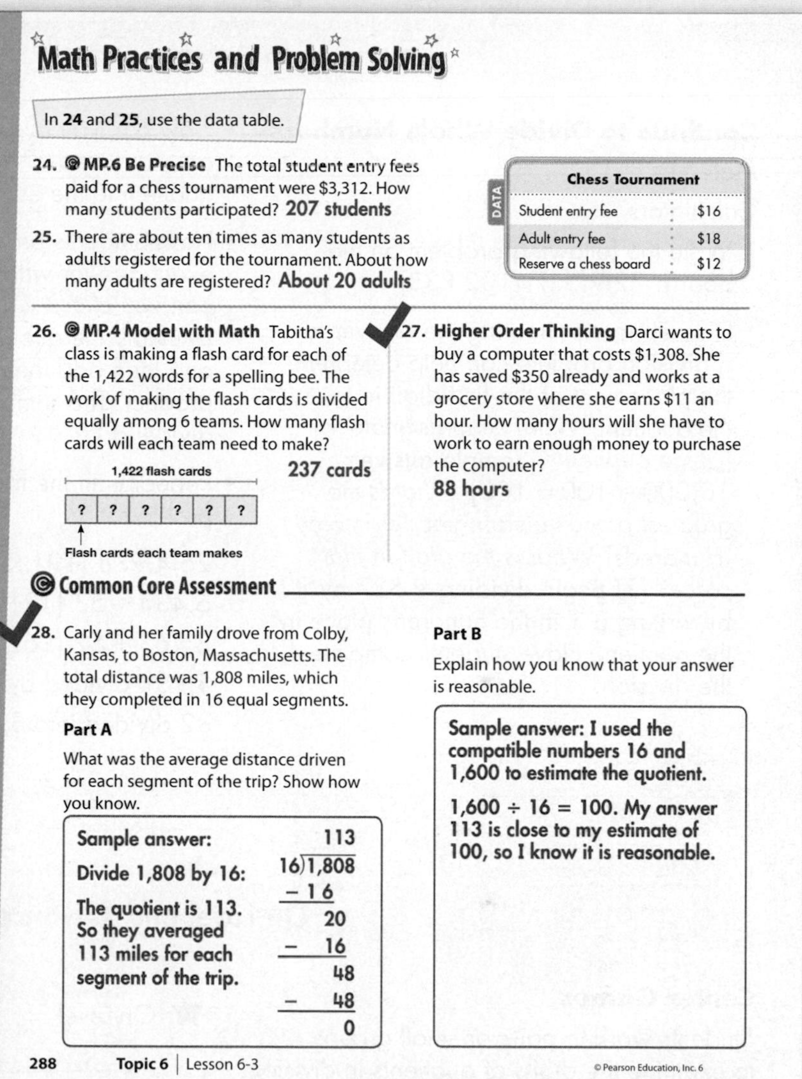

**Math Practices and Problem Solving**

In **24** and **25**, use the data table.

| Chess Tournament | |
|---|---|
| Student entry fee | $16 |
| Adult entry fee | $18 |
| Reserve a chess board | $12 |

24. **MP.6 Be Precise** The total student entry fees paid for a chess tournament were $3,312. How many students participated? **207 students**

25. There are about ten times as many students as adults registered for the tournament. About how many adults are registered? **About 20 adults**

26. **MP.4 Model with Math** Tabitha's class is making a flash card for each of the 1,422 words for a spelling bee. The work of making the flash cards is divided equally among 6 teams. How many flash cards will each team need to make? **237 cards**



27. **Higher Order Thinking** Darci wants to buy a computer that costs $1,308. She has saved $350 already and works at a grocery store where she earns $11 an hour. How many hours will she have to work to earn enough money to purchase the computer? **88 hours**

**Common Core Assessment**

28. Carly and her family drove from Colby, Kansas, to Boston, Massachusetts. The total distance was 1,808 miles, which they completed in 16 equal segments.

**Part A**

What was the average distance driven for each segment of the trip? Show how you know.

**Sample answer: Divide 1,808 by 16: The quotient is 113. So they averaged 113 miles for each segment of the trip.**

**16)1,808 = 113; − 16, 20, − 16, 48, − 48, 0**

**Part B**

Explain how you know that your answer is reasonable.

**Sample answer: I used the compatible numbers 16 and 1,600 to estimate the quotient. 1,600 ÷ 16 = 100. My answer 113 is close to my estimate of 100, so I know it is reasonable.**





**Item 1 MP.8 Generalize** Students should become adept at using an estimate to determine in which place the first digit of the quotient should be placed. *How can you use estimation to decide where to begin dividing?* [Sample answer: The greatest place in the estimate is where you should start dividing. You may have to adjust the place depending on how close the estimate is to the actual quotient.]

**Error Intervention: Item 6**

**If** students have difficulty placing the first digit in the quotient,

**then** ask: *How can you estimate the quotient by using compatible numbers?* [Sample answer: 6,000 ÷ 60 = 100] *Based on this estimate, where would you expect to begin dividing?* [In the hundreds place] *How do you know that you cannot begin dividing in the hundreds place?* [Sample answer: The divisor, 62, is greater than 58, so you cannot start dividing in the hundreds place.]

**Reteaching** Assign Reteaching Set B on p. 311.

**Item 24 MP.6 Be Precise** Encourage students to attend to precision by keeping their division work organized and aligned by place value. You may wish to provide students with grid paper or have them record their work on lined paper that is turned sideways. By lining up digits of the same place value in columns, they are less likely to make errors that result from misaligned digits and they will be able to check their work more easily.

**Item 27 Higher Order Thinking** Some students might incorrectly set up the division problem as $1,308 ÷ 11. Help them to establish the steps needed to solve the problem. *If Darci has already saved $350, how much money does she need to earn?* [$1,308 − $350 = $958] *How would you estimate the quotient?* [Sample answers: 1,000 ÷ 10 = 100, 990 ÷ 11 = 90] *What would a remainder in the quotient mean?* [Darci will earn $958 in a certain number of hours plus a fractional part of an hour. To give a whole-number answer, round to the next full hour.]

**Multi-Step Problems** *Page 288 Items 27 and 28; Page 290 Items 19, 20, and 22*

# ASSESS AND DIFFERENTIATE

**2** RtI

Use the **QUICK CHECK** on the previous page to prescribe differentiated instruction.

**I Intervention** 0–3 points on the Quick Check

**O On-Level** 4 points on the Quick Check

**A Advanced** 5 points on the Quick Check

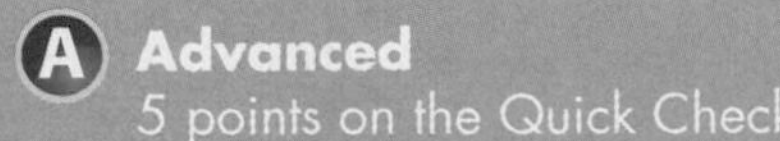

## Intervention Activity 

### Continue to Divide Whole Numbers

**Materials**

Calculators

- Write the following problem on the board: 72)9,537 [132 R33]
- Discuss how estimating the answer to a division problem can help determine the placement of the first digit in the quotient. *What is an estimate for the quotient?* [Sample answer: 10,000 ÷ 100 = 100] *What is the greatest place value in your estimate?* [Hundreds] *What is the digit in that place?* [1] Begin dividing 9,537 by 72 by writing a 1 in the hundreds place in the quotient. Have students complete the division.
- *How can you check whether your answer is reasonable?* [Compare the quotient to the estimate.]
- Have students practice checking the exact answer with a calculator. *How can you check your exact answer?* [Multiply the quotient by the divisor, and then add the remainder to that product. The sum should match the dividend.]
- Repeat with the following division problems:

26)4,978 [191 R12]

6,434 ÷ 53 [121 R21]

8,463 ÷ 52 [162 R39]

8,984 divided by 45 [199 R29]

32 divided into 8,529 [266 R17]

## Reteach I

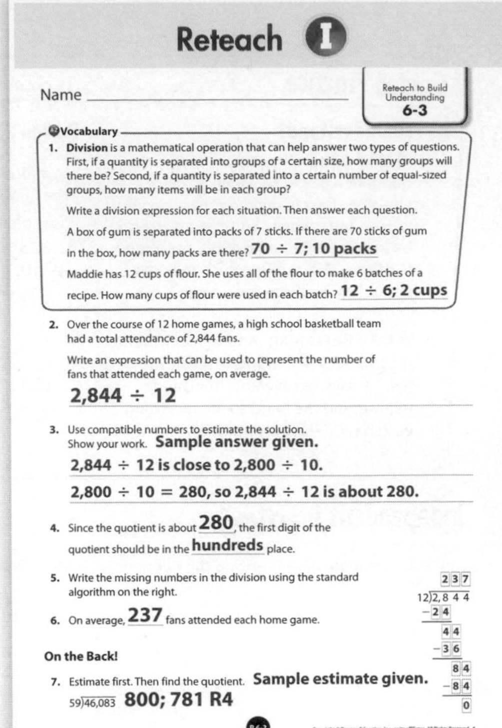

Name ______

Reteach to Build Understanding **6-3**

**Vocabulary**

1. **Division** is a mathematical operation that can help answer two types of questions. First, if a quantity is separated into groups of a certain size, how many groups will there be? Second, if a quantity is separated into a certain number of equal-sized groups, how many items will be in each group?

Write a division expression for each situation. Then answer each question.

A box of gum is separated into packs of 7 sticks. If there are 70 sticks of gum in the box, how many packs are there? **70 ÷ 7; 10 packs**

Maddie has 12 cups of flour. She uses all of the flour to make 6 batches of a recipe. How many cups of flour were used in each batch? **12 ÷ 6; 2 cups**

2. Over the course of 12 home games, a high school basketball team had a total attendance of 2,844 fans.

Write an expression that can be used to represent the number of fans that attended each game, on average.

**2,844 ÷ 12**

3. Use compatible numbers to estimate the solution. Show your work. **Sample answer given.**

**2,844 ÷ 12 is close to 2,800 ÷ 10.**

**2,800 ÷ 10 = 280, so 2,844 ÷ 12 is about 280.**

4. Since the quotient is about **280**, the first digit of the quotient should be in the **hundreds** place.

5. Write the missing numbers in the division using the standard algorithm on the right.

6. On average, **237** fans attended each home game.

```
    237
12)2,844
  -24
    44
   -36
     84
    -84
      0
```

**On the Back!**

7. Estimate first. Then find the quotient. **Sample estimate given.**
59)46,083 **800; 781 R4**

R 6-3



## On-Level and Advanced Activity Centers  

### Center Games

Students work in pairs or small groups to examine the digits of quotients in division problems. Have students record their work as they play the game.

★ On-Level

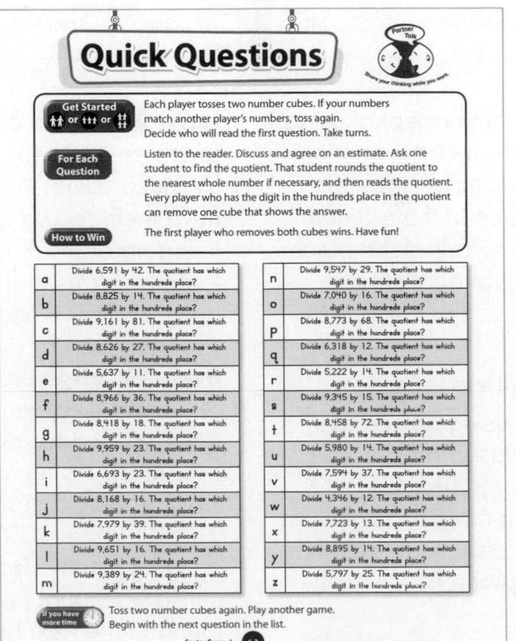

**Quick Questions**



**Get Started** (2 or 3 or 4 players) Each player tosses two number cubes. If your numbers match another player's numbers, toss again. Decide who will read the first question. Take turns.

**For Each Question** Listen to the reader. Discuss and agree on an estimate. Ask one student to find the quotient. That student rounds the quotient to the nearest whole number if necessary, and then reads the quotient. Every player who has the digit in the hundreds place in the quotient can remove one cube that shows the answer.

**How to Win** The first player who removes both cubes wins. Have fun!

| | | | |
|---|---|---|---|
| a | Divide 6,591 by 42. The quotient has which digit in the hundreds place? | n | Divide 9,547 by 29. The quotient has which digit in the hundreds place? |
| b | Divide 8,825 by 14. The quotient has which digit in the hundreds place? | o | Divide 7,040 by 16. The quotient has which digit in the hundreds place? |
| c | Divide 9,161 by 81. The quotient has which digit in the hundreds place? | p | Divide 8,773 by 68. The quotient has which digit in the hundreds place? |
| d | Divide 8,626 by 27. The quotient has which digit in the hundreds place? | q | Divide 6,318 by 12. The quotient has which digit in the hundreds place? |
| e | Divide 5,637 by 11. The quotient has which digit in the hundreds place? | r | Divide 5,222 by 14. The quotient has which digit in the hundreds place? |
| f | Divide 8,966 by 36. The quotient has which digit in the hundreds place? | s | Divide 9,345 by 15. The quotient has which digit in the hundreds place? |
| g | Divide 8,418 by 18. The quotient has which digit in the hundreds place? | t | Divide 8,458 by 72. The quotient has which digit in the hundreds place? |
| h | Divide 9,959 by 23. The quotient has which digit in the hundreds place? | u | Divide 5,980 by 14. The quotient has which digit in the hundreds place? |
| i | Divide 6,693 by 23. The quotient has which digit in the hundreds place? | v | Divide 7,594 by 37. The quotient has which digit in the hundreds place? |
| j | Divide 8,168 by 16. The quotient has which digit in the hundreds place? | w | Divide 4,346 by 12. The quotient has which digit in the hundreds place? |
| k | Divide 7,979 by 39. The quotient has which digit in the hundreds place? | x | Divide 7,723 by 13. The quotient has which digit in the hundreds place? |
| l | Divide 9,651 by 16. The quotient has which digit in the hundreds place? | y | Divide 8,895 by 14. The quotient has which digit in the hundreds place? |
| m | Divide 9,389 by 24. The quotient has which digit in the hundreds place? | z | Divide 5,797 by 25. The quotient has which digit in the hundreds place? |

**If you have more time** Toss two number cubes again. Play another game. Begin with the next question in the list.

Center Game ★ 6-3



★★ Advanced

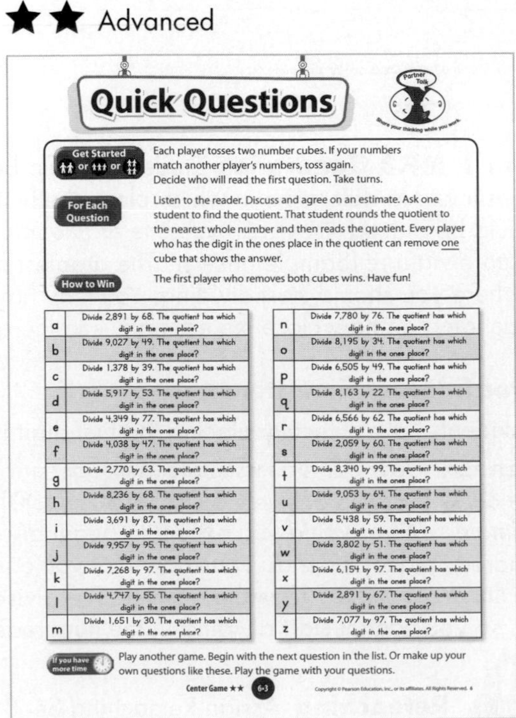

**Quick Questions**



**Get Started** (2 or 3 or 4 players) Each player tosses two number cubes. If your numbers match another player's numbers, toss again. Decide who will read the first question. Take turns.

**For Each Question** Listen to the reader. Discuss and agree on an estimate. Ask one student to find the quotient. That student rounds the quotient to the nearest whole number and then reads the quotient. Every player who has the digit in the ones place in the quotient can remove one cube that shows the answer.

**How to Win** The first player who removes both cubes wins. Have fun!

| | | | |
|---|---|---|---|
| a | Divide 2,891 by 68. The quotient has which digit in the ones place? | n | Divide 7,780 by 76. The quotient has which digit in the ones place? |
| b | Divide 9,027 by 49. The quotient has which digit in the ones place? | o | Divide 8,195 by 34. The quotient has which digit in the ones place? |
| c | Divide 1,378 by 39. The quotient has which digit in the ones place? | p | Divide 6,505 by 49. The quotient has which digit in the ones place? |
| d | Divide 5,917 by 53. The quotient has which digit in the ones place? | q | Divide 8,163 by 22. The quotient has which digit in the ones place? |
| e | Divide 4,349 by 77. The quotient has which digit in the ones place? | r | Divide 6,566 by 62. The quotient has which digit in the ones place? |
| f | Divide 4,038 by 47. The quotient has which digit in the ones place? | s | Divide 2,059 by 60. The quotient has which digit in the ones place? |
| g | Divide 2,770 by 63. The quotient has which digit in the ones place? | t | Divide 8,340 by 99. The quotient has which digit in the ones place? |
| h | Divide 8,236 by 68. The quotient has which digit in the ones place? | u | Divide 9,053 by 64. The quotient has which digit in the ones place? |
| i | Divide 3,691 by 87. The quotient has which digit in the ones place? | v | Divide 5,438 by 59. The quotient has which digit in the ones place? |
| j | Divide 9,957 by 95. The quotient has which digit in the ones place? | w | Divide 3,802 by 51. The quotient has which digit in the ones place? |
| k | Divide 7,268 by 97. The quotient has which digit in the ones place? | x | Divide 6,154 by 97. The quotient has which digit in the ones place? |
| l | Divide 4,747 by 55. The quotient has which digit in the ones place? | y | Divide 2,891 by 67. The quotient has which digit in the ones place? |
| m | Divide 1,651 by 30. The quotient has which digit in the ones place? | z | Divide 7,077 by 97. The quotient has which digit in the ones place? |

**If you have more time** Play another game. Begin with the next question in the list. Or make up your own questions like these. Play the game with your questions.

Center Game ★★ 6-3

## TIMING

The time allocated to Step 3 will depend on the teacher's instructional decisions and differentiation routines.

15–30 min

Help

Practice Buddy

Tools

Games

## Technology Center   

 Tools  Games

### Math Tools and Math Games

A link to a specific math tools activity or math game to use with this lesson is provided at PearsonRealize.com.

## Leveled Assignment

 Items 1–9, 16–17, 20–22  Items 7–12, 16–22  Items 10–22

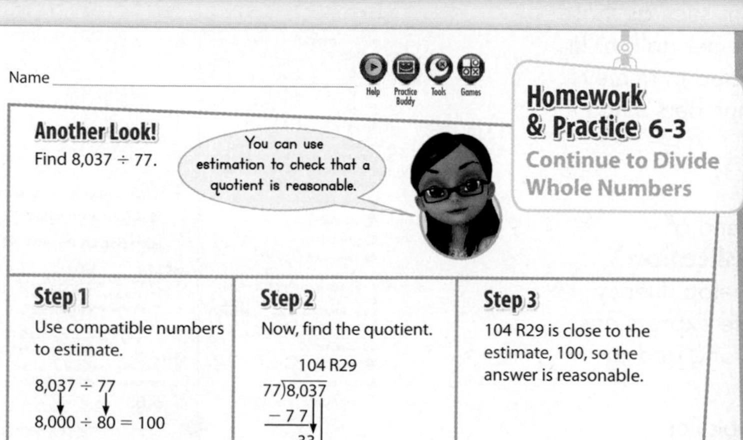

Name ______________________ Help Practice Buddy Tools Games

### Homework & Practice 6-3

**Continue to Divide Whole Numbers**

**Another Look!**

Find 8,037 ÷ 77.



| Step 1 | Step 2 | Step 3 |
|---|---|---|
| Use compatible numbers to estimate.<br>8,037 ÷ 77<br>8,000 ÷ 80 = 100<br>The quotient should be close to 100. | Now, find the quotient.<br>104 R29<br>77)8,037<br>− 77<br>33<br>− 0<br>337<br>− 308<br>29 | 104 R29 is close to the estimate, 100, so the answer is reasonable. |

In **1–15**, estimate first. Then find the quotient. **Sample estimates are given.**

1. 78)3,796 **50; 48 R52**
2. 51)2,588 **50; 50 R38**
3. 38)22,952 **600; 604**
4. 37)7,492 **200; 202 R18**
5. 46)6,725 **140; 146 R9**
6. 62)9,911 **200; 159 R53**
7. 869 ÷ 3 **300; 289 R2**
8. 7,727 ÷ 41 **200; 188 R19**
9. 8,905 ÷ 33 **300; 269 R28**
10. 6,025 ÷ 18 **300; 334 R13**
11. 4,900 ÷ 88 **50; 55 R60**
12. 90,503 ÷ 9 **10,000; 10,055 R8**
13. 608 ÷ 30 **20; 20 R8**
14. 8,855 ÷ 6 **1,800; 1,475 R5**
15. 49,790 ÷ 54 **1,000; 922 R2**



In **16** and **17**, use the data table.

| Distances by Plane | |
|---|---|
| San Francisco to New York | 4,140 km |
| New York to Rome | 6,907 km |
| Rome to New Delhi | 5,929 km |
| New Delhi to Tokyo | 5,857 km |

16. **MP.6 Be Precise** It took the Riger family 6 hours to travel from San Francisco to New York. How many kilometers did they travel per hour? **690 km per h**

17. **MP.3 Critique Reasoning** Chris said that to get from New Delhi to Tokyo in 8 hours, the plane would need to travel 650 kilometers per hour. Do you agree? Why or why not? **No. Sample answer: 650 × 8 = 5,200, which is much less than the distance of 5,857 km.**

18. A baseball team has hit a total of 10,009 home runs over the past 72 seasons. How many home runs has the team averaged per season? **139 R1**

19. **Higher Order Thinking** Zak wants to buy a used car that costs $2,625. He works at a bank where he earns $15 an hour. He has already saved $880 for the car. How many hours will he have to work to earn enough money to purchase the car? **117 hours**

20. **Algebra** Evaluate the following expression for $m = 2$. $5m + 2(m + 8) + 3$ **33**

21. There are 12 inches in 1 foot. How many inches are there in 120 feet? **1,440 inches**

### Common Core Assessment

22. Percy and his family drove from Durham, North Carolina, to Omaha, Nebraska. The total distance was 1,235 miles, which they completed in 13 equal segments.

**Part A**

What is the average number of miles they drove for each segment of the trip? Show how you know.

**Sample answer: Divide 1,235 by 13: The quotient is 95 with a remainder of 0. So they averaged 95 miles for each segment of the trip.**

95
13)1235
− 117
65
− 65
0

**Part B**

Explain how you know your answer is reasonable.

**Sample answer: I used the compatible numbers 13 and 1,300 to estimate the quotient. 1,300 ÷ 13 = 100. My answer 95 is close to my estimate of 100, so I know it is reasonable.**

# LESSON 6-4

# EVALUATE EXPRESSIONS

## DIGITAL RESOURCES PearsonRealize.com

 eText — Student and Teacher eTexts

 PD — Listen and Look For Lesson Video

 Think — Today's Challenge

 Solve — Solve and Share

Learn — Visual Learning Animation Plus

 Glossary — Animated Glossary

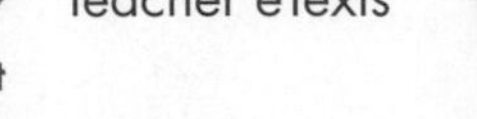

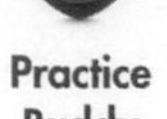 Practice Buddy — Online Personalized Practice

 Tools — Math Tools

 Assessment — Quick Check

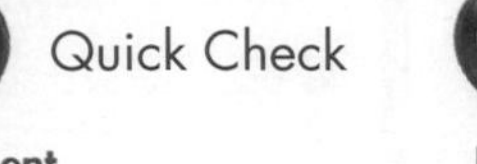

 Help — Another Look Homework Video

Games — Math Games

## LESSON OVERVIEW FCR FOCUS • COHERENCE • RIGOR

### FOCUS

**Domain 6.EE** Expressions and Equations

**Cluster 6.EE.A** Apply and extend previous understandings of arithmetic to algebraic expressions.

**Content Standard 6.EE.A.2c** Evaluate expressions at specific values of their variables. Include expressions that arise from formulas used in real-world problems. Perform arithmetic operations, including those involving whole-number exponents, in the conventional order when there are no parentheses to specify a particular order (Order of Operations). *For example, use the formulas* $V = s^3$ *and* $A = 6s^2$ *to find the volume and surface area of a cube with sides of length* $s = \frac{1}{2}$. Also **6.NS.B.2**.

**Mathematical Practices MP.3, MP.4, MP.7**

**Objective** Evaluate expressions involving division by using substitution and order of operations.

**Essential Understanding** Formulas involving division can be evaluated by substituting given values for the variables and then performing the arithmetic operations.

### COHERENCE

Students learned how to evaluate algebraic expressions and formulas in Topic 1. In this topic, they continue to develop fluency with division of multi-digit whole numbers using the standard algorithm. In this lesson, students apply both skills as they evaluate formulas that require division, such as those for density, speed, and miles per gallon. In Grade 6, students are expected to achieve fluency dividing multi-digit numbers using the standard algorithm.

### RIGOR

This lesson emphasizes a blend of **procedural skill** with **application**. Students will continue to develop fluency with division as they evaluate expressions and formulas to solve real-world and mathematical problems.

PD Watch the Listen and Look For Lesson Video.

## MATH ANYTIME

### Daily Common Core Review

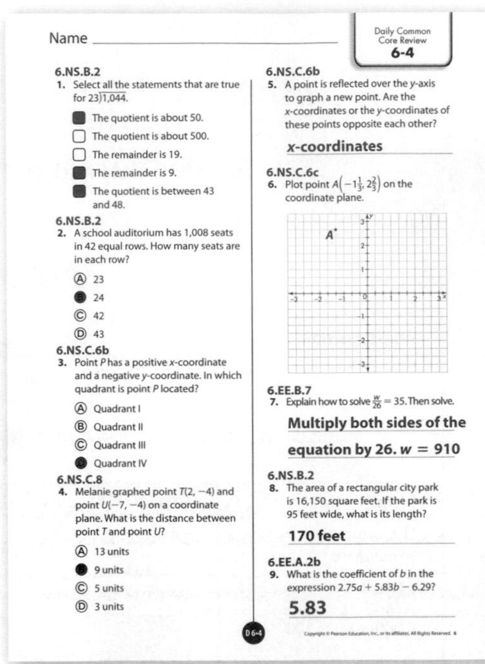

Name ________________

Daily Common Core Review 6-4

**6.NS.B.2**
1. Select all the statements that are true for 23)1,044.
   - ■ The quotient is about 50.
   - □ The quotient is about 500.
   - □ The remainder is 19.
   - ■ The remainder is 9.
   - ■ The quotient is between 43 and 48.

**6.NS.B.2**
2. A school auditorium has 1,008 seats in 42 equal rows. How many seats are in each row?
   - Ⓐ 23
   - ● 24
   - Ⓒ 42
   - Ⓓ 43

**6.NS.C.6b**
3. Point *P* has a positive *x*-coordinate and a negative *y*-coordinate. In which quadrant is point *P* located?
   - Ⓐ Quadrant I
   - Ⓑ Quadrant II
   - Ⓒ Quadrant III
   - ● Quadrant IV

**6.NS.C.8**
4. Melanie graphed point $T(2, -4)$ and point $U(-7, -4)$ on a coordinate plane. What is the distance between point *T* and point *U*?
   - Ⓐ 13 units
   - ● 9 units
   - Ⓒ 5 units
   - Ⓓ 3 units

**6.NS.C.6b**
5. A point is reflected over the *y*-axis to graph a new point. Are the *x*-coordinates or the *y*-coordinates of these points opposite each other?

   ***x*-coordinates**

**6.NS.C.6c**
6. Plot point $A\left(-1\frac{1}{3}, 2\frac{2}{3}\right)$ on the coordinate plane.

**6.EE.B.7**
7. Explain how to solve $\frac{w}{26} = 35$. Then solve.

   **Multiply both sides of the equation by 26. $w = 910$**

**6.NS.B.2**
8. The area of a rectangular city park is 16,150 square feet. If the park is 95 feet wide, what is its length?

   **170 feet**

**6.EE.A.2b**
9. What is the coefficient of *b* in the expression $2.75a + 5.83b - 6.29$?

   **5.83**

D 6-4



### Today's Challenge

Think Use the Topic 6 problems any time during this topic.

## ENGLISH LANGUAGE LEARNERS ELL

**Listening** Listen to ideas and information.

*Use with the Visual Learning Bridge on Student's Edition p. 292.*

Read the Visual Learning Bridge as students listen. Write *m* = miles per gallon, *d* = total miles driven, and *g* = total number of gallons. Explain the letters are used as placeholders until numbers can be determined. Point to the formula. *To find miles per gallon (point to m), divide the total number of miles (point to d) by the number of gallons (point to g). Look at the chart.*

**Beginning** *Find the total number of miles driven.* Demonstrate finding *d* by adding the numbers in the second column. Continue by finding *g*. Point to the formula. *Rewrite the formula using numbers.* Instruct students to listen to partners respond using the sentence stem: The formula is *m* = ___/___.

**Intermediate** *Find the total miles driven by adding the numbers in the second column.* Have students work with partners to find *d*. Repeat this process for the number of gallons. Point to the formula. *How can the formula be rewritten using numbers?* Instruct students to listen to partners respond using the sentence stem: The formula is *m* = ___/___ because ___.

**Advanced** Instruct students to find the total number of miles driven, the number of gallons used, and then rewrite the formula using numbers. Have students listen to partners explain how information from the chart is used to rewrite the formula.

**Summarize** How did substituting numbers in the formula help find the missing value?

# DEVELOP: PROBLEM-BASED LEARNING

**COHERENCE: Engage learners by connecting prior knowledge to new ideas.**
Students continue to develop fluency with division as they evaluate formulas and algebraic expressions involving division.

10–15 min

Solve

## BEFORE

**1. Pose the Solve-and-Share Problem**
**MP.7 Use Structure** Listen and look for students who use substitution and the division algorithm to evaluate the formula.

**2. Build Understanding**
*What is a formula?* [A rule that uses symbols to relate two or more quantities] *What do the variables in the formula* $s = \frac{d}{t}$ *represent?* [$s$ = speed, $d$ = distance, 504 miles, and $t$ = time, 8 hours.]

## DURING

**3. Ask Guiding Questions As Needed**
*In the formula* $s = \frac{d}{t}$*, what operation does the fraction expression* $\frac{d}{t}$ *represent?* [Division] *Which variable represents the dividend?* [$d$] *The divisor?* [$t$] *What values should be substituted for the variables in the formula?* [$d = 504$, $t = 8$]

## AFTER

**4. Share and Discuss Solutions**
Start with students' solutions. If needed, project Jenny's work to discuss how to evaluate the formula.

**5. Transition to the Visual Learning Bridge**
*In addition to calculating speed, you can find gas mileage and other rates using formulas requiring division.*

**6. Extension for Early Finishers**
*Mr. Brown drove another 246 miles on the rest of his trip. He drove for a total of 10 hours. What was his average speed for the entire trip?* [75 miles per hour]

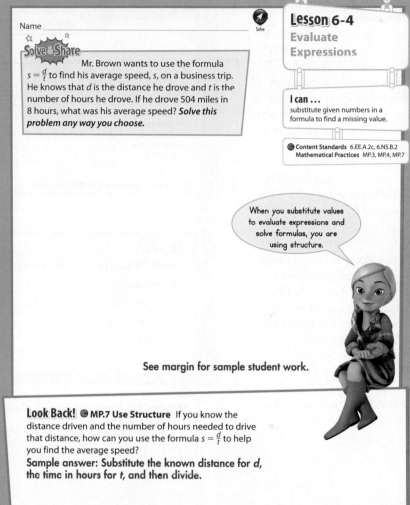

Name

Solve & Share

Mr. Brown wants to use the formula $s = \frac{d}{t}$ to find his average speed, $s$, on a business trip. He knows that $d$ is the distance he drove and $t$ is the number of hours he drove. If he drove 504 miles in 8 hours, what was his average speed? ***Solve this problem any way you choose.***

**Lesson 6-4**
**Evaluate Expressions**

**I can ...**
substitute given numbers in a formula to find a missing value.

Content Standards 6.EE.A.2c, 6.NS.B.2
Mathematical Practices MP.3, MP.4, MP.7

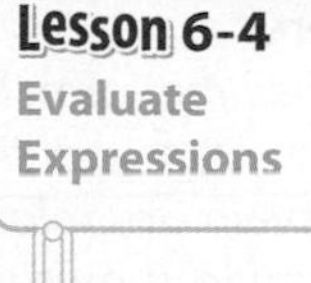

When you substitute values to evaluate expressions and solve formulas, you are using structure.

**See margin for sample student work.**

**Look Back!** **MP.7 Use Structure** If you know the distance driven and the number of hours needed to drive that distance, how can you use the formula $s = \frac{d}{t}$ to help you find the average speed?
**Sample answer: Substitute the known distance for $d$, the time in hours for $t$, and then divide.**

Digital Resources at PearsonRealize.com    Topic 6 | Lesson 6-4    291

## Analyze Student Work

Jenny's Work

$$\begin{array}{r} 63 \\ 8\overline{)504} \\ \underline{48} \\ 24 \\ \underline{24} \\ 0 \end{array}$$

$d = 504$ miles
$t = 8$ hours
$\frac{d}{t} = \frac{504 \text{ miles}}{8 \text{ hours}}$
$= 63 \frac{\text{miles}}{\text{hour}}$

Jenny substitutes values for the variables in the formula, then uses the division algorithm to evaluate the expression.

Becca's Work

$504 \div 8 = ?$
$60 \times 8 = 480$
$3 \times 8 = 24$
$(63) \times 8 = 504$

$$\begin{array}{r} 504 \\ -480 \\ \hline 24 \end{array}$$

The speed is $63 \frac{\text{miles}}{\text{hour}}$.

Becca uses multiplication to find the solution.

# DEVELOP: VISUAL LEARNING

The *Visual Learning Bridge* connects students' thinking in Solve & Share to important math ideas in the lesson. Use the *Visual Learning Bridge* to make these ideas explicit. Also available as a *Visual Learning Animation Plus* at PearsonRealize.com

PEARSON realize.
PearsonRealize.com

Learn Glossary

**MP.1 Make Sense and Persevere** *How does the formula show how the quantities in the problem are related?* [The formula shows that the miles driven divided by the total gallons of gas equals the gas mileage.] *How does the information in the table relate to the quantities in the formula?* [The table shows the data needed to find *d* and *g*.]

*Why do you have to add all of the miles driven to find the value of* d*?* [It's needed to calculate the mileage for the 4-day trip.] *Why do you have to add the numbers of gallons bought to find the value of* g*?* [To find the total number of gallons of gas used for the trip]

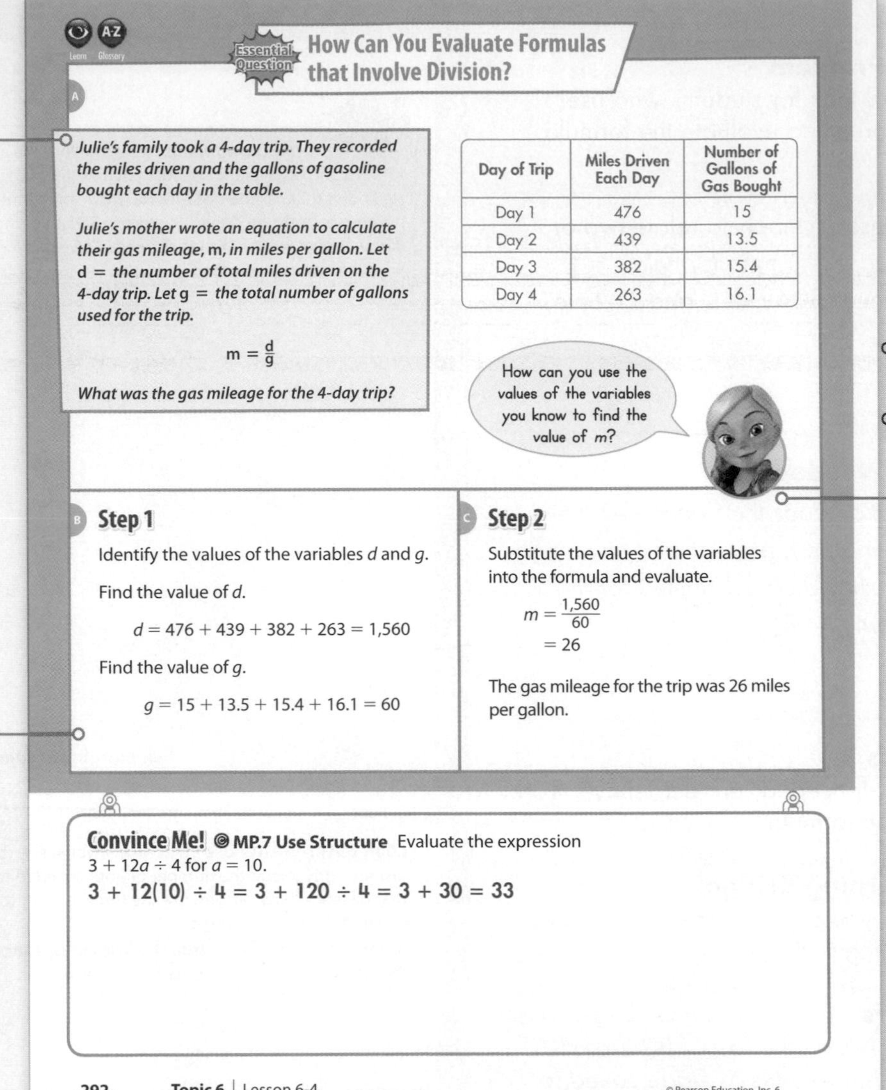

Essential Question **How Can You Evaluate Formulas that Involve Division?**

A

*Julie's family took a 4-day trip. They recorded the miles driven and the gallons of gasoline bought each day in the table.*

*Julie's mother wrote an equation to calculate their gas mileage, m, in miles per gallon. Let d = the number of total miles driven on the 4-day trip. Let g = the total number of gallons used for the trip.*

$$m = \frac{d}{g}$$

*What was the gas mileage for the 4-day trip?*

| Day of Trip | Miles Driven Each Day | Number of Gallons of Gas Bought |
|---|---|---|
| Day 1 | 476 | 15 |
| Day 2 | 439 | 13.5 |
| Day 3 | 382 | 15.4 |
| Day 4 | 263 | 16.1 |

How can you use the values of the variables you know to find the value of *m*?

B **Step 1**

Identify the values of the variables *d* and *g*.

Find the value of *d*.

$d = 476 + 439 + 382 + 263 = 1{,}560$

Find the value of *g*.

$g = 15 + 13.5 + 15.4 + 16.1 = 60$

C **Step 2**

Substitute the values of the variables into the formula and evaluate.

$m = \frac{1{,}560}{60}$

$= 26$

The gas mileage for the trip was 26 miles per gallon.

Visual Learning Bridge

**Convince Me!** **MP.7 Use Structure** Evaluate the expression $3 + 12a \div 4$ for $a = 10$.

$3 + 12(10) \div 4 = 3 + 120 \div 4 = 3 + 30 = 33$

292 Topic 6 | Lesson 6-4 © Pearson Education, Inc. 6

*Which operation does the fraction $\frac{1{,}560}{60}$ represent?* [Division] *How can you use multiplication to check your answer?* [$26 \times 60 = 1{,}560$]

**Convince Me!** **MP.7 Use Structure** *How do you begin evaluating the expression?* [Substitute 10 for *a*] *What is the first operation you perform?* [Multiply 12 and 10] *What operation do you perform next?* [$120 \div 4$]

**Coherence** Students were formally introduced to evaluating algebraic expressions and formulas in Topic 1. Students apply this understanding to evaluate algebraic expressions and formulas involving division of multi-digit numbers.

Revisit the Essential Question. Students can evaluate algebraic expressions involving division by substituting given values for the variables and then performing the necessary operations.

## QUICK CHECK

Check mark indicates items for prescribing differentiation on the next page.
Item 9 is worth 1 point. Items 19 and 21 are each worth up to 2 points.

20–30 min

Practice Buddy

Tools

Assessment

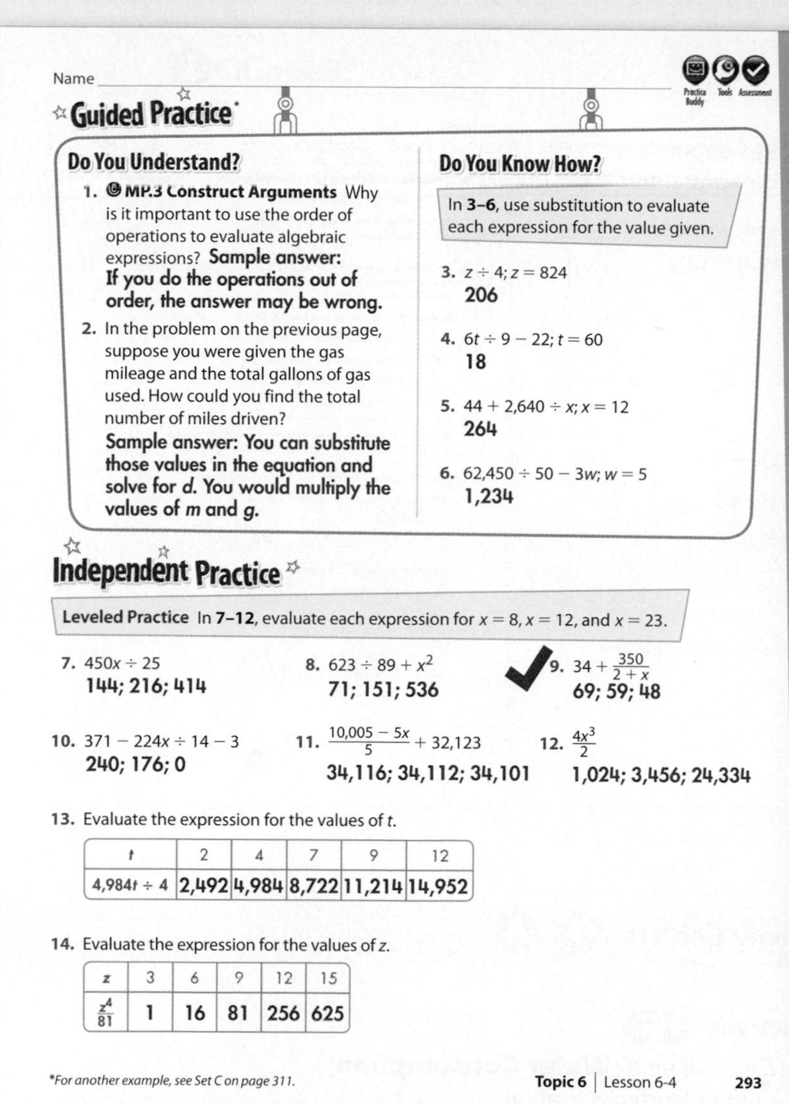

Name

### Guided Practice*

**Do You Understand?**

1. **MP.3 Construct Arguments** Why is it important to use the order of operations to evaluate algebraic expressions? **Sample answer: If you do the operations out of order, the answer may be wrong.**
2. In the problem on the previous page, suppose you were given the gas mileage and the total gallons of gas used. How could you find the total number of miles driven? **Sample answer: You can substitute those values in the equation and solve for *d*. You would multiply the values of *m* and *g*.**

**Do You Know How?**

In **3–6**, use substitution to evaluate each expression for the value given.

3. $z \div 4$; $z = 824$ **206**
4. $6t \div 9 - 22$; $t = 60$ **18**
5. $44 + 2{,}640 \div x$; $x = 12$ **264**
6. $62{,}450 \div 50 - 3w$; $w = 5$ **1,234**

### Independent Practice

**Leveled Practice** In **7–12**, evaluate each expression for $x = 8$, $x = 12$, and $x = 23$.

7. $450x \div 25$ **144; 216; 414**
8. $623 \div 89 + x^2$ **71; 151; 536**
9. $34 + \frac{350}{2 + x}$ **69; 59; 48**
10. $371 - 224x \div 14 - 3$ **240; 176; 0**
11. $\frac{10{,}005 - 5x}{5} + 32{,}123$ **34,116; 34,112; 34,101**
12. $\frac{4x^3}{2}$ **1,024; 3,456; 24,334**

13. Evaluate the expression for the values of *t*.

| $t$ | 2 | 4 | 7 | 9 | 12 |
|---|---|---|---|---|---|
| $4{,}984t \div 4$ | 2,492 | 4,984 | 8,722 | 11,214 | 14,952 |

14. Evaluate the expression for the values of *z*.

| $z$ | 3 | 6 | 9 | 12 | 15 |
|---|---|---|---|---|---|
| $\frac{z^4}{81}$ | 1 | 16 | 81 | 256 | 625 |

*For another example, see Set C on page 311.

Topic 6 | Lesson 6-4 293

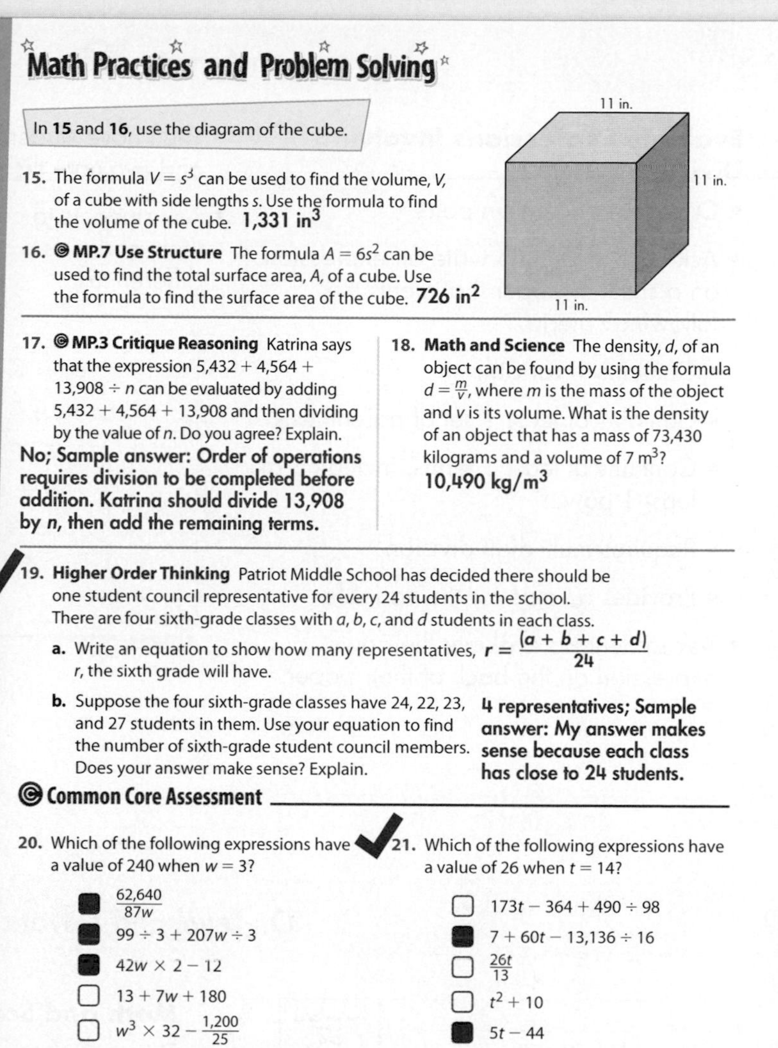

### Math Practices and Problem Solving

In **15** and **16**, use the diagram of the cube.

11 in.
11 in.
11 in.

15. The formula $V = s^3$ can be used to find the volume, *V*, of a cube with side lengths *s*. Use the formula to find the volume of the cube. **1,331 in$^3$**
16. **MP.7 Use Structure** The formula $A = 6s^2$ can be used to find the total surface area, *A*, of a cube. Use the formula to find the surface area of the cube. **726 in$^2$**
17. **MP.3 Critique Reasoning** Katrina says that the expression $5{,}432 + 4{,}564 + 13{,}908 \div n$ can be evaluated by adding 5,432 + 4,564 + 13,908 and then dividing by the value of *n*. Do you agree? Explain. **No; Sample answer: Order of operations requires division to be completed before addition. Katrina should divide 13,908 by *n*, then add the remaining terms.**
18. **Math and Science** The density, *d*, of an object can be found by using the formula $d = \frac{m}{v}$, where *m* is the mass of the object and *v* is its volume. What is the density of an object that has a mass of 73,430 kilograms and a volume of 7 m$^3$? **10,490 kg/m$^3$**
19. **Higher Order Thinking** Patriot Middle School has decided there should be one student council representative for every 24 students in the school. There are four sixth-grade classes with *a*, *b*, *c*, and *d* students in each class.
   a. Write an equation to show how many representatives, *r*, the sixth grade will have. $r = \frac{(a + b + c + d)}{24}$
   b. Suppose the four sixth-grade classes have 24, 22, 23, and 27 students in them. Use your equation to find the number of sixth-grade student council members. Does your answer make sense? Explain. **4 representatives; Sample answer: My answer makes sense because each class has close to 24 students.**

**Common Core Assessment**

20. Which of the following expressions have a value of 240 when $w = 3$?
   - ■ $\frac{62{,}640}{87w}$
   - ■ $99 \div 3 + 207w \div 3$
   - ■ $42w \times 2 - 12$
   - ☐ $13 + 7w + 180$
   - ☐ $w^3 \times 32 - \frac{1{,}200}{25}$
21. Which of the following expressions have a value of 26 when $t = 14$?
   - ☐ $173t - 364 + 490 \div 98$
   - ■ $7 + 60t - 13{,}136 \div 16$
   - ☐ $\frac{26t}{13}$
   - ☐ $t^2 + 10$
   - ■ $5t - 44$

294 Topic 6 | Lesson 6-4

© Pearson Education, Inc. 6

**Error Intervention: Item 2**

**If** students have trouble explaining how to find the miles driven, **then** suggest that they use the formula $m = \frac{d}{g}$ and substitute quantities for the variables *m* and *g*. *How do you solve for d?* [Multiply both sides of the equation by the value of *g*]

**Item 9** *After you substitute 8 for the variable x, what is the first operation you perform?* [Add 2 + 8] *What operation do you do next?* [Divide 350 by 10]

**Reteaching** Assign Reteaching Set C on p. 311.

**Item 16 MP.7 Use Structure** Remind students that the Order of Operations requires that the power $s^2$ be evaluated before multiplying by 6.

**Item 18 Math and Science** Consider using a balance to have students practice their skills with additional density problems. Have partners compute the volume of small objects using measurements or water immersion. Find the mass and then use the formula to calculate the density.

**Item 19 Higher Order Thinking** *What operation can you use to find the number of student council representatives?* [Division] *What quantities will you divide?* [The total number of sixth graders by 24] *How do you represent the total number of sixth graders in this situation?* [$a + b + c + d$]

**Multi-Step Problems** *Page 294 Items 15, 16, 18–21; Page 296 Items 10, 13, and 14*

# ASSESS AND DIFFERENTIATE

2 RtI

Use the **QUICK CHECK** on the previous page to prescribe differentiated instruction.

**I Intervention** 0–3 points on the Quick Check

**O On-Level** 4 points on the Quick Check

**A Advanced** 5 points on the Quick Check

## Intervention Activity I

### Evaluate Expressions Involving Division

- Organize students in pairs.
- Ask each student to write an expression on a sheet of paper that meets the following criteria.
  - Contains 1 variable
  - Contains at least 1 set of parenthesis
  - Contains at least 3 terms, including at least 1 power
  - Requires multi-digit division
  - Provides a value for the variable
- Ask students to evaluate their own expression on the back of their paper.
- Then have students exchange papers and evaluate their partner's expression.
- Ask students to compare their work with their partner's work and discuss any differences.

$6 + 8^2 - (3x \div 2)$

$x = 24$

$6 + 8^2 - (3 \cdot 24 \div 2)$

$6 + 8^2 - (72 \div 2)$

$6 + 8^2 - 36$

$6 + 64 - 36$

$70 - 36$

$34$

## Reteach I

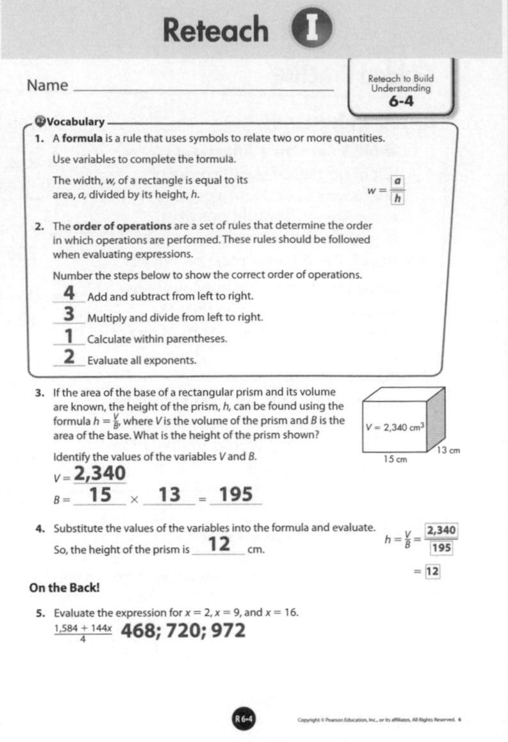

Name ______________________

Reteach to Build Understanding 6-4

**Vocabulary**

1. A **formula** is a rule that uses symbols to relate two or more quantities.

   Use variables to complete the formula.

   The width, $w$, of a rectangle is equal to its area, $a$, divided by its height, $h$. $w = \frac{a}{h}$

2. The **order of operations** are a set of rules that determine the order in which operations are performed. These rules should be followed when evaluating expressions.

   Number the steps below to show the correct order of operations.

   **4** Add and subtract from left to right.
   **3** Multiply and divide from left to right.
   **1** Calculate within parentheses.
   **2** Evaluate all exponents.

3. If the area of the base of a rectangular prism and its volume are known, the height of the prism, $h$, can be found using the formula $h = \frac{V}{B}$, where $V$ is the volume of the prism and $B$ is the area of the base. What is the height of the prism shown?

   $V$ = 2,340 cm³; 15 cm; 13 cm

   Identify the values of the variables $V$ and $B$.

   $V$ = **2,340**

   $B$ = **15** × **13** = **195**

4. Substitute the values of the variables into the formula and evaluate.

   So, the height of the prism is **12** cm. $h = \frac{V}{B} = \frac{2,340}{195} = 12$

**On the Back!**

5. Evaluate the expression for $x = 2$, $x = 9$, and $x = 16$.

   $\frac{1,584 + 144x}{4}$ **468; 720; 972**

R 6-4 Copyright © Pearson Education, Inc., or its affiliates. All Rights Reserved. 6

## On-Level and Advanced Activity Centers O A

Name ______________________

Math and Science Activity 6-4

### Conserving Water

Did You Know? About 70% of water used in households is used indoors. The bathroom is where most of the indoor water is used. There are many ways to conserve water in the bathroom. Shutting off the faucet while brushing teeth can save more than 50 gallons of water each week.

Indoor Water Use: Toilet 27%; Washing Machine 22%; Shower 17%; Faucet 16%; Leaks 14%; Other 4%

1. A leaking toilet wastes up to 200 gallons of water each day. Jonas writes the equation $r = \frac{g}{t}$ to calculate the leak rate, $r$, in gallons per hour. The number of gallons that leak out is $g$ and the total time of the leak is $t$.

   What is the leak rate, in gallons per hour, of the toilet?

   **$8\frac{1}{3}$ gallons per hour**

2. **Represent** Caroline conserves 1,300 gallons of water by shutting off the faucet while brushing her teeth. For about how many weeks has Caroline been shutting off the faucet while brushing her teeth?

   **1,300 ÷ 50; 26 weeks**

3. **Extension** A hotel has 15 leaking faucets, 12 leaking toilets, and 1 leaking sprinkler. Each faucet wastes 42 gallons per week. Each toilet wastes 63 gallons per week. The sprinkler wastes 84 gallons each week. As part of her weekly report, the hotel manager writes an expression to calculate the number of gallons of water wasted each day, $g$.

   Write and evaluate an expression to find how much water would be saved each day by fixing the leaks.

   **(15 • 42 + 12 • 63 + 1 • 84) ÷ 7;**

   **210 gallons**

Math and Science Activity 6-4 Copyright © Pearson Education, Inc., or its affiliates. All Rights Reserved. 6

### Math and Science Activity STEM

This activity revisits the science theme, **Water Consumption**, introduced on page 271 in the Student's Edition.

### Sample Student Work

3. $f = 42$, $t = 63$, $s = 84$

$g = \frac{15f + 12t + s}{7}$

$= \frac{15(42) + 12(63) + 84}{7}$

$= \frac{1470}{7}$

$= 210$ gallons per day

PEARSON realize. PearsonRealize.com

Help | Practice Buddy | Tools | Games

**TIMING**

The time allocated to Step 3 will depend on the teacher's instructional decisions and differentiation routines.

15–30 min

## Technology Center I O A

Tools Games

**Math Tools and Math Games**

A link to a specific math tools activity or math game to use with this lesson is provided at PearsonRealize.com.

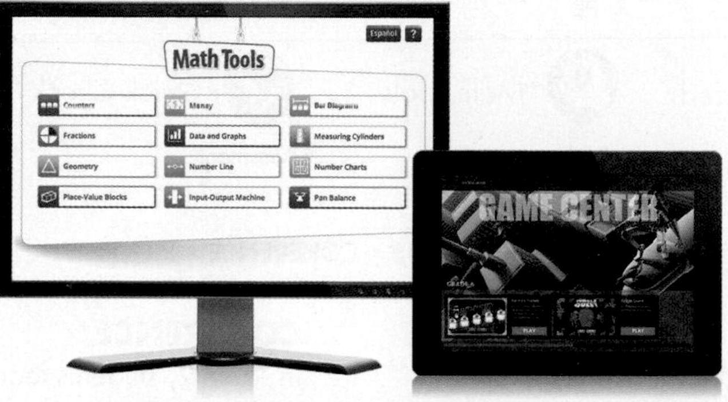


## Leveled Assignment

 Items 1–4, 8, 12–14  Items 4–8, 10, 12–14  Items 5, 7–14

Name ______________________

Help Practice Buddy Tools Games

**Homework & Practice 6-4**
**Evaluate Expressions**

**Another Look!**

The cost, $c$, to attend the annual class trip is given by the equation

$c = 2a + 3b + 3c + d \div 48$

where $a$ is the cost of a room for one night, $b$ is the cost of meals for one day, $c$ is the cost of tickets for one day, and $d$ is the cost for the bus rental. There are 48 students.

What will it cost each student to go on the class trip?

Remember to use the order of operations when evaluating the equation.

| Step 1 | Step 2 |
|---|---|
| Identify the value of each variable. | Substitute the value of each variable into the equation and evaluate. |
| $a = 50$ | $c = 2 \cdot 50 + 3 \cdot 40 + 3 \cdot 20 + 1{,}392 \div 48$ |
| $b = 40$ | $c = 100 + 120 + 60 + 29$ |
| $c = 20$ | $c = 309$ |
| $d = 1{,}392$ | It will cost each student \$309 to go on the class trip. |

In **1–7**, evaluate each expression for $z = 3$, $z = 7$, and $z = 12$.

1. $\frac{14{,}952 - 6z}{3}$ **4,978; 4,970; 4,960**
2. $378z \div 7$ **162; 378; 648**
3. $(7 \cdot 24) \div z$ **56; 24; 14**
4. $34 + 34z \div 17$ **40; 48; 58**
5. $45z + 4{,}565 + 9{,}078 \div 89$ **4,802; 4,982; 5,207**
6. $\frac{156 + 84z + 144}{12}$ **46; 74; 109**
7. $\frac{4z^4 + 26}{10}$ **35; 963; 8,297**

8. Evaluate the expression for the values of $x$.

| $x$ | 2 | 3 | 5 | 7 | 9 |
|---|---|---|---|---|---|
| $\frac{48x + 16 + 35}{3}$ | **49** | **65** | **97** | **129** | **161** |

9. Evaluate the expression for the values of $t$.

| $t$ | 2 | 4 | 8 | 9 | 21 |
|---|---|---|---|---|---|
| $\frac{26{,}418}{5t - 3}$ | **3,774** | **1,554** | **714** | **629** | **259** |



10. **Higher Order Thinking** A school district can send a representative to the state spelling bee for every 50 students in the school district. There are 5 schools with $a$, $b$, $c$, $d$, and $e$ students in each school.
    a. Write an equation to show how many representatives, $r$, the school district will have. $r = \frac{(a + b + c + d + e)}{50}$
    b. Suppose there are 1,587, 985, 2,052, 824, and 752 students, respectively, in each of the schools. Use your equation to find the number of students the school district can send to the state spelling bee. Does your answer make sense? Explain.
    **124 representatives; Sample answer: My answer makes sense because $124 \times 50 = 6{,}200$.**

In **11** and **12**, use the menu.

11. **MP.4 Model with Math** Two friends ordered 2 steaks, 2 drinks, and some Caesar salads. Write an expression that shows the cost per person when the total cost is split equally between the two friends.
    **Sample answer: $\frac{(2 \cdot 15) + (2 \cdot 2) + 9x}{2}$**

12. The 24 members of the middle school swim team ordered 9 steaks, 13 orders of spaghetti, 16 drinks, and some bowls of soup. Write an expression that shows the total cost of their order split equally among the 24 members.
    **Sample answer: $\frac{(9 \cdot 15) + (13 \cdot 11) + (16 \cdot 2) + 5x}{24}$**

Dinner Menu
Steak $15
Spaghetti $11
Soup $5
Caesar Salad $9
Drink $2


**Common Core Assessment**

13. Which of the following expressions have a value of 13 when $n = 5$?
    - ■ $3n - 2$
    - ■ $9n \div 3 - 6 \div 3$
    - ☐ $13n \times 2 - 10$
    - ☐ $13 + 7n - 2$
    - ■ $\frac{n^5 - 1{,}838}{99}$

14. Which of the following expressions have a value of 112 when $z = 7$?
    - ☐ $732 \div 12 + z^2$
    - ☐ $7z + 3{,}136 \div 49 - 3$
    - ■ $103 + 27z \div 21$
    - ■ $67 + z^2 - 4$
    - ■ $\frac{707 - 5z}{6}$

# LESSON 6-5

# SOLVE DIVISION EQUATIONS

## DIGITAL RESOURCES PearsonRealize.com

Student and Teacher eTexts — eText

Listen and Look For Lesson Video — PD

Today's Challenge — Think

Solve and Share — Solve

Visual Learning Animation Plus — Learn

Animated Glossary — Glossary

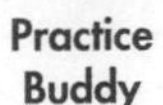
Online Personalized Practice — Practice Buddy

Math Tools — Tools

Quick Check — Assessment

Another Look Homework Video — Help

Math Games — Games

## LESSON OVERVIEW FCR FOCUS • COHERENCE • RIGOR

### FOCUS

**Domain 6.EE** Expressions and Equations

**Cluster 6.EE.B** Reason about and solve one-variable equations and inequalities.

**Content Standard 6.EE.B.7** Solve real-world and mathematical problems by writing and solving equations of the form $x + p = q$ and $px = q$ for cases in which $p$, $q$ and $x$ are all nonnegative rational numbers. Also **6.NS.B.2**.

**Mathematical Practices MP.2, MP.3, MP.4, MP.7, MP.8**

**Objective** Solve one-step equations involving division.

**Essential Understanding** Inverse relationships and properties of equality can be used to solve equations that involve division.

### COHERENCE

In Topic 2, students learned how to solve one-step division equations with one-digit divisors. In this topic, students have developed fluency with multi-digit division and are becoming proficient solving problems involving 2-digit divisors. In this lesson, students apply these skills to write and solve equations that require multi-digit division. Students will use these skills in Grade 7 when they solve more complicated equations.

### RIGOR

This lesson emphasizes a blend of **procedural skill** with **application**. Students use their skills solving one-step division problems to solve real-world and mathematical problems.

PD Watch the Listen and Look For Lesson Video.

## MATH ANYTIME

### Daily Common Core Review

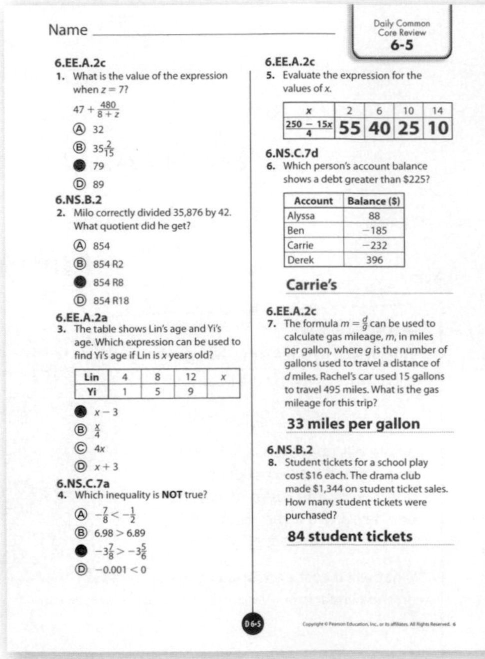

Name ____________

Daily Common Core Review 6-5

6.EE.A.2c
1. What is the value of the expression when $z = 7$?

$47 + \frac{480}{8 + z}$

Ⓐ 32
Ⓑ $35\frac{2}{15}$
● 79
Ⓓ 89

6.NS.B.2
2. Milo correctly divided 35,876 by 42. What quotient did he get?

Ⓐ 854
Ⓑ 854 R2
● 854 R8
Ⓓ 854 R18

6.EE.A.2a
3. The table shows Lin's age and Yi's age. Which expression can be used to find Yi's age if Lin is $x$ years old?

| Lin | 4 | 8 | 12 | $x$ |
|---|---|---|---|---|
| Yi | 1 | 5 | 9 | |

● $x - 3$
Ⓑ $\frac{x}{4}$
Ⓒ $4x$
Ⓓ $x + 3$

6.NS.C.7a
4. Which inequality is **NOT** true?

Ⓐ $-\frac{7}{8} < -\frac{1}{2}$
Ⓑ $6.98 > 6.89$
● $-3\frac{7}{8} > -3\frac{5}{6}$
Ⓓ $-0.001 < 0$

6.EE.A.2c
5. Evaluate the expression for the values of $x$.

| $x$ | 2 | 6 | 10 | 14 |
|---|---|---|---|---|
| $\frac{250 - 15x}{4}$ | **55** | **40** | **25** | **10** |

6.NS.C.7d
6. Which person's account balance shows a debt greater than $225?

| Account | Balance ($) |
|---|---|
| Alyssa | 88 |
| Ben | −185 |
| Carrie | −232 |
| Derek | 396 |

**Carrie's**

6.EE.A.2c
7. The formula $m = \frac{d}{g}$ can be used to calculate gas mileage, $m$, in miles per gallon, where $g$ is the number of gallons used to travel a distance of $d$ miles. Rachel's car used 15 gallons to travel 495 miles. What is the gas mileage for this trip?

**33 miles per gallon**

6.NS.B.2
8. Student tickets for a school play cost $16 each. The drama club made $1,344 on student ticket sales. How many student tickets were purchased?

**84 student tickets**

D 6-5



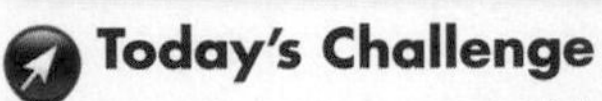

### Today's Challenge

Think Use the Topic 6 problems any time during this topic.

## ENGLISH LANGUAGE LEARNERS 

**Listening** Demonstrate listening comprehension by responding to questions.

*Use with the Solve & Share on Student's Edition p. 297.*

Read the Solve & Share as students listen. *What is the problem asking us to find?* Write the following: $s$ = each person's share, $c$ = total cost of trip, $p$ = number of people. *What formula can be used to solve the problem?* Write $s = \frac{c}{p}$.

**Beginning** Write $s$, $c$, and $p$, each person's share, total cost of trip, number of people. Point to $s$. *What does s represent?* Students respond by pointing. Continue this process with $c$ and $p$. Point to $s = \frac{c}{p}$ and the chart. *What is the total cost of the trip?* Erase the $c$ in the formula and write $19,111. Erase the $p$ in the formula and write 29.

**Intermediate** *What information in the Solve & Share is needed to solve the problem?* Point to the chart. *What information in the chart is needed to solve the problem?* Point to $s = \frac{c}{p}$. *How can the formula be rewritten using these numbers?*

**Advanced** Ask students to find the needed information in the Solve & Share and on the chart to solve the problem. *How can the formula be rewritten?* Instruct students to listen to partners explain their reasoning.

**Summarize** What information was needed to write the formula?

# DEVELOP: PROBLEM-BASED LEARNING

**COHERENCE: Engage learners by connecting prior knowledge to new ideas.**
Students build on their ability to use division to evaluate expressions as they solve equations requiring division.

10–15 min

Solve

## BEFORE

1. **Pose the Solve-and-Share Problem**
**MP.8 Generalize** Listen and look for students who write and solve a division equation to solve the problem.

2. **Build Understanding**
*What two quantities are given in this problem?* [Total cost of the trip, number of people going] *Will the cost be the same for each person? Explain.* [Yes; the problem says they will share the cost equally.]

## DURING

3. **Ask Guiding Questions As Needed**
*What is the unknown in this situation?* [The cost of the trip for each person] *How can you represent the unknown to write an equation?* [Sample answer: You can define a variable to represent the cost per person.]

## AFTER

4. **Share and Discuss Solutions**
Solve Start with students' solutions. If needed, project David's work to discuss how to write a division equation, and then use the division algorithm to solve.

5. **Transition to the Visual Learning Bridge**
*You can use what you know about writing and solving equations and dividing to solve problems.*

6. **Extension for Early Finishers**
*Seventeen people in the group decide to add on a visit to Philadelphia. The total cost for the extension is $10,846. Write and solve an equation to find how much each person must pay for the additional visit.* [$638]

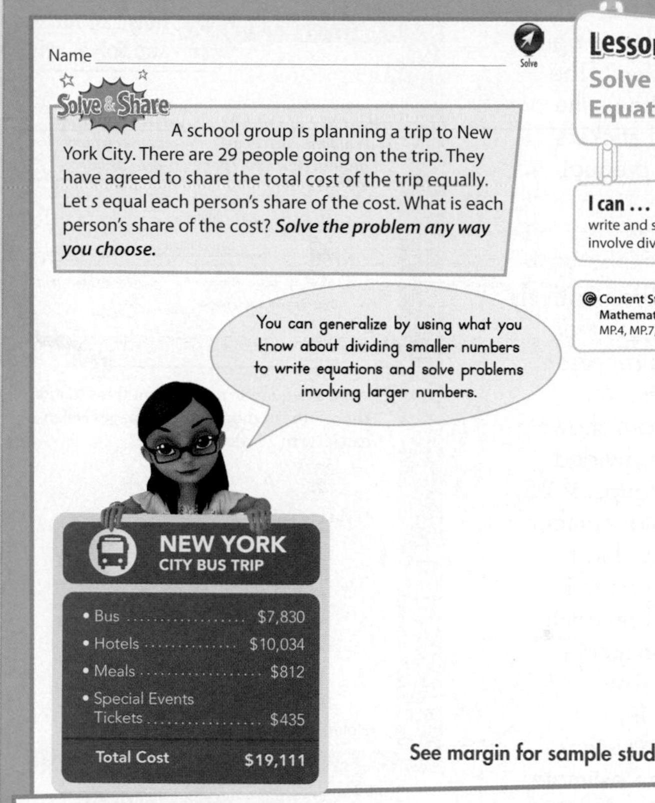

Name
Solve
Lesson 6-5
Solve Division Equations
Solve & Share
A school group is planning a trip to New York City. There are 29 people going on the trip. They have agreed to share the total cost of the trip equally. Let s equal each person's share of the cost. What is each person's share of the cost? Solve the problem any way you choose.
I can ...
write and solve equations that involve division.
Content Standards 6.EE.B.7, 6.NS.B.2
Mathematical Practices MP.2, MP.3, MP.4, MP.7, MP.8
You can generalize by using what you know about dividing smaller numbers to write equations and solve problems involving larger numbers.
NEW YORK CITY BUS TRIP
Bus $7,830
Hotels $10,034
Meals $812
Special Events Tickets $435
Total Cost $19,111
See margin for sample student work.
Look Back! MP.3 Construct Arguments Can you use the same strategy you used above to find each person's share of the hotel bill? Explain your reasoning.
Yes; Sample answer: I can divide the $10,034 cost of the hotel bill by 29 to find each person's share of the hotel bill. Let h = one person's share.
10,034 ÷ 29 = h
Divide to solve for h.
10,034 ÷ 29 = 346
Each person's share of the hotel bill is $346.
Digital Resources at PearsonRealize.com
Topic 6 | Lesson 6-5
297


## Analyze Student Work

**David's Work**

$\$19{,}111 \div 29 = s$

```
      659
29 ) 19111
    -174
      171
     -145
       261
      -261
         0
```

Each person's share of the total is $659.

David writes a division equation and divides using the standard algorithm to solve the problem.

**Eric's Work**

Let $s$ = cost per person for the trip.

$29s = 19{,}111$

$\frac{29s}{29} = \frac{19{,}111}{29}$

$s = \$659$

```
      659
29 ) 19111
    -174
      171
     -145
       261
      -261
         0
```

Each person must pay $659.

Eric writes a multiplication equation to solve the problem.

# DEVELOP: VISUAL LEARNING

PearsonRealize.com

Learn Glossary

The *Visual Learning Bridge* connects students' thinking in Solve & Share to important math ideas in the lesson. Use the *Visual Learning Bridge* to make these ideas explicit. Also available as a *Visual Learning Animation Plus* at PearsonRealize.com

ELL Visual Learning

**MP.7 Use Structure**
*How does the bar diagram represent division?* [The bar diagram shows the total number of stickers is divided into $p$ equal groups of 25.]

**MP.2 Reason Quantitatively**
*How do you know that both equations represent the problem situation?* [The bar diagram shows the stickers are divided into $p$ equal groups of 25, or that if the total number of stickers is divided by the number of pages in the album, $p$, then each page has 25 stickers.] *How do you know to place the first digit of the quotient in the tens place?* [You can estimate that $25 \times 100 = 2{,}500$, and since that estimate is too high, the quotient will be less than 100.]

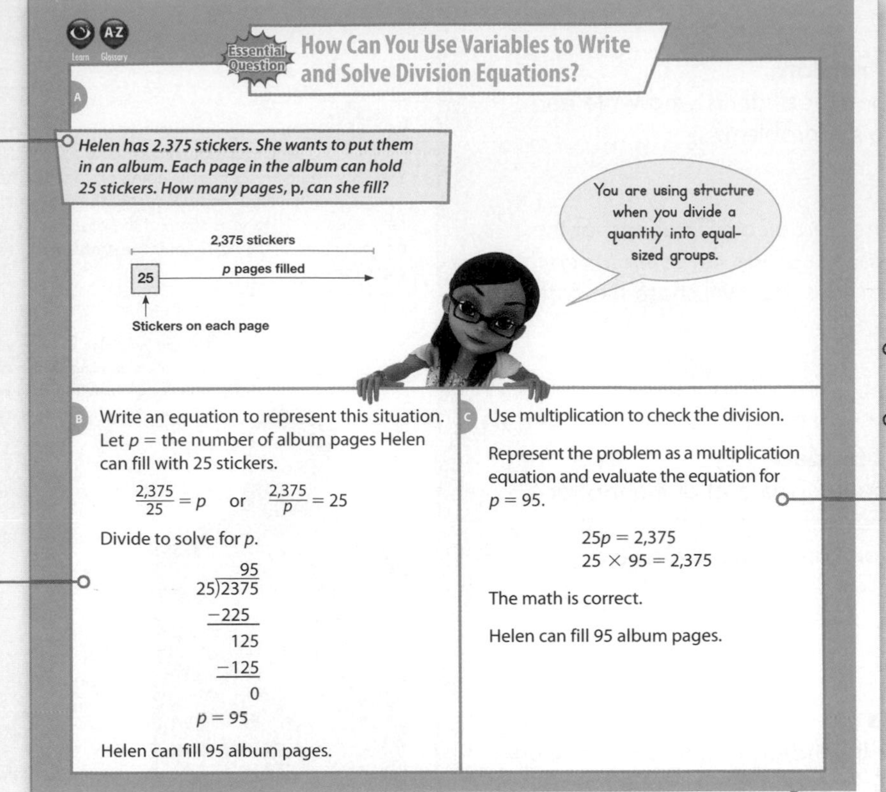

Essential Question **How Can You Use Variables to Write and Solve Division Equations?**

A

*Helen has 2,375 stickers. She wants to put them in an album. Each page in the album can hold 25 stickers. How many pages, p, can she fill?*



B Write an equation to represent this situation. Let $p$ = the number of album pages Helen can fill with 25 stickers.

$\frac{2{,}375}{25} = p$ or $\frac{2{,}375}{p} = 25$

Divide to solve for $p$.

$$\begin{array}{r} 95 \\ 25\overline{)2375} \\ -225 \\ 125 \\ -125 \\ 0 \end{array}$$

$p = 95$

Helen can fill 95 album pages.

C Use multiplication to check the division.

Represent the problem as a multiplication equation and evaluate the equation for $p = 95$.

$25p = 2{,}375$
$25 \times 95 = 2{,}375$

The math is correct.

Helen can fill 95 album pages.

*Why do you use multiplication to check your work?* [Multiplication is the inverse operation of division.]

Visual Learning Bridge

**Convince Me!** **MP.7 Look for Relationships** What similarities do you see between the division equation $2{,}375 \div 25 = p$ and the multiplication equation $25p = 2{,}375$? Explain why both can be used to find how many album pages Helen can fill.
**Sample answer: Both equations include the total number of stickers and the number of stickers that can fit on one page. They also use the variable $p$ to represent the unknown number of total pages that Helen can fill with 25 stickers. Division is used to break apart 2,375 into equal groups of 25 to solve for $p$, and multiplication combines equal groups of 25 $p$ times until the total equals 2,375.**

298 Topic 6 | Lesson 6-5 © Pearson Education, Inc. 6

**Convince Me! MP.7 Look for Relationships** *What does 25p represent?* [25 times the number of pages in the album] *How do you solve the equation 25p = 2,375?* [Divide by 25 on both sides of the equation.] *After you divide by 25 on both sides of the equation, what do you notice about how that equivalent equation compares with the equation 2,375 ÷ 25 = p?* [They are the same.]

Revisit the Essential Question. Students will use variables to represent the unknown value in a division equation and solve the equation using inverse operations and the properties of equality.

## QUICK CHECK

Check mark indicates items for prescribing differentiation on the next page. Items 6 and 16 are worth 1 point. Item 15 is worth up to 3 points.

20–30 min

PEARSON realize.
PearsonRealize.com

Practice Buddy

Tools

Assessment

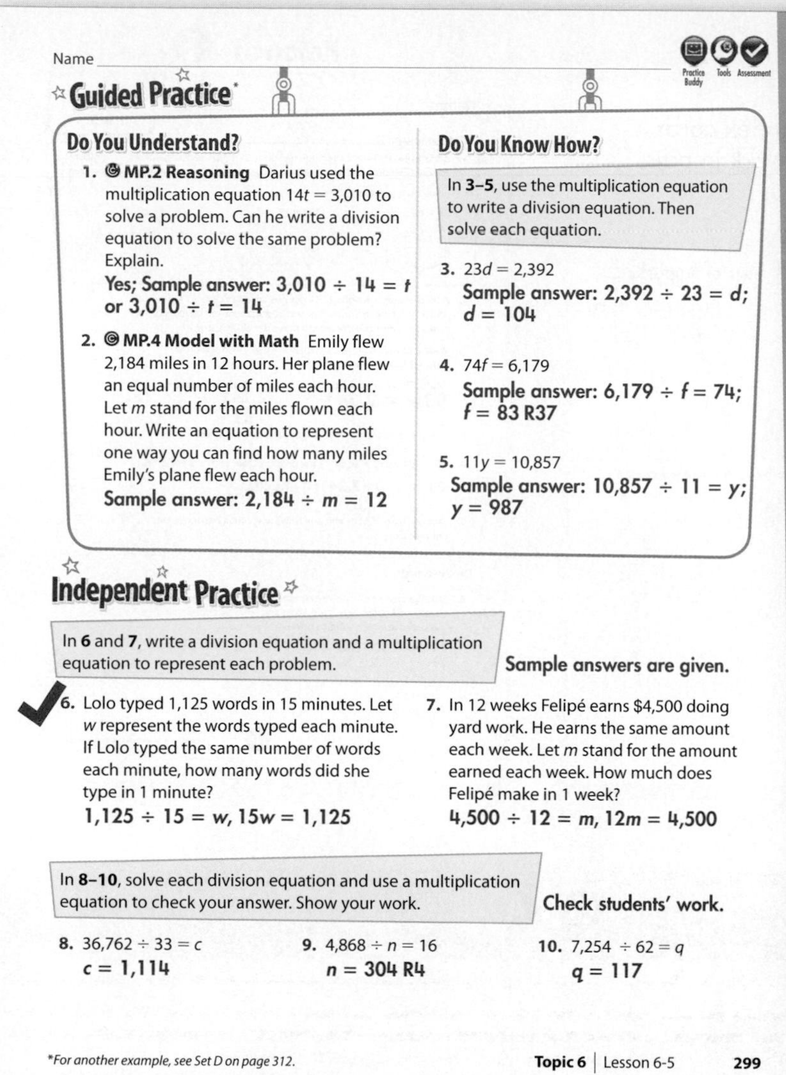

Name

### Guided Practice*

**Do You Understand?**

1. **MP.2 Reasoning** Darius used the multiplication equation $14t = 3{,}010$ to solve a problem. Can he write a division equation to solve the same problem? Explain.
**Yes; Sample answer: $3{,}010 \div 14 = t$ or $3{,}010 \div t = 14$**

2. **MP.4 Model with Math** Emily flew 2,184 miles in 12 hours. Her plane flew an equal number of miles each hour. Let *m* stand for the miles flown each hour. Write an equation to represent one way you can find how many miles Emily's plane flew each hour.
**Sample answer: $2{,}184 \div m = 12$**

**Do You Know How?**

In **3–5**, use the multiplication equation to write a division equation. Then solve each equation.

3. $23d = 2{,}392$
**Sample answer: $2{,}392 \div 23 = d$; $d = 104$**

4. $74f = 6{,}179$
**Sample answer: $6{,}179 \div f = 74$; $f = 83$ R37**

5. $11y = 10{,}857$
**Sample answer: $10{,}857 \div 11 = y$; $y = 987$**

### Independent Practice*

In **6** and **7**, write a division equation and a multiplication equation to represent each problem. **Sample answers are given.**

6. Lolo typed 1,125 words in 15 minutes. Let *w* represent the words typed each minute. If Lolo typed the same number of words each minute, how many words did she type in 1 minute?
**$1{,}125 \div 15 = w$, $15w = 1{,}125$**

7. In 12 weeks Felipé earns $4,500 doing yard work. He earns the same amount each week. Let *m* stand for the amount earned each week. How much does Felipé make in 1 week?
**$4{,}500 \div 12 = m$, $12m = 4{,}500$**

In **8–10**, solve each division equation and use a multiplication equation to check your answer. Show your work. **Check students' work.**

8. $36{,}762 \div 33 = c$
**$c = 1{,}114$**

9. $4{,}868 \div n = 16$
**$n = 304$ R4**

10. $7{,}254 \div 62 = q$
**$q = 117$**

*For another example, see Set D on page 312.



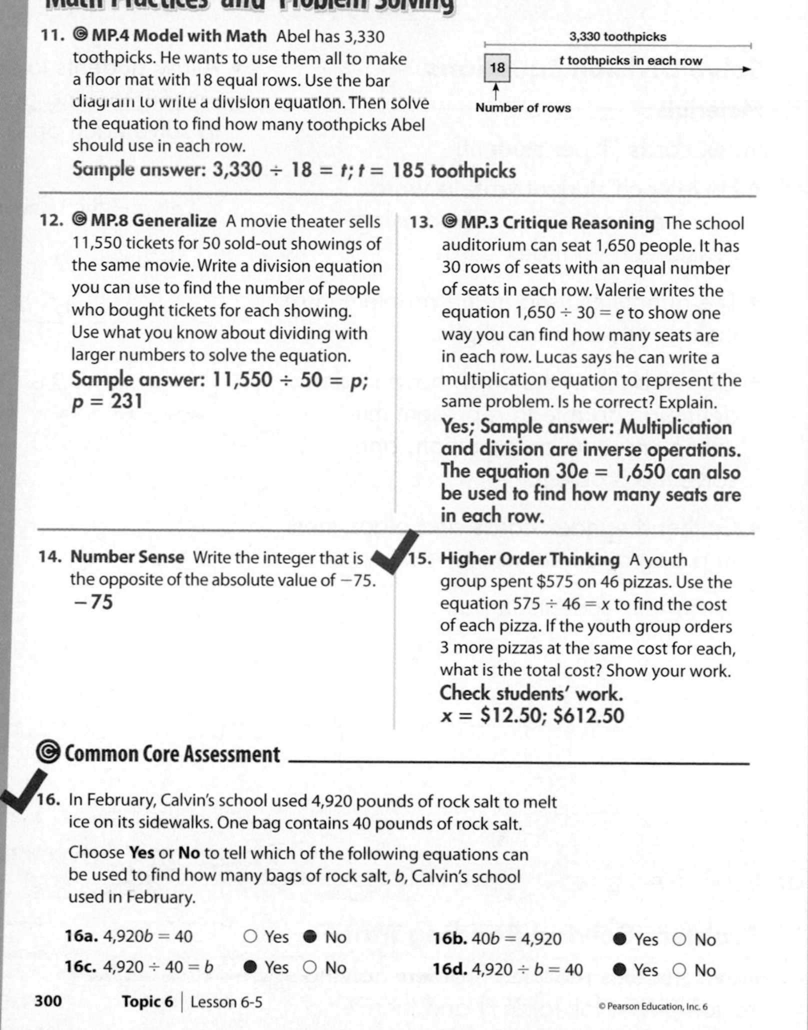

### Math Practices and Problem Solving*

11. **MP.4 Model with Math** Abel has 3,330 toothpicks. He wants to use them all to make a floor mat with 18 equal rows. Use the bar diagram to write a division equation. Then solve the equation to find how many toothpicks Abel should use in each row.
**Sample answer: $3{,}330 \div 18 = t$; $t = 185$ toothpicks**



12. **MP.8 Generalize** A movie theater sells 11,550 tickets for 50 sold-out showings of the same movie. Write a division equation you can use to find the number of people who bought tickets for each showing. Use what you know about dividing with larger numbers to solve the equation.
**Sample answer: $11{,}550 \div 50 = p$; $p = 231$**

13. **MP.3 Critique Reasoning** The school auditorium can seat 1,650 people. It has 30 rows of seats with an equal number of seats in each row. Valerie writes the equation $1{,}650 \div 30 = e$ to show one way you can find how many seats are in each row. Lucas says he can write a multiplication equation to represent the same problem. Is he correct? Explain.
**Yes; Sample answer: Multiplication and division are inverse operations. The equation $30e = 1{,}650$ can also be used to find how many seats are in each row.**

14. **Number Sense** Write the integer that is the opposite of the absolute value of −75.
**−75**

15. **Higher Order Thinking** A youth group spent $575 on 46 pizzas. Use the equation $575 \div 46 = x$ to find the cost of each pizza. If the youth group orders 3 more pizzas at the same cost for each, what is the total cost? Show your work.
**Check students' work.**
**$x = \$12.50$; $612.50**

#### Common Core Assessment

16. In February, Calvin's school used 4,920 pounds of rock salt to melt ice on its sidewalks. One bag contains 40 pounds of rock salt.

Choose **Yes** or **No** to tell which of the following equations can be used to find how many bags of rock salt, *b*, Calvin's school used in February.

16a. $4{,}920b = 40$ ○ Yes ● No
16b. $40b = 4{,}920$ ● Yes ○ No
16c. $4{,}920 \div 40 = b$ ● Yes ○ No
16d. $4{,}920 \div b = 40$ ● Yes ○ No





**Item 1 MP.2 Reason Quantitatively** *What property of equality can Darius use to write this equation as a division equation?* [The Division Property of Equality] *What can both sides of the equation be divided by to write an equivalent division equation?* [You can divide by 14 or by *t*.]

**Error Intervention: Item 2**

**If** students are unsure of which operation to use to solve the problem, **then** encourage them to represent the situation with a bar diagram model to show how the quantities are related. *What is given in the problem?* [The plane flew 2,184 miles in 12 hours. The plane flew an equal number of miles each hour.]

**Reteaching** Assign Reteaching Set D on p. 312.

**Items 6 and 7** Some students will recognize the situations as either multiplication or division situations. Encourage these students to recognize that they can use the relationship between multiplication and division to write the corresponding equation.

**Item 13 MP.3 Critique Reasoning** Students may write either multiplication or division equations to model these problems. Encourage them to explain why either equation represents the situation.

**Item 14** *What is the absolute value of −75?* [75] *What is the opposite of 75?* [−75]

**Multi-Step Problems** *Page 300 Items 11, 12, and 15; Page 302 Items 7 and 8*

# ASSESS AND DIFFERENTIATE

Use the **QUICK CHECK** on the previous page to prescribe differentiated instruction.

**I Intervention** 0–3 points on the Quick Check

**O On-Level** 4 points on the Quick Check

**A Advanced** 5 points on the Quick Check

## Intervention Activity 

### Solve Division Equations

**Materials**

Index cards (1 per student)

- Have each student write a word problem that can be solved using division on an index card.
- The quantities used in the problem must include two or more digits.
- On the back of the card, have students define a variable to represent the unknown, write an equation, and solve the problem.
- Gather the index cards and place them in a bag or container.
- Organize students in pairs.
- Allow students to choose index cards without looking and then work in pairs to solve each problem.

Let $a$ = the total number of bags of apples.

$$\frac{1,512}{a} = 12$$

$$a = \frac{1,512}{12}$$

$$a = 126$$

## Reteach I

Name ______________________

Reteach to Build Understanding
6-5

**Vocabulary**

1. A **variable** is a letter or symbol, such as $n$, that represents an unknown number. To solve an equation, find the value of the variable that makes the equation true.

   Solve each equation. The first one is done for you.

   $7n = 63$ $n = 9$ | $320 \div 10 = y$ $y = 32$ | $\frac{16}{2} = z$ $z = 8$

   $\frac{63}{n} = 7$ $n = 9$ | $10y = 320$ $y = 32$ | $\frac{16}{z} = 2$ $z = 8$

2. A load of mulch weighs 2,241 pounds. Jack can carry 83 pounds of mulch at a time in a wheelbarrow. How many wheelbarrows full of mulch, $w$, will it take for Jack to move the entire load?

   Write a multiplication equation and a division equation to represent the problem.

   **Multiplication equation** $83w = 2,241$ **Division equation** $\frac{2,241}{83} = w$

3. Divide to find the number of wheelbarrows of mulch.

   $$\begin{array}{r} 27 \\ 83\overline{)2,241} \\ -166 \\ \hline 581 \\ -581 \\ \hline 0 \end{array}$$

4. Use multiplication to check the division. Does your answer check?

   **$83 \times 27 = 2,241$; It checks.**

5. Jack will take **27** wheelbarrows full of mulch to move the entire load.

**On the Back!**

6. Shanika drives 567 miles in 9 hours. Suppose she drives the same speed, $s$, throughout her trip. Write and solve an equation to find the speed at which Shanika drives.

   **Sample answer: $567 \div 9 = s$; $s = 63$**

R 6-5



## On-Level and Advanced Activity Centers  

### Problem-Solving Reading Mat

Have students read the Problem-Solving Reading Mat for Topic 6 and then complete Problem-Solving Reading Activity 6-5.

See the Problem-Solving Reading Activity Guide for other suggestions on how to use this mat.

PEARSON realize.
PearsonRealize.com

**TIMING**

The time allocated to Step 3 will depend on the teacher's instructional decisions and differentiation routines.

15–30 min

Help | Practice Buddy | Tools | Games

## Technology Center    

Tools Games

### Math Tools and Math Games

A link to a specific math tools activity or math game to use with this lesson is provided at PearsonRealize.com.

## Leveled Assignment  Items 1, 3–6, 8–11  Items 2, 4–11  Items 2–4, 6–11

Name ____________

Help Practice Buddy Tools Games

**Homework & Practice 6-5**
**Solve Division Equations**

**Another Look!**

A book club purchased 27 copies of the same book. Each member gets 1 book. The total number of pages is 9,450. If all of the book club members complete the book, how many pages will each person read?

You can use a variable to represent an unknown quantity when writing equations to solve real-world problems.


Write an equation to represent the problem. Let $b$ = the number of pages in each book.

**Divide to solve for $b$.**

$9,450 \div 27 = b$

```
      350
27)9,450   Divide the hundreds.
  − 81     Multiply and subtract.
    135    Continue the process.
  − 135
      0
```

$b = 350$

**Multiply to check your work.**

$27b = 9,450$. Let $b = 350$.

So, $27 \times 350$ pages = 9,450 pages.

The math is correct.

Each person will read 350 pages.

In **1** and **2**, write a division equation and a multiplication equation to represent each problem. **Sample answers are given.**

**1.** Gillian read 3,135 words in 19 minutes. Let $w$ represent the words read each minute. If Gillian read the same number of words each minute, how many words did she read in one minute?
**$3,135 \div 19 = w$, $3,135 = 19 \times w$**

**2.** Colin is a math tutor. He charges the same amount, $s$, for every tutoring session. After 21 sessions he has earned \$1,575. How much does Colin charge for one tutoring session?
**$1,575 \div 21 = s$, $s \times 21 = 1,575$**

In **3–5**, solve each division equation and use a multiplication equation to check your answer. Show your work. **Check students' work.**

**3.** $9,522 \div 9 = k$
**$k = 1,058$**

**4.** $7,848 \div w = 36$
**$w = 218$**

**5.** $56,259 \div 57 = i$
**$i = 987$**



**6.** **MP.2 Reasoning** On a calm day, the 32 windmills on the Bosley family wind farm each complete 120 revolutions every minute. Which operation would you use to find the total number of revolutions the 32 windmills complete in one minute? Explain.
**Sample answer: Multiplication. The problem involves joining equal groups into one large group to find the total number of revolutions all 32 windmills make each minute. When working with larger numbers, multiplication is better than addition.**

**7.** **Higher Order Thinking** The Columbus junior soccer league is selling raffle tickets to raise money for new uniforms and equipment. So far league members have earned \$1,218 and sold 84 tickets. Use the equation $1,218 \div 84 = r$ to find the cost of each raffle ticket. Then use the answer to find the total earnings after 90 raffle tickets have been sold. Show your work.
**Check students' work.**
**$r = \$14.50$; \$1,305**

**8.** **MP.4 Model with Math** The 46 golf balls in Stavin's golf bag have 15,180 dimples on them. Each golf ball has the same number of dimples. Complete the bar diagram. Then write and solve an equation to find the number of dimples on each ball in Stavin's bag.
**$15,180 \div 46 = d$; $d = 330$ dimples**

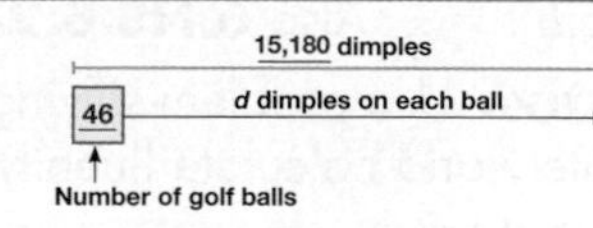


**9.** **Vocabulary** The mathematical phrase $\$13.25 \times w$ is an example of what type of expression?
**algebraic expression**

**10.** **Math and Science** There are 45 houses in Grey's Lake subdivision. Each house uses 400 gallons of water each day. Write a division equation to represent the total number of gallons of water used daily in Grey's Lake subdivision.
**Sample answer: $w \div 45 = 400$**

### Common Core Assessment

**11.** In May, a landscaping crew used 8,500 pounds of potting soil. One bag contains 50 pounds of potting soil.

Choose **Yes** or **No** to tell which of the following equations can be used to find how many bags of potting soil the landscaping crew used in May.

**11a.** $8,500 \div 50 = p$ ● Yes ○ No
**11b.** $50p = 8,500$ ● Yes ○ No
**11c.** $8,500p = 50$ ○ Yes ● No
**11d.** $50 \div p = 8,500$ ○ Yes ● No

# PRECISION

## DIGITAL RESOURCES PearsonRealize.com

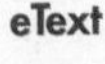
eText — Student and Teacher eTexts

PD — Listen and Look For Lesson Video

Think — Today's Challenge

Solve — Solve and Share

Learn — Visual Learning Animation Plus

Glossary — Animated Glossary

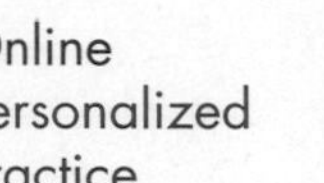
Practice Buddy — Online Personalized Practice

Tools — Math Tools

Assessment — Quick Check

Help — Another Look Homework Video

Games — Math Games

MP — Math Practices Animations

## LESSON OVERVIEW — FCR FOCUS • COHERENCE • RIGOR

### FOCUS

**Mathematical Practices MP.6** Attend to precision. Also **MP.1, MP.2, MP.3**

**Domain 6.EE** Expressions and Equations

**Cluster 6.EE.A** Apply and extend previous understandings of arithmetic to algebraic expressions.

**Content Standard 6.EE.A.2c** Evaluate expressions at specific values of their variables. Include expressions that arise from formulas used in real-world problems. Perform arithmetic operations, including those involving whole-number exponents, in the conventional order when there are no parentheses to specify a particular order (Order of Operations). *For example, use the formulas* $V = s^3$ *and* $A = 6s^2$ *to find the volume and surface area of a cube with sides of length* $s = \frac{1}{2}$. Also **6.NS.B.2**.

**Objective** Use problem-solving strategies accurately and calculate fluently.

**Essential Understanding** Good math thinkers are careful about what they write and say, so their ideas about math are clear.

### COHERENCE

Students have previously engaged MP.6, attending to precision, as they practiced and gained fluency with the standard algorithms for adding, subtracting, multiplying, and dividing whole numbers. This lesson provides an opportunity to focus on the thinking habits that mathematically proficient students use when they solve problems with precision. Students will rely on and further develop these thinking habits as they continue to gain fluency and attend to precision throughout Grade 6 and beyond.

### RIGOR

This lesson emphasizes **application**. All of the problems in this lesson elicit the use of multiple mathematical practices, which should be explicitly discussed. However, classroom conversation should focus on attending to precision, MP.6, as students apply what they learned about dividing whole numbers in this topic to solve problems.

PD Watch the Listen and Look For Lesson Video.

## MATH ANYTIME

### Daily Common Core Review

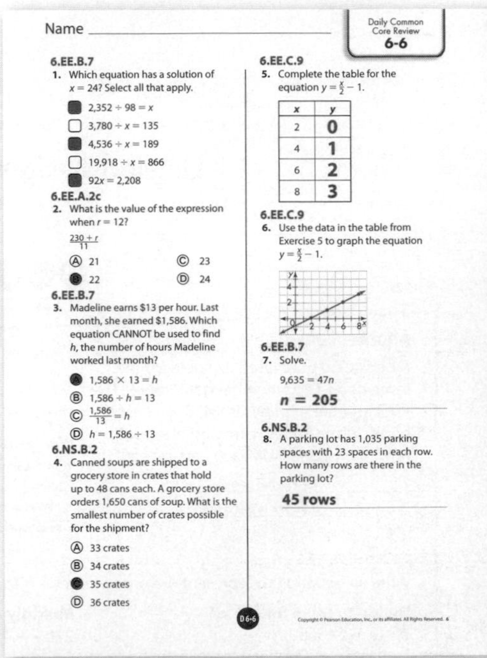
Name ____________

Daily Common Core Review 6-6

6.EE.B.7
1. Which equation has a solution of $x = 24$? Select all that apply.
   - ■ $2,352 \div 98 = x$
   - □ $3,780 \div x = 135$
   - ■ $4,536 \div x = 189$
   - □ $19,918 \div x = 866$
   - ■ $92x = 2,208$

6.EE.A.2c
2. What is the value of the expression when $r = 12$?
   $\frac{230 + r}{11}$
   Ⓐ 21 Ⓑ 22 Ⓒ 23 Ⓓ 24

6.EE.B.7
3. Madeline earns $13 per hour. Last month, she earned $1,586. Which equation CANNOT be used to find $h$, the number of hours Madeline worked last month?
   Ⓐ $1,586 \times 13 = h$
   Ⓑ $1,586 \div h = 13$
   Ⓒ $\frac{1,586}{13} = h$
   Ⓓ $h = 1,586 \div 13$

6.NS.B.2
4. Canned soups are shipped to a grocery store in crates that hold up to 48 cans each. A grocery store orders 1,650 cans of soup. What is the smallest number of crates possible for the shipment?
   Ⓐ 33 crates
   Ⓑ 34 crates
   Ⓒ 35 crates
   Ⓓ 36 crates

6.EE.C.9
5. Complete the table for the equation $y = \frac{x}{2} - 1$.

| x | y |
|---|---|
| 2 | 0 |
| 4 | 1 |
| 6 | 2 |
| 8 | 3 |

6.EE.C.9
6. Use the data in the table from Exercise 5 to graph the equation $y = \frac{x}{2} - 1$.

6.EE.B.7
7. Solve.
   $9,635 = 47n$
   $n = 205$

6.NS.B.2
8. A parking lot has 1,035 parking spaces with 23 spaces in each row. How many rows are there in the parking lot?
   45 rows

D 6-6

### Today's Challenge

Think Use the Topic 6 problems any time during this topic.

## ENGLISH LANGUAGE LEARNERS

**Speaking** Describe information.

*Use with the Solve & Share on Student's Edition p. 303.*

Read the Solve & Share. Have students describe the information in the Solve & Share to partners. Read and project the Thinking Habits on the board. Draw a diagram to support information in the Solve & Share. Draw a length of fabric labeled as 76 inches long, add another 76 inches, and then add 12 inches. Underneath show a length of 9 inches with a cost of $15.

**Beginning** Instruct students to describe the diagram to partners using gestures, single words, or simple sentences. Point to Thinking Habits, Bullet 1. *What numbers will be used?* Have students circle numbers in the Solve & Share. *What units will be used?* Have students underline *inches*. *What symbols will be used?* Have students describe the symbols by writing them in the air. Continue the discussion with the remaining Thinking Habits bullets.

**Intermediate** Ask students to describe the diagram to partners using complete sentences. Point to Thinking Habits, Bullet 1. *What numbers, units, and symbols will be used to solve the problem?* Have students locate information in the Solve & Share. Continue the discussion with the remaining Thinking Habits bullets.

**Advanced** Have students describe the diagram to partners and use the Thinking Habits bullets to solve the problem. Ask students to describe the process they used to solve the problem.

**Summarize** Why is it important to use numbers, units, and symbols correctly when solving problems?

# DEVELOP: PROBLEM-BASED LEARNING

PearsonRealize.com

**COHERENCE: Engage learners by connecting prior knowledge to new ideas.**
Students extend their understanding of using appropriate units and converting between units of length as they focus on precision in their work to solve a multi-step problem.

10–15 min

Solve

## BEFORE

**1. Pose the Solve-and-Share Problem**
**MP.6 Be Precise** Listen and look for students who make sure they use the correct units, divide accurately, and check their answer.

**2. Build Understanding**
*What does it mean that the least amount of fabric you can buy is a quarter of a yard?* [The fabric is sold is quarter-yard units.] *Why might the directions double the length and add 1 foot to the length?* [Sample answer: The curtain may have 2 sections or it may be folded to make a lining. The extra foot is for hems.]

## DURING

**3. Ask Guiding Questions As Needed**
*How do you combine quantities that are measured in different units?* [Change all quantities to the same unit.] *How many inches of material are needed?* [$76 \times 2 + 12 = 164$ inches] *How many inches of fabric cost $15?* [$\frac{1}{4} \times 36 = 9$ inches] *How will a remainder in the division problem affect the answer?* [The number of quarter-yards will be rounded to the next whole number.]

## AFTER

**4. Share and Discuss Solutions**
Solve Start with students' solutions. If needed, project Stuart's work to discuss how to solve the problem efficiently using inches.

**5. Transition to the Visual Learning Bridge**
*Solving multi-step problems requires organization, accurate calculations, and the use of precision.*

**6. Extension for Early Finishers**
*How much would it cost to make the same curtain with fabric that is sold in half-yards that cost $30?* [$300]

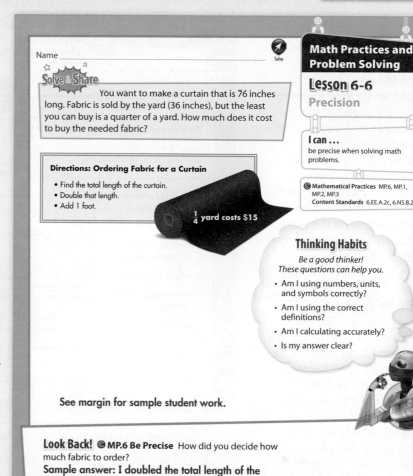

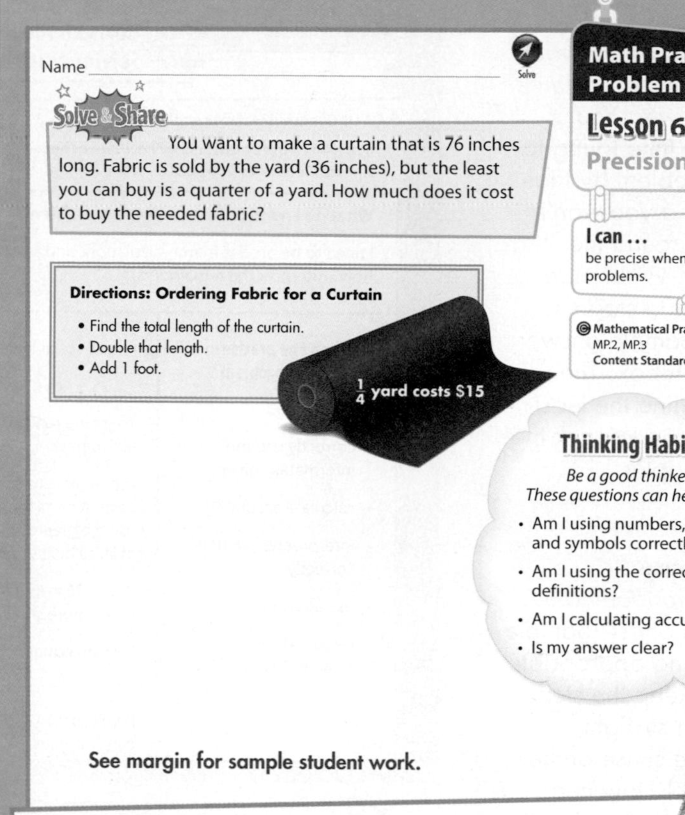

Name

Solve & Share

You want to make a curtain that is 76 inches long. Fabric is sold by the yard (36 inches), but the least you can buy is a quarter of a yard. How much does it cost to buy the needed fabric?

**Math Practices and Problem Solving**

**Lesson 6-6**
**Precision**

**I can ...**
be precise when solving math problems.

Mathematical Practices MP.6, MP.1, MP.2, MP.3
Content Standards 6.EE.A.2c, 6.NS.B.2

**Directions: Ordering Fabric for a Curtain**
- Find the total length of the curtain.
- Double that length.
- Add 1 foot.

$\frac{1}{4}$ yard costs $15

**Thinking Habits**
*Be a good thinker! These questions can help you.*
- Am I using numbers, units, and symbols correctly?
- Am I using the correct definitions?
- Am I calculating accurately?
- Is my answer clear?

**See margin for sample student work.**

**Look Back!** **MP.6 Be Precise** How did you decide how much fabric to order?
**Sample answer: I doubled the total length of the curtain, $76 \times 2 = 152$ inches. Then I added 1 foot or 12 inches, $152 + 12 = 164$ inches. Then I divided by 36 inches to find yards of fabric, $\frac{164}{36} = 4$ R20, so I should order at least $4\frac{3}{4}$ yards.**

Digital Resources at PearsonRealize.com    Topic 6 | Lesson 6-6    303

## Analyze Student Work

**Stuart's Work**

$76 \times 2 + 12 = 164$ inches required
$\frac{1}{4}$ yard $= \frac{1}{4} \times 36 = 9$ inches; 9 inches cost $15.
$\frac{164}{9} = 18$ R2
More than $18\ \frac{1}{4}$-yards are needed
so you need to buy $19\ \frac{1}{4}$-yards.
$19 \times \$15 = \$285$
The curtain costs $285.

Stuart efficiently solves the problem using inches as the unit of measurement.

**Matt's Work**

$\frac{76}{12} = 6\frac{1}{3}$
$(6\frac{1}{3}) \times 2 + 1 = 13\frac{2}{3}$ ft needed
$\frac{1}{4}$ yd $= 9$ inches  $\frac{9}{12} = \frac{3}{4}$ ft
$\frac{3}{4}$ ft cost $15.
$13\frac{2}{3} \div \frac{3}{4} = \frac{41}{3} \times \frac{4}{3} = \frac{164}{9} = 18$ R2
More than $18\ \frac{3}{4}$-ft pieces are needed. Buy $19\ \frac{1}{4}$-yd
$\$15 \times 19 = \$285$

Matt converts all the lengths to feet before solving the problem. His work involves division with fractions, which students will formally learn in Topic 12.

# STEP 2 DEVELOP: VISUAL LEARNING

The *Visual Learning Bridge* connects students' thinking in Solve & Share to important math ideas in the lesson. Use the *Visual Learning Bridge* to make these ideas explicit. Also available as a *Visual Learning Animation Plus* at PearsonRealize.com

ELL Visual Learning

PEARSON realize. PearsonRealize.com

Learn

Glossary

*Why might you want to devise a plan before you try to solve this problem?* [Sample answer: You could waste time trying to solve the problem by trial-and-error and you won't be sure you found the lowest cost.] *What plan do you have to start the problem?* [Sample answer: Fill 1 of each box. Then try to determine the least expensive way to pack the rest of the apples.]

**MP.6 Be Precise**
*Why is it important to use appropriate units?* [Sample answer: Using appropriate units helps keep the steps of a solution straight, and to make sense of the calculations.] *How can you make your answer clear?* [Use a complete sentence that answers the question asked in the problem.]

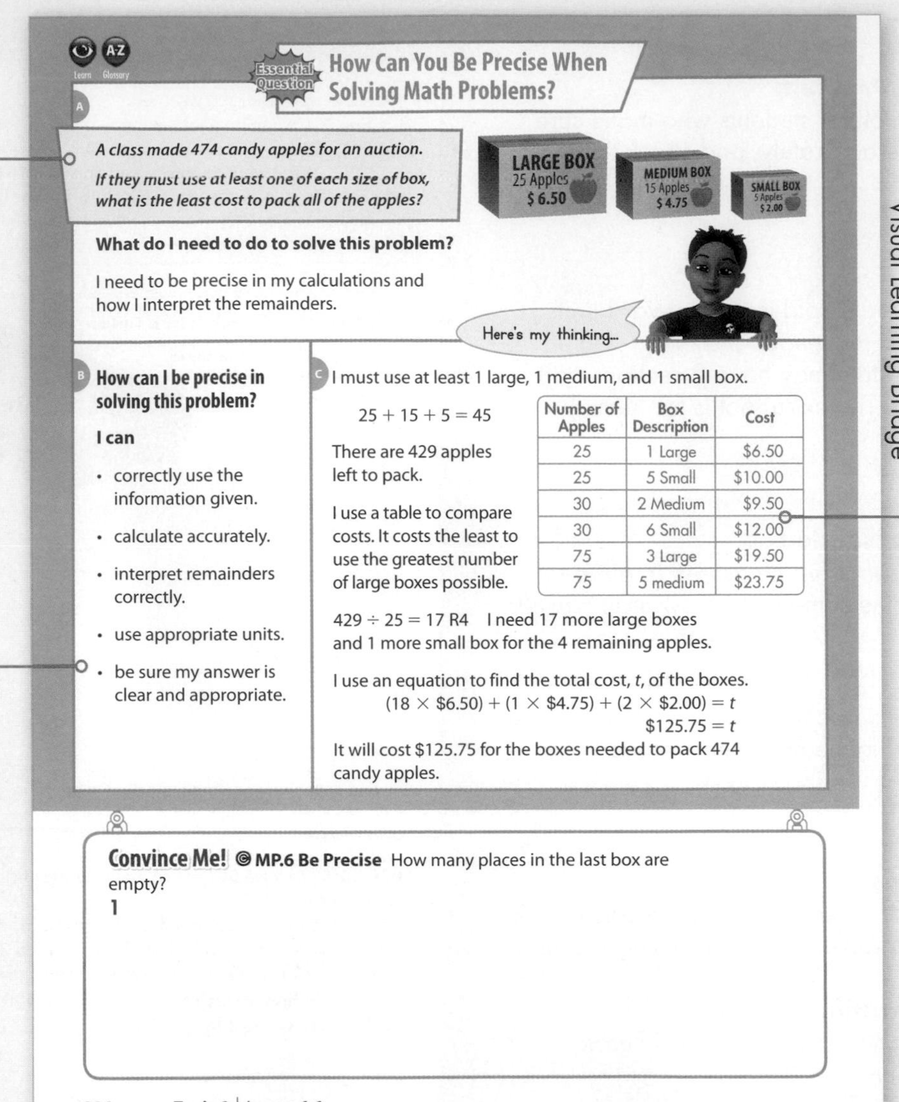

Essential Question **How Can You Be Precise When Solving Math Problems?**

A

*A class made 474 candy apples for an auction.*
*If they must use at least one of each size of box, what is the least cost to pack all of the apples?*



**What do I need to do to solve this problem?**

I need to be precise in my calculations and how I interpret the remainders.

B **How can I be precise in solving this problem?**

**I can**

- correctly use the information given.
- calculate accurately.
- interpret remainders correctly.
- use appropriate units.
- be sure my answer is clear and appropriate.

C I must use at least 1 large, 1 medium, and 1 small box.

$25 + 15 + 5 = 45$

There are 429 apples left to pack.

I use a table to compare costs. It costs the least to use the greatest number of large boxes possible.

| Number of Apples | Box Description | Cost |
|---|---|---|
| 25 | 1 Large | $6.50 |
| 25 | 5 Small | $10.00 |
| 30 | 2 Medium | $9.50 |
| 30 | 6 Small | $12.00 |
| 75 | 3 Large | $19.50 |
| 75 | 5 medium | $23.75 |

$429 \div 25 = 17$ R4 I need 17 more large boxes and 1 more small box for the 4 remaining apples.

I use an equation to find the total cost, $t$, of the boxes.

$(18 \times \$6.50) + (1 \times \$4.75) + (2 \times \$2.00) = t$

$\$125.75 = t$

It will cost $125.75 for the boxes needed to pack 474 candy apples.

**Convince Me!** **MP.6 Be Precise** How many places in the last box are empty?
1

304 Topic 6 | Lesson 6-6 © Pearson Education, Inc. 6

Visual Learning Bridge

*The information given in the table compares the number of large boxes with small, medium with small, and large with medium boxes that hold the same number of apples. What does this information tell you?* [The large boxes are the least expensive option, and the small boxes are the most expensive.] Make sure students are able to come to this conclusion. Have them discuss the rows in pairs. *What should you do with any apples that are the "remainders"?* [Put them in the smallest box that holds them.] *Does the solution meet the conditions of the problem? Explain.* [Yes, all the apples are boxed, and at least one of each box is used. The least expensive boxes were used as often as possible.]

**Convince Me!** **MP.6 Be Precise** Students attend to precision as they analyze and interpret their division work for the original apple-packing problem. *What types of boxes were used to pack the apples?* [17 large boxes and 1 small box] *Which boxes were completely full? Which boxes weren't?* [The 17 large boxes were completely full, and the 1 small box wasn't.] *How many apples fit in a small box?* [5 apples] *How many apples were packed in the small box?* [4 apples] Students should reason that there is one empty place in the small box.

**Coherence** The apple-packing problem requires students to organize a great deal of information and make a plan that requires several steps to find the solution. They apply what they learned about multi-digit division in this topic, and engage MP.6 by using the information given and checking their results as they carry out each step of their plan.

Revisit the Essential Question. Attending to precision involves careful calculations with appropriate units, accurate problem-solving strategies, good communication, and checking one's work.

## QUICK CHECK

Check mark indicates items for prescribing differentiation on the next page.
Items 3 and 4 are worth 1 point. Items 5–7 are worth up to 3 points.

20–30 min

Practice Buddy

Tools

Assessment

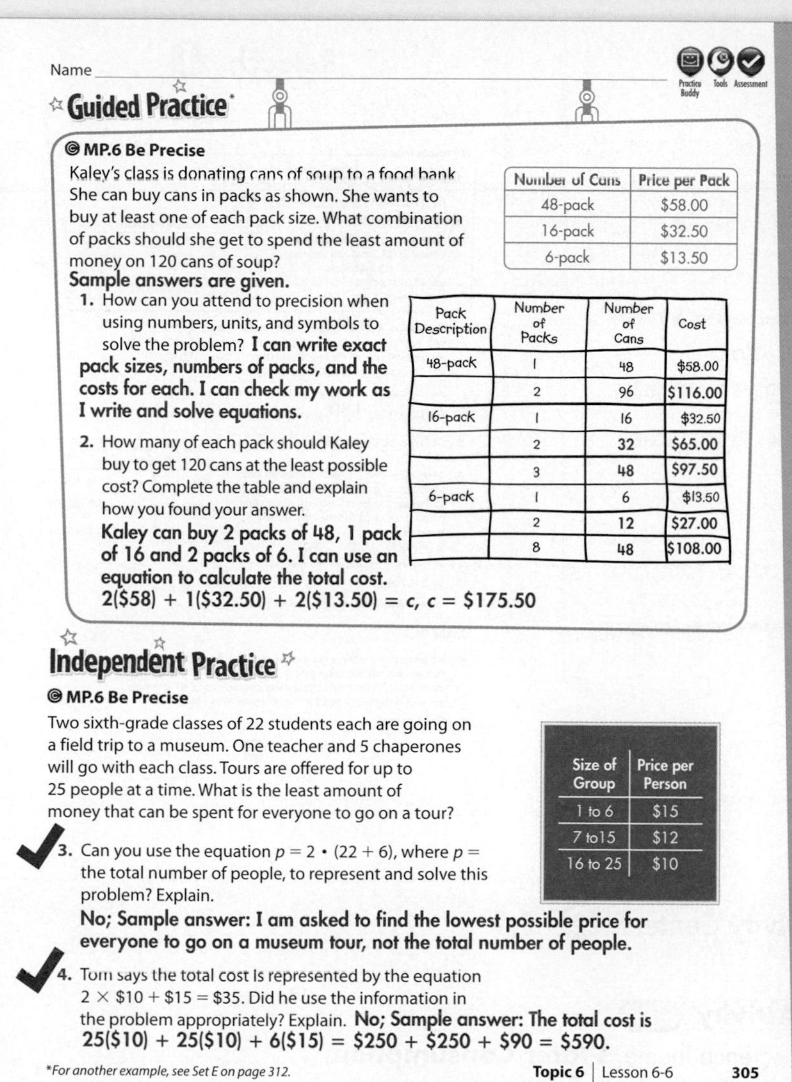

Name

### Guided Practice*

**MP.6 Be Precise**

Kaley's class is donating cans of soup to a food bank. She can buy cans in packs as shown. She wants to buy at least one of each pack size. What combination of packs should she get to spend the least amount of money on 120 cans of soup?

| Number of Cans | Price per Pack |
|---|---|
| 48-pack | $58.00 |
| 16-pack | $32.50 |
| 6-pack | $13.50 |

**Sample answers are given.**

1. How can you attend to precision when using numbers, units, and symbols to solve the problem? **I can write exact pack sizes, numbers of packs, and the costs for each. I can check my work as I write and solve equations.**

2. How many of each pack should Kaley buy to get 120 cans at the least possible cost? Complete the table and explain how you found your answer. **Kaley can buy 2 packs of 48, 1 pack of 16 and 2 packs of 6. I can use an equation to calculate the total cost. 2($58) + 1($32.50) + 2($13.50) = c, c = $175.50**

| Pack Description | Number of Packs | Number of Cans | Cost |
|---|---|---|---|
| 48-pack | 1 | 48 | $58.00 |
| | 2 | 96 | $116.00 |
| 16-pack | 1 | 16 | $32.50 |
| | 2 | 32 | $65.00 |
| | 3 | 48 | $97.50 |
| 6-pack | 1 | 6 | $13.50 |
| | 2 | 12 | $27.00 |
| | 8 | 48 | $108.00 |

### Independent Practice

**MP.6 Be Precise**

Two sixth-grade classes of 22 students each are going on a field trip to a museum. One teacher and 5 chaperones will go with each class. Tours are offered for up to 25 people at a time. What is the least amount of money that can be spent for everyone to go on a tour?

| Size of Group | Price per Person |
|---|---|
| 1 to 6 | $15 |
| 7 to 15 | $12 |
| 16 to 25 | $10 |

3. Can you use the equation $p = 2 \cdot (22 + 6)$, where $p$ = the total number of people, to represent and solve this problem? Explain. **No; Sample answer: I am asked to find the lowest possible price for everyone to go on a museum tour, not the total number of people.**

4. Tom says the total cost is represented by the equation $2 \times \$10 + \$15 = \$35$. Did he use the information in the problem appropriately? Explain. **No; Sample answer: The total cost is 25($10) + 25($10) + 6($15) = $250 + $250 + $90 = $590.**

*For another example, see Set E on page 312.



### Math Practices and Problem Solving

**Common Core Performance Assessment**

**Tiling a Hallway**

Mrs. Wu wants to tile her hallway, which is twice the size of the pattern of tiles shown. She needs to buy boxes of tiles. She cannot buy a partial box.

To find the least she could spend to buy enough tiles for the hallway, Mrs. Wu made a table. Then she wrote the equation $t = (2 \times \$5) + (3 \times \$5.25) + (3 \times \$4)$. She determined she will spend $37.75 on the tiles. Do you agree with her calculations?

9 × 18

9 × 9

18 × 18

| Tile size (inches) | Number of tiles Needed | Number in Box | Price per Box |
|---|---|---|---|
| 9 × 9 | 10 | 6 | $5.00 |
| 9 × 18 | 8 | 3 | $5.25 |
| 18 × 18 | 6 | 2 | $4.00 |

When you critique reasoning, you ask questions to help you understand someone's thinking.

5. **MP.1 Make Sense and Persevere** How did Mrs. Wu figure out the number of tiles of each size she needed? Explain.

**Sample answer: She counted the number of tiles of each size in the pattern and then doubled the number. The pattern shows five 9 × 9 tiles, four 9 × 18 tiles, and three 18 × 18 tiles. Doubling the number of each size gave her ten 9 × 9 tiles, eight 9 × 18 tiles, and six 18 × 18 tiles.**

6. **MP.3 Critique Reasoning** How did Mrs. Wu decide the number of boxes of each size tile she needed? Was her reasoning logical? Explain.

**Sample answer: Yes, her reasoning is logical. She compared the number of tiles needed to the number in a box. For the 9 × 9 tiles, she needs 10 tiles, so 2 boxes of 6, or 12 tiles. For the 9 × 18 tiles, she needs 8 tiles, so 3 boxes of 3, or 9 tiles. For the 18 × 18 tiles, she needs 6 tiles, so 3 boxes of 2, or 6.**

7. **MP.6 Be Precise** Is the equation that Mrs. Wu wrote accurate? Explain.

**Sample answer: Yes, the equation is accurate. The total price was found by multiplying the number of boxes times the price of each box.**





**MP.6 Be Precise** Listen and look for these behaviors as evidence that students are exhibiting proficiency with MP.6.

- Calculates efficiently, accurately, and fluently
- Uses numbers, symbols, and units appropriately
- Accurately uses problem-solving strategies

**Items 1 and 2 MP.6 Be Precise** Students attend to precision to calculate the missing information and complete the table. Make sure they pay close attention to the units and symbols needed.

**Items 3 and 4 MP.6 Be Precise** If students have difficulty making sense of the problem, suggest that they reread the problem and underline the words: two sixth-grade classes, 22 students each, and one teacher and 5 chaperones [will go with] each class. First, ask students to find the total number of people going on the field trip. Then have them divide the total number of people into groups of the largest size in each category, and calculate the total cost.

1 RtI **Reteaching** Assign Reteaching Set E on p. 312.

**Item 5 MP.1 Make Sense and Persevere** Have students count the number of tiles of each size in the pattern shown. *Why are the numbers in the second column different from the numbers you counted in the diagram?* [The problem says that Mrs. Wu's hallway is twice the size of the pattern of tiles shown. You need to double the numbers.]

**Item 6 MP.3 Critique Reasoning** As students evaluate Mrs. Wu's reasoning, they must understand that there could be leftover tiles in the boxes.

**Item 7 MP.6 Be Precise** Have students describe the relationships that determine the total price. Encourage them to check the solution in different ways to determine its accuracy.

# ASSESS AND DIFFERENTIATE

Use the **QUICK CHECK** on the previous page to prescribe differentiated instruction.

**I Intervention** 0–3 points on the Quick Check

**O On-Level** 4 points on the Quick Check

**A Advanced** 5 points on the Quick Check

## Intervention Activity I

### Math Practices and Problem Solving: Precision

- Write the following problem on the board: Elizabeth served 125 12-ounce glasses of iced green tea at a reception. About how many gallons of tea did she serve?
- Have students work together in pairs to complete each of the following steps:
  1 Determine what you need to find.
  2 Discuss a strategy for converting ounces to gallons.
  3 Solve the problem and write a clear, complete answer.
  4 Check your answer for reasonableness.

$125 \times 12$: 250, 1250, 1500

Number of ounces: 125 glasses × 12 ounces each = 1,500 ounces

Number of ounces in each gallon:

$8\,\frac{\text{ounces}}{\text{cup}} \times 4\,\frac{\text{cups}}{\text{quart}} \times 4\,\frac{\text{quarts}}{\text{gallon}} = 128$ ounces in each gallon

Number of gallons needed: $1{,}500 \div 128 \approx 12$ gallons

$1500 \div 128 = 11$ R92: $1500 - 128 = 220$; $220 - 128 = 92$

## Reteach I

Name ____________ Reteach to Build Understanding 6-6

**Vocabulary**

1. In mathematics, a **table** is often used to organize data. Column headings are used to describe the data.

Fill in the table to organize the data given in this situation.

A baker is packing gourmet granola into gift bags. Small and large bags hold 2 pounds and 10 pounds of granola. The prices of the bags of granola are $28 and $110.

| Gourmet Granola | | |
|---|---|---|
| Bag Size | Weight | Price |
| Small | 2 pounds | $28 |
| Large | 10 pounds | $110 |

2. Mrs. Ferguson needs 360 pounds of clay for an art project. The store sells 3 different-sized boxes of clay: small: 25 pounds for $24.88, medium: 50 pounds for $48.00, and large: 75 pounds for $70.00. Mrs. Ferguson already has 1 box of each size.

How many pounds of clay does Mrs. Ferguson need to buy?

She already has **150** pounds. She needs **210** pounds.

3. Fill in the table to compare costs of clay.

4. What is the least expensive combination of boxes of clay that Mrs. Ferguson can buy so that she has exactly enough clay for her project? Divide to find the number of large boxes needed.

210 ÷ **75** = **2** R **60**

| Pounds of Clay | Box Description | Cost |
|---|---|---|
| 150 | **2** large | $140.00 |
| 150 | 3 medium | **$144.00** |
| 150 | **6** small | $149.28 |

5. So, Mrs. Ferguson should buy **2** large box(es), **1** medium box(es), and **1** small box(es).

**On the Back!**

6. An average of 2,900 commuters use a train system each weekday. The transit authority estimates that in 5 years, the number of commuters will increase by $\frac{2}{5}$. Each train in the system can carry up to 300 passengers per day. How many trains will the system need in 5 years?

**14 trains**

## On-Level and Advanced Activity Centers O A

Name ____________ Math and Science Activity 6-6

### Reducing Water Usage

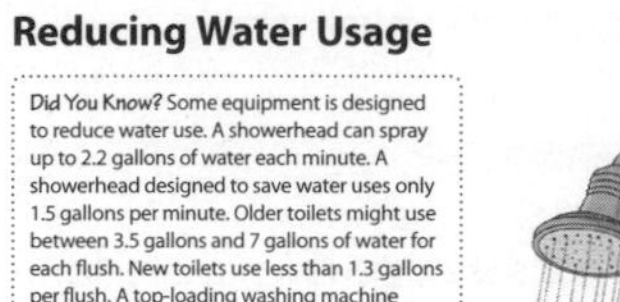

*Did You Know?* Some equipment is designed to reduce water use. A showerhead can spray up to 2.2 gallons of water each minute. A showerhead designed to save water uses only 1.5 gallons per minute. Older toilets might use between 3.5 gallons and 7 gallons of water for each flush. New toilets use less than 1.3 gallons per flush. A top-loading washing machine might use 40 gallons of water to wash a load of clothes. A front-loading washing machine can use half of that.

1. Keiko's younger sister shortens her showers from 10 minutes long to 7 minutes long in order to conserve water. If her showerhead sprays 2 gallons of water per minute, how much water does Keiko's sister conserve per shower?
**6 gallons**

2. Last week, Keiko used 560 gallons of water for baths. Each bath used 70 gallons of water. How many baths did Keiko take last week?
**8 baths**

3. **Represent** This week, Keiko switches from taking baths to taking showers. If Keiko takes 9-minute showers, how many showers could she take this week and still use less water than the water used taking baths last week? Write an expression to represent the situation. Then evaluate to answer the question.
**560 ÷ (2 × 9) = 31 R2; Keiko could take 31 showers in one week and still use less water than if she took baths.**

4. **Extension** Keiko's family has a washing machine that uses 20 gallons of water per load. How many loads of laundry can Keiko's family wash with the water saved in one week by Keiko switching from baths to showers? Assume Keiko plans to take the same number of showers as she took baths.
**20.8 loads, or 20 full loads of laundry**

Math and Science Activity 6-6



### Math and Science Activity STEM

This activity revisits the science theme, **Water Consumption**, introduced on page 271 in the Student's Edition.

### Sample Student Work

4. 8 baths use 560 gallons of water

8 showers at 18 gallons each use 144 gallons of water

$18 \times 8 = 144$

Keiko saves $560 - 144 = 416$ gallons each week.

Each load of laundry uses 20 gallons.

$416 \div 20 = 20$ R16 loads of laundry $\approx 21$ loads

$416 \div 20 = 20$ R16: $416 - 400 = 16$

## TIMING

The time allocated to Step 3 will depend on the teacher's instructional decisions and differentiation routines.

15–30 min

PEARSON realize. PearsonRealize.com

Help | Practice Buddy | Tools | Games

## Technology Center    

Tools Games

### Math Tools and Math Games

A link to a specific math tools activity or math game to use with this lesson is provided at PearsonRealize.com.

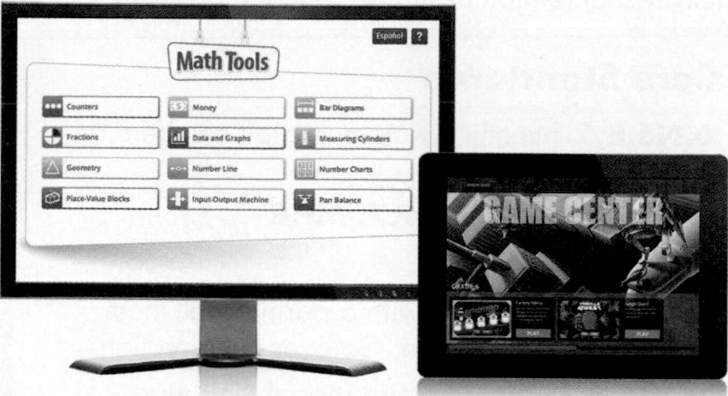


## Leveled Assignment  Items 1–5  Items 1–5  Items 1–5

Name ______

Help Practice Buddy Tools Games

**Homework & Practice 6-6**
**Precision**

### Another Look!

Ethan wants to make apple pies for a banquet. He needs enough pie to serve 75 people. Which size baskets of apples can he buy for $25 or less to make enough apple pies?

3 lb apples per pie - Serves 8

**How can you be precise when solving this problem?**

- I can use units, numbers, and symbols correctly to find the number of pies and pounds of apples needed to serve 75 people.
- I can check my work when using a table and writing equations to find a way Ethan can serve everyone for $25 or less.

| Number of pounds of basket | Number of Baskets | Total Cost |
|---|---|---|
| $2\frac{1}{2}$ | 12 | $30.00 |
| 5 | 6 | $24.60 |
| 12 | 3 | $33.00 |

**Attend to precision when solving the problem.**

I can divide to find the number of pies needed to serve 75 people:
$75 \div 8 = 9$ R3. The remainder means Ethan will need 10 pies, or 30 lb of apples.
Buying six 5-lb baskets of apples is the cheapest option.
I can multiply to find the total cost: $6 \times \$4.10 = \$24.60$. The total cost is $0.40 less than $25.

**MP.6 Be Precise**

A school has 218 sixth-grade students. The town predicts that in 10 years there will be $\frac{1}{4}$ more sixth-grade students. If a maximum of 25 students can fit in a classroom, how many classes of sixth graders would there be in 10 years?

When you are precise, you pay attention to what the remainder means in a problem and use it correctly.

1. How can you find the predicted number of students in 10 years? Explain.
   **Sample answer: Find $\frac{1}{4}$ of $218 = \frac{218}{4} = 54$ R2 or $54\frac{1}{2}$. I cannot use one half a person, so I add 1 to the quotient. In 10 years, there will be $218 + 55 = 273$ students.**
2. Steve says that there will be 10 sixth-grade classes in 10 years. Is he correct? Explain your answer. **Sample answer: Steve is incorrect. 11 classes will be needed: $273 \div 25 = 10$ R23. Steve forgot to account for the 23 leftover students who also need a classroom.**



### Common Core Performance Assessment

**Mixing Paint**

Mia painted several rooms in her house. She has paint left over that she wants to use for the play room. The room has 2 windows and 2 doors. If Mia mixes together all of her leftover paint, does she have enough paint for the walls of the room?

$\frac{3}{4}$ gal blue
3 qt green
2 pt white
1 pt yellow

Directions: Find the number of square feet to be painted using the formula $A = 2(\ell \cdot h) + 2(w \cdot h)$, where $A$ = area of the four walls, $\ell$ = length, $w$ = width, and $h$ = height.

Subtract 20 square feet for each door.

Subtract 15 square feet for each window.

Each quart covers $87\frac{1}{2}$ square feet.

8 ft, 15 ft, 18 ft

3. **MP.6 Be Precise** Mia knows that there are 2 pints in a quart and 4 quarts in a gallon. How can Mia precisely calculate the amount of paint she has?
   **Sample answer: Change each amount of paint to the same measurement unit. She can use quarts: $\frac{3}{4}$ gal = 3 quarts; 2 pt = 1 qt; 1 pt = $\frac{1}{2}$ qt; $3 + 3 + 1 + \frac{1}{2} = 7\frac{1}{2}$ quarts in all.**
4. **MP.3 Critique Reasoning** Mia wrote the equation $8(15 + 15 + 18 + 18) = 528$ to find the area she needs to paint without considering the doors and windows. Is it correct? Explain.
   **Yes; Sample answer: Mia noticed that the area of each wall will be the height of the room times the length of the wall. She reasoned that multiplying 8 feet by each length and finding the sum would be the same as finding the sum of the lengths first and then multiplying the sum by the height.**
5. **MP.2 Construct Arguments** Mia decided that she did not have enough paint. Do you agree? Explain.
   **No; Sample answer: After subtracting the area of the windows and doors, Mia needs to cover 458 square feet. She has $7\frac{1}{2}$ quarts. Her left over paint will cover $7.5 \times 87.5 = 656.25$ square feet.**

Be precise by converting measurements accurately.

# FLUENCY PRACTICE ACTIVITY

PEARSON realize.
PearsonRealize.com

Games

Practice Buddy

## FLUENCY PRACTICE ACTIVITY

Students practice fluently dividing multi-digit whole numbers during a partner activity that reinforces mathematical practices.

### Common Core Standards

**Content Standard 6.NS.B.2** Fluently divide multi-digit numbers using the standard algorithm.

**Mathematical Practices MP.3, MP.6, MP.7, MP.8**

**Getting Started** Ask students to work with a partner. Tell them to record their matches on their own page. Go over the directions.

Both students should solve each problem and record their work. Tell students to take turns identifying the match.

**As Students Do the Activity** Remind students that each clue can be matched with only one problem.

Encourage students to use estimation to help choose the matches, then solve each problem. Some students may find all of the answers first and then match the clues.

**Another Activity** Have students work together to write a new set of clues for the problems on the page. Ask them to record the new rules on a separate sheet of paper.

**Extra Challenge** *Create your own Find a Match activity. Use the same clues on your page. You may change the letters so they spell a new 8-letter word or phrase. Write a new problem for each clue. Then trade your activity with your partner and complete your partner's Find a Match activity.*

Games

**Online Game** The Game Center at PearsonRealize.com provides opportunities for fluency practice.

Practice Buddy

**Steps to Fluency Success** To ensure all students achieve fluency, see pages 271K–271N for additional resources including practice/assessment masters and online practice/assessment on fluency subskills. You can also use the ExamView® CD-ROM to generate worksheets with multiple-choice or free-response items on fluency subskills.

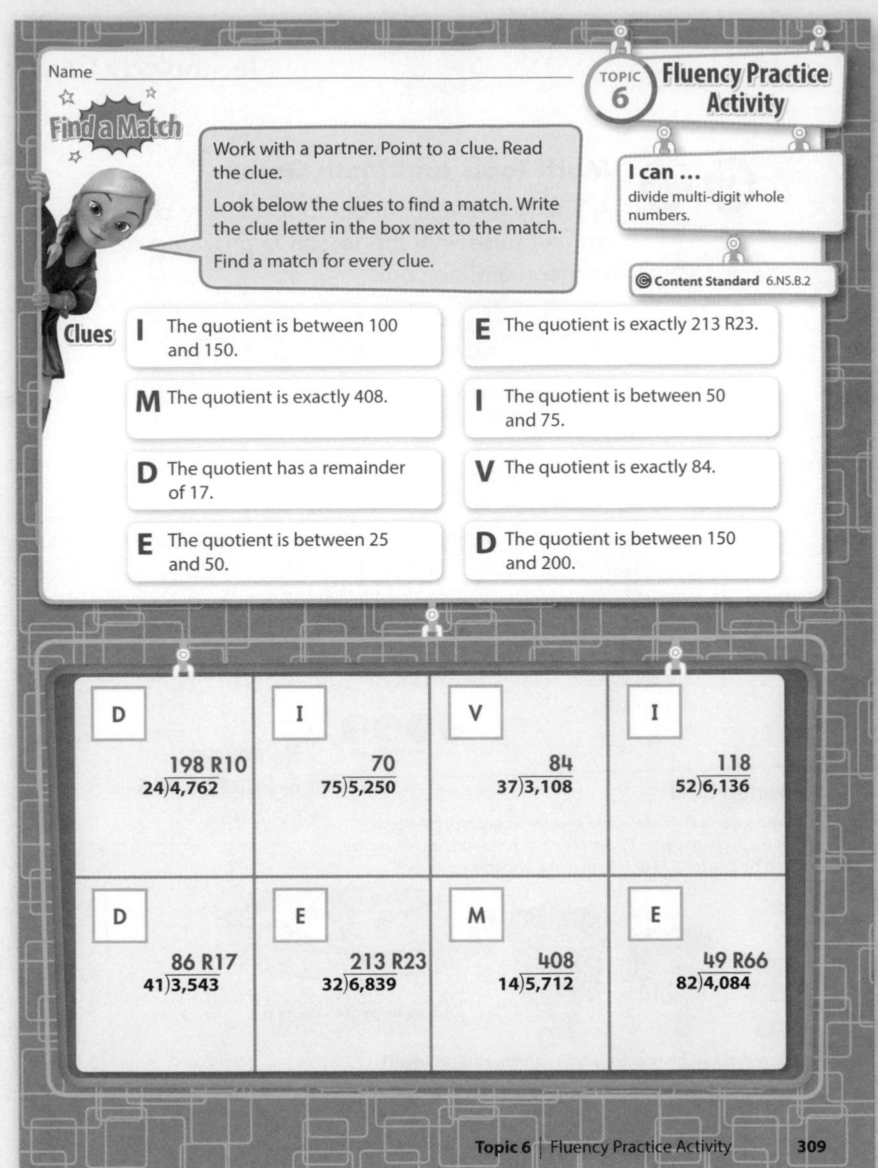

Name ______________________

Find a Match

TOPIC 6 Fluency Practice Activity

Work with a partner. Point to a clue. Read the clue.

Look below the clues to find a match. Write the clue letter in the box next to the match.

Find a match for every clue.

**I can …** divide multi-digit whole numbers.

Content Standard 6.NS.B.2

**Clues**

| | |
|---|---|
| **I** The quotient is between 100 and 150. | **E** The quotient is exactly 213 R23. |
| **M** The quotient is exactly 408. | **I** The quotient is between 50 and 75. |
| **D** The quotient has a remainder of 17. | **V** The quotient is exactly 84. |
| **E** The quotient is between 25 and 50. | **D** The quotient is between 150 and 200. |

| | | | |
|---|---|---|---|
| D<br>198 R10<br>24)4,762 | I<br>70<br>75)5,250 | V<br>84<br>37)3,108 | I<br>118<br>52)6,136 |
| D<br>86 R17<br>41)3,543 | E<br>213 R23<br>32)6,839 | M<br>408<br>14)5,712 | E<br>49 R66<br>82)4,084 |

Topic 6 | Fluency Practice Activity 309

 Glossary  Games

**Understand Vocabulary**

Choose the best term from the Word List. Write it on the blank.

**Word List**
- algebraic expression
- compatible numbers
- dividend
- divisor
- estimate
- equation
- evaluate
- quotient
- substitution
- variable

1. The letter $p$ in $2{,}064 \div 2p = 24$ is the **variable**.
2. Both of the sides of a(n) **equation** are always equal in value.
3. The number 37 in $1{,}924 \div 37 = 52$ is the **divisor**.
4. A(n) **algebraic expression** has at least one variable and one operation.
5. To evaluate an expression, use **substitution** to replace a variable with a number.
6. Write **E** next to each *equation*. Write **A** next to each *algebraic expression*.

$44p = 3{,}784$ **E** $225n \div 35$ **A** $\frac{26x^2}{14}$ **A** $5{,}712 \div 56 = q$ **E**

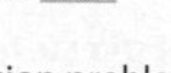

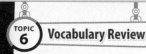

7. Circle the *dividend* in each division problem below.

$3{,}645 \div 45 = p$ $\frac{18{,}904}{34w}$ $36\overline{)3{,}312}$ (92) $2{,}518 \div 63 = 39$ R61

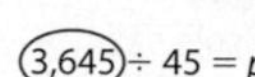

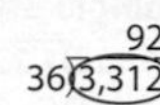
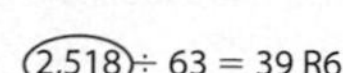

Draw a line from each division problem in Column A to the best *estimate* of its quotient in Column B.

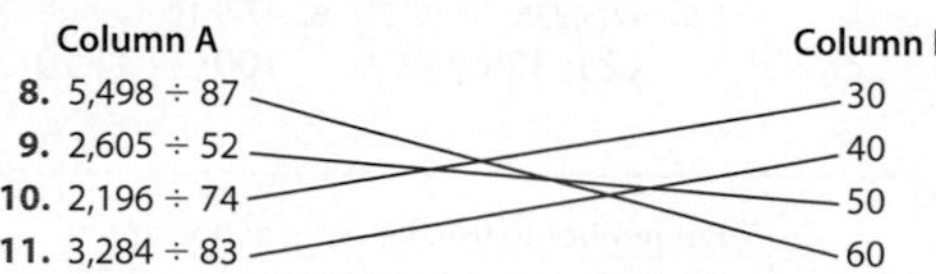

| Column A | Column B |
|---|---|
| 8. $5{,}498 \div 87$ | 30 |
| 9. $2{,}605 \div 52$ | 40 |
| 10. $2{,}196 \div 74$ | 50 |
| 11. $3{,}284 \div 83$ | 60 |

**Use Vocabulary in Writing**

12. Describe how to estimate $2{,}448 \div 78$. Use at least 4 words from the Word List.

**Sample answer: To *estimate* the *quotient* of $2{,}448 \div 78$, use *compatible numbers* 2,400 and 80 for the *dividend* and *divisor*. $2{,}400 \div 80 = 30$, so the *quotient* of $2{,}448 \div 78$ is about 30.**

310 **Topic 6** | Vocabulary Review



## VOCABULARY REVIEW

Students review vocabulary words used in the topic.

**Oral Language** Before students complete the page, you might reinforce oral language through a class discussion involving one or more of the following activities.

- Have students define the terms in their own words.
- Write two or more vocabulary terms on the board. Ask students to make connections between the terms.
- Play a "What's My Word?" guessing game in which you or a student thinks about one of the words and gives a clue so others can guess the word.
- As an alternative, play a "Picture My Word" game. Have students work with a partner and decide who is going to draw and who is going to guess. Without revealing the vocabulary term, one partner chooses a term from the Word List and silently draws a picture representing the term using numbers and symbols only. The other partner tries to guess the vocabulary term until the correct one is identified. The partners switch roles to draw and guess another word. To speed up the game, students might want to use a timer or play against other teams.

**Writing in Math** After students complete the page, you might further reinforce writing in math by doing one or more of the following activities.

- Have students write a math instruction manual. Identify several math operations or processes that involve three or more of the vocabulary terms from the Word List. Have students provide an example, and then write step-by-step instructions using the vocabulary terms in their proper contexts.
- Have students write an acrostic-style poem. Students choose one vocabulary term from the Word List. They spell out the word letter-by-letter horizontally on a sheet of paper. On each line, they write an adjective, phrase, or sentence beginning with the letter that describes or relates to the word.

Games

**Online Game** The Game Center at PearsonRealize.com includes a vocabulary game that students can access any time.

# RETEACHING

## FLUENTLY DIVIDE WHOLE NUMBERS

### RtI Item Analysis for Diagnosis and Intervention

| Reteaching Sets | Standard | MDIS |
|---|---|---|
| Set A | 6.NS.B.2 | G72 |
| Set B | 6.NS.B.2 | G75 |
| Set C | 6.EE.A.2c, 6.NS.B.2 | F41, F45, G75 |
| Set D | 6.EE.B.7, 6.NS.B.2 | F50, F54, G75 |
| Set E | MP.6, MP.1, MP.2, MP.3 | F51, F54, G75 |

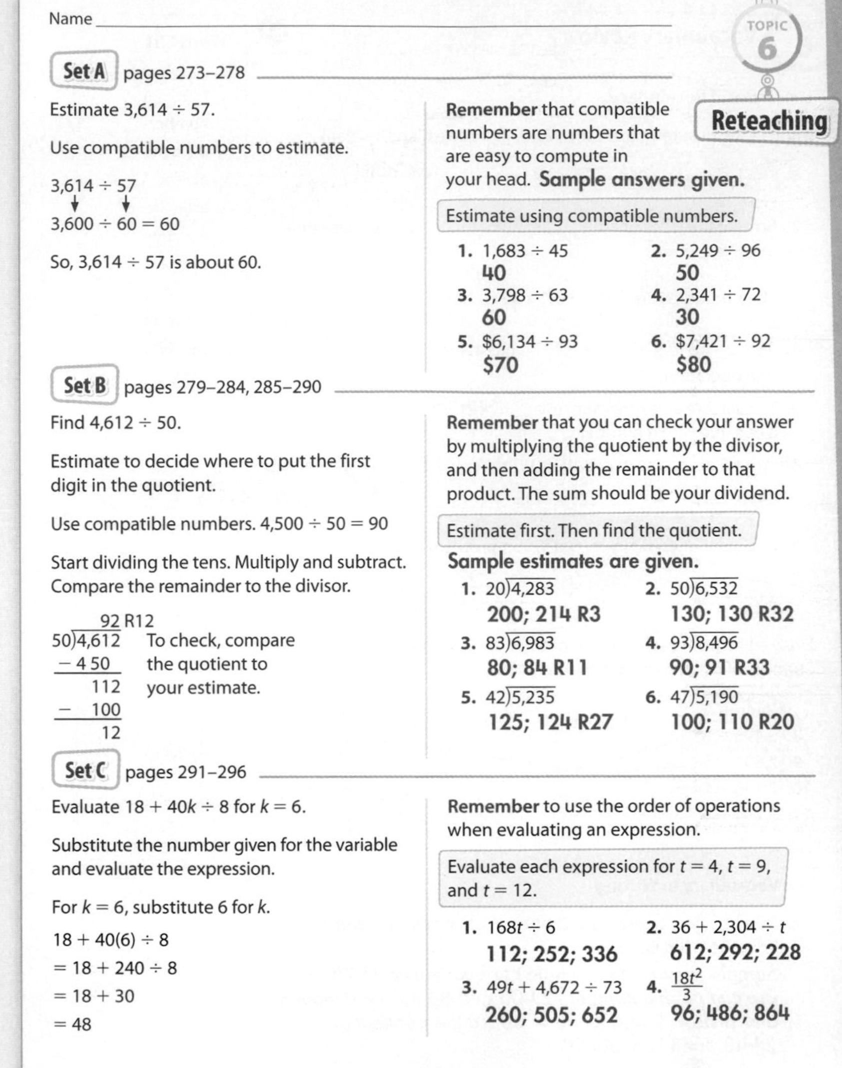

Name ______________________

TOPIC 6

**Reteaching**

**Set A** pages 273–278

Estimate 3,614 ÷ 57.

Use compatible numbers to estimate.

3,614 ÷ 57
↓ ↓
3,600 ÷ 60 = 60

So, 3,614 ÷ 57 is about 60.

**Remember** that compatible numbers are numbers that are easy to compute in your head. **Sample answers given.**

Estimate using compatible numbers.

1. 1,683 ÷ 45 **40**
2. 5,249 ÷ 96 **50**
3. 3,798 ÷ 63 **60**
4. 2,341 ÷ 72 **30**
5. \$6,134 ÷ 93 **\$70**
6. \$7,421 ÷ 92 **\$80**

**Set B** pages 279–284, 285–290

Find 4,612 ÷ 50.

Estimate to decide where to put the first digit in the quotient.

Use compatible numbers. 4,500 ÷ 50 = 90

Start dividing the tens. Multiply and subtract. Compare the remainder to the divisor.

```
     92 R12
50)4,612
 – 4 50
    112
 –  100
     12
```

To check, compare the quotient to your estimate.

**Remember** that you can check your answer by multiplying the quotient by the divisor, and then adding the remainder to that product. The sum should be your dividend.

Estimate first. Then find the quotient.

**Sample estimates are given.**

1. 20)4,283 **200; 214 R3**
2. 50)6,532 **130; 130 R32**
3. 83)6,983 **80; 84 R11**
4. 93)8,496 **90; 91 R33**
5. 42)5,235 **125; 124 R27**
6. 47)5,190 **100; 110 R20**

**Set C** pages 291–296

Evaluate $18 + 40k \div 8$ for $k = 6$.

Substitute the number given for the variable and evaluate the expression.

For $k = 6$, substitute 6 for $k$.

$18 + 40(6) \div 8$
$= 18 + 240 \div 8$
$= 18 + 30$
$= 48$

**Remember** to use the order of operations when evaluating an expression.

Evaluate each expression for $t = 4$, $t = 9$, and $t = 12$.

1. $168t \div 6$ **112; 252; 336**
2. $36 + 2{,}304 \div t$ **612; 292; 228**
3. $49t + 4{,}672 \div 73$ **260; 505; 652**
4. $\frac{18t^2}{3}$ **96; 486; 864**

Topic 6 | Reteaching 311

**Set D** pages 297–302

A company packs and ships games to a store. Forty-eight games fit in a box. How many boxes are needed for 2,448 games? Write a division equation to represent the problem. Then solve the equation.

Let $n$ represent the number of boxes.
$2{,}448 \div 48 = n$ or $2{,}448 \div n = 48$

Divide to solve for $n$.

$$\begin{array}{r} 51 \\ 48\overline{)2{,}448} \\ -\,2\,40 \\ \hline 48 \\ -\quad 48 \\ \hline 0 \end{array}$$

Divide the tens.
Multiply and subtract.
Continue the process.

$n = 51$
The company needs 51 boxes to pack the games.

**Remember** that you can use a multiplication equation to check your answer.

Write a division equation to represent each problem. Then solve the equation.

1. An online movie store made $1,494 on poster sales last week. It charged $18 for each poster. How many posters did the store sell?
   **Sample answer: $1{,}494 \div 18 = p$; $p = 83$; The store sold 83 posters.**
2. A bicycle club logged 9,860 miles. If the 29 members of the club each rode the same number of miles, how many miles did each member ride?
   **Sample answer: $9{,}860 \div m = 29$; $m = 340$; Each member rode 340 miles.**

**Set E** pages 303–308

Think about these questions to help you **attend to precision.**

**Thinking Habits**

- Am I using numbers, units, and symbols correctly?
- Am I using the correct definitions?
- Am I calculating accurately?
- Is my answer clear?

**Remember** that you need to interpret the remainder to be precise.

Four teachers, 7 assistants, and three classes of 24 students each are going to a kite festival. Each person gets a kite. What is the least amount of money they can spend?

| Kite Bundles | Cost per Kite |
|---|---|
| 1 kite | $18 |
| 20 kites | $15 |
| 30 kites | $12 |

1. How can you find the least total cost?
   **Sample answer: The largest bundle costs the least per kite. Divide the number of kites needed, 83, by 30 and then by 20 to find the number of each type of bundle to buy.**
2. Write and solve an equation to find the least total cost. **$2(30 \times 12) + 1(20 \times 15) + 3(1 \times 18) = 1{,}074$; The least total cost is $1,074.**

## Response to Intervention

### Ongoing Intervention

- Lessons with guiding questions to assess understanding
- Support to prevent misconceptions and to reteach

### Strategic Intervention

- Targeted to small groups that need more support
- Easy to implement

### Intensive Intervention

- Instruction to accelerate progress
- Instruction focused on foundational skills

# TOPIC ASSESSMENT

## FLUENTLY DIVIDE WHOLE NUMBERS

Name ____________________

TOPIC 6 Assessment

1. Which of the following results is the most reasonable estimate of $4,875 \div 64$? **1 point**

   Ⓐ $6,000 \div 60$

   Ⓑ $5,000 \div 60$

   ● $4,900 \div 70$

   Ⓓ $4,800 \div 70$

2. Eliana started a new bank account and saved the same amount each week for a year. Now she has $2,860 in her account. Let $a$ be the amount she saved each week.

   **Part A** **2 points**

   Write an equation to represent how much Eliana saved each week.

   **Sample answer: $2,860 \div 52 = a$**

   **Part B**

   Solve your equation to find how much Eliana saved each week.

   **Eliana saved $55 each week.**

3. Select each expression that has a value of 15 when $x = 15$. **1 point**

   ■ $\frac{x}{3} + 10$

   □ $15,521 \div x$

   ■ $(3,015 \div x) - 186$

   □ $20x^2 \div 30$

   □ $\frac{2x^2}{5} - 25$

4. Chloe served 320 cups of lemonade at a family reunion. There are 4 cups in a quart and 4 quarts in a gallon. How many gallons of lemonade did she serve? Explain how you solved the problem. **1 point**

   **20 gallons; Sample answer: There are 4 cups in 1 quart and 4 quarts in 1 gallon, so $4 \times 4 = 16$ cups in 1 gallon; $320 \div 16 = 20$.**

5. There are 17,600 yards in 10 miles. Samuel's father can run 10 miles in 65 minutes. If he runs the same speed for the entire distance, about how many yards does Samuel's father run each minute? **1 point**

   **Sample answer: About 300 yards**

6. A city has 1,242 law enforcement officers in the police department. If the officers are equally divided into 18 groups, how many officers will be in each group? **1 point**

   Ⓐ 60 officers

   Ⓑ 68 officers

   ● 69 officers

   Ⓓ 70 officers

Topic 6 | Assessment 313

7. There are 1,070 people going on a trip to New York City. The travel group organizing the trip can use any of the vehicles shown in the table. **3 points**

| Type of Vehicle | Number of Passengers | Cost |
|---|---|---|
| Mini Van | 8 | $35 |
| Large Van | 12 | $50 |
| Bus | 40 | $120 |

**Part A**

If the travel group decides to use only one type of vehicle, how many will they need to transport 1,070 people?

mini vans **134** large vans **90** buses **27**

**Part B**

Twenty more people join the travel group at the last minute. How many buses does the group need now? Is there a less expensive option than transporting everyone by bus? Explain.

**28 buses; Yes; Sample answer: $1,090 \div 40 = 27$ R10. So, 27 buses are full and 1 bus has 10 passengers. The group could rent a large van for $50 instead of paying $120 for another bus.**

8. The table shows the number of employees going to a conference. Read each of the following problem situations. Draw lines to match each number to the question it answers. **2 points**

DATA

| Group | Number of Employees |
|---|---|
| Accounting | 521 |
| Marketing | 536 |
| Central Office | 172 |

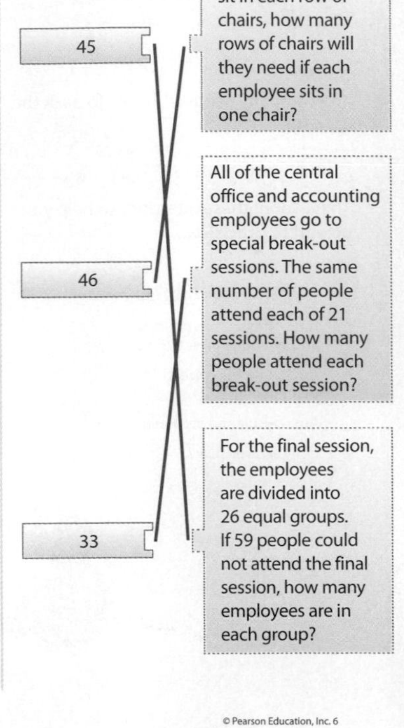

45
46
33
If 27 employees can sit in each row of chairs, how many rows of chairs will they need if each employee sits in one chair?
All of the central office and accounting employees go to special break-out sessions. The same number of people attend each of 21 sessions. How many people attend each break-out session?
For the final session, the employees are divided into 26 equal groups. If 59 people could not attend the final session, how many employees are in each group?

314 Topic 6 | Assessment



## ANSWERING THE TOPIC ESSENTIAL QUESTION

**How are quotients of multi-digit numbers found?**

Restate the Topic Essential Question from the Topic Opener or project it from the Student's Edition eText.

Ask students to answer the Essential Question (verbally or in writing) and give examples that support their answers. The following are key elements of the answer to the Essential Question. Be sure these are made explicit when discussing students' answers.

- Compatible numbers can be used to estimate quotients. An estimate helps determine the place-value structure of the quotient.

  **Example:** The quotient of $963 \div 17$ can be estimated as $900 \div 15 = 60$ or $1,000 \div 20 = 50$. Either way, the value of the quotient is in the tens.

- Use your estimate to find the first digit of the quotient. Sometimes this needs to be adjusted, but the number should be close.

  **Example:** Based on the estimate of $963 \div 17$, begin by putting a 6 or 5 in the tens place of the quotient. Then compare the product of that number and the divisor to the number of tens in the dividend. $6 \times 17 = 102 > 96$. $5 \times 17 = 85 < 96$. Choose the number 5 since the product is less than the corresponding number of tens in the dividend.

- Perform the division using the standard algorithm: estimate, multiply, subtract, compare, bring down, and repeat until the remainder is less than the divisor.

  **Example:**

```
    56 R11
17)963
  - 85
    113
  - 102
     11
```

Assessment

## ONLINE TOPIC ASSESSMENT

An auto-scored Topic Assessment is provided at PearsonRealize.com.

## EXAMVIEW® TEST GENERATOR

ExamView can be used to create a blackline-master Topic Assessment with multiple-choice and free-response items.

## Topic Assessment Masters

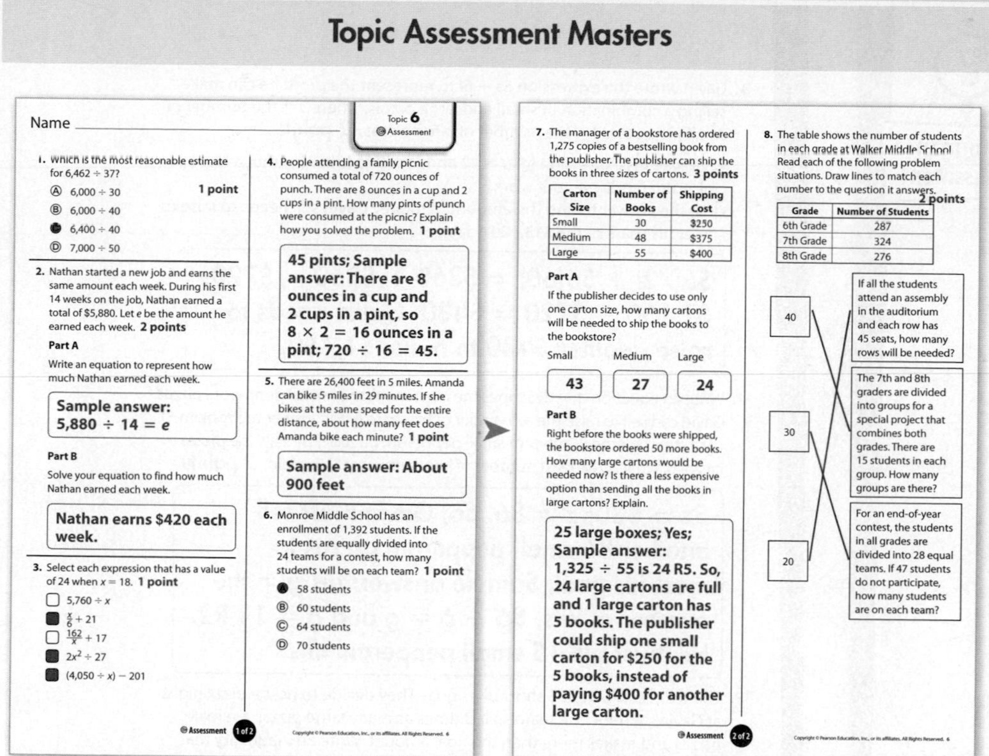

Name ______________________

Topic 6
Assessment

1. Which is the most reasonable estimate for $6,462 \div 37$? **1 point**
   - Ⓐ $6,000 \div 30$
   - Ⓑ $6,000 \div 40$
   - ● $6,400 \div 40$
   - Ⓓ $7,000 \div 50$

2. Nathan started a new job and earns the same amount each week. During his first 14 weeks on the job, Nathan earned a total of $5,880. Let *e* be the amount he earned each week. **2 points**

   **Part A**

   Write an equation to represent how much Nathan earned each week.

   **Sample answer: $5,880 \div 14 = e$**

   **Part B**

   Solve your equation to find how much Nathan earned each week.

   **Nathan earns $420 each week.**

3. Select each expression that has a value of 24 when $x = 18$. **1 point**
   - ☐ $5,760 \div x$
   - ■ $\frac{x}{6} + 21$
   - ☐ $\frac{162}{x} + 17$
   - ■ $2x^2 \div 27$
   - ■ $(4,050 \div x) - 201$

4. People attending a family picnic consumed a total of 720 ounces of punch. There are 8 ounces in a cup and 2 cups in a pint. How many pints of punch were consumed at the picnic? Explain how you solved the problem. **1 point**

   **45 pints; Sample answer: There are 8 ounces in a cup and 2 cups in a pint, so $8 \times 2 = 16$ ounces in a pint; $720 \div 16 = 45$.**

5. There are 26,400 feet in 5 miles. Amanda can bike 5 miles in 29 minutes. If she bikes at the same speed for the entire distance, about how many feet does Amanda bike each minute? **1 point**

   **Sample answer: About 900 feet**

6. Monroe Middle School has an enrollment of 1,392 students. If the students are equally divided into 24 teams for a contest, how many students will be on each team? **1 point**
   - ● 58 students
   - Ⓑ 60 students
   - Ⓒ 64 students
   - Ⓓ 70 students

Assessment 1 of 2



7. The manager of a bookstore has ordered 1,275 copies of a bestselling book from the publisher. The publisher can ship the books in three sizes of cartons. **3 points**

| Carton Size | Number of Books | Shipping Cost |
|---|---|---|
| Small | 30 | $250 |
| Medium | 48 | $375 |
| Large | 55 | $400 |

**Part A**

If the publisher decides to use only one carton size, how many cartons will be needed to ship the books to the bookstore?

Small **43** Medium **27** Large **24**

**Part B**

Right before the books were shipped, the bookstore ordered 50 more books. How many large cartons would be needed now? Is there a less expensive option than sending all the books in large cartons? Explain.

**25 large boxes; Yes; Sample answer: $1,325 \div 55$ is 24 R5. So, 24 large cartons are full and 1 large carton has 5 books. The publisher could ship one small carton for $250 for the 5 books, instead of paying $400 for another large carton.**

8. The table shows the number of students in each grade at Walker Middle School Read each of the following problem situations. Draw lines to match each number to the question it answers. **2 points**

| Grade | Number of Students |
|---|---|
| 6th Grade | 287 |
| 7th Grade | 324 |
| 8th Grade | 276 |

40 — The 7th and 8th graders are divided into groups for a special project that combines both grades. There are 15 students in each group. How many groups are there?

30 — For an end-of-year contest, the students in all grades are divided into 28 equal teams. If 47 students do not participate, how many students are on each team?

20 — If all the students attend an assembly in the auditorium and each row has 45 seats, how many rows will be needed?

Assessment 2 of 2



## RtI Item Analysis for Diagnosis and Intervention

| Item | Standard | DOK | MDIS |
|---|---|---|---|
| 1 | 6.NS.B.2 | 1 | G72 |
| 2A | 6.EE.B.7 | 2 | F54 |
| 2B | 6.EE.B.7, 6.NS.B.2 | 1 | G75 |
| 3 | 6.EE.A.2c, 6.NS.B.2 | 1 | F45, G75 |
| 4 | 6.NS.B.2 | 2 | I33, G73 |
| 5 | 6.NS.B.2 | 2 | I32, G72 |
| 6 | 6.NS.B.2 | 1 | G75 |
| 7A | 6.NS.B.2 | 2 | G75 |
| 7B | 6.NS.B.2, MP.6 | 3 | G75 |
| 8 | 6.NS.B.2 | 2 | G75 |

The Topic Assessment Masters assess the same content item for item as the Topic Assessment in the Student's Edition.

## Scoring Guide

| Item | Points | Topic Assessment (Student's Edition and Masters) |
|---|---|---|
| 1 | 1 | Correct choice selected |
| 2A | 1 | Correct equation |
| 2B | 1 | Correct solution |
| 3 | 1 | All correct choices selected |
| 4 | 1 | Correct answer and explanation |
| 5 | 1 | Reasonable estimate |
| 6 | 1 | Correct choice selected |
| 7A | 1 | Three correct answers |
| 7B | 2 | Correct answers and explanation |
| | 1 | Correct answers with incomplete or missing explanation |
| 8 | 2 | All matches correct |
| | 1 | One match correct |

# TOPIC 6 TOPIC PERFORMANCE ASSESSMENT

## FLUENTLY DIVIDE WHOLE NUMBERS

Name ____________________

**Pizza Money**
Gavin's basketball team needs to raise $13,800 to pay for their uniforms and travel expenses. There are 12 players on the team. The coach has decided to sell pizzas to raise the money they need.

**1.** Each player agrees to raise the same amount of money. At least how much money does each player need to raise for an equal share? **1 point**

**13,800 ÷ 12 = 1,150. Each player needs to raise at least $1,150.**

**2.** The pizzas to be sold are purchased in kits with 6 small pizzas or 4 large pizzas in each. The team intends to make a profit of $5 on each small pizza and $6 on each large pizza sold.

**Part A 1 point**

Let $p$ = the profit made on each pizza. Complete the table by evaluating the expression $k \div n + p$ to find the selling price for one of each type of pizza.

| Pizza Type | Pizzas in Each Kit ($n$) | Cost of Kit ($k$) | Selling Price Each Pizza ($k \div n + p$) |
|---|---|---|---|
| Small Cheese | 6 | $30 | **$10** |
| Small Pepperoni | 6 | $36 | **$11** |
| Large Cheese | 4 | $32 | **$14** |
| Large Pepperoni | 4 | $36 | **$15** |

**Part B 1 point**

Let $c$ = the selling price of 1 large cheese pizza. Solve the equation $4c = t$ to find the total selling price, $t$, of 1 large cheese pizza kit.

**4 × $14 = $56**



**3.** Gavin wrote the expression $5s + 6l$ to represent the profit he can make selling a combination of small and large pizzas, where $s$ = the number of small pizzas and $l$ = the number of large pizzas. **2 points**

- Evaluate his expression for $s = 72$ and $l = 60$ to find how much he has raised so far. Show your work.
- Use the answer to find the amount of money Gavin still needs to raise to meet his share of the $13,800 goal.

**$5(72) + $6(60) = $360 + $360 = $720; $1,150 − $720 = $430. Gavin needs to raise another $430 to make $1,150.**

**4.** Write an equation that describes the least number of small pepperoni pizzas Gavin can sell to raise the remainder of his share (your answer to Problem 3). Let $z$ stand for the number of small pepperoni pizzas. If he sells the pizzas in kits of 6, what is the least number of kits he must sell? Explain. **2 points**

**$5z = 430$; $z = 86$. So, Gavin must sell another 86 small pepperoni pizzas to meet his goal; Sample answer: Let $g$ = the number of kits. 86 ÷ 6 = $g$ and $g$ = 14 R2. He must sell 15 small pepperoni kits.**

**5.** The team is still $1,536 short of its goal. They decide to host a pizza night at Gavin's school. The team sells 3 times as many large pizzas as small pizzas and makes more than the goal amount. Write an inequality that can be used to find possible numbers of large and small pizzas sold on pizza night. Find one possible solution. **3 points**

**Check students' work; Sample answer: I wrote the inequality $5s + 6l$ > $1,536 and tried different values for $s$ and $l$, where $3s = l$. $5(70) + $6(210) = $350 + $1,260 = $1,610 > $1,536, so the team could have sold 70 small pizzas and 210 large pizzas on pizza night.**





### Scoring Guide

| Item | Points | Topic Performance Assessment in the Student's Edition |
|---|---|---|
| 1 | 1 | Correct answer |
| 2A | 1 | All correct answers in table |
| 2B | 1 | Correct answer |
| 3 | 2<br>1 | Correct evaluation and answer<br>Correct evaluation or correct answer based on incorrect evaluation |
| 4 | 2<br>1 | Correct equation, answer, and explanation<br>Incorrect equation, answer, or explanation |
| 5 | 3<br>2<br>1 | Correct inequality and possible solution<br>Correct possible solution based on incorrect inequality<br>Correct inequality with incorrect or missing solution |

### Item Analysis for Diagnosis and Intervention

| Item | Standard | DOK | MDIS |
|---|---|---|---|
| 1 | 6.NS.B.2, MP.1 | 1 | G75 |
| 2A | 6.EE.A.2c, 6.NS.B.2, MP.7 | 1 | F45 |
| 2B | 6.EE.A.2c, MP.7 | 2 | F47 |
| 3 | 6.EE.A.2c, MP.6 | 2 | F45, J5 |
| 4 | 6.EE.B.7, 6.NS.B.2, MP.3 | 2 | F54, F51 |
| 5 | 6.EE.B.8, 6.EE.A.2c, MP.4 | 3 | F61, J13 |

## Topic Performance Assessment Masters

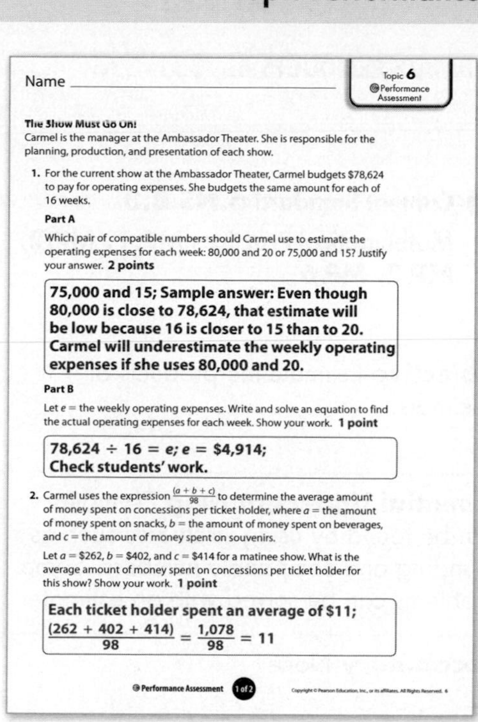

Name ______________________

Topic 6 Performance Assessment

**The Show Must Go On!**

Carmel is the manager at the Ambassador Theater. She is responsible for the planning, production, and presentation of each show.

1. For the current show at the Ambassador Theater, Carmel budgets $78,624 to pay for operating expenses. She budgets the same amount for each of 16 weeks.

**Part A**

Which pair of compatible numbers should Carmel use to estimate the operating expenses for each week: 80,000 and 20 or 75,000 and 15? Justify your answer. **2 points**

**75,000 and 15; Sample answer: Even though 80,000 is close to 78,624, that estimate will be low because 16 is closer to 15 than to 20. Carmel will underestimate the weekly operating expenses if she uses 80,000 and 20.**

**Part B**

Let $e$ = the weekly operating expenses. Write and solve an equation to find the actual operating expenses for each week. Show your work. **1 point**

**$78{,}624 \div 16 = e$; $e = \$4{,}914$; Check students' work.**

2. Carmel uses the expression $\frac{(a+b+c)}{98}$ to determine the average amount of money spent on concessions per ticket holder, where $a$ = the amount of money spent on snacks, $b$ = the amount of money spent on beverages, and $c$ = the amount of money spent on souvenirs.

Let $a$ = $262, $b$ = $402, and $c$ = $414 for a matinee show. What is the average amount of money spent on concessions per ticket holder for this show? Show your work. **1 point**

**Each ticket holder spent an average of $11;**
$$\frac{(262 + 402 + 414)}{98} = \frac{1{,}078}{98} = 11$$

Performance Assessment 1 of 2



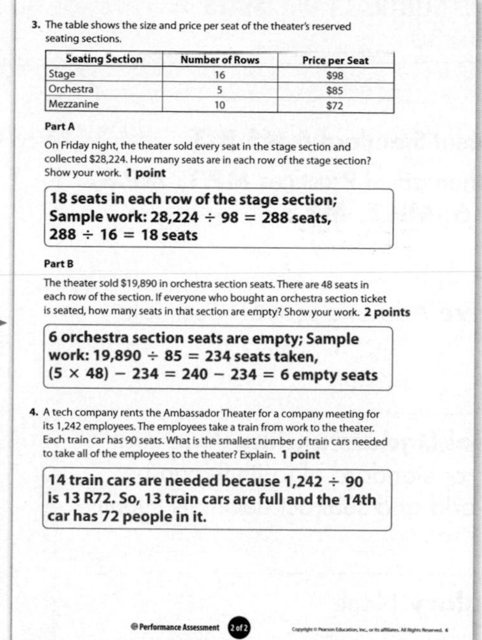

3. The table shows the size and price per seat of the theater's reserved seating sections.

| Seating Section | Number of Rows | Price per Seat |
|---|---|---|
| Stage | 16 | $98 |
| Orchestra | 5 | $85 |
| Mezzanine | 10 | $72 |

**Part A**

On Friday night, the theater sold every seat in the stage section and collected $28,224. How many seats are in each row of the stage section? Show your work. **1 point**

**18 seats in each row of the stage section; Sample work: 28,224 ÷ 98 = 288 seats, 288 ÷ 16 = 18 seats**

**Part B**

The theater sold $19,890 in orchestra section seats. There are 48 seats in each row of the section. If everyone who bought an orchestra section ticket is seated, how many seats in that section are empty? Show your work. **2 points**

**6 orchestra section seats are empty; Sample work: 19,890 ÷ 85 = 234 seats taken, (5 × 48) − 234 = 240 − 234 = 6 empty seats**

4. A tech company rents the Ambassador Theater for a company meeting for its 1,242 employees. The employees take a train from work to the theater. Each train car has 90 seats. What is the smallest number of train cars needed to take all of the employees to the theater? Explain. **1 point**

**14 train cars are needed because 1,242 ÷ 90 is 13 R72. So, 13 train cars are full and the 14th car has 72 people in it.**

Performance Assessment 2 of 2



## RtI Item Analysis for Diagnosis and Intervention

| Item | Standard | DOK | MDIS |
|---|---|---|---|
| 1A | 6.NS.B.2, MP.3 | 3 | G72 |
| 1B | 6.EE.B.7, 6.NS.B.2, MP.6 | 1 | F54, G75 |
| 2 | 6.EE.A.2c, 6.NS.B.2, MP.7 | 2 | F45, G75 |
| 3A | 6.NS.B.2, MP.2 | 2 | G75 |
| 3B | 6.NS.B.2, MP.1 | 3 | G75, J5 |
| 4 | 6.NS.B.2, MP.6 | 2 | G75 |

## Scoring Guide

| Item | Points | Topic Performance Assessment Masters |
|---|---|---|
| 1A | 2 | Correct answer and explanation |
| | 1 | Correct answer or explanation |
| 1B | 1 | Correct equation and answer |
| 2 | 1 | Correct answer and work shown |
| 3A | 1 | Correct answer and work shown |
| 3B | 2 | Correct answer and work shown |
| | 1 | Correct answer with incomplete or missing work |
| 4 | 1 | Correct answer and explanation |

# TOPIC PLANNER

## FLUENTLY ADD, SUBTRACT, MULTIPLY, AND DIVIDE DECIMALS

### Lesson 7-1

**ESTIMATE SUMS AND DIFFERENCES**
pp. 319–324

**Content Standard 6.NS.B.3**
**Mathematical Practices MP.1, MP.2, MP.3, MP.4, MP.6, MP.7**

**Objective** Estimate the sums and differences of decimals.

**Essential Understanding** Estimates can be found by using strategies such as rounding and compatible numbers. Some problems can be solved with an estimate.

**Vocabulary** None

**ELL Learning Strategies:** Monitor language production.

**Materials** None

**On-Level and Advanced Activity Centers**
- Center Games

### Lesson 7-2

**ADD AND SUBTRACT DECIMALS**
pp. 325–330

**Content Standard 6.NS.B.3**
**Mathematical Practices MP.1, MP.3, MP.6, MP.7, MP.8**

**Objective** Add and subtract decimals.

**Essential Understanding** A general method, or standard algorithm, can be used to add and subtract decimals fluently.

**Vocabulary** None

**ELL Listening:** Demonstrate listening comprehension by retelling.

**Materials** Grid paper (TT 17), index cards, markers

**On-Level and Advanced Activity Centers**
- Math and Science Activity

### Lesson 7-3

**ESTIMATE PRODUCTS** pp. 331–336

**Content Standard 6.NS.B.3**
**Mathematical Practices MP.1, MP.2, MP.3, MP.6**

**Objective** Estimate the products of decimals.

**Essential Understanding** Estimates can be found by using strategies such as rounding and compatible numbers. Some problems can be solved with an estimate.

**Vocabulary** None

**ELL Reading:** Demonstrate comprehension by taking notes.

**Materials** Grocery store advertisement

**On-Level and Advanced Activity Centers**
- Center Games

## LESSON RESOURCES

**Digital**

**Print**

- Student's Edition
- Daily Common Core Review
- Reteach to Build Understanding
- Center Games
- Math and Science Activity
- Problem-Solving Reading Mat
- Problem-Solving Reading Activity

**Digital**

- Listen and Look For PD Lesson Video
- Student's Edition eText
- Today's Challenge
- Solve & Share
- Visual Learning Animation Plus
- Animated Glossary
- Math Tools
- Practice Buddy Online Practice
- Quick Check
- Another Look Homework Video
- Math Games

Digital

## Lesson 7-4

**MULTIPLY DECIMALS** pp. 337–342

**Content Standard 6.NS.B.3**
**Mathematical Practices MP.2, MP.3, MP.5, MP.7, MP.8**

**Objective** Multiply decimals.

**Essential Understanding** A general method, or standard algorithm, can be used to multiply decimals fluently.

**Vocabulary** None

**ELL Speaking:** Speak using content area vocabulary in context.

**Materials** Decimal models (TT 31), Grid paper (TT 17), Number cubes (or TT 23)

**On-Level and Advanced Activity Centers**
- Center Games

## Lesson 7-5

**DIVIDE DECIMALS BY A WHOLE NUMBER** pp. 343–348

**Content Standards 6.NS.B.2, 6.NS.B.3**
**Mathematical Practices MP.2, MP.3, MP.7**

**Objective** Divide decimals by whole numbers.

**Essential Understanding** A general method, or standard algorithm, can be used to divide decimals fluently.

**Vocabulary** None

**ELL Listening:** Seek clarification of spoken word.

**Materials** Index cards, colored pencils

**On-Level and Advanced Activity Centers**
- Center Games

## Lesson 7-6

**DIVIDE DECIMALS** pp. 349–354

**Content Standards 6.NS.B.2, 6.NS.B.3**
**Mathematical Practices MP.2, MP.4, MP.6, MP.7**

**Objective** Find quotients of two decimals.

**Essential Understanding** A general method, or standard algorithm, can be used to divide decimals fluently.

**Vocabulary** None

**ELL Reading:** Use reading supports: illustrations.

**Materials** Decimal models (TT 31)

**On-Level and Advanced Activity Centers**
- Center Games

## TOPIC RESOURCES

Digital

Print

**Start of Topic**
- Steps to Fluency Success
- Math and Science Project
- Home-School Connection
- Review What You Know

**End of Topic**
- Fluency Practice Activity
- Vocabulary Review
- Reteaching
- Topic Assessment
- Topic Performance Assessment

Digital

**Start of Topic**
- Topic Overview PD Video

**End of Topic**
- Math Practices Animations
- Online Topic Assessment
- ExamView® Test Generator
- Practice Buddy Fluency Practice/Assessment

PearsonRealize.com

TOPIC 7

# TOPIC PLANNER

## FLUENTLY ADD, SUBTRACT, MULTIPLY, AND DIVIDE DECIMALS

### Lesson 7-7

**CONTINUE TO DIVIDE DECIMALS** pp. 355–360

Content Standards **6.NS.B.2, 6.NS.B.3**
Mathematical Practices **MP.1, MP.2, MP.4, MP.7**

**Objective** Divide decimals to solve real-world problems.

**Essential Understanding** A general method, or standard algorithm, can be used to divide decimals fluently.

**Vocabulary** None

**ELL** Speaking: Share information in cooperative learning interactions.

**Materials** Index cards

**On-Level and Advanced Activity Centers**
- Math and Science Activity

### Lesson 7-8

**EVALUATE EXPRESSIONS WITH DECIMALS** pp. 361–366

Content Standards **6.EE.A.2a, 6.EE.A.2c, 6.NS.B.2, 6.NS.B.3**
Mathematical Practices **MP.3, MP.4, MP.6, MP.7, MP.8**

**Objective** Evaluate algebraic expressions that involve decimals.

**Essential Understanding** The value of an algebraic expression can be found by replacing the variables with given numbers and doing the calculation that results.

**Vocabulary** None

**ELL** Listening: Demonstrate listening comprehension by taking notes.

**Materials** Colored pencils

**On-Level and Advanced Activity Centers**
- Problem-Solving Reading Mat

### Lesson 7-9

**SOLVE EQUATIONS WITH DECIMALS** pp. 367–372

Content Standards **6.EE.B.7, 6.NS.B.2, 6.NS.B.3**
Mathematical Practices **MP.2, MP.3, MP.4, MP.7**

**Objective** Solve algebraic equations that involve decimals.

**Essential Understanding** Solving an equation involves finding the value of the variable that makes the equation true.

**Vocabulary** None

**ELL** Learning Strategies: Use prior knowledge to understand meanings.

**Materials** Strips of paper, container

**On-Level and Advanced Activity Centers**
- Center Games

## Notes

Digital

## Lesson 7-10

**MATH PRACTICES AND PROBLEM SOLVING: USE APPROPRIATE TOOLS**
pp. 373–378

**Mathematical Practices MP.5 Also, MP.4, MP.7, MP.8**
**Content Standards 6.NS.B.3, 6.NS.B.2**

**Objective** Use appropriate tools strategically to solve problems involving decimals.

**Essential Understanding** Good math thinkers know how to pick the right tools to solve math problems.

**Vocabulary** None

**ELL Reading:** Expand comprehension by predicting.

**Materials** Calculators (optional), computer with Internet access (optional)

**On-Level and Advanced Activity Centers**
- Problem-Solving Reading Mat

# STEPS TO FLUENCY SUCCESS

## FLUENTLY ADD, SUBTRACT, MULTIPLY, AND DIVIDE DECIMALS

In Grade 6, students are expected to fluently add, subtract, multiply, and divide decimals using the standard algorithm. (6.NS.B.3) To help all students achieve fluency follow the 6 steps outlined below and use the support materials described on pages 317F, 317G, and 317H.

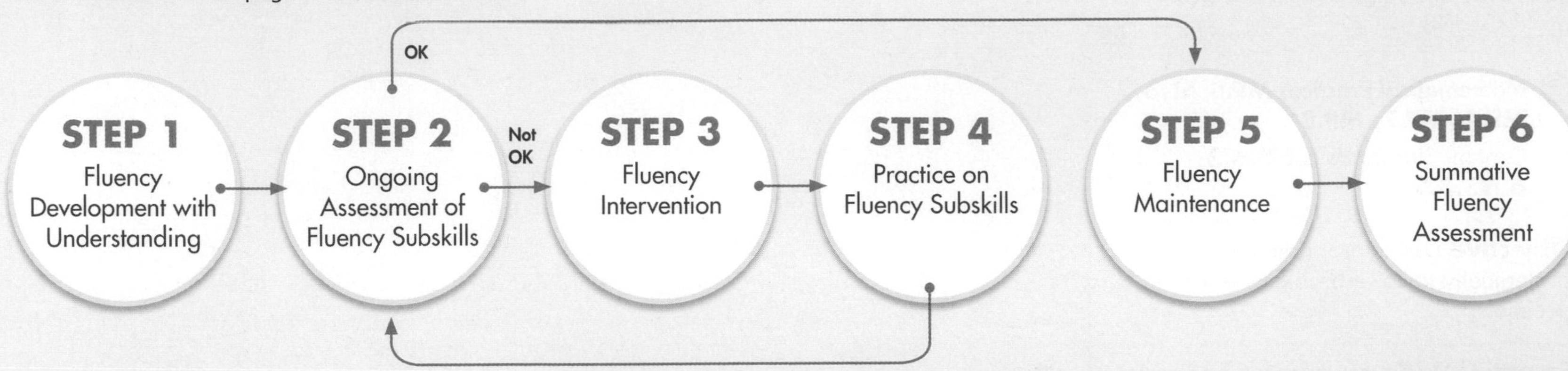


| Resources | Step 1 | Step 2 | Step 3 | Step 4 | Step 5 | Step 6 |
|---|---|---|---|---|---|---|
| **Student's Edition Resources** | | | | | | |
| Topic 7 Lessons | ● | | | | | |
| Fluency Practice Activities | | | | | ● | |
| **Fluency Practice/Assessment Worksheets** | | | | | | |
| Teacher's Resource Masters | | ● | | ● | ● | ● |
| ExamView® CD-ROM | | ● | | ● | ● | ● |
| **Math Diagnosis and Intervention System 2.0** | | | | | | |
| Diagnostic Tests | | | ● | | | |
| Intervention Lessons | | | ● | | | |
| Practice Buddy **Online Practice/Assessment** | | | | | | |
| Auto-Scored Items | | ● | | ● | ● | ● |
| On-Screen Help | | | ● | | | |
| Games **Game Center Online** | | | | | | |
| Games | | | | | ● | |
| **"My Fluency Progress" Form** | | | | | | |
| Teaching Tool 4 | | ● | | | | |

Practice Buddy

Games

## Student's Edition Resources

- **Topic 7 Lessons** Topic 7 provides the development with understanding that students need to fluently add, subtract, multiply, and divide decimals using the standard algorithm. This work builds on foundations for fluency from earlier work.

**Foundations For Fluency**

**Grade 4, Topic 12** Understand and Compare Decimals

**Grade 4, Topic 13** Measurement: Find Equivalence in Units of Measure

**Grade 5, Topic 1** Understand Place Value

**Grade 5, Topic 2** Add and Subtract Decimals to Hundredths

**Grade 5, Topic 4** Use Models and Strategies to Multiply Decimals

**Grade 5, Topic 6** Use Models and Strategies to Divide Decimals

- **Fluency Practice Activities** To support fluency for 6.NS.B.3, use the fluency activity found at the end of each of Topics 7, 9, 11, 13, and 15. Students can collaborate on these activities to help each other as needed.

Each Fluency Practice Activity is in one of the following formats: *Point & Tally*, *Find a Match*, or *Follow the Path*.

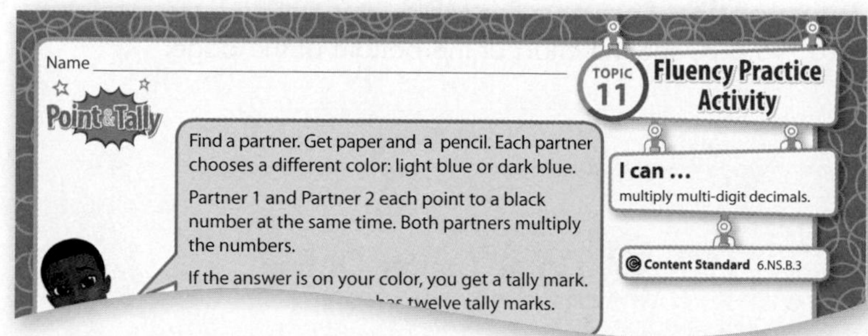


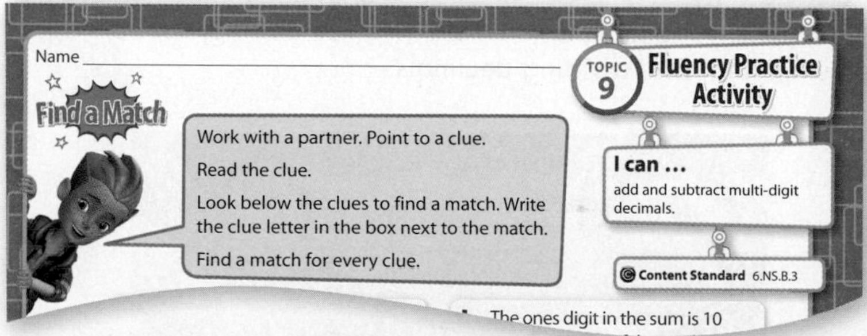


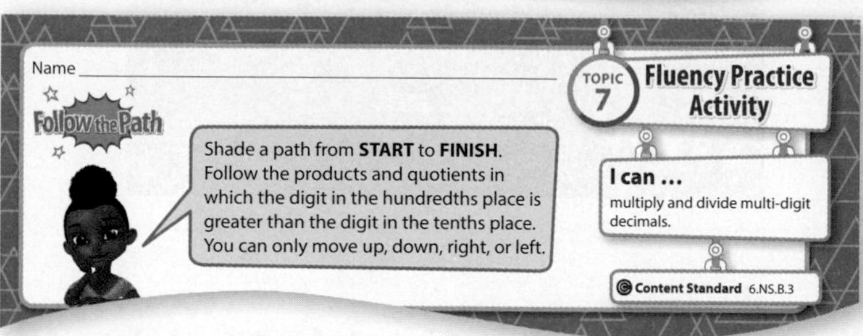


## Fluency Practice/Assessment Worksheets

- **Teacher's Resource Masters** Teacher's Resource Masters for Fluency Practice/Assessment are organized around 4 subskills of 6.NS.B.3. These worksheets can be used for practice on fluency subskills, for maintenance, or for assessment.

- **ExamView® CD-ROM** You can use ExamView to generate worksheets that cover the same content as the items on the Fluency Practice/Assessment Masters.

***Go to pages 317G–317H*** to see the Fluency Practice/Assessment Masters and a list of the subskills for 6.NS.B.3.

# STEPS TO FLUENCY SUCCESS

## FLUENTLY ADD, SUBTRACT, MULTIPLY, AND DIVIDE DECIMALS

### Math Diagnosis and Intervention System 2.0

- **Diagnostic Tests** After covering Topic 7, if a student cannot fluently add, subtract, multiply, and divide decimals, you might want to give a *Math Diagnosis and Intervention System 2.0* Diagnostic Test. These tests can diagnose the need for remediation of on-level content as well as prerequisite content such as addition facts, subtraction facts, place value, and using models to represent operations with decimals.

- **Intervention Lessons** For MDIS intervention lessons related to 6.NS.B.3, see the chart at the bottom of the page.

### Online Practice/Assessment

- **Auto-Scored Items** The online practice/assessment includes items on subskills of 6.NS.B.3. Items are auto-scored to give students instant feedback, and a report is sent to the teacher.

- **On-Screen Help** If students are uncertain how to complete an item, or if they answer incorrectly, intervention is available through on-screen help. This includes "Help Me Solve This" which guides the student through a solution, and "View an Example" which shows a worked-out solution for a similar item.

### Game Center Online

- **Games** The Game Center at PearsonRealize.com includes the Factory Frenzy Game which involves adding, subtracting, multiplying, and dividing decimals.

### "My Fluency Progress" Form

- **Teaching Tool 4** To help students become personally responsible for monitoring their progress on 6.NS.B.3, have them use the "My Fluency Progress" Form, Teaching Tool 4. This form gives students a place to record progress on fluency subskills.

### RtI Item Analysis for Diagnosis and Intervention

| Item | Fluency Subskills for 6.NS.B.3 | | MDIS |
|---|---|---|---|
| 1–4 | A | Add multi-digit decimals. | H56, H59 |
| 5–8 | B | Subtract multi-digit decimals. | H57, H59 |
| 9–12 | C | Multiply multi-digit decimals. | H60, H64 |
| 13–16 | D | Divide multi-digit decimals. | H67, H69 |

PEARSON realize.
PearsonRealize.com

Practice Buddy

Games

# Fluency Practice/Assessment Worksheets

Name ____________________ Topic 7 Fluency Practice/Assessment

## Fluently Add, Subtract, Multiply, and Divide Multi-Digit Decimals

1. 1.56 + 672.3 = **673.86**
2. 43.613 + 224.73 = **268.343**
3. 52.6 + 2.5 = **55.1**
4. 0.286 + 55.057 = **55.343**
5. 17.7 − 7.94 = **9.76**
6. 58.156 − 0.180 = **57.976**
7. 16.373 − 0.859 = **15.514**
8. 75.234 − 52.5 = **22.734**
9. 72.83 × 8.6 = **626.338**
10. 4.9 × 5.6 = **27.44**
11. 7.23 × 0.55 = **3.9765**
12. 4.62 × 98.9 = **456.918**
13. 8.49)71.316 **8.4**
14. 0.7)5.32 **7.6**
15. 5.8)295.626 **50.97**
16. 9.9)11.88 **1.2**

17. For the first three weeks of the month, a bakery had $5,108.16 in sales. During the fourth week, sales were $1,145.73. What were the total sales for the month? Show your work.

**$6,253.89; 5,108.16 + 1,145.73 = 6,253.89**




Name ____________________ Topic 7 Fluency Practice/Assessment

## Fluently Add, Subtract, Multiply, and Divide Multi-Digit Decimals

1. 64.9 + 72.07 = **136.97**
2. 9.048 + 9.93 = **18.978**
3. 26.3 + 1.8 = **28.1**
4. 235.80 + 285.24 = **521.04**
5. 384.41 − 9.5 = **374.91**
6. 88.52 − 1.50 = **87.02**
7. 135.890 − 98.831 = **37.059**
8. 669.76 − 89.413 = **580.347**
9. 901.59 × 3.3 = **2,975.247**
10. 398.7 × 16.9 = **6,738.03**
11. 102.7 × 6.17 = **633.659**
12. 16.92 × 77.6 = **1,312.992**
13. 7.52)221.84 **29.5**
14. 0.8)49.44 **61.8**
15. 55.9)181.675 **3.25**
16. 6.45)54.825 **8.5**

17. Insert one digit in each box to complete the subtraction problem. You will not use the same digit twice.

**4 7 0.8 6 3 − 5.0 5 0 = 4 6 5.8 1 3**




Name ____________________ Topic 7 Fluency Practice/Assessment

## Fluently Add, Subtract, Multiply, and Divide Multi-Digit Decimals

1. 883.10 + 9.09 = **892.19**
2. 5.742 + 49.528 = **55.270**
3. 3.74 + 931.1 = **934.84**
4. 90.2 + 142.285 = **232.485**
5. 53.35 − 9.1 = **44.25**
6. 73.670 − 5.797 = **67.873**
7. 41.2 − 27.228 = **13.972**
8. 87.502 − 3.782 = **83.720**
9. 236.2 × 48.3 = **11,408.46**
10. 95.96 × 5.8 = **556.568**
11. 95.44 × 5.89 = **562.1416**
12. 36.91 × 36.8 = **1,358.288**
13. 8.1)416.34 **51.4**
14. 2.2)0.836 **0.38**
15. 5.5)254.65 **46.3**
16. 5.64)50.76 **9**

17. Two decimal numbers are multiplied. None of the digits in either factor or the product are zero. One of the factors has three digits to the right of the decimal point. The product has four digits to the right of the decimal point. How many digits are to the right of the decimal point in the second factor? Explain your answer.

**One; Sample answer: Since the number of decimal places in the product is the sum of the decimal places in the factors, $3 + x = 4$. So $x = 1$, and the second factor has 1 digit to the right of the decimal point.**




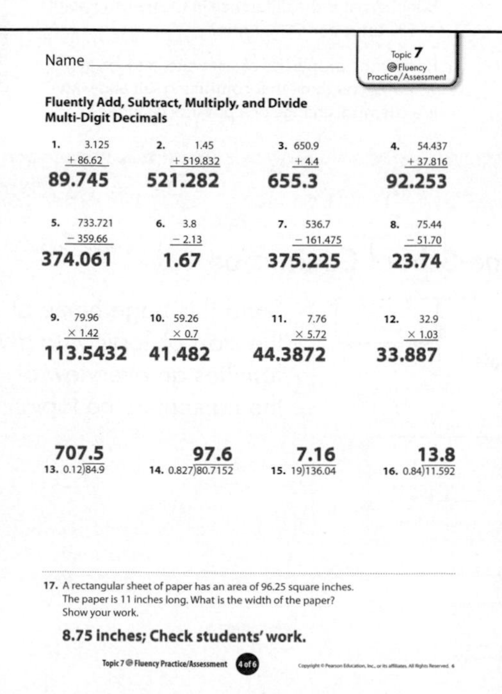
Name ____________________ Topic 7 Fluency Practice/Assessment

## Fluently Add, Subtract, Multiply, and Divide Multi-Digit Decimals

1. 3.125 + 86.62 = **89.745**
2. 1.45 + 519.832 = **521.282**
3. 650.9 + 4.4 = **655.3**
4. 54.437 + 37.816 = **92.253**
5. 733.721 − 359.66 = **374.061**
6. 3.8 − 2.13 = **1.67**
7. 536.7 − 161.475 = **375.225**
8. 75.44 − 51.70 = **23.74**
9. 79.96 × 1.42 = **113.5432**
10. 59.26 × 0.7 = **41.482**
11. 7.76 × 5.72 = **44.3872**
12. 32.9 × 1.03 = **33.887**
13. 0.12)84.9 **707.5**
14. 0.827)80.7152 **97.6**
15. 19)136.04 **7.16**
16. 0.84)11.592 **13.8**

17. A rectangular sheet of paper has an area of 96.25 square inches. The paper is 11 inches long. What is the width of the paper? Show your work.

**8.75 inches; Check students' work.**

Name ____________________ Topic 7 Fluency Practice/Assessment

## Fluently Add, Subtract, Multiply, and Divide Multi-Digit Decimals

1. 5.22 + 23.22 = **28.44**
2. 6.8 + 89.958 = **96.758**
3. 906.077 + 813.2 = **1,719.277**
4. 131.400 + 6.414 = **137.814**
5. 62.5 − 7.857 = **54.643**
6. 4.57 − 4.30 = **0.27**
7. 70.6 − 35.64 = **34.96**
8. 99.089 − 1.77 = **97.319**
9. 24.02 × 6.53 = **156.8506**
10. 70.56 × 0.49 = **34.5744**
11. 691.1 × 12.4 = **8,569.64**
12. 62.75 × 9.42 = **591.105**
13. 8.5)1.0795 **0.127**
14. 8.3)744.51 **89.7**
15. 0.72)457.56 **635.5**
16. 3.7)0.4699 **0.127**

17. The quotient of $72.644 \div 2.54 = 28.6$. Without calculating, what is the product of 28.6 and 2.54? Explain how you know.

**72.644; Sample answer: Multiplication and division are inverse operations.**




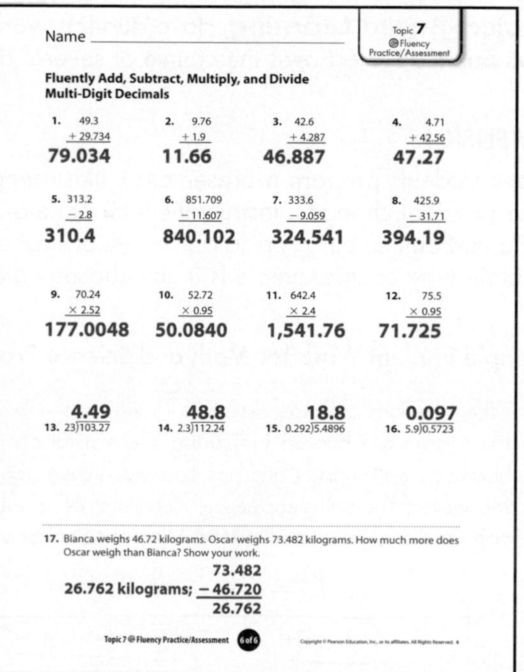
Name ____________________ Topic 7 Fluency Practice/Assessment

## Fluently Add, Subtract, Multiply, and Divide Multi-Digit Decimals

1. 49.3 + 29.734 = **79.034**
2. 9.76 + 1.9 = **11.66**
3. 42.6 + 4.287 = **46.887**
4. 4.71 + 42.56 = **47.27**
5. 313.2 − 2.8 = **310.4**
6. 851.709 − 11.607 = **840.102**
7. 333.6 − 9.059 = **324.541**
8. 425.9 − 31.71 = **394.19**
9. 70.24 × 2.52 = **177.0048**
10. 52.72 × 0.95 = **50.0840**
11. 642.4 × 2.4 = **1,541.76**
12. 75.5 × 0.95 = **71.725**
13. 23)103.27 **4.49**
14. 2.3)112.24 **48.8**
15. 0.292)5.4896 **18.8**
16. 5.9)0.5723 **0.097**

17. Bianca weighs 46.72 kilograms. Oscar weighs 73.482 kilograms. How much more does Oscar weigh than Bianca? Show your work.

**26.762 kilograms; 73.482 − 46.720 = 26.762**

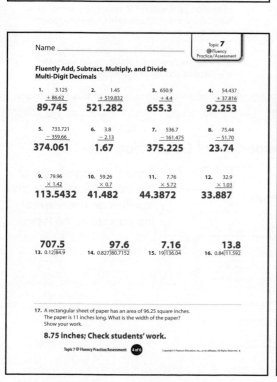

# TOPIC OPENER

# FLUENTLY ADD, SUBTRACT, MULTIPLY, AND DIVIDE DECIMALS

## TOPIC ESSENTIAL QUESTION

**How can you fluently add, subtract, multiply, and divide decimals?**

Revisit the Topic Essential Question throughout the topic, and see a note about answering the question in the Teacher's Edition for the Topic Assessment.

## MATH AND SCIENCE PROJECT STEM

**Science Theme** The science theme for this project is **Freezing Points**. This theme will be revisited in the Math and Science Activities in Lessons 7-2 and 7-7 and in some lesson exercises.

Changes in matter can be classified as physical or chemical. Physical changes result in a new form or state of matter, but no chemical reaction. Examples include crushing a can, whipping cream, or chopping wood. Chemical changes require that chemical bonds in molecules are created or broken. Examples include rusting iron and burning wood. Some changes, such as boiling coffee, can be broken down into simpler steps, some of which are chemical while others are physical. Thus, the overall process is difficult to categorize.

A solution of salt and water is called brine. Saturated brine contains a bit more than 25% salt by weight. In a saturated solution, no more solvent will dissolve.

**Project-Based Learning** Have students work on the **Math and Science Project** over the course of several days.

## EXTENSION

Have students prepare a presentation illustrating chemical and physical changes. Instruct them to make a poster, create a PowerPoint or blog, or do a live demonstration. Have them explain why each example is in the chosen category.

### Sample Student Work for Math and Science Project

When sodium chloride dissolves in water, the bonds between the atoms are broken indicating a chemical change. However, new bonds are not formed. When you evaporate the water, the salt reappears. Recovery of a substance in its original form is characteristic of a physical change.

Freezing Points of Brine

| % Salt | Temperature in C° |
|---|---|
| 0 | 0 |
| 5 | − 3.05 |
| 10 | − 6.56 |
| 20 | − 16.46 |
| saturated | − 21.13 |

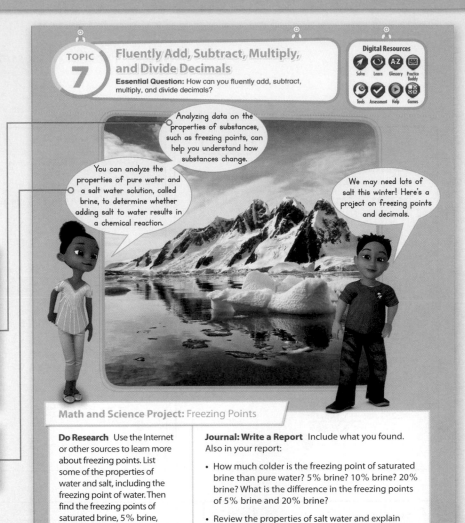

**Math and Science Project:** Freezing Points

**Do Research** Use the Internet or other sources to learn more about freezing points. List some of the properties of water and salt, including the freezing point of water. Then find the freezing points of saturated brine, 5% brine, 10% brine, and 20% brine. Round to the nearest hundredth °C.

**Journal: Write a Report** Include what you found. Also in your report:

- How much colder is the freezing point of saturated brine than pure water? 5% brine? 10% brine? 20% brine? What is the difference in the freezing points of 5% brine and 20% brine?
- Review the properties of salt water and explain whether you think that combining salt and water is a chemical change or a physical change.

Topic 7 317

## Home-School Connection

Name ______________________

Home-School Connection Topic 7

**Fluently Add, Subtract, Multiply, and Divide Decimals**

**Topic 7 Standards**
6.NS.B.2, 6.NS.B.3, 6.EE.A.2a, 6.EE.A.2c, 6.EE.B.7
*See the front of the Student's Edition for complete standards.*

Dear Family,

Your child is learning how to estimate with decimals and how to use estimation to check that his or her answers are reasonable. Your child will learn how to add, subtract, multiply and divide decimals, and how to evaluate expressions with decimals and find solutions to decimal equations.

Here is an activity you can do with your child to help him or her develop estimation skills.

**Rolling Decimals**

**Materials** number cube

**Step 1** Roll a number cube six times. Write two three-digit numbers using the digits you rolled. Insert a decimal point in both numbers. For example, you might write 23.6 and 0.125.

**Step 2** Write an equation for each of the operations using the two numbers. Estimate the answers to the equations. Compare the results with your estimations.

**Step 3** After you and your child take turns making up numbers and estimating the results of different operations, choose an estimation goal, such as 100 or 25.5. Challenge your child to write equations with decimals that will come as close to the estimate as possible.

**Observe Your Child**

**Focus on Mathematical Practice 2**
Reason abstractly and quantitatively.

Help your child become proficient with Mathematical Practice 2. Be sure to have your child write or record all estimates for computations with decimals. Solving the computations and comparing the results with the estimates confirms your child's ability to reason abstractly and quantitatively.



Send this page home at the start of Topic 7 to give families an overview of the content in the topic.

Name

# Review What You Know

## Vocabulary

Choose the best term from the box. Write it on the blank.

- compatible numbers
- decimal
- difference
- estimate
- product
- quotient
- sum

1. The result of multiplying two numbers is called the **product**.
2. A(n) **estimate** is an approximate answer.
3. Numbers that are easy to compute mentally are **compatible numbers**.
4. In the equation 497 − 265 = 232, the number 232 is the **difference**.

## Whole Number Operations

Calculate each value.

5. $4\overline{)348}$ **87**
6. 9,007 − 3,128 **5,879**
7. 35 × 17 **595**
8. 7,964 + 3,872 **11,836**
9. $22\overline{)4{,}638}$ **210 R18**
10. 181 × 42 **7,602**

## Evaluating Expressions

Evaluate each expression for $x = 3$ and $x = 7$.

11. $5x$ **15; 35**
12. $84 - 2x$ **78; 70**
13. $4 + 21 \div x$ **11; 7**
14. $3x + 98 \div 14$ **16; 28**
15. $6x \div x - 2$ **4; 4**
16. $28 + 4x \div 2$ **34; 42**

## Decimals

17. What decimal does this model represent? Explain how you know.

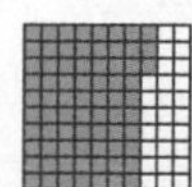

**0.73; Sample answer: The grid represents 1 whole and has 100 parts. 73 parts or 73 hundredths are shaded.**





## Vocabulary Review Activity

Have students work in pairs, using cards like the ones drawn below. Instruct students to use compatible numbers to estimate the answers to the operations shown on each card. Then have them use the correct vocabulary word *sum, difference, product,* or *quotient* to describe the result of the operation.

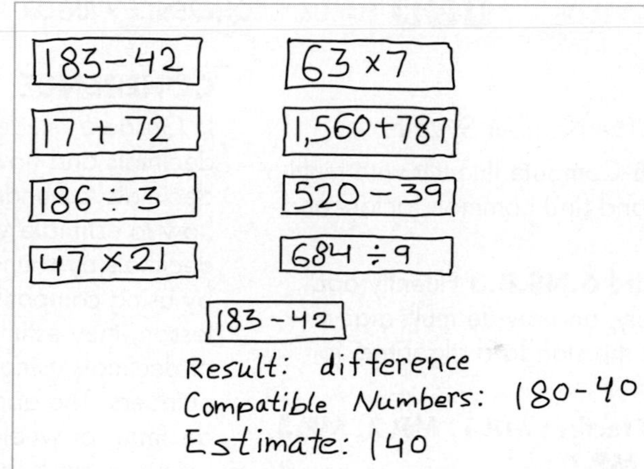


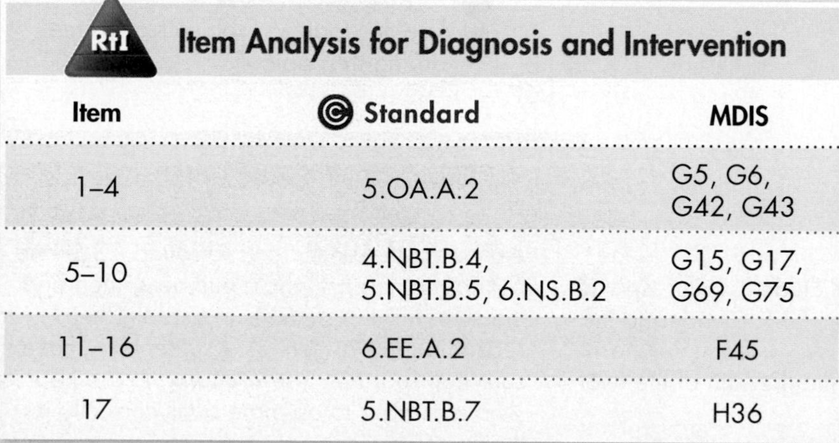

### Item Analysis for Diagnosis and Intervention

| Item | Standard | MDIS |
|---|---|---|
| 1–4 | 5.OA.A.2 | G5, G6, G42, G43 |
| 5–10 | 4.NBT.B.4, 5.NBT.B.5, 6.NS.B.2 | G15, G17, G69, G75 |
| 11–16 | 6.EE.A.2 | F45 |
| 17 | 5.NBT.B.7 | H36 |

# LESSON 7-1

# ESTIMATE SUMS AND DIFFERENCES

## DIGITAL RESOURCES PearsonRealize.com

eText — Student and Teacher eTexts

PD — Listen and Look For Lesson Video

Think — Today's Challenge

Solve — Solve and Share

Learn — Visual Learning Animation Plus

Glossary — Animated Glossary

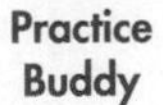
Practice Buddy — Online Personalized Practice

Tools — Math Tools

Assessment — Quick Check

Help — Another Look Homework Video

Games — Math Games

## LESSON OVERVIEW FCR FOCUS • COHERENCE • RIGOR

### FOCUS

**Domain 6.NS** The Number System

**Cluster 6.NS.B** Compute fluently with multi-digit numbers and find common factors and multiples.

**Content Standard 6.NS.B.3** Fluently add, subtract, multiply, and divide multi-digit decimals using the standard algorithm for each operation.

**Mathematical Practices MP.1, MP.2, MP.3, MP.4, MP.6, MP.7**

**Objective** Estimate the sums and differences of decimals.

**Essential Understanding** Estimates can be found by using strategies such as rounding and compatible numbers. Some problems can be solved with an estimate.

### COHERENCE

In Grade 5, students learned how to round decimals and how to add and subtract decimals to hundredths. They also learned how to estimate sums and differences of decimals by rounding to a whole number or by using compatible whole numbers. In this lesson, they estimate sums and differences of decimals using rounding and compatible numbers. The approximations may be either decimals or whole numbers.

### RIGOR

This lesson emphasizes **conceptual understanding** and **procedural skill**. Students use number sense to estimate sums and differences of decimals.

PD Watch the Listen and Look For Lesson Video.

## MATH ANYTIME

### Daily Common Core Review

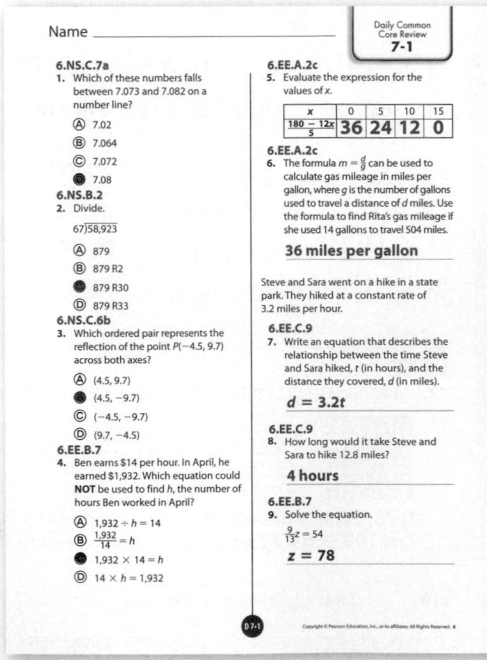
Name ____________ Daily Common Core Review 7-1

6.NS.C.7a
1. Which of these numbers falls between 7.073 and 7.082 on a number line?
Ⓐ 7.02
Ⓑ 7.064
Ⓒ 7.072
● 7.08

6.NS.B.2
2. Divide.
67)58,923
Ⓐ 879
Ⓑ 879 R2
● 879 R30
Ⓓ 879 R33

6.NS.C.6b
3. Which ordered pair represents the reflection of the point $P(-4.5, 9.7)$ across both axes?
Ⓐ (4.5, 9.7)
● (4.5, −9.7)
Ⓒ (−4.5, −9.7)
Ⓓ (9.7, −4.5)

6.EE.B.7
4. Ben earns $14 per hour. In April, he earned $1,932. Which equation could **NOT** be used to find $h$, the number of hours Ben worked in April?
Ⓐ $1,932 \div h = 14$
Ⓑ $\frac{1,932}{14} = h$
● $1,932 \times 14 = h$
Ⓓ $14 \times h = 1,932$

6.EE.A.2c
5. Evaluate the expression for the values of $x$.

| $x$ | 0 | 5 | 10 | 15 |
|---|---|---|---|---|
| $\frac{180 - 12x}{5}$ | **36** | **24** | **12** | **0** |

6.EE.A.2c
6. The formula $m = \frac{d}{g}$ can be used to calculate gas mileage in miles per gallon, where $g$ is the number of gallons used to travel a distance of $d$ miles. Use the formula to find Rita's gas mileage if she used 14 gallons to travel 504 miles.
**36 miles per gallon**

Steve and Sara went on a hike in a state park. They hiked at a constant rate of 3.2 miles per hour.

6.EE.C.9
7. Write an equation that describes the relationship between the time Steve and Sara hiked, $t$ (in hours), and the distance they covered, $d$ (in miles).
$d = 3.2t$

6.EE.C.9
8. How long would it take Steve and Sara to hike 12.8 miles?
**4 hours**

6.EE.B.7
9. Solve the equation.
$\frac{9}{13}z = 54$
$z = 78$

D 7-1

### Today's Challenge

Think Use the Topic 7 problems any time during this topic.

## ENGLISH LANGUAGE LEARNERS 

**Learning Strategies** Monitor language production.

*Use with the Solve & Share on Student's Edition p. 319.*

Read the Solve & Share. Say the term *estimate* and instruct students to repeat it. *What does it mean to estimate?* Write *round*. *What does it mean to round numbers?* Write *round to the nearest whole number*. *What does it mean to use rounding to estimate sums and differences?* Write 13.9.

**Beginning** *How do you round 13.9 to the nearest whole number?* Students will respond using the sentence stem: 13.9 rounded to the nearest whole number is ___. Continue the process for 6.4. Then find the sum of the two whole numbers.

**Intermediate** *What is 13.9 rounded to the nearest whole number? How do you know?* Students will respond using the sentence stem: 13.9 rounded to the nearest whole number is ___ because ___. Continue the process for 6.4. Then find the sum of the two whole numbers.

**Advanced** Ask students to round 13.9 and 6.4 to the nearest whole numbers, then find the sum. Instruct students to explain their reasoning to partners. Ask students to make sure their partners use *rounding to the nearest whole number to estimate sums* correctly in their explanations.

**Summarize** What does it mean to use rounding to estimate sums and differences?

# DEVELOP: PROBLEM-BASED LEARNING

**COHERENCE: Engage learners by connecting prior knowledge to new ideas.**
Students expand their ability to compute with decimals by estimating sums or differences using rounding or compatible numbers.

10–15 min

Solve

## BEFORE

1. **Pose the Solve-and-Share Problem**
   **MP.7 Use Structure** Listen and look for students who use place value to round the amounts of snow to the nearest whole numbers in order to estimate the total snowfall.

2. **Build Understanding**
   *Do you need to find an exact answer or an approximate answer to solve the problem? Explain how you know.* [You can find an approximate answer because the problem asks about how much snow fell.] *What operation will you use to find the total amount of snow?* [Addition]

## DURING

3. **Ask Guiding Questions As Needed**
   *What strategies are used for estimating?* [Rounding or compatible numbers] *What are the decimals rounded to the nearest whole numbers?* [13.9 rounds to 14 and 6.4 rounds to 6] *What are compatible numbers for the amounts of snowfall?* [Sample answer: 14 and 7] *About how much snow did the town receive altogether?* [About 20 or 21 inches]

## AFTER

4. **Share and Discuss Solutions**
   Solve Start with students' solutions. If needed, project Alexa's work to discuss how to estimate the answer using rounding.

5. **Transition to the Visual Learning Bridge**
   *Sometimes an exact answer is not needed and you can use an estimate to solve a problem.*

6. **Extension for Early Finishers**
   *Write a problem that can be solved with an estimate that uses decimals and has an estimated sum of 15.* [Check students' answers.]

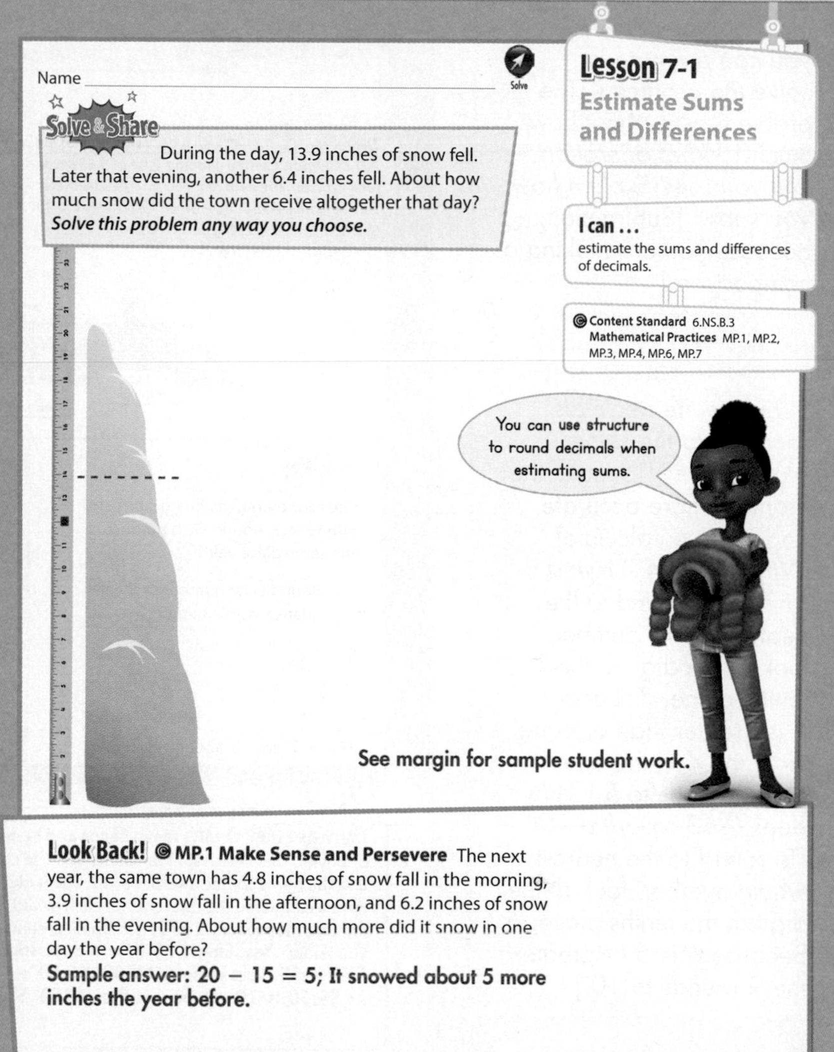

Name
Solve & Share
During the day, 13.9 inches of snow fell. Later that evening, another 6.4 inches fell. About how much snow did the town receive altogether that day?
*Solve this problem any way you choose.*
Lesson 7-1
Estimate Sums and Differences
I can ...
estimate the sums and differences of decimals.
Content Standard 6.NS.B.3
Mathematical Practices MP.1, MP.2, MP.3, MP.4, MP.6, MP.7
You can use structure to round decimals when estimating sums.
See margin for sample student work.
Look Back! MP.1 Make Sense and Persevere The next year, the same town has 4.8 inches of snow fall in the morning, 3.9 inches of snow fall in the afternoon, and 6.2 inches of snow fall in the evening. About how much more did it snow in one day the year before?
Sample answer: 20 − 15 = 5; It snowed about 5 more inches the year before.
Digital Resources at PearsonRealize.com
Topic 7 | Lesson 7-1
319


## Analyze Student Work

**Alexa's Work**

$13.9 \rightarrow 14$

$+6.4 \rightarrow +6$

$20$

The town received about 20 inches of snowfall that day.

Alexa rounds the decimals to the nearest whole numbers to estimate the total snowfall.

**Jon's Work**

$13.9 \rightarrow 14$

$+6.4 \rightarrow +7$

$21$

The town got about 21 inches of snow.

Jon uses compatible numbers to estimate the total snowfall.

# DEVELOP: VISUAL LEARNING

The *Visual Learning Bridge* connects students' thinking in Solve & Share to important math ideas in the lesson. Use the *Visual Learning Bridge* to make these ideas explicit. Also available as a *Visual Learning Animation Plus* at PearsonRealize.com

ELL Visual Learning

PEARSON realize. PearsonRealize.com

 Learn  Glossary

*How do you know that you can estimate to solve the problem?* [The problem asks about how much.] *What operation will you use? Explain how you know.* [Subtraction, because you are making a comparison.]

*Why are the decimals rounded to the same place value?* [To make the estimate more accurate and easy to calculate] *Why does 14.7 round to 15?* [To round to the nearest whole number, look at the digit in the tenths place, 7. Because 7 is greater than or equal to 5, the 4 in the ones place rounds to 5.] *Why does 9.63 round to 10?* [To round to the nearest whole number, look at the digit in the tenths place, 6. Because 6 is 5 or greater, the 9 rounds to 10.]

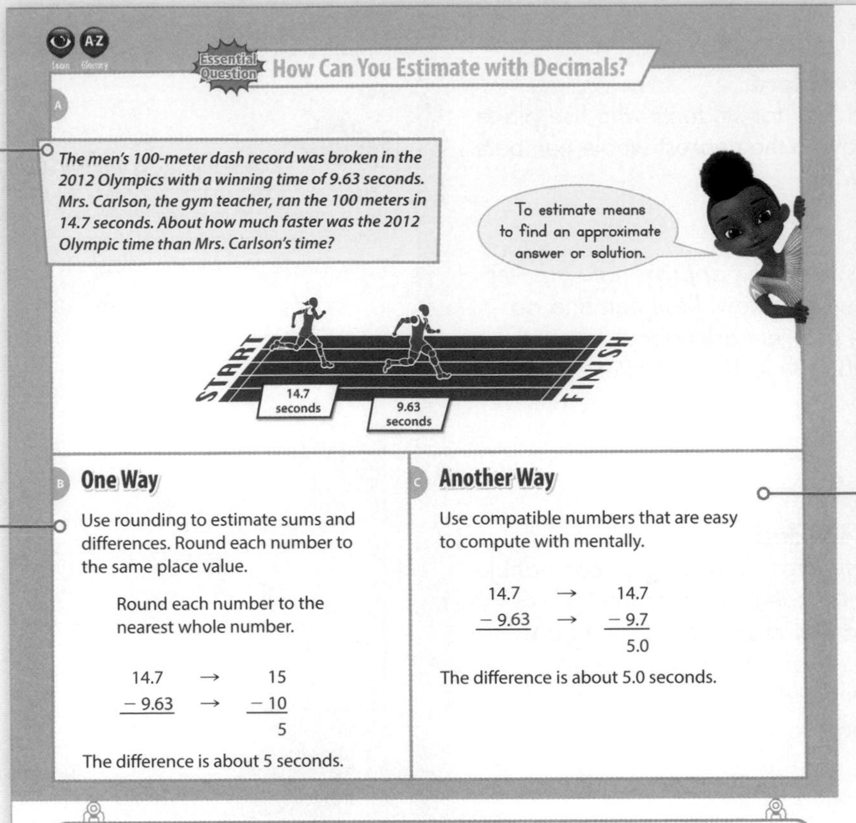

Essential Question **How Can You Estimate with Decimals?**

A

*The men's 100-meter dash record was broken in the 2012 Olympics with a winning time of 9.63 seconds. Mrs. Carlson, the gym teacher, ran the 100 meters in 14.7 seconds. About how much faster was the 2012 Olympic time than Mrs. Carlson's time?*



B **One Way**

Use rounding to estimate sums and differences. Round each number to the same place value.

Round each number to the nearest whole number.

| | | |
|---|---|---|
| 14.7 | → | 15 |
| − 9.63 | → | − 10 |
| | | 5 |

The difference is about 5 seconds.

C **Another Way**

Use compatible numbers that are easy to compute with mentally.

| | | |
|---|---|---|
| 14.7 | → | 14.7 |
| − 9.63 | → | − 9.7 |
| | | 5.0 |

The difference is about 5.0 seconds.

Visual Learning Bridge

**MP.2 Reason Quantitatively** *Why are 14.7 and 9.7 compatible numbers?* [Because they are close to the original numbers and can be subtracted easily.] *Are there other compatible numbers that can be used to find this estimate?* [Yes; the numbers 14.5 and 9.5 are also compatible and give an estimate of 5.]

**Convince Me!** **MP.1 Make Sense and Persevere** Emma is in charge of buying the awards for the science fair. The cost for each award is $5.43 and the frame for the award is $3.82. She is given a budget of $100. Emma estimated the total cost for each award and said she will have enough money for 10 awards. Is Emma's estimate reasonable? Show how you know. **Yes, Emma's estimate is reasonable; Sample answer: $5.43 is close to $5.50; $3.82 is close to $4.00; $5.50 + $4.00 = $9.50; I know 10 × 10 = 100, so $9.50 × 10 will be less than $100. She will have enough money for 10 awards.**

320 Topic 7 | Lesson 7-1 © Pearson Education, Inc. 6

**Convince Me! MP.1 Make Sense and Persevere** *How would you find the total cost for each award?* [Add $5.43 and $3.82] *How can you estimate the sum?* [Sample answer: $5.43 rounds to $5 and $3.82 rounds to $4, so about $9 per award.] *If Emma plans on 10 awards for $100, what is the maximum price each award can cost? Explain.* [$10; $100 ÷ 10 = $10]

Revisit the Essential Question. Students should recognize that they can estimate with decimals by rounding the decimals to the same place value or by using compatible numbers. Estimated values should be close to the actual decimals and easy to calculate.

PEARSON realize. PearsonRealize.com

## QUICK CHECK

Check mark indicates items for prescribing differentiation on the next page. Items 14 and 24 are worth 1 point. Item 25 is worth up to 3 points.

20–30 min

Practice Buddy

Tools

Assessment

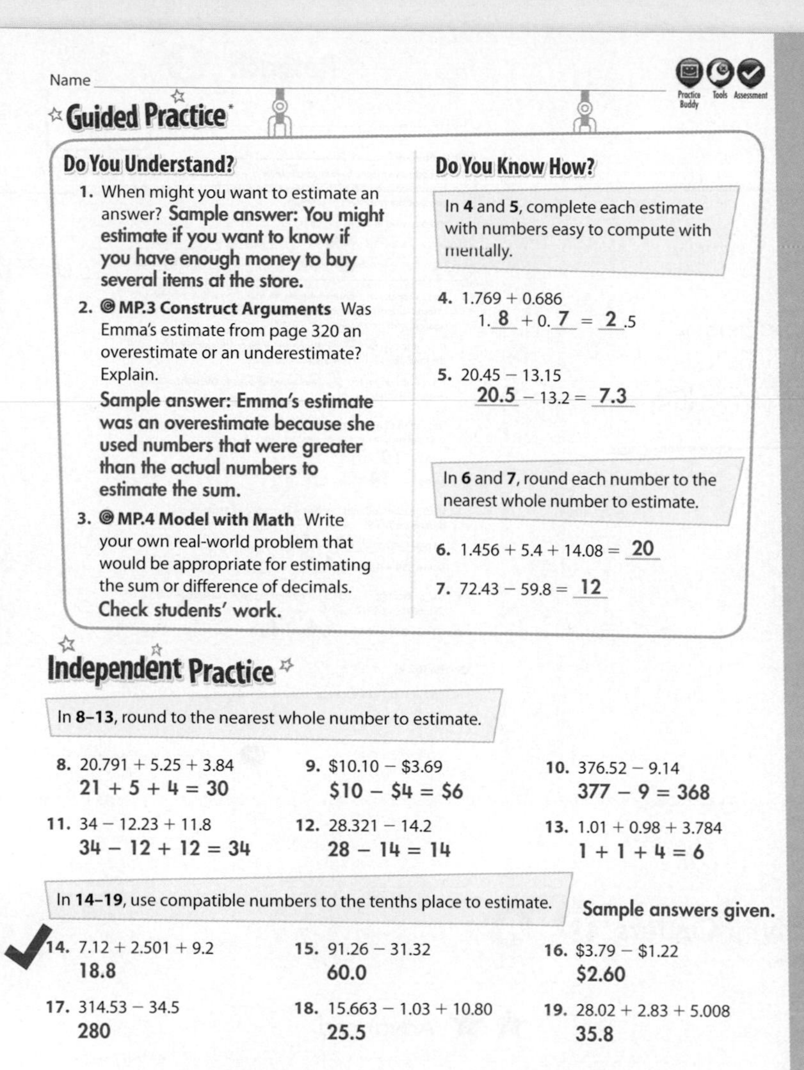

Name

### Guided Practice*

**Do You Understand?**

1. When might you want to estimate an answer? **Sample answer: You might estimate if you want to know if you have enough money to buy several items at the store.**
2. **MP.3 Construct Arguments** Was Emma's estimate from page 320 an overestimate or an underestimate? Explain. **Sample answer: Emma's estimate was an overestimate because she used numbers that were greater than the actual numbers to estimate the sum.**
3. **MP.4 Model with Math** Write your own real-world problem that would be appropriate for estimating the sum or difference of decimals. **Check students' work.**

**Do You Know How?**

In **4** and **5**, complete each estimate with numbers easy to compute with mentally.

4. 1.769 + 0.686
 1.__8__ + 0.__7__ = __2__.5
5. 20.45 − 13.15
 __20.5__ − 13.2 = __7.3__

In **6** and **7**, round each number to the nearest whole number to estimate.

6. 1.456 + 5.4 + 14.08 = __20__
7. 72.43 − 59.8 = __12__

### Independent Practice

In **8–13**, round to the nearest whole number to estimate.

8. 20.791 + 5.25 + 3.84
 **21 + 5 + 4 = 30**
9. $10.10 − $3.69
 **$10 − $4 = $6**
10. 376.52 − 9.14
 **377 − 9 = 368**
11. 34 − 12.23 + 11.8
 **34 − 12 + 12 = 34**
12. 28.321 − 14.2
 **28 − 14 = 14**
13. 1.01 + 0.98 + 3.784
 **1 + 1 + 4 = 6**

In **14–19**, use compatible numbers to the tenths place to estimate. **Sample answers given.**

14. 7.12 + 2.501 + 9.2
 **18.8**
15. 91.26 − 31.32
 **60.0**
16. $3.79 − $1.22
 **$2.60**
17. 314.53 − 34.5
 **280**
18. 15.663 − 1.03 + 10.80
 **25.5**
19. 28.02 + 2.83 + 5.008
 **35.8**

*For another example, see Set A on page 381.

Topic 7 | Lesson 7-1 321

### Math Practices and Problem Solving*

20. **Number Sense** Rachel is shopping and needs to buy bread, lunchmeat, and pretzels to make lunch. She has a ten-dollar bill. Use estimation to find whether she will have enough money. Explain your reasoning.
 **$2 + $5 + $2 = $9; Sample answer: I got an overestimate by rounding to the nearest whole number. Since she has $10, she will have enough money.**

Grocery List
Bread $1.82
Lunchmeat $4.93
Pretzels $2.03


21. Cooper, a 2-year-old stallion, ran a lap in 8.71 seconds. He ran a second lap in 7.32 seconds. Estimate Cooper's combined time to the nearest second.
 **Sample answer: Cooper ran two laps in about 16 seconds.**
22. **MP.3 Construct Arguments** Camilla estimated the sum of 8.614 + 3.099 + 7.301 to be about 19. She added 8.6 + 3.1 + 7.3 to get the sum. Is her estimate an overestimate or an underestimate? Explain your reasoning.
 **Sample answer: Camilla's estimate is an underestimate because she rounded 8.614 to 8.6, a difference of 14 hundredths less. Rounding the other two decimals did not change their combined value.**
23. The jeweler made a new crown for the Queen. It was made with an 8.74-carat diamond, a 7.086-carat ruby, and a 4.93-carat sapphire. What is the approximate total weight, in carats, of all the gems in the Queen's crown?
 **Sample answer: The Queen's crown has a total weight of about 21 carats.**
24. **Higher Order Thinking** In a certain manufacturing process, a chemical must be heated to exactly 236.75°F. If the temperature showed 210.964°F, would you use an estimate to find the needed increase in temperature? Explain.
 **Sample answer: No. The chemical needs to be heated to an exact temperature, so an estimate is not precise enough.**

**Common Core Assessment**

25. Kira wants to buy a movie ticket, popcorn, and a drink. The movie ticket costs $7.75, and the snack and drink combo costs $2.85. If Kira brings $10, will she have enough money for the ticket and snack combo? Estimate to explain your reasoning.
 **No; Sample answer: Kira needs more than $10 because $2.85 is close to $3, and $3 added to $7.75 is more than $10.**

322 Topic 7 | Lesson 7-1



**Error Intervention: Item 4**

**If** students have difficulty finding the missing numbers,

**then** ask: *What is 1.769 rounded to the nearest tenth?* [1.8] *What is 0.686 rounded to the nearest tenth?* [0.7]

**Item 8** Encourage students to round each of the three decimals first, and then to apply strategies for mental math to add the three whole numbers. For example, to find the sum 21 + 5 + 4, add 5 + 4 = 9 first, then add 21 + 9 = 30.

**Reteaching** Assign Reteaching Set A on p. 381.

**Item 20 Number Sense** Remind students that sometimes the estimating strategy is important to determining an accurate estimate. In situations like this, underestimating the cost could mean a lack of money to afford the items. *Would you use rounding or compatible numbers to determine whether Rachel has enough money?* [Sample answer: You could use either. For example, you could round to the nearest whole number or use compatible numbers to estimate 2 + 5 + 2 = 9.]

**Item 22 MP.3 Construct Arguments** Remind students that a good math argument uses words and math to justify a solution. This item requires reasoning to explain why the numbers were chosen.

**Multi-Step Problems** *Page 322 Items 20 and 25; Page 324 Items 16, 17, 19, and 21*

# ASSESS AND DIFFERENTIATE

Use the **QUICK CHECK** on the previous page to prescribe differentiated instruction.

**I Intervention** 0–3 points on the Quick Check

**O On-Level** 4 points on the Quick Check

**A Advanced** 5 points on the Quick Check

## Intervention Activity I

### Estimating Sums and Differences

**Materials**

Sheets of paper each displaying a digit 0–9, +, −, or a decimal point (.)

- Distribute the sheets of paper to students.
- Ask students to stand in a line to create an addition problem using decimals.
- Have students decide which strategy they would use to estimate the sum. Then have students record the addition problem and the estimate.
- Repeat the activity with a variety of decimal addition and subtraction problems.

35.7 + 65.2

Use compatible numbers.

35.7 + 65.2 → 35 + 65 = 100

## Reteach I

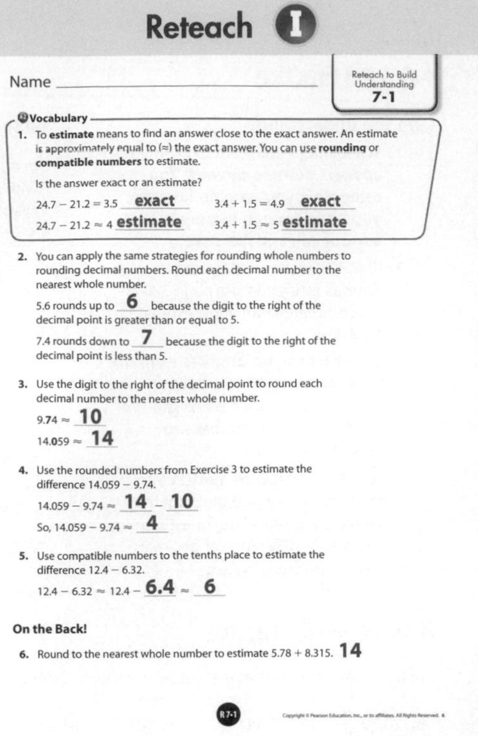

Name ______________

Reteach to Build Understanding 7-1

**Vocabulary**

1. To **estimate** means to find an answer close to the exact answer. An estimate is approximately equal to (≈) the exact answer. You can use **rounding** or **compatible numbers** to estimate.

Is the answer exact or an estimate?

$24.7 - 21.2 = 3.5$ **exact** $3.4 + 1.5 = 4.9$ **exact**

$24.7 - 21.2 \approx 4$ **estimate** $3.4 + 1.5 \approx 5$ **estimate**

2. You can apply the same strategies for rounding whole numbers to rounding decimal numbers. Round each decimal number to the nearest whole number.

5.6 rounds up to **6** because the digit to the right of the decimal point is greater than or equal to 5.

7.4 rounds down to **7** because the digit to the right of the decimal point is less than 5.

3. Use the digit to the right of the decimal point to round each decimal number to the nearest whole number.

$9.74 \approx$ **10**

$14.059 \approx$ **14**

4. Use the rounded numbers from Exercise 3 to estimate the difference 14.059 − 9.74.

$14.059 - 9.74 \approx$ **14** − **10**

So, $14.059 - 9.74 \approx$ **4**

5. Use compatible numbers to the tenths place to estimate the difference 12.4 − 6.32.

$12.4 - 6.32 \approx 12.4 -$ **6.4** $\approx$ **6**

**On the Back!**

6. Round to the nearest whole number to estimate 5.78 + 8.315. **14**

R7-1



## On-Level and Advanced Activity Centers 

### Center Games

Students work in pairs or small groups to estimate decimal sums and differences. Have students record their work as they play the game.

★ On-Level

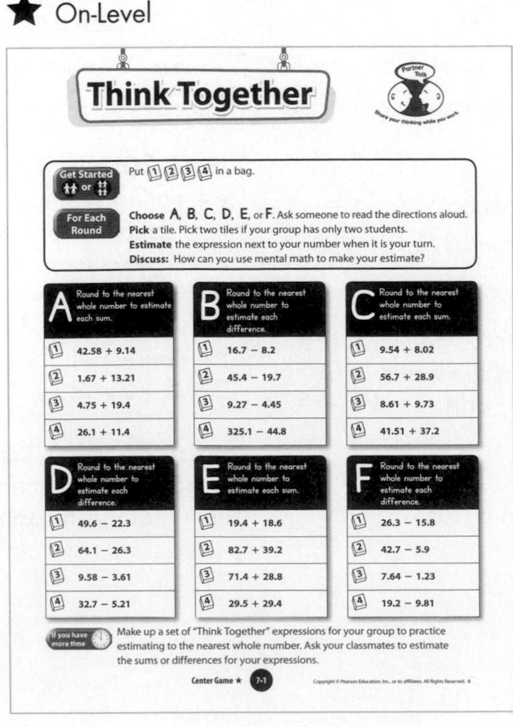

**Think Together**

Partner Talk — Share your thinking while you work.

**Get Started** Put 1 2 3 4 in a bag.

**For Each Round** **Choose** A, B, C, D, E, or F. Ask someone to read the directions aloud. **Pick** a tile. Pick two tiles if your group has only two students. **Estimate** the expression next to your number when it is your turn. **Discuss:** How can you use mental math to make your estimate?

| | A Round to the nearest whole number to estimate each sum. | B Round to the nearest whole number to estimate each difference. | C Round to the nearest whole number to estimate each sum. |
|---|---|---|---|
| 1 | 42.58 + 9.14 | 16.7 − 8.2 | 9.54 + 8.02 |
| 2 | 1.67 + 13.21 | 45.4 − 19.7 | 56.7 + 28.9 |
| 3 | 4.75 + 19.4 | 9.27 − 4.45 | 8.61 + 9.73 |
| 4 | 26.1 + 11.4 | 325.1 − 44.8 | 41.51 + 37.2 |

| | D Round to the nearest whole number to estimate each difference. | E Round to the nearest whole number to estimate each sum. | F Round to the nearest whole number to estimate each difference. |
|---|---|---|---|
| 1 | 49.6 − 22.3 | 19.4 + 18.6 | 26.3 − 15.8 |
| 2 | 64.1 − 26.3 | 82.7 + 39.2 | 42.7 − 5.9 |
| 3 | 9.58 − 3.61 | 71.4 + 28.8 | 7.64 − 1.23 |
| 4 | 32.7 − 5.21 | 29.5 + 29.4 | 19.2 − 9.81 |

**If you have more time** Make up a set of "Think Together" expressions for your group to practice estimating to the nearest whole number. Ask your classmates to estimate the sums or differences for your expressions.

Center Game ★ 7-1



★★ Advanced

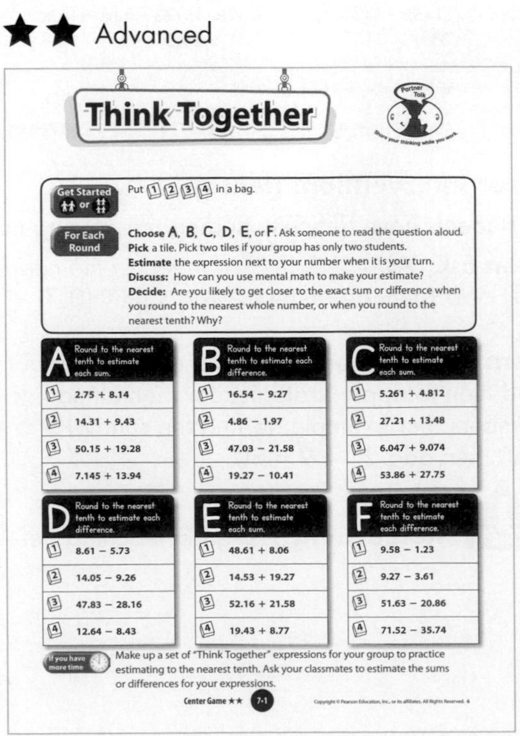

**Think Together**

Partner Talk — Share your thinking while you work.

**Get Started** Put 1 2 3 4 in a bag.

**For Each Round** **Choose** A, B, C, D, E, or F. Ask someone to read the question aloud. **Pick** a tile. Pick two tiles if your group has only two students. **Estimate** the expression next to your number when it is your turn. **Discuss:** How can you use mental math to make your estimate? **Decide:** Are you likely to get closer to the exact sum or difference when you round to the nearest whole number, or when you round to the nearest tenth? Why?

| | A Round to the nearest tenth to estimate each sum. | B Round to the nearest tenth to estimate each difference. | C Round to the nearest tenth to estimate each sum. |
|---|---|---|---|
| 1 | 2.75 + 8.14 | 16.54 − 9.27 | 5.261 + 4.812 |
| 2 | 14.31 + 9.43 | 4.86 − 1.97 | 27.21 + 13.48 |
| 3 | 50.15 + 19.28 | 47.03 − 21.58 | 6.047 + 9.074 |
| 4 | 7.145 + 13.94 | 19.27 − 10.41 | 53.86 + 27.75 |

| | D Round to the nearest tenth to estimate each difference. | E Round to the nearest tenth to estimate each sum. | F Round to the nearest tenth to estimate each difference. |
|---|---|---|---|
| 1 | 8.61 − 5.73 | 48.61 + 8.06 | 9.58 − 1.23 |
| 2 | 14.05 − 9.26 | 14.53 + 19.27 | 9.27 − 3.61 |
| 3 | 47.83 − 28.16 | 52.16 + 21.58 | 51.63 − 20.86 |
| 4 | 12.64 − 8.43 | 19.43 + 8.77 | 71.52 − 35.74 |

**If you have more time** Make up a set of "Think Together" expressions for your group to practice estimating to the nearest tenth. Ask your classmates to estimate the sums or differences for your expressions.

Center Game ★★ 7-1

PEARSON realize.
PearsonRealize.com

**TIMING**

The time allocated to Step 3 will depend on the teacher's instructional decisions and differentiation routines.

15–30 min

Help | Practice Buddy | Tools | Games

## Technology Center   

 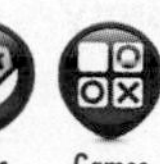

Tools Games

### Math Tools and Math Games

A link to a specific math tools activity or math game to use with this lesson is provided at PearsonRealize.com.

## Leveled Assignment

I Items 1–6, 10–12, 16, 17, 19, 21  Items 4–6, 13–15, 16, 18–21  Items 7–9, 13–15, 16–21

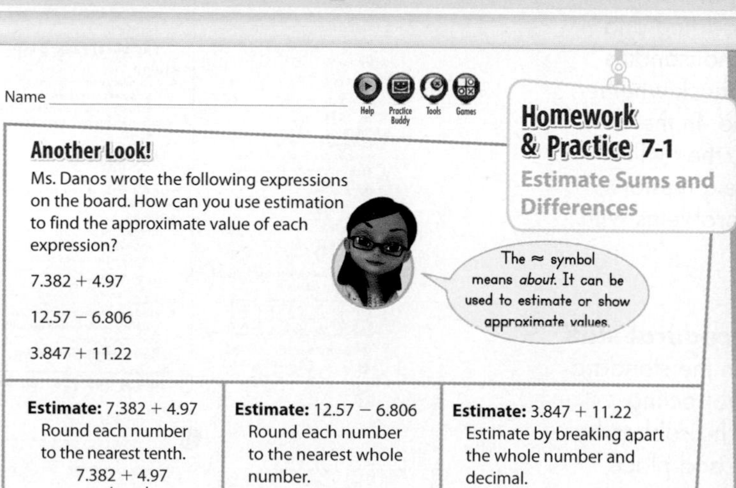

Name ____________________

Help Practice Buddy Tools Games

**Homework & Practice 7-1**
**Estimate Sums and Differences**

**Another Look!**

Ms. Danos wrote the following expressions on the board. How can you use estimation to find the approximate value of each expression?

7.382 + 4.97

12.57 − 6.806

3.847 + 11.22



| **Estimate:** 7.382 + 4.97 | **Estimate:** 12.57 − 6.806 | **Estimate:** 3.847 + 11.22 |
|---|---|---|
| Round each number to the nearest tenth.<br>7.382 + 4.97<br>↓ ↓<br>7.4 + 5<br>Add to estimate:<br>7.4 + 5 = 12.4<br>7.382 + 4.97 ≈ 12.4 | Round each number to the nearest whole number.<br>12.57 − 6.806<br>↓ ↓<br>13 − 7<br>Subtract to estimate:<br>13 − 7 = 6<br>12.57 − 6.806 ≈ 6 | Estimate by breaking apart the whole number and decimal.<br>3.847 → 3 .8<br>+ 11.22 → + 11 .2<br>↓ ↓<br>14 + 1.0 = 15<br>3.847 + 11.22 ≈ 15 |

In **1–9**, round to the nearest whole number to estimate.

**1.** 4.38 + 9.179 **13** **2.** 62.873 − 12.7 **50** **3.** 52.83 + 97.288 **150**

**4.** 131.049 − 82.604 **48** **5.** 79.14 + 32.546 **112** **6.** 48.468 + 63.029 **111**

**7.** 112.658 − 81.903 **31** **8.** 586.735 − 204.63 **382** **9.** 107.139 + 90.621 **198**

In **10–15**, use compatible numbers to the tenths place to estimate.

**10.** 9.13 − 5.1 **4** **11.** \$15.56 + \$2.19 **\$17.80** **12.** 20.22 + 22.81 + 25.278 **68.3**

**13.** 89.36 + 253.5 **342.9** **14.** 25.6 − 12.22 + 10.8 **24.2** **15.** 86.89 − 45.69 **41.2**



**16.** **MP.6 Be Precise** In baseball, an earned run average (ERA) is the average of earned runs given up by a pitcher every nine innings pitched.

DATA

| Player | Earned Run Average (ERA) |
|---|---|
| Eddie | 1.82 |
| John | 2.10 |
| Mario | 2.06 |
| Scott | 2.04 |
| Josh | 1.89 |

**a** Order the ERAs in the table from greatest to least. **2.10, 2.06, 2.04, 1.89, 1.82**

**b** About how many tenths difference is there between the lowest and highest ERAs in the table? **About 3 tenths**

**17.** **MP.2 Reasoning** Alexis has a \$5-bill, two \$10-bills, and a \$20-bill. She wants to buy a DVD for \$17.89, a mug for \$5.12, and a shirt for \$12.99. Estimate the sum to the nearest dollar. Tell which bills she should hand to the cashier to pay for her items. **\$18 + \$5 + \$13 = \$36. She should give the cashier a \$20-bill and 2 \$10-bills.**

**18.** **Higher Order Thinking** When rounding to the nearest whole number, the decimal 9.5 would typically be rounded to 10. How would you round the numbers 9.5 and 7.5 in the equation $9.5 + 4.7 + 3.2 + 7.5 = x$ if you want your estimate to be as close as possible to the actual sum? **Sample answer: To get an answer as close as possible, I would round one of the 0.5 numbers down and the other up. 10 + 7 = 17, I can use this sum and do the math in my head to get 17 + 4.7 + 3.2 = 24.9.**

**19.** **Algebra** When evaluating the expression $8(4 + 6^2) \div 20 - (3^2 + 3)$, James said its value was 40. Is he correct? Use the order of operations to explain how you know. **No; Sample answer: James subtracted 12 from 20 before he divided 320 by 20. The correct answer is 4.**

**20.** The area of the Garrett's living room is 18.087 square yards. Their bedroom has an area of 15.98 square yards. Round to the nearest tenth and estimate the total amount of carpet they need for both rooms. **Sample answer: 18.1 + 16.0 = 34.1 square yards.**

**Common Core Assessment**

**21.** Bill, Tory, and Jessica ran a 300-meter relay race. Each ran 100 meters. Bill ran his leg of the race in 13.73 seconds, Tory ran hers in 14.22 seconds, and Jessica ran the final leg in 15.09 seconds. Bill estimates that they beat the 44.2-second time they ran last year. Estimate to show whether or not Bill is correct.

**Sample answer: Bill is correct. 13 + 14 + 15 = 42; 0.7 + 0.2 + 0.1 = 1; 42 + 1 = 43; They ran the relay in about 43 seconds, which is less than the previous 44.2-second record.**

# LESSON 7-2

## ADD AND SUBTRACT DECIMALS

### DIGITAL RESOURCES PearsonRealize.com

eText — Student and Teacher eTexts

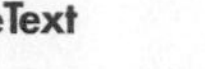

PD — Listen and Look For Lesson Video

Think — Today's Challenge

Solve — Solve and Share

Learn — Visual Learning Animation Plus

Glossary — Animated Glossary

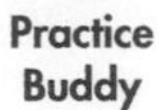
Practice Buddy — Online Personalized Practice

Tools — Math Tools

Assessment — Quick Check

Help — Another Look Homework Video

Games — Math Games

### LESSON OVERVIEW FCR FOCUS • COHERENCE • RIGOR

#### FOCUS

**Domain 6.NS** The Number System

**Cluster 6.NS.B** Compute fluently with multi-digit numbers and find common factors and multiples.

**Content Standard 6.NS.B.3** Fluently add, subtract, multiply, and divide multi-digit decimals using the standard algorithm for each operation.

**Mathematical Practices MP.1, MP.3, MP.6, MP.7, MP.8**

**Objective** Add and subtract decimals.

**Essential Understanding** A general method, or standard algorithm, can be used to add and subtract decimals fluently.

**Materials** Grid paper (Teaching Tool 17)

#### COHERENCE

In Grade 5, students learned how to read, write, and compare decimals to thousandths and how to use place value understanding to add and subtract decimals to hundredths. In Lesson 7-1, they learned to estimate sums and differences of decimals. In this lesson, students develop fluency in adding and subtracting decimals to the thousandths place and use estimates to check whether their answers are reasonable. In the last three lessons of Topic 7, they will use this fluency to evaluate expressions, solve equations, and solve problems with decimals.

#### RIGOR

This lesson emphasizes **procedural skill** and **fluency**. Students learn the standard algorithm for adding and subtracting decimals. They structure each problem by lining up the decimal points and place values before performing the operation.

PD Watch the Listen and Look For Lesson Video.

### MATH ANYTIME

#### Daily Common Core Review

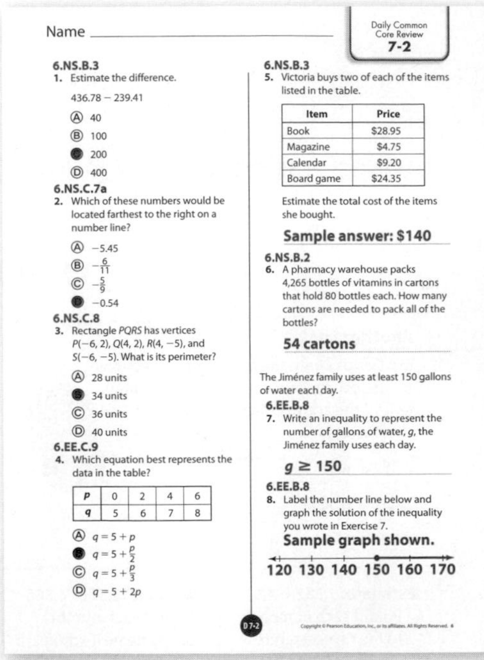

Name ______

Daily Common Core Review 7-2

6.NS.B.3
1. Estimate the difference.

436.78 − 239.41

Ⓐ 40
Ⓑ 100
● 200
Ⓓ 400

6.NS.C.7a
2. Which of these numbers would be located farthest to the right on a number line?

Ⓐ $-5.45$
Ⓑ $-\frac{6}{11}$
Ⓒ $-\frac{5}{9}$
● $-0.54$

6.NS.C.8
3. Rectangle *PQRS* has vertices $P(-6, 2)$, $Q(4, 2)$, $R(4, -5)$, and $S(-6, -5)$. What is its perimeter?

Ⓐ 28 units
● 34 units
Ⓒ 36 units
Ⓓ 40 units

6.EE.C.9
4. Which equation best represents the data in the table?

| *p* | 0 | 2 | 4 | 6 |
|---|---|---|---|---|
| *q* | 5 | 6 | 7 | 8 |

Ⓐ $q = 5 + p$
● $q = 5 + \frac{p}{2}$
Ⓒ $q = 5 + \frac{p}{3}$
Ⓓ $q = 5 + 2p$

6.NS.B.3
5. Victoria buys two of each of the items listed in the table.

| Item | Price |
|---|---|
| Book | $28.95 |
| Magazine | $4.75 |
| Calendar | $9.20 |
| Board game | $24.35 |

Estimate the total cost of the items she bought.

**Sample answer: $140**

6.NS.B.2
6. A pharmacy warehouse packs 4,265 bottles of vitamins in cartons that hold 80 bottles each. How many cartons are needed to pack all of the bottles?

**54 cartons**

The Jiménez family uses at least 150 gallons of water each day.

6.EE.B.8
7. Write an inequality to represent the number of gallons of water, *g*, the Jiménez family uses each day.

$g \geq 150$

6.EE.B.8
8. Label the number line below and graph the solution of the inequality you wrote in Exercise 7.

**Sample graph shown.**

120 130 140 150 160 170

D7-2

#### Today's Challenge

Think Use the Topic 7 problems any time during this topic.

### ENGLISH LANGUAGE LEARNERS ELL

**Listening** Demonstrate listening comprehension by retelling.

*Use with the Visual Learning Bridge on Student's Edition p. 326.*

Read Box A. Instruct students to retell the information to partners. *What information is needed to solve the problem?* Read Frame B. Write 50.9 + 0.26 vertically, lining up the decimal points. *What does it mean to annex a zero so each place has a digit?*

**Beginning** Point to 50.9. *To solve the equation, annex a zero.* Demonstrate annexing a zero by writing 50.90. *Line up the place values to add.* Work with students to find the sum. *To find the sum, we annexed a zero. What did we do to find the sum?* Students will retell using the sentence stem: We ____ a zero.

**Intermediate** *To find the sum, annex a zero to line up the place values.* Demonstrate annexing a zero by writing 50.90. Instruct students to work with partners to find the sum. *What did we do to find the sum? Why?* Students will retell information using the sentence stem: We ____ a ___ because ___.

**Advanced** Instruct students to read Box B with partners. *What does it mean to annex a zero and how is this used to find the sum?* Students will retell information to partners. *Does annexing a zero make finding the sum easier or more difficult? Why?* Students will explain their reasoning to partners.

**Summarize** What does it mean to annex a zero?

# DEVELOP: PROBLEM-BASED LEARNING

**COHERENCE: Engage learners by connecting prior knowledge to new ideas.**
Students use what they know about the base-ten number system to add decimals when finding a combined length.

10–15 min

Solve

## BEFORE

1. **Pose the Solve-and-Share Problem**
**MP.7 Use Structure** Listen and look for students who align the decimal points and digits in correct place-value columns to add the lengths of the boards.

2. **Build Understanding**
*Which operation would you use to find the combined length of the boards? How do you know?* [Addition; because addition combines amounts] *What addition expression represents the combined length of the boards?* [1.15 + 0.7] *Use compatible numbers to estimate 1.15 + 0.7.* [Sample answer: 1.2 + 0.5 = 1.7]

## DURING

3. **Ask Guiding Questions As Needed**
*When you add whole numbers, how do you know which digits to add?* [You add the digits that have the same place value.] *How would you align the decimal numbers to make sure that you add the digits with the same place value?* [You line up the decimal points.]

## AFTER

4. **Share and Discuss Solutions**
Solve: Start with students' solutions. If needed, project Claire's work to discuss how to line up the place values.

5. **Transition to the Visual Learning Bridge**
*You can use a standard method to add and subtract decimals.*

6. **Extension for Early Finishers**
*What is 2.18 + 0.77? Estimate first, and then add.* [Sample answer: 2 + 0.75 = 2.75; 2.95]

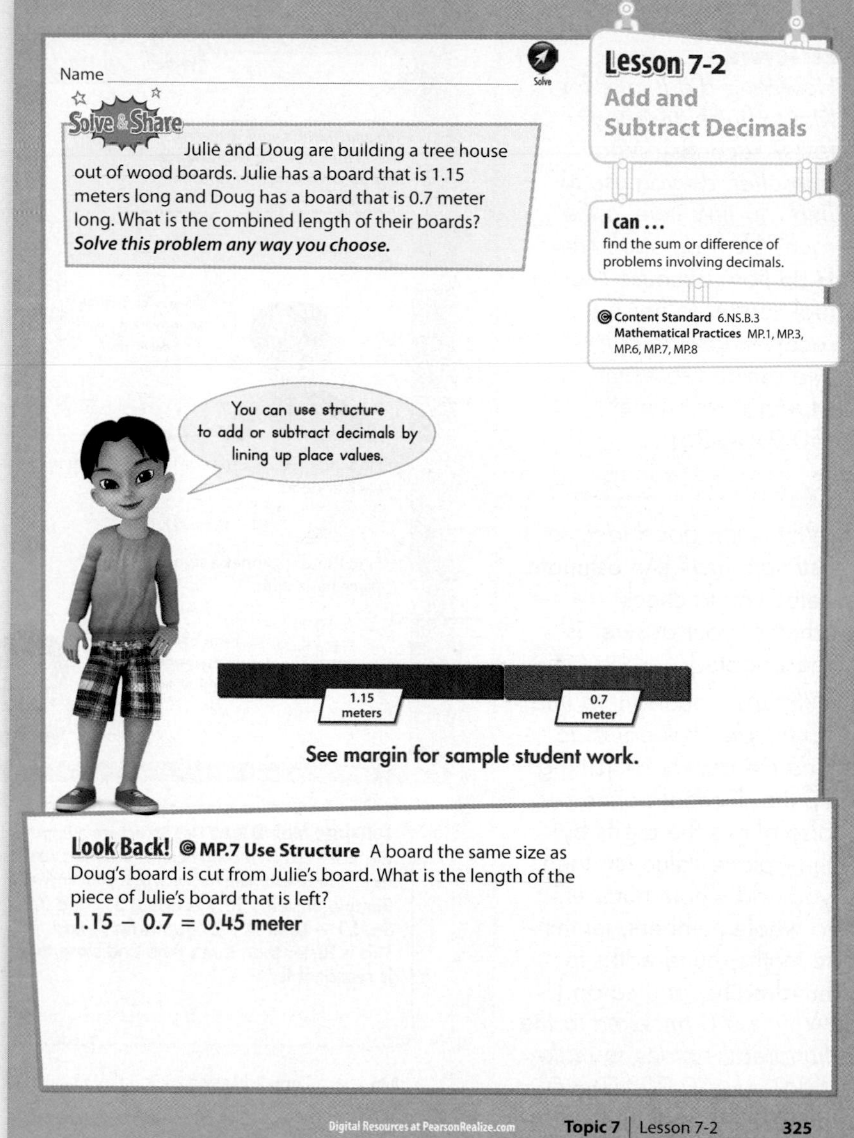

Name

**Solve & Share** Julie and Doug are building a tree house out of wood boards. Julie has a board that is 1.15 meters long and Doug has a board that is 0.7 meter long. What is the combined length of their boards? ***Solve this problem any way you choose.***

**Lesson 7-2**
**Add and Subtract Decimals**

**I can ...**
find the sum or difference of problems involving decimals.

**Content Standard** 6.NS.B.3
**Mathematical Practices** MP.1, MP.3, MP.6, MP.7, MP.8

You can use structure to add or subtract decimals by lining up place values.
1.15 meters
0.7 meter



**See margin for sample student work.**

**Look Back!** **MP.7 Use Structure** A board the same size as Doug's board is cut from Julie's board. What is the length of the piece of Julie's board that is left?
**1.15 − 0.7 = 0.45 meter**

Digital Resources at PearsonRealize.com **Topic 7** | Lesson 7-2 **325**

## Analyze Student Work

Claire's Work

$$\begin{array}{r} 1.15 \\ +\ 0.70 \\ \hline 1.85 \end{array}$$

The combined length of the boards is 1.85 meters.

Claire lines up the decimals and adds the digits in each place-value column to find the sum.

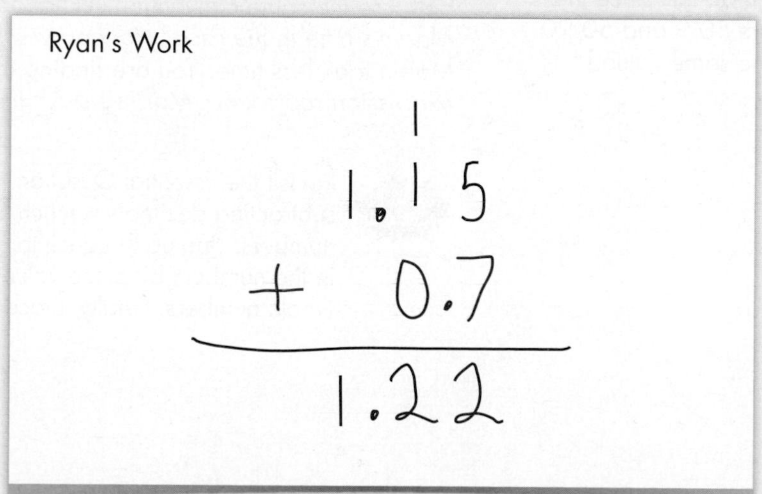


Ryan incorrectly right aligns the numbers before adding.

# DEVELOP: VISUAL LEARNING

The *Visual Learning Bridge* connects students' thinking in Solve & Share to important math ideas in the lesson. Use the *Visual Learning Bridge* to make these ideas explicit. Also available as a *Visual Learning Animation Plus* at PearsonRealize.com

ELL Visual Learning

PEARSON realize. PearsonRealize.com

Learn Glossary

**MP.1 Make Sense and Persevere**
*How long did it take for Kim to finish the race?* [50.9 seconds] *What operation do you use to find Martin's time in the race? How do you know?* [Addition; because Martin took longer to finish the race] *What addition expression represents Martin's swim time?* [50.9 + 0.26]

*Why is it a good idea to estimate first?* [An estimate helps you to check whether your answer is reasonable.] *Why is it important to line up the decimal points to add the decimals?* [Lining up the decimal points also aligns the digits by their place value, so then you add whole numbers to whole numbers, tenths to tenths, hundredths to hundredths, and so on.] *Why is a 0 annexed to the hundredths place to make 50.9 into 50.90?* [The 0 is annexed so that the number of decimal places in both addends is the same. You can do this since the numbers 50.9 and 50.90 have the same value.]

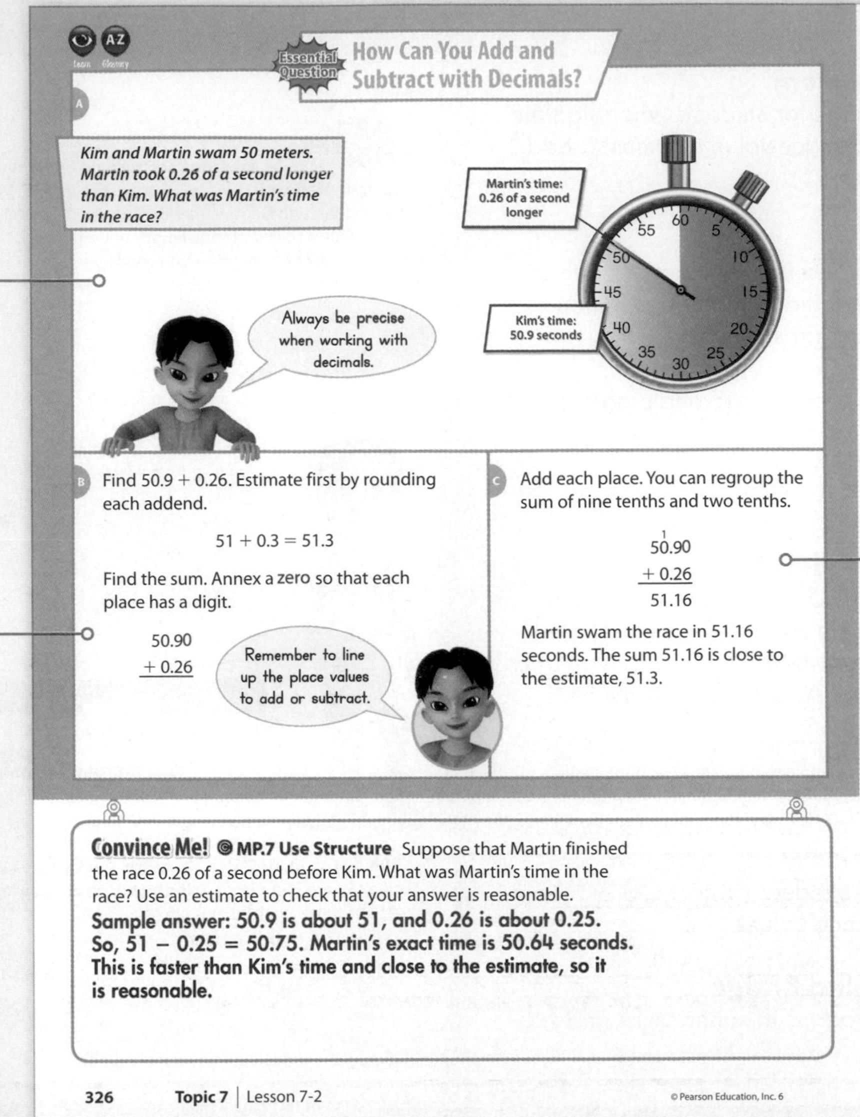

Essential Question How Can You Add and Subtract with Decimals?
Kim and Martin swam 50 meters. Martin took 0.26 of a second longer than Kim. What was Martin's time in the race?
Martin's time: 0.26 of a second longer
Kim's time: 50.9 seconds
Always be precise when working with decimals.
Find 50.9 + 0.26. Estimate first by rounding each addend.
51 + 0.3 = 51.3
Find the sum. Annex a zero so that each place has a digit.
50.90
+ 0.26
Remember to line up the place values to add or subtract.
Add each place. You can regroup the sum of nine tenths and two tenths.
50.90
+ 0.26
51.16
Martin swam the race in 51.16 seconds. The sum 51.16 is close to the estimate, 51.3.
Convince Me! MP.7 Use Structure Suppose that Martin finished the race 0.26 of a second before Kim. What was Martin's time in the race? Use an estimate to check that your answer is reasonable.
Sample answer: 50.9 is about 51, and 0.26 is about 0.25. So, 51 − 0.25 = 50.75. Martin's exact time is 50.64 seconds. This is faster than Kim's time and close to the estimate, so it is reasonable.
326 Topic 7 | Lesson 7-2
© Pearson Education, Inc. 6


Visual Learning Bridge

**MP.7 Be Precise**
*How is adding decimals like adding whole numbers?* [Sample answer: You add the digits in the same way that you add whole numbers.] *How is adding decimals different from adding whole numbers?* [Sample answer: You line up the decimal points, annex zeros when needed, and place the decimal point in the answer.] *How do you know whether the answer is reasonable?* [Because it is close to the estimate]

**Prevent Misconceptions** 
Remind students that whole numbers have decimal points, too. Although the decimal point is not needed, it belongs to the right of the ones place in a whole number. Therefore, the same concept of aligning place values applies to whole numbers and decimal numbers.

**Convince Me! MP.7 Use Structure** Encourage students to use what they just learned about place value structure. Addition and subtraction both use the same convention. *What operation would you use to find Martin's time in the race? How do you know?* [Subtraction; because Martin took less time. You are finding the difference.] *What subtraction expression represent's Martin's swim time?* [50.9 − 0.26]

Revisit the Essential Question. Students recognize that adding and subtracting decimals is much like adding and subtracting whole numbers. Line up the decimal points in order to align all the digits in the numbers by place value. Then add or subtract as you would whole numbers. Finally, place the decimal point in the answer.

Pearson realize. PearsonRealize.com

20–30 min

Practice Buddy

Tools

Assessment

## QUICK CHECK

Check mark indicates items for prescribing differentiation on the next page. Items 7 and 16 are worth 1 point. Item 17 is worth up to 3 points.

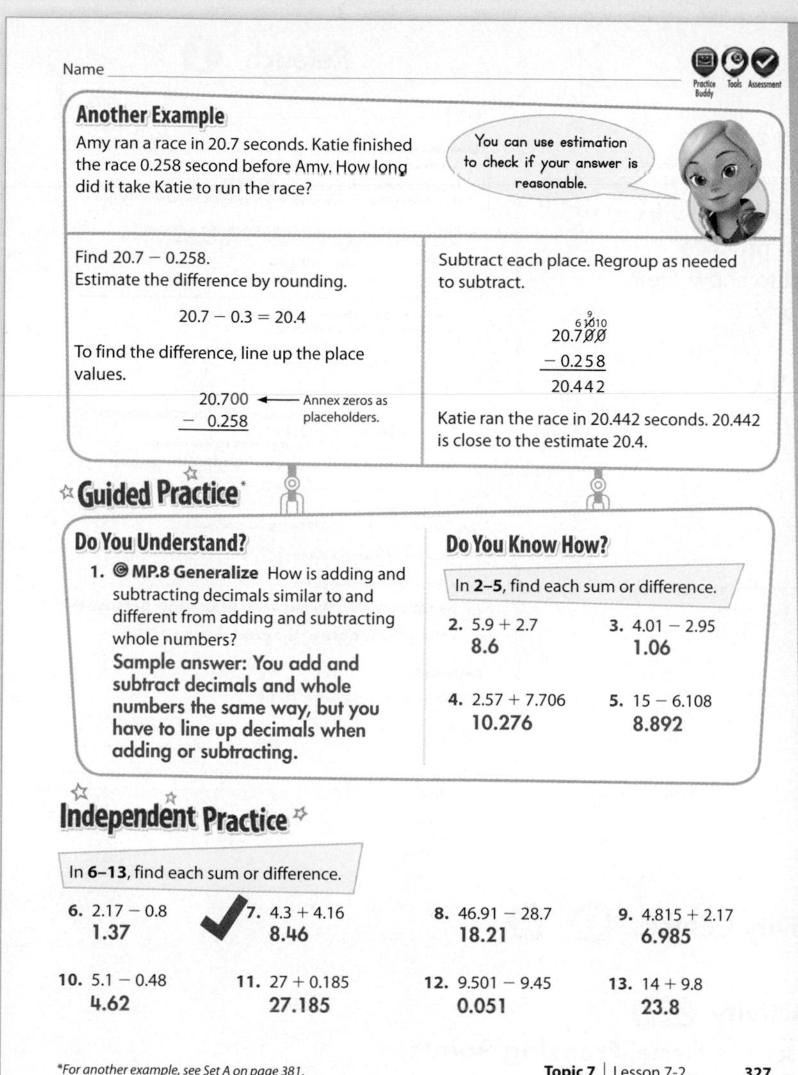

Name

### Another Example

Amy ran a race in 20.7 seconds. Katie finished the race 0.258 second before Amy. How long did it take Katie to run the race?

You can use estimation to check if your answer is reasonable.



Find 20.7 − 0.258.
Estimate the difference by rounding.

20.7 − 0.3 = 20.4

To find the difference, line up the place values.

20.700 ← Annex zeros as placeholders.
− 0.258

Subtract each place. Regroup as needed to subtract.

20.700
− 0.258
20.442

Katie ran the race in 20.442 seconds. 20.442 is close to the estimate 20.4.

### Guided Practice*

**Do You Understand?**

1. MP.8 Generalize How is adding and subtracting decimals similar to and different from adding and subtracting whole numbers?
**Sample answer: You add and subtract decimals and whole numbers the same way, but you have to line up decimals when adding or subtracting.**

**Do You Know How?**

In **2–5**, find each sum or difference.

2. 5.9 + 2.7 **8.6**
3. 4.01 − 2.95 **1.06**
4. 2.57 + 7.706 **10.276**
5. 15 − 6.108 **8.892**

### Independent Practice

In **6–13**, find each sum or difference.

6. 2.17 − 0.8 **1.37**
7. 4.3 + 4.16 **8.46**
8. 46.91 − 28.7 **18.21**
9. 4.815 + 2.17 **6.985**
10. 5.1 − 0.48 **4.62**
11. 27 + 0.185 **27.185**
12. 9.501 − 9.45 **0.051**
13. 14 + 9.8 **23.8**

*For another example, see Set A on page 381.



### Math Practices and Problem Solving

14. MP.6 Be Precise The U.S. Census Bureau tracks travel times to work. Use the information in the table to compare the travel time to work in New York to the travel time to work in Chicago. Write an equation to show your work.
**35.3 − 29.1 = 6.2; The travel time to work in New York is 6.2 minutes longer than in Chicago.**

| Location | Average Travel Time to Work (minutes) |
|---|---|
| United States | 23.2 |
| Los Angeles, CA | 26.5 |
| Chicago, IL | 29.1 |
| New York, NY | 35.3 |

15. Algebra Anna's running time for a race was 23.1 seconds. Another runner's time was 5.86 seconds faster. Write and evaluate an equation with a variable to find the difference between Anna's time and the other runner's time.
**Sample answer: Let $a$ = the other runner's time; 23.1 − $a$ = 5.86 seconds; 23.1 − 5.86 = 17.24; So, the other runner's time was 17.24 seconds.**

16. Higher Order Thinking Matthew bought a jersey for $39.99, a pennant for $10.25, and a hat for $13.75. He paid with a $50 bill and the rest he borrowed from his friend. If Matthew got $6.01 in change from the cashier, how much did he borrow from his friend to pay for all the items?
**$20**

**Common Core Assessment**

17. Use the information in the table to solve each problem. Use estimation to check that your answers are reasonable.

| Trails in Joshua Tree National Park | |
|---|---|
| Trail | Length (kilometers) |
| Lost Horse Mine | 6.4 |
| Lost Palms Oasis | 11.6 |
| Mastodon Peak | 4.8 |
| Skull Rock | 2.7 |

**Part A**

What is the combined length of the Lost Horse Mine trail and the Mastodon Peak trail?

**6.4 + 4.8 = 11.2 kilometers; 6.4 is about 6, and 4.8 is about 5. So, 6 + 5 = 11. My answer is reasonable because 11.2 is close to 11.**

**Part B**

How much longer is the Lost Palms Oasis trail than the Skull Rock trail?

**11.6 − 2.7 = 8.9 kilometers 11.6 is close to 12, and 2.7 is close to 3. So, 12 − 3 = 9. My answer is reasonable because 9 is close to 8.9.**





**Another Example** *Why is important to annex the zero as a placeholder in the hundredths place?* [Sample answer: You have to subtract 5 from something, so you need to place the zero in order to subtract in the hundredths place.]

**Error Intervention: Item 5**

**If** students simply bring down the digits 108 since there are no decimal digits in 15 to subtract from,

**then** have students write the numbers on grid paper, making sure the decimal points line up. *Where is the decimal point in the number 15?* [After the 5] *How many zeros should you annex to 15 so that both numbers have the same number of digits to the right of the decimal point?* [Three zeros should be annexed to 15, so you should write 15 as 15.000.]

**Reteaching** Assign Reteaching Set A on p. 381.

**Item 14 MP.6 Be Precise** *What information in the table do you need to solve the problem?* [The average travel times to work in New York and Chicago] *What equation can you write to compare these travel times?* [35.3 − 29.1 = 6.2] Encourage students to use precision by calculating correctly and using appropriate math language to state the solution to the problem.

**Item 15 Algebra** Remind students to define the variable that they use in the equation they write.

**Item 16 Higher Order Thinking** This item requires several steps to solve. Encourage students to make a plan for solving the problem before beginning their work.

**Item 17 Coherence** Students use what they learned about estimating sums and differences in the previous lesson to explain how to check that their answer is reasonable.

**Multi-Step Problems** *Page 328 Items 16 and 17; Page 330 Items 19–22*

# ASSESS AND DIFFERENTIATE

Use the **QUICK CHECK** on the previous page to prescribe differentiated instruction.

2 RtI

**I Intervention** 0–3 points on the Quick Check

**O On-Level** 4 points on the Quick Check

**A Advanced** 5 points on the Quick Check

## Intervention Activity I

### Adding and Subtracting Decimals

**Materials**

Grid paper (Teaching Tool 17) (1 for each student), index cards, markers

- Prepare index cards by writing one number or symbol per card and creating: three sets of digits 0 to 9, five extra zeros, one addition sign, one subtraction sign, and three decimal points.
- Have students use the index cards to create problems with the following structures:

x.x + x.xxx

xx.xxx − x.xxxx

xx.xxx − x.xx

x.xxx + x.xxxxx

- Have students use the extra zeros to annex zeros as necessary.
- Encourage students to record their work on grid paper to help them practice lining up the decimals and to show their math work neatly and clearly.

9.3 + 4.621

```
  9.300
+ 4.621
-------
 13.921
```

## Reteach I

Name ____________

Reteach to Build Understanding 7-2

**Vocabulary**

1. To **annex** means to add as an extra part.

   To annex a zero to a decimal means to **write** a zero to the right of the last digit in the decimal. Sometimes, you may have to write two or more **zeros**.

2. When you annex a zero, the zero acts as a **placeholder**. Annex one or more zeros in the following addition or subtraction problems.

   1.45**0** + 3.589    27,779.7**00** − 18,998.925    4.1111 + 0.6**000**

3. It rained 1.8 inches on Tuesday and 0.24 inch on Wednesday. How many inches did it rain altogether?

   Write an expression you could use to solve this problem. Write a number or operation symbol in each box.

   **1.8** **+** **0.24**

4. Estimate the number of inches it rained altogether. **Sample answer: $1.8 + 0.24 \approx 1.8 + 0.2 \approx 2$**

5. Rewrite the expression by lining up the decimal points vertically.

   The decimal 1.8 needs a placeholder in the **hundredths** place.

   1.80 ← Annex a zero in the hundredths place in 1.8.
   + 0.24
   2.04 ← Add and regroup as necessary.

   It rained **2.04** inches altogether.

6. Is your answer reasonable? Explain.

   **Sample answer: My answer is reasonable because the estimate 2 is close to the exact answer 2.04.**

**On the Back!**

7. Find the difference 15.25 − 7.14. **8.11**

R 7-2



## On-Level and Advanced Activity Centers O A

Name ____________

Math and Science Activity 7-2

### Mass Conservation

*Did You Know?* Matter is a general term for the objects around us. Matter occupies space and has mass. Spiders, rocks, air, apples, and you are all examples of matter. The law of conservation of mass states that matter can be neither created nor destroyed. This means that in an ordinary chemical reaction, the sum of the masses of the reactants (the substances undergoing change) equals the sum of the masses of the products.

Law of Conservation of Mass

mass of reactants = mass of product

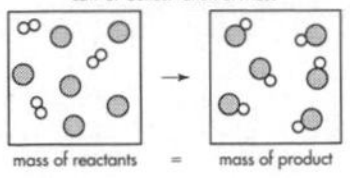

1. When hydrogen (H) combines with oxygen (O) to form water ($H_2O$), a chemical reaction takes place. Hydrogen and oxygen are the reactants and water is the product. Suppose 4.032 grams of hydrogen combine with 31.998 grams of oxygen. According to the law of conservation of mass, how many grams of water does the reaction produce?

   **36.03 g**

2. **Represent** Hydrochloric acid (HCl) reacts with sodium hydroxide (NaOH) to form sodium chloride (NaCl) and water ($H_2O$). The equation below represents the reaction.

   36.461 g (HCl) + ? g (NaOH) = 58.442 g (NaCl) + 18.015 g ($H_2O$)

   How many grams of NaOH are required to react with HCl to form the products?

   **39.996 g**

3. **Extension** Suppose 2 carbon (C) atoms react with 2 oxygen (O) atoms to form 2 molecules of carbon monoxide (CO). One molecule of carbon monoxide is made up of 1 atom of carbon and 1 atom of oxygen. The mass of 1 carbon atom is 12.010 atomic mass units and the mass of 1 oxygen atom is 15.999 atomic mass units.

   What is the mass of 1 molecule of carbon monoxide?

   **28.009 atomic mass units**

Math and Science Activity 7-2



### Math and Science Activity STEM

This activity revisits the science theme, **Freezing Points**, introduced on page 317 in the Student's Edition.

### Sample Student Work

2.

$$36.461 + x = 58.442 + 18.015$$
$$36.461 + x = 76.457$$
$$x + 36.461 - 36.461 = 76.457 - 36.461$$
$$x = 39.996 \text{ grams}$$

## TIMING

The time allocated to Step 3 will depend on the teacher's instructional decisions and differentiation routines.

15–30 min

PEARSON realize. PearsonRealize.com

Help

Practice Buddy

Tools

Games

## Technology Center   

Tools Games

### Math Tools and Math Games

A link to a specific math tools activity or math game to use with this lesson is provided at PearsonRealize.com.

## Leveled Assignment  Items 1–9, 16–20, 22  Items 7–12, 15–17, 19, 21, 22  Items 10–15, 17–22

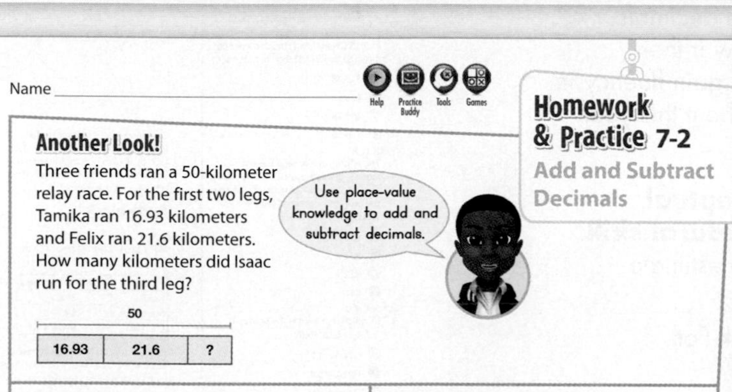


| Add to find the total distance Tamika and Felix ran. | Subtract to find how far Isaac ran. |
|---|---|
| Estimate: 16.93 ≈ 17 and 21.6 ≈ 22<br>17 + 22 = 39<br>16.93<br>+ 21.60 ← Annex a zero.<br>38.53<br>38.53 is close to 39, so the answer is reasonable. | Estimate: 38.53 ≈ 39<br>50 − 39 = 11<br>50.00 ← Annex 2 zeros.<br>− 38.53<br>11.47<br>11.47 is close to 11, so the answer is reasonable.<br>Isaac ran 11.47 kilometers. |

In **1–15**, find each sum or difference.

1. 45.6 + 26.3 **71.9**
2. 14.25 − 5.14 **9.11**
3. 17.2 + 6.08 **23.28**
4. 24.84 − 22.7 **2.14**
5. 13.64 − 8.3 **5.34**
6. 0.214 + 15.9 **16.114**
7. 3.652 − 1.41 **2.242**
8. 18.06 + 9.798 **27.858**
9. 8.006 − 6.38 **1.626**
10. 34.89 − 12.2 **22.69**
11. 22.31 − 4.22 **18.09**
12. 1.01 + 3.69 **4.7**
13. 87.5 + 85.05 **172.55**
14. 1.09 − 1.03 **0.06**
15. 100.02 − 64.58 **35.44**

Digital Resources at PearsonRealize.com    Topic 7 | Lesson 7-2    329

16. **MP.7 Look for Relationships** Complete the sequence of numbers in this set. Explain the pattern.
7.5  6.25  5  **3.75**  **2.5**
**Subtract 1.25.**

17. **MP.3 Critique Reasoning** Jaime wrote 4.4 − 0.33 = 1.1. Is his answer reasonable? Explain why or why not.
**Sample answer: Estimate would be 4 − 0 = 4, so his answer is not reasonable.**

18. The weights of 3 kittens at one week old were 3.6 ounces, 4.2 ounces, and 3.3 ounces. If each kitten gained 2.3 ounces, how much would each of the kittens weigh?
**5.9 ounces, 6.5 ounces, 5.6 ounces**

19. A movie theater is having a special. If a group of four pays $7.25 each for tickets, each person can get popcorn and a drink for $5.75. Use the expression 4(5.75 + 7.25) to find the total cost for 4 friends.
**4(5.75 + 7.25) = 4 × 13 = 52; The total cost is $52.**

20. **MP.1 Make Sense and Persevere** A factory makes parts for toys in different quantities as shown in the table. How much would 11 parts cost? **$4.95**

| Number of Parts | 2 | 7 | 12 | 15 |
|---|---|---|---|---|
| Cost | $0.90 | $3.15 | $5.40 | $6.75 |

21. **Higher Order Thinking** The perimeter of a 5-sided figure is 45.56 meters. Two of the sides have the same length. The sum of the other three side lengths is 24.2 meters. About how long is each of the same-length sides? Explain how you decided.
**Sample answer: About 10.5 meters; First, I subtracted 45.56 − 24.2 = 21.36 meters. Then I rounded 21.36 to 21 and divided by 2.**

### Common Core Assessment

22. Use the information in the table to solve each problem. Use estimation to check that your answers are reasonable.

| Craft Supplies | |
|---|---|
| Poster board | $1.29/sheet |
| Markers | $4.50/pack |
| Tape | $1.99/roll |
| Glue | $2.39/tube |
| Construction paper | $3.79/pack |

**Part A**

How much more does 1 tube of glue cost than 1 roll of tape?

**$2.39 − $1.99 = $0.40; $2.39 is about $2.50, and $1.99 is about 2. So, $2.50 − $2 = $0.50. My answer is reasonable because $0.40 is close to $0.50.**

**Part B**

What is the total cost for 2 packs of markers and a pack of construction paper?

**$9 + $3.79 = $12.79; $3.79 is about $4 and $4 + $9 = $13. My answer is reasonable because $12.79 is close to $13.**

330    Topic 7 | Lesson 7-2    

# LESSON 7-3

# ESTIMATE PRODUCTS

## DIGITAL RESOURCES PearsonRealize.com

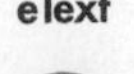
Student and Teacher eTexts
eText

Listen and Look For Lesson Video
PD

Today's Challenge
Think

Solve and Share
Solve

Visual Learning Animation Plus
Learn

Animated Glossary
Glossary

Online Personalized Practice
Practice Buddy

Math Tools
Tools

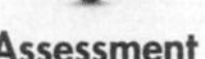
Quick Check
Assessment

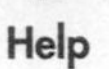
Another Look Homework Video
Help

Math Games
Games

## LESSON OVERVIEW FCR FOCUS • COHERENCE • RIGOR

### FOCUS

**Domain 6.NS** The Number System

**Cluster 6.NS.B** Compute fluently with multi-digit numbers and find common factors and multiples.

**Content Standard 6.NS.B.3** Fluently add, subtract, multiply, and divide multi-digit decimals using the standard algorithm for each operation.

**Mathematical Practices MP.1, MP.2, MP.3, MP.6**

**Objective** Estimate the products of decimals.

**Essential Understanding** Estimates can be found by using strategies such as rounding and compatible numbers. Some problems can be solved with an estimate.

### COHERENCE

In Grade 5, students learned how to round decimals and how to estimate the product of a whole number and a decimal by rounding or by using compatible numbers. In this lesson, those procedures are reviewed and extended to estimate the products of whole numbers and decimals or two decimals. Estimation helps students know if their answer is reasonable as they gain fluency in decimal multiplication throughout this year.

### RIGOR

This lesson emphasizes **conceptual understanding** and **procedural skill**. Students use number sense to estimate products of decimals.

PD Watch the Listen and Look For Lesson Video.

## MATH ANYTIME

### Daily Common Core Review

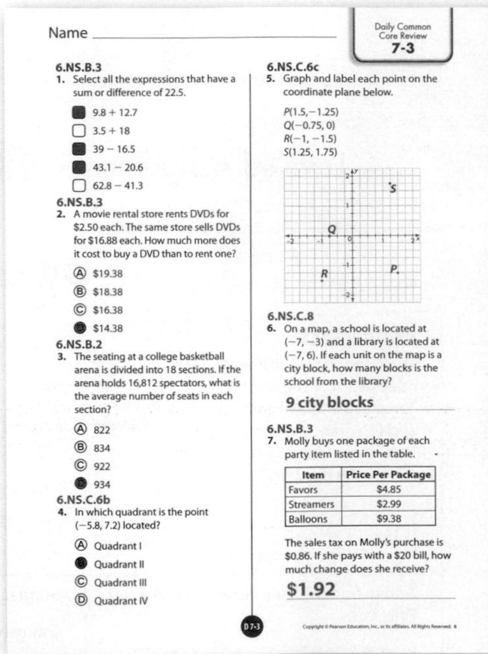

Name ______

Daily Common Core Review 7-3

**6.NS.B.3**
1. Select all the expressions that have a sum or difference of 22.5.
   - ■ 9.8 + 12.7
   - □ 3.5 + 18
   - ■ 39 − 16.5
   - ■ 43.1 − 20.6
   - □ 62.8 − 41.3

**6.NS.B.3**
2. A movie rental store rents DVDs for \$2.50 each. The same store sells DVDs for \$16.88 each. How much more does it cost to buy a DVD than to rent one?
   - Ⓐ \$19.38
   - Ⓑ \$18.38
   - Ⓒ \$16.38
   - ● \$14.38

**6.NS.B.2**
3. The seating at a college basketball arena is divided into 18 sections. If the arena holds 16,812 spectators, what is the average number of seats in each section?
   - Ⓐ 822
   - Ⓑ 834
   - Ⓒ 922
   - ● 934

**6.NS.C.6b**
4. In which quadrant is the point (−5.8, 7.2) located?
   - Ⓐ Quadrant I
   - ● Quadrant II
   - Ⓒ Quadrant III
   - Ⓓ Quadrant IV

**6.NS.C.6c**
5. Graph and label each point on the coordinate plane below.
   $P(1.5, -1.25)$
   $Q(-0.75, 0)$
   $R(-1, -1.5)$
   $S(1.25, 1.75)$



**6.NS.C.8**
6. On a map, a school is located at (−7, −3) and a library is located at (−7, 6). If each unit on the map is a city block, how many blocks is the school from the library?
   **9 city blocks**

**6.NS.B.3**
7. Molly buys one package of each party item listed in the table.

| Item | Price Per Package |
|---|---|
| Favors | \$4.85 |
| Streamers | \$2.99 |
| Balloons | \$9.38 |

The sales tax on Molly's purchase is \$0.86. If she pays with a \$20 bill, how much change does she receive?
**\$1.92**

D 7-3

### Today's Challenge

Think Use the Topic 7 problems any time during this topic.

## ENGLISH LANGUAGE LEARNERS 

**Reading** Demonstrate comprehension by taking notes.

*Use with the Visual Learning Bridge on Student's Edition p. 332.*

Write *estimate, rounding,* and *compatible numbers.* Ask students to write definitions for the terms in their notes. Read Box A. Instruct students to write information needed to solve the problem in their notes. *To solve the problem, estimate the product of a whole number and decimal.* Instruct students to make a T-chart in their notes, labeling as follows: *Estimate by Rounding* and *Estimate with Compatible Numbers.*

**Beginning** Read Box B to students. Instruct students to write the equation $42 \times \$9.25 \approx 40 \times \$9 \approx \$360$ on their T-charts. Continue process with Box C. *Which strategy would you use to solve the problem?* Instruct students to circle the strategy they would use and respond using the sentence frame: I would use ____.

**Intermediate** Read Boxes B and C with students. Instruct students to write the equations $42 \times \$9.25 \approx 40 \times \$9 \approx \$360$ and $42 \times \$9.25 \approx 40 \times \$10 \approx \$420$ on their T-charts. *Which strategy would you use to solve the problem? Why?* Students will respond using the sentence frame: I would use ____ because ____.

**Advanced** Instruct students to read Boxes B and C with partners and to record information on their T-charts. *Which strategy do you think comes closest to the actual answer? Why?* Instruct students to write their responses in their notes.

**Summarize** What strategies can be used to estimate the products of decimals?

# DEVELOP: PROBLEM-BASED LEARNING

**COHERENCE: Engage learners by connecting prior knowledge to new ideas.**
Students use what they know about estimation strategies to estimate the product of a whole number and a decimal to solve a multi-step problem.

10–15 min

Solve

## BEFORE

**1. Pose the Solve-and-Share Problem**
**MP.2 Use Reasoning** Listen and look for students who reason quantitatively to estimate the difference of the regular cost and the group rate cost.

**2. Build Understanding**
*What is the cost per person for a regular ticket?* [$8.95] *For a group rate ticket?* [$7.65] *Do you need to find an exact answer to solve this problem? Explain.* [No; an estimate is okay since the problem asks about how much.]

## DURING

**3. Ask Guiding Questions As Needed**
*To what place could you round the costs in this problem?* [The nearest whole number, or dollar] *What are $8.95 and $7.65 rounded to the nearest dollar?* [$9 and $8] *How could you estimate the total cost for 54 people?* [Sample answer: Multiply each rounded ticket rate by the compatible number 50.] *How do you find the savings?* [Subtract the total group rate cost from the total regular rate cost.]

## AFTER

**4. Share and Discuss Solutions**
Solve Start with students' solutions. If needed, project Max's and Julia's work to discuss how to estimate the costs and find how much money the school would save.

**5. Transition to the Visual Learning Bridge**
*You can estimate products of decimals to solve some problems.*

**6. Extension for Early Finishers**
*Sam paid $8.81 for 3.4 pounds of grapes at a farmer's market. About how much did each pound of grapes cost?* [≈ $3/lb]

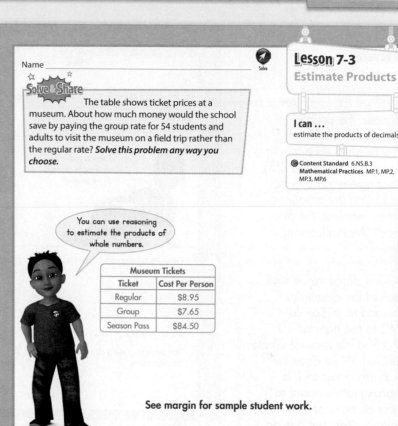

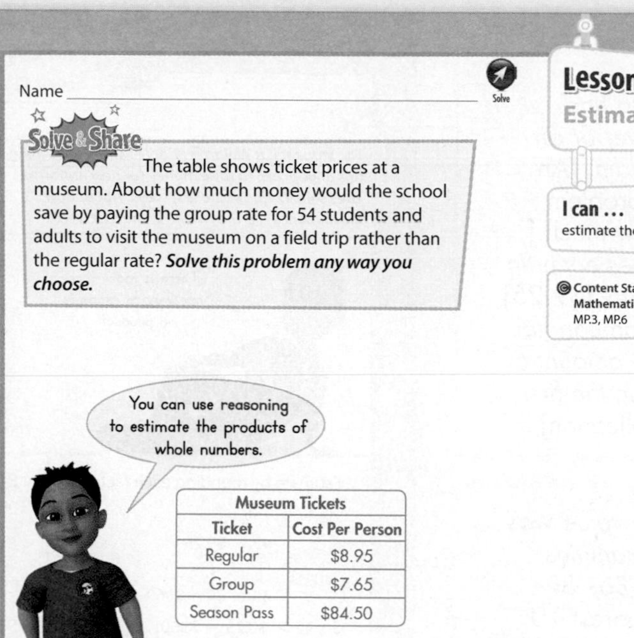

Name ______

Solve & Share

The table shows ticket prices at a museum. About how much money would the school save by paying the group rate for 54 students and adults to visit the museum on a field trip rather than the regular rate? ***Solve this problem any way you choose.***

**Lesson 7-3**
**Estimate Products**

**I can ...**
estimate the products of decimals.

**Content Standard** 6.NS.B.3 **Mathematical Practices** MP.1, MP.2, MP.3, MP.6

You can use reasoning to estimate the products of whole numbers.



Museum Tickets

| Ticket | Cost Per Person |
|---|---|
| Regular | $8.95 |
| Group | $7.65 |
| Season Pass | $84.50 |

**See margin for sample student work.**

**Look Back!** **MP.2 Reasoning** Six of the people on the field trip decided to buy season passes. Estimate the total cost of 6 season passes. Explain your reasoning.
**Sample answer: The cost of a season pass is $84.50, which is close to $85. If I think of 85 as 80 and 5, I can multiply compatible numbers: 80 × 6 = 480 and 5 × 6 = 30. The estimated total cost is about $480 + $30 = $510.**

Digital Resources at PearsonRealize.com **Topic 7** | Lesson 7-3 331

## Analyze Student Work

Max's Work

Regular Rate $9 \times 50 = 450$
Group Rate $8 \times 50 = 400$

$450 - 400 = 50$

The School saves about $50.

Max estimates the total costs for each ticket type and then subtracts to find the savings.

Julia's Work

Regular Rate − Group Rate → $9 − $8 = $1
The School saves about $1 per ticket,
So they save about $54.

Julia estimates the difference in cost per ticket type, and then multiplies this by the number of students and adults on the field trip.

# STEP 2 DEVELOP: VISUAL LEARNING

The *Visual Learning Bridge* connects students' thinking in Solve & Share to important math ideas in the lesson. Use the *Visual Learning Bridge* to make these ideas explicit. Also available as a *Visual Learning Animation Plus* at PearsonRealize.com

Pearson realize. PearsonRealize.com

**MP.1 Make Sense and Persevere**
*Do you need to find an exact answer or an estimate? Explain.* [An estimate; the problem asks about how much.] *How much does each tin of popcorn cost?* [$9.25] *What operation can you use to find the amount of money made in the first week?* [Multiplication]

*To what place value was each of the quantities rounded to in Box B?* [$42 to the nearest 10; $9.25 to the nearest whole number] *What does the ≈ symbol mean?* ["Is approximately equal to"] *Is this an accurate estimate? Explain.* [Yes; but it is an underestimate because each rounded quantity is less than the actual quantity.]

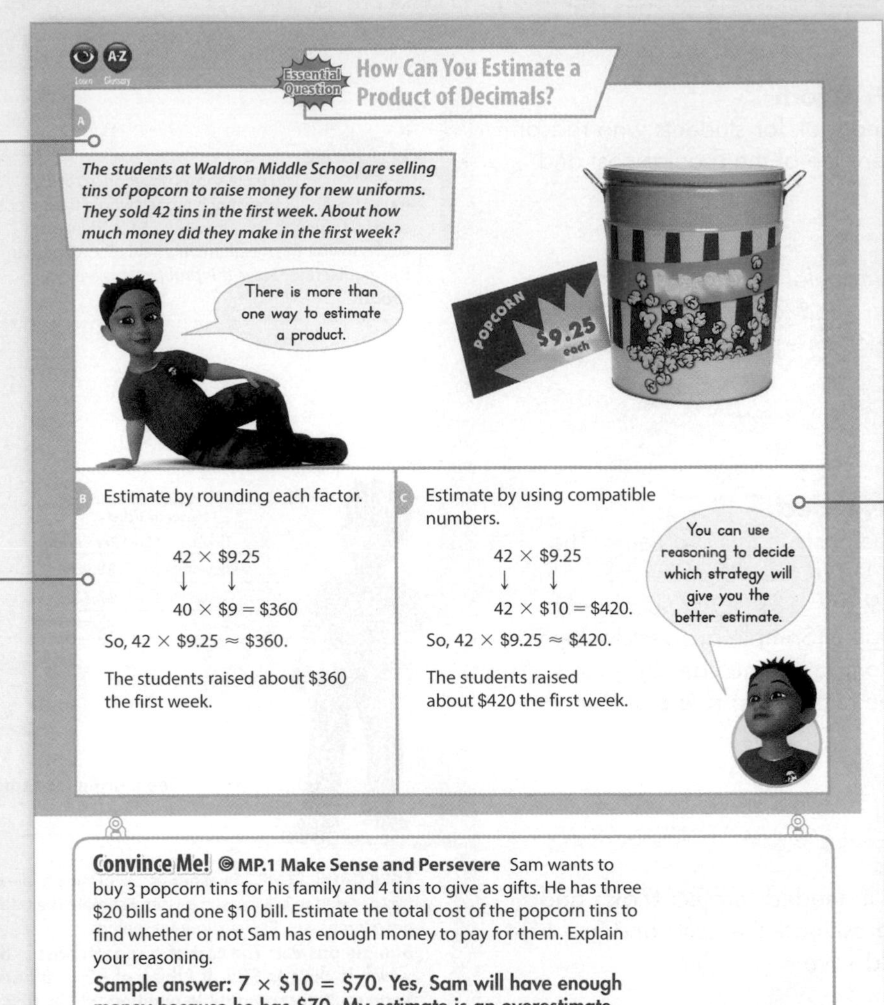

Essential Question
How Can You Estimate a Product of Decimals?
A
The students at Waldron Middle School are selling tins of popcorn to raise money for new uniforms. They sold 42 tins in the first week. About how much money did they make in the first week?
There is more than one way to estimate a product.
POPCORN
$9.25 each
B
Estimate by rounding each factor.
42 × $9.25
40 × $9 = $360
So, 42 × $9.25 ≈ $360.
The students raised about $360 the first week.
C
Estimate by using compatible numbers.
42 × $9.25
42 × $10 = $420.
So, 42 × $9.25 ≈ $420.
The students raised about $420 the first week.
You can use reasoning to decide which strategy will give you the better estimate.
Visual Learning Bridge


**Convince Me!** MP.1 Make Sense and Persevere Sam wants to buy 3 popcorn tins for his family and 4 tins to give as gifts. He has three $20 bills and one $10 bill. Estimate the total cost of the popcorn tins to find whether or not Sam has enough money to pay for them. Explain your reasoning.

**Sample answer: 7 × $10 = $70. Yes, Sam will have enough money because he has $70. My estimate is an overestimate so it is reasonable to say Sam will have enough money.**

332 Topic 7 | Lesson 7-3 © Pearson Education, Inc. 6

**MP.2 Reason Quantitatively**
*Why are 42 and 10 compatible numbers?* [Because 42 and 10 are close to the actual quantities and 42 × 10 is easy to calculate] *What other compatible numbers could you use to find this estimate?* [Sample answer: 40 and 10] *Is this an accurate estimate? Explain.* [Yes; but it is an overestimate since $9.25 was rounded up to $10.]

**Prevent Misconceptions**

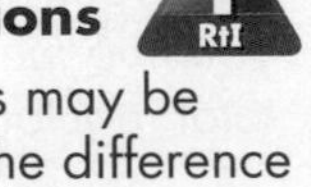

Some students may be confused by the difference in the two estimates.

Explain that both estimates are accurate because they use quantities that make sense and are about the same difference from the actual amount of money made $388.50. The best estimate would fall somewhere between $360 and $420.

**Convince Me! MP.1 Make Sense and Persevere** *How many tins of popcorn does Sam want to buy in total?* [7] *How much money does Sam have to spend?* [$70] *What is the most Sam can pay for each tin of popcorn? Explain.* [$10: $70 ÷ 7 = $10]

Revisit the Essential Question. Students can use rounding or compatible numbers to estimate the product of decimals. By changing the decimal numbers to whole numbers, they use the standard algorithm for multiplication to find an approximate answer.

## QUICK CHECK

Check mark indicates items for prescribing differentiation on the next page.
Item 14 is worth 1 point. Items 18 and 21 are worth 2 points.

20–30 min

PEARSON realize.
PearsonRealize.com

Practice Buddy

Tools

Assessment

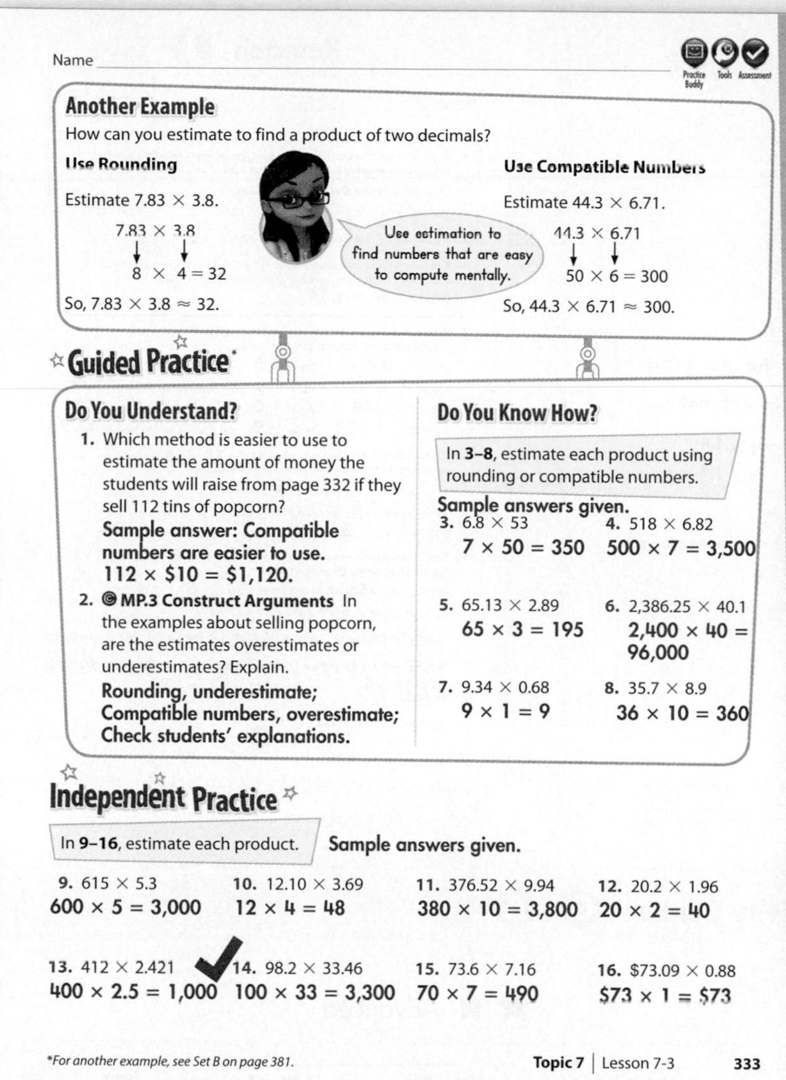

Name

**Another Example**

How can you estimate to find a product of two decimals?

**Use Rounding**

Estimate 7.83 × 3.8.

7.83 × 3.8
↓ ↓
8 × 4 = 32

So, 7.83 × 3.8 ≈ 32.

**Use Compatible Numbers**

Estimate 44.3 × 6.71.

44.3 × 6.71
↓ ↓
50 × 6 = 300

So, 44.3 × 6.71 ≈ 300.

Use estimation to find numbers that are easy to compute mentally.



**Guided Practice***

**Do You Understand?**

1. Which method is easier to use to estimate the amount of money the students will raise from page 332 if they sell 112 tins of popcorn?
**Sample answer: Compatible numbers are easier to use. 112 × $10 = $1,120.**

2. MP.3 Construct Arguments In the examples about selling popcorn, are the estimates overestimates or underestimates? Explain.
**Rounding, underestimate; Compatible numbers, overestimate; Check students' explanations.**

**Do You Know How?**

In **3–8**, estimate each product using rounding or compatible numbers.

**Sample answers given.**

3. 6.8 × 53 **7 × 50 = 350**
4. 518 × 6.82 **500 × 7 = 3,500**
5. 65.13 × 2.89 **65 × 3 = 195**
6. 2,386.25 × 40.1 **2,400 × 40 = 96,000**
7. 9.34 × 0.68 **9 × 1 = 9**
8. 35.7 × 8.9 **36 × 10 = 360**

**Independent Practice**

In **9–16**, estimate each product. **Sample answers given.**

9. 615 × 5.3 **600 × 5 = 3,000**
10. 12.10 × 3.69 **12 × 4 = 48**
11. 376.52 × 9.94 **380 × 10 = 3,800**
12. 20.2 × 1.96 **20 × 2 = 40**
13. 412 × 2.421 **400 × 2.5 = 1,000**
✓14. 98.2 × 33.46 **100 × 33 = 3,300**
15. 73.6 × 7.16 **70 × 7 = 490**
16. $73.09 × 0.88 **$73 × 1 = $73**

*For another example, see Set B on page 381.

Topic 7 | Lesson 7-3 333

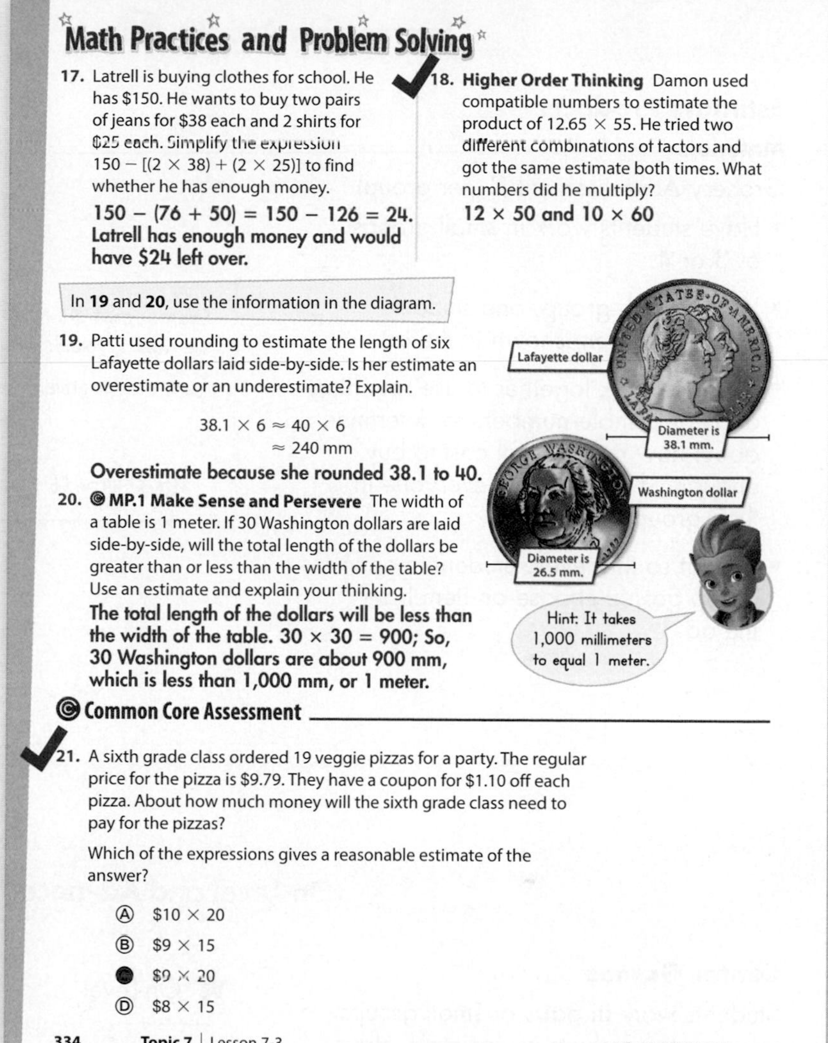

**Math Practices and Problem Solving**

17. Latrell is buying clothes for school. He has $150. He wants to buy two pairs of jeans for $38 each and 2 shirts for $25 each. Simplify the expression 150 − [(2 × 38) + (2 × 25)] to find whether he has enough money.
**150 − (76 + 50) = 150 − 126 = 24. Latrell has enough money and would have $24 left over.**

✓18. **Higher Order Thinking** Damon used compatible numbers to estimate the product of 12.65 × 55. He tried two different combinations of factors and got the same estimate both times. What numbers did he multiply?
**12 × 50 and 10 × 60**

In **19** and **20**, use the information in the diagram.

19. Patti used rounding to estimate the length of six Lafayette dollars laid side-by-side. Is her estimate an overestimate or an underestimate? Explain.

38.1 × 6 ≈ 40 × 6
≈ 240 mm

**Overestimate because she rounded 38.1 to 40.**

20. MP.1 Make Sense and Persevere The width of a table is 1 meter. If 30 Washington dollars are laid side-by-side, will the total length of the dollars be greater than or less than the width of the table? Use an estimate and explain your thinking.
**The total length of the dollars will be less than the width of the table. 30 × 30 = 900; So, 30 Washington dollars are about 900 mm, which is less than 1,000 mm, or 1 meter.**



Diameter is 26.5 mm.
Hint: It takes 1,000 millimeters to equal 1 meter.

**Common Core Assessment**

✓21. A sixth grade class ordered 19 veggie pizzas for a party. The regular price for the pizza is $9.79. They have a coupon for $1.10 off each pizza. About how much money will the sixth grade class need to pay for the pizzas?

Which of the expressions gives a reasonable estimate of the answer?

Ⓐ $10 × 20
Ⓑ $9 × 15
● $9 × 20
Ⓓ $8 × 15

334 Topic 7 | Lesson 7-3

© Pearson Education, Inc. 6

**Another Example** Students see that they can use rounding or compatible numbers to estimate a product involving two decimal numbers. *How could you use compatible numbers to estimate 7.83 × 3.8?* [8 × 4 = 32] *How could you use rounding to estimate 44.3 × 6.71?* [44 × 7 = 308]

**Error Intervention: Item 1**

**If** students have difficulty explaining which strategy is easier,

**then** encourage students to estimate using rounding and by using compatible numbers, and then to compare these strategies. In general, multiplying by a power of 10 is easy since the appropriate number of zeros can just be added to the end of the other factor.

**Reteaching** Assign Reteaching Set B on p. 381.

**Item 17** Remind students to use the order of operations to evaluate the expression. You may also want to reinforce understanding and have students explain what each term of the expression represents in the problem.

**Item 18 Higher Order Thinking** Ask student volunteers to identify pairs of compatible numbers that can be used to estimate the product. List the factors on the board and then find the products in order to identify two pairs of factors that result in the same product.

**Item 20 MP.1 Make Sense and Persevere** *The width of the table is 1 meter, so what is the width of the table in millimeters?* [1,000 mm] *About how wide is a Washington dollar?* [About 25 mm]

Diameter is 38.1 mm.

**Multi-Step Problems** *Page 334 Items 17 and 20; Page 336 Items 13 and 16*

# ASSESS AND DIFFERENTIATE

Use the **QUICK CHECK** on the previous page to prescribe differentiated instruction.

**I Intervention** 0–3 points on the Quick Check

**O On-Level** 4 points on the Quick Check

**A Advanced** 5 points on the Quick Check

## Intervention Activity 

### Estimate Products

**Materials**

Grocery Advertisement (1 per group)

- Have students work in small groups of 3 or 4.
- Within each group, one student chooses an item shown in the ad.
- Students work together to use rounding and compatible numbers to determine about how much it will cost to buy enough of that item for everyone in their group.
- Repeat so that every student in each group gets to choose an item from the ad.

Grapes cost \$1.49 per pound
We need 4 pounds of grapes for our group
Use compatible numbers to estimate.
$4 \times 1.49 \rightarrow 4 \times 1.5$
$4 \times 1.5 = 6$
$4 \times \$1.49 \approx \$6$

## Reteach I

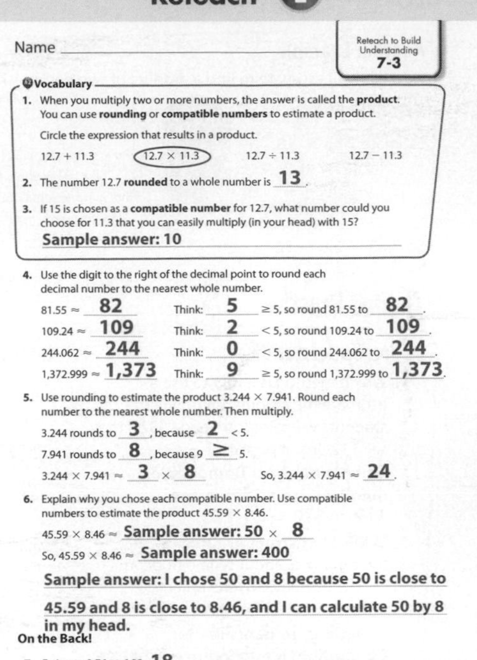

Name ______ Reteach to Build Understanding 7-3

Vocabulary

1. When you multiply two or more numbers, the answer is called the **product**. You can use **rounding** or **compatible numbers** to estimate a product.
Circle the expression that results in a product.
12.7 + 11.3    (12.7 × 11.3)    12.7 ÷ 11.3    12.7 − 11.3
2. The number 12.7 **rounded** to a whole number is **13**.
3. If 15 is chosen as a **compatible number** for 12.7, what number could you choose for 11.3 that you can easily multiply (in your head) with 15?
**Sample answer: 10**
4. Use the digit to the right of the decimal point to round each decimal number to the nearest whole number.
81.55 ≈ **82** Think: **5** ≥ 5, so round 81.55 to **82**.
109.24 ≈ **109** Think: **2** < 5, so round 109.24 to **109**.
244.062 ≈ **244** Think: **0** < 5, so round 244.062 to **244**.
1,372.999 ≈ **1,373** Think: **9** ≥ 5, so round 1,372.999 to **1,373**.
5. Use rounding to estimate the product 3.244 × 7.941. Round each number to the nearest whole number. Then multiply.
3.244 rounds to **3**, because **2** < 5.
7.941 rounds to **8**, because 9 **≥** 5.
3.244 × 7.941 ≈ **3** × **8** So, 3.244 × 7.941 ≈ **24**.
6. Explain why you chose each compatible number. Use compatible numbers to estimate the product 45.59 × 8.46.
45.59 × 8.46 ≈ **Sample answer: 50** × **8**
So, 45.59 × 8.46 ≈ **Sample answer: 400**
**Sample answer: I chose 50 and 8 because 50 is close to 45.59 and 8 is close to 8.46, and I can calculate 50 by 8 in my head.**

On the Back!

7. Estimate 2.76 × 6.23. **18**

R 7-3

## On-Level and Advanced Activity Centers 

### Center Games

Students work in pairs or small groups to estimate products of decimals. Have students record their estimates as they play the game.

★ On-Level

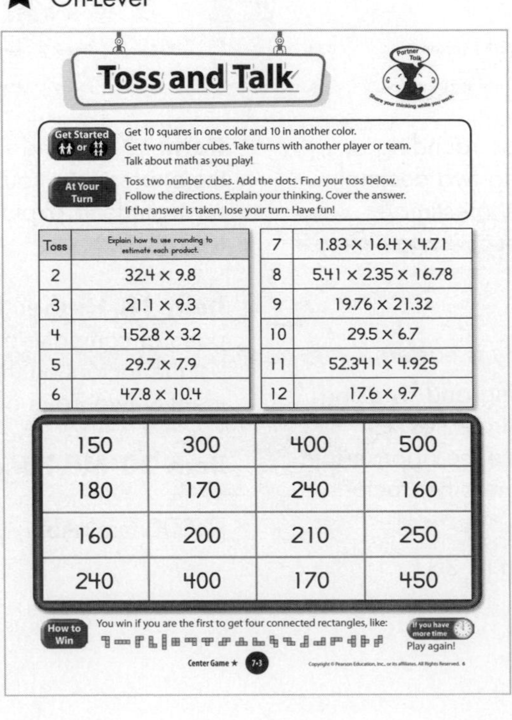

Toss and Talk

Partner Talk — Share your thinking while you work.

Get Started: Get 10 squares in one color and 10 in another color. Get two number cubes. Take turns with another player or team. Talk about math as you play!

At Your Turn: Toss two number cubes. Add the dots. Find your toss below. Follow the directions. Explain your thinking. Cover the answer. If the answer is taken, lose your turn. Have fun!

| Toss | Explain how to use rounding to estimate each product. | Toss | |
|---|---|---|---|
| 2 | 32.4 × 9.8 | 7 | 1.83 × 16.4 × 4.71 |
| 3 | 21.1 × 9.3 | 8 | 5.41 × 2.35 × 16.78 |
| 4 | 152.8 × 3.2 | 9 | 19.76 × 21.32 |
| 5 | 29.7 × 7.9 | 10 | 29.5 × 6.7 |
| 6 | 47.8 × 10.4 | 11 | 52.341 × 4.925 |
| | | 12 | 17.6 × 9.7 |

| | | | |
|---|---|---|---|
| 150 | 300 | 400 | 500 |
| 180 | 170 | 240 | 160 |
| 160 | 200 | 210 | 250 |
| 240 | 400 | 170 | 450 |

How to Win: You win if you are the first to get four connected rectangles, like:

If you have more time: Play again!

Center Game ★ 7-3

★★ Advanced

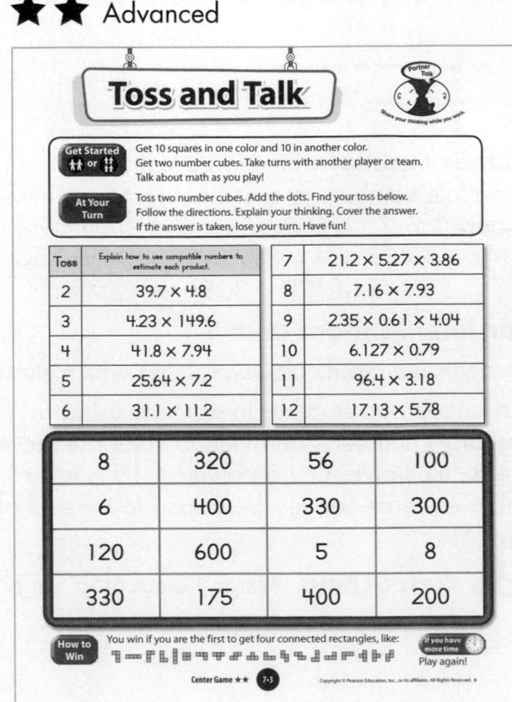

Toss and Talk

Partner Talk — Share your thinking while you work.

Get Started: Get 10 squares in one color and 10 in another color. Get two number cubes. Take turns with another player or team. Talk about math as you play!

At Your Turn: Toss two number cubes. Add the dots. Find your toss below. Follow the directions. Explain your thinking. Cover the answer. If the answer is taken, lose your turn. Have fun!

| Toss | Explain how to use compatible numbers to estimate each product. | Toss | |
|---|---|---|---|
| 2 | 39.7 × 4.8 | 7 | 21.2 × 5.27 × 3.86 |
| 3 | 4.23 × 149.6 | 8 | 7.16 × 7.93 |
| 4 | 41.8 × 7.94 | 9 | 2.35 × 0.61 × 4.04 |
| 5 | 25.64 × 7.2 | 10 | 6.127 × 0.79 |
| 6 | 31.1 × 11.2 | 11 | 96.4 × 3.18 |
| | | 12 | 17.13 × 5.78 |

| | | | |
|---|---|---|---|
| 8 | 320 | 56 | 100 |
| 6 | 400 | 330 | 300 |
| 120 | 600 | 5 | 8 |
| 330 | 175 | 400 | 200 |

How to Win: You win if you are the first to get four connected rectangles, like:

If you have more time: Play again!

Center Game ★★ 7-3

**TIMING**

The time allocated to Step 3 will depend on the teacher's instructional decisions and differentiation routines.

15–30 min

PEARSON realize. PearsonRealize.com

 Help  Practice Buddy  Tools Games

## Technology Center    

 Tools  Games

### Math Tools and Math Games

A link to a specific math tools activity or math game to use with this lesson is provided at PearsonRealize.com.

## Leveled Assignment  Items 1–9, 13, 15, 17  Items 7–14, 16, 17  Items 8–17

Name ______________________

**Homework & Practice 7-3**
**Estimate Products**

**Another Look!**

In 15 minutes, a food vendor at the ball game sold 28 hot dogs. Each hot dog costs \$4.25. How much money did the vendor make selling hot dogs in 15 minutes?

**Rounding:**

Round each factor to the nearest ten or whole number.

$28 \times \$4.25$

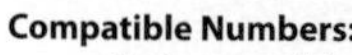

$30 \times \$4 = \$120$

So, $28 \times \$4.25 \approx \$120$.

The vendor made about \$120 selling hot dogs in 15 minutes.

**Compatible Numbers:**

Find compatible numbers and multiply.

$28 \times 4.25$

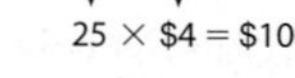

$25 \times \$4 = \$100$

So, $28 \times \$4.25 \approx \$100$.

The vendor made about \$100 selling hot dogs in 15 minutes.

Remember, compatible numbers are easy to compute with mentally.

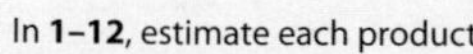

In **1–12**, estimate each product. **Sample answers are given.**

1. $3.73 \times 8.16$ **$4 \times 8 = 32$**
2. $35.518 \times 9.722$ **$36 \times 10 = 360$**
3. $7.349 \times 5.62$ **$7 \times 6 = 42$**
4. $4.178 \times 12.513$ **$4 \times 12 = 48$**
5. $8.498 \times 5.602$ **$8 \times 6 = 48$**
6. $24.534 \times 7.96$ **$25 \times 8 = 200$**
7. $55.93 \times 8.34$ **$60 \times 8 = 480$**
8. $61.438 \times 8.72$ **$60 \times 9 = 540$**
9. $122.899 \times 5.36$ **$120 \times 5 = 600$**
10. $16.954 \times 3.5$ **$15 \times 4 = 60$**
11. $17.158 \times 8.99$ **$17 \times 10 = 170$**
12. $38.753 \times 8.461$ **$40 \times 8 = 320$**



In **13** and **14**, use the diagram to solve.

**Mandy's Bedroom**

11.4 ft

8.65 ft

13. **MP.6 Be Precise** Estimate the area of Mandy's bedroom. Tell which estimation strategy you used and why.
**Sample answer: $11 \times 9 = 99$ sq ft. I used rounding to the nearest whole number because by subtracting 0.40 from 11 and adding 0.35 to 8.65, the estimated product will be close to the actual product.**

14. **Higher Order Thinking** Mandy needs carpet for her bedroom. Why should the estimate for the area be an overestimate instead of an underestimate?
**Sample answer: The carpet needs to cover the entire floor. If you underestimate the area, you may not have enough carpet.**

15. Julie estimates that she can produce 28 puzzles in one week. She sells each puzzle for \$12.25. Estimate the amount of money Julie can earn in a month. Tell which estimation technique you used.
**Sample answer: About \$1,500; $30 \times 5 \times 10 = 1{,}500$; I used compatible numbers.**

16. **MP.1 Make Sense and Persevere** The length of a library bookshelf is 46.725 inches. It was designed for their new MP3 audio book players. When the MP3 players arrived, the librarian found that each of the 24 cases was 1.65 inches. Will all 24 cases fit on the shelf? Use estimation to explain your reasoning.
**Sample answer: Yes, the cases will fit. $24 \times 1 = 24$; 0.65 is closer to 0.50, or $\frac{1}{2}$, than to 1; $\frac{24}{2} = 12$; $24 + 12 = 36$. The estimate of 36 inches is much less than 46.725.**

**Common Core Assessment**

17. At a food manufacturer, 8.8 pounds of peanuts are added to other fruits, grains, and nuts to make one batch of granola bars. About how many pounds of peanuts are needed to make 54 batches of granola bars?

Which of the expressions would **NOT** give a reasonable estimate of the answer?

Ⓐ $8 \times 50$
● $10 \times 100$
Ⓒ $10 \times 50$
Ⓓ $9 \times 50$

# LESSON 7-4

# MULTIPLY DECIMALS

## DIGITAL RESOURCES PearsonRealize.com

eText — Student and Teacher eTexts

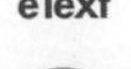

PD — Listen and Look For Lesson Video

Think — Today's Challenge

Solve — Solve and Share

Learn — Visual Learning Animation Plus

Glossary — Animated Glossary

Practice Buddy — Online Personalized Practice

Tools — Math Tools

Assessment — Quick Check

Help — Another Look Homework Video

Games — Math Games

## LESSON OVERVIEW FCR FOCUS • COHERENCE • RIGOR

### FOCUS

**Domain 6.NS** The Number System

**Cluster 6.NS.B** Compute fluently with multi-digit numbers and find common factors and multiples.

**Content Standard 6.NS.B.3** Fluently add, subtract, multiply, and divide multi-digit decimals using the standard algorithm for each operation.

**Mathematical Practices MP.2, MP.3, MP.5, MP.7, MP.8**

**Objective** Multiply decimals.

**Essential Understanding** A general method, or standard algorithm, can be used to multiply decimals fluently.

**Materials** Decimal models (Teaching Tool 31), Grid paper (Teaching Tool 17)

### COHERENCE

In Grade 5, students used models to multiply two decimals with products to the hundredths place. In this lesson, they extend the multiplication of decimals with products to the thousandths place. They also multiply the decimals by changing them to fractions with denominators that are a power of ten. This process with fractions shows why the standard algorithm for multiplying decimals works and helps students develop fluency.

### RIGOR

This lesson emphasizes **conceptual understanding**, **procedural skill**, and **fluency**. Students use models and operations with fractions to understand the standard algorithm for multiplying two decimals.

PD Watch the Listen and Look For Lesson Video.

## MATH ANYTIME

### Daily Common Core Review

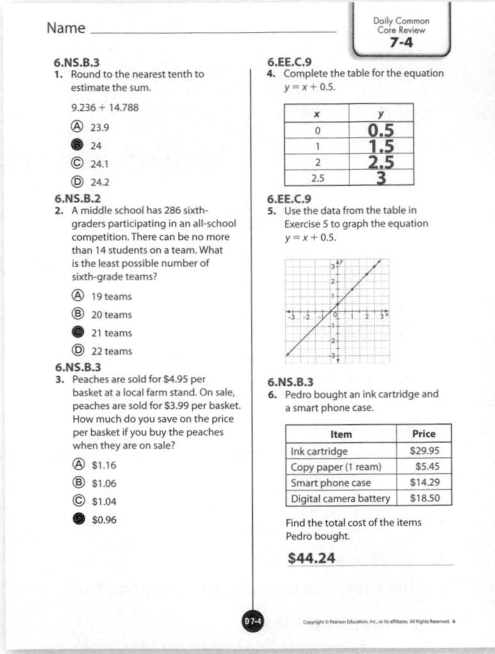
Name ______

Daily Common Core Review 7-4

6.NS.B.3
1. Round to the nearest tenth to estimate the sum.

9.236 + 14.788

Ⓐ 23.9
● 24
Ⓒ 24.1
Ⓓ 24.2

6.NS.B.2
2. A middle school has 286 sixth-graders participating in an all-school competition. There can be no more than 14 students on a team. What is the least possible number of sixth-grade teams?

Ⓐ 19 teams
Ⓑ 20 teams
● 21 teams
Ⓓ 22 teams

6.NS.B.3
3. Peaches are sold for $4.95 per basket at a local farm stand. On sale, peaches are sold for $3.99 per basket. How much do you save on the price per basket if you buy the peaches when they are on sale?

Ⓐ $1.16
Ⓑ $1.06
Ⓒ $1.04
● $0.96

6.EE.C.9
4. Complete the table for the equation $y = x + 0.5$.

| $x$ | $y$ |
|---|---|
| 0 | 0.5 |
| 1 | 1.5 |
| 2 | 2.5 |
| 2.5 | 3 |

6.EE.C.9
5. Use the data from the table in Exercise 5 to graph the equation $y = x + 0.5$.

6.NS.B.3
6. Pedro bought an ink cartridge and a smart phone case.

| Item | Price |
|---|---|
| Ink cartridge | $29.95 |
| Copy paper (1 ream) | $5.45 |
| Smart phone case | $14.29 |
| Digital camera battery | $18.50 |

Find the total cost of the items Pedro bought.

$44.24

D 7-4

### Today's Challenge

Think Use the Topic 7 problems any time during this topic.

## ENGLISH LANGUAGE LEARNERS

**Speaking** Speak using content area vocabulary in context.

*Use with the Visual Learning Bridge on Student's Edition p. 338.*

Read Box A. Write: $A = \ell w$. *To find the area of a rectangle, use the formula: Area = length times width.* Read Boxes B and C. *How was the area of the map found by changing the decimal to fractions? By multiplying decimals like whole numbers?* Instruct students to explain information using the terms: *area, decimal, fraction,* and/or *factors.*

**Beginning** Reread Boxes B and C to students. *How were the decimals written to solve the problem? How many decimal places?* Students will respond using the sentence stems: The decimals were written as ___. There are ___ ___ places.

**Intermediate** Reread Boxes B and C with students. *Why were the decimals written as fractions to solve the problem? Why was the decimal point moved three places in the product?* Students will respond using the sentence stems: The ___ were written as ___ because ___. There are ___ ___ places because ___.

**Advanced** Instruct students to reread Boxes B and C with partners. Ask students to write area, decimal, fraction, factors on index cards and to place the cards face up. *Explain how to solve the problem by changing the decimals to fractions and by multiplying the decimals like whole numbers.* As students use each word in their explanations, they turn the card over.

**Summarize** What strategies can be used to multiply decimals?

# DEVELOP: PROBLEM-BASED LEARNING

**COHERENCE: Engage learners by connecting prior knowledge to new ideas.**
Students use decimal grids as a tool to multiply a whole number and a decimal as they did in Grade 5.

10–15 min

Solve

## BEFORE

**1. Pose the Solve-and-Share Problem**
You may wish to provide decimal models (Teaching Tool 31).

**MP.5 Use Appropriate Tools Strategically** Listen and look for students who use the decimal models to represent and find the product of 0.28 × 4.

**2. Build Understanding**
*How can you find the total length of the connected tubes?* [Sample answers: Multiply 4 × 0.28, or add 0.28 four times.] *What does each square in the grid represent?* [0.01] *What does an entire square represent?* [1.0]

## DURING

**3. Ask Guiding Questions As Needed**
*How can you use the decimal grids to represent the combined length of the tubes?* [Shade 0.28 four times.] *How many squares will you shade to represent 0.28?* [28] *How do you use the shading to solve the problem?* [You count the total number of squares shaded.]

## AFTER

**4. Share and Discuss Solutions**
Solve Start with students' solutions. If needed, project Tom's work to discuss how to use the decimal grids to solve the problem.

**5. Transition to the Visual Learning Bridge**
*In 5th grade, you learned how to use decimal models to multiply decimals. Now you will learn how to use a general method, or standard algorithm, to multiply decimals.*

**6. Extension for Early Finishers**
*Show how to use decimal grids to represent and find the product of 0.17 × 3.* [Check students' work; 0.51]

Name

**Solve & Share**

Maxine is making a model windmill for a science fair. She is connecting 4 cardboard tubes together vertically. Each tube is 0.28 meter in length. What is the combined measure of the connected tubes? ***Solve this problem any way you choose.***

**Lesson 7-4**
**Multiply Decimals**

**I can …**
multiply decimals.

Content Standard 6.NS.B.3
Mathematical Practices MP.2, MP.3, MP.5, MP.7, MP.8

You can use tools, like decimal grids, to calculate with decimals.

See margin for sample student work.

**Look Back!** **MP.7 Look for Relationships** Suppose that Maxine made another windmill model by connecting 4 cardboard tubes that are 2.8 meters long. What is the combined measure of this model? What relationships do you see in the factors you used here and above? Explain how this helps you solve the problem.
**11.2 meters; Sample answer: The digits in the factors are the same and the number of decimal places in the product will be the same as the number of decimal places in both the factors.**



## Analyze Student Work

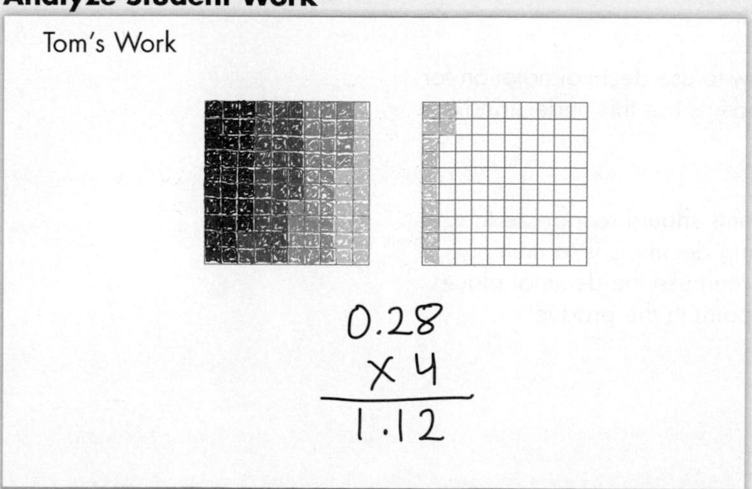


Tom shades 0.28 four times, using different colors, and then counts the total squares shaded to solve the problem.

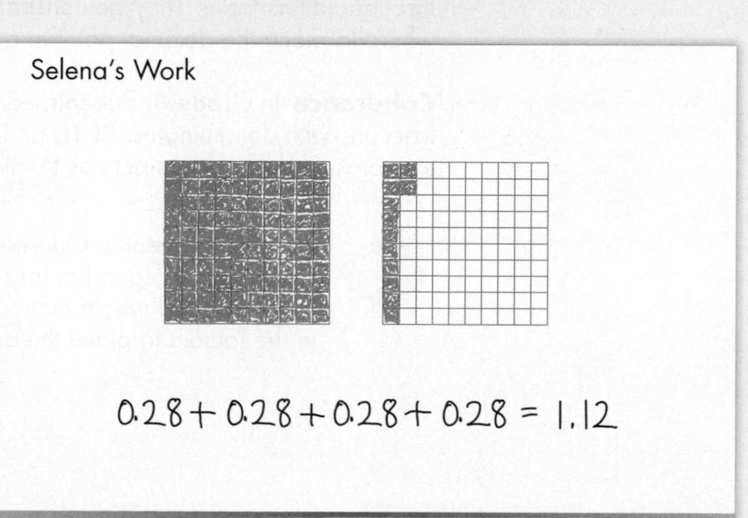


Selena shades 0.28 four times, and then adds the decimals to solve the problem.

# DEVELOP: VISUAL LEARNING

The *Visual Learning Bridge* connects students' thinking in Solve & Share to important math ideas in the lesson. Use the *Visual Learning Bridge* to make these ideas explicit. Also available as a *Visual Learning Animation Plus* at PearsonRealize.com

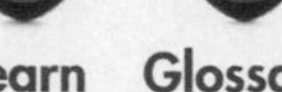

*How do you find the area of the rectangular map?* [Multiply the length and width.] *What is the length of the map?* [2.5 ft] *What is the width of the map?* [3.25 ft]

**MP.7 Use Structure**

*How do you know that 2.5 is the same as $\frac{25}{10}$? How do you know that 3.25 is the same as $\frac{325}{100}$?* [The number of digits to the right of the decimal place tells the number of zeros in the denominator.] *How do you multiply fractions?* [Multiply the numerators and then the denominators.]

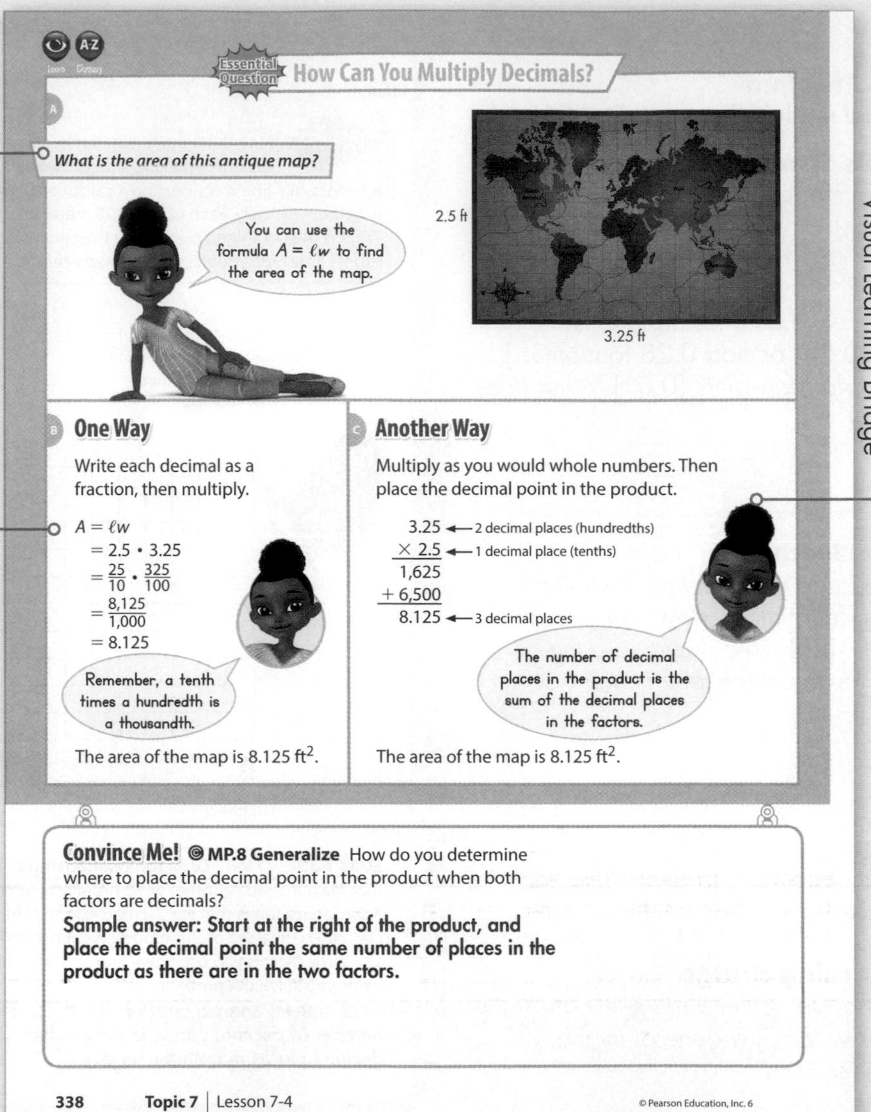

How Can You Multiply Decimals?
What is the area of this antique map?
You can use the formula $A = \ell w$ to find the area of the map.
2.5 ft
3.25 ft
One Way
Write each decimal as a fraction, then multiply.
$A = \ell w$
$= 2.5 \cdot 3.25$
$= \frac{25}{10} \cdot \frac{325}{100}$
$= \frac{8,125}{1,000}$
$= 8.125$
Remember, a tenth times a hundredth is a thousandth.
The area of the map is 8.125 ft$^2$.
Another Way
Multiply as you would whole numbers. Then place the decimal point in the product.
3.25 ← 2 decimal places (hundredths)
× 2.5 ← 1 decimal place (tenths)
1,625
+ 6,500
8.125 ← 3 decimal places
The number of decimal places in the product is the sum of the decimal places in the factors.
The area of the map is 8.125 ft$^2$.
Convince Me! MP.8 Generalize How do you determine where to place the decimal point in the product when both factors are decimals?
Sample answer: Start at the right of the product, and place the decimal point the same number of places in the product as there are in the two factors.
338 Topic 7 | Lesson 7-4
© Pearson Education, Inc. 6
Visual Learning Bridge


*How do you know that there are two decimal places in 3.25?* [There are two digits to the right of the decimal point.] *How do you know that there are 3 decimal places in the product?* [You add the decimal places in each factor, 2 + 1 = 3.]

**Prevent Misconceptions**

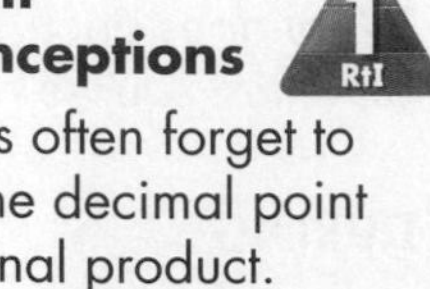


Students often forget to place the decimal point in the final product. Encourage them to estimate the product first, and then check that their answer is reasonable. If they did forget to place the decimal, the estimate is likely not close to the actual product. This can alert students to check that the decimal point is in their final answer.

**Convince Me! MP.8 Generalize** Students will continue to work to achieve fluency with multiplying decimals using the standard algorithm throughout this topic. They demonstrate understanding by explaining where to place the decimal point in a product.

**Coherence** In Grade 4, students learned how to use decimal notation for fractions with denominators of 10 or 100. Students use this understanding to represent decimal numbers as fractions.

Revisit the Essential Question. Students should recognize that the standard algorithm for multiplying decimals is to multiply as they would whole numbers and then use the decimal places in the factors to place the decimal point in the product.

Practice Buddy | Tools | Assessment

## QUICK CHECK

Check mark indicates items for prescribing differentiation on the next page.
Item 14 is worth 1 point. Items 18 and 22 are worth up to 2 points each.

20–30 min

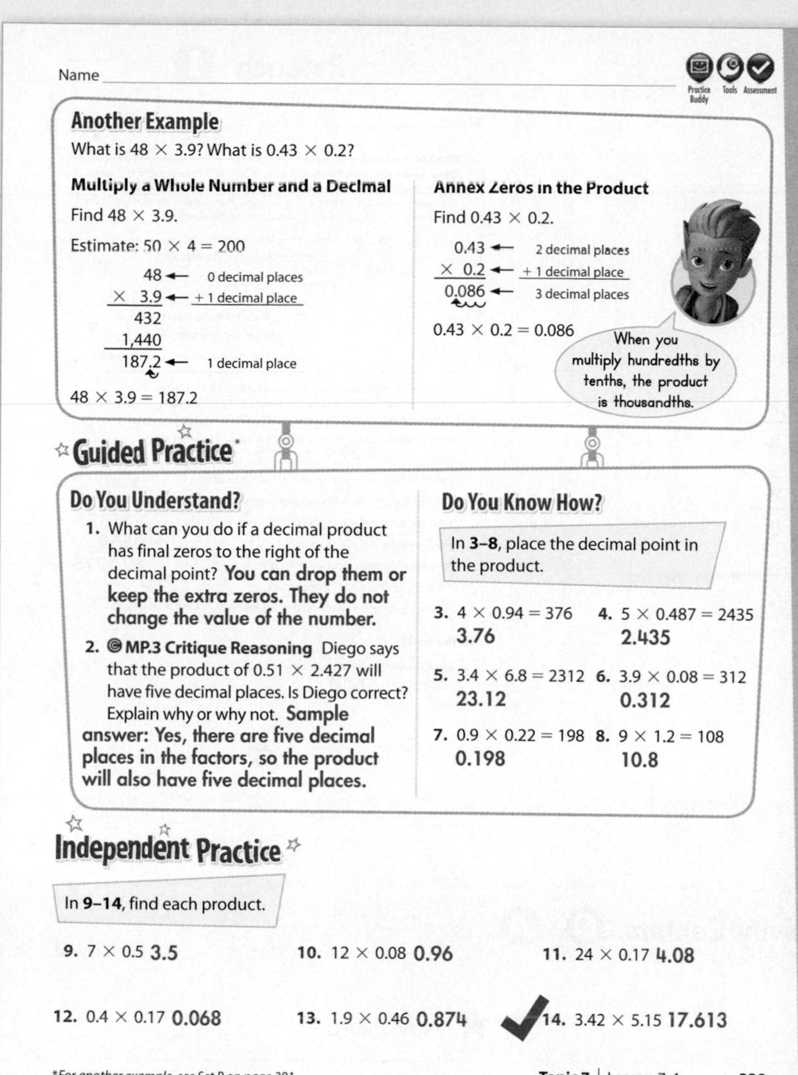

Name

### Another Example

What is 48 × 3.9? What is 0.43 × 0.2?

**Multiply a Whole Number and a Decimal**

Find 48 × 3.9.

Estimate: 50 × 4 = 200

```
   48  ← 0 decimal places
 × 3.9 ← + 1 decimal place
  432
1,440
187.2  ← 1 decimal place
```

48 × 3.9 = 187.2

**Annex Zeros in the Product**

Find 0.43 × 0.2.

```
  0.43 ← 2 decimal places
 × 0.2 ← + 1 decimal place
 0.086 ← 3 decimal places
```

0.43 × 0.2 = 0.086

When you multiply hundredths by tenths, the product is thousandths.



### Guided Practice*

**Do You Understand?**

1. What can you do if a decimal product has final zeros to the right of the decimal point? **You can drop them or keep the extra zeros. They do not change the value of the number.**
2. **MP.3 Critique Reasoning** Diego says that the product of 0.51 × 2.427 will have five decimal places. Is Diego correct? Explain why or why not. **Sample answer: Yes, there are five decimal places in the factors, so the product will also have five decimal places.**

**Do You Know How?**

In **3–8**, place the decimal point in the product.

3. 4 × 0.94 = 376 **3.76**
4. 5 × 0.487 = 2435 **2.435**
5. 3.4 × 6.8 = 2312 **23.12**
6. 3.9 × 0.08 = 312 **0.312**
7. 0.9 × 0.22 = 198 **0.198**
8. 9 × 1.2 = 108 **10.8**

### Independent Practice*

In **9–14**, find each product.

9. 7 × 0.5 **3.5**
10. 12 × 0.08 **0.96**
11. 24 × 0.17 **4.08**
12. 0.4 × 0.17 **0.068**
13. 1.9 × 0.46 **0.874**
14. 3.42 × 5.15 **17.613**

*For another example, see Set B on page 381.



### Math Practices and Problem Solving*

15. **Number Sense** Write a number sentence that illustrates the following. A number with two decimal places multiplied by a number with one decimal place. The product has only two nonzero digits. **Sample answer: 0.09 × 0.7 = 0.063**
16. The Bright-O Shampoo factory includes 1.078 ounces of vanilla oil in a 6.35-ounce bottle of shampoo. How much of the bottle of shampoo is **NOT** vanilla oil? **5.272 ounces**
17. Write the expanded form of the expression $8^5$ and then evaluate the expression. **8 × 8 × 8 × 8 × 8 = 32,768**
18. **Higher Order Thinking** Explain why 0.25 × 0.4 has only one decimal place in the product. **Sample answer: The zeros in the answer, 0.100, are not included in the answer.**

In **19–21**, use the graph to solve.

**Fastest Sporting Speeds**

| Human Activity | Miles per hour |
|---|---|
| Fastest swimming | 5.35 |
| Fastest running | 27.79 |
| Fastest rowing | 13.99 |
| Fastest luge | 95.69 |
| Fastest thrown baseball | 106 |

19. The fastest speed a table tennis ball has been hit is about 13.07 times as fast as the speed for the fastest swimming. What is the speed for the table tennis ball? **About 69.9245 miles per hour**
20. **MP.7 Look for Relationships** How fast would 1.5 times the fastest rowing speed be? Before you solve, tell the number of decimal places in your answer. **3 decimal places; 20.985 miles per hour**
21. Which activity has a recorded speed about 7 times as fast as the fastest rowing speed? **Luge**

#### Common Core Assessment

22. The wings of some hummingbirds beat 52 times per second.

**Part A**

If a hummingbird hovers for 35.5 seconds, how many times do its wings beat?

**1,846 beats**

**Part B**

Estimate the number of times its wings would beat in a minute.

**Sample answer: About 3,000 beats per minute.**





**Another Example** *What is the total number of decimal places in the factors of 0.43 × 0.2?* [3] *Where should the decimal point be placed in the product?* [Three places from the right in the product] *Why is it important to annex the zero to the left of the product?* [There are 3 decimal places in the product, so you need to include a zero as a placeholder.]

**Error Intervention: Item 3**

**If** students have difficulty placing the decimal in the product,
**then** ask: *How many digits are to the right of the decimal point in 4?* [0] *In 0.94?* [2] *How many places from the right do you place the decimal point in the product? Explain.* [2; 0 + 2 = 2]

**Items 9–14** Students may have trouble recording their work neatly. You may wish to provide Grid paper (Teaching Tool 16) for these students and encourage them to use one square for each digit.

**Reteaching** Assign Reteaching Set B on p. 381.

**Item 18 Higher Order Thinking** *How many decimal places would you expect in the product of 0.25 × 0.4?* [Three] *What must be true about the last two digits to the right of the decimal point in the product?* [They must be zeros.] Remind students that zeros can be annexed to the end of a decimal number without changing the value of the number so these zeros do not need to be written in the final number.

**Item 20 MP.7 Look for Relationships** *What is the fastest rowing speed?* [13.99 miles per hour] Encourage students to use compatible numbers to estimate. For example, 14 × 1.5 = 14(1) + 14(0.5) = 14 + 7 = 21.

**Multi-Step Problems** *Page 340 Item 22; Page 342 Item 22*

STEP 3

# ASSESS AND DIFFERENTIATE

Use the **QUICK CHECK** on the previous page to prescribe differentiated instruction.

**I Intervention** 0–3 points on the Quick Check

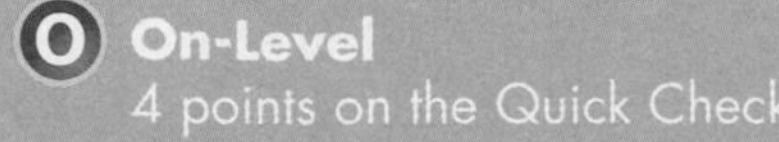

**O On-Level** 4 points on the Quick Check

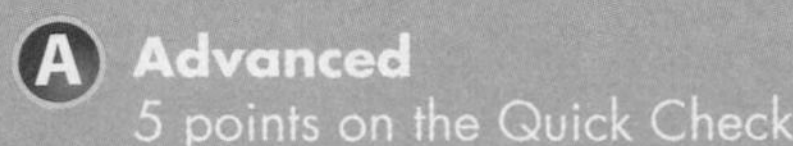

**A Advanced** 5 points on the Quick Check

## Intervention Activity I

### Multiply Decimals

**Materials**

Number cubes (or Teaching Tool 23)

- Organize students in pairs.
- To start, have one student roll the number cube 5 times and use the results to write a decimal number.
- Have the other student roll the number cube 2 times and use the results to write another decimal number.
- Ask students to multiply the two decimals they wrote.
- Student pairs check each other's work and agree on the correct product.
- Continue the game, encouraging students to write decimals with varying numbers of decimal places.

$$\begin{array}{r} 56.124 \\ \times \quad 2.1 \\ \hline 56124 \\ +\ 1122480 \\ \hline 117.8604 \end{array}$$

## Reteach I

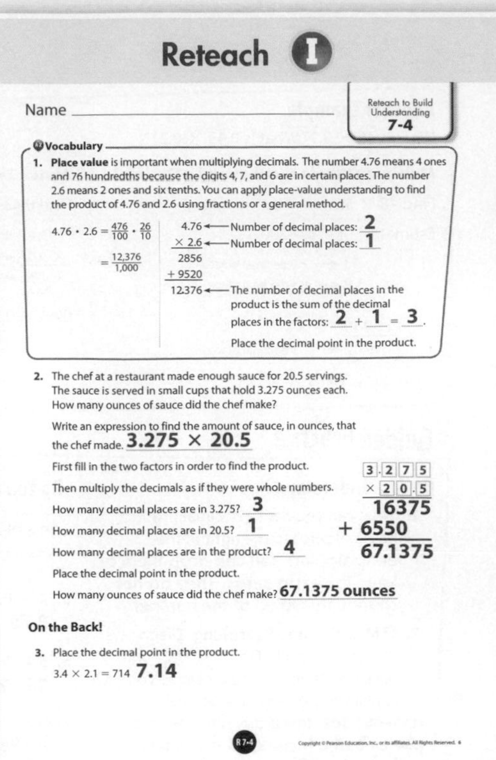

Name ______________

Reteach to Build Understanding 7-4

**Vocabulary**

1. **Place value** is important when multiplying decimals. The number 4.76 means 4 ones and 76 hundredths because the digits 4, 7, and 6 are in certain places. The number 2.6 means 2 ones and six tenths. You can apply place-value understanding to find the product of 4.76 and 2.6 using fractions or a general method.

$4.76 \cdot 2.6 = \frac{476}{100} \cdot \frac{26}{10} = \frac{12{,}376}{1{,}000}$

4.76 ← Number of decimal places: **2**
× 2.6 ← Number of decimal places: **1**
2856
+ 9520
12.376 ← The number of decimal places in the product is the sum of the decimal places in the factors: **2** + **1** = **3**.

Place the decimal point in the product.

2. The chef at a restaurant made enough sauce for 20.5 servings. The sauce is served in small cups that hold 3.275 ounces each. How many ounces of sauce did the chef make?

Write an expression to find the amount of sauce, in ounces, that the chef made. **3.275 × 20.5**

First fill in the two factors in order to find the product.

Then multiply the decimals as if they were whole numbers.

How many decimal places are in 3.275? **3**

How many decimal places are in 20.5? **1**

How many decimal places are in the product? **4**

Place the decimal point in the product.

How many ounces of sauce did the chef make? **67.1375 ounces**

$$\begin{array}{r} 3.275 \\ \times \ 20.5 \\ \hline 16375 \\ +\ 6550 \\ \hline 67.1375 \end{array}$$

**On the Back!**

3. Place the decimal point in the product.

3.4 × 2.1 = 714 **7.14**

R 7-4



## On-Level and Advanced Activity Centers O A

### Center Games

Students work in pairs or small groups to multiply decimals. Have students record their work as they play the game.

★ On-Level

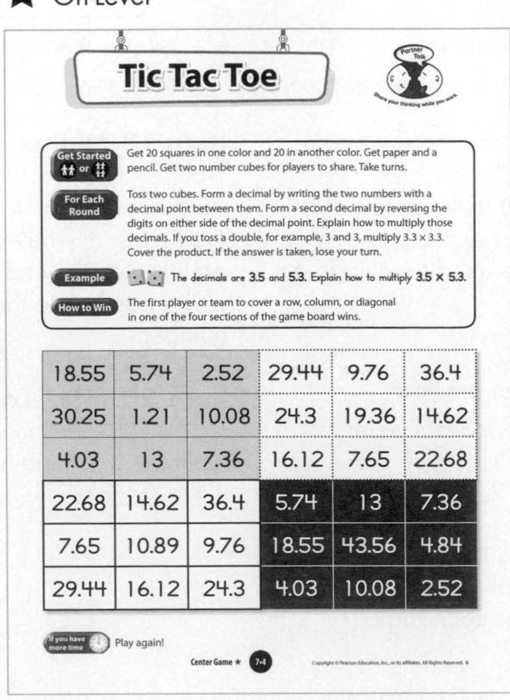

**Tic Tac Toe**



**Get Started** Get 20 squares in one color and 20 in another color. Get paper and a pencil. Get two number cubes for players to share. Take turns.

**For Each Round** Toss two cubes. Form a decimal by writing the two numbers with a decimal point between them. Form a second decimal by reversing the digits on either side of the decimal point. Explain how to multiply those decimals. If you toss a double, for example, 3 and 3, multiply 3.3 × 3.3. Cover the product. If the answer is taken, lose your turn.

**Example** The decimals are 3.5 and 5.3. Explain how to multiply 3.5 × 5.3.

**How to Win** The first player or team to cover a row, column, or diagonal in one of the four sections of the game board wins.

| 18.55 | 5.74 | 2.52 | 29.44 | 9.76 | 36.4 |
|---|---|---|---|---|---|
| 30.25 | 1.21 | 10.08 | 24.3 | 19.36 | 14.62 |
| 4.03 | 13 | 7.36 | 16.12 | 7.65 | 22.68 |
| 22.68 | 14.62 | 36.4 | 5.74 | 13 | 7.36 |
| 7.65 | 10.89 | 9.76 | 18.55 | 43.56 | 4.84 |
| 29.44 | 16.12 | 24.3 | 4.03 | 10.08 | 2.52 |

If you have more time Play again!

Center Game ★ 7-4



★★ Advanced

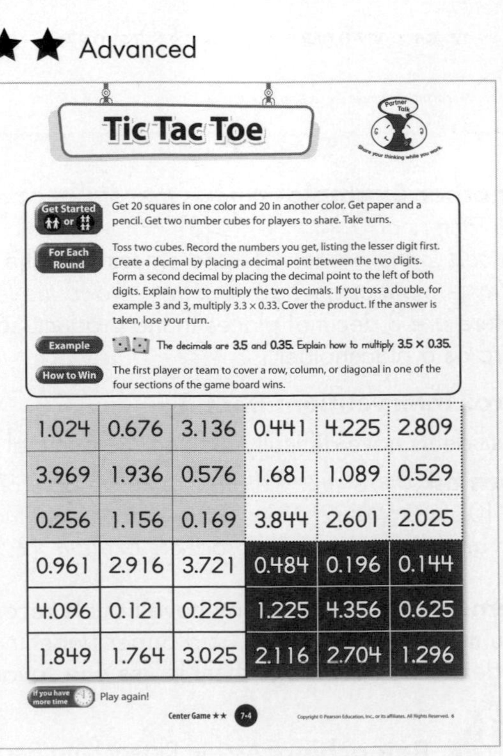

**Tic Tac Toe**



**Get Started** Get 20 squares in one color and 20 in another color. Get paper and a pencil. Get two number cubes for players to share. Take turns.

**For Each Round** Toss two cubes. Record the numbers you get, listing the lesser digit first. Create a decimal by placing a decimal point between the two digits. Form a second decimal by placing the decimal point to the left of both digits. Explain how to multiply the two decimals. If you toss a double, for example 3 and 3, multiply 3.3 × 0.33. Cover the product. If the answer is taken, lose your turn.

**Example** The decimals are 3.5 and 0.35. Explain how to multiply 3.5 × 0.35.

**How to Win** The first player or team to cover a row, column, or diagonal in one of the four sections of the game board wins.

| 1.024 | 0.676 | 3.136 | 0.441 | 4.225 | 2.809 |
|---|---|---|---|---|---|
| 3.969 | 1.936 | 0.576 | 1.681 | 1.089 | 0.529 |
| 0.256 | 1.156 | 0.169 | 3.844 | 2.601 | 2.025 |
| 0.961 | 2.916 | 3.721 | 0.484 | 0.196 | 0.144 |
| 4.096 | 0.121 | 0.225 | 1.225 | 4.356 | 0.625 |
| 1.849 | 1.764 | 3.025 | 2.116 | 2.704 | 1.296 |

If you have more time Play again!

Center Game ★★ 7-4

15–30 min

**TIMING**

The time allocated to Step 3 will depend on the teacher's instructional decisions and differentiation routines.

PEARSON realize. PearsonRealize.com

 Help
 Practice Buddy
 Tools
Games

## Technology Center   

 Tools
 Games

### Math Tools and Math Games

A link to a specific math tools activity or math game to use with this lesson is provided at PearsonRealize.com.

## Leveled Assignment

 Items 1–9, 16–20, 22  Items 3–6, 10–12, 18–22  Items 4–6, 13–22

Name ______________

Help Practice Buddy Tools Games

## Homework & Practice 7-4
### Multiply Decimals

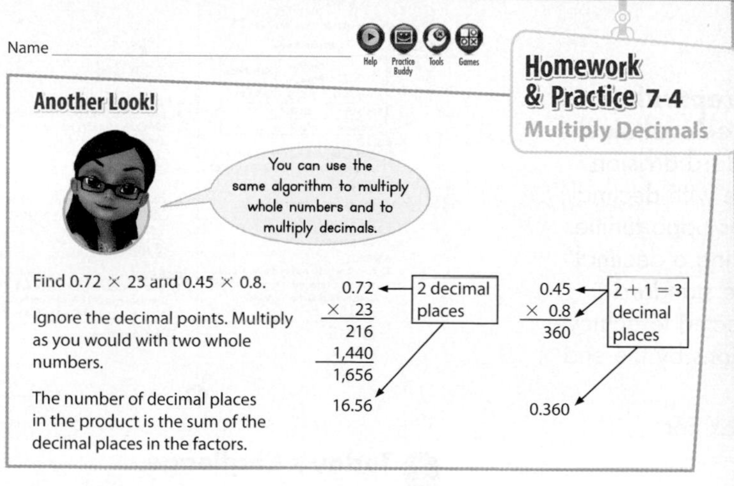

Another Look!
You can use the same algorithm to multiply whole numbers and to multiply decimals.
Find 0.72 × 23 and 0.45 × 0.8.
Ignore the decimal points. Multiply as you would with two whole numbers.
The number of decimal places in the product is the sum of the decimal places in the factors.
0.72
× 23
216
1,440
1,656
16.56
2 decimal places
0.45
× 0.8
360
0.360
2 + 1 = 3 decimal places


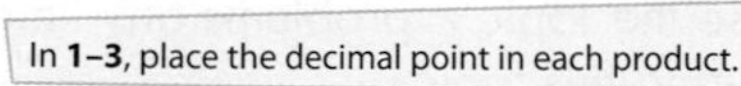
In **1–3**, place the decimal point in each product.

**1.** 1.2 × 3.6 = 432
**4.32**

**2.** 5.5 × 3.77 = 20735
**20.735**

**3.** 4.4 × 2.333 = 102652
**10.2652**

In **4–15**, find each product.

**4.** 532.1 × 4.2
**2,234.82**

**5.** 47.50 × 0.03
**1.425**

**6.** 210.7 × 17.4
**3,666.18**

**7.** 4.3 × 2.1 =
**9.03**

**8.** 40.45 × 0.01 =
**0.4045**

**9.** 6.1 × 0.3 =
**1.83**

**10.** 4.89 × 2.2
**10.758**

**11.** 2.01 × 0.43
**0.8643**

**12.** 54.1 × 0.69
**37.329**

**13.** 0.5 × 0.05
**0.025**

**14.** 14.09 × 1.3
**18.317**

**15.** 10.92 × 4.08
**44.5536**



**16.** **MP.2 Reasoning** If you multiply two decimals less than 1, can you predict whether the product will be less than or greater than either of the factors? Explain.
**Sample answer: If two numbers less than 1 are multiplied, the product will be less than either factor. You are taking part of a part of one, so it will be less.**

**17.** **Number Sense** Two factors are multiplied and their product is 34.44. One factor is a whole number. How many decimal places are in the other factor? Tell how you know.
**2 decimal places; The product has the total number of decimal places of the factors, so 0 + 2 = 2.**

In **18** and **19**, use the graph to solve.

**18.** Renaldo owns a used car lot. What is the total number of cars Renaldo sold during the three months?
**57 cars**

**19.** Renaldo makes $956.75 for each car that he sells. Estimate how much money he made during the three months.
**Sample answer: $57,000**

**20.** **MP.3 Critique Reasoning** Kim multiplied 8 × 0.952 and got 76.16. How can you use estimation to show that Kim's answer is wrong?
**Sample answer: The number 0.952 can be rounded to 1; 8 × 1 = 8, so 7.616 is the reasonable answer. Kim placed the decimal point in the wrong place.**

**21.** **Higher Order Thinking** The decimal 104.3 becomes 1,043 when multiplied by 10. The same number becomes 10.43 when multiplied by 0.10. Explain why.
**Sample answer: Multiplying by 10 makes the number greater by a factor of 10. Multiplying by a decimal, like 0.10, will give a product that is only part of the number, and smaller by a factor of 10.**

### Common Core Assessment

**22.** A wolf is able to hear the howl of another wolf in the forest up to 1.8 kilometers away. Wolves are also very quick and can jump up to 4.5 meters.

**Part A**

If a kangaroo can jump 1.68 times that of a wolf, how many meters can a kangaroo jump?

**7.56 meters**

**Part B**

An elephant is able to hear 5.4 times the distance of a wolf's hearing ability. How many kilometers away is that?

**9.72 kilometers**

# LESSON 7-5

# DIVIDE DECIMALS BY A WHOLE NUMBER

## DIGITAL RESOURCES PearsonRealize.com

eText — Student and Teacher eTexts

PD — Listen and Look For Lesson Video

Think — Today's Challenge

Solve — Solve and Share

Learn — Visual Learning Animation Plus

Glossary — Animated Glossary

Practice Buddy — Online Personalized Practice

Tools — Math Tools

Assessment — Quick Check

Help — Another Look Homework Video

Games — Math Games

## LESSON OVERVIEW FCR FOCUS • COHERENCE • RIGOR

### FOCUS

**Domain 6.NS** The Number System

**Cluster 6.NS.B** Compute fluently with multi-digit numbers and find common factors and multiples.

**Content Standard 6.NS.B.2** Fluently divide multi-digit numbers using the standard algorithm. Also **6.NS.B.3**.

**Mathematical Practices MP.2, MP.3, MP.7**

**Objective** Divide decimals by whole numbers.

**Essential Understanding** A general method, or standard algorithm, can be use to divide decimals fluently.

### COHERENCE

In Topic 6, students developed fluency in dividing multi-digit whole numbers. In the first four lessons of this topic, students applied a standard algorithm to add, subtract, and multiply decimal numbers. In this lesson, they begin to develop fluency in dividing decimals by whole numbers using the standard algorithm.

### RIGOR

This lesson emphasizes **conceptual understanding** and **procedural skill**. Students learn how the standard division algorithm is extended for use with decimal numbers. The lesson provides opportunities for students to practice dividing a decimal by a whole number using the standard algorithm. Students are expected to achieve fluency with decimal operations by the end of Grade 6.

PD Watch the Listen and Look For Lesson Video.

## MATH ANYTIME

### Daily Common Core Review

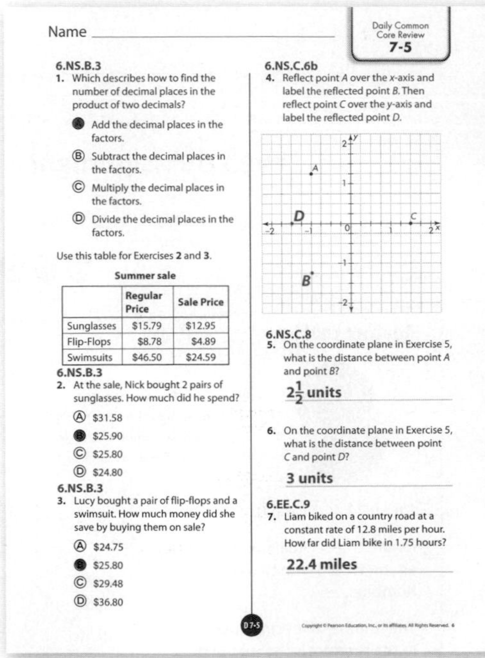

Name ____________

Daily Common Core Review 7-5

6.NS.B.3
1. Which describes how to find the number of decimal places in the product of two decimals?
   - (A) Add the decimal places in the factors. ●
   - (B) Subtract the decimal places in the factors.
   - (C) Multiply the decimal places in the factors.
   - (D) Divide the decimal places in the factors.

Use this table for Exercises **2** and **3**.

**Summer sale**

| | Regular Price | Sale Price |
|---|---|---|
| Sunglasses | $15.79 | $12.95 |
| Flip-Flops | $8.78 | $4.89 |
| Swimsuits | $46.50 | $24.59 |

6.NS.B.3
2. At the sale, Nick bought 2 pairs of sunglasses. How much did he spend?
   - (A) $31.58
   - (B) $25.90 ●
   - (C) $25.80
   - (D) $24.80

6.NS.B.3
3. Lucy bought a pair of flip-flops and a swimsuit. How much money did she save by buying them on sale?
   - (A) $24.75
   - (B) $25.80 ●
   - (C) $29.48
   - (D) $36.80

6.NS.C.6b
4. Reflect point $A$ over the $x$-axis and label the reflected point $B$. Then reflect point $C$ over the $y$-axis and label the reflected point $D$.



6.NS.C.8
5. On the coordinate plane in Exercise 5, what is the distance between point $A$ and point $B$?
   **$2\frac{1}{2}$ units**

6. On the coordinate plane in Exercise 5, what is the distance between point $C$ and point $D$?
   **3 units**

6.EE.C.9
7. Liam biked on a country road at a constant rate of 12.8 miles per hour. How far did Liam bike in 1.75 hours?
   **22.4 miles**

D7-5

### Today's Challenge

Think Use the Topic 7 problems any time during this topic.

## ENGLISH LANGUAGE LEARNERS ELL

**Listening** Seek clarification of spoken word.

*Use with the Solve & Share on Student's Edition p. 343.*

Read the Solve & Share. Instruct students to retell information to partners. Ask students to give thumbs up if they understand their partner's explanation. *What is the total cost of the snack? What operation is used to solve the problem?*

**Beginning** Write $10.96, ÷ , and 4 on index cards. Read the Solve & Share. *What is the total cost of the snack? What operation is used to solve the problem? What is the divisor?* Students will respond by selecting the correct cards.

**Intermediate** Distribute three index cards to each student. Read the Solve & Share. *What is the total cost of the snack?* Students will write the correct response on an index card and hold it up. Continue the process with questions: *What operation is used to solve the problem? What equation is used to solve the problem?*

**Advanced** Instruct students to read the Solve & Share with partners. Have students work in pairs. Distribute three index cards to each group. Ask students to write the following on the index cards: *amount owed, divided by 4 because, equally*. One student will use the cards to explain the problem. If the partner understands the explanation, she or he will give thumbs up. Students will reverse roles.

**Summarize** What operation is used to find equal amounts?

# DEVELOP: PROBLEM-BASED LEARNING

**COHERENCE: Engage learners by connecting prior knowledge to new ideas.**
Students apply what they know about division and using the standard algorithm to divide a decimal by a whole number.

10–15 min

Solve

## BEFORE

1. **Pose the Solve-and-Share Problem**
**MP.2 Reason Quantitatively** Listen and look for students who divide as they would whole numbers and then reason about the quantities to solve the problem.

2. **Build Understanding**
*What mathematical operation would the girls use to share the cost equally?* [Division] *What division expression represents the problem?* [$10.96 ÷ 4]

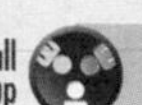

## DURING

3. **Ask Guiding Questions As Needed**
*How is dividing decimals different from dividing whole numbers?* [You need to figure out where to place the decimal point in the quotient.] *How could you use what you know about dividing whole numbers to solve the problem?* [Sample answer: Divide $10 by 4 and divide 96 cents by 4, and then add the money amounts.]

## AFTER

4. **Share and Discuss Solutions**
Solve Start with students' solutions. If needed, project Tim's work to discuss how to use the division algorithm and estimation to solve the problem.

5. **Transition to the Visual Learning Bridge**
*The standard algorithm for division with whole numbers can be used to divide decimals. You just need to know where to place the decimal point in the quotient.*

6. **Extension for Early Finishers**
*Lola, Tanish, Sarita, and Tia share a desert. How much will each girl owe now that their final bill is $17.44?* [$4.36]

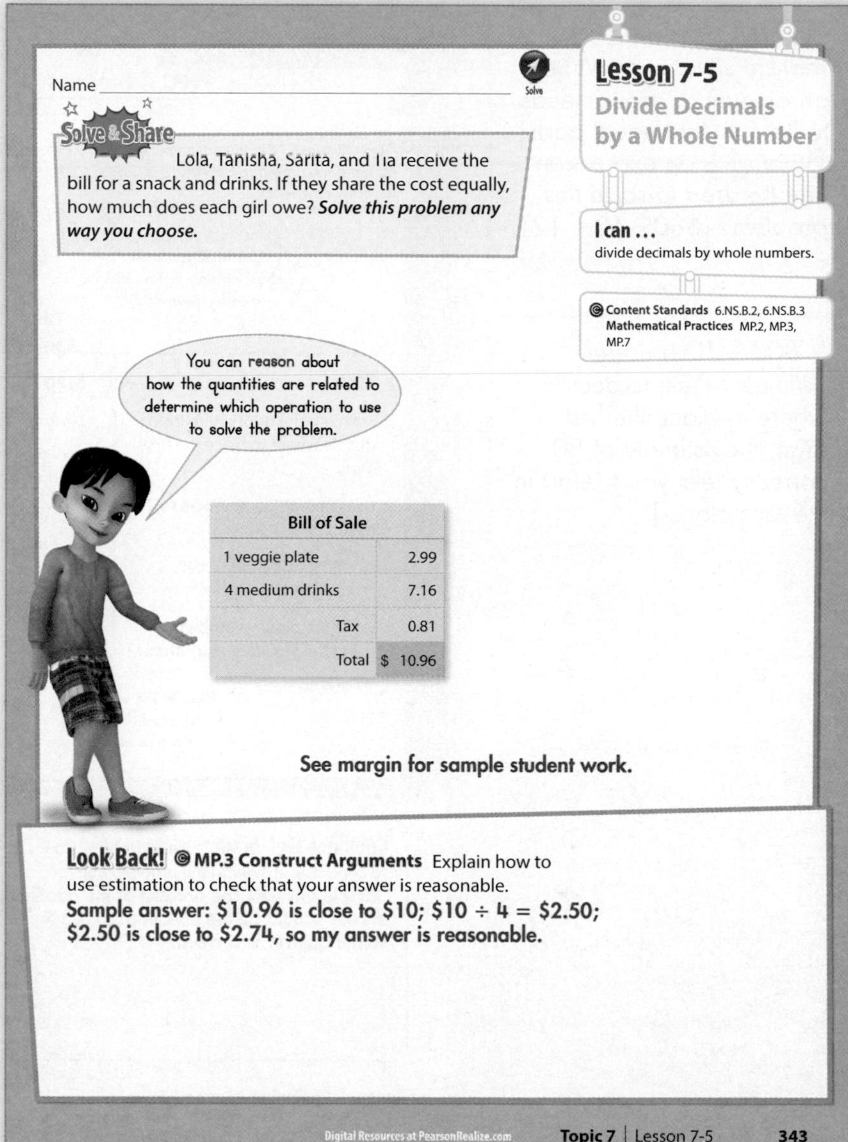

Name

Solve & Share

Lola, Tanisha, Sarita, and Tia receive the bill for a snack and drinks. If they share the cost equally, how much does each girl owe? ***Solve this problem any way you choose.***

**Lesson 7-5**
**Divide Decimals by a Whole Number**

**I can ...**
divide decimals by whole numbers.

Content Standards 6.NS.B.2, 6.NS.B.3
Mathematical Practices MP.2, MP.3, MP.7

You can reason about how the quantities are related to determine which operation to use to solve the problem.

| Bill of Sale | |
|---|---|
| 1 veggie plate | 2.99 |
| 4 medium drinks | 7.16 |
| Tax | 0.81 |
| Total | $ 10.96 |

**See margin for sample student work.**

**Look Back!** **MP.3 Construct Arguments** Explain how to use estimation to check that your answer is reasonable.
**Sample answer: $10.96 is close to $10; $10 ÷ 4 = $2.50; $2.50 is close to $2.74, so my answer is reasonable.**

Digital Resources at PearsonRealize.com **Topic 7** | Lesson 7-5 **343**

## Analyze Student Work

**Tim's Work**

10.96 ÷ 4 = n
Estimate: 10 ÷ 4 = 2.5

```
     274
 4 ) 10.96
    -8
     29
    -28
      16
     -16
       0
```

The digits in the answer are 274. The actual answer is $2.74 because it must be close to the estimate of $2.75.

Tim divides as with whole numbers and determines where to put the decimal by using his estimate.

**Vicki's Work**

Divide both $10 and 96¢ by 4, then add the amounts.

Use mental math:
$10 ÷ 4 = $2.50

```
   24 cents
 4 ) 96
     8
     16
     16
      0
```

$2.50 + $0.24 = $2.74
Each person pays $2.74.

Vicki divides $10 and 96 cents by 4, then adds the two quotients.

# DEVELOP: VISUAL LEARNING

The *Visual Learning Bridge* connects students' thinking in Solve & Share to important math ideas in the lesson. Use the *Visual Learning Bridge* to make these ideas explicit. Also available as a *Visual Learning Animation Plus* at PearsonRealize.com

PEARSON realize. PearsonRealize.com

Learn Glossary

*When is division used in real-life situations?* [When an amount or group needs to be split into equal parts] *What division expression can be used to solve this problem?* [$809.40 ÷ 12]

*Is 800 ÷ 10 a useful estimate?* [Yes; to decide where to place the first digit, the estimate of 80 correctly tells you to start in the tens place.]

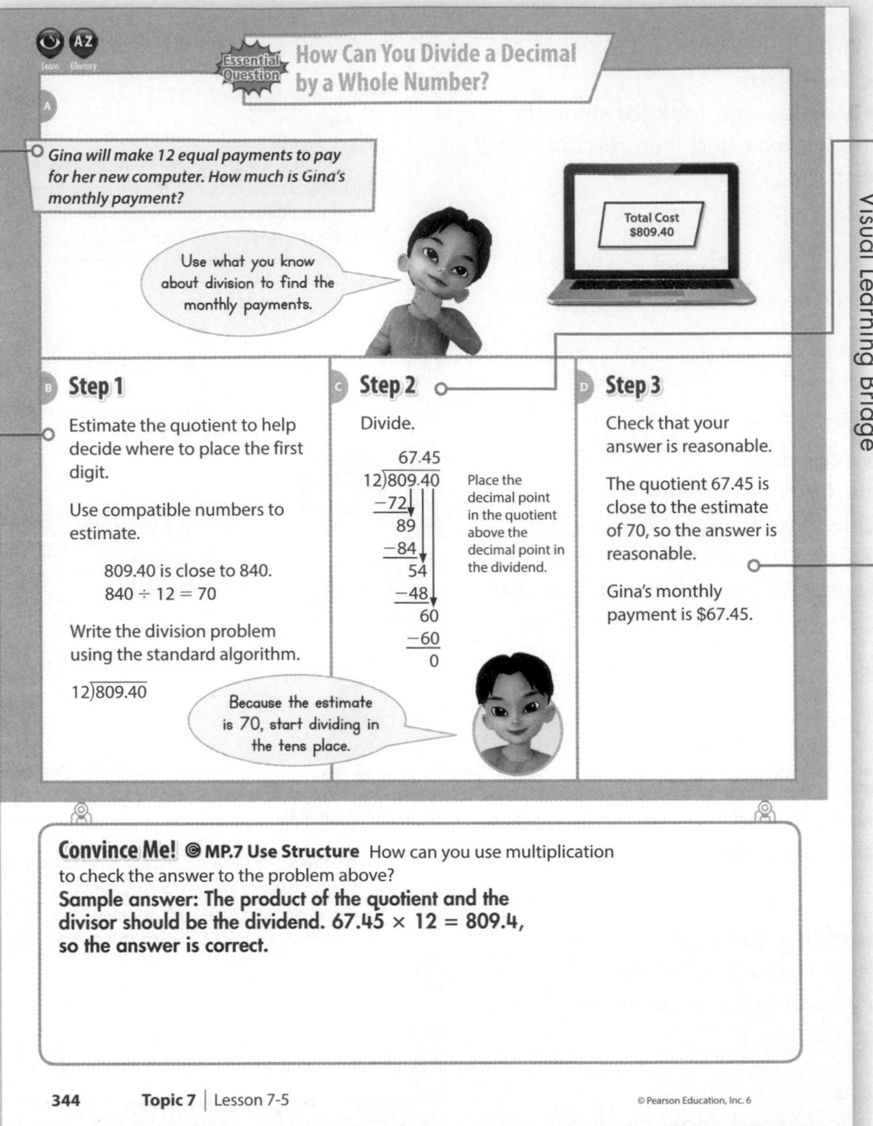

Essential Question
How Can You Divide a Decimal by a Whole Number?
Gina will make 12 equal payments to pay for her new computer. How much is Gina's monthly payment?
Total Cost $809.40
Use what you know about division to find the monthly payments.
Step 1
Estimate the quotient to help decide where to place the first digit.
Use compatible numbers to estimate.
809.40 is close to 840.
840 ÷ 12 = 70
Write the division problem using the standard algorithm.
12)809.40
Step 2
Divide.
67.45
12)809.40
−72
89
−84
54
−48
60
−60
0
Place the decimal point in the quotient above the decimal point in the dividend.
Because the estimate is 70, start dividing in the tens place.
Step 3
Check that your answer is reasonable.
The quotient 67.45 is close to the estimate of 70, so the answer is reasonable.
Gina's monthly payment is $67.45.
Visual Learning Bridge
Convince Me! MP.7 Use Structure How can you use multiplication to check the answer to the problem above?
Sample answer: The product of the quotient and the divisor should be the dividend. 67.45 × 12 = 809.4, so the answer is correct.
344 Topic 7 | Lesson 7-5
© Pearson Education, Inc. 6


**MP.7 Use Structure**
*Why is it important to use structure when applying the division algorithm?* [The place value structure of decimals indicates the location of the decimal point. By aligning digits by their place value, you keep the decimal point in the same relative place in both the dividend and quotient.]

*Why is an estimate so beneficial when making calculations with decimal numbers?* [It is easy to misplace the decimal point; an estimate lets you know immediately if this has happened.]

**Convince Me! MP.7 Use Structure** *Which operation has an inverse relationship with division?* [Multiplication] *How would you use this inverse relationship to check your answer?* [Multiply the quotient by the divisor; the product should be the dividend.]

**Coherence** Students solve the computer problem by dividing a multi-digit decimal by a 2-digit whole number. They also estimate the quotient and check that their answer is reasonable. This extends work in Topic 6 where students learned the algorithm for division, developed fluency in dividing multi-digit whole numbers, and estimated quotients.

Revisit the Essential Question. Students use the standard division algorithm and learn where to place the decimal point when dividing a decimal by a whole number.

## QUICK CHECK

Check mark indicates items for prescribing differentiation on the next page. Item 8 is worth 1 point. Items 18 and 19 are worth up to 2 points.

20–30 min

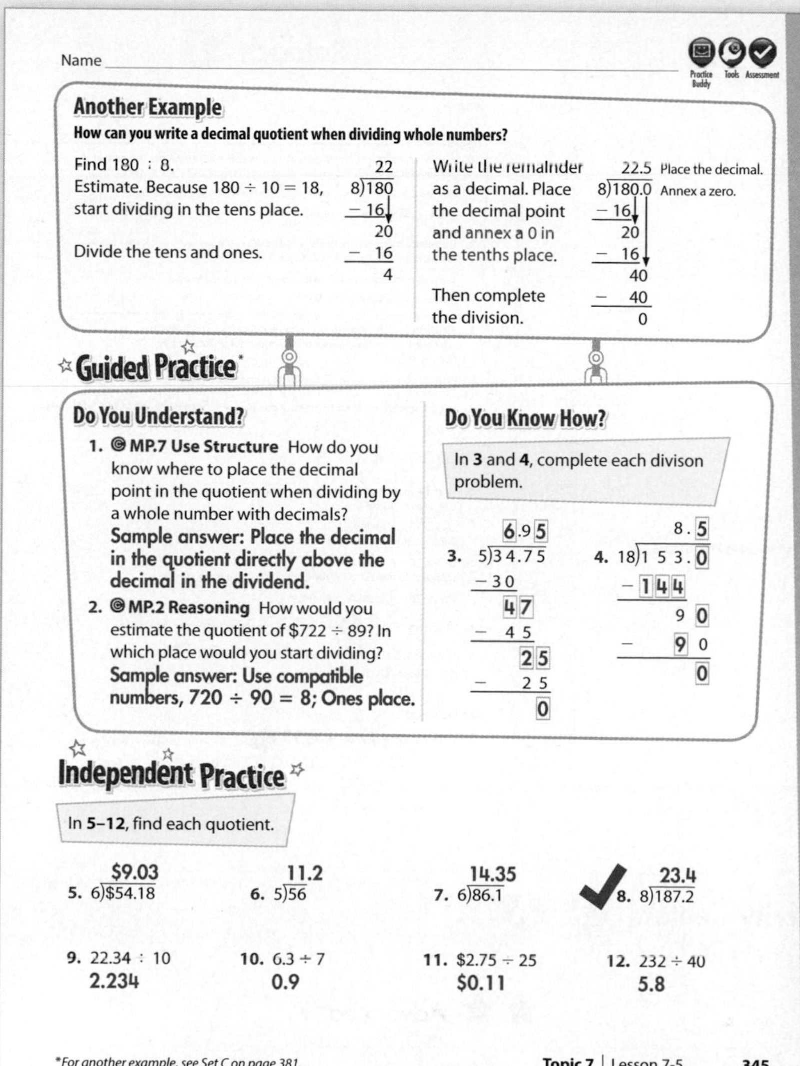

Name ______________________

### Another Example

**How can you write a decimal quotient when dividing whole numbers?**

Find 180 ÷ 8.
Estimate. Because 180 ÷ 10 = 18, start dividing in the tens place.

Divide the tens and ones.

$$\begin{array}{r} 22 \\ 8\overline{)180} \\ -16\phantom{0} \\ \hline 20 \\ -16 \\ \hline 4 \end{array}$$

Write the remainder as a decimal. Place the decimal point and annex a 0 in the tenths place.

Then complete the division.

$$\begin{array}{r} 22.5 \\ 8\overline{)180.0} \\ -16\phantom{0.0} \\ \hline 20\phantom{.0} \\ -16\phantom{.0} \\ \hline 4\,0 \\ -4\,0 \\ \hline 0 \end{array}$$

Place the decimal. Annex a zero.

### Guided Practice*

**Do You Understand?**

1. **MP.7 Use Structure** How do you know where to place the decimal point in the quotient when dividing by a whole number with decimals?
**Sample answer: Place the decimal in the quotient directly above the decimal in the dividend.**

2. **MP.2 Reasoning** How would you estimate the quotient of \$722 ÷ 89? In which place would you start dividing?
**Sample answer: Use compatible numbers, 720 ÷ 90 = 8; Ones place.**

**Do You Know How?**

In **3** and **4**, complete each divison problem.

3. $\begin{array}{r} 6.95 \\ 5\overline{)34.75} \\ -30\phantom{.75} \\ \hline 4\,7\phantom{5} \\ -4\,5\phantom{5} \\ \hline 25 \\ -25 \\ \hline 0 \end{array}$

4. $\begin{array}{r} 8.5 \\ 18\overline{)153.0} \\ -144\phantom{.0} \\ \hline 9\,0 \\ -9\,0 \\ \hline 0 \end{array}$

### Independent Practice*

In **5–12**, find each quotient.

5. 6)\$54.18 **\$9.03**
6. 5)56 **11.2**
7. 6)86.1 **14.35**
8. ✓ 8)187.2 **23.4**
9. 22.34 ÷ 10 **2.234**
10. 6.3 ÷ 7 **0.9**
11. \$2.75 ÷ 25 **\$0.11**
12. 232 ÷ 40 **5.8**

*For another example, see Set C on page 381.



### Math Practices and Problem Solving*

13. **Vocabulary** Write an example of a *formula*.
**Sample answer: $A = \ell \cdot w$**

14. The longest spin of a basketball on one finger is 255 minutes. How many hours is this? **4.25 h**

15. **MP.3 Critique Reasoning** Henrieta divided 0.80 by 20 as shown. Is her work correct? If not, explain why and give a correct response.

$$\begin{array}{r} 0.40 \\ 20\overline{)0.80} \\ -80 \\ \hline 0 \end{array}$$

**No; Sample answer: The division should begin in the hundredths place. The correct answer is 0.04.**

16. Which brand of fruit snacks costs less per pound? How much less?

| Fruit Snacks | | |
|---|---|---|
| Brand A | 15 lbs | \$16.20 |
| Brand B | 25 lbs | \$22.25 |

**Sample answer: Brand A costs \$1.08 per pound. Brand B costs \$0.89 per pound. Brand B costs \$0.19 less per pound.**

17. How might you best estimate the quotient of 479.25 ÷ 24?
**Sample answer: Use compatible numbers 500 and 25; 500 ÷ 25 = 20; about 20.**

18. ✓ **Higher Order Thinking** Kendra has 5.5 pounds of popcorn and wants to package it equally in 50 bags. How can she use place-value reasoning to find the amount of popcorn to put in each bag?
**Sample answer: The divisor, 50, is about 10 times as much as the dividend, 5.5. Kendra can annex a zero in the hundredths place and divide 5.50 by 50. Each share is 0.11 pound.**

#### Common Core Assessment

19. ✓ Draw lines to connect each division expression in Column A with its quotient in Column B.

| Column A | Column B |
|---|---|
| 21.6 ÷ 3 | 7.2 |
| 315.7 ÷ 41 | 7.5 |
| 90 ÷ 12 | 7.7 |





**Another Example** Before students look at this page, have students do the problem 114 ÷ 5. *What is the solution to 114 ÷ 5?* [Sample answer: 22 R4]. Then work through this example. Have students return to 114 ÷ 5. *What is an equivalent answer for 114 ÷ 5?* [22.8] Tell students they can always use this method instead of writing a remainder.

**Error Intervention: Item 1**

**If** students have difficulty placing the decimal point,

**then** remind them to place the decimal point in the quotient directly above the decimal point in the dividend.

**Item 2 MP.2 Reason Quantitatively** *Is 700 ÷ 100 close enough to answer the question? Explain.* [Yes; the estimate 7 is close enough to know you can start in the ones place. If the estimate is between 9 and 11, you should try to find a better estimate so you know whether to start in the ones place or tens place.]

**Reteaching** Assign Reteaching Set C on p. 381.

**Item 15 MP.3 Critique Reasoning** *When you assess someone else's work, what should you look for?* [Sample answers: Does the strategy used make sense? Can I find a flaw in the thinking? Can I improve or clarify the reasoning?]

**Item 19** Since all the numbers in Column B are between 7 and 8, it is difficult to use estimation to match the division expressions with the quotients. However, encourage students to look for relationships that can help. Since division and multiplication have an inverse relationship, encourage students to work backward to find the matches. *Look at the first row in each column. What is the last digit of 7.2 × 3?* [6] *Is this a reasonable match?* [Yes] *Look at the second row. What is the last digit of 7.5 × 41?* [5] *What digits do you multiply to get the last digit?* [5 × 1] *Is the second row a match? Explain.* [No; the dividend 315.7 does not end in 5.] *Is the combination 90 ÷ 12 = 7.5 reasonable? Explain.* [Yes; 7.5 × 12 ends in 0.]

**Multi-Step Problems** *Page 346 Items 16 and 19; Page 348 Items 20 and 23*

# ASSESS AND DIFFERENTIATE

Use the **QUICK CHECK** on the previous page to prescribe differentiated instruction.

2 RtI

**I Intervention** 0–3 points on the Quick Check

**O On-Level** 4 points on the Quick Check

**A Advanced** 5 points on the Quick Check

## Intervention Activity I

### Dividing Decimals by a Whole Number

**Materials**

Colored pencils

- Write the following division problems on the board and have students copy them in their notes.

  7)65.1 [9.3]

  12)992.88 [82.74]

- Instruct students to use a colored pencil to draw a small square indicating where the decimal point should go in the quotient.
- Have students solve each division problem and place the decimal point inside the drawn square.

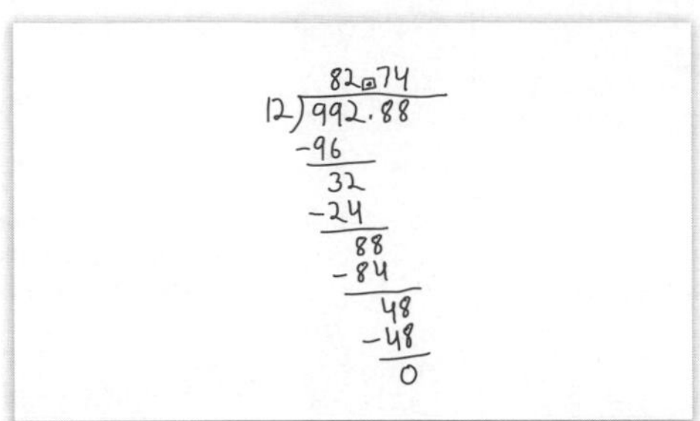


## Reteach I

Name ______________________

Reteach to Build Understanding 7-5

**Vocabulary**

1. In a division problem, the **dividend** is the number being divided, the **divisor** is the number by which you are dividing, and the **quotient** is the answer.

   Identify the dividend, divisor, and quotient in the division to the right. 4)86.72 = 21.68

   dividend: **86.72** divisor: **4** quotient: **21.68**

2. The **whole numbers** are the set of all positive integers and zero. So the whole numbers are 0, 1, 2, 3, 4, 5, 6, 7, 8, 9, and so on.

   In the division above, which is a whole number, the dividend, divisor, or quotient? **divisor**

3. Alejandra has 19.8 pounds of potting soil. She wants to divide the soil equally among 4 flowerpots. How much soil will she put in each flowerpot?

   Fill in the box to write an expression to represent this problem. 19.8 [÷] 4

4. Use compatible numbers to estimate the quotient. **Sample answers given.**

   19.8 ÷ 4 → **20** ÷ **4** = **5**

5. Find the quotient. Fill in the boxes at the right as you complete the steps to divide.

   Divide 19 ÷ 4. Multiply.
   Subtract. Bring down the tenths.

   Divide 38 ÷ 4. Multiply.
   Subtract. Annex a 0 to the dividend. Bring down the hundredths.

   Divide 20 ÷ 4. Multiply. Subtract.

   4)19.8[0] = [4].[9][5]; −[1][6]; [3]8; −[3][6]; [2]0; −[2][0]; [0]

6. Alejandra will put **4.95** pounds of potting soil in each flowerpot.

7. Is the answer reasonable? Explain. **Yes, because 4.95 is close to the estimate**.

**On the Back!**

8. Find the quotient 37.4 ÷ 4. **9.35** R7•5



## On-Level and Advanced Activity Centers O A

### Center Games

Students work in pairs or small groups to find quotients when the dividend is a decimal. Have students record their work as they play the game.

★ On-Level

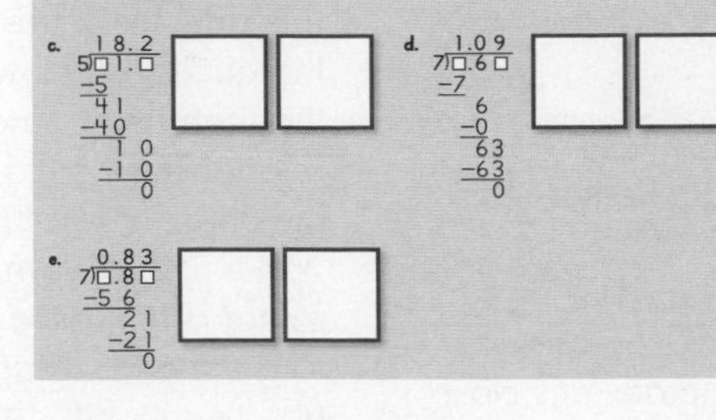

If you have more time: Make up other division puzzles like these. Ask your partner to display the answers with 0–9 tiles.

Center Game ★ 7-5

★★ Advanced

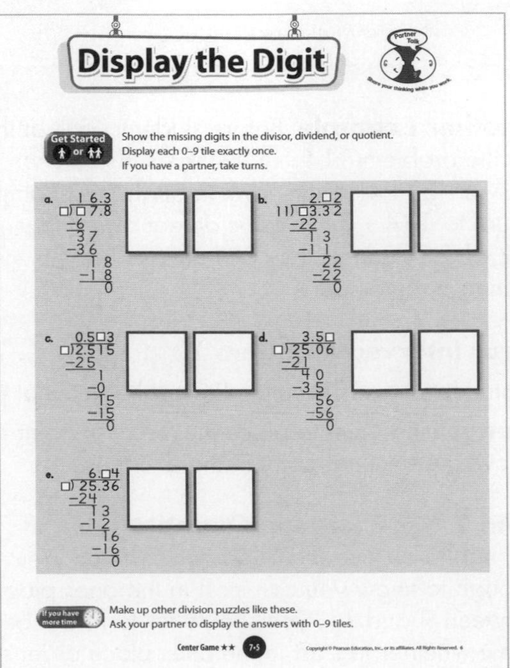

TIMING

The time allocated to Step 3 will depend on the teacher's instructional decisions and differentiation routines.

15–30 min

PEARSON realize.
PearsonRealize.com

Help

Practice Buddy

Tools

Games

## Technology Center   

Tools Games

**Math Tools and Math Games**

A link to a specific math tools activity or math game to use with this lesson is provided at PearsonRealize.com.

## Leveled Assignment  Items 1–10, 17–20, 23  Items 1–4, 13–18, 20–23  Items 9–23

Name ____________________

Help Practice Buddy Tools Games

**Homework & Practice 7-5**
**Divide Decimals by a Whole Number**

### Another Look!

The school Gaming Club spent $196.80 on snacks and prizes for a party. There are 32 members in the club. Each agrees to pay an equal share for the snacks and prizes. Find 196.8 divided by 32.

**Step 1**

Put the decimal point in the quotient right above the decimal point in the dividend. Divide. Subtract.

```
     6.
32)196.8
 − 192
     4
```

**Step 2**

Fill in the next place value with the 8. Divide. Subtract.

```
     6.1
32)196.8
 − 192↓
     48
   − 32
     16
```

**Step 3**

Annex a zero to the end of the dividend. Divide. Subtract.

```
     6.15
32)196.80
 − 192↓
     48
   − 32↓
     160
   − 160
       0
```

Each member pays $6.15.

Remember, you can use estimation to see if your answer is reasonable. $180 \div 30 = 6$

In **1–16**, find each quotient.

1. $12\overline{)\$44.40}$ **$3.70**
2. $9\overline{)20.7}$ **2.3**
3. $4\overline{)26}$ **6.5**
4. $7\overline{)22.61}$ **3.23**
5. $42.78 ÷ 3 **$14.26**
6. 73.5 ÷ 6 **12.25**
7. 34 ÷ 10 **3.4**
8. 59.6 ÷ 8 **7.45**
9. 188.4 ÷ 60 **3.14**
10. 9 ÷ 90 **0.1**
11. 231 ÷ 42 **5.5**
12. 11.2 ÷ 25 **0.448**
13. 32.9 ÷ 5 **6.58**
14. 0.34 ÷ 34 **0.01**
15. 12.8 ÷ 64 **0.2**
16. 31 ÷ 62 **0.5**



17. Yolanda bought 8 tickets to a concert for $214. What was the cost of each ticket?
**$26.75**

18. **Number Sense** Vicky makes jewelry. She uses 42 beads for each necklace she makes and has 500 beads. How many necklaces can she make? Explain.
**11 necklaces; Sample answer: The quotient 11 R 38 means that Vicky can make 11 necklaces but does not have enough beads for 12.**

19. **MP.3 Critique Reasoning** Dana said that 0.6 ÷ 30 = 0.02. Is she correct? Explain how you know.
**Dana is correct. Sample answer: She needed to annex a zero in the hundredths place to divide 0.60 by 30. So, I know the quotient will have 2 decimal places. Also, 30 × 0.02 = 0.6.**

20. Which bag of potatoes costs more per pound? How much more?

| Potatoes | |
|---|---|
| 12-pound bag | $6.96 |
| 25-pound bag | $15.75 |

**Sample answer: A 12-pound bag costs $0.58 per pound. A 25-pound bag costs $0.63 per pound. The 25-pound bag costs $0.05 more per pound.**

21. Tony bought a 72-ounce box of dog biscuits. How many pounds of dog biscuits did he buy? **4.5 pounds**

22. **Higher Order Thinking** When you divide 7.7 by 700, how many decimal places will the quotient have? Use place-value reasoning to explain how you know.
**3 places; Sample answer: The divisor is about 100 times as much as the dividend. I can annex a zero in the hundredths place and divide 7.70 by 700 to get a quotient of 0.011.**

### Common Core Assessment

23. Draw lines to connect each division expression in Column A with its quotient in Column B.

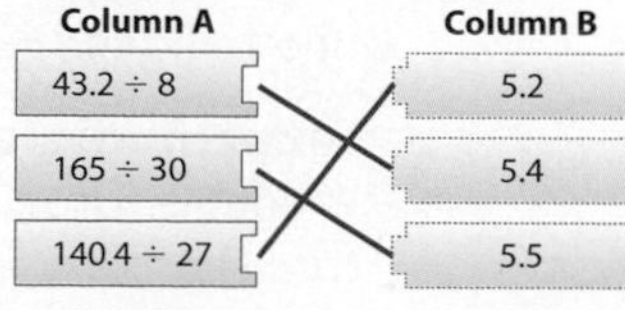

# LESSON 7-6

# DIVIDE DECIMALS

## DIGITAL RESOURCES PearsonRealize.com

 eText — Student and Teacher eTexts 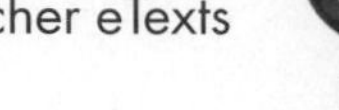

 PD — Listen and Look For Lesson Video

 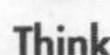 Think — Today's Challenge

 Solve — Solve and Share

 Learn — Visual Learning Animation Plus

 Glossary — Animated Glossary

 Practice Buddy — Online Personalized Practice

 Tools — Math Tools

  Assessment — Quick Check

 Help — Another Look Homework Video

 Games — Math Games

## LESSON OVERVIEW FCR FOCUS • COHERENCE • RIGOR

### FOCUS

**Domain 6.NS** The Number System

**Cluster 6.NS.B** Compute fluently with multi-digit numbers and find common factors and multiples.

**Content Standard 6.NS.B.2** Fluently divide multi-digit numbers using the standard algorithm. Also **6.NS.B.3**.

**Mathematical Practices MP.2, MP.4, MP.6, MP.7**

**Objective** Find quotients of two decimals.

**Essential Understanding** A general method, or standard algorithm, can be used to divide decimals fluently.

**Materials** Decimal models (Teaching Tool 31)

### COHERENCE

In Grade 5, students learned patterns involving powers of 10 and how to divide two simple decimals using visual models. In this lesson, they extend this understanding to divide more complicated decimals using the standard algorithm. Students will continue to practice division with decimals in Lesson 7-7. Then they will be familiar with all four operations with decimals and can apply their fluency to real-world situations.

### RIGOR

This lesson emphasizes **conceptual understanding**, **procedural skill**, and **fluency**. Students use models to understand the standard algorithm for dividing a decimal by a decimal. Then they practice the process to gain fluency.

PD Watch the Listen and Look For Lesson Video.

## MATH ANYTIME

### Daily Common Core Review

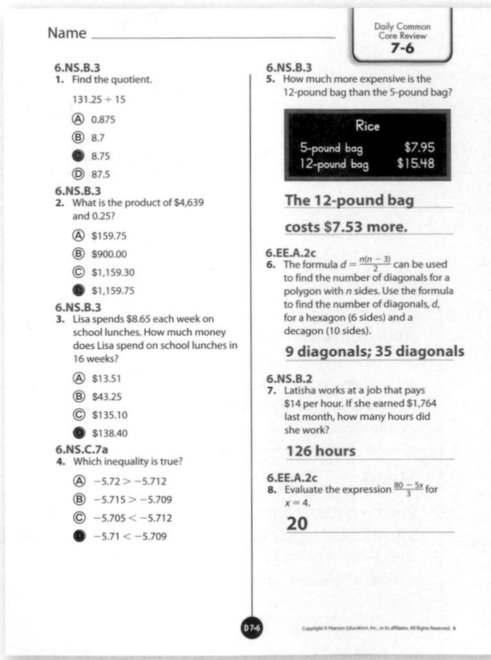

Name ____________

Daily Common Core Review 7-6

6.NS.B.3
1. Find the quotient.

131.25 ÷ 15

Ⓐ 0.875
Ⓑ 8.7
● 8.75
Ⓓ 87.5

6.NS.B.3
2. What is the product of $4,639 and 0.25?

Ⓐ $159.75
Ⓑ $900.00
Ⓒ $1,159.30
● $1,159.75

6.NS.B.3
3. Lisa spends $8.65 each week on school lunches. How much money does Lisa spend on school lunches in 16 weeks?

Ⓐ $13.51
Ⓑ $43.25
Ⓒ $135.10
● $138.40

6.NS.C.7a
4. Which inequality is true?

Ⓐ $-5.72 > -5.712$
Ⓑ $-5.715 > -5.709$
Ⓒ $-5.705 < -5.712$
● $-5.71 < -5.709$

6.NS.B.3
5. How much more expensive is the 12-pound bag than the 5-pound bag?

| Rice | |
|---|---|
| 5-pound bag | $7.95 |
| 12-pound bag | $15.48 |

**The 12-pound bag costs $7.53 more.**

6.EE.A.2c
6. The formula $d = \frac{n(n-3)}{2}$ can be used to find the number of diagonals for a polygon with $n$ sides. Use the formula to find the number of diagonals, $d$, for a hexagon (6 sides) and a decagon (10 sides).

**9 diagonals; 35 diagonals**

6.NS.B.2
7. Latisha works at a job that pays $14 per hour. If she earned $1,764 last month, how many hours did she work?

**126 hours**

6.EE.A.2c
8. Evaluate the expression $\frac{80-5x}{3}$ for $x = 4$.

**20**

D 7-6

### Today's Challenge

Think Use the Topic 7 problems any time during this topic.

## ENGLISH LANGUAGE LEARNERS ELL

**Reading** Use reading supports: illustrations.

*Use with the Solve & Share on Student's Edition p. 349.*

Read the Solve & Share. *Use models to divide decimals.* Point to the illustration of the two grids. *Think of each column as $0.10.* Point to the first grid. *If each column is $0.10, how much is the whole grid?* Point to the second grid. *If one grid is $1.00, how many columns will be used in the second grid to represent $0.50?*

**Beginning** Read the Solve & Share to students. Draw an arc over 3 columns. *This represents the cost of 1 bead.* Draw an arc over the next 3 columns. *How many beads do we have now?* Continue the process for the remaining columns.

**Intermediate** Read the Solve & Share with students. Draw an arc over 3 columns. *This arc represents the cost of one bead.* Instruct students to work with partners and use the illustration to determine the total number of beads purchased.

**Advanced** Instruct students to read the Solve & Share with partners. Draw an arc over 3 columns. *How is this arc used to represent the cost of one bead? How will this structure be used to determine the total number of beads purchased?* Instruct students to explain to partners how the illustration is used to determine the total number of beads purchased.

**Summarize** How are models used to illustrate division?

# DEVELOP: PROBLEM-BASED LEARNING

**COHERENCE: Engage learners by connecting prior knowledge to new ideas.**
Students use what they know about division and about representing decimals with grids to find the quotient of two decimals.

10–15 min

Solve

## BEFORE

1. **Pose the Solve-and-Share Problem**
**MP.4 Model with Math** Listen and look for students who represent the problem using decimal grids.

2. **Build Understanding**
*What division expression represents this situation?* [1.5 ÷ 0.3]
*How is this problem different than the problems in the last lesson?* [The divisor also has a decimal.]

## DURING

3. **Ask Guiding Questions As Needed**
*How can you show 1.5 on a decimal model?* [Shade 1 whole grid and half of a second grid.] *How can you show 0.3?* [Shade three columns or rows.] *How many groups of 0.3 are in 1.5?* [5]

## AFTER

4. **Share and Discuss Solutions**
Start with students' solutions. If needed, project Joan's work to discuss how to model the problem with decimal grids.

5. **Transition to the Visual Learning Bridge**
*You can learn to divide decimals by converting the decimal divisor into a whole number. Then you can use the standard algorithm.*

6. **Extension for Early Finishers**
*Find the quotient of 1.8 ÷ 0.09. What power of 10 did you use to make the divisor a whole number?* [20; $10^2$]

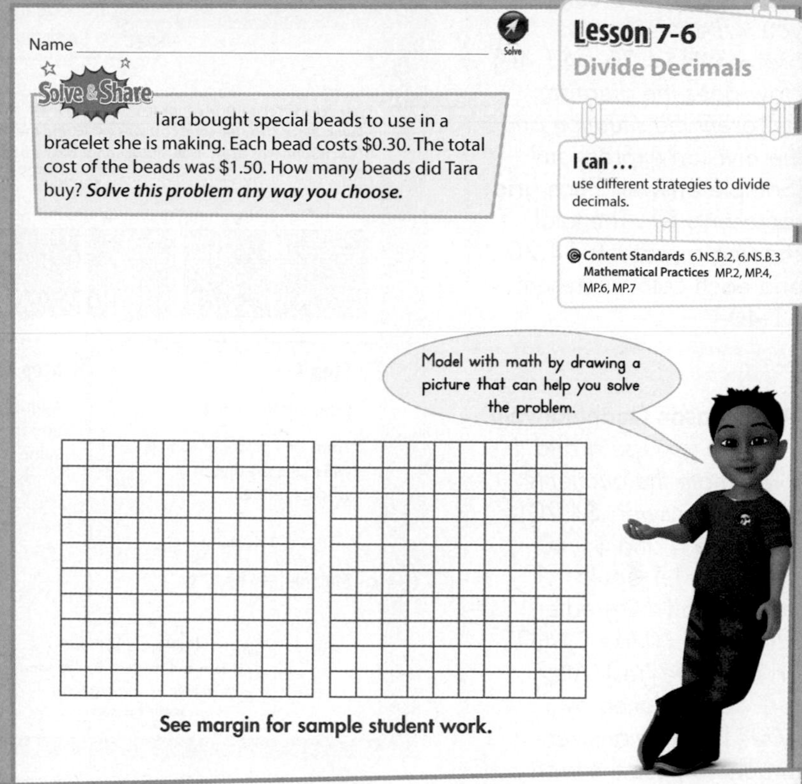

Name ____________

Solve & Share

Tara bought special beads to use in a bracelet she is making. Each bead costs $0.30. The total cost of the beads was $1.50. How many beads did Tara buy? ***Solve this problem any way you choose.***

**Lesson 7-6**
**Divide Decimals**

**I can …**
use different strategies to divide decimals.

**Content Standards** 6.NS.B.2, 6.NS.B.3
**Mathematical Practices** MP.2, MP.4, MP.6, MP.7

Model with math by drawing a picture that can help you solve the problem.



**See margin for sample student work.**

**Look Back!** **MP.2 Reasoning** Think of the cost of the beads as 150 cents rather than $1.50. How might this make the division easier? Explain your reasoning.

**Sample answer: When I divide 150 cents by 30 cents, I am using whole numbers. There are no decimal places to consider, and I get the same quotient.**

$$\begin{array}{r} 5 \\ 30\overline{)150} \\ -150 \\ \hline 0 \end{array}$$

Digital Resources at PearsonRealize.com    **Topic 7** | Lesson 7-6    **349**

## Analyze Student Work

Joan's Work

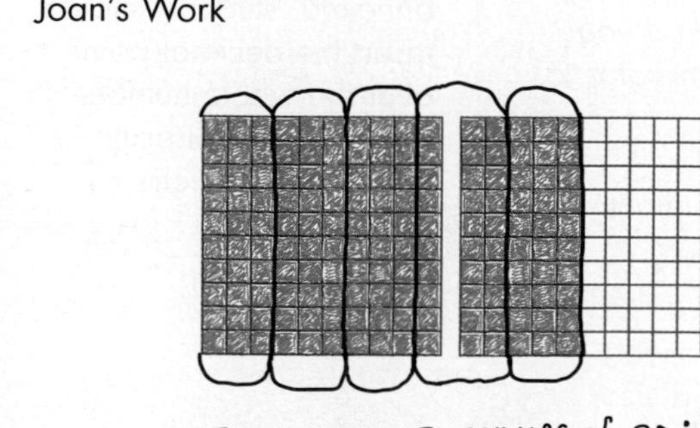

There are 5 groups of 30 in 150.
Tara bought 5 beads.


Joan uses the decimal grids to represent and solve the problem.

David's Work

What is $1.50 ÷ $0.30?

Use mental math:

5 × 3 = 15

5 × 30 = 150

so 150 ÷ 30 = 5

Tara bought 5 beads.

David uses mental math and the inverse operation of multiplication to solve the problem.

STEP 2

# DEVELOP: VISUAL LEARNING

The *Visual Learning Bridge* connects students' thinking in Solve & Share to important math ideas in the lesson. Use the *Visual Learning Bridge* to make these ideas explicit. Also available as a *Visual Learning Animation Plus* at PearsonRealize.com

Visual Learning

Learn Glossary

*What expression could you write to solve this problem?* [\$4.20 ÷ \$1.40] *How does the diagram represent the situation and the division expression?* [Sample answer: Each grid represents \$1. The total shading represents \$4.20 and each color represents \$1.40.]

**MP.2 Reason Quantitatively** *Why do you use 4 and 1 to estimate the quotient?* [Sample answer: \$4.20 rounds to 4 and \$1.40 rounds to 1.] *Could you multiply by greater powers of 10 like 1,000 or 10,000?* [Yes] *Why is 1.40 multiplied by 100?* [Sample answer: In general, use the least power of 10 that converts the divisor to a whole number to keep the problem simple.]

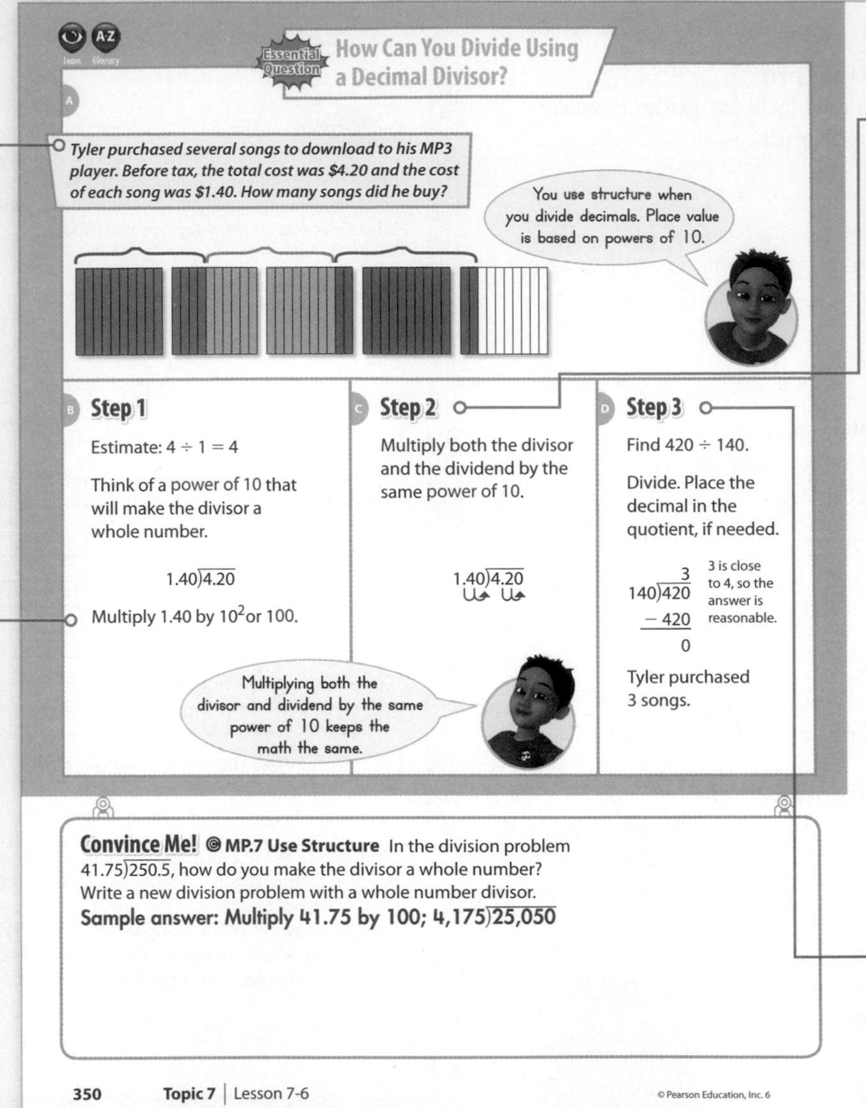

Essential Question **How Can You Divide Using a Decimal Divisor?**

A Tyler purchased several songs to download to his MP3 player. Before tax, the total cost was \$4.20 and the cost of each song was \$1.40. How many songs did he buy?

You use structure when you divide decimals. Place value is based on powers of 10.

B **Step 1**

Estimate: 4 ÷ 1 = 4

Think of a power of 10 that will make the divisor a whole number.

1.40)4.20

Multiply 1.40 by $10^2$ or 100.

C **Step 2**

Multiply both the divisor and the dividend by the same power of 10.

1.40)4.20

Multiplying both the divisor and dividend by the same power of 10 keeps the math the same.

D **Step 3**

Find 420 ÷ 140.

Divide. Place the decimal in the quotient, if needed.

$$\begin{array}{r} 3 \\ 140\overline{)420} \\ -\,420 \\ \hline 0 \end{array}$$

3 is close to 4, so the answer is reasonable.

Tyler purchased 3 songs.

**Convince Me!** MP.7 Use Structure In the division problem 41.75)250.5, how do you make the divisor a whole number? Write a new division problem with a whole number divisor.

**Sample answer: Multiply 41.75 by 100; 4,175)25,050**

350 Topic 7 | Lesson 7-6 © Pearson Education, Inc. 6

Visual Learning Bridge

**MP.7 Use Structure** Guide students to understand why multiplying the divisor and dividend by the same power of 10 results in an equivalent division expression. *How can you write 4.20 ÷ 1.40 as a fraction?* [$\frac{4.20}{1.40}$] *By what power of 10 do you multiply the numerator and denominator to write the equivalent fraction $\frac{420}{140}$?* [$10^2$ or 100] *How can you write the fraction $\frac{420}{140}$ as a division expression?* [140)420] *What do the arrows under the numbers mean?* [When you multiply both numbers by 100 the decimal point moves 2 places to the right.]

**Prevent Misconceptions**

Some students might think that the decimal point "disappears" from this problem since both the divisor and dividend are whole numbers. It is important to note that if the problem had a remainder and zeros needed to be annexed, students should insert the decimal point after the whole number dividend and directly above in the quotient.

**Convince Me! MP.7 Use Structure** Students learned how to divide a decimal number by a whole number in Lesson 7-5. *How would you write this problem as a fraction?* [$\frac{250.5}{41.75}$] *What power of 10 would you need to multiply the divisor by in order to make it a whole number?* [$10^2$] *If you multiply the denominator by 100, what should you do to the numerator to make it an equivalent fraction?* [Multiply it by 100 also.]

**Coherence** Students apply the standard algorithm for whole number division that they learned in Topic 6 to divide decimals.

Revisit the Essential Question. Students learn how to convert a problem with decimals to one with a whole number divisor so they can use the standard division algorithm to find the quotient.

realize. PearsonRealize.com

Practice Buddy · Tools · Assessment

20–30 min

## QUICK CHECK

Check mark indicates items for prescribing differentiation on the next page. Item 10 is worth 1 point. Items 18 and 19 are worth up to 2 points.

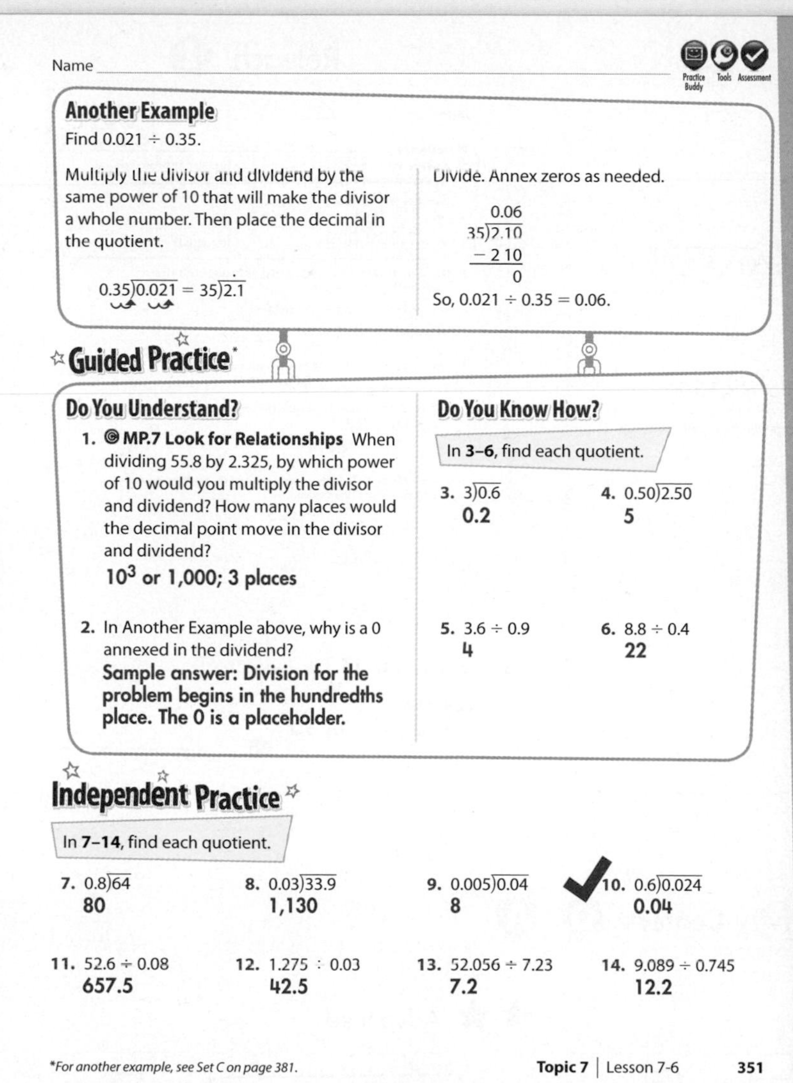

Name

### Another Example

Find 0.021 ÷ 0.35.

Multiply the divisor and dividend by the same power of 10 that will make the divisor a whole number. Then place the decimal in the quotient.

0.35)0.021 = 35)2.1

Divide. Annex zeros as needed.

```
   0.06
35)2.10
 - 2 10
      0
```

So, 0.021 ÷ 0.35 = 0.06.

### Guided Practice*

**Do You Understand?**

1. MP.7 Look for Relationships When dividing 55.8 by 2.325, by which power of 10 would you multiply the divisor and dividend? How many places would the decimal point move in the divisor and dividend?
   **$10^3$ or 1,000; 3 places**
2. In Another Example above, why is a 0 annexed in the dividend?
   **Sample answer: Division for the problem begins in the hundredths place. The 0 is a placeholder.**

**Do You Know How?**

In **3–6**, find each quotient.

3. 3)0.6 **0.2**
4. 0.50)2.50 **5**
5. 3.6 ÷ 0.9 **4**
6. 8.8 ÷ 0.4 **22**

### Independent Practice

In **7–14**, find each quotient.

7. 0.8)64 **80**
8. 0.03)33.9 **1,130**
9. 0.005)0.04 **8**
10. ✓ 0.6)0.024 **0.04**
11. 52.6 ÷ 0.08 **657.5**
12. 1.275 ÷ 0.03 **42.5**
13. 52.056 ÷ 7.23 **7.2**
14. 9.089 ÷ 0.745 **12.2**

*For another example, see Set C on page 381.

Topic 7 | Lesson 7-6 351

### Math Practices and Problem Solving

15. An electric company charges \$0.15 for each kilowatt-hour of electricity. If your electric bill is \$67.50, how many kilowatt-hours of electricity did you use?
    **450 kilowatt-hours**
16. **Number Sense** How can you decide which quotient is greater, 127.34 ÷ 0.673 or 127.34 ÷ 0.671, without doing the division?
    **Sample answer: 127.34 ÷ 0.671 > 127.34 ÷ 0.673 because the dividends are the same and 0.671 is the lesser divisor.**
17. MP.6 Be Precise How many times as much does each item cost in 2010 as in 1960?

    Movie ticket **13 times as much**
    Regular popcorn **16.4 times as much**
    Regular drink **8.8 times as much**

| Item | 1960 Cost | 2010 Cost |
|---|---|---|
| Movie Ticket | \$0.75 | \$9.75 |
| Regular Popcorn | \$0.25 | \$4.10 |
| Regular drink | \$0.35 | \$3.08 |

18. ✓ **Higher Order Thinking** You and a friend are paid \$38.25 for doing yard work. You worked 2.5 hours and your friend worked 2 hours. You split the money according to the amount of time each of you worked. How much is your share of the money? Explain.
    **\$21.25; Sample answer: Together we worked 4.5 hours; \$38.25 ÷ 4.5 = \$8.50 for each hour worked; \$8.50 • 2.5 = \$21.25.**

**Common Core Assessment**

19. ✓ A farmer harvested 634.5 bushels of sweet corn from a 4.5 acre corn field. If the same number of bushels were harvested from each acre, how many bushels are there per acre? **Sample answers are given.**

    Explain how to find 634.5 ÷ 4.5.

    **Multiply both 634.5 and 4.5 by 10. Then divide.**

```
     141  bushels per acre
 45)6,345
   - 4 5
     184
   - 180
      45
   -  45
       0
```

352 Topic 7 | Lesson 7-6 © Pearson Education, Inc. 6

**Another Example** In the example on the previous page, multiplying by a power of 10 to make the divisor a whole number also resulted in a whole-number dividend. In Another Example, even though the divisor is made into a whole number, the dividend remains a decimal number. *If the dividend remains a decimal number, what should you do before starting the division algorithm?* [Place the decimal point in the quotient, directly above the decimal point in the dividend.]

**Error Intervention: Item 2**

**If** students don't understand why they need to write a zero in the dividend,

**then** remind them of the importance of lining up the place-value columns. Since the division continues in the hundredths place, then 0 is used as a placeholder in that column, rather than leaving an empty space.

**Reteaching** Assign Reteaching Set C on p. 381.

**Item 10** Make sure that students know to place a zero in the tenths place after the decimal point in the divisor. *By what power of 10 would you multiply the divisor and dividend?* [$10^1$] *How many places would the decimal point move in the divisor and dividend?* [1] *Where do you place the decimal in the quotient?* [Directly above the decimal in the dividend] *Does 6 go into 2?* [No] *So, what digit would you write above the 2? In other words, what digit would you use as a place holder?* [0] *How many times does 6 go into 24?* [4]

**Item 17 MP.6 Be Precise** *What expression can you write to represent how many times as much a movie ticket costs in 2010 than in 1960?* [9.75 ÷ 0.75] Watch for students who divide efficiently, accurately, and fluently.

**Item 18 Higher Order Thinking** *What are the hidden questions that need answering before you can complete this problem?* [Sample answers: What is the total number of hours worked? What is the pay per hour?]

**Multi-Step Problems** *Page 352 Items 17 and 18; Page 354 Item 26*

# ASSESS AND DIFFERENTIATE

Use the **QUICK CHECK** on the previous page to prescribe differentiated instruction.

**I Intervention** 0–3 points on the Quick Check

**O On-Level** 4 points on the Quick Check

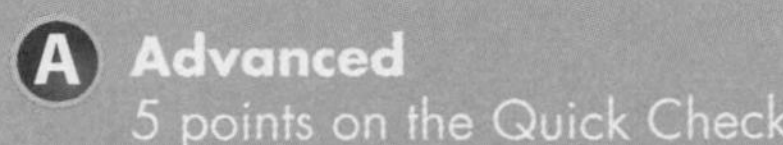
**A Advanced** 5 points on the Quick Check

## Intervention Activity I

### Dividing Decimals

- Model this example on the board to show students how to prepare division problems by indicating the movement of the decimal points.

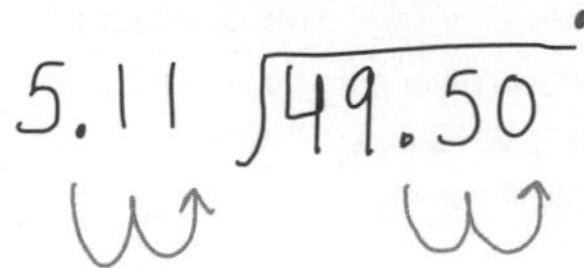


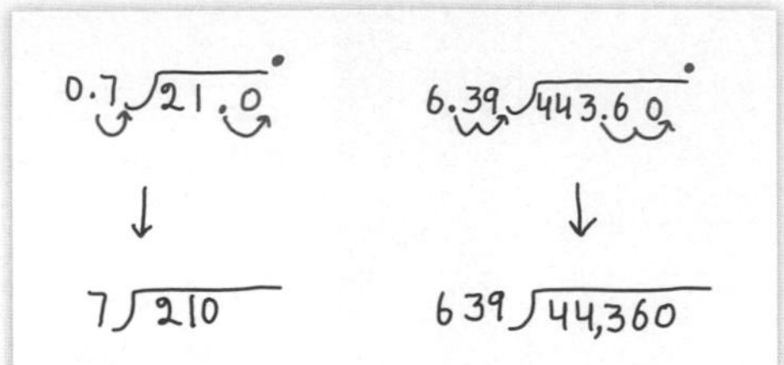


- Write these division problems on the board.

  3.2)85.6 0.05)9.325
  0.7)21 6.39)443.6

- Have students mark the decimal movement to prepare these problems for division.

## Reteach I

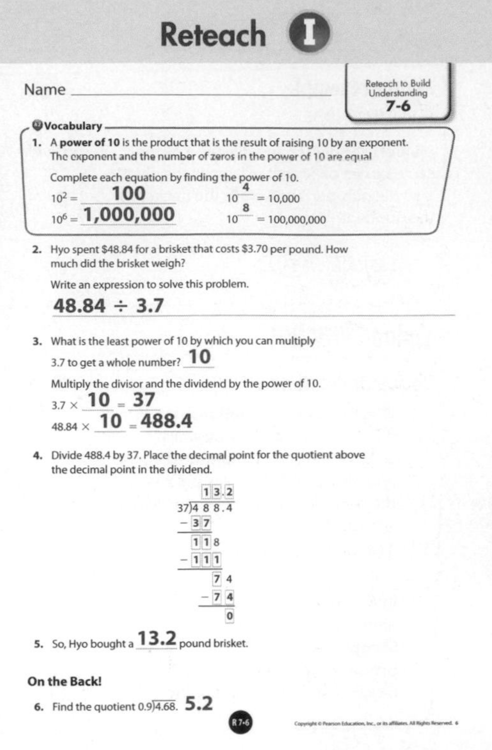

Name ______

Reteach to Build Understanding 7-6

**Vocabulary**

1. A **power of 10** is the product that is the result of raising 10 by an exponent. The exponent and the number of zeros in the power of 10 are equal.

   Complete each equation by finding the power of 10.

   $10^2$ = **100** $10^{\mathbf{4}}$ = 10,000
   $10^6$ = **1,000,000** $10^{\mathbf{8}}$ = 100,000,000

2. Hyo spent $48.84 for a brisket that costs $3.70 per pound. How much did the brisket weigh?

   Write an expression to solve this problem.

   **48.84 ÷ 3.7**

3. What is the least power of 10 by which you can multiply 3.7 to get a whole number? **10**

   Multiply the divisor and the dividend by the power of 10.

   3.7 × **10** = **37**
   48.84 × **10** = **488.4**

4. Divide 488.4 by 37. Place the decimal point for the quotient above the decimal point in the dividend.

   13.2
   37)488.4
   − 37
   118
   − 111
   74
   − 74
   0

5. So, Hyo bought a **13.2** pound brisket.

**On the Back!**

6. Find the quotient 0.9)4.68. **5.2**

R 7-6



## On-Level and Advanced Activity Centers O A

### Center Games

Students work in pairs or small groups to find quotients when dividing a decimal by another decimal. Have students record their work as they play the game.

★ On-Level

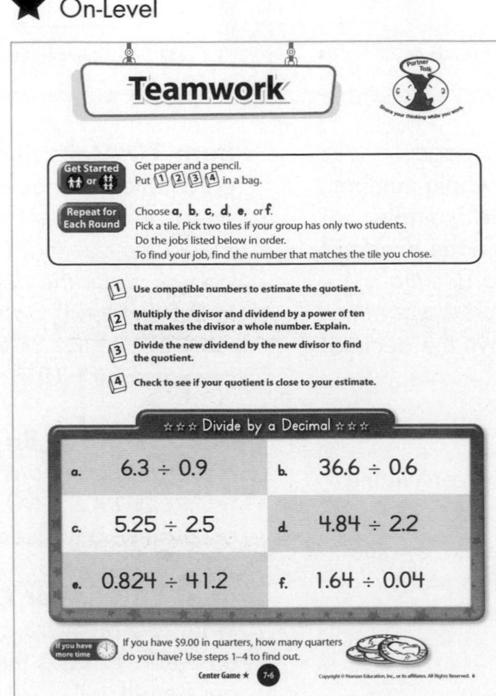

**Teamwork**

Partner Talk — Share your thinking while you work.

**Get Started** Get paper and a pencil. Put 1 2 3 4 in a bag.

**Repeat for Each Round** Choose **a**, **b**, **c**, **d**, **e**, or **f**. Pick a tile. Pick two tiles if your group has only two students. Do the jobs listed below in order. To find your job, find the number that matches the tile you chose.

1. Use compatible numbers to estimate the quotient.
2. Multiply the divisor and dividend by a power of ten that makes the divisor a whole number. Explain.
3. Divide the new dividend by the new divisor to find the quotient.
4. Check to see if your quotient is close to your estimate.

★★★ Divide by a Decimal ★★★

| | | | |
|---|---|---|---|
| a. | 6.3 ÷ 0.9 | b. | 36.6 ÷ 0.6 |
| c. | 5.25 ÷ 2.5 | d. | 4.84 ÷ 2.2 |
| e. | 0.824 ÷ 41.2 | f. | 1.64 ÷ 0.04 |

If you have more time: If you have $9.00 in quarters, how many quarters do you have? Use steps 1–4 to find out.

Center Game ★ 7-6



★★ Advanced

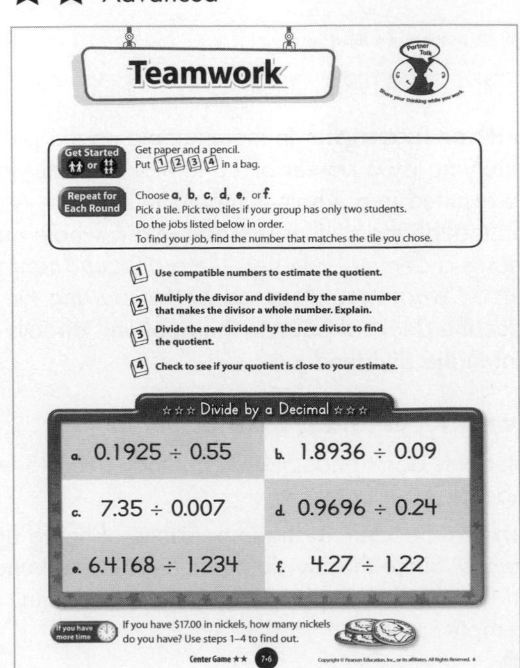

**Teamwork**

Partner Talk — Share your thinking while you work.

**Get Started** Get paper and a pencil. Put 1 2 3 4 in a bag.

**Repeat for Each Round** Choose **a**, **b**, **c**, **d**, **e**, or **f**. Pick a tile. Pick two tiles if your group has only two students. Do the jobs listed below in order. To find your job, find the number that matches the tile you chose.

1. Use compatible numbers to estimate the quotient.
2. Multiply the divisor and dividend by the same number that makes the divisor a whole number. Explain.
3. Divide the new dividend by the new divisor to find the quotient.
4. Check to see if your quotient is close to your estimate.

★★★ Divide by a Decimal ★★★

| | | | |
|---|---|---|---|
| a. | 0.1925 ÷ 0.55 | b. | 1.8936 ÷ 0.09 |
| c. | 7.35 ÷ 0.007 | d. | 0.9696 ÷ 0.24 |
| e. | 6.4168 ÷ 1.234 | f. | 4.27 ÷ 1.22 |

If you have more time: If you have $17.00 in nickels, how many nickels do you have? Use steps 1–4 to find out.

Center Game ★★ 7-6

**TIMING**

The time allocated to Step 3 will depend on the teacher's instructional decisions and differentiation routines.

15–30 min

PEARSON realize. PearsonRealize.com

Help

Practice Buddy

Tools

Games

## Technology Center    

Tools

Games

### Math Tools and Math Games

A link to a specific math tools activity or math game to use with this lesson is provided at PearsonRealize.com.

## Leveled Assignment

 Items 1–12, 23, 25–27  Items 7–18, 23, 24, 27  Items 13–27

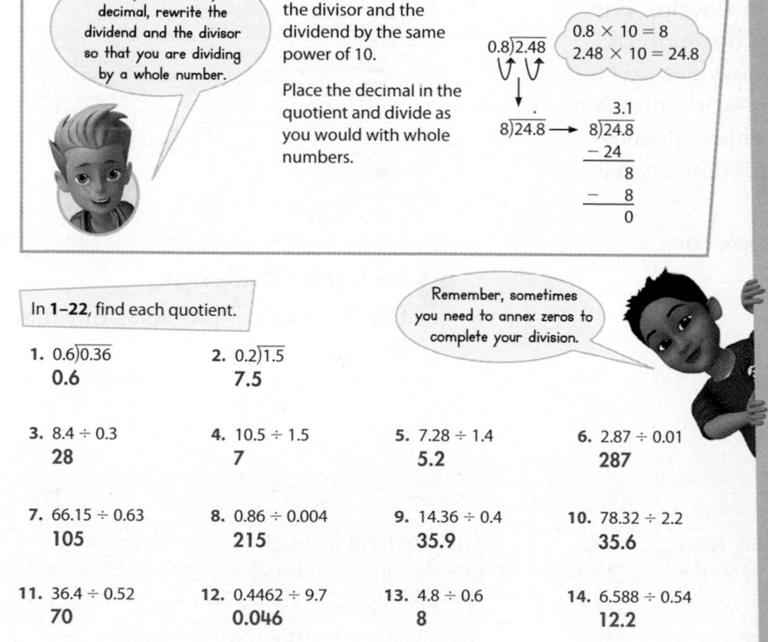

Name ____________________

Help Practice Buddy Tools Games

**Homework & Practice 7-6**
**Divide Decimals**

**Another Look!**

Find 2.48 ÷ 0.8.

When you divide by a decimal, rewrite the dividend and the divisor so that you are dividing by a whole number.

To make the divisor a whole number, multiply the divisor and the dividend by the same power of 10.

$0.8\overline{)2.48}$

$0.8 \times 10 = 8$
$2.48 \times 10 = 24.8$

Place the decimal in the quotient and divide as you would with whole numbers.

$$\begin{array}{r} 3.1 \\ 8\overline{)24.8} \\ -\,24 \\ 8 \\ -\,8 \\ 0 \end{array}$$

Remember, sometimes you need to annex zeros to complete your division.

In **1–22**, find each quotient.

1. $0.6\overline{)0.36}$ **0.6**
2. $0.2\overline{)1.5}$ **7.5**
3. 8.4 ÷ 0.3 **28**
4. 10.5 ÷ 1.5 **7**
5. 7.28 ÷ 1.4 **5.2**
6. 2.87 ÷ 0.01 **287**
7. 66.15 ÷ 0.63 **105**
8. 0.86 ÷ 0.004 **215**
9. 14.36 ÷ 0.4 **35.9**
10. 78.32 ÷ 2.2 **35.6**
11. 36.4 ÷ 0.52 **70**
12. 0.4462 ÷ 9.7 **0.046**
13. 4.8 ÷ 0.6 **8**
14. 6.588 ÷ 0.54 **12.2**
15. 23.6 ÷ 5 **4.72**
16. 89.54 ÷ 11 **8.14**
17. 21 ÷ 0.2 **105**
18. 100.8 ÷ 8.4 **12**
19. 10.25 ÷ 4.1 **2.5**
20. 76.23 ÷ 0.03 **2,541**
21. 2.8 ÷ 1.4 **2**
22. 9.3 ÷ 3.1 **3**

Digital Resources at PearsonRealize.com Topic 7 | Lesson 7-6 353

23. **Math and Science** Alec researched the melting points of different elements. Sodium melts at 97.72°C. Lead melts at 327.5°C. How much hotter is the melting point of lead than sodium?
**229.78°C**

24. **Higher Order Thinking** How do you know that 1.016 ÷ 4.064 ≠ 0.025 without doing the division?
**Sample answer: I know that 1.016 ÷ 4.064 is about $\frac{1}{4}$, which equals 0.25. So 0.025 is not a reasonable quotient.**

25. **MP.4 Model with Math** Ricky wants to buy plants to put in his garden. Each plant with pot costs $1.60. How many plants can he buy with $10.00? Draw a picture and write an equation to show how you can get the answer.
**6 plants; $1.60 × 6 = $9.60**

26. Mr. Timm rented a truck for $39.95 for the day, plus $0.54 for each mile he drives. His total bill, not including gasoline, was $72.62. How many miles did he drive?
**60.5 mi; $72.62 − $39.95 = $32.67; 32.67 ÷ 0.54 = 60.5**

**Common Core Assessment**

27. A farmer harvested 1,627.5 bushels of soybeans from 38.75 acres. If the same number of bushels were harvested from each acre, how many bushels are there per acre? **Sample answers are given.**

Explain how to find 1,627.5 ÷ 38.75.

**Multiply both 1,627.5 and 38.75 by 100. Then divide.**

$$\begin{array}{r} 42 \\ 3{,}875\overline{)162{,}750} \\ -\,155\,00 \\ 7750 \\ -\,7750 \\ 0 \end{array}$$

**bushels per acre**

354 Topic 7 | Lesson 7-6

# LESSON 7-7

# CONTINUE TO DIVIDE DECIMALS

## DIGITAL RESOURCES PearsonRealize.com

eText — Student and Teacher eTexts

PD — Listen and Look For Lesson Video

Think — Today's Challenge

Solve — Solve and Share

Learn — Visual Learning Animation Plus

Glossary — Animated Glossary

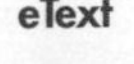
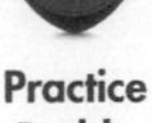
Practice Buddy — Online Personalized Practice

Tools — Math Tools

Assessment — Quick Check

Help — Another Look Homework Video

Games — Math Games

## LESSON OVERVIEW

FCR FOCUS • COHERENCE • RIGOR

### FOCUS

**Domain 6.NS** The Number System

**Cluster 6.NS.B** Compute fluently with multi-digit numbers and find common factors and multiples.

**Content Standard 6.NS.B.2** Fluently divide multi-digit numbers using the standard algorithm. Also **6.NS.B.3**.

**Mathematical Practices MP.1, MP.2, MP.4, MP.7**

**Objective** Divide decimals to solve real-world problems.

**Essential Understanding** A general method, or standard algorithm, can be used to divide decimals fluently.

### COHERENCE

In Grade 5, students used concrete models, including drawings, place-value strategies, and properties of operations to multiply decimals to hundredths. In Lesson 7-6, students extended this understanding by using models in order to generalize and develop the standard algorithm for dividing two decimals. In this lesson, students continue to develop fluency in dividing any two decimals.

### RIGOR

This lesson emphasizes **procedural skill** and **fluency**. Students develop and maintain fluency in dividing decimals as they divide decimals and apply this skill to solve mathematical and real-world problems. Students are expected to achieve fluency with multi-digit decimal operations by the end of Grade 6.

PD Watch the Listen and Look For Lesson Video.

## MATH ANYTIME

### Daily Common Core Review

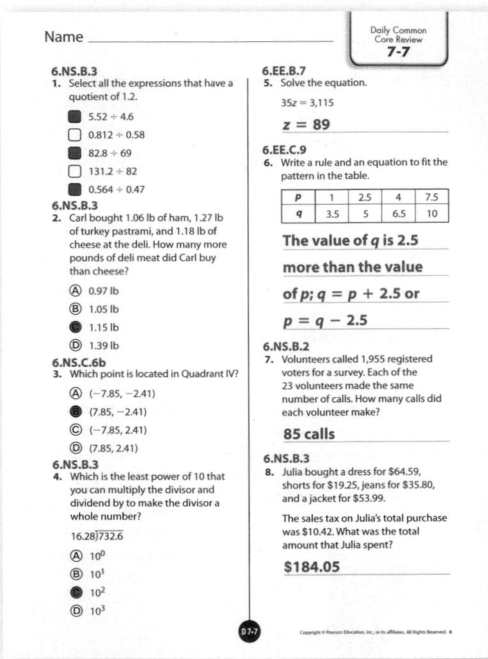

Name ____________

Daily Common Core Review 7-7

6.NS.B.3
1. Select all the expressions that have a quotient of 1.2.
   - ■ 5.52 ÷ 4.6
   - □ 0.812 ÷ 0.58
   - ■ 82.8 ÷ 69
   - □ 131.2 ÷ 82
   - ■ 0.564 ÷ 0.47

6.NS.B.3
2. Carl bought 1.06 lb of ham, 1.27 lb of turkey pastrami, and 1.18 lb of cheese at the deli. How many more pounds of deli meat did Carl buy than cheese?
   - Ⓐ 0.97 lb
   - Ⓑ 1.05 lb
   - ● 1.15 lb
   - Ⓓ 1.39 lb

6.NS.C.6b
3. Which point is located in Quadrant IV?
   - Ⓐ (−7.85, −2.41)
   - ● (7.85, −2.41)
   - Ⓒ (−7.85, 2.41)
   - Ⓓ (7.85, 2.41)

6.NS.B.3
4. Which is the least power of 10 that you can multiply the divisor and dividend by to make the divisor a whole number?

   $16.28\overline{)732.6}$
   - Ⓐ $10^0$
   - Ⓑ $10^1$
   - ● $10^2$
   - Ⓓ $10^3$

6.EE.B.7
5. Solve the equation.

   $35z = 3{,}115$

   **$z = 89$**

6.EE.C.9
6. Write a rule and an equation to fit the pattern in the table.

| $p$ | 1 | 2.5 | 4 | 7.5 |
|---|---|---|---|---|
| $q$ | 3.5 | 5 | 6.5 | 10 |

   **The value of $q$ is 2.5 more than the value of $p$; $q = p + 2.5$ or $p = q - 2.5$**

6.NS.B.2
7. Volunteers called 1,955 registered voters for a survey. Each of the 23 volunteers made the same number of calls. How many calls did each volunteer make?

   **85 calls**

6.NS.B.3
8. Julia bought a dress for $64.59, shorts for $19.25, jeans for $35.80, and a jacket for $53.99.

   The sales tax on Julia's total purchase was $10.42. What was the total amount that Julia spent?

   **$184.05**

D 7-7

### Today's Challenge

Think Use the Topic 7 problems any time during this topic.

## ENGLISH LANGUAGE LEARNERS 

**Speaking** Share information in cooperative learning interactions.

*Use with the Visual Learning Bridge on Student's Edition p. 356.*

Read Box A. Ask students to retell information to partners. *What formula is used to find the area of a rectangle? What information is given that can be used to solve the problem?* Write $7.75 = \ell \cdot 1.25$. *This formula can be rewritten so it is a division equation.* Write $7.75 \div 1.25 = \ell$. *To find the length, divide the area by the width.*

**Beginning** Instruct students to work as a group to solve the equation $7.75 \div 1.25 = \ell$. *What is the length of the flowerbed?* Students will respond using the sentence stem: The ___ of the flower bed is ___.

**Intermediate** Instruct students to work in groups of 3 to solve the equation $7.75 \div 1.25 = \ell$. *What is the length of the flowerbed? How did your group divide the decimals?* Students will respond using the sentence stem: The ___ of the flower bed is ___. We divided the decimals by ___.

**Advanced** Instruct students with partners to solve the equation $7.75 \div 1.25 = \ell$. Ask students to work with partners to write a step-by-step plan for dividing decimals.

**Summarize** How are decimals divided?

# DEVELOP: PROBLEM-BASED LEARNING

**COHERENCE: Engage learners by connecting prior knowledge to new ideas.**
Students continue to develop fluency in division with decimals as they solve real-world problems.

10–15 min

Solve

## BEFORE

1. **Pose the Solve-and-Share Problem**
**MP.2 Reason Quantitatively** Listen and look for students who use a diagram or an equation to solve the problem.

2. **Build Understanding**
*What information are you given?* [Some friends shared a $27 lunch bill and each paid $6.75.] *Will your answer be a whole number? How do you know?.* [Yes, because we are counting the number of people.]

## DURING

3. **Ask Guiding Questions As Needed**
*How can you use an equation to represent this problem?* [Sample answer: Let $n$ = the number of people who went to lunch; $n = 27 \div 6.25$] *How do you write an equivalent division expression so that you can divide by a whole number?* [You multiply the dividend and divisor by 100 to get a whole number divisor.]

## AFTER

4. **Share and Discuss Solutions**
Solve Start with students' solutions. If needed, project Mark's work to discuss how to solve by using the division algorithm.

5. **Transition to the Visual Learning Bridge**
*Remember, you can divide a decimal by a decimal by multiplying the divisor and dividend by the same power of ten so that the divisor becomes a whole number.*

6. **Extension for Early Finishers**
*Find the total cost per person for the lunch after adding a $5.40 tip. Assume that sales tax is included.* [$8.10]

Name ______ Solve

**Solve & Share** Some friends went to lunch and split the bill equally. If each person paid $6.75, how many people went to lunch? Use a diagram or equation to explain your thinking. ***Solve this problem any way you choose.***

**Lesson 7-7**
**Continue to Divide Decimals**

**I can ...**
divide decimals to find solutions to real-world problems.

Content Standards 6.NS.B.2, 6.NS.B.3
Mathematical Practices MP.1, MP.2, MP.4, MP.7

You can use reasoning to solve the problem.

| RECEIPT | |
|---|---|
| Food | $$$ |
| Drinks | $$$ |
| Total | $27 |

**See margin for sample student work.**

**Look Back!** MP.2 Reasoning Suppose $7.00 was added to the bill for a dessert that everyone shared. How much more does each person have to pay? Explain how you found the answer.
**Each person owes an additional $1.75; Sample answer: $34 \div 4 = 8.5$; $8.50 - 6.75 = 1.75$. I put a decimal at the end of the dividend, annexing as many zeros to the right of the decimal point as needed. I subtracted my first answer from the new quotient to find the additional amount each person should pay.**

Digital Resources at PearsonRealize.com  **Topic 7** | Lesson 7-7  355

## Analyze Student Work

Mark's Work

Let $n$ = number of people.

$\$6.75 \times n = \$27$

$n = \$27 \div \$6.75$

$$\begin{array}{r} 4. \\ 6.75\overline{)27.00} \\ -2700 \\ \hline 0 \end{array}$$

4 people split the cost.

Mark writes an equation and uses the division algorithm to find the number of people that went to lunch.

Jane's Work

| person | cost | |
|---|---|---|
| 1 | $6.75 | |
| | | > + $6.75 |
| 2 | $13.50 | |
| | | > + $6.75 |
| 3 | $20.25 | |
| | | > + $6.75 |
| 4 | $27.00 | |

4 people = $27.

Jane makes a table and finds the correct solution by using addition.

## STEP 2 DEVELOP: VISUAL LEARNING

The *Visual Learning Bridge* connects students' thinking in Solve & Share to important math ideas in the lesson. Use the *Visual Learning Bridge* to make these ideas explicit. Also available as a *Visual Learning Animation Plus* at PearsonRealize.com

PEARSON realize. PearsonRealize.com

Learn Glossary

**MP.1 Make Sense and Persevere** *What information from the illustration is needed to solve this problem?* [The width and area of the flowerbed] *Show how to solve the formula for ℓ and use it to write an equation.* [$\frac{A}{w} = \frac{\ell w}{w} \rightarrow \frac{A}{w} = \ell$; $\ell = \frac{A}{w} = \frac{7.75}{1.25} = \frac{775}{125}$]

**MP.2 Reason Quantitatively** *Why do you multiply the divisor and the dividend by 100?* [You multiply by 100 so that the 1.25 becomes a whole number.] *How do you know that 7.75 ÷ 1.25 will give the same quotient as 775 ÷ 125?* [The expressions are equivalent. If you multiply $\frac{7.75}{1.25} \times \frac{100}{100}$ you get $\frac{775}{125}$.]

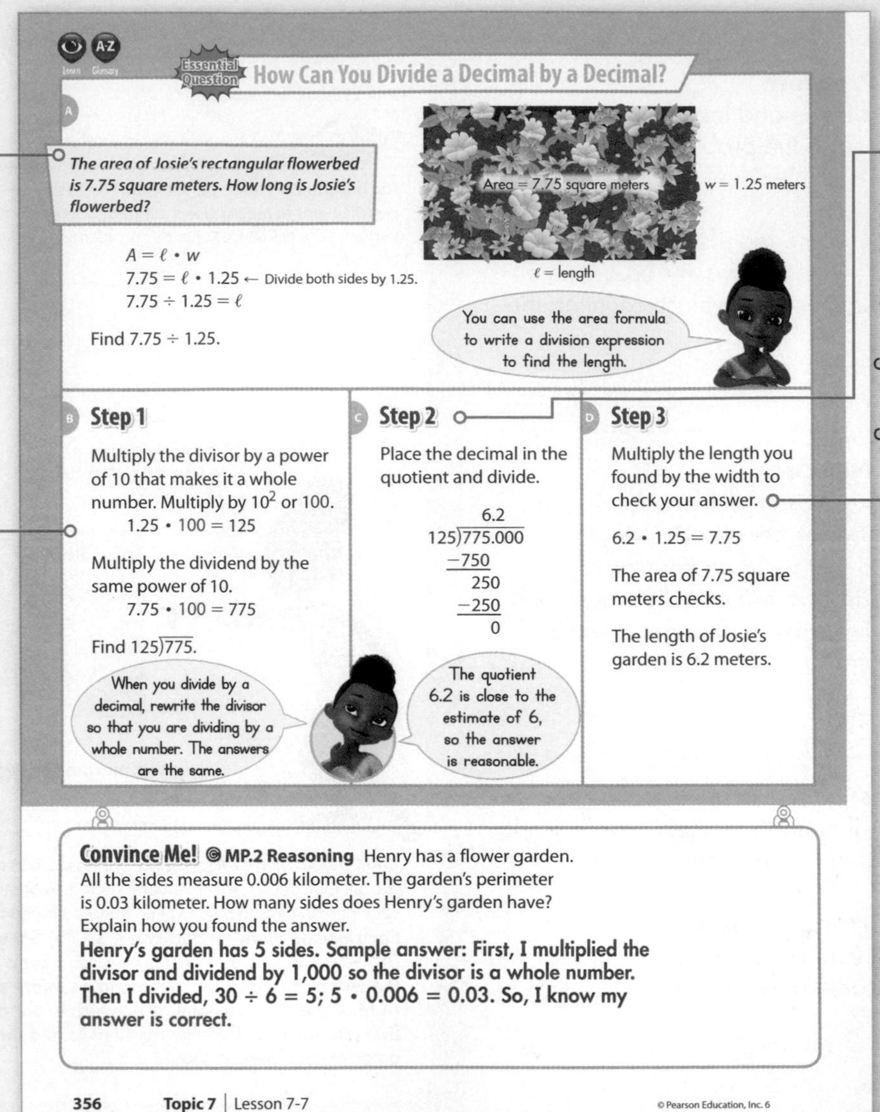

Essential Question **How Can You Divide a Decimal by a Decimal?**

A *The area of Josie's rectangular flowerbed is 7.75 square meters. How long is Josie's flowerbed?*



$A = \ell \cdot w$

$7.75 = \ell \cdot 1.25$ ← Divide both sides by 1.25.

$7.75 \div 1.25 = \ell$

Find 7.75 ÷ 1.25.

You can use the area formula to write a division expression to find the length.



**B Step 1**

Multiply the divisor by a power of 10 that makes it a whole number. Multiply by $10^2$ or 100.

$1.25 \cdot 100 = 125$

Multiply the dividend by the same power of 10.

$7.75 \cdot 100 = 775$

Find 125)775.

When you divide by a decimal, rewrite the divisor so that you are dividing by a whole number. The answers are the same.



**C Step 2**

Place the decimal in the quotient and divide.

```
      6.2
125)775.000
   -750
     250
    -250
       0
```

The quotient 6.2 is close to the estimate of 6, so the answer is reasonable.



**D Step 3**

Multiply the length you found by the width to check your answer.

$6.2 \cdot 1.25 = 7.75$

The area of 7.75 square meters checks.

The length of Josie's garden is 6.2 meters.

Visual Learning Bridge

**Convince Me!** **MP.2 Reasoning** Henry has a flower garden. All the sides measure 0.006 kilometer. The garden's perimeter is 0.03 kilometer. How many sides does Henry's garden have? Explain how you found the answer.

**Henry's garden has 5 sides. Sample answer: First, I multiplied the divisor and dividend by 1,000 so the divisor is a whole number. Then I divided, 30 ÷ 6 = 5; 5 • 0.006 = 0.03. So, I know my answer is correct.**

356 Topic 7 | Lesson 7-7 © Pearson Education, Inc. 6

**MP.7 Use Structure** *Why might you want to add zeros to the end of the dividend?* [If there is a remainder, you can keep dividing to find the decimal equivalent.] *Are 3 zeros needed in this problem? Explain.* [No; they are not needed. You write the quotient as 6.2 instead of 6.200.]

*What is another way you can check your answer?* [Divide 7.75 by 6.2 to see if you get 1.25]

**Convince Me!** **MP.2 Reason Quantitatively** *What is the unknown in this situation?* [The number of sides] *In general, how do you find the perimeter?* [Add up all the sides.] *What do you know about the sides?* [They are all the same length, 0.006 km.] *What equation could you use to solve this problem?* [$0.006s = 0.03$]

**Coherence** In the flowerbed problem, students combine what they know about formulas from Lesson 1-9 and solving multiplication and division equations from Lesson 2-4. This problem also provides an opportunity for students to continue to develop fluency with dividing decimals learned in this topic.

Revisit the Essential Question. To divide a decimal by a decimal, multiply the divisor and the dividend by the same power of 10 to make the divisor a whole number, divide as you would whole numbers, and then place the decimal in the quotient.

## ☑ QUICK CHECK

Check mark indicates items for prescribing differentiation on the next page.
Item 8 is worth 1 point. Items 19 and 20 are worth up to 2 points.

20–30 min

PEARSON realize.
PearsonRealize.com

Practice Buddy

Tools

Assessment

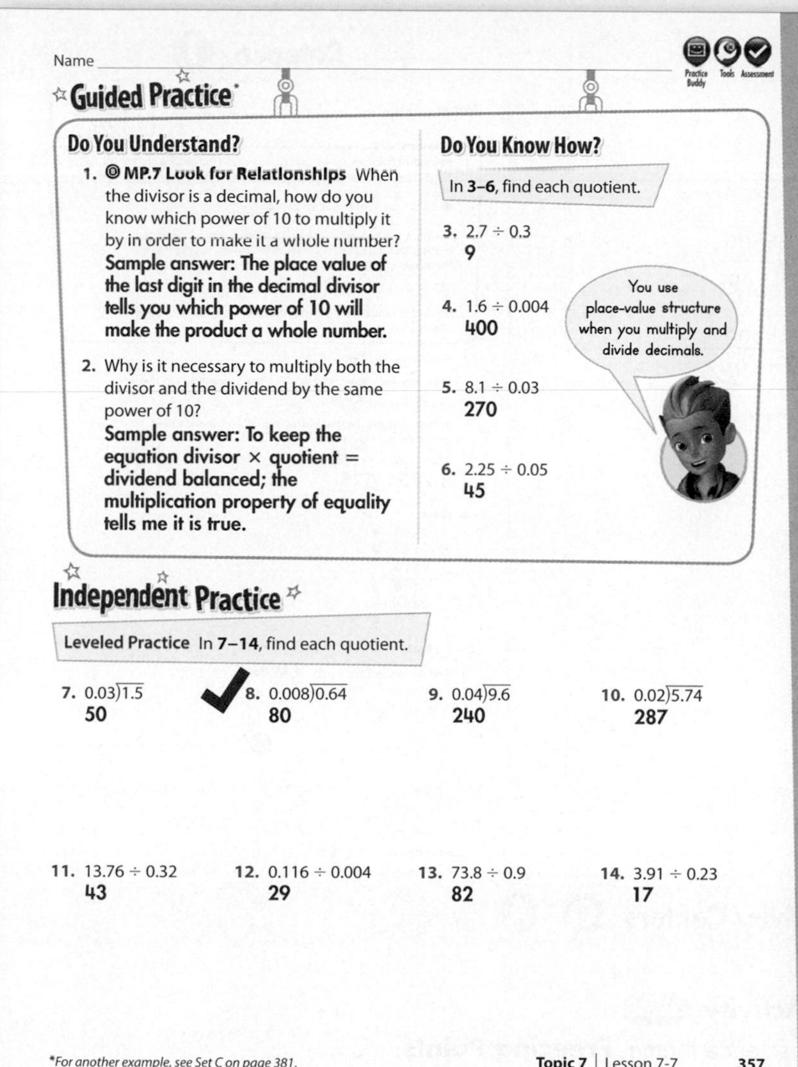

Name

### Guided Practice*

**Do You Understand?**

1. MP.7 Look for Relationships When the divisor is a decimal, how do you know which power of 10 to multiply it by in order to make it a whole number?
**Sample answer: The place value of the last digit in the decimal divisor tells you which power of 10 will make the product a whole number.**

2. Why is it necessary to multiply both the divisor and the dividend by the same power of 10?
**Sample answer: To keep the equation divisor × quotient = dividend balanced; the multiplication property of equality tells me it is true.**

**Do You Know How?**

In **3–6**, find each quotient.

3. $2.7 \div 0.3$ **9**
4. $1.6 \div 0.004$ **400**
5. $8.1 \div 0.03$ **270**
6. $2.25 \div 0.05$ **45**

You use place-value structure when you multiply and divide decimals.

### Independent Practice*

**Leveled Practice** In **7–14**, find each quotient.

7. $0.03\overline{)1.5}$ **50**
8. ✔ $0.008\overline{)0.64}$ **80**
9. $0.04\overline{)9.6}$ **240**
10. $0.02\overline{)5.74}$ **287**
11. $13.76 \div 0.32$ **43**
12. $0.116 \div 0.004$ **29**
13. $73.8 \div 0.9$ **82**
14. $3.91 \div 0.23$ **17**

*For another example, see Set C on page 381.

Topic 7 | Lesson 7-7 357

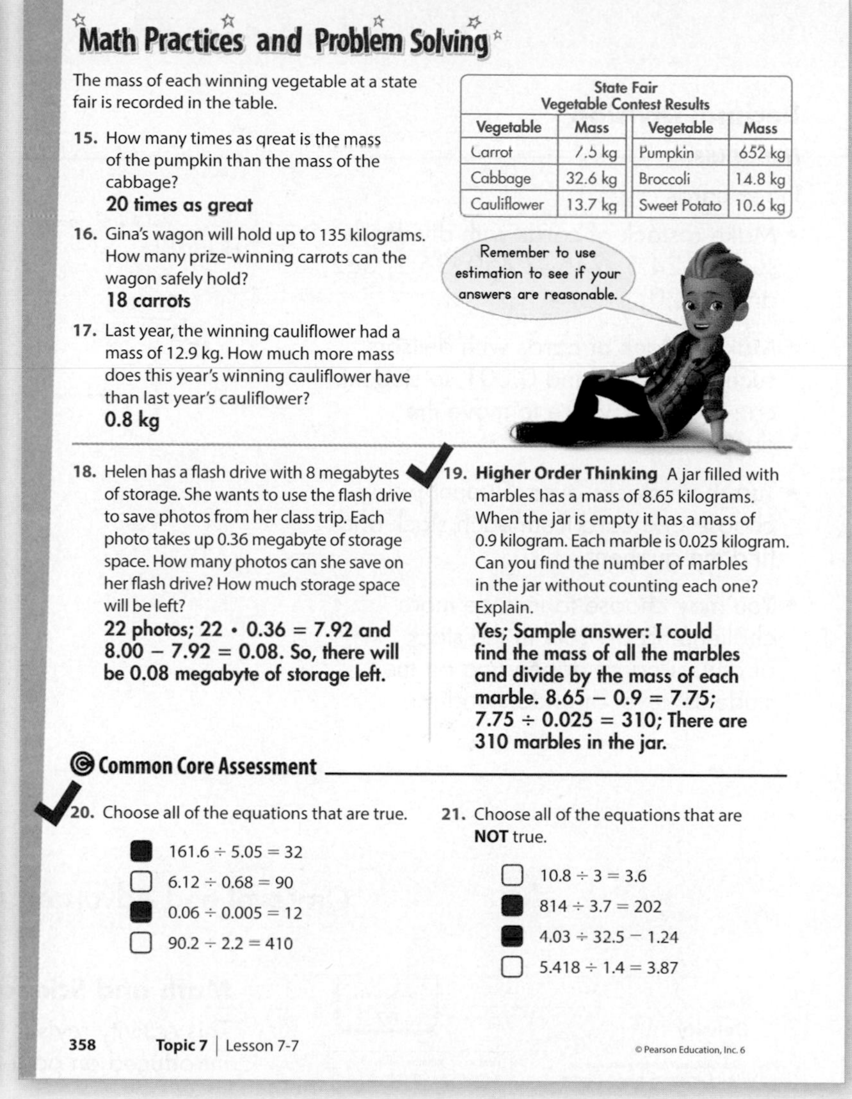

### Math Practices and Problem Solving*

The mass of each winning vegetable at a state fair is recorded in the table.

State Fair Vegetable Contest Results

| Vegetable | Mass | Vegetable | Mass |
|---|---|---|---|
| Carrot | 7.5 kg | Pumpkin | 652 kg |
| Cabbage | 32.6 kg | Broccoli | 14.8 kg |
| Cauliflower | 13.7 kg | Sweet Potato | 10.6 kg |

15. How many times as great is the mass of the pumpkin than the mass of the cabbage?
**20 times as great**

16. Gina's wagon will hold up to 135 kilograms. How many prize-winning carrots can the wagon safely hold?
**18 carrots**

17. Last year, the winning cauliflower had a mass of 12.9 kg. How much more mass does this year's winning cauliflower have than last year's cauliflower?
**0.8 kg**

Remember to use estimation to see if your answers are reasonable.

18. Helen has a flash drive with 8 megabytes of storage. She wants to use the flash drive to save photos from her class trip. Each photo takes up 0.36 megabyte of storage space. How many photos can she save on her flash drive? How much storage space will be left?
**22 photos; 22 • 0.36 = 7.92 and 8.00 − 7.92 = 0.08. So, there will be 0.08 megabyte of storage left.**

19. ✔ **Higher Order Thinking** A jar filled with marbles has a mass of 8.65 kilograms. When the jar is empty it has a mass of 0.9 kilogram. Each marble is 0.025 kilogram. Can you find the number of marbles in the jar without counting each one? Explain.
**Yes; Sample answer: I could find the mass of all the marbles and divide by the mass of each marble. 8.65 − 0.9 = 7.75; 7.75 ÷ 0.025 = 310; There are 310 marbles in the jar.**

**Common Core Assessment**

20. ✔ Choose all of the equations that are true.
- ■ $161.6 \div 5.05 = 32$
- ☐ $6.12 \div 0.68 = 90$
- ■ $0.06 \div 0.005 = 12$
- ☐ $90.2 \div 2.2 = 410$

21. Choose all of the equations that are **NOT** true.
- ☐ $10.8 \div 3 = 3.6$
- ■ $814 \div 3.7 = 202$
- ■ $4.03 \div 32.5 = 1.24$
- ☐ $5.418 \div 1.4 = 3.87$

358 Topic 7 | Lesson 7-7 © Pearson Education, Inc. 6

**Error Intervention: Item 2**

**If** students do not understand why they multiply the dividend, **then** show them an example such as $1 \div 2$. Write the division expression as a fraction and find equivalent fractions. Elicit answers such as $\frac{2}{4}$, $\frac{10}{20}$, $\frac{50}{100}$, and $\frac{100}{200}$. Remind students that they multiplied the numerator and the denominator by the same number to generate equivalent fractions. Explain that the equivalent fractions can be written as equivalent division expressions that result in the same quotient.

**Item 9** *By what power of ten do you multiply to make the divisor a whole number?* [100] *What is the equivalent division expression?* [$960 \div 4$]

**Reteaching** Assign Reteaching Set C on p. 381.

**Item 15 MP.4 Model with Math** *What operation can you use to find how many times as great the mass of the pumpkin is than the cabbage?* [Sample answer: Division] *What division expression represents this situation?* [$652 \div 32.6$]

**Item 19 Higher Order Thinking** *What does 8.65 kilograms measure?* [The mass of all the marbles and the mass of the jar.] *How do you find the mass of the marbles?* [Subtract the mass of the jar from the total mass.]

**Items 20–21 Coherence** Students can also use what they know about the relationship between multiplication and division to solve these problems. For example, in Item 20, the first equation is true because $32 \times 5.05 = 161.6$. This computation may be faster than dividing 161.6 by 5.05. Remind students to estimate the quotients. If the estimate is not close, then that problem can be eliminated.

**Multi-Step Problems** *Page 358 Items 18–21; Page 360 Items 13–15*

STEP 3

# ASSESS AND DIFFERENTIATE

2 RtI

Use the **QUICK CHECK** on the previous page to prescribe differentiated instruction.

**I Intervention** 0–3 points on the Quick Check

**O On-Level** 4 points on the Quick Check

**A Advanced** 5 points on the Quick Check

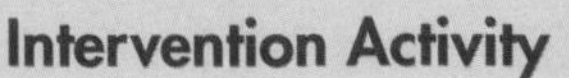

## Intervention Activity I

### Decimal Division

**Materials**

Index cards

- Make a stack of cards with dividends such as 24.5, 245, 2,450, 36.2, 362, and 3,620.
- Make a stack of cards with divisors such as 1, 0.1, and 0.001 so students can focus on where to move the decimal.
- Turn both stacks over. Student pairs choose one card from each stack and find the quotient.
- You may choose to include more challenging divisors in the stack of divisor cards depending on the students' level of understanding.

$0.1\overline{)24.5}$ = 245.  $0.001\overline{)24.500}$ = 24500.

$0.1\overline{)245.0}$ = 2450.  $0.001\overline{)245.000}$ = 245000.

## Reteach I

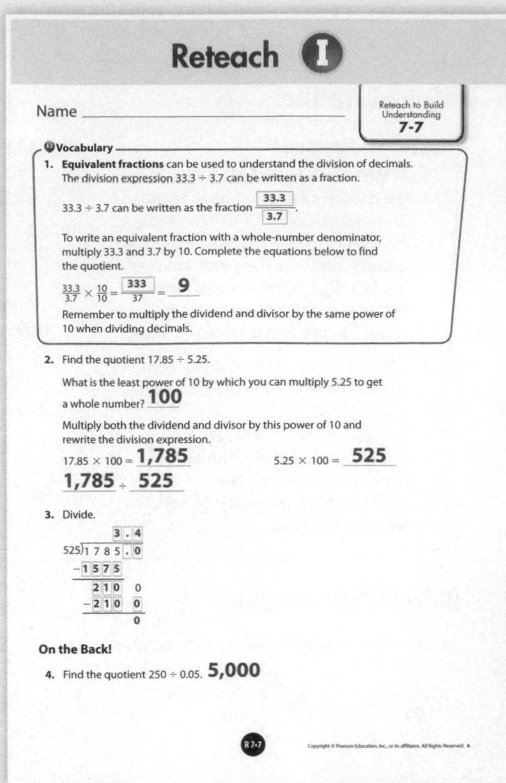

Name ______________________

Reteach to Build Understanding 7-7

**Vocabulary**

1. **Equivalent fractions** can be used to understand the division of decimals. The division expression 33.3 ÷ 3.7 can be written as a fraction.

33.3 ÷ 3.7 can be written as the fraction $\frac{33.3}{3.7}$.

To write an equivalent fraction with a whole-number denominator, multiply 33.3 and 3.7 by 10. Complete the equations below to find the quotient.

$\frac{33.3}{3.7} \times \frac{10}{10} = \frac{333}{37} = 9$

Remember to multiply the dividend and divisor by the same power of 10 when dividing decimals.

2. Find the quotient 17.85 ÷ 5.25.

What is the least power of 10 by which you can multiply 5.25 to get a whole number? **100**

Multiply both the dividend and divisor by this power of 10 and rewrite the division expression.

17.85 × 100 = **1,785**  5.25 × 100 = **525**

**1,785** ÷ **525**

3. Divide.

$525\overline{)1785.0}$ = 3.4
−1575
210 0
−210 0
0

**On the Back!**

4. Find the quotient 250 ÷ 0.05. **5,000**

R 7-7



## On-Level and Advanced Activity Centers O A

Name ______________________

Math and Science Activity 7-7

**Density**

Did You Know? A pure substance can be characterized by its various physical properties, such as its boiling point, freezing point, or density. The density of a substance is the relationship between the mass of the substance and how much space it takes up (volume). The density of a substance is found by dividing the mass of the substance by its volume. If we know the density of a pure substance, we can identify the substance.

| Densities of Common Substances (grams per cubic centimeter = $\frac{g}{cm^3}$) | |
|---|---|
| Water | 1 |
| Silver | 10.49 |
| Gold | 19.3 |
| Platinum | 21.09 |
| Lead | 11.34 |
| Iron | 7.874 |
| Copper | 8.92 |
| Titanium | 4.507 |

density = $\frac{mass}{volume}$ volume = $\frac{mass}{density}$

mass = density × volume

1. A metal sample has a mass of 28.544 grams and a volume of 3.2 cm³. Which metal could this sample be?

**copper**

2. Liam determines the mass of a pure silver coin to be 68.185 grams. How many cubic centimeters of silver were used to make the coin?

**6.5 cm³**

3. **Extension** King Hiero of Syracuse, who reigned from 270 to 215 BC, commissioned a new crown to be made of pure gold. King Hiero provided the goldsmith with the gold to make the crown. When the crown was delivered, King Hiero suspected that the goldsmith added some other metal to the gold so that he could keep some of the gold for himself and still have enough metal to make the crown. The crown had a mass of 998.58 grams and a volume of 53.4 cm³. Did the goldsmith cheat the king? Justify your answer.

**Yes; Sample answer: density of crown = 998.58 g ÷ 53.4 cm³ = 18.7 g/cm³. The density of the crown is less than the density of pure gold, so the goldsmith cheated the king.**

Math and Science Activity 7-7



### Math and Science Activity STEM

This activity revisits the science theme, **Freezing Points**, introduced on page 317 in the Student's Edition.

### Sample Student Work

3. $D = \frac{mass}{volume} = \frac{998.58}{53.4}$

$53.4\overline{)998.58}$ = 18.7
−534
4645
−4272
3738
−3738
0

**TIMING**

The time allocated to Step 3 will depend on the teacher's instructional decisions and differentiation routines.

15–30 min

PEARSON realize. PearsonRealize.com

 Help  Practice Buddy  Tools Games

## Technology Center    

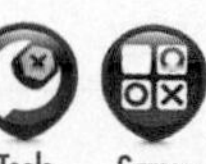 Tools Games

### Math Tools and Math Games

A link to a specific math tools activity or math game to use with this lesson is provided at PearsonRealize.com.

## Leveled Assignment  Items 1–6, 9, 10, 13–15  Items 3–11, 13–15  Items 4–15

Name ______________

## Homework & Practice 7-7

### Continue to Divide Decimals

### Another Look!

If all the plastic bottles collected by the Quinn family for recycling during a given month were laid end to end, they would measure 35.2 meters long. How many plastic bottles were collected if each plastic bottle measures 0.16 meter?

Find $35.2 \div 0.16$.

When you divide by a decimal, rewrite the divisor so that you are dividing by a whole number.

**Step 1** Make the divisor a whole number. Multiply the divisor and the dividend by the same power of 10. Place the decimal in the quotient.

$$\begin{array}{r} 220 \\ 0.16\overline{)35.20} \\ -\underline{32}\phantom{0} \\ 32 \\ -\underline{32} \\ 0 \end{array}$$

$0.16 \times 100 = 16$
$35.2 \times 100 = 3{,}520$

**Step 2** Divide as you would with whole numbers. Remember that sometimes you may need to annex zeros.

$220 \times 0.16 = 35.2$
220 bottles is reasonable.

**Step 3** Multiply to check that your answer is reasonable.

There is no remainder, so there are no decimal places in the quotient.

In **1–8**, find each quotient.

1. $0.25\overline{)500}$ **2,000**
2. $0.68\overline{)0.816}$ **1.2**
3. $0.9\overline{)0.36}$ **0.4**
4. $0.5\overline{)0.004}$ **0.008**
5. $15.4 \div 0.308$ **50**
6. $7.37 \div 0.67$ **11**
7. $4.848 \div 0.4$ **12.12**
8. $1.16 \div 0.008$ **145**



Samantha visits her local farm market to buy apples and oranges to make a fruit salad. She has $10.00 to spend.

9. If Samantha buys only apples, how many can she buy? **38 apples**
10. If Samantha buys only oranges, how many can she buy? **26 oranges**
11. **Higher Order Thinking** Samantha decides to buy both apples and oranges. Give two different solutions to tell how many apples and how many oranges she might buy.
**Sample answer: 20 apples and 12 oranges; 10 apples and 19 oranges**

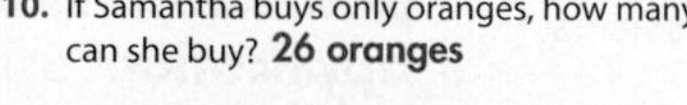

12. **MP.4 Model with Math** Jared draws several figures that each have equal side lengths of 1.4 meters. He records the perimeter, in meters, of each figure in the table below.
Let $n$ = the number of sides of each figure. Write an equation to represent the perimeter and complete the table.

| Number of Sides, $n$ | 3 | 4 | 5 | 6 | 8 |
|---|---|---|---|---|---|
| Perimeter | 4.2 | **5.6** | 7 | **8.4** | **11.2** |

**$P = 1.4n$**

13. **MP.1 Make Sense and Persevere** You have $15.60 to buy juice boxes for the school picnic. Each juice box costs $0.80. How many juice boxes can you buy? Should you expect to get change when you pay for the juice boxes? If so, how much?
**19 juice boxes. Sample answer: Yes, $15.60 \div 0.8 = 19.5$, so I can buy 19 juice boxes and get the change for the 0.5 of a juice box I can't buy. I will pay $15.20 and get $0.40 back.**

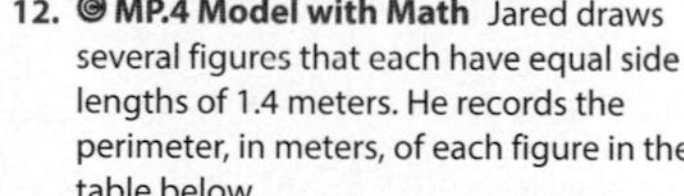

### Common Core Assessment

14. Choose all of the equations that are true.
- ☐ $157.59 \div 35.02 = 4$
- ■ $2.244 \div 3.4 = 0.66$
- ☐ $222.5 \div 0.89 = 25$
- ■ $4.428 \div 1.2 = 3.69$

15. Choose all of the equations that are **NOT** true.
- ■ $8.5 \div 2.5 = 0.34$
- ■ $5.60 \div 7.0 = 8$
- ☐ $3.311 \div 1.4 = 2.365$
- ☐ $2.58 \div 0.3 = 8.6$

# LESSON 7-8

# EVALUATE EXPRESSIONS WITH DECIMALS

## DIGITAL RESOURCES PearsonRealize.com

eText — Student and Teacher eTexts

PD — Listen and Look For Lesson Video

Think — Today's Challenge

Solve — Solve and Share

Learn — Visual Learning Animation Plus

Glossary — Animated Glossary

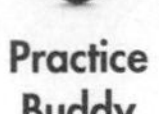
Practice Buddy — Online Personalized Practice

Tools — Math Tools

Assessment — Quick Check

Help — Another Look Homework Video

Games — Math Games

## LESSON OVERVIEW FCR FOCUS • COHERENCE • RIGOR

### FOCUS

**Domain 6.EE** Expressions and Equations

**Cluster 6.EE.A** Apply and extend previous understandings of arithmetic to algebraic expressions.

**Content Standard 6.EE.A.2a** Write expressions that record operations with numbers and with letters standing for numbers. *For example, express the calculation "Subtract* y *from 5" as* $5 - y$. Also **6.EE.A.2c, 6.NS.B.2, 6.NS.B.3**.

**Mathematical Practices MP.3, MP.4, MP.6, MP.7, MP.8**

**Objective** Evaluate algebraic expressions that involve decimals.

**Essential Understanding** The value of an algebraic expression can be found by replacing the variables with given numbers and doing the calculation that results.

### COHERENCE

In Topic 1, students wrote and evaluated algebraic expressions. They also extended their understanding of the order of operations, first introduced in Grade 3. In this topic, students have developed fluency in adding, subtracting, multiplying, and dividing decimals. In this lesson, they combine these skills to write and evaluate algebraic expressions that require decimal operations.

### RIGOR

This lesson emphasizes a blend of **procedural skill** and **fluency** with **application**. Students apply what they know about writing and evaluating algebraic expressions to write and evaluate expressions involving decimals to solve real-world and mathematical problems.

PD Watch the Listen and Look For Lesson Video.

## MATH ANYTIME

### Daily Common Core Review

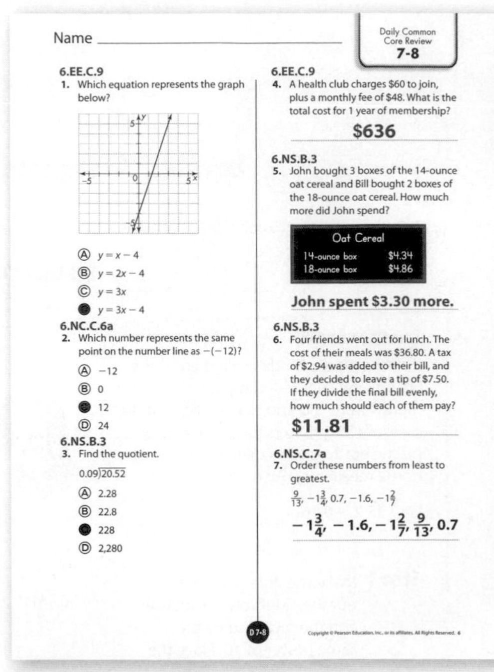

Name ____________

Daily Common Core Review 7-8

6.EE.C.9
1. Which equation represents the graph below?



Ⓐ $y = x - 4$
Ⓑ $y = 2x - 4$
Ⓒ $y = 3x$
● $y = 3x - 4$

6.NC.C.6a
2. Which number represents the same point on the number line as $-(-12)$?

Ⓐ −12
Ⓑ 0
● 12
Ⓓ 24

6.NS.B.3
3. Find the quotient.

$0.09\overline{)20.52}$

Ⓐ 2.28
Ⓑ 22.8
● 228
Ⓓ 2,280

6.EE.C.9
4. A health club charges $60 to join, plus a monthly fee of $48. What is the total cost for 1 year of membership?

**$636**

6.NS.B.3
5. John bought 3 boxes of the 14-ounce oat cereal and Bill bought 2 boxes of the 18-ounce oat cereal. How much more did John spend?

| Oat Cereal | |
|---|---|
| 14-ounce box | $4.34 |
| 18-ounce box | $4.86 |

**John spent $3.30 more.**

6.NS.B.3
6. Four friends went out for lunch. The cost of their meals was $36.80. A tax of $2.94 was added to their bill, and they decided to leave a tip of $7.50. If they divide the final bill evenly, how much should each of them pay?

**$11.81**

6.NS.C.7a
7. Order these numbers from least to greatest.

$\frac{9}{13}, -1\frac{3}{4}, 0.7, -1.6, -1\frac{2}{7}$

$\mathbf{-1\frac{3}{4}, -1.6, -1\frac{2}{7}, \frac{9}{13}, 0.7}$

D 7-8



### Today's Challenge

Think Use the Topic 7 problems any time during this topic.

## ENGLISH LANGUAGE LEARNERS ELL

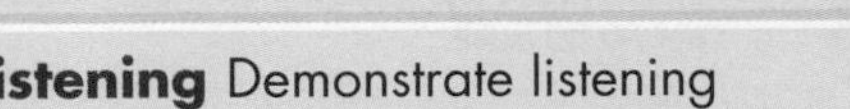

**Listening** Demonstrate listening comprehension by taking notes.

*Use with the Visual Learning Bridge on Student's Edition p. 362.*

Write the following anchor chart: An Algebraic Expression has one or more 1) Numbers, 2) Variables, 3) Operations. Instruct students to write the information in their notes. Read the first paragraph of Box A as students listen.

**Beginning** Reread the first paragraph of Box A as students listen. Point to the illustration. *Each ticket costs $4.25.* Ask students to write $4.25 in their notes. *We do not know how many people need tickets.* Ask students to write $4.25$x$ in their notes. *How many people will share the cost?* Ask students to write $4.25x \div 2 =$ _____ in their notes.

**Intermediate** Reread the first paragraph of Box A as students listen. Ask students to write the amount of each ticket in their notes. *Do we know how many people need tickets?* Have students represent the number of people with an $x$. *What operation will be used? How many people will share the cost of the tickets equally?* Instruct students to check to see if they've written an algebraic expression by reviewing their anchor chart notes.

**Advanced** Instruct students to reread the first paragraph in Box A. Ask students to write an algebraic expression in their notes based on the information given and to check to see if each component of an algebraic expression is evident in their expressions. Ask students to listen to their partners explain their expressions.

**Summarize** What is an algebraic expression?

# DEVELOP: PROBLEM-BASED LEARNING

**COHERENCE: Engage learners by connecting prior knowledge to new ideas.**
Students extend their understanding of algebraic expressions and the order of operations to write and evaluate expressions involving decimals.

10–15 min

Solve

## BEFORE

**1. Pose the Solve-and-Share Problem**
**MP.4 Model with Math** Listen and look for students who write an expression with decimals to represent the costs at a bike shop.

**2. Build Understanding**
*What is the per hour bike rental fee?* [$12.50] *What is the variable described in the problem situation and what quantity does it represent?* [*h*; The number of hours the bike was rented]

## DURING

**3. Ask Guiding Questions As Needed**
*What expression can you write to represent the cost to rent a bike for h hours?* [12.50*h*] *How can you use this expression to represent the total rental cost, including the helmet?* [Sample answer: Add the cost of $5.25 for renting a helmet to the expression 12.50*h*.]

## AFTER

**4. Share and Discuss Solutions**
Solve Start with students' solutions. If needed, project John's work to discuss how to solve the problem by writing and evaluating an algebraic expression.

**5. Transition to the Visual Learning Bridge**
*You can write and evaluate algebraic expressions to solve a variety of real-world problems that involve decimals.*

**6. Extension for Early Finishers**
*Evaluate this expression* $(1.3d + 0.2s) \div 5$ *for* $d = 2.5$ *and* $s = 4$.
[0.81]

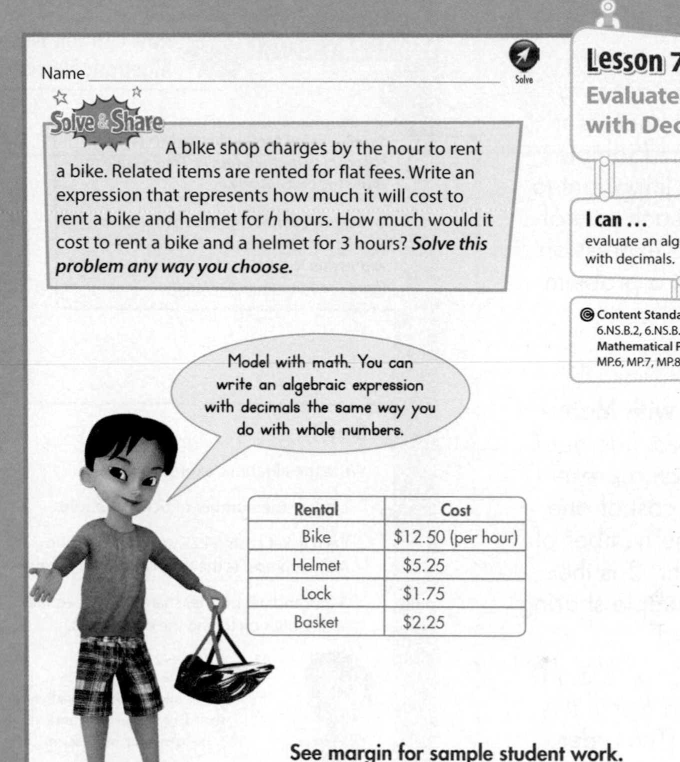

Name

Solve & Share

A bike shop charges by the hour to rent a bike. Related items are rented for flat fees. Write an expression that represents how much it will cost to rent a bike and helmet for *h* hours. How much would it cost to rent a bike and a helmet for 3 hours? *Solve this problem any way you choose.*

**Lesson 7-8**
**Evaluate Expressions with Decimals**

**I can ...**
evaluate an algebraic expression with decimals.

**Content Standards** 6.EE.A.2a, 6.EE.A.2c, 6.NS.B.2, 6.NS.B.3
**Mathematical Practices** MP.3, MP.4, MP.6, MP.7, MP.8

Model with math. You can write an algebraic expression with decimals the same way you do with whole numbers.

| Rental | Cost |
|---|---|
| Bike | $12.50 (per hour) |
| Helmet | $5.25 |
| Lock | $1.75 |
| Basket | $2.25 |

**See margin for sample student work.**

**Look Back!** **MP.7 Use Structure** Write an expression that represents renting a bike, lock, and basket for *h* hours. What is the cost of renting this equipment for 4 hours?
**Sample answer: 12.50*h* + (1.75 + 2.25); 12.50(4) + 4.00 = 54.00; It would cost $54.00 to rent a bike for 4 hours, a lock, and a basket.**

Digital Resources at PearsonRealize.com Topic 7 | Lesson 7-8 361

## Analyze Student Work

**John's Work**

Bike Cost × Time + Helmet Cost
12.50 × h + 5.25
h = 3
12.50 × 3 + 5.25
37.50 + 5.25 = 42.75

Total cost: $42.75

John writes the correct expression and evaluates the expression correctly to find the total cost.

**Tim's Work**

Cost of bike + Cost of helmet × number of hours
(Cost of bike + Cost of helmet) × # hours
(12.50 + 5.25) h =
17.75 h
Let h = 3
17.75 h =
17.75(3) =
53.25
The total cost is $53.25.

Tim writes an incorrect expression to represent this situation, but evaluates the expression correctly.

# DEVELOP: VISUAL LEARNING

The *Visual Learning Bridge* connects students' thinking in Solve & Share to important math ideas in the lesson. Use the *Visual Learning Bridge* to make these ideas explicit. Also available as a *Visual Learning Animation Plus* at PearsonRealize.com

Visual Learning

PEARSON realize. PearsonRealize.com

Learn Glossary

**MP.6 Be Precise**
*Why is it important to be precise by defining a variable to represent the unknown?* [Sample answer: It is important to know what each part of an algebraic expression represents in a problem situation.]

**MP.4 Model with Math**
*What does each term of the expression represent?* [4.25 is the cost of one ticket, $x$ is the number of tickets bought, 2 is the number of people sharing the total cost.]
*Which operation should be performed first in this expression?* [The order of operations states multiplication and division in order from left to right. Multiply 4.25 times $x$ first.]

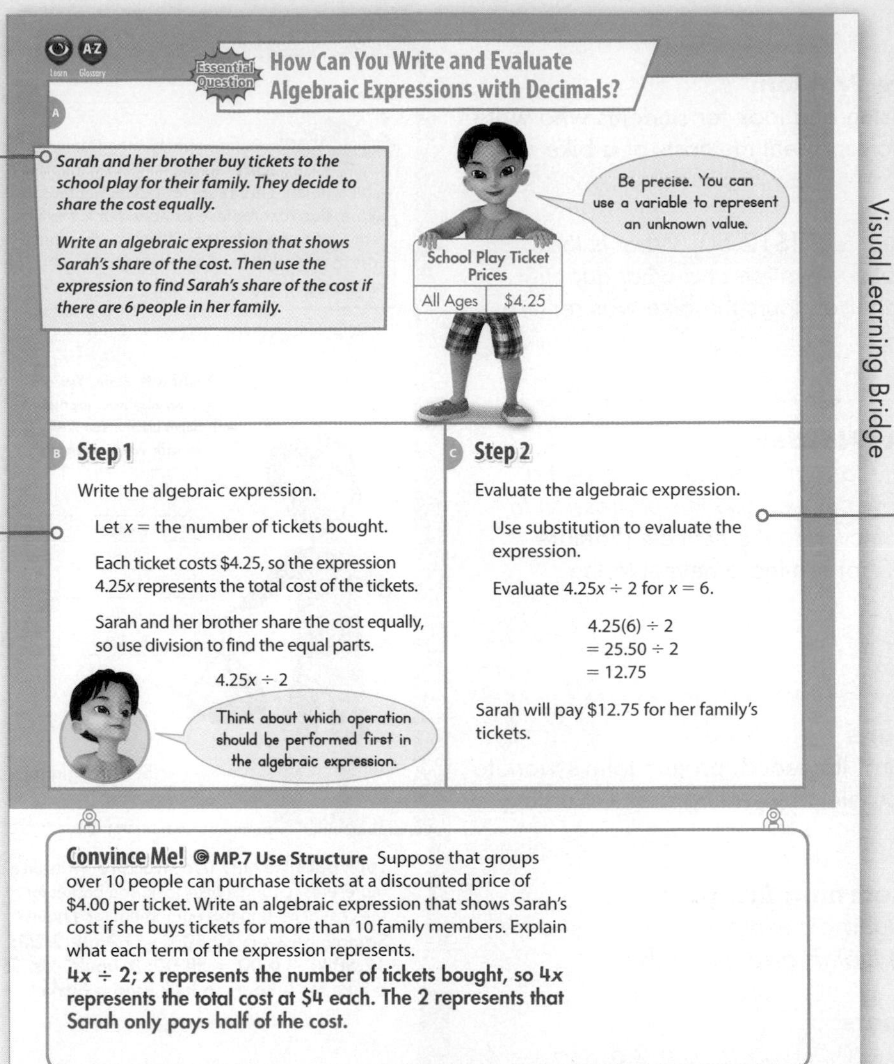

Essential Question
How Can You Write and Evaluate Algebraic Expressions with Decimals?
Sarah and her brother buy tickets to the school play for their family. They decide to share the cost equally.
Write an algebraic expression that shows Sarah's share of the cost. Then use the expression to find Sarah's share of the cost if there are 6 people in her family.
Be precise. You can use a variable to represent an unknown value.
School Play Ticket Prices
All Ages $4.25
Step 1
Write the algebraic expression.
Let x = the number of tickets bought.
Each ticket costs $4.25, so the expression 4.25x represents the total cost of the tickets.
Sarah and her brother share the cost equally, so use division to find the equal parts.
4.25x ÷ 2
Think about which operation should be performed first in the algebraic expression.
Step 2
Evaluate the algebraic expression.
Use substitution to evaluate the expression.
Evaluate 4.25x ÷ 2 for x = 6.
4.25(6) ÷ 2
= 25.50 ÷ 2
= 12.75
Sarah will pay $12.75 for her family's tickets.
Visual Learning Bridge


**Convince Me!** MP.7 Use Structure Suppose that groups over 10 people can purchase tickets at a discounted price of $4.00 per ticket. Write an algebraic expression that shows Sarah's cost if she buys tickets for more than 10 family members. Explain what each term of the expression represents.
**$4x \div 2$; $x$ represents the number of tickets bought, so $4x$ represents the total cost at $4 each. The 2 represents that Sarah only pays half of the cost.**

362 Topic 7 | Lesson 7-8 © Pearson Education, Inc. 6

**MP.2 Reason Quantitatively**
*Why do you substitute 6 for x?* [Sarah and her brother need to buy 6 tickets, one for each family member.] *How can you estimate the value of the expression 4.25(6) ÷ 2?* [4(6) ÷ 2 = 12] *Compare your actual answer to your estimate. Is your answer reasonable?* [Yes. 12 is close to 12.75.] *How could you check your answer knowing that Sarah paid for half of the six total tickets?* [Sample answer: $4.25 × 3 = $12.75]

**Convince Me! MP.7 Use Structure** Students look for and make use of structure by recognizing how each part of the algebraic expression above represents the problem situation and by replacing the coefficient of $x$ with the discounted price of $4. *What quantity has changed from the previous problem to this situation?* [The cost per ticket] *What part of the expression represents the cost of each ticket?* [The coefficient of $x$]

**Coherence** Students learned how to write and evaluate an algebraic expression in Topic 1. Throughout this topic, they have developed fluency in decimal computations. Students apply both of these skills in order to solve the school play ticket problem.

Revisit the Essential Question. Students can evaluate an algebraic expression by substituting the variables with given numbers, including decimals, and doing the calculation that results.

## ☑ QUICK CHECK

Check mark indicates items for prescribing differentiation on the next page.
Item 12 is worth one point. Items 21 and 24 are worth up to 2 points.

20–30 min

PearsonRealize.com

Practice Buddy

Tools

Assessment

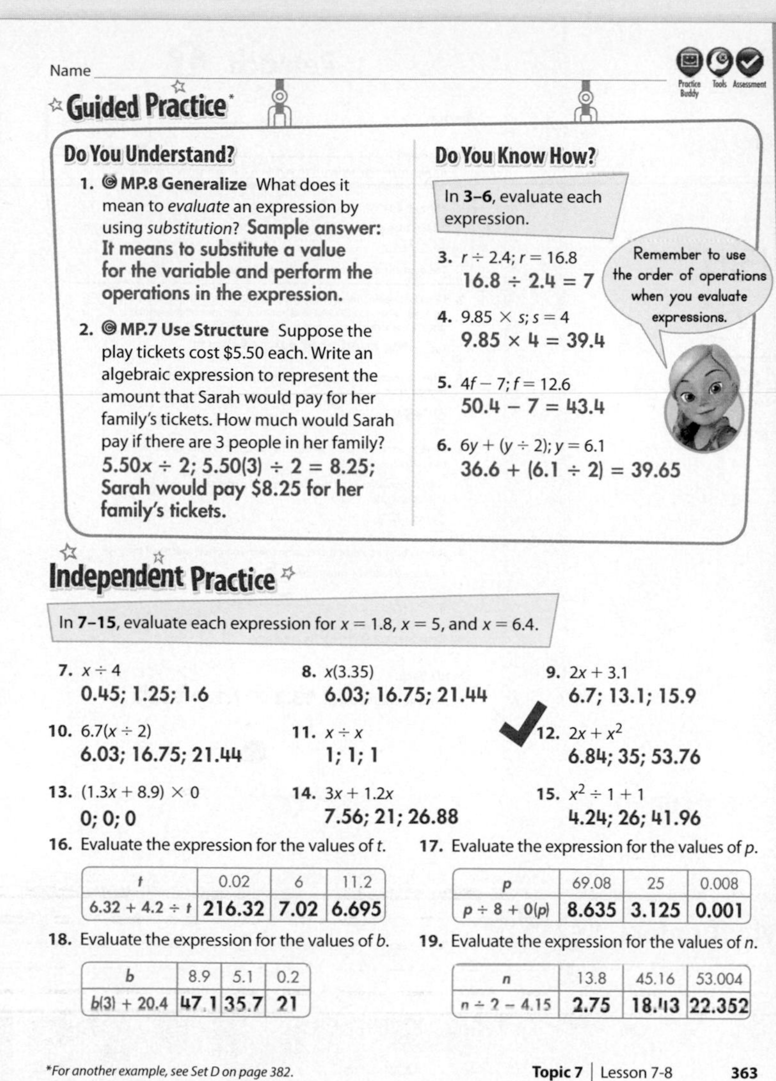

Name

### Guided Practice*

**Do You Understand?**

1. MP.8 Generalize What does it mean to *evaluate* an expression by using *substitution*? **Sample answer: It means to substitute a value for the variable and perform the operations in the expression.**
2. MP.7 Use Structure Suppose the play tickets cost $5.50 each. Write an algebraic expression to represent the amount that Sarah would pay for her family's tickets. How much would Sarah pay if there are 3 people in her family? **$5.50x \div 2$; $5.50(3) \div 2 = 8.25$; Sarah would pay $8.25 for her family's tickets.**

**Do You Know How?**

In **3–6**, evaluate each expression.

3. $r \div 2.4$; $r = 16.8$ **$16.8 \div 2.4 = 7$**
4. $9.85 \times s$; $s = 4$ **$9.85 \times 4 = 39.4$**
5. $4f - 7$; $f = 12.6$ **$50.4 - 7 = 43.4$**
6. $6y + (y \div 2)$; $y = 6.1$ **$36.6 + (6.1 \div 2) = 39.65$**

Remember to use the order of operations when you evaluate expressions.

### Independent Practice*

In **7–15**, evaluate each expression for $x = 1.8$, $x = 5$, and $x = 6.4$.

7. $x \div 4$ **0.45; 1.25; 1.6**
8. $x(3.35)$ **6.03; 16.75; 21.44**
9. $2x + 3.1$ **6.7; 13.1; 15.9**
10. $6.7(x \div 2)$ **6.03; 16.75; 21.44**
11. $x \div x$ **1; 1; 1**
12. ✓ $2x + x^2$ **6.84; 35; 53.76**
13. $(1.3x + 8.9) \times 0$ **0; 0; 0**
14. $3x + 1.2x$ **7.56; 21; 26.88**
15. $x^2 \div 1 + 1$ **4.24; 26; 41.96**

16. Evaluate the expression for the values of *t*.

| $t$ | 0.02 | 6 | 11.2 |
|---|---|---|---|
| $6.32 + 4.2 \div t$ | **216.32** | **7.02** | **6.695** |

17. Evaluate the expression for the values of *p*.

| $p$ | 69.08 | 25 | 0.008 |
|---|---|---|---|
| $p \div 8 + 0(p)$ | **8.635** | **3.125** | **0.001** |

18. Evaluate the expression for the values of *b*.

| $b$ | 8.9 | 5.1 | 0.2 |
|---|---|---|---|
| $b(3) + 20.4$ | **47.1** | **35.7** | **21** |

19. Evaluate the expression for the values of *n*.

| $n$ | 13.8 | 45.16 | 53.004 |
|---|---|---|---|
| $n \div 2 - 4.15$ | **2.75** | **18.43** | **22.352** |

*For another example, see Set D on page 382.

Topic 7 | Lesson 7-8 363

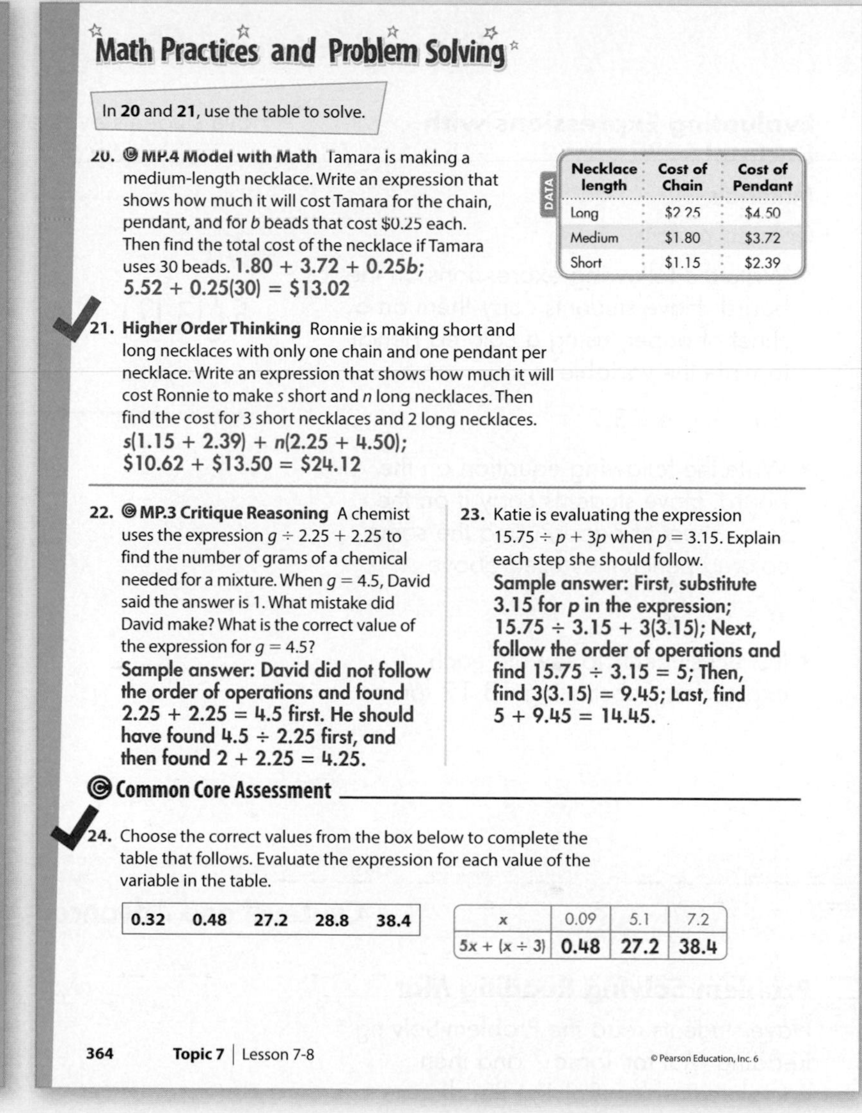

### Math Practices and Problem Solving*

In **20** and **21**, use the table to solve.

| Necklace length | Cost of Chain | Cost of Pendant |
|---|---|---|
| Long | $2.25 | $4.50 |
| Medium | $1.80 | $3.72 |
| Short | $1.15 | $2.39 |

20. MP.4 Model with Math Tamara is making a medium-length necklace. Write an expression that shows how much it will cost Tamara for the chain, pendant, and for *b* beads that cost $0.25 each. Then find the total cost of the necklace if Tamara uses 30 beads. **$1.80 + 3.72 + 0.25b$; $5.52 + 0.25(30) = \$13.02$**
21. ✓ Higher Order Thinking Ronnie is making short and long necklaces with only one chain and one pendant per necklace. Write an expression that shows how much it will cost Ronnie to make *s* short and *n* long necklaces. Then find the cost for 3 short necklaces and 2 long necklaces. **$s(1.15 + 2.39) + n(2.25 + 4.50)$; $\$10.62 + \$13.50 = \$24.12$**
22. MP.3 Critique Reasoning A chemist uses the expression $g \div 2.25 + 2.25$ to find the number of grams of a chemical needed for a mixture. When $g = 4.5$, David said the answer is 1. What mistake did David make? What is the correct value of the expression for $g = 4.5$? **Sample answer: David did not follow the order of operations and found $2.25 + 2.25 = 4.5$ first. He should have found $4.5 \div 2.25$ first, and then found $2 + 2.25 = 4.25$.**
23. Katie is evaluating the expression $15.75 \div p + 3p$ when $p = 3.15$. Explain each step she should follow. **Sample answer: First, substitute 3.15 for *p* in the expression; $15.75 \div 3.15 + 3(3.15)$; Next, follow the order of operations and find $15.75 \div 3.15 = 5$; Then, find $3(3.15) = 9.45$; Last, find $5 + 9.45 = 14.45$.**

**Common Core Assessment**

24. ✓ Choose the correct values from the box below to complete the table that follows. Evaluate the expression for each value of the variable in the table.

| 0.32 | 0.48 | 27.2 | 28.8 | 38.4 |
|---|---|---|---|---|

| $x$ | 0.09 | 5.1 | 7.2 |
|---|---|---|---|
| $5x + (x \div 3)$ | **0.48** | **27.2** | **38.4** |

364 Topic 7 | Lesson 7-8



**Error Intervention: Item 5**

**If** students get an answer of 49.7,

**then** remind them to line up the decimal points. They should write 7 as 7.0 to make sure they are subtracting the 7 from the ones column and not from the last digit of the product $4 \times 12.6$.

**Items 5 and 6 Coherence** Remind students to use the order of operations as they evaluate the expression.

*If the parenthesis in Item 6 were omitted, would the answer be the same? Explain.* [Yes; according to the order of operations, all division must be completed before addition.]

**Reteaching** Assign Reteaching Set D on p. 382.

**Items 11 and 13 Coherence** Encourage students to apply the properties of operations they learned in Grade 4 rather than evaluating the expression for each value of *x*. For example, they learned that any number (except zero) divided by itself is 1; so $x \div x = 1$ for any value of *x*. The Zero Property of Multiplication applies to Item 13; so the expression has a value of 0 for any value of *x*.

**Item 22 MP.3 Critique Reasoning** Encourage students to ask the following questions when they critique the reasoning of others. Does the strategy used make sense? Are the properties of equality used correctly? Can I clarify or improve the reasoning?

**Item 23** Students will add, multiply, and divide decimals as they evaluate the algebraic expression. Encourage them to apply the standard algorithms for operations with decimals and to record their work neatly and carefully as they complete each computation.

**Multi-Step Problems** *Page 364 Items 20–24; Page 366 Items 14–16 and 21*

# ASSESS AND DIFFERENTIATE

Use the **QUICK CHECK** on the previous page to prescribe differentiated instruction.

**Ⓘ Intervention** 0–3 points on the Quick Check

**Ⓞ On-Level** 4 points on the Quick Check

**Ⓐ Advanced** 5 points on the Quick Check

## Intervention Activity Ⓘ

**Evaluating Expressions with Decimals**

**Materials**

Colored pencils

- Write the following expressions on the board. Have students copy them on a sheet of paper, using a colored pencil to write the variable *a*.

  $5a$ $\quad a \div 3.2$

- Write the following equation on the board. Have students copy it on the same sheet of paper, using the same colored pencil they used above.

  $a = 13.12$

- Instruct students to rewrite each expression, substituting 13.12 for *a*.
- Have students evaluate each expression. [65.6; 4.1]

5a

5(13.12)

13.12
X 5
65.60

## Reteach 

Name ____________

Reteach to Build Understanding 7-8

**Vocabulary**

1. An **algebraic expression**, such as $0.4n \div 2$, uses numbers, variables, and symbols to express a value. Expressions do not include equal signs.

   Write an algebraic expression for each situation.

   7.2 less than a number *f* **$f - 7.2$**

   The product of 6.4 and a number *n* **$6.4n$**

   The quotient of a number *x* divided by a number *y* **$x \div y$**

2. Elena is shopping for several pairs of athletic shorts. The regular price for a pair of shorts is \$9.99. Elena has a coupon for $\frac{1}{3}$ off the regular price. Write an expression to find the amount Elena will pay.

   Let $x$ = **the number of pairs of shorts**.

3. Write an expression to represent the total cost of the shorts at the regular price.

   **$9.99x$**

4. Write an expression to represent the total cost of the shorts after the coupon is applied.

   The coupon gives $\frac{1}{3}$ off the regular price, so the sale price is $\frac{2}{3}$ of the regular price.

   $\frac{2}{3}(9.99\ \boldsymbol{x})$

5. If Elena buys 5 pairs of shorts using the coupon, how much will she pay?

   Evaluate $\frac{2}{3}(9.99x)$ by substituting **5** for *x*.

   $\frac{2}{3}(9.99 \times \boxed{5}) = \frac{2}{3} \times \boxed{49.95} = \frac{\boxed{99.90}}{3} = \boxed{33.30}$

6. Elena will pay \$**33.30** for the shorts.

**On the Back!**

7. Evaluate $13.2a$ for $a = 7.1$. **$13.2 \times 7.1 = 93.72$**

R 7-8



## On-Level and Advanced Activity Centers  

**Problem-Solving Reading Mat**

Have students read the Problem-Solving Reading Mat for Topic 7 and then complete Problem-Solving Reading Activity 7-8.

See the Problem-Solving Reading Activity Guide for other suggestions on how to use this mat.

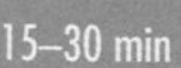

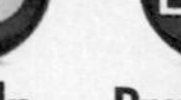

**TIMING**

The time allocated to Step 3 will depend on the teacher's instructional decisions and differentiation routines.

15–30 min

PEARSON realize. PearsonRealize.com

Help | Practice Buddy | Tools | Games

## Technology Center   

Tools Games

**Math Tools and Math Games**

A link to a specific math tools activity or math game to use with this lesson is provided at PearsonRealize.com.

## Leveled Assignment  Items 1–6, 11, 16–21  Items 7–9 12–15, 17–21  Items 10–21

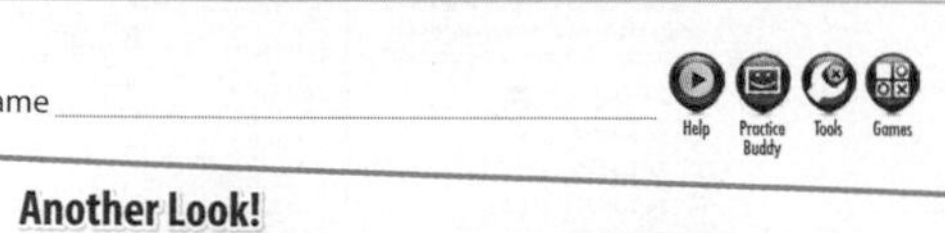


### Homework & Practice 7-8
### Evaluate Expressions with Decimals

**Another Look!**

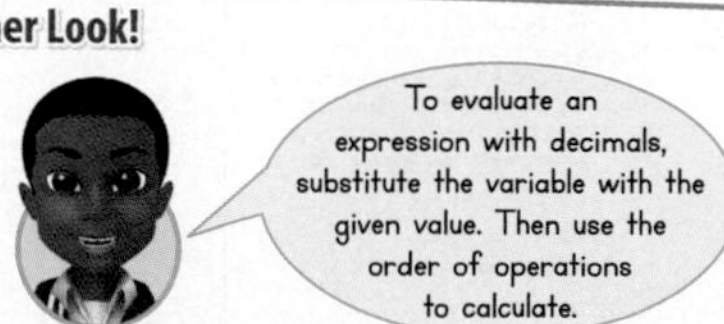

To evaluate an expression with decimals, substitute the variable with the given value. Then use the order of operations to calculate.


Evaluate $5.1 + 3n$ for $n = 2.6$.

Replace $n$ with 2.6. → $5.1 + 3(2.6)$

Multiply first. → $5.1 + 7.8$

Then add. → $12.9$

The value of the expression is 12.9.

Evaluate $x^2 + 2x - x \div 3$ for $x = 3.3$.

Replace $x$ with 3.3. → $3.3^2 + 2(3.3) - 3.3 \div 3$

Evaluate terms with exponents first. → $10.89 + 2(3.3) - 3.3 \div 3$

Then multiply and divide. → $10.89 + 6.6 - 1.1$

Then add and subtract. → $16.39$

The value of the expression is 16.39.

In **1–3**, evaluate each expression by using substitution.

**1.** $6n$; $n = 2.3$
**$6 \times 2.3 = 13.8$**

**2.** $3x - 8.1$; $x = 6.4$
**$3 \times 6.4 - 8.1 = 11.1$**

**3.** $r + 53.3 \div r$; $r = 6.5$
**$6.5 + 53.3 \div 6.5 = 14.7$**

In **4–9**, evaluate each expression for $x = 3.1$, $x = 6.2$, and $x = 8.3$.

**4.** $5x$
**15.5; 31; 41.5**

**5.** $8.2 + x \div 2$
**9.75; 11.3; 12.35**

**6.** $2x + 1.5x$
**10.85; 21.7; 29.05**

**7.** $12x - 14.5$
**22.7; 59.9; 85.1**

**8.** $(0.85 + x) \div 5$
**0.79; 1.41; 1.83**

**9.** $8.92 - (x + 0.47)$
**5.35; 2.25; 0.15**

**10.** Evaluate the expression for the values of $f$.

| $f$ | 0.6 | 24 | 100 |
|---|---|---|---|
| $2.6f + f \div 8$ | **1.635** | **65.4** | **272.5** |

**11.** Evaluate the expression for the values of $v$.

| $v$ | 1.8 | 13.2 | 200.89 |
|---|---|---|---|
| $v - 0.8 + 0.5 \cdot v$ | **1.9** | **19** | **300.535** |

**12.** Evaluate the expression for the values of $s$.

| $s$ | 0.002 | 2.89 | 34.74 |
|---|---|---|---|
| $4.09s \div s$ | **4.09** | **4.09** | **4.09** |

**13.** Evaluate the expression for the values of $t$.

| $t$ | 0.01 | 1 | 2.5 |
|---|---|---|---|
| $\frac{9.5}{t} + 3.2t$ | **950.032** | **12.7** | **11.8** |



**14. Higher Order Thinking** The deli sells ham for \$3.95 per pound, turkey for \$4.30 per pound, and cheese for \$3.10 per pound. Write an expression that shows how much it will cost to buy $h$ pounds of ham, $t$ pounds of turkey, and $c$ pounds of cheese. Then find the cost for 1 pound of ham, 1.5 pounds of turkey, and 2.3 pounds of cheese.
**$3.95h + 4.30t + 3.10c$; $3.95(1) + 4.30(1.5) + 3.10(2.3) = \$17.53$**

**15. MP.4 Model with Math** Juan rented a paddleboard for \$5.75 per hour plus a \$17.50 fee. Write an expression that shows how much it will cost Juan to rent the paddleboard for $x$ hours. Then evaluate the expression for 3 hours.
**$5.75x + 17.5$; \$34.75**

**16. MP.6 Be Precise** The table shows how much a frozen yogurt shop charges for its yogurt. Write an expression to show how much it costs to buy a small yogurt with no toppings and a large yogurt with $x$ toppings. Then find the total cost for a small yogurt with no toppings and a large yogurt with 3 toppings.
**$2.85 + 4.65 + 0.35x$; \$8.55**

DATA

| Size of cup | Cost of cup | Cost per topping |
|---|---|---|
| Small | \$2.85 | \$0.25 |
| Medium | \$3.75 | \$0.30 |
| Large | \$4.65 | \$0.35 |

**17. Math and Science** The heart of an adult human being pumps about 83.3 gallons of blood per hour. Write an expression to tell how many gallons of blood an adult heart pumps in $h$ hours.
**$83.3h$**

**18.** Evaluate the expression from Exercise 17 to find how many gallons of blood the heart of an adult human being pumps in 3 hours and in 10 hours.
**249.9 gallons; 833 gallons**

**19. Vocabulary** Multiplication and division have an *inverse relationship*. How are multiplication and division related?
**Sample answer: Multiplication and division "undo" each other. If you multiply a number by 3, then divide by 3, you get back the original number.**

**20.** Order the follow numbers from least to greatest.

$\frac{3}{4}, -\frac{1}{8}, |\frac{1}{4}|, -3, -\frac{1}{2}, |-1|$

**$-3, -\frac{1}{2}, -\frac{1}{8}, |\frac{1}{4}|, \frac{3}{4}, |-1|$**

**Common Core Assessment**

**21.** Choose the correct values from the box below to complete the table that follows. Evaluate the expression for each value of the variable in the table.

| 0.71 | 0.97 | 3.13 | 3.73 | 4.13 |
|---|---|---|---|---|

| $r$ | 0.59 | 1.8 | 2.3 |
|---|---|---|---|
| $3r - (r + 0.47)$ | **0.71** | **3.13** | **4.13** |

# LESSON 7-9

# SOLVE EQUATIONS WITH DECIMALS

## DIGITAL RESOURCES PearsonRealize.com

Student and Teacher eTexts
eText

Listen and Look For Lesson Video
PD

Today's Challenge
Think

Solve and Share
Solve

Visual Learning Animation Plus
Learn

Animated Glossary
Glossary

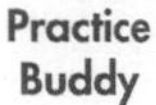
Online Personalized Practice
Practice Buddy

Math Tools
Tools

Quick Check
Assessment

Another Look Homework Video
Help

Math Games
Games

## LESSON OVERVIEW FCR FOCUS • COHERENCE • RIGOR

### FOCUS

**Domain 6.EE** Expressions and Equations

**Cluster 6.EE.B** Reason about and solve one-variable equations and inequalities.

**Content Standard 6.EE.B.7** Solve real-world and mathematical problems by writing and solving equations of the form $x + p = q$ and $px = q$ for cases in which $p$, $q$ and $x$ are all nonnegative rational numbers.
Also **6.NS.B.2, 6.NS.B.3**.

**Mathematical Practices MP.2, MP.3, MP.4, MP.7**

**Objective** Solve algebraic equations that involve decimals.

**Essential Understanding** Solving an equation involves finding the value of the variable that makes the equation true.

### COHERENCE

In Topic 2, students learned the properties of equality and used them to solve one-step equations. In this lesson, they use the properties of equality and inverse relationships to solve one-step equations that include decimals.

### RIGOR

This lesson emphasizes a blend of **procedural skill** and **fluency** with **application**. Students apply what they know about writing equations and using properties of equality and inverse relationships to solve real-world and mathematical problems involving decimals.

PD Watch the Listen and Look For Lesson Video.

## MATH ANYTIME

### Daily Common Core Review

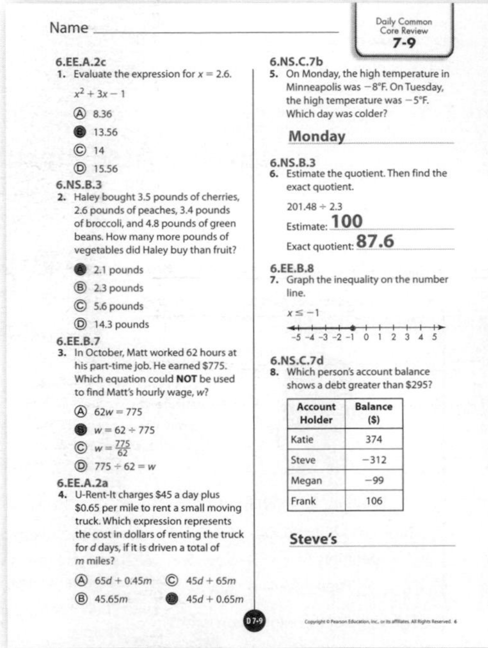
Name ____________

Daily Common Core Review 7-9

6.EE.A.2c
1. Evaluate the expression for $x = 2.6$.
$x^2 + 3x - 1$
Ⓐ 8.36
● 13.56
Ⓒ 14
Ⓓ 15.56

6.NS.B.3
2. Haley bought 3.5 pounds of cherries, 2.6 pounds of peaches, 3.4 pounds of broccoli, and 4.8 pounds of green beans. How many more pounds of vegetables did Haley buy than fruit?
● 2.1 pounds
Ⓑ 2.3 pounds
Ⓒ 5.6 pounds
Ⓓ 14.3 pounds

6.EE.B.7
3. In October, Matt worked 62 hours at his part-time job. He earned $775. Which equation could **NOT** be used to find Matt's hourly wage, $w$?
Ⓐ $62w = 775$
● $w = 62 \div 775$
Ⓒ $w = \frac{775}{62}$
Ⓓ $775 \div 62 = w$

6.EE.A.2a
4. U-Rent-It charges $45 a day plus $0.65 per mile to rent a small moving truck. Which expression represents the cost in dollars of renting the truck for $d$ days, if it is driven a total of $m$ miles?
Ⓐ $65d + 0.45m$
Ⓑ $45.65m$
Ⓒ $45d + 65m$
● $45d + 0.65m$

6.NS.C.7b
5. On Monday, the high temperature in Minneapolis was −8°F. On Tuesday, the high temperature was −5°F. Which day was colder?
Monday

6.NS.B.3
6. Estimate the quotient. Then find the exact quotient.
$201.48 \div 2.3$
Estimate: 100
Exact quotient: 87.6

6.EE.B.8
7. Graph the inequality on the number line.
$x \leq -1$
−5 −4 −3 −2 −1 0 1 2 3 4 5

6.NS.C.7d
8. Which person's account balance shows a debt greater than $295?

| Account Holder | Balance ($) |
|---|---|
| Katie | 374 |
| Steve | −312 |
| Megan | −99 |
| Frank | 106 |

Steve's

D 7-9



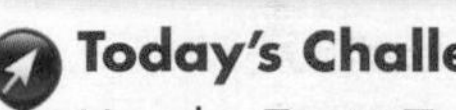
### Today's Challenge

Think Use the Topic 7 problems any time during this topic.

## ENGLISH LANGUAGE LEARNERS 

**Learning Strategies** Use prior knowledge to understand meanings.

*Use with the Solve & Share on Student's Edition p. 367.*

Read the Solve & Share. *How have you solved similar problems in the past?* Students will share prior knowledge with partners. *You've written algebraic equations in the past. What are the components of an algebraic equation? What algebraic equation could be written to solve this problem?*

**Beginning** *How many total miles did the family hike?* Write 22.2 miles. Point to the illustration. *How many miles was each hike?* Write 3.7. Instruct students to work as a group to create an algebraic equation using the given information. Write $3.7h = 22.2$ and $22.2 \div 3.7 = h$. Explain to students both equations can be used to solve the problem.

**Intermediate** *How many total miles did the family hike? How many miles was each hike?* Instruct students to work with partners to create an algebraic equation. *Is your equation operation multiplication or division?* Write $3.7h = 22.2$ and $22.2 \div 3.7 = h$. Explain to students both equations can be used to solve the problem.

**Advanced** Divide students into partner groups. Student A will write a multiplication equation and Student B will write a division equation. Ask students to explain to partners their reasoning for writing their equations.

**Summarize** How are multiplication or division algebraic equations used to solve problems?

# DEVELOP: PROBLEM-BASED LEARNING

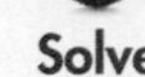

**COHERENCE: Engage learners by connecting prior knowledge to new ideas.**
Students apply what they know about writing and solving equations and about decimal computation to solve a real-world problem.

10–15 min

Solve

## BEFORE

**1. Pose the Solve-and-Share Problem**
**MP.2 Reason Quantitatively** Listen and look for students who reason about the quantities in the problem to write an equation and use it to solve the problem.

**2. Build Understanding**
*What is the unknown quantity in this problem?* [The number of times the family hiked the trail] *How can you represent an unknown quantity in an equation?* [By assigning a variable to represent the unknown quantity]

## DURING

**3. Ask Guiding Questions As Needed**
*What equation shows an unknown number of times, t, that the family hiked the Shore Coast Trail?* [$3.7t = 22.2$] *How would you solve this equation?* [Divide both sides of the equation by 3.7] *What property of equality would you use to solve this equation?* [Division Property of Equality]

## AFTER

**4. Share and Discuss Solutions**
Solve Start with students' solutions. If needed, project James's work to discuss how to write and solve an equation to solve the problem.

**5. Transition to the Visual Learning Bridge**
*Just like with whole numbers and fractions, you can use inverse relationships to solve equations involving decimals.*

**6. Extension for Early Finishers**
*On the board, write the equation 2.45r = 17.15. Ask students to write a problem that could be represented by the equation and then solve for r.* [Sample answer: Teddy spent $17.15 on juice drinks that each cost $2.45 each. How many drinks did he buy?; 7]

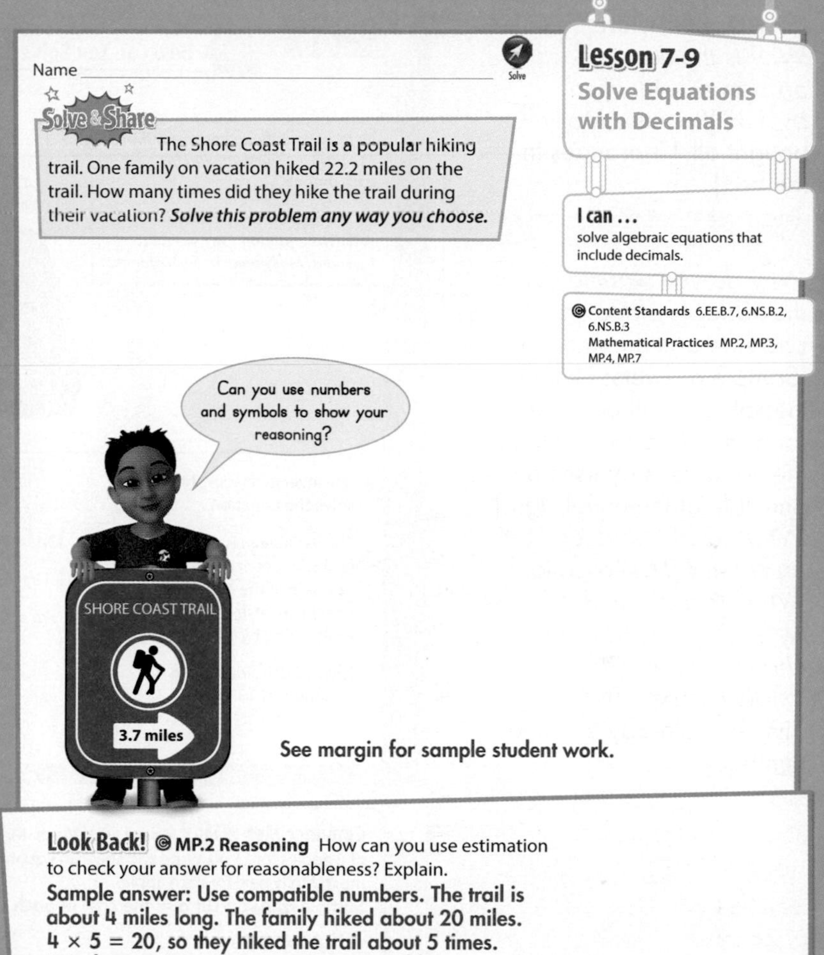

Name

Solve & Share

The Shore Coast Trail is a popular hiking trail. One family on vacation hiked 22.2 miles on the trail. How many times did they hike the trail during their vacation? ***Solve this problem any way you choose.***

**Lesson 7-9**
**Solve Equations with Decimals**

**I can . . .**
solve algebraic equations that include decimals.

Content Standards 6.EE.B.7, 6.NS.B.2, 6.NS.B.3
Mathematical Practices MP.2, MP.3, MP.4, MP.7

Can you use numbers and symbols to show your reasoning?
SHORE COAST TRAIL
3.7 miles

**See margin for sample student work.**

**Look Back!** **MP.2 Reasoning** How can you use estimation to check your answer for reasonableness? Explain.
**Sample answer: Use compatible numbers. The trail is about 4 miles long. The family hiked about 20 miles. 4 × 5 = 20, so they hiked the trail about 5 times. 5 is close to 6, so my answer is reasonable.**

Digital Resources at PearsonRealize.com  **Topic 7** | Lesson 7-9  **367**

## Analyze Student Work

**James's Work**

$3.7t = 22.2$

$t = 22.2 \div 3.7$

$$\begin{array}{r} 6. \\ 3.7 \overline{)22.2} \\ -22.2 \\ \hline 0 \end{array}$$

$t = 6$ times

James writes and solves an equation to solve the problem.

**Danny's Work**

$3.7t = 22.2$

Estimate $4t = 20$

$t = 5$

$$\begin{array}{r} \overset{3}{3.7} \\ \times\ 5 \\ \hline 18.5 \end{array} \qquad \begin{array}{r} \overset{4}{3.7} \\ \times\ 6 \\ \hline 22.2 \end{array}$$

The family hiked the trail 6 times.

Danny solves the problem using estimation and multiplication.

# DEVELOP: VISUAL LEARNING

The *Visual Learning Bridge* connects students' thinking in Solve & Share to important math ideas in the lesson. Use the *Visual Learning Bridge* to make these ideas explicit. Also available as a *Visual Learning Animation Plus* at PearsonRealize.com

Visual Learning

PEARSON realize. PearsonRealize.com

Learn

Glossary

**MP.7 Use Structure**
*Why is the cost of each orange m, multiplied by 13?* [Because Molly bought all 13 oranges in the box]

*Why do you want to get the variable alone on one side of the equation?* [Sample answers: I know the solution will be in the form $m = ?$; In the solution, the variable is by itself on one side of the equal sign.] *What operation does 13m represent?* [Multiplication] *When you divide 7.15 by 13, do you have to change the divisor to a whole number?* [No; the divisor is already a whole number.]

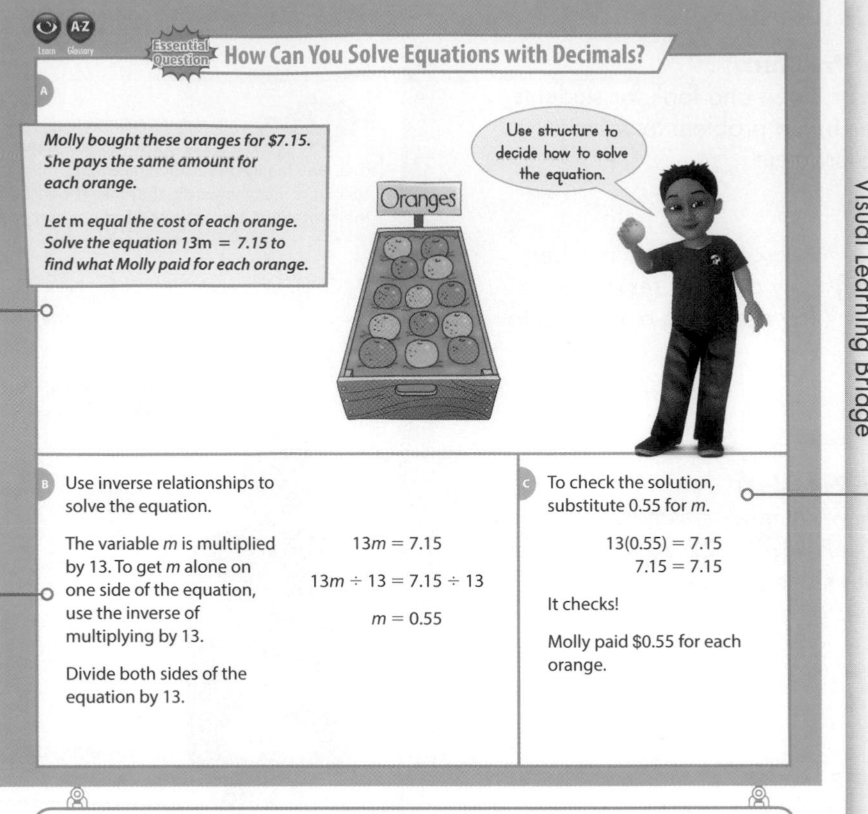

Essential Question How Can You Solve Equations with Decimals?
Molly bought these oranges for $7.15. She pays the same amount for each orange.
Let m equal the cost of each orange. Solve the equation 13m = 7.15 to find what Molly paid for each orange.
Use structure to decide how to solve the equation.
Oranges
Use inverse relationships to solve the equation.
The variable m is multiplied by 13. To get m alone on one side of the equation, use the inverse of multiplying by 13.
Divide both sides of the equation by 13.
13m = 7.15
13m ÷ 13 = 7.15 ÷ 13
m = 0.55
To check the solution, substitute 0.55 for m.
13(0.55) = 7.15
7.15 = 7.15
It checks!
Molly paid $0.55 for each orange.
Visual Learning Bridge


*What does it mean for an equation to be true?* [The expressions on both sides of the equation are equal to each other.]

**Convince Me!** **MP.4 Model with Math** Molly also buys a bag of 8 apples for $3.60. Write and solve an equation to find how much Molly paid for each apple.
**Sample answer: Let $a$ = the cost of each apple.**

$$8a = 3.60$$
$$8a \div 8 = 3.60 \div 8$$
$$a = 0.45$$

**Molly paid $0.45 for each apple.**

368 Topic 7 | Lesson 7-9 © Pearson Education, Inc. 6

**Convince Me! MP.4 Model with Math** *How can you use numbers and symbols to represent this situation?* [Sample answer: $3.60 \div 8 = a$, $a$ = *price of an apple*]

**Coherence** In the orange problem, students use inverse relationships and the properties of equality to solve a one-step multiplication equation involving decimals. Students already solved multiplication and division equations involving whole numbers and fractions in Topic 2. Now, they apply their understanding of decimal computations from Topic 7 to solve equations that include decimal numbers.

Revisit the Essential Question. Students can solve equations with decimals using the order of operations and the properties of equality.

## ☑ QUICK CHECK

Check mark indicates items for prescribing differentiation on the next page. Item 10 is worth 1 point. Items 14 and 16 are worth up to 2 points.

20–30 min

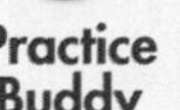


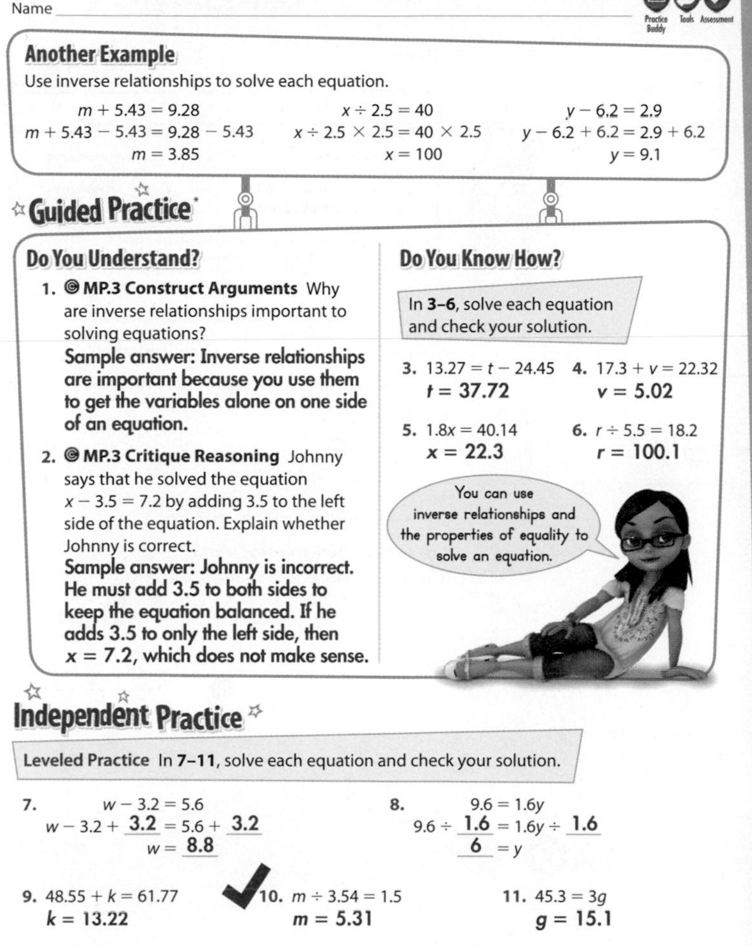

Name ____________

**Another Example**

Use inverse relationships to solve each equation.

| | | |
|---|---|---|
| $m + 5.43 = 9.28$ | $x \div 2.5 = 40$ | $y - 6.2 = 2.9$ |
| $m + 5.43 - 5.43 = 9.28 - 5.43$ | $x \div 2.5 \times 2.5 = 40 \times 2.5$ | $y - 6.2 + 6.2 = 2.9 + 6.2$ |
| $m = 3.85$ | $x = 100$ | $y = 9.1$ |

**Guided Practice***

**Do You Understand?**

1. **MP.3 Construct Arguments** Why are inverse relationships important to solving equations?
**Sample answer: Inverse relationships are important because you use them to get the variables alone on one side of an equation.**

2. **MP.3 Critique Reasoning** Johnny says that he solved the equation $x - 3.5 = 7.2$ by adding 3.5 to the left side of the equation. Explain whether Johnny is correct.
**Sample answer: Johnny is incorrect. He must add 3.5 to both sides to keep the equation balanced. If he adds 3.5 to only the left side, then $x = 7.2$, which does not make sense.**

**Do You Know How?**

In **3–6**, solve each equation and check your solution.

3. $13.27 = t - 24.45$
**$t = 37.72$**

4. $17.3 + v = 22.32$
**$v = 5.02$**

5. $1.8x = 40.14$
**$x = 22.3$**

6. $r \div 5.5 = 18.2$
**$r = 100.1$**

You can use inverse relationships and the properties of equality to solve an equation.

**Independent Practice**

Leveled Practice In **7–11**, solve each equation and check your solution.

7. $w - 3.2 = 5.6$
$w - 3.2 + \underline{3.2} = 5.6 + \underline{3.2}$
$w = \underline{8.8}$

8. $9.6 = 1.6y$
$9.6 \div \underline{1.6} = 1.6y \div \underline{1.6}$
$\underline{6} = y$

9. $48.55 + k = 61.77$
**$k = 13.22$**

✔ 10. $m \div 3.54 = 1.5$
**$m = 5.31$**

11. $45.3 = 3g$
**$g = 15.1$**

*For another example, see Set D on page 382.

Topic 7 | Lesson 7-9 369

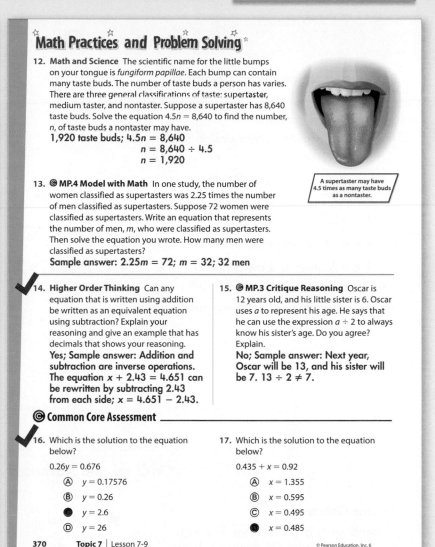

## Math Practices and Problem Solving

12. **Math and Science** The scientific name for the little bumps on your tongue is *fungiform papillae*. Each bump can contain many taste buds. The number of taste buds a person has varies. There are three general classifications of taste: supertaster, medium taster, and nontaster. Suppose a supertaster has 8,640 taste buds. Solve the equation $4.5n = 8,640$ to find the number, $n$, of taste buds a nontaster may have.
**1,920 taste buds; $4.5n = 8,640$**
**$n = 8,640 \div 4.5$**
**$n = 1,920$**

A supertaster may have 4.5 times as many taste buds as a nontaster.

13. **MP.4 Model with Math** In one study, the number of women classified as supertasters was 2.25 times the number of men classified as supertasters. Suppose 72 women were classified as supertasters. Write an equation that represents the number of men, $m$, who were classified as supertasters. Then solve the equation you wrote. How many men were classified as supertasters?
**Sample answer: $2.25m = 72$; $m = 32$; 32 men**

✔ 14. **Higher Order Thinking** Can any equation that is written using addition be written as an equivalent equation using subtraction? Explain your reasoning and give an example that has decimals that shows your reasoning.
**Yes; Sample answer: Addition and subtraction are inverse operations. The equation $x + 2.43 = 4.651$ can be rewritten by subtracting 2.43 from each side; $x = 4.651 - 2.43$.**

15. **MP.3 Critique Reasoning** Oscar is 12 years old, and his little sister is 6. Oscar uses $a$ to represent his age. He says that he can use the expression $a \div 2$ to always know his sister's age. Do you agree? Explain.
**No; Sample answer: Next year, Oscar will be 13, and his sister will be 7. $13 \div 2 \neq 7$.**

**Common Core Assessment**

✔ 16. Which is the solution to the equation below?
$0.26y = 0.676$
Ⓐ $y = 0.17576$
Ⓑ $y = 0.26$
● $y = 2.6$
Ⓓ $y = 26$

17. Which is the solution to the equation below?
$0.435 + x = 0.92$
Ⓐ $x = 1.355$
Ⓑ $x = 0.595$
Ⓒ $x = 0.495$
● $x = 0.485$

370 Topic 7 | Lesson 7-9



**Another Example** Students solve addition, subtraction, and division equations with decimals using inverse relationships and the properties of equality.

**Error Intervention: Item 2 MP.3 Critique Reasoning**

**If** students have difficulty deciding whether Johnny is correct,

**then** say: *Is addition the correct operation to use in this problem? Explain.* [Yes; it has an inverse relationship with subtraction.] *Did Johnny use the properties of equality correctly? Explain.* [No; he did not apply the Property of Addition to both sides of the equation to keep it balanced.]

**Items 7–11** Students can check their work by substituting their solution for the variable in the original equation. Use Item 7 as an example. *How can you check the solution $w = 8.8$?* [Test whether $8.8 - 3.2 = 5.6$ is a true statement.]

**Reteaching** Assign Reteaching Set D on p. 382.

**Item 13 MP.4 Model with Math** *How do you use the quantities in the problem to write an algebraic expression that represents the number of women classified as supertasters?* [$2.25m$] *What numerical expression also represents the number of women classified as supertasters?* [72]

**Items 16–17 Coherence** Extend what students already know about using inverse relationships and properties of equality to solve equations that involve decimals. *What operation is used in $0.26y = 0.676$?* [Multiplication] *What operation has an inverse relationship with multiplication?* [Division] *How do you solve the equation $0.26y = 0.676$?* [Divide both sides of the equation by 0.26] *How can you check your solution?* [Substitute the solution for $y$ into the original equation to see if it makes the equation true, $0.26 \times 2.6 = 0.676$.]

**Multi-Step Problems** *Page 370 Items 13 and 14; Page 372 Items 15, 16, and 18*

# ASSESS AND DIFFERENTIATE

Use the **QUICK CHECK** on the previous page to prescribe differentiated instruction.

**I Intervention** 0–3 points on the Quick Check

**O On-Level** 4 points on the Quick Check

**A Advanced** 5 points on the Quick Check

## Intervention Activity 

### Solving Equations with Decimals

**Materials**

Strips of paper, container

- Write the following equations on small strips of paper.

| | |
|---|---|
| $7b = 21$ | $g \div 9 = 4$ |
| $y \div 6 = 70$ | $w \times 10 = 99$ |
| $p(12) = 27$ | $\frac{u}{14} = 16.4$ |

- Place the strips of paper in a container.
- Ask a volunteer to draw a strip of paper and write the equation on the board.
- Identify how to isolate the variable.

$\frac{7b}{7} = \frac{21}{7}$ divide by 7

$y \div 6 = 70$

$6[y \div 6] = 6[70]$ multiply by 6

## Reteach 

Name ______________________ Reteach to Build Understanding 7-9

**Vocabulary**

1. **Inverse relationships** are used to solve equations. For example, to solve $2x = 6$ the variable $x$ is isolated by undoing multiplication by 2 with the inverse operation, which is division by 2. So $x = 3$.

Which operation has an inverse relationship to the operation in the equation and can be used to isolate the variable?

$y + 4.12 = 12.42$ **subtraction** $x \times 2.4 = 7.2$ **division**

$z \div 9 = 4.1$ **multiplication** $a - 2.3 = 5.4$ **addition**

2. At the beginning of football practice, one of the water coolers contained 5.2 liters of water. Some water was added to the cooler until it contained 22.1 liters of water. How many times as many liters are there after water is added compared to the beginning amount?

Solve the equation $5.2x = 22.1$ to find out how many times greater the new amount of water is.

In the equation $5.2x = 22.1$, the operation of **multiplication** is used.

3. The inverse operation that can be used to get $x$ alone is **division**.

4. Solve the equation.

$5.2x = 22.1$

$5.2x \div$ **5.2** $= 22.1 \div 5.2$

**x** $=$ **4.25**

5. So, there was **4.25** times as many liters of water.

**On the Back! Check students' work.**

6. Solve the equation $p \div 8.2 = 9.3$ and check your solution.

$p \div 8.2 \times 8.2 = 9.3 \times 8.2$ $76.26 \div 8.2 = 9.3$

$p = 76.26$ $9.3 = 9.3$

R 7-9



## On-Level and Advanced Activity Centers 

### Center Games

Students work in pairs or small groups to solve equations with decimals. Have students discuss the property of equality they should use to solve each equation as they play the game.

★ On-Level

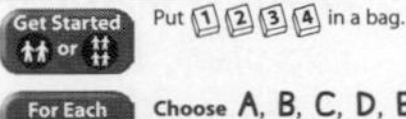

Get Started: Put 1 2 3 4 in a bag.

For Each Round: Choose A, B, C, D, E, or F. **Pick** a tile. Pick two tiles if your group has only two students. **Explain** how to solve the equation next to your tile number when it is your turn. **Discuss:** Which equations have the same solution?

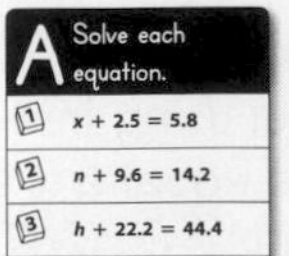

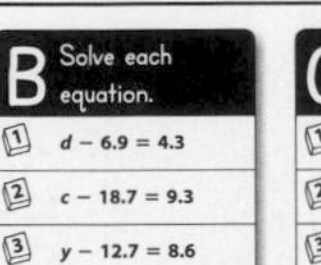

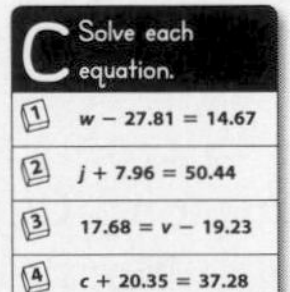

**A** Solve each equation.
1. $x + 2.5 = 5.8$
2. $n + 9.6 = 14.2$
3. $h + 22.2 = 44.4$
4. $z + 11.7 = 16.3$

**B** Solve each equation.
1. $d - 6.9 = 4.3$
2. $c - 18.7 = 9.3$
3. $y - 12.7 = 8.6$
4. $q - 4.3 = 23.7$

**C** Solve each equation.
1. $w - 27.81 = 14.67$
2. $j + 7.96 = 50.44$
3. $17.68 = v - 19.23$
4. $c + 20.35 = 37.28$

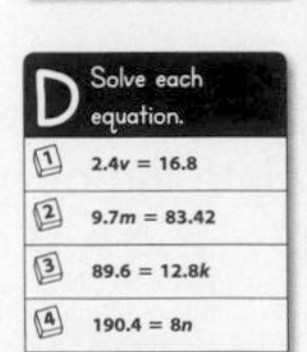

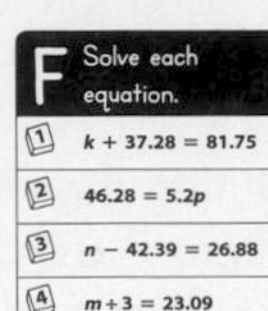

**D** Solve each equation.
1. $2.4v = 16.8$
2. $9.7m = 83.42$
3. $89.6 = 12.8k$
4. $190.4 = 8n$

**E** Solve each equation.
1. $x \div 3.5 = 2.2$
2. $v \div 9.6 = 1.5$
3. $g \div 13.8 = 1.2$
4. $h \div 6 = 2.4$

**F** Solve each equation.
1. $k + 37.28 = 81.75$
2. $46.28 = 5.2p$
3. $n - 42.39 = 26.88$
4. $m \div 3 = 23.09$

If you have more time: Make up three equations that have the same solution.

Center Game ★ 7-9



★★ Advanced

Get Started: Put 1 2 3 4 in a bag.

For Each Round: Choose A, B, C, or D. **Pick** a tile. Pick two tiles if your group has only two students. **Follow** the directions next to your tile number when it is your turn.

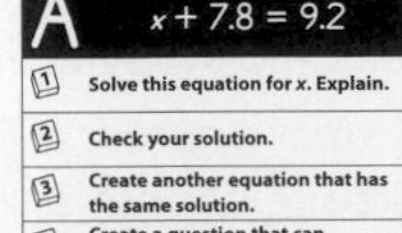

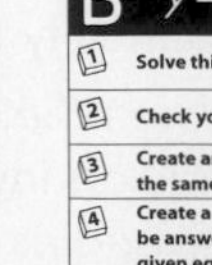

**A** $x + 7.8 = 9.2$
1. Solve this equation for $x$. Explain.
2. Check your solution.
3. Create another equation that has the same solution.
4. Create a question that can be answered by solving the given equation.

**B** $y - 12.74 = 6.29$
1. Solve this equation for $y$. Explain.
2. Check your solution.
3. Create another equation that has the same solution.
4. Create a question that can be answered by solving the given equation.

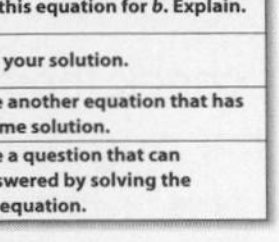

**C** $25.74 = 4.29b$
1. Solve this equation for $b$. Explain.
2. Check your solution.
3. Create another equation that has the same solution.
4. Create a question that can be answered by solving the given equation.

**D** $z \div 22.6 = 7.9$
1. Solve this equation for $z$. Explain.
2. Check your solution.
3. Create another equation that has the same solution.
4. Create a question that can be answered by solving the given equation.

If you have more time: Make up another equation. Complete steps 1–4 for your equation.

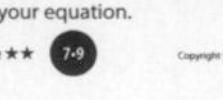

Center Game ★★ 7-9

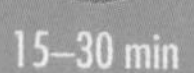

**TIMING**

The time allocated to Step 3 will depend on the teacher's instructional decisions and differentiation routines.

15–30 min

PEARSON realize. PearsonRealize.com

 Help  Practice Buddy  Tools Games

## Technology Center   

Tools Games

### Math Tools and Math Games

A link to a specific math tools activity or math game to use with this lesson is provided at PearsonRealize.com.

## Leveled Assignment  Items 1–10, 15–17, 20, 21  Items 3–15, 18–21  Items 7–21

Name ____________

Help Practice Buddy Tools Games

### Homework & Practice 7-9
Solve Equations with Decimals

**Another Look!**

Equations can be solved by using inverse relationships and the properties of equality to get a variable alone on one side of the equation.

Remember that you need to do the same thing to both sides of the equation to keep the equation equal.


Solve the equation $5.2 + c = 13.6$.

To get $c$ alone, undo adding 5.2 by subtracting 5.2 from both sides.

$$5.2 + c = 13.6$$
$$5.2 + c - \mathbf{5.2} = 13.6 - \mathbf{5.2}$$
$$c = 8.4$$

Check your solution by substituting 8.4 for $c$ in the equation.

$$5.2 + c = 13.6$$
$$5.2 + 8.4 = 13.6$$
$$13.6 = 13.6 \text{ It checks.}$$

Solve the equation $t \div 2.5 = 11.7$.

To get $t$ alone, undo dividing by 2.5 by multiplying by 2.5 on both sides.

$$t \div 2.5 = 11.7$$
$$t \div 2.5 \times \mathbf{2.5} = 11.7 \times \mathbf{2.5}$$
$$t = 29.25$$

Check your solution by substituting 29.25 for $t$ in the equation.

$$t \div 2.5 = 11.7$$
$$29.25 \div 2.5 = 11.7$$
$$11.7 = 11.7 \text{ It checks.}$$

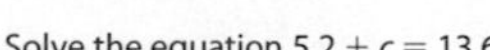

In **1–14**, solve each equation and check your solution.

1. $t \div 5.4 = 9.01$
$t \div 5.4 \times \underline{5.4} = 9.01 \times \underline{5.4}$
$t = \underline{48.654}$

2. $43.9 = m + 8.84$
$43.9 - \underline{8.84} = m + 8.84 - \underline{8.84}$
$m = \underline{35.06}$

3. $w \div 1.9 = 9$ **$w = 17.1$**

4. $10.4 = 0.2t$ **$t = 52$**

5. $51 = b \div 3.25$ **$b = 165.75$**

6. $\frac{v}{2.6} = 88.9$ **$v = 231.14$**

7. $x \div 3.25 = 5.6$ **$x = 18.2$**

8. $2.7k = 54.0$ **$k = 20$**

9. $5.89 + j = 9.34$ **$j = 3.45$**

10. $m - 7.62 = 9.5$ **$m = 17.12$**

11. $k + 24.75 = 36.12$ **$k = 11.37$**

12. $x \div 45.2 = 2.3$ **$x = 103.96$**

13. $12.85 = x - 4.34$ **$x = 17.19$**

14. $15.95 = 3.19n$ **$n = 5$**



15. In a 400-meter relay race, 4 runners pass a baton, each running 100 meters of the race. The table shows the split times for the first 3 runners of a relay team. Suppose the team has set a goal of running the race in 210 seconds. Solve the equation $(53.715 + 51.3 + 52.62) + n = 210$ to find the number of seconds, $n$, the 4th runner must run to meet their goal.

DATA

| 400 Meter Relay Team Split Times (seconds) | |
|---|---|
| 1st runner | 53.715 |
| 2nd runner | 51.3 |
| 3rd runner | 52.62 |
| 4th runner | $n$ |

**52.365 s; $(53.715 + 51.3 + 52.62) + n = 210$**
**$157.635 + n = 210$**
**$n = 210 - 157.635$**
**$n = 52.365$**

16. **Number Sense** Suppose the team in Exercise 15 meets their goal and runs the race in 210 seconds. Write 210 seconds as a decimal in minutes. Then write 210 seconds as minutes and seconds.
**3.5 min; 3 min 30 s**

17. **MP.4 Model with Math** The winning team in a 400 meter relay race had a time of 198.608 seconds. Suppose all 4 of the split times were the same. Write an equation to find the split times. Then solve the equation you wrote. What was the split time for each runner?
**Sample answer: $4t = 198.608$; $t = 49.652$; 49.652 s**

18. **Higher Order Thinking** Can any equation that is written using multiplication be written as an equivalent equation using division? Explain your reasoning and give an example that has decimals that shows your reasoning.
**Yes; Sample answer: Multiplication and division are inverse operations. The equation $2.34 \cdot x = 8.252$ can be rewritten by dividing each side by 2.34; $x = 8.252 \div 2.34$.**

19. **MP.7 Use Structure** Teresa placed parentheses in the expression below so that its value was greater than 80. Write the expression to show where Teresa placed the parentheses.
$10.5 + 9.5 \times 3 - 1 \times 2.5$
**$(10.5 + 9.5) \times (3 - 1) \times 2.5$**

**Common Core Assessment**

20. Which is the solution to the equation below?
$y \div 2.5 = 1.95$
Ⓐ $y = 0.78$
● $y = 4.875$
Ⓒ $y = 48.75$
Ⓓ $y = 4{,}875$

21. Which is the solution to the equation below?
$x - 4.21 = 6.047$
Ⓐ $x = 10.68$
● $x = 10.257$
Ⓒ $x = 10.247$
Ⓓ $x = 1.837$

MATH PRACTICES AND PROBLEM SOLVING | LESSON **7-10**

# USE APPROPRIATE TOOLS

## DIGITAL RESOURCES PearsonRealize.com

 Student and Teacher eTexts — **eText**

 Listen and Look For Lesson Video — **PD**

 Today's Challenge — **Think**

 Solve and Share — **Solve**

 Visual Learning Animation Plus — **Learn**

 Animated Glossary — **Glossary**

 Online Personalized Practice — **Practice Buddy**

 Math Tools — **Tools**

 Quick Check — **Assessment**

 Another Look Homework Video — **Help**

 Math Games — **Games**

 Math Practices Animations — **MP**

## LESSON OVERVIEW

FCR FOCUS • COHERENCE • RIGOR

### FOCUS

**Mathematical Practices MP.5** Use appropriate tools strategically. Also **MP.4, MP.7, MP.8**

**Domain 6.NS** The Number System

**Cluster 6.NS.B** Compute fluently with multi-digit numbers and find common factors and multiples.

**Content Standard 6.NS.B.3** Fluently add, subtract, multiply, and divide multi-digit decimals using the standard algorithm for each operation. Also **6.NS.B.2**.

**Objective** Use appropriate tools strategically to solve problems involving decimals.

**Essential Understanding** Good math thinkers know how to pick the right tools to solve math problems.

**Materials** Calculators (optional), Computer with Internet access (optional)

### COHERENCE

Students engage MP.5, Use Appropriate Tools Strategically, throughout grades K–6. This lesson provides an opportunity to focus on the thinking habits good problem solvers use in order to choose and use appropriate tools strategically. In this lesson, students use technology to find accurate and precise information to help them to solve problems involving computations with decimals.

### RIGOR

This lesson emphasizes **fluency** and **application**. Mathematically proficient students select and engage multiple mathematical practices as they solve mathematical and real-world problems. Any mathematical practices engaged in the work on this lesson should be made explicit. However, the classroom conversation should focus on the meaning and use of the thinking habits shown on the Solve & Share task for MP.5.

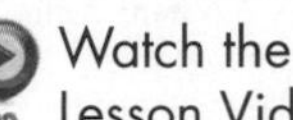 Watch the Listen and Look For Lesson Video.

## MATH ANYTIME

### Daily Common Core Review

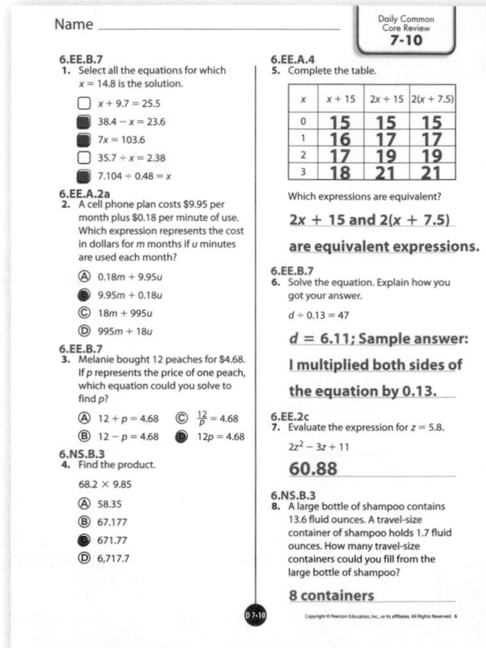

Name ______

Daily Common Core Review 7-10

6.EE.B.7
1. Select all the equations for which $x = 14.8$ is the solution.
- [ ] $x + 9.7 = 25.5$
- [x] $38.4 - x = 23.6$
- [x] $7x = 103.6$
- [ ] $35.7 \div x = 2.38$
- [x] $7.104 \div 0.48 = x$

6.EE.A.2a
2. A cell phone plan costs $9.95 per month plus $0.18 per minute of use. Which expression represents the cost in dollars for *m* months if *u* minutes are used each month?
- Ⓐ $0.18m + 9.95u$
- ● $9.95m + 0.18u$
- Ⓒ $18m + 995u$
- Ⓓ $995m + 18u$

6.EE.B.7
3. Melanie bought 12 peaches for $4.68. If *p* represents the price of one peach, which equation could you solve to find *p*?
- Ⓐ $12 + p = 4.68$
- Ⓑ $12 - p = 4.68$
- Ⓒ $\frac{12}{p} = 4.68$
- ● $12p = 4.68$

6.NS.B.3
4. Find the product.

$68.2 \times 9.85$
- Ⓐ 58.35
- Ⓑ 67.177
- ● 671.77
- Ⓓ 6,717.7

6.EE.A.4
5. Complete the table.

| $x$ | $x + 15$ | $2x + 15$ | $2(x + 7.5)$ |
|---|---|---|---|
| 0 | 15 | 15 | 15 |
| 1 | 16 | 17 | 17 |
| 2 | 17 | 19 | 19 |
| 3 | 18 | 21 | 21 |

Which expressions are equivalent?

**$2x + 15$ and $2(x + 7.5)$ are equivalent expressions.**

6.EE.B.7
6. Solve the equation. Explain how you got your answer.

$d \div 0.13 = 47$

**$d = 6.11$; Sample answer: I multiplied both sides of the equation by 0.13.**

6.EE.2c
7. Evaluate the expression for $z = 5.8$.

$2z^2 - 3z + 11$

**60.88**

6.NS.B.3
8. A large bottle of shampoo contains 13.6 fluid ounces. A travel-size container of shampoo holds 1.7 fluid ounces. How many travel-size containers could you fill from the large bottle of shampoo?

**8 containers**

D 7-10

### Today's Challenge

Think Use the Topic 7 problems any time during this topic.

## ENGLISH LANGUAGE LEARNERS 

**Reading** Expand comprehension by predicting.

*Use with the Visual Learning Bridge on Student's Edition p. 374.*

Read Box A. Ask students to predict what missing information is needed to solve the problem. Write predictions as students state them. Read the list. As each prediction is read, ask students to decide if it is or is not reasonable.

**Beginning** *What information is missing?* Read Bullet 1. *Where is this information found?* Read Bullet 2. *Use the Internet to find the width of a quarter.* Write *1.75*. *The width of a quarter is 1.75 millimeters.* Ask students to predict if James has more or fewer than 2,000 quarters.

**Intermediate** Read Box B with students. *What information do you need to find using the Internet?* Write *1.75*. Ask students to work with partners to write the equation used to solve the problem. Instruct students to predict if James has more than or fewer than 2,000 quarters.

**Advanced** Instruct students to read Box B with partners and then use the Internet to find the width of a quarter. Ask students to write an equation, predict about how many quarters James has by rounding, and then solve the equation. Instruct students to share with partners how predicting by rounding helped solve the problem.

**Summarize** What tool was used to help solve the problem? Why was it an effective tool?

# DEVELOP: PROBLEM-BASED LEARNING

**COHERENCE: Engage learners by connecting prior knowledge to new ideas.**
Students continue to develop fluency with addition and subtraction of decimals and choose an appropriate tool, such as pencil and paper or a calculator, to complete a magic square.

10–15 min

Solve

## BEFORE

**1. Pose the Solve-and-Share Problem**
You may wish to provide students with calculators to use.

**MP.5 Use Appropriate Tools Strategically** Listen and look for students who choose an appropriate tool and use it strategically to complete the magic square.

**2. Build Understanding**
*What is the magic number for this magic square?* [21] *What do you need to do to solve this problem?* [Fill in each square so that the numbers in each row, column, and diagonal add to 21.]

## DURING

**3. Ask Guiding Questions As Needed**
*Which tools could you use to help you solve this problem?* [Sample answer: a calculator and paper and pencil] *Which tool will you choose to help you solve this problem? Why?* [Sample answer: A calculator so that I can calculate the sums efficiently and accurately.] *Which square can you fill in first?* [Sample answer: The top, center square is 4 because $10 + 7 = 17$ and $17 + 4 = 21$.]

## AFTER

**4. Share and Discuss Solutions**
Solve Start with students' solutions. If needed, project Eliza's work to discuss how to solve the magic square.

**5. Transition to the Visual Learning Bridge**
*It is important for good math thinkers to choose appropriate tools, like calculators, protractors, or the Internet, and to use them properly to solve problems.*

**6. Extension for Early Finishers**
*Choose a magic number. Make a magic square that uses at least two decimal addends.* [Check students' work.]

---

Name ______________________ Solve

**Solve & Share**

You are going to play a math game called Magic Squares. You will solve a magic square by finding the missing values so that each row, column, and diagonal has the same sum, known as the magic number. Find the missing numbers using the most efficient and accurate way to solve.

Choose an appropriate tool to help you solve this problem.

**Math Practices and Problem Solving**

**Lesson 7-10**
**Use Appropriate Tools**

**I can ...**
choose an appropriate tool and use it strategically to solve a problem.

**Mathematical Practices** MP.5, MP.4, MP.7, MP.8
**Content Standards** 6.NS.B.2, 6.NS.B.3

Magic Number: 21

| | | |
|---|---|---|
| | | |
| | 7 | |
| | 10 | 4.75 |

**Thinking Habits**
*Be a good thinker! These questions can help you.*
- Which tools can I use?
- Why should I use this tool to help me solve the problem?
- Is there a different tool I could use?
- Am I using the tool appropriately?

**See margin for sample student work.**

**Look Back!** MP.5 Use Appropriate Tools Suppose the values in each square of the magic square were fractions and the magic number was a mixed number. Would the tool you used to find the decimal values be appropriate to find the fraction values? Explain why or why not.

**Sample answer: No; I used a calculator to find the decimal values for the magic squares. If I had to find fraction values, I would choose fraction strips to help me find the magic number.**

Digital Resources at PearsonRealize.com **Topic 7** | Lesson 7-10 373

---

### Analyze Student Work

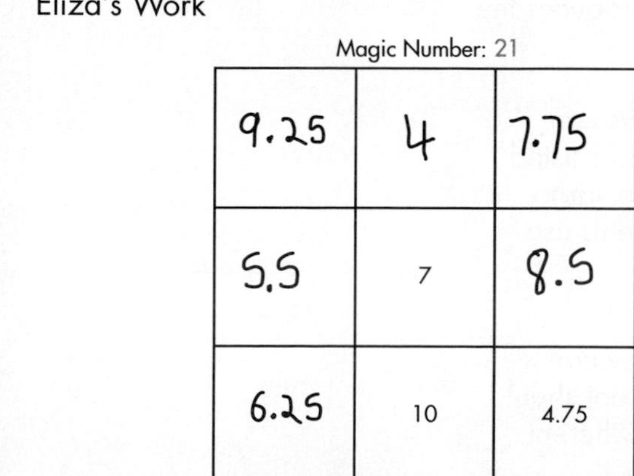

Eliza's Work

Magic Number: 21

| | | |
|---|---|---|
| 9.25 | 4 | 7.75 |
| 5.5 | 7 | 8.5 |
| 6.25 | 10 | 4.75 |

Eliza uses a calculator and records the addends in the appropriate squares.

Juan's Work

Magic Number: 21

| | | |
|---|---|---|
| 9.25 | 4 | 7.75 |
| 5.5 | 7 | 8.5 |
| 6.25 | 10 | 4.75 |

21 − 17 = 4
4.75 + 7 = 11.75
21.00 − 11.75 = 9.25
21.00 − 13.25 = 7.75
7.75 + 4.75 = 12.50
21.00 − 12.50 = 8.50
21.00 − 15.50 = 5.50
21.00 − 14.75 = 6.25

Juan uses paper and pencil to find each sum and solve the magic square.

# DEVELOP: VISUAL LEARNING

The *Visual Learning Bridge* connects students' thinking in Solve & Share to important math ideas in the lesson. Use the *Visual Learning Bridge* to make these ideas explicit. Also available as a *Visual Learning Animation Plus* at PearsonRealize.com

PEARSON realize. PearsonRealize.com

*What unit of measurement is used to measure the total width of all of the rolls?* [Meters] *Does the picture accurately depict the problem? Why or why not?* [No; it would take a lot more rolls of quarters to measure about 2 meters.] *How can you use this information to find the number of quarters James has?* [You can divide the total width by the width, or thickness, of one quarter to find the total number of quarters.]

**MP.5 Use Appropriate Tools Strategically**
*Which tools would be appropriate to use to solve this problem?* [The Internet or a precision measuring tool] *How do you know whether the Internet was used correctly to help solve this problem?* [Sample answer: Use a reputable web page, like the United States Mint website.]

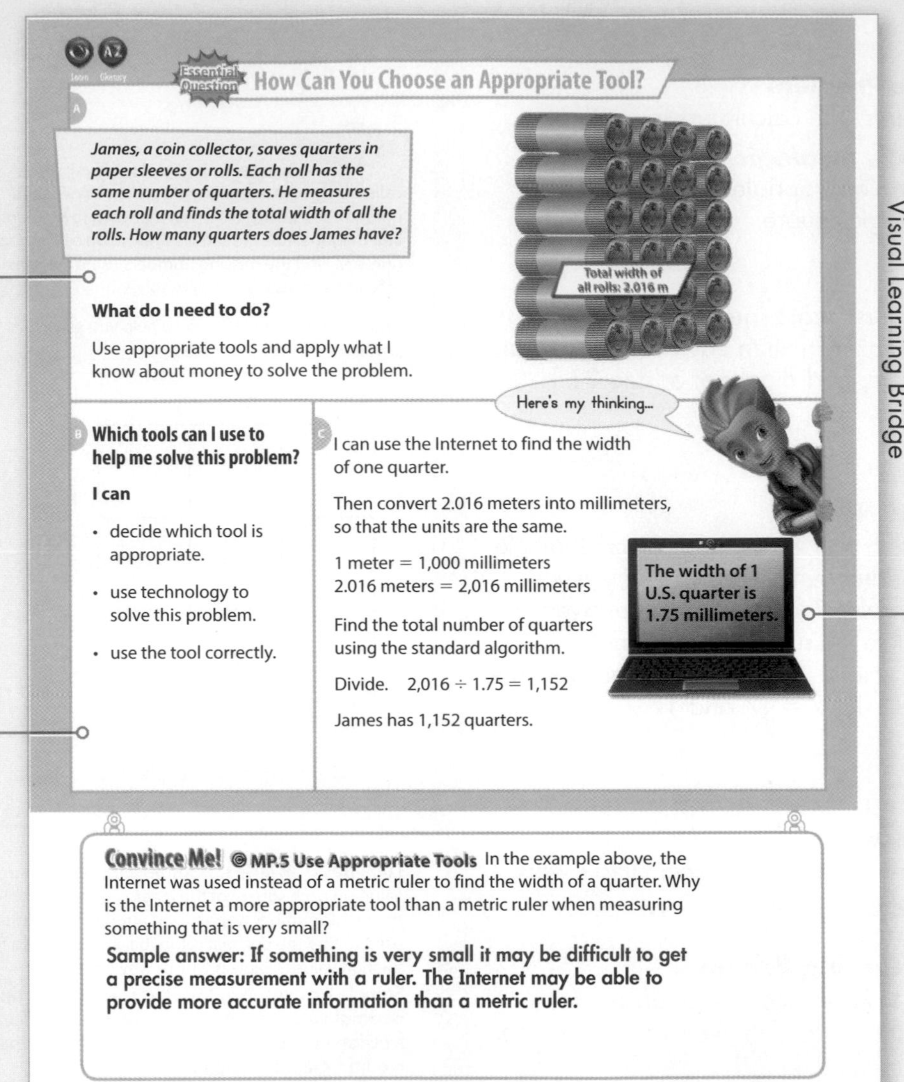

Essential Question **How Can You Choose an Appropriate Tool?**

A

*James, a coin collector, saves quarters in paper sleeves or rolls. Each roll has the same number of quarters. He measures each roll and finds the total width of all the rolls. How many quarters does James have?*



**What do I need to do?**

Use appropriate tools and apply what I know about money to solve the problem.

B

**Which tools can I use to help me solve this problem?**

**I can**

- decide which tool is appropriate.
- use technology to solve this problem.
- use the tool correctly.

C



I can use the Internet to find the width of one quarter.

Then convert 2.016 meters into millimeters, so that the units are the same.

1 meter = 1,000 millimeters
2.016 meters = 2,016 millimeters



Find the total number of quarters using the standard algorithm.

Divide. $2{,}016 \div 1.75 = 1{,}152$

James has 1,152 quarters.

Visual Learning Bridge

**Convince Me!** **MP.5 Use Appropriate Tools** In the example above, the Internet was used instead of a metric ruler to find the width of a quarter. Why is the Internet a more appropriate tool than a metric ruler when measuring something that is very small?
**Sample answer: If something is very small it may be difficult to get a precise measurement with a ruler. The Internet may be able to provide more accurate information than a metric ruler.**

374 Topic 7 | Lesson 7-10 © Pearson Education, Inc. 6

*How does the Internet help you solve this problem?* [You can find an accurate measure for the width of a quarter.] *Why do you need to convert 2.016 meters to millimeters?* [Because the width, or thickness, of a quarter is given in millimeters and you have to divide like units to solve this problem.]

**Convince Me!** **MP.5 Use Appropriate Tools Strategically** Students should recognize that a typical ruler is not precise enough to measure the width of a quarter and that there is also possible human error introduced when a quarter is measured. Explain that only the U.S. Mint produces the quarters, and does so to exact specifications.

**Coherence** Focus the classroom conversation on how students can use appropriate tools strategically, by emphasizing the behaviors listed in Box B of the Visual Learning Bridge. These behaviors are similar to those emphasized in other grades; however, in Grade 6, students use technology such as calculators and the Internet.

Revisit the Essential Question. Students learn that they can choose a tool to provide accurate information. The tool should enable students to be precise when used correctly. Different tools are appropriate for different types of problems.

## QUICK CHECK

Check mark indicates items for prescribing differentiation on the next page. Items 3 and 5 are worth 1 point. Items 6–7 are worth up to 3 points.

PEARSON realize
PearsonRealize.com

Name

## Guided Practice*

**MP.5 Use Appropriate Tools**

May made a pan of lasagna. She evenly spread 2.45 pounds of cheese in the pan for the recipe. If May cuts the lasagna into 10 equal pieces, how many ounces of cheese are there in each piece of lasagna?

1 lb = 16 oz

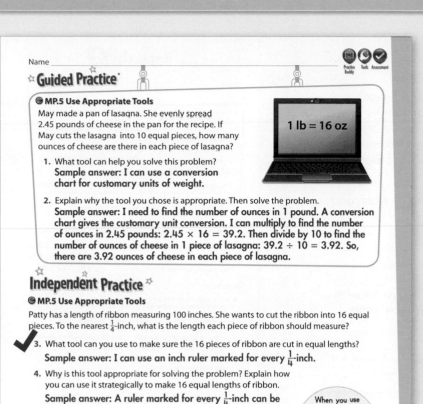

1. What tool can help you solve this problem?
   **Sample answer: I can use a conversion chart for customary units of weight.**
2. Explain why the tool you chose is appropriate. Then solve the problem.
   **Sample answer: I need to find the number of ounces in 1 pound. A conversion chart gives the customary unit conversion. I can multiply to find the number of ounces in 2.45 pounds: $2.45 \times 16 = 39.2$. Then divide by 10 to find the number of ounces of cheese in 1 piece of lasagna: $39.2 \div 10 = 3.92$. So, there are 3.92 ounces of cheese in each piece of lasagna.**

## Independent Practice

**MP.5 Use Appropriate Tools**

Patty has a length of ribbon measuring 100 inches. She wants to cut the ribbon into 16 equal pieces. To the nearest $\frac{1}{4}$-inch, what is the length each piece of ribbon should measure?

3. What tool can you use to make sure the 16 pieces of ribbon are cut in equal lengths?
   **Sample answer: I can use an inch ruler marked for every $\frac{1}{4}$-inch.**
4. Why is this tool appropriate for solving the problem? Explain how you can use it strategically to make 16 equal lengths of ribbon.
   **Sample answer: A ruler marked for every $\frac{1}{4}$-inch can be used to find the precise measure in customary units; I can divide to find an exact length for each piece of ribbon: $100 \div 16 = 6.25$. The decimal 6.25 can be written as the mixed number $6\frac{1}{4}$. I can then use the ruler to measure and cut the ribbon into 16 pieces each measuring $6\frac{1}{4}$ inches.**
5. Can you use a different tool to solve this problem another way? Explain your reasoning.
   **Sample answer: Yes; I can use a sheet of paper that is 100 inches long to model the ribbon. Then I can fold the length of paper in half 4 times, marking it each time until the paper is folded into 16 equal sections. Finally, I can use a ruler to make sure each section measures $6\frac{1}{4}$ inches.**

When you use tools strategically, you are using them in ways that make sense and help you solve the problem correctly.

*For another example, see Set E on page 382.



## Math Practices and Problem Solving

**Common Core Performance Assessment**

**Swim Competition**

A swim team has six members: Jordan, Allison, Kylie, Oscar, Matt, and Luis. Each competed in two races at a swim meet. The fastest swimmer had the lowest combined time. Complete the chart to find the fastest swimmer on the team.

| Swimmer | First Race (seconds) | Second Race (seconds) | Combined Time (seconds) |
|---|---|---|---|
| Matt | 42.11 | 42.55 | **84.66** |
| Allison | 39.65 | 40.03 | **79.68** |
| Oscar | 43.03 | 42.94 | **85.97** |
| Kylie | 39.25 | 39.14 | **78.39** |
| Luis | 41.8 | 41.83 | **83.63** |
| Jordan | 40.82 | 40.29 | **81.11** |

- Jordan's combined time was 81.11 seconds.
- Allison finished four tenths of a second behind the fastest swimmer on the team in the first race.
- Kylie's time for the first race was 0.11 of a second slower than her time for the second race.
- Luis took 0.03 of a second longer to finish the second race than to finish the first race.
- It took Oscar about 43 seconds to complete the first race.

6. **MP.5 Use Appropriate Tools** Can the table help you solve the problem? Explain.
   **Yes; Sample answer: The table shows the numbers that are needed to solve each of the clues and match each swimmer with his or her times.**
7. **MP.7 Use Structure** How can you use place-value relationships to solve the clues and find the fastest swimmer on the team?
   **Sample answer: Each of the the clues involves adding or subtracting decimals to match a swimmer with his or her times. Once the table is completed, I can use place value to compare each of the combined times to the others and find the fastest swimmer. Kylie's combined time of 78.39 seconds makes her the fastest swimmer on the team.**

You use structure when you add or subtract decimals.





**MP.5 Use Appropriate Tools Strategically** Listen and look for these behaviors as evidence that students are exhibiting proficiency with MP.5.

- Identifies available tools
- Uses tools correctly and accurately
- Knows when to use a particular tool
- Considers options before selecting a particular tool
- Decides if the results obtained using a tool make sense
- Thinks about using tools to explore and solve problems, without prompting from the teacher

**Reteaching** Assign Reteaching Set E on p. 382.

**Items 1 and 2 MP.5 Use Appropriate Tools Strategically** If students have trouble explaining how to choose an appropriate tool, have them make a list of all possible tools and then decide whether each tool could be used effectively to help them solve the problem.

**Item 6 MP.5 Use Appropriate Tools Strategically** *What information will you record in the table?* [Each swimmer's name and their combined times from Race 1 and Race 2] *How can that information help you solve the problem?* [You can compare the combined times to find which swimmer is the fastest.]

**Item 7 MP.7 Use Structure** *How is adding and subtracting decimals different from multiplying decimals?* [You align decimals to add and subtract; you do not need to align decimals to multiply.] *How do you use place value to add and subtract decimals?* [When you align the decimal points, you align each digit by its place so that you are adding digits with the same place value.]

# ASSESS AND DIFFERENTIATE

Use the **QUICK CHECK** on the previous page to prescribe differentiated instruction.

**I Intervention**
0–3 points on the Quick Check

**O On-Level**
4 points on the Quick Check

**A Advanced**
5 points on the Quick Check

## Intervention Activity 

**Math Practices and Problem Solving: Use Appropriate Tools**

- Display the following on the board: Gina fills a 10-gallon water cooler with water to serve during a school field day. She wants to set it on a small table that has a weight capacity of 100 pounds. Should Gina use the table for the water cooler? Explain your recommendation.
- Have students make a plan, including choosing an appropriate tool, to solve this problem. *What information do you need to know to solve this problem?* [The weight of 10 gallons of water and the weight of the water cooler] *What tools can you use to help you solve this problem?* [You can use the Internet to find out how much 1 gallon of water weighs and how much a typical 10-gallon water cooler weighs.] *How can you make sure that you are using the tool correctly?* [You can make sure that you are using websites that you know are reliable.]
- Have students solve the problem and share their solutions.

I used the Internet to find:
A 10-gallon water cooler weighs 2.2 pounds.
A gallon of water weighs 8.34 pounds.

8.34 x 10 = 83.4 pounds
83.4 + 2.2 = 85.6 pounds

Gina can use the table because it should hold the weight of cooler full of water.

## Reteach 

Name ______________________

Reteach to Build Understanding
**7-10**

**Vocabulary**

1. Some of the **tools** used to solve math problems include computers, calculators, rulers, and conversion charts.

   Identify a tool that could be used in each situation. **Sample answers given.**

   Multiplying greater numbers: **calculator**

   Finding the number of inches in a mile: **conversion chart**

   Calculating the area of a textbook: **ruler to measure length and width and calculator to multiply**

   Finding the height of the Washington Monument: **computer (Internet)**

2. Hanna made 7 quarts of picante sauce. She put the picante sauce in 3.5-ounce jars. What tool can Hanna use to find the number of ounces of sauce that she made?

   **Sample answer: A conversion chart for liquid measures**

3. Use the tool you chose in Exercise 2. How many ounces are in 1 quart? **32 oz**

   How many ounces of sauce did Hanna make? 7 × **32** = **224 oz**

   How many 3.5-ounce jars did Hanna fill? **224** ÷ 3.5 = **64**

**On the Back!**

4. Suppose that you can mow a lawn that is 162 square feet using one tank of gas. Is one tank of gas enough to mow a rectangular lawn that is 10.3 feet wide and 14.8 feet long? What tool can help you to solve this problem? Why would you use this tool? Explain how to use this tool strategically to solve the problem.

   **Sample answer: Use a calculator to quickly and easily multiply 10.3 × 14.8 to find the area of the yard, 152.44 $ft^2$. Because 152.44 $ft^2 < 162$ $ft^2$, one tank of gas will be enough gas.**

## On-Level and Advanced Activity Centers  

**Problem-Solving Reading Mat**

Have students read the Problem-Solving Reading Mat for Topic 7 and then complete Problem-Solving Reading Activity 7-10.

See the Problem-Solving Reading Activity Guide for other suggestions on how to use this mat.

realize
PearsonRealize.com

## TIMING

The time allocated to Step 3 will depend on the teacher's instructional decisions and differentiation routines.

15–30 min

 Help  Practice Buddy  Tools Games

## Technology Center   

 Tools  Games

### Math Tools and Math Games

A link to a specific math tools activity or math game to use with this lesson is provided at PearsonRealize.com.

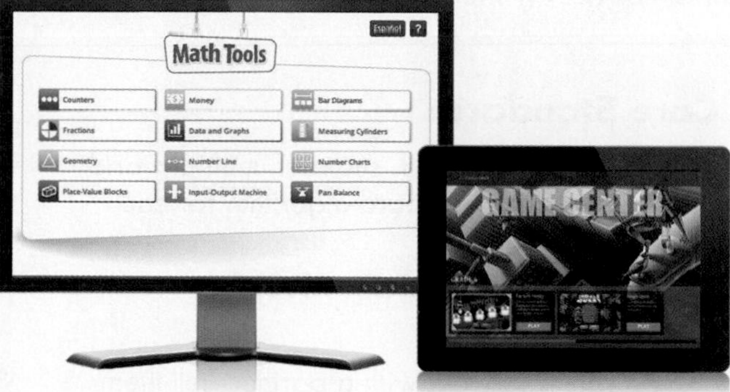


## Leveled Assignment  Items 1–5  Items 1–5  Items 1–5

Name ______________________

Help Practice Buddy Tools Games

### Homework & Practice 7-10

**Use Appropriate Tools**

#### Another Look!

Deidre wants to cover all the sides and the top of a cube with blue denim fabric. She calculates the surface area to be covered. Then she rounds to the next $\frac{1}{4}$ yard to make sure she has enough fabric. How much fabric does Deidre need to buy?

21.6 in.

**Tell how you can use tools to solve the problem.**

- I can use paper and pencil to diagram the problem.

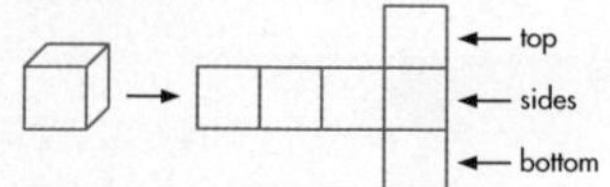


- I can use a conversion chart or the Internet to make sure that 36 inches = 1 yard.

**Solve the problem. Explain how to use the tools strategically to find the solution.**

The diagram shows 5 square sides that need to be covered. Multiply to find the total area.
$5 \times 21.6 \times 21.6 = 2{,}332.8$ square inches

Fabric is sold in yard lengths that are 60 inches wide. Multiply to find the number of square inches in 1 yard of fabric.
1 yard = 36 inches
$36 \times 60 = 2{,}160$ square inches

Divide to find the number of yards of fabric needed.
$2{,}332.8 \div 2{,}160 = 1.08$
Deidre needs 1.08 yards, so she will have to buy 1.25 yards of fabric.

**MP.5 Use Appropriate Tools**
Harris has a laptop that takes up an area of 135.9 in$^2$ when closed. He receives a computer sleeve that measures 15.75 inches by 13.2 inches as a gift. Will the sleeve work with his computer? Explain how you decided.

When you use appropriate tools, such as technology, be sure to use them correctly.

1. What tool can help you solve this problem? Why would you use this tool?
**Sample answer: I can use a calculator to calculate the area of the sleeve or to check that my math is correct.**
2. Explain how to use this tool strategically to solve the problem.
**Sample answer: Multiply to find the area that the laptop sleeve can cover: $13.2 \times 15.75 = 207.9$ in$^2$. The sleeve will work with Harris' computer.**



### Common Core Performance Assessment

**Money Measures**
Zack found this table on the Internet. He has a stack of quarters and dimes that is 12 mm tall. Three of the coins are quarters, the rest are dimes. What is the value of his stack of coins? What is the mass of his coins?

| | Penny | Nickel | Dime | Quarter | Half Dollar |
|---|---|---|---|---|---|
| Mass | 2.500 g | 5.000 g | 2.268 g | 5.670 g | 11.340 g |
| Thickness | 1.52 mm | 1.95 mm | 1.35 mm | 1.75 mm | 2.15 mm |

3. **MP.5 Use Appropriate Tools** How can you use the table strategically to help solve the problem?
**Sample answer: I can use the information in the Dime and Quarter columns to find the mass and thickness for different quantities of these coins. Then I can use what I have discovered to determine the value and mass of Zack's stack of coins.**

4. **MP.4 Model with Math** Explain how you can use words, numbers, and symbols to find the number and value of Zack's coins.
**Sample answer: I know three of the coins are quarters and the stack is 12 mm tall. I can write and solve an equation to find the number of dimes. Let $n$ = the number of dimes. $1.35n = 12 - (3 \times 1.75)$, $1.35n = 12 - 5.25$, $1.35n = 6.75$. Divide both sides of the equation by 1.35. $1.35n \div 1.35 = 6.75 \div 1.35$, $n = 5$ There are 5 dimes and 3 quarters. \$0.50 + \$0.75 = \$1.25.**

You can write and solve equations to model with math.

5. **MP.8 Generalize** Can you use the same strategy to find the total mass of Zack's coins? Explain your reasoning.
**Sample answer: Yes; I know there are 5 dimes and 3 quarters. I can write and solve an equation using the information in the table to calculate the mass of Zack's stack of coins. $(5 \times 2.268) + (3 \times 5.670) = 11.34 + 17.01 = 28.35$ So, the mass of Zack's stack of coins is 28.35 grams.**

# FLUENCY PRACTICE ACTIVITY

## FLUENCY PRACTICE ACTIVITY

Students practice fluently multiplying and dividing multi-digit decimals during a partner activity that reinforces mathematical practices.

### Common Core Standards

**Content Standard 6.NS.B.3** Fluently add, subtract, multiply, and divide multi-digit decimals using the standard algorithm for each operation.

**Mathematical Practices MP.3, MP.6, MP.7, MP.8**

**Getting Started** Ask students to work with a partner. Tell them to record their answers and shade the path on their own page. Go over the directions.

Both students should solve each problem and record their work on a separate sheet of paper. Tell students to take turns choosing which square to try next.

**As Students Do the Activity** Remind students that the path may go up, down, left, or right. There may be several options they must try before they find the square with the problem that follows the rule. Remind students to compare and discuss their answers.

Encourage students to use estimation to help choose the squares that are likely to be on the path.

**Another Activity** Ask students to find the answers to all of the problems in the remaining squares. Have students record the answers in each square.

**Extra Challenge** *Look at all of the answers in the squares. Write a new rule that results in a different path from start to finish. Your path may go up, down, left, right, or diagonally. Shade the new path in a different color.*

**Online Game** The Game Center at PearsonRealize.com provides opportunities for fluency practice.

**Steps to Fluency Success** To ensure all students achieve fluency, see pages 317E–317H for additional resources including practice/assessment masters and online practice/assessment on fluency subskills. You can also use the ExamView® CD-ROM to generate worksheets with multiple-choice or free-response items on fluency subskills.

---

Name ____________________

TOPIC 7 **Fluency Practice Activity**

**Follow the Path**

Shade a path from **START** to **FINISH**. Follow the products and quotients in which the digit in the hundredths place is greater than the digit in the tenths place. You can only move up, down, right, or left.

**I can …** multiply and divide multi-digit decimals.

Content Standard 6.NS.B.3

Start

| | | | | |
|---|---|---|---|---|
| 22.04<br>× 9<br>198.36 | 5.85<br>7.2)42.12 | 53.08<br>× 2.4<br>127.392 | 0.18<br>× 1.5<br>0.27 | 0.04<br>7)0.28 |
| 1.12<br>25)28 | 3.71<br>× 0.6<br>2.226 | 9.34<br>2.5)23.35 | 0.106<br>9)0.954 | 0.9<br>× 0.27<br>0.243 |
| 12.4<br>× 14.6<br>181.04 | 1.78<br>1.3)2.314 | 86.35<br>× 7<br>604.45 | 2.65<br>0.4)1.06 | 12.12<br>6)72.72 |
| 0.75<br>1.2)0.9 | 1.05<br>× 1.05<br>1.1025 | 3.625<br>2.4)8.7 | 7.2<br>× 0.06<br>0.432 | 0.24<br>75)18 |
| 86.3<br>× 0.4<br>34.52 | 0.0025<br>16)0.04 | 0.55<br>8)4.4 | 5.2<br>× 3.8<br>19.76 | 22.3<br>× 1.8<br>40.14 |

Finish

Topic 7 | Fluency Practice Activity 379

# VOCABULARY REVIEW

Glossary

Games

A-Z Glossary

**Word List**

- compatible numbers
- decimal
- difference
- equation
- estimate
- evaluate
- inverse relationship
- product
- quotient
- round
- sum

**Understand Vocabulary**

Choose the best term from the Word List. Write it on the blank.

1. A number that is close to an exact answer is a(n) **estimate**.
2. A mathematical sentence stating that two expressions are equal is a(n) **equation**.
3. A number with one or more digits to the right of the decimal point is a(n) **decimal**.
4. The answer to an addition problem is called a(n) **sum**.
5. **Evaluate** an expression to find its value.

Which operation represents the *inverse relationship* that can be used to solve each equation? Write *addition, subtraction, multiplication,* or *division.*

6. $3n = 4.8$ **division**
7. $a - 0.52 = 1.02$ **addition**
8. $3.8 + z = 5.55$ **subtraction**
9. $0.4 \div d = 0.16$ **multiplication**

Draw a line from each *equation* in Column A to its solution in Column B.

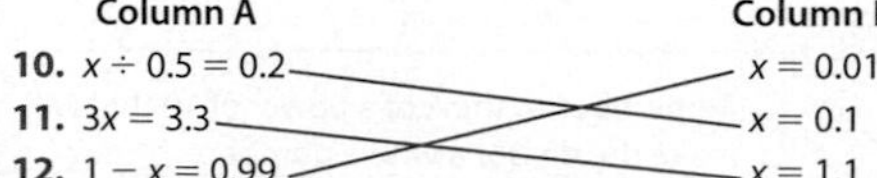

| | Column A | Column B |
|---|---|---|
| 10. | $x \div 0.5 = 0.2$ | $x = 0.01$ |
| 11. | $3x = 3.3$ | $x = 0.1$ |
| 12. | $1 - x = 0.99$ | $x = 1.1$ |

**Use Vocabulary in Writing**

13. Explain two ways to estimate $12.741 - 9.8$. Use at least 4 words from the Word List.
**Sample answer: One way to *estimate* the *difference* of 12.741 and 9.8 is to *round* both numbers to the nearest whole number. Round 12.741 to 13 and 9.8 to 10. Subtract 13 − 10 to give an *estimate* of about 3. Another way is to use *compatible numbers.* Use 12.8 and 9.8 to give an *estimate* of about 3.**

380 Topic 7 | Vocabulary Review



## VOCABULARY REVIEW

Students review vocabulary words used in the topic.

**Oral Language** Before students complete the page, you might reinforce oral language through a class discussion involving one or more of the following activities.

- Have students define the vocabulary terms in their own words and use the terms in math sentences.
- Have student pairs ask and answer math questions that use the words.
- On the board, write addition, subtraction, multiplication, and division equations involving decimals. Have students come to the board and use at least one vocabulary term from the Word List in a sentence to describe what they see.
- Say one of the vocabulary terms aloud. Ask students what they already know about the term, where they have seen or heard the term before, and give an example.

**Writing in Math** After students complete the page, you might further reinforce writing in math by doing one or more of the following activities.

- Have students work in pairs to create a word search using the terms in the Word List. Provide grid paper or allow students to use an online word search activity maker. Encourage students to use definitions, examples, or models, rather than the terms themselves, for the word search clues.
- Have students work with a partner. Each partner writes three math riddles that either use the vocabulary terms or ask questions about a vocabulary term. Then students trade papers to solve each other's riddles.

Games

**Online Game** The Game Center at PearsonRealize.com includes a vocabulary game that students can access any time.

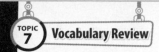

# RETEACHING

## FLUENTLY ADD, SUBTRACT, MULTIPLY, AND DIVIDE DECIMALS

### RtI Item Analysis for Diagnosis and Intervention

| Reteaching Sets | Standard | MDIS |
|---|---|---|
| Set A | 6.NS.B.3 | H55, H56, H57 |
| Set B | 6.NS.B.3 | H62, H64 |
| Set C | 6.NS.B.2, 6.NS.B.3 | H67, H68, H69 |
| Set D | 6.EE.A.2c, 6.EE.B.7, 6.NS.B.2, 6.NS.B.3 | F52 |
| Set E | MP.5, MP.4, MP.7, MP.8 | F46 |

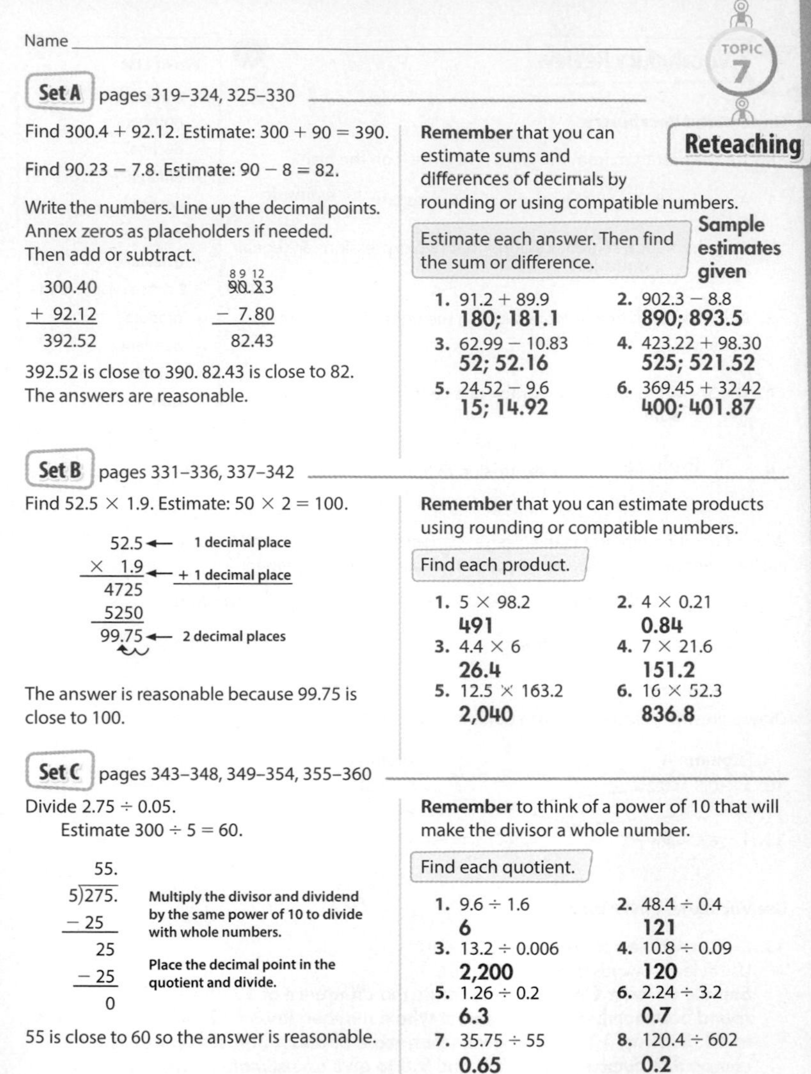

Name ______

TOPIC 7

**Reteaching**

**Set A** pages 319–324, 325–330

Find 300.4 + 92.12. Estimate: 300 + 90 = 390.

Find 90.23 − 7.8. Estimate: 90 − 8 = 82.

Write the numbers. Line up the decimal points. Annex zeros as placeholders if needed. Then add or subtract.

$$\begin{array}{r} 300.40 \\ +\ 92.12 \\ \hline 392.52 \end{array} \qquad \begin{array}{r} 90.23 \\ -\ 7.80 \\ \hline 82.43 \end{array}$$

392.52 is close to 390. 82.43 is close to 82. The answers are reasonable.

**Remember** that you can estimate sums and differences of decimals by rounding or using compatible numbers.

Estimate each answer. Then find the sum or difference. **Sample estimates given**

1. 91.2 + 89.9 **180; 181.1**
2. 902.3 − 8.8 **890; 893.5**
3. 62.99 − 10.83 **52; 52.16**
4. 423.22 + 98.30 **525; 521.52**
5. 24.52 − 9.6 **15; 14.92**
6. 369.45 + 32.42 **400; 401.87**

**Set B** pages 331–336, 337–342

Find 52.5 × 1.9. Estimate: 50 × 2 = 100.

$$\begin{array}{r} 52.5 \\ \times\ 1.9 \\ \hline 4725 \\ 5250 \\ \hline 99.75 \end{array}$$

52.5 ← 1 decimal place
1.9 ← + 1 decimal place
99.75 ← 2 decimal places

The answer is reasonable because 99.75 is close to 100.

**Remember** that you can estimate products using rounding or compatible numbers.

Find each product.

1. 5 × 98.2 **491**
2. 4 × 0.21 **0.84**
3. 4.4 × 6 **26.4**
4. 7 × 21.6 **151.2**
5. 12.5 × 163.2 **2,040**
6. 16 × 52.3 **836.8**

**Set C** pages 343–348, 349–354, 355–360

Divide 2.75 ÷ 0.05.
Estimate 300 ÷ 5 = 60.

$$\begin{array}{r} 55. \\ 5\overline{)275.} \\ -\ 25 \\ \hline 25 \\ -\ 25 \\ \hline 0 \end{array}$$

Multiply the divisor and dividend by the same power of 10 to divide with whole numbers.

Place the decimal point in the quotient and divide.

55 is close to 60 so the answer is reasonable.

**Remember** to think of a power of 10 that will make the divisor a whole number.

Find each quotient.

1. 9.6 ÷ 1.6 **6**
2. 48.4 ÷ 0.4 **121**
3. 13.2 ÷ 0.006 **2,200**
4. 10.8 ÷ 0.09 **120**
5. 1.26 ÷ 0.2 **6.3**
6. 2.24 ÷ 3.2 **0.7**
7. 35.75 ÷ 55 **0.65**
8. 120.4 ÷ 602 **0.2**

Topic 7 | Reteaching 381

**Set D** pages 361–366, 367–372

Evaluate 2.4 • *m* for *m* = 6.

Substitute 6 for the value of *m* in the expression.

$2.4 \cdot m = 2.4 \cdot 6 = 14.4$

Solve $x \div 5.3 = 6.2$. Use inverse operations to get the variable by itself on one side of the equation.

$x \div 5.3 = 6.2$

$x \div 5.3 \times 5.3 = 6.2 \times 5.3$ ← **Multiply both sides by 5.3.**

$x = 32.86$

**Remember** to use substitution and check your solution.

In **1–3**, evaluate each expression.

1. $6.7 + x; x = 2$ **8.7**
2. $x(3.4); x = 5.4$ **18.36**
3. $5n^2 + 2d \div 4; n = 3, d = 6$ **48**

In **4** and **5**, solve each equation.

4. $x \div 7.9 = 50.56$ **x = 399.424**
5. $0.02x = 0.82$ **x = 41**

**Set E** pages 373–378

Think about these questions to help you **use appropriate tools strategically**.

**Thinking Habits**

- Which tools can I use?
- Why should I use this tool to help me solve the problem?
- Is there a different tool I could use?
- Am I using the tool appropriately?

**Remember** to choose the tool that is most helpful in solving the problem.

Eva joins a gym for 12 months and wants 5 training sessions. Option A is \$45 per month and \$79 per training session. Option B is \$55 per month plus \$245 for 5 training sessions. Which is the better option for Eva?

1. What tool can help you solve the problem? **Sample answer: A calculator.**
2. Use the tool to solve the problem. **Option B; Sample answer: It will cost 12(\$55) + \$245 = \$905. The cost of the first option is 12(\$45) + 5(\$79) = \$935. Eva will save \$30 taking the second option.**





## Response to Intervention

**Ongoing Intervention**

- Lessons with guiding questions to assess understanding
- Support to prevent misconceptions and to reteach

**Strategic Intervention**

- Targeted to small groups that need more support
- Easy to implement

**Intensive Intervention**

- Instruction to accelerate progress
- Instruction focused on foundational skills

# TOPIC ASSESSMENT

## FLUENTLY ADD, SUBTRACT, MULTIPLY, AND DIVIDE DECIMALS

Name ____________

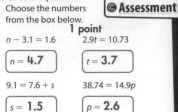

1. The table gives the areas of 3 parks. Which is the best estimate of the difference between the sizes of Shady Heights and Pine Island? **1 point**

| Park Area | Size in Acres |
|---|---|
| Shady Heights | 58.38 |
| Pine Island | 27.5 |
| Oak Woods | 792.84 |

- Ⓐ 30 acres (selected)
- Ⓑ 35 acres
- Ⓒ 38 acres
- Ⓓ 40 acres

2. Mrs. Jenks bought 53 erasers for the students in her class. Mr. Bailey bought 9 more erasers than Mrs. Jenks bought. Each eraser cost $0.14. How much did the teachers spend for the erasers? Explain how you found your answer. **2 points**

**$16.10; Sample answer: Mrs. Jenks bought 53 erasers; Mr. Bailey bought 53 + 9 = 62 erasers. Together they bought 53 + 62 = 115 erasers. 115 × $0.14 = $16.10.**

3. Russ has a car that averages 9.8 miles per gallon. Mike's car averages 39.2 miles per gallon. How many times more miles per gallon does Mike's car average than Russ's car? **1 point**

**4 times as many miles per gallon**

4. Write the correct solution for each equation. Choose the numbers from the box below. **1 point**

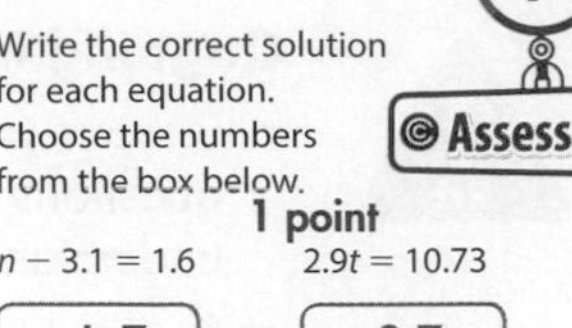

$n - 3.1 = 1.6$   $n =$ **4.7**

$2.9t = 10.73$   $t =$ **3.7**

$9.1 = 7.6 + s$   $s =$ **1.5**

$38.74 = 14.9p$   $p =$ **2.6**

1.1   1.5   4.7   3.7   0.5   2.6

5. Choose all the expressions that have a quotient of 0.7. **1 point**

- ☐ 1.61 ÷ 0.23
- ■ 1.61 ÷ 2.3
- ■ 2.87 ÷ 4.1
- ☐ 0.287 ÷ 41

6. Chris and Jeff sold 15.5 pounds of trail mix. They sold the trail mix for $3.98 per pound. How much money did they collect? Explain how you found your answer. **2 points**

**$61.69; Sample answer: I multiplied 15.5 by $3.98.**

7. Ilana needs $d$ more dollars to buy a new scrapbook that costs $8.35. She has $4.88. Solve the equation $4.88 + $d$ = $8.35 to find how much more money Ilana needs. **1 point**

- Ⓐ $d$ = $3.57
- Ⓑ $d$ = $3.47 (selected)
- Ⓒ $d$ = $3.42
- Ⓓ $d$ = $4.12



8. Evaluate the expression $6.908 - g$ for $g = 0.173$. **1 point**

**6.735**

9. Draw lines to connect each division expression in Column A with its quotient in Column B. **1 point**

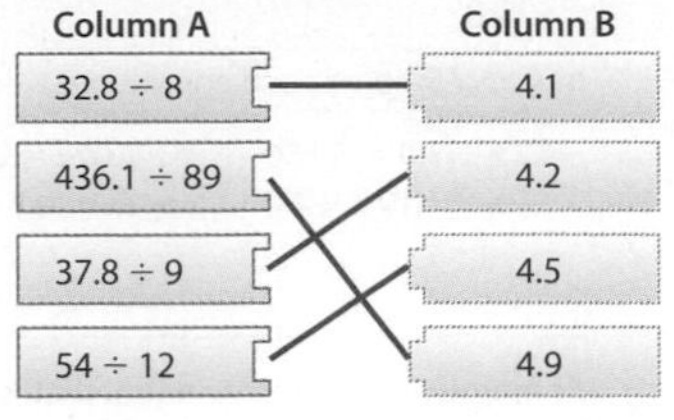

| Column A | Column B |
|---|---|
| 32.8 ÷ 8 | 4.1 |
| 436.1 ÷ 89 | 4.2 |
| 37.8 ÷ 9 | 4.5 |
| 54 ÷ 12 | 4.9 |

(Answer lines: 32.8 ÷ 8 → 4.1; 436.1 ÷ 89 → 4.9; 37.8 ÷ 9 → 4.2; 54 ÷ 12 → 4.5)

10. Diego and Ashley estimated the product 23.879 × 2.995. Diego estimated 25 × 3 = 75. Ashley estimated 23 × 3 = 69.

What method did each student use? Are they both correct? Explain. **2 points**

**Sample answer: Diego used compatible numbers. The numbers 25 and 3 are close to the original numbers and easy to compute. Diego's estimate is correct. Ashley rounded to estimate. 2.995 rounds to 3, but 23.879 rounds to 24. 24 × 3 = 72 would have been a more reasonable estimate.**

11. Abby, Brianna, and Maria competed in a figure skating competition. The table shows how one judge scored each skater on a scale from 0 to 6.0. Which statements about their scores are true? Select all that apply. **1 point**

| Skater | Scores | |
|---|---|---|
| Abby | Technical | 5.8 |
| | Presentation | 5.9 |
| Brianna | Technical | 5.7 |
| | Presentation | 5.6 |
| Maria | Technical | 5.8 |
| | Presentation | 5.4 |

- ☐ Brianna has the lowest combined score.
- ■ The difference between Brianna's and Abby's combined scores is 0.4.
- ☐ The difference between Abby's and Maria's combined scores is 0.05.
- ■ Maria's technical score is 0.1 more than Brianna's technical score.

12. Milo wants to ship both items shown below. He finds out that a special rate is available for a large box as long as no dimension is greater than 30.48 cm. Will his items fit in one large box? Explain. **2 points**

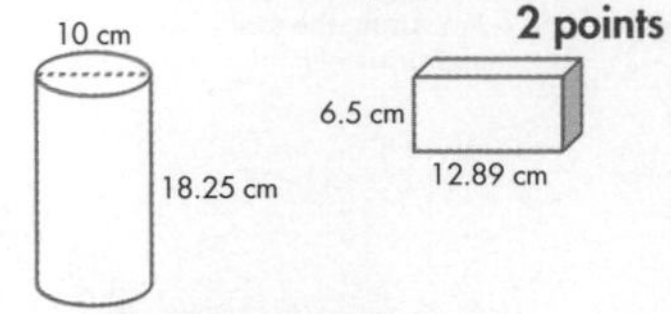


**Yes; Sample answer: The items can be placed side-by side. The shorter dimensions of 10 + 6.5 = 16.5 cm. The longer dimension will only be 18.25 cm.**





## ANSWERING THE TOPIC ESSENTIAL QUESTION

**How can you fluently add, subtract, multiply, and divide decimals?**

Restate the Topic Essential Question from the Topic Opener or project it from the Student's Edition eText.

Ask students to answer the Essential Question (verbally or in writing) and give examples that support their answers. The following are key elements of the answer to the Essential Question. Be sure these are made explicit when discussing students' answers.

- To add or subtract decimals, line up the decimal points so that place-value positions correspond. Annex zeros as needed. Add or subtract as you would whole numbers, and place the decimal in the answer.

**Examples:** Add 17.6 + 3.56. Subtract 2.045 − 0.29.

$$\begin{array}{r} \overset{1}{1}\overset{1}{7}.60 \\ +\,3.56 \\ \hline 21.16 \end{array} \qquad \begin{array}{r} 2.045 \\ -\,0.290 \\ \hline 1.755 \end{array}$$

- To multiply decimals, multiply as you would whole numbers, then place the decimal point in the product by starting at the right and counting the number of places equal to the sum of the number of decimal places in each factor.
- To divide decimals, multiply the divisor and dividend by the same power of 10 so that the divisor is a whole number. Then use the standard algorithm for whole-number division. Annex zeros to the dividend as needed.

**Examples:** Multiply 36.9 × 4.26. Divide 56.5 ÷ 2.5.

$$\begin{array}{r} 36.9 \\ \times\,4.26 \\ \hline 2214 \\ 7380 \\ +147600 \\ \hline 157.194 \end{array}$$

36.9 ← one decimal place; × 4.26 ← two decimal places; 157.194 ← three decimal places

$$\begin{array}{r} 22.6 \\ 25\overline{)565.0} \\ -50 \\ \hline 65 \\ -50 \\ \hline 150 \\ -150 \\ \hline 0 \end{array}$$

PearsonRealize.com

Assessment

**ONLINE TOPIC ASSESSMENT**

An auto-scored Topic Assessment is provided at PearsonRealize.com.

**EXAMVIEW® TEST GENERATOR**

ExamView can be used to create a blackline-master Topic Assessment with multiple-choice and free-response items.

## Topic Assessment Masters

Name ______________________

Topic 7 Assessment

**1.** The table gives the estimated median age, in years, for the population of 3 countries in 2014. Which is the best estimate of the difference between the median ages in Germany and Ghana? **1 point**

| Country | Median Age |
|---|---|
| Germany | 46.1 |
| Ghana | 20.8 |
| United States | 37.6 |

Ⓐ 21 years
● 25 years
Ⓒ 29 years
Ⓓ 32 years

**2.** For a school Halloween party, Mrs. Gomez bought 24 packages of paper plates and 5 fewer packages of paper cups. Each package of plates or cups cost \$0.89. What was the total amount she spent for the plates and cups? Explain how you found your answer. **2 points**

**\$38.27; Sample answer: Mrs. Gomez bought 24 packages of paper plates and 24 − 5 = 19 packages of paper cups. This was a total of 24 + 19 = 43 packages. 43 × \$0.89 = \$38.27.**

**3.** Tom weighs 168.5 pounds. His 2-year old son Nicholas weighs 33.7 pounds. How many times as much as Nicholas does Tom weigh? **1 point**

**5 times as much**

**4.** Write the correct solution for each equation. Choose the numbers from the box below. **1 point**

$w - 1.8 = 4.5$   $w =$ **6.3**

$3.6x = 9.72$   $x =$ **2.7**

$15.3 = 9.5 + y$   $y =$ **5.8**

$63.36 = 13.2z$   $z =$ **4.8**

2.7   3.8   4.8   5.8   6.3   24.8

**5.** Choose all the expressions that have a quotient of 0.6. **1 point**

■ 0.618 ÷ 1.03
□ 61.8 ÷ 10.3
□ 28.2 ÷ 0.47
■ 2.82 ÷ 4.7

**6.** Marissa bought 12.8 pounds of potatoes for \$1.35 per pound. How much did Marissa spend for the potatoes? Explain how you found your answer. **2 points**

**\$17.28; Sample answer: I multiplied 12.8 by \$1.35.**

**7.** Gabriel needs *d* more dollars to buy a new video game console that costs \$156.75. He has saved \$98.26. Solve the equation \$98.26 + *d* = \$156.75 to find how much more money Gabriel needs. **1 point**

Ⓐ *d* = \$57.49
● *d* = \$58.49
Ⓒ *d* = \$58.59
Ⓓ *d* = \$68.59

Assessment 1 of 2



**8.** Evaluate the expression $8.952 + p$ for $p = 0.276$. **1 point**

**9.228**

**9.** Draw lines to connect each division expression in Column A with its quotient in Column B. **1 point**

| Column A | Column B |
|---|---|
| 91 ÷ 14 | 6.1 |
| 285.6 ÷ 42 | 6.3 |
| 67.1 ÷ 11 | 6.5 |
| 56.7 ÷ 9 | 6.8 |

**10.** Mia and Max estimated the product 37.628 × 5.109. Mia estimated 40 × 5 = 200. Max estimated 38 × 5 = 190.

What method did each student use? Are they both correct? Explain. **2 points**

**Sample answer: Yes, they are both correct. Mia used compatible numbers. The numbers 40 and 5 are close to the original numbers and easy to compute. Max rounded to estimate. 5.109 rounds to 5, 37.628 rounds to 38 and 38 × 5 = 190.**

**11.** Jonathan, Kevin, and Emilio are trying out for the track team at their high school. The table shows their times on two trials of the 100-meter dash. Which statements about their times are true? Select all that apply. **1 point**

| Runner | Times (seconds) | |
|---|---|---|
| Jonathan | 1st Trial | 11.9 |
| | 2nd Trial | 12.3 |
| Kevin | 1st Trial | 13.1 |
| | 2nd Trial | 12.8 |
| Emilio | 1st Trial | 14.1 |
| | 2nd Trial | 13.7 |

□ Kevin has the lowest combined time.
■ The difference between Kevin's and Jonathan's combined times is 1.7 seconds.
■ The difference between Emilio's times on the two trials is 0.4 second.
□ The difference between Emilio's and Jonathan's combined times is 4.6 seconds.

**12.** The dimensions of a bookcase are shown in the diagram below. Chelsea buys 3 of these bookcases for her office. The length of one office wall is 73 inches. Will the 3 bookcases fit against the wall? Explain. **2 points**

32.6 in.
24.5 in.
8.2 in.

**No; 3 bookcases set side-by-side are 3 × 24.5, or 73.5, inches long.**

Assessment 2 of 2



## Scoring Guide

| Item | Points | Topic Assessment (Student's Edition and Masters) |
|---|---|---|
| 1 | 1 | Correct choice selected |
| 2 | 2 | Correct answer and explanation |
| | 1 | Correct answer or explanation |
| 3 | 1 | Correct answer |
| 4 | 1 | All correct answers |
| 5 | 1 | All correct choices selected |
| 6 | 2 | Correct answer and explanation |
| | 1 | Correct answer or explanation |
| 7 | 1 | Correct choice selected |
| 8 | 1 | Correct answer |
| 9 | 1 | All matches correct |
| 10 | 2 | Correct methods and explanation |
| | 1 | Correct methods or explanation |
| 11 | 1 | All correct choices selected |
| 12 | 2 | Correct answer and explanation |
| | 1 | Correct answer or explanation |

## RtI Item Analysis for Diagnosis and Intervention

| Item | Standard | DOK | MDIS |
|---|---|---|---|
| 1 | 6.NS.B.3 | 1 | H55 |
| 2 | 6.NS.B.3 | 2 | H60 |
| 3 | 6.NS.B.2, 6.NS.B.3 | 1 | H69 |
| 4 | 6.EE.B.7, 6.NS.B.3 | 1 | F52 |
| 5 | 6.NS.B.2, 6.NS.B.3 | 1 | H69 |
| 6 | 6.NS.B.3 | 2 | H64 |
| 7 | 6.EE.B.7, 6.NS.B.3 | 1 | F52 |
| 8 | 6.EE.A.2c, 6.NS.B.3 | 1 | H59, F45 |
| 9 | 6.NS.B.2, 6.NS.B.3 | 1 | H65, H67 |
| 10 | 6.NS.B.3 | 3 | H29, H62 |
| 11 | 6.NS.B.3, MP.5 | 2 | H56, H57 |
| 12 | 6.NS.B.3 | 3 | H56, H57 |

The Topic Assessment Masters assess the same content item for item as the Topic Assessment in the Student's Edition.

# TOPIC PERFORMANCE ASSESSMENT

## FLUENTLY ADD, SUBTRACT, MULTIPLY, AND DIVIDE DECIMALS

Name ____________________

TOPIC 7

Performance Assessment

**Food Bank**

Volunteers at the Food Bank package meals to feed a family of four. The table shows the foods that are available, the number of people served by each food, and the weight of the food.

- One selection from each category is packed into a box.
- Each box can hold a maximum of 3.5 pounds, or 56 ounces.

DATA

| Main Course | | | Side Dish | | |
|---|---|---|---|---|---|
| **Food** | **Serves** | **Weight** | **Food** | **Serves** | **Weight** |
| Roast Beef | 4 | 16 oz | Potato | 1 | 4 oz |
| Chicken | 2 | 12.6 oz | Cole Slaw | 4 | 12.4 oz |
| Stew | 1 | 5.2 oz | Green salad | 2 | 5.6 oz |
| Lasagna | 4 | 28 oz | Baked beans | 4 | 14.2 oz |
| Chili | 1 | 8.6 oz | Pasta | 2 | 5.2 oz |
| **Vegetables** | | | **Dessert** | | |
| Carrots | 2 | 6 oz | Custard cup | 1 | 3.2 oz |
| Corn | 2 | 5.8 oz | Carrot cake | 4 | 10.4 oz |
| Green beans | 1 | 3.2 oz | Frozen yogurt | 2 | 2.7 oz |
| Peas | 4 | 14.8 oz | Apple | 1 | 5 oz |

**1.** Suppose you pack 2 carrots, 4 potatoes, and 2 frozen yogurts.

**Part A**

Write an equation for the number of ounces that are still available for a main course. Let $x$ = the number of ounces. **1 point**

**Sample answer:**
$(2 \times 6) + (4 \times 4) + (2 \times 2.7) + x = 56$

**Part B**

Which main dishes can you use to complete the meal under the food bank's guidelines? Explain how you know. **2 points**

**Roast beef and stew; Answers will vary. Check students' work.**



**2.** Describe a meal that you could make that weighs 3.5 pounds or less. Include the number of servings and total weight of each food. **2 points**

**Answers will vary. Check students' work.**

**3.** The Food Bank has 110.9 pounds, or 1,774.4 ounces, of chicken. To the nearest whole number, how many servings of chicken does this provide? **1 point**

**282 servings of chicken**

**4.** If donations to the Food Bank increase, they will be able to offer meals for a family of six, too.

**Part A**

Would boxes with a weight limit of 5.1 pounds, or 81.6 ounces, be enough to make good meals for 6 people? Explain your thinking. **1 point**

**Answers will vary. Check students' work.**

**Part B**

Decide on a weight limit for each box for a family of six. Justify your choice. Then make a meal that will fit in the box. **2 points**

**Answers will vary. Check students' work.**





### Scoring Guide

| Item | Points | Topic Performance Assessment in the Student's Edition |
|---|---|---|
| 1A | 1 | Correct equation |
| 1B | 2<br>1 | Correct answer and explanation<br>Correct answer or explanation |
| 2 | 2<br>1 | Correct answer and description<br>Correct answer without description |
| 3 | 1 | Correct answer |
| 4A | 1 | Reasonable answer and explanation |
| 4B | 2<br>1 | Reasonable answer and explanation<br>Reasonable answer without explanation |

### Item Analysis for Diagnosis and Intervention

| Item | Standard | DOK | MDIS |
|---|---|---|---|
| 1A | 6.EE.B.7, MP.4 | 2 | F53, F54 |
| 1B | 6.NS.B.3, MP.3 | 2 | F52, H60 |
| 2 | 6.NS.B.3, MP.6 | 3 | H60, H56 |
| 3 | 6.NS.B.2, 6.NS.B.3, MP.2 | 2 | H69 |
| 4A | 6.NS.B.3, MP.1 | 3 | H60, H56 |
| 4B | 6.NS.B.3, MP.3 | 3 | H60, H56 |

## Topic Performance Assessment Masters

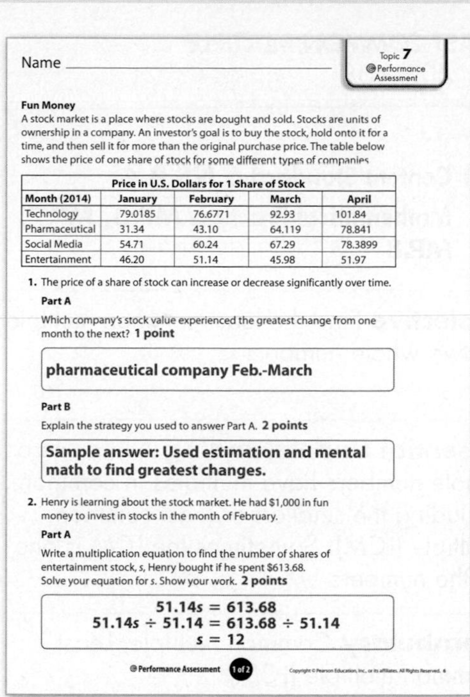

Name ______________________

Topic 7
Performance Assessment

**Fun Money**

A stock market is a place where stocks are bought and sold. Stocks are units of ownership in a company. An investor's goal is to buy the stock, hold onto it for a time, and then sell it for more than the original purchase price. The table below shows the price of one share of stock for some different types of companies

| Price in U.S. Dollars for 1 Share of Stock | | | | |
|---|---|---|---|---|
| **Month (2014)** | **January** | **February** | **March** | **April** |
| Technology | 79.0185 | 76.6771 | 92.93 | 101.84 |
| Pharmaceutical | 31.34 | 43.10 | 64.119 | 78.841 |
| Social Media | 54.71 | 60.24 | 67.29 | 78.3899 |
| Entertainment | 46.20 | 51.14 | 45.98 | 51.97 |

**1.** The price of a share of stock can increase or decrease significantly over time.

**Part A**

Which company's stock value experienced the greatest change from one month to the next? **1 point**

**pharmaceutical company Feb.-March**

**Part B**

Explain the strategy you used to answer Part A. **2 points**

**Sample answer: Used estimation and mental math to find greatest changes.**

**2.** Henry is learning about the stock market. He had $1,000 in fun money to invest in stocks in the month of February.

**Part A**

Write a multiplication equation to find the number of shares of entertainment stock, *s*, Henry bought if he spent $613.68. Solve your equation for *s*. Show your work. **2 points**

$$51.14s = 613.68$$
$$51.14s \div 51.14 = 613.68 \div 51.14$$
$$s = 12$$

Performance Assessment 1 of 2



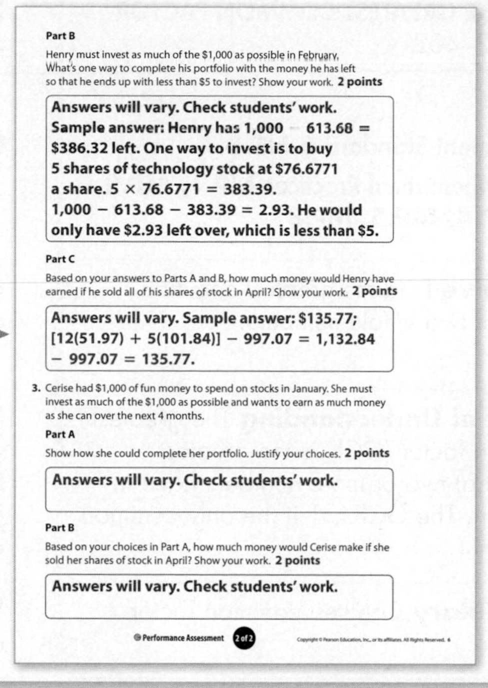

**Part B**

Henry must invest as much of the $1,000 as possible in February. What's one way to complete his portfolio with the money he has left so that he ends up with less than $5 to invest? Show your work. **2 points**

**Answers will vary. Check students' work. Sample answer: Henry has 1,000 − 613.68 = $386.32 left. One way to invest is to buy 5 shares of technology stock at $76.6771 a share. 5 × 76.6771 = 383.39. 1,000 − 613.68 − 383.39 = 2.93. He would only have $2.93 left over, which is less than $5.**

**Part C**

Based on your answers to Parts A and B, how much money would Henry have earned if he sold all of his shares of stock in April? Show your work. **2 points**

**Answers will vary. Sample answer: $135.77; [12(51.97) + 5(101.84)] − 997.07 = 1,132.84 − 997.07 = 135.77.**

**3.** Cerise had $1,000 of fun money to spend on stocks in January. She must invest as much of the $1,000 as possible and wants to earn as much money as she can over the next 4 months.

**Part A**

Show how she could complete her portfolio. Justify your choices. **2 points**

**Answers will vary. Check students' work.**

**Part B**

Based on your choices in Part A, how much money would Cerise make if she sold her shares of stock in April? Show your work. **2 points**

**Answers will vary. Check students' work.**

Performance Assessment 2 of 2



## RtI Item Analysis for Diagnosis and Intervention

| Item | Standard | DOK | MDIS |
|---|---|---|---|
| 1A | 6.NS.B.3, MP.2 | 2 | H58, H59 |
| 1B | 6.NS.B.3, MP.3 | 2 | H58, H59 |
| 2A | 6.EE.B.7, 6.NS.B.3, MP.4 | 2 | F52, F54 |
| 2B | 6.NS.B.3, MP.3 | 3 | F52, J23 |
| 2C | 6.NS.B.3, MP.6 | 2 | F52 |
| 3A | 6.NS.B.3, MP.3 | 3 | F52, J24 |
| 3B | 6.NS.B.3, MP.6 | 2 | F52 |

## Scoring Guide

| Item | Points | Topic Performance Assessment Masters |
|---|---|---|
| 1A | 1 | Correct answer |
| 1B | 2 | Reasonable answer and explanation |
| | 1 | Reasonable answer without explanation |
| 2A | 2 | Correct equation and answer |
| | 1 | Correct equation or answer |
| 2B | 2 | Reasonable answer and explanation |
| | 1 | Reasonable answer without explanation |
| 2C | 2 | Reasonable answer and explanation |
| | 1 | Reasonable answer without explanation |
| 3A | 2 | Reasonable answer and explanation |
| | 1 | Reasonable answer without explanation |
| 3B | 2 | Reasonable answer and explanation |
| | 1 | Reasonable answer without explanation |

TOPIC 8

# TOPIC PLANNER

## COMMON FACTORS AND MULTIPLES

### Lesson 8-1

PRIME AND COMPOSITE NUMBERS
pp. 391–396

Content Standard **6.NS.B.4**
Mathematical Practices **MP.2, MP.3, MP.6, MP.7**

**Objective** Identify prime and composite numbers, and write the prime factorization of a number.

**Essential Understanding** Any number can be written as a unique product of prime numbers called its prime factorization.

**Vocabulary** Prime factorization, Factor tree

**ELL Speaking:** Speak using content area vocabulary in context.

**Materials** Index cards

**On-Level and Advanced Activity Centers**
- Math and Science Activity

### Lesson 8-2

FIND THE GREATEST COMMON FACTOR
pp. 397–402

Content Standard **6.NS.B.4**
Mathematical Practices **MP.1, MP.2, MP.4, MP.5, MP.8**

**Objective** Find the greatest common factor of two whole numbers.

**Essential Understanding** The greatest common factor (GCF) is the greatest factor that two or more numbers have in common. The GCF is 1 if the only common factor is 1.

**Vocabulary** Greatest common factor (GCF)

**ELL Listening:** Learn basic/academic vocabulary.

**Materials** None

**On-Level and Advanced Activity Centers**
- Problem-Solving Reading Mat

### Lesson 8-3

LEAST COMMON MULTIPLE
pp. 403–408

Content Standard **6.NS.B.4**
Mathematical Practices **MP.3, MP.7, MP.8**

**Objective** Find the least common multiple of two whole numbers.

**Essential Understanding** All non-zero whole numbers have multiples in common, including the smallest or least common multiple (LCM). Sometimes the LCM is one of the numbers.

**Vocabulary** Common multiple, Least common multiple (LCM)

**ELL Reading:** Expand comprehension by predicting.

**Materials** Index cards

**On-Level and Advanced Activity Centers**
- Problem-Solving Reading Mat

## LESSON RESOURCES

Digital

Print

- Student's Edition
- Daily Common Core Review
- Reteach to Build Understanding
- Math and Science Activity
- Problem-Solving Reading Mat
- Problem-Solving Reading Activity

Digital

- Listen and Look For PD Lesson Video
- Student's Edition eText
- Today's Challenge
- Solve & Share
- Visual Learning Animation Plus
- Animated Glossary
- Math Tools
- Practice Buddy Online Practice
- Quick Check
- Another Look Homework Video
- Math Games

Digital

## Lesson 8-4

**MATH PRACTICES AND PROBLEM SOLVING: CRITIQUE REASONING** pp. 409–414

**Mathematical Practices MP.3 Also MP.1, MP.6, MP.7**
**Content Standard 6.NS.B.4**

**Objective** Critique the reasoning of others using what is known about factors and multiples.

**Essential Understanding** Good math thinkers use math to explain why they are right. They can talk about the math that others do, too.

**Vocabulary** Counterexample

**ELL Learning Strategies:** Use prior knowledge to understand meanings.

**Materials** None

**On-Level and Advanced Activity Centers**
- Math and Science Activity

## TOPIC RESOURCES

Digital

Print

**Start of Topic**
- Math and Science Project
- Home-School Connection
- Review What You Know
- My Word Cards

**End of Topic**
- Fluency Practice Activity
- Vocabulary Review
- Reteaching
- Topic Assessment
- Topic Performance Assessment
- Cumulative/Benchmark Assessment

Digital

**Start of Topic**
- Topic Overview PD Video

**End of Topic**
- Math Practices Animations
- Online Topic Assessment
- ExamView® Test Generator
- Practice Buddy Fluency Practice/Assessment

PearsonRealize.com

# COMMON FACTORS AND MULTIPLES

## TOPIC ESSENTIAL QUESTION

**How can you find common factors and multiples of numbers?**

Revisit the Topic Essential Question throughout the topic, and see a note about answering the question in the Teacher's Edition for the Topic Assessment.

## MATH AND SCIENCE PROJECT STEM

**Science Theme** The science theme for this project is **Cryptography**. This theme will be revisited in the Math and Science Activities in Lessons 8-1 and 8-4 and in some lesson exercises.

Encryption, or encoding, is the process of using a code to represent information. Decryption, or decoding, is the reverse process that uses coded information to obtain the original information.

Prime numbers are used to encrypt and decrypt important information like a credit card number when sending data over the Internet. A popular algorithm depends on the fact that it is easy to multiply two very large prime numbers. Since these products have hundreds of digits, it is extremely hard to do the opposite—find their prime factorization. The two original prime numbers are used to decode the information.

**Project-Based Learning** Have students work on the **Math and Science Project** over the course of several days.

### EXTENSION

Have students research Samuel Morse's invention of the telegraph and Morse code. Have each student work with a partner and send a message written using Morse code to another student pair to decipher.

### Sample Student Work for Math and Science Project

Original message:

John said he would meet us at the movies.

Use a shift (+3) encryption technique.

Encrypted message:

Mrkq vdlg kh zrxog phhw xv dw wkh prylhv.

TOPIC 8

## Common Factors and Multiples

**Essential Question:** How can you find common factors and multiples of numbers?



**Math and Science Project:** Cryptography

**Do Research** Use the Internet or other sources to learn about various encryption techniques. Find examples of techniques that are easy to reproduce.

**Journal: Write a Report** Include what you found. Also in your report:

- Describe at least three basic encryption techniques.
- Choose one of the encryption techniques you described to encrypt a secret message. State the secret message and then show its encrypted form.

Topic 8 387

## Home-School Connection

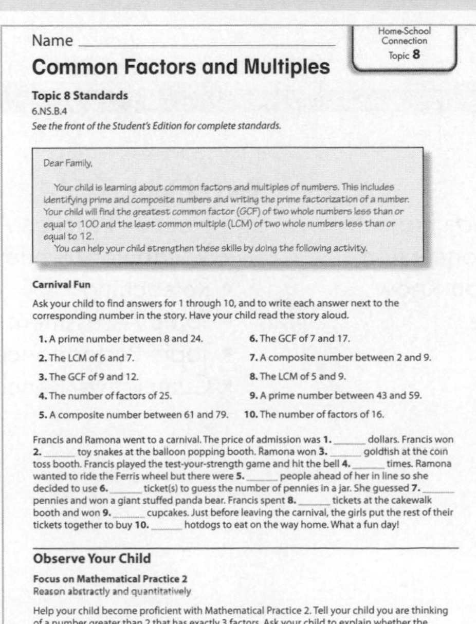

Name ______________________

Home-School Connection Topic 8

### Common Factors and Multiples

**Topic 8 Standards**

6.NS.B.4

*See the front of the Student's Edition for complete standards.*

Dear Family,

Your child is learning about common factors and multiples of numbers. This includes identifying prime and composite numbers and writing the prime factorization of a number. Your child will find the greatest common factor (GCF) of two whole numbers less than or equal to 100 and the least common multiple (LCM) of two whole numbers less than or equal to 12.

You can help your child strengthen these skills by doing the following activity.

**Carnival Fun**

Ask your child to find answers for 1 through 10, and to write each answer next to the corresponding number in the story. Have your child read the story aloud.

**1.** A prime number between 8 and 24.
**2.** The LCM of 6 and 7.
**3.** The GCF of 9 and 12.
**4.** The number of factors of 25.
**5.** A composite number between 61 and 79.
**6.** The GCF of 7 and 17.
**7.** A composite number between 2 and 9.
**8.** The LCM of 5 and 9.
**9.** A prime number between 43 and 59.
**10.** The number of factors of 16.

Francis and Ramona went to a carnival. The price of admission was **1.** ______ dollars. Francis won **2.** ______ toy snakes at the balloon popping booth. Ramona won **3.** ______ goldfish at the coin toss booth. Francis played the test-your-strength game and hit the bell **4.** ______ times. Ramona wanted to ride the Ferris wheel but there were **5.** ______ people ahead of her in line so she decided to use **6.** ______ ticket(s) to guess the number of pennies in a jar. She guessed **7.** ______ pennies and won a giant stuffed panda bear. Francis spent **8.** ______ tickets at the cakewalk booth and won **9.** ______ cupcakes. Just before leaving the carnival, the girls put the rest of their tickets together to buy **10.** ______ hotdogs to eat on the way home. What a fun day!

**Observe Your Child**

**Focus on Mathematical Practice 2**
Reason abstractly and quantitatively

Help your child become proficient with Mathematical Practice 2. Tell your child you are thinking of a number greater than 2 that has exactly 3 factors. Ask your child to explain whether the number is a prime or a composite number.



Send this page home at the start of Topic 8 to give families an overview of the content in the topic.

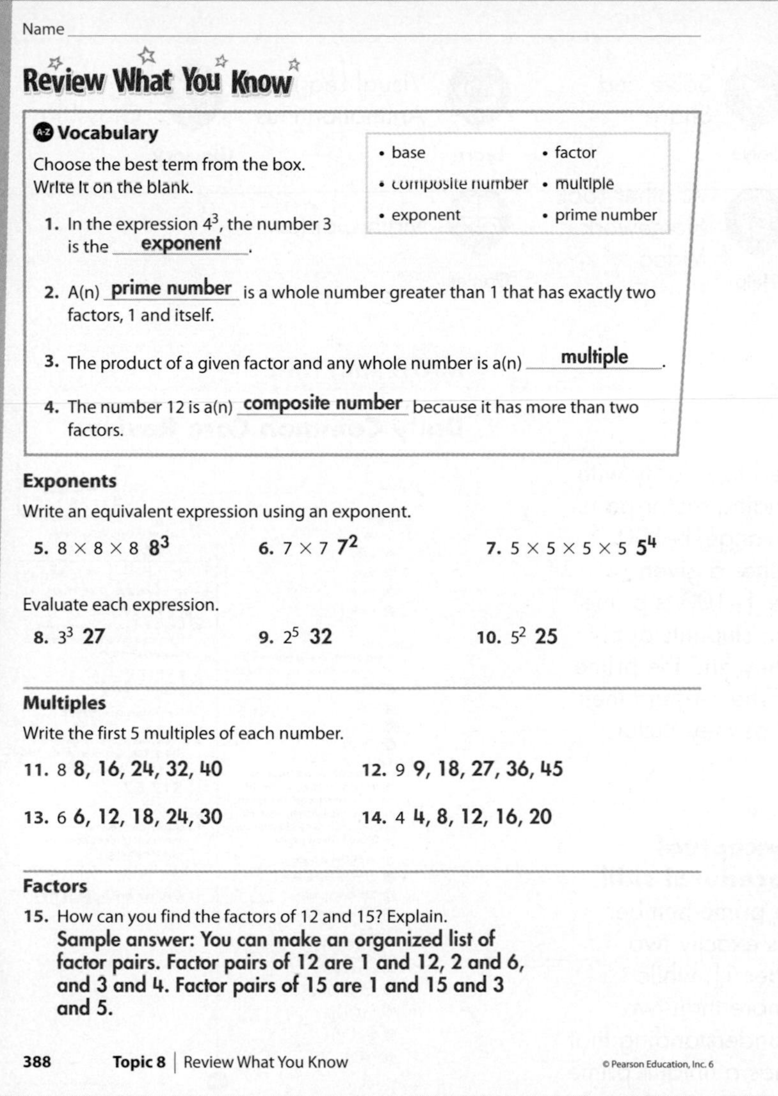

Name ____________

## Review What You Know

**Vocabulary**

Choose the best term from the box. Write it on the blank.

- base
- composite number
- exponent
- factor
- multiple
- prime number

1. In the expression $4^3$, the number 3 is the **exponent**.
2. A(n) **prime number** is a whole number greater than 1 that has exactly two factors, 1 and itself.
3. The product of a given factor and any whole number is a(n) **multiple**.
4. The number 12 is a(n) **composite number** because it has more than two factors.

**Exponents**

Write an equivalent expression using an exponent.

5. $8 \times 8 \times 8$ **$8^3$**
6. $7 \times 7$ **$7^2$**
7. $5 \times 5 \times 5 \times 5$ **$5^4$**

Evaluate each expression.

8. $3^3$ **27**
9. $2^5$ **32**
10. $5^2$ **25**

**Multiples**

Write the first 5 multiples of each number.

11. 8 **8, 16, 24, 32, 40**
12. 9 **9, 18, 27, 36, 45**
13. 6 **6, 12, 18, 24, 30**
14. 4 **4, 8, 12, 16, 20**

**Factors**

15. How can you find the factors of 12 and 15? Explain.
**Sample answer: You can make an organized list of factor pairs. Factor pairs of 12 are 1 and 12, 2 and 6, and 3 and 4. Factor pairs of 15 are 1 and 15 and 3 and 5.**

388 Topic 8 | Review What You Know



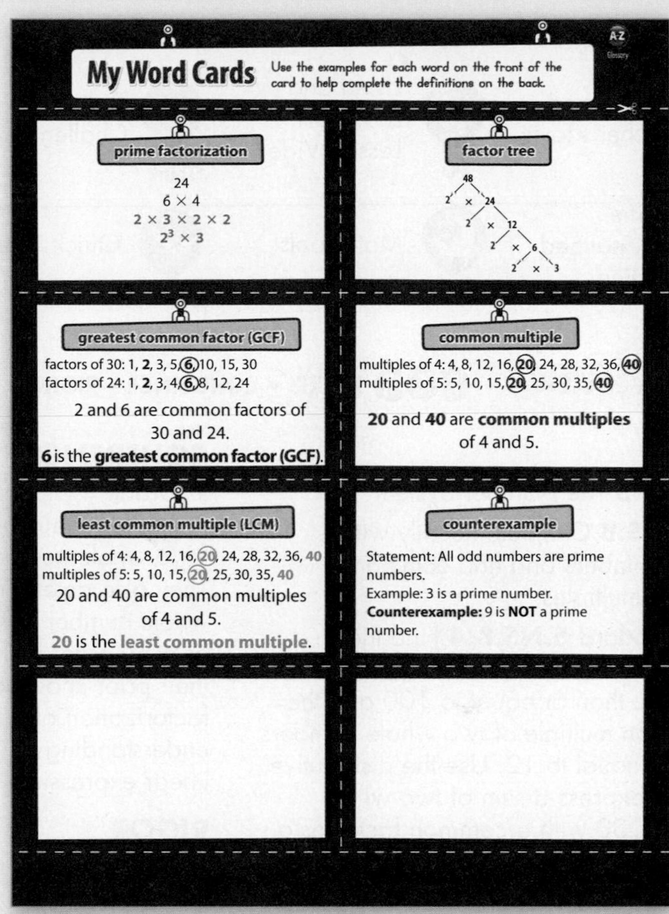

**My Word Cards** Use the examples for each word on the front of the card to help complete the definitions on the back.

**prime factorization**
24
$6 \times 4$
$2 \times 3 \times 2 \times 2$
$2^3 \times 3$

**factor tree**
48
$2 \times 24$
$2 \times 12$
$2 \times 6$
$2 \times 3$

**greatest common factor (GCF)**
factors of 30: 1, 2, 3, 5, 6, 10, 15, 30
factors of 24: 1, 2, 3, 4, 6, 8, 12, 24
2 and 6 are common factors of 30 and 24.
**6** is the **greatest common factor (GCF)**.

**common multiple**
multiples of 4: 4, 8, 12, 16, 20, 24, 28, 32, 36, 40
multiples of 5: 5, 10, 15, 20, 25, 30, 35, 40
**20** and **40** are **common multiples** of 4 and 5.

**least common multiple (LCM)**
multiples of 4: 4, 8, 12, 16, 20, 24, 28, 32, 36, 40
multiples of 5: 5, 10, 15, 20, 25, 30, 35, 40
20 and 40 are common multiples of 4 and 5.
**20** is the **least common multiple.**

**counterexample**
Statement: All odd numbers are prime numbers.
Example: 3 is a prime number.
**Counterexample:** 9 is **NOT** a prime number.

**My Word Cards** Complete the definition. Extend learning by writing your own definitions.

A diagram that shows the prime factorization of a number is called a **factor tree**.

A number written as a product of prime factors is called a **prime factorization**.

A multiple of two or more numbers is a **common multiple**.

The greatest number that is a factor of two or more numbers is the **greatest common factor (GCF)**.

An example that shows that a statement is false is a **counterexample**.

The least number, not including 0, that is a common multiple of two or more numbers is the **least common multiple (LCM)**.

## RtI Item Analysis for Diagnosis and Intervention

| Item | Standard | MDIS |
|---|---|---|
| 1–4 | 4.OA.B.4, 6.EE.A.1 | G57, G60 |
| 5–10 | 6.EE.A.1 | G60 |
| 11–14 | 4.OA.B.4 | G24, G27, G28 |
| 15 | 4.OA.B.4 | G57 |

## Topic 8 Vocabulary Words Activity

Use the Topic 1 activity on p. 3–4 with the Topic 8 words at the right.

# LESSON 8-1

## PRIME AND COMPOSITE NUMBERS

### DIGITAL RESOURCES PearsonRealize.com

 Student and Teacher eTexts
eText

 Listen and Look For Lesson Video
PD

 Today's Challenge
Think

 Solve and Share
Solve

 Visual Learning Animation Plus
Learn

 Animated Glossary
Glossary

 Online Personalized Practice
Practice Buddy

  Math Tools
Tools

 Quick Check
Assessment

Another Look Homework Video
Help

  Math Games
Games

### LESSON OVERVIEW FCR FOCUS • COHERENCE • RIGOR

**FOCUS**

**Domain 6.NS** The Number System

**Cluster 6.NS.B** Compute fluently with multi-digit numbers and find common factors and multiples.

**Content Standard 6.NS.B.4** Find the greatest common factor of two whole numbers less than or equal to 100 and the least common multiple of two whole numbers less than or equal to 12. Use the distributive property to express a sum of two whole numbers 1–100 with a common factor as a multiple of a sum of two whole numbers with no common factor. *For example, express 36 + 8 as 4 (9 + 2).*

**Mathematical Practices MP.2, MP.3, MP.6, MP.7**

**Objective** Identify prime and composite numbers, and write the prime factorization of a number.

**Essential Understanding** Any number can be written as a unique product of prime numbers called its prime factorization.

**Vocabulary** Prime factorization, Factor tree

**COHERENCE**

In Grade 4, students gained familiarity with factors and multiples by finding factor pairs for a whole number in the range 1–100. They also determined whether a given whole number in the range 1–100 is prime or composite. In this lesson, students apply their prior knowledge as they find the prime factorization of a number. They extend their understanding in Grade 7 as they factor linear expressions.

**RIGOR**

This lesson emphasizes **conceptual understanding** and **procedural skill**. Students understand that a prime number is a whole number that has exactly two factors (itself and the number 1), while a composite number has more than two factors. They develop the understanding that every composite number has a unique prime factorization and learn how to use a factor tree to find it.

 Watch the Listen and Look For Lesson Video.

### MATH ANYTIME

**Daily Common Core Review**

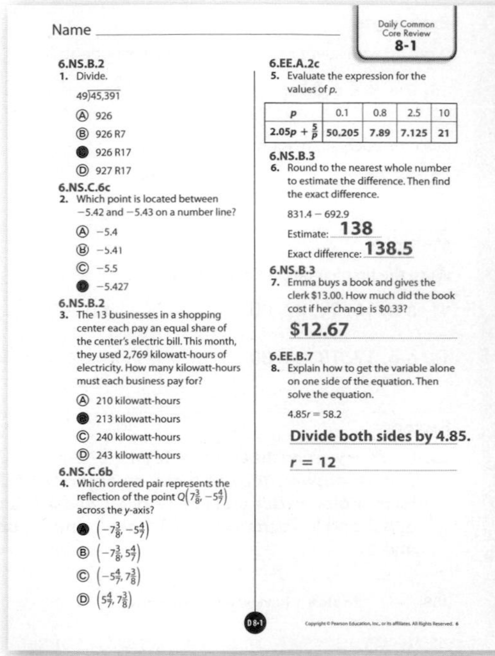

Name ____________

Daily Common Core Review 8-1

6.NS.B.2
1. Divide.
$49\overline{)45,391}$
Ⓐ 926
Ⓑ 926 R7
● 926 R17
Ⓓ 927 R17

6.NS.C.6c
2. Which point is located between −5.42 and −5.43 on a number line?
Ⓐ −5.4
Ⓑ −5.41
Ⓒ −5.5
● −5.427

6.NS.B.2
3. The 13 businesses in a shopping center each pay an equal share of the center's electric bill. This month, they used 2,769 kilowatt-hours of electricity. How many kilowatt-hours must each business pay for?
Ⓐ 210 kilowatt-hours
● 213 kilowatt-hours
Ⓒ 240 kilowatt-hours
Ⓓ 243 kilowatt-hours

6.NS.C.6b
4. Which ordered pair represents the reflection of the point $Q\left(7\frac{3}{8}, -5\frac{4}{7}\right)$ across the $y$-axis?
● $\left(-7\frac{3}{8}, -5\frac{4}{7}\right)$
Ⓑ $\left(-7\frac{3}{8}, 5\frac{4}{7}\right)$
Ⓒ $\left(-5\frac{4}{7}, 7\frac{3}{8}\right)$
Ⓓ $\left(5\frac{4}{7}, 7\frac{3}{8}\right)$

6.EE.A.2c
5. Evaluate the expression for the values of $p$.

| $p$ | 0.1 | 0.8 | 2.5 | 10 |
|---|---|---|---|---|
| $2.05p + \frac{5}{p}$ | 50.205 | 7.89 | 7.125 | 21 |

6.NS.B.3
6. Round to the nearest whole number to estimate the difference. Then find the exact difference.
831.4 − 692.9
Estimate: 138
Exact difference: 138.5

6.NS.B.3
7. Emma buys a book and gives the clerk $13.00. How much did the book cost if her change is $0.33?
$12.67

6.EE.B.7
8. Explain how to get the variable alone on one side of the equation. Then solve the equation.
$4.85r = 58.2$
Divide both sides by 4.85.
$r = 12$

D 8-1

Copyright © Pearson Education, Inc., or its affiliates. All Rights Reserved. 6

**Today's Challenge**

Think Use the Topic 8 problems any time during this topic.

### ENGLISH LANGUAGE LEARNERS ELL

**Speaking** Speak using content area vocabulary in context.

*Use with the Visual Learning Bridge on Student's Edition p. 392.*

Read Box A. Write *prime number* and *composite number*. *A prime number has exactly two factors, 1 and itself. A composite number has more than two factors.* Write 5 = 1 × 5. *5 is a prime number because its only factors are 1 and 5.* Write 12 = 1 × 12, 12 = 2 × 6, 12 = 3 × 4. *12 is a composite number because it has more than two factors.*

**Beginning** Write 2. *Is 2 a prime or composite number?* Have students respond using the sentence stem: 2 is a ____ ____. [prime number] *How do you know?* Have students respond using the sentence stem: 2 has only ___ ____. [two factors] Continue the process with the numbers 14, 7, and 20.

**Intermediate** Write 2. *Is 2 a prime or composite number? How do you know?* Have students respond using the sentence stem: 2 is a ____ ____ because _____. Continue the process with the numbers 14, 7, and 20.

**Advanced** Write the numbers 2, 7, 14, and 20. Ask students to work with partners to determine whether each number is prime or composite and explain their reasoning. Instruct students to find additional examples. Have student pairs share their prime and composite numbers with other pairs and explain why each number is prime or composite.

**Summarize** What are *prime* and *composite numbers?*

# DEVELOP: PROBLEM-BASED LEARNING

**COHERENCE: Engage learners by connecting prior knowledge to new ideas.**
Students apply their understanding of factors and multiples as they find all the possible factor pairs for a given whole number and interpret the factor pairs within a real-world context.

10–15 min

Solve

## BEFORE

**1. Pose the Solve-and-Share Problem**
**MP.7 Use Structure** Listen and look for students who write factor pairs in an orderly and structured way as they find the possible lengths and widths of the garden.

**2. Build Understanding**
*How do you find the area of a rectangle?* [Use the formula $A = \ell \times w$.] *Why is there more than one answer to the problem?* [Sample answer: Different number combinations for the dimensions of the garden can result in an area of 24 square units.]

## DURING

**3. Ask Guiding Questions As Needed**
*What operations can you use to solve this problem?* [Multiplication and division] *What are factors of a number?* [All of the numbers that can be multiplied to get that number] *What is the product in this problem?* [24]

## AFTER

**4. Share and Discuss Solutions**
Solve Start with students' solutions. If needed, project Rachel's work to discuss how to use all of the factors of 24 to list the possible garden dimensions.

**5. Transition to the Visual Learning Bridge**
*You can represent whole numbers as a product of two factors, called a factor pair. A prime number has only two factors, 1 and itself. A composite number has the factors 1 and itself, as well as other whole numbers.*

**6. Extension for Early Finishers**
Have students work in pairs. *Find whole-number dimensions for a garden with an area of 31 square units.* [31 by 1 and 1 by 31]

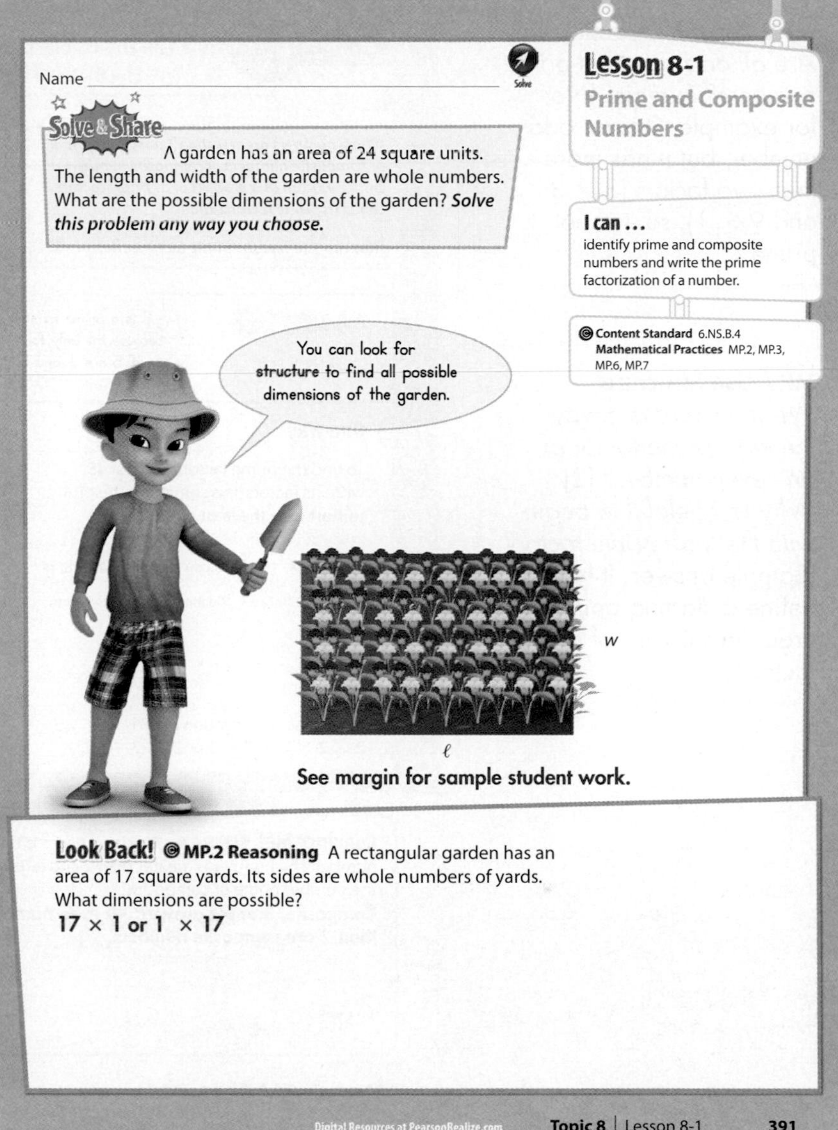

Name

Solve & Share

A garden has an area of 24 square units. The length and width of the garden are whole numbers. What are the possible dimensions of the garden? *Solve this problem any way you choose.*

**Lesson 8-1**
Prime and Composite Numbers

**I can ...**
identify prime and composite numbers and write the prime factorization of a number.

**Content Standard** 6.NS.B.4
**Mathematical Practices** MP.2, MP.3, MP.6, MP.7

You can look for structure to find all possible dimensions of the garden.
w
ℓ



**See margin for sample student work.**

**Look Back!** **MP.2 Reasoning** A rectangular garden has an area of 17 square yards. Its sides are whole numbers of yards. What dimensions are possible?
**17 × 1 or 1 × 17**

Digital Resources at PearsonRealize.com **Topic 8** | Lesson 8-1 **391**

## Analyze Student Work

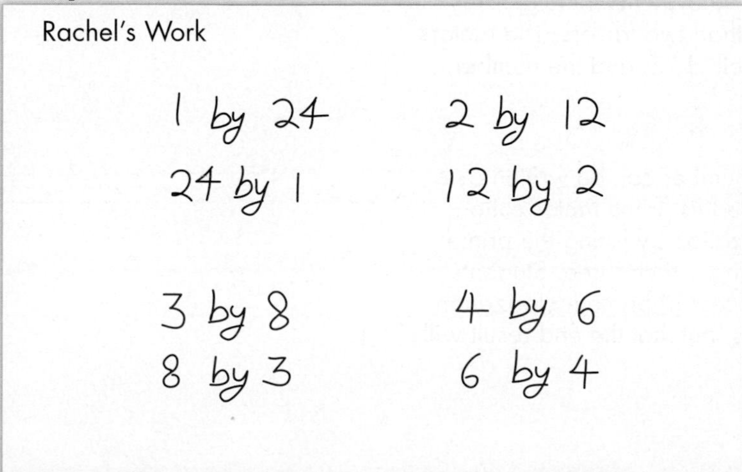

Rachel's Work
1 by 24
24 by 1
2 by 12
12 by 2
3 by 8
8 by 3
4 by 6
6 by 4



Rachel correctly lists all of the possible factor pairs of 24 as possible garden dimensions.

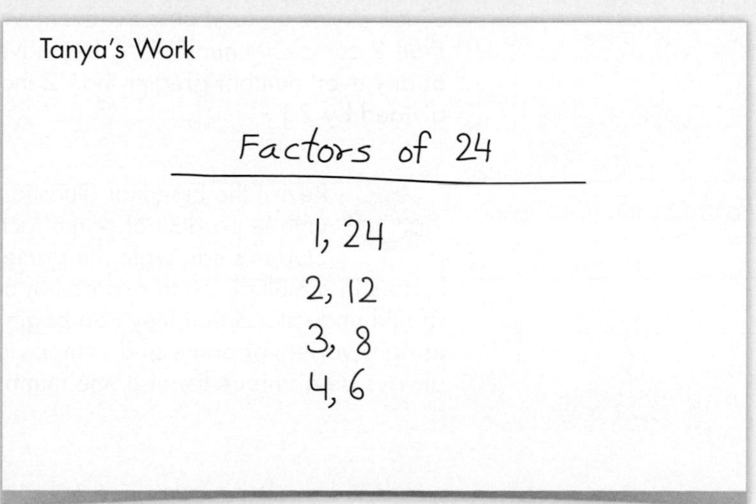

Tanya's Work
Factors of 24
1, 24
2, 12
3, 8
4, 6



Tanya lists all of the possible factors of 24, but she does not interpret them as possible dimensions for the garden.

# DEVELOP: VISUAL LEARNING

The *Visual Learning Bridge* connects students' thinking in Solve & Share to important math ideas in the lesson. Use the *Visual Learning Bridge* to make these ideas explicit. Also available as a *Visual Learning Animation Plus* at PearsonRealize.com

ELL Visual Learning

PEARSON realize. PearsonRealize.com

Learn Glossary

**MP.2 Reason Quantitatively** *Are all odd numbers prime numbers? Explain.* [No; for example, 9 is an odd number, but it has more than two factors (3 × 3 and 9 × 1), so it is not prime.]

**MP.7 Use Structure** *What number is always the least prime factor of any even number?* [2] *Why is it helpful to begin with the least prime factor?* [Sample answer: It helps define a starting point and organizes the list of prime factors.]

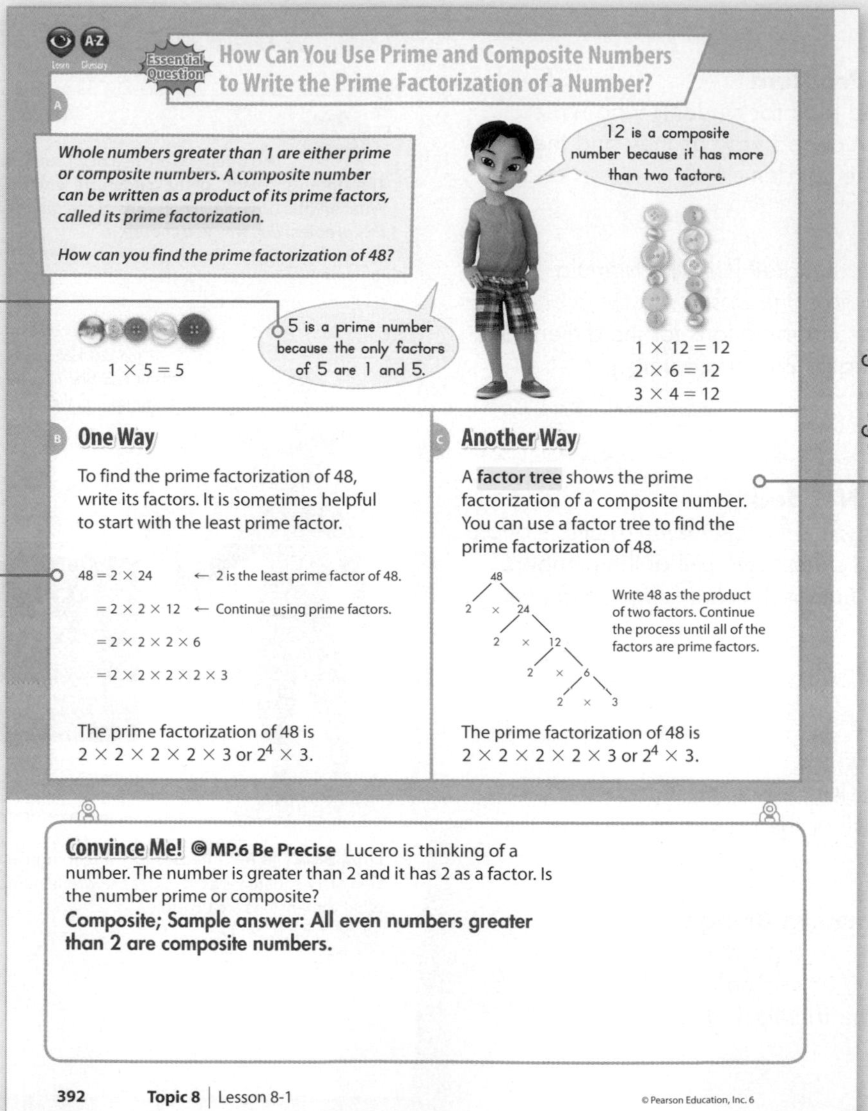


Visual Learning Bridge

**MP.7 Use Structure** *Could you use 4 × 12 as the first pair of factors in the factor tree? Explain.* [Yes; Sample answer: You can start with any two factors. You just need to continue finding factors until they are all prime.] *How can you check that the prime factorization is correct?* [You can multiply all of the prime factors and confirm that the product is 48.]

**Convince Me! MP.6 Be Precise** *Is the number 2 prime or composite? Explain.* [Prime; its only factors are 2 and 1.] *If a number is divisible by 2, what type of number is it?* [Even] *Why are all even numbers greater than 2 composite numbers?* [They have more than two factors. The factors of any even number greater than 2 include itself, 1, 2, and the number divided by 2.]

Essential Question Revisit the Essential Question. Any number can be written as a unique product of prime factors called its prime factorization. Students can write the prime factorization by listing the prime factors in a multiplication expression or by using a factor tree. Students should understand that they can begin the process of prime factorization using a variety of prime and composite factors, but that the end result will always be a unique list of prime numbers.

**QUICK CHECK**

Check mark indicates items for prescribing differentiation on the next page. Items 13 and 23 are worth 1 point. Item 21 is worth up to 3 points.

20–30 min

Practice Buddy

Tools

Assessment

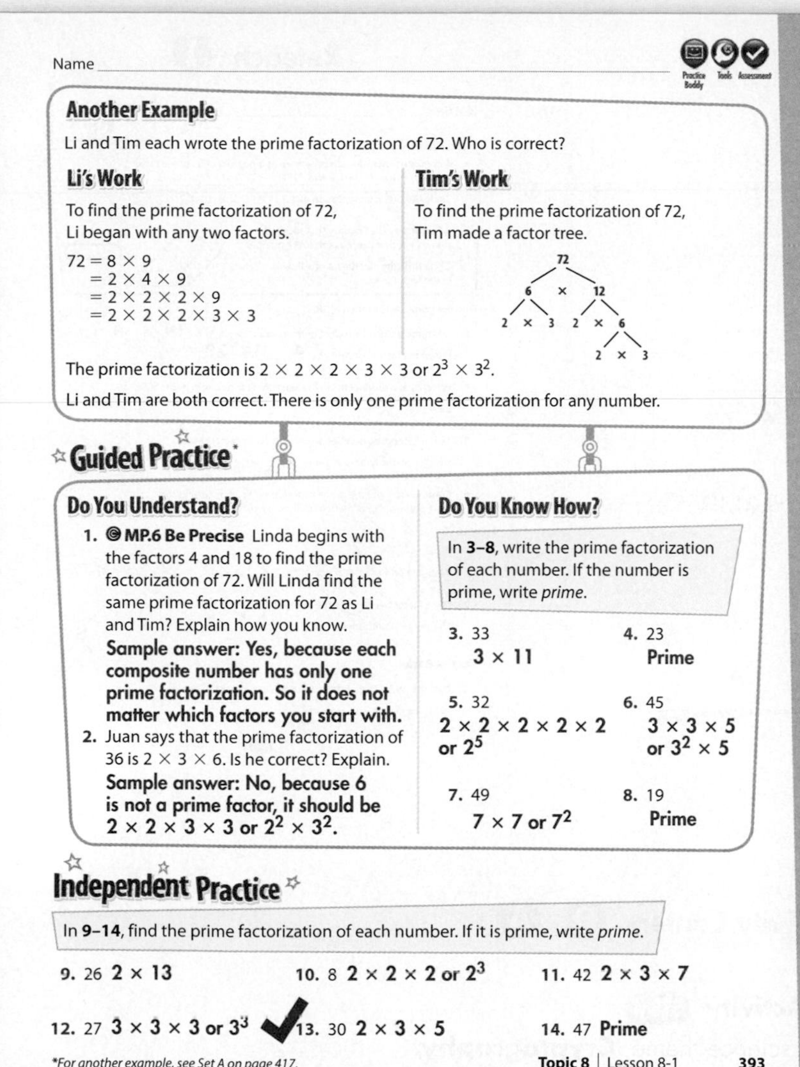

Name ______

## Another Example

Li and Tim each wrote the prime factorization of 72. Who is correct?

**Li's Work**

To find the prime factorization of 72, Li began with any two factors.

72 = 8 × 9
= 2 × 4 × 9
= 2 × 2 × 2 × 9
= 2 × 2 × 2 × 3 × 3

**Tim's Work**

To find the prime factorization of 72, Tim made a factor tree.



The prime factorization is $2 \times 2 \times 2 \times 3 \times 3$ or $2^3 \times 3^2$.

Li and Tim are both correct. There is only one prime factorization for any number.

## Guided Practice*

**Do You Understand?**

1. MP.6 Be Precise Linda begins with the factors 4 and 18 to find the prime factorization of 72. Will Linda find the same prime factorization for 72 as Li and Tim? Explain how you know.
**Sample answer: Yes, because each composite number has only one prime factorization. So it does not matter which factors you start with.**

2. Juan says that the prime factorization of 36 is 2 × 3 × 6. Is he correct? Explain.
**Sample answer: No, because 6 is not a prime factor, it should be $2 \times 2 \times 3 \times 3$ or $2^2 \times 3^2$.**

**Do You Know How?**

In **3–8**, write the prime factorization of each number. If the number is prime, write *prime*.

3. 33 **3 × 11**
4. 23 **Prime**
5. 32 **$2 \times 2 \times 2 \times 2 \times 2$ or $2^5$**
6. 45 **$3 \times 3 \times 5$ or $3^2 \times 5$**
7. 49 **$7 \times 7$ or $7^2$**
8. 19 **Prime**

## Independent Practice

In **9–14**, find the prime factorization of each number. If it is prime, write *prime*.

9. 26 **2 × 13**
10. 8 **$2 \times 2 \times 2$ or $2^3$**
11. 42 **2 × 3 × 7**
12. 27 **$3 \times 3 \times 3$ or $3^3$**
13. 30 **2 × 3 × 5** ✔
14. 47 **Prime**

*For another example, see Set A on page 417.



## Math Practices and Problem Solving

15. A triangle has a 60°, a 30°, and a 90° angle. Is the triangle acute, right, or obtuse?
**Right**

16. Chris says that the expression $31{,}521g \div 61 - 15{,}205 + 13{,}908$ can be evaluated by dividing 31,521*g* by 61, then subtracting 15,205, and finally adding 13,908. Do you agree? Explain.
**Sample answer: Chris is correct; The order of operations was correctly followed.**

17. MP.3 Critique Reasoning Gabrielle and John each wrote the prime factorization of 64. Analyze their work and explain any errors.
**Sample answer: Both Gabrielle and John found the correct prime factorization of 64. John listed the factors until all factors are prime numbers and Gabrielle used a factor tree.**

Gabrielle's Work: 64; 8, 8; 2, 4, 2, 4; 2, 2, 2, 2; 64 = 2 × 2 × 2 × 2 × 2 × 2 = $2^6$

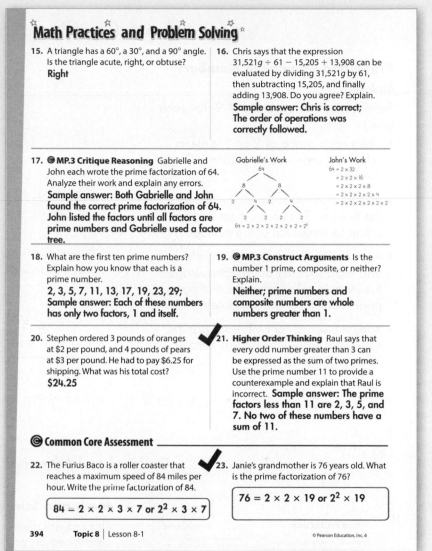

John's Work:
64 = 2 × 32
= 2 × 2 × 16
= 2 × 2 × 2 × 8
= 2 × 2 × 2 × 2 × 4
= 2 × 2 × 2 × 2 × 2 × 2

18. What are the first ten prime numbers? Explain how you know that each is a prime number.
**2, 3, 5, 7, 11, 13, 17, 19, 23, 29; Sample answer: Each of these numbers has only two factors, 1 and itself.**

19. MP.3 Construct Arguments Is the number 1 prime, composite, or neither? Explain.
**Neither; prime numbers and composite numbers are whole numbers greater than 1.**

20. Stephen ordered 3 pounds of oranges at $2 per pound, and 4 pounds of pears at $3 per pound. He had to pay $6.25 for shipping. What was his total cost?
**$24.25**

21. ✔ Higher Order Thinking Raul says that every odd number greater than 3 can be expressed as the sum of two primes. Use the prime number 11 to provide a counterexample and explain that Raul is incorrect. **Sample answer: The prime factors less than 11 are 2, 3, 5, and 7. No two of these numbers have a sum of 11.**

### Common Core Assessment

22. The Furius Baco is a roller coaster that reaches a maximum speed of 84 miles per hour. Write the prime factorization of 84.
**$84 = 2 \times 2 \times 3 \times 7$ or $2^2 \times 3 \times 7$**

23. ✔ Janie's grandmother is 76 years old. What is the prime factorization of 76?
**$76 = 2 \times 2 \times 19$ or $2^2 \times 19$**





**Another Example** *How are the two methods for finding the prime factorization of 72 alike?* [They both start with two composite factors, and they both result in the same prime factorization.] *How are they different?* [They start with different factors of 72; one method lists the factors in a multiplication expression, and the other uses a factor tree.]

**Error Intervention: Items 3–8**

**If** students are having trouble finding the prime factorizations,

**then** suggest students try dividing the given number by a very small number like 2 or 3. Some numbers like 49 do not divide evenly by 2 or 3, so students should persevere until they can conclude that there are no factors other than 1 and the number itself.

**Reteaching** Assign Reteaching Set A on p. 417.

**Items 9–14** Encourage students to use divisibility rules to help them determine whether a number is prime or composite.

**Item 17 MP.3 Critique Reasoning** Have students compare the two methods of prime factorization and show why both final expressions are the same.

**Item 19 MP.3 Construct Arguments** Ask students to read the definitions of prime numbers and composite numbers from the glossary or another math dictionary. Encourage them to apply the constraints included in the definition to determine whether the number 1 is prime, composite, or neither.

**Multi-Step Problems** *Page 394 Item 20; Page 396 Items 19, 22, and 23*

# STEP 3 ASSESS AND DIFFERENTIATE

Use the **QUICK CHECK** on the previous page to prescribe differentiated instruction.

**I Intervention** 0–3 points on the Quick Check

**O On-Level** 4 points on the Quick Check

**A Advanced** 5 points on the Quick Check

## Intervention Activity 

### Prime and Composite Numbers

**Materials**

Set of index cards labeled 0–9, for each group

- Have each group of 2 or 3 students select two index cards to form a 2-digit number.
- Instruct students to list all the factors for the number. Then have them find the prime factorization of the number.
- Ask volunteers to write their numbers and factors on the board. Encourage the class to tell whether the number is a prime number or a composite number.
- Repeat this activity by having groups select two more index cards to form another 2-digit number.

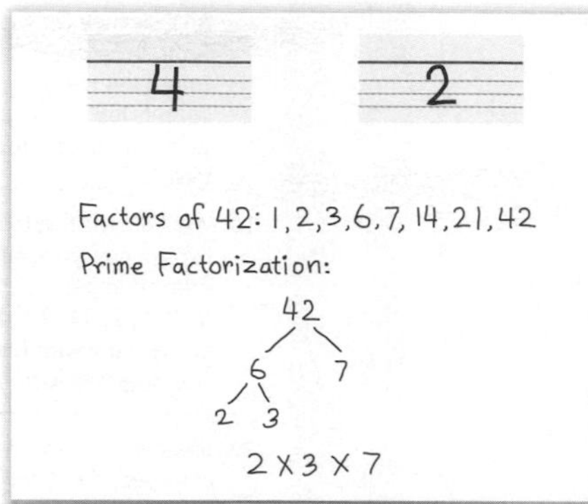


## Reteach I

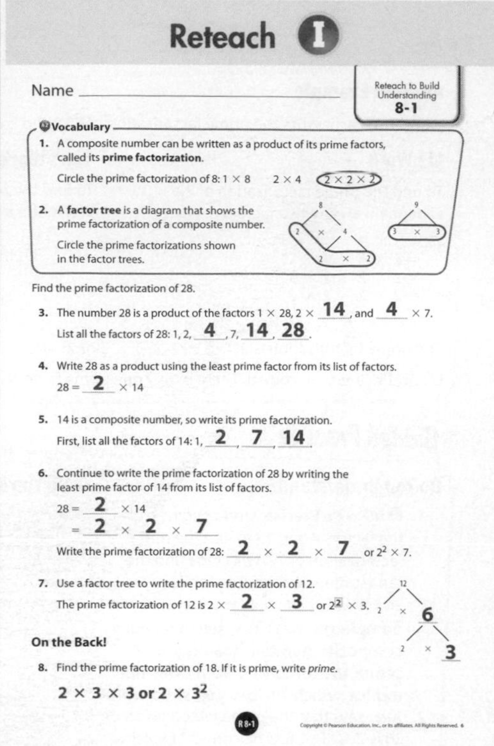

Name ______

Reteach to Build Understanding 8-1

**Vocabulary**

1. A composite number can be written as a product of its prime factors, called its **prime factorization**.

   Circle the prime factorization of 8: 1 × 8 2 × 4 (2 × 2 × 2)

2. A **factor tree** is a diagram that shows the prime factorization of a composite number.

   Circle the prime factorizations shown in the factor trees.

Find the prime factorization of 28.

3. The number 28 is a product of the factors 1 × 28, 2 × **14**, and **4** × 7.

   List all the factors of 28: 1, 2, **4**, 7, **14**, **28**.

4. Write 28 as a product using the least prime factor from its list of factors.

   28 = **2** × 14

5. 14 is a composite number, so write its prime factorization.

   First, list all the factors of 14: 1, **2**, **7**, **14**.

6. Continue to write the prime factorization of 28 by writing the least prime factor of 14 from its list of factors.

   28 = **2** × 14
   = **2** × **2** × **7**

   Write the prime factorization of 28: **2** × **2** × **7** or $2^2 \times 7$.

7. Use a factor tree to write the prime factorization of 12.

   The prime factorization of 12 is 2 × **2** × **3** or $2^{\mathbf{2}} \times 3$.

**On the Back!**

8. Find the prime factorization of 18. If it is prime, write *prime*.

   **$2 \times 3 \times 3$ or $2 \times 3^2$**

R 8-1



## On-Level and Advanced Activity Centers  

Name ______

Math and Science Activity 8-1

### Prime Protection

*Did You Know?* Prime numbers are used to generate public keys that are used to encrypt private information, like personal data and bank and credit card account numbers. Two very large prime numbers are multiplied together to generate a composite number, or public key, that is difficult to factor. The prime factors are the private keys and are the only keys that can be used to access or decode the encrypted data.

Public Key RSA-210 = 2452466449
0027821197651766357308801846
7026787678332759743414451715
0616008300385872169522083993
3207154910362682719167986407
9776723243005600592035631246
5612184658179041001318592996
1993381701214933503487587055
1067

1. Multiplying a prime number between 300 and 310 by another prime number between 707 and 710 generates an encryption key used to encode a message. What are the two private keys and the encryption key?

   **307 × 709 = 217,663**

2. The relatively weak security key 13191623 was used to encrypt personal data. Multiplying two prime numbers less than 4,000 generated the code. There are 550 prime numbers less than 4,000. Explain how you can break the code.

   **Sample answer: You can divide 13,191,623 by each prime number less than 4,000 until you get a quotient that is also prime.**

3. If you know that 3,307 is one of the prime factors used to generate the encryption key in Problem 2, what is the other private key you need to decode the message? Explain how you know.

   **3,989; Because the encryption key 13,191,623 is a product of two primes, and I know one of those primes is 3,307, I can divide 13,191,623 ÷ 3,307 = 3,989.**

4. **Extension** Generate your own encryption key by multiplying two prime numbers. Use the Internet and other technology to find prime number factors greater than 10,000.

   **Check students' work.**

Math and Science Activity 8-1



### Math and Science Activity STEM

This activity revisits the science theme, **Cryptography,** introduced on page 387 in the Student's Edition.

### Sample Student Work

4. Two prime numbers greater than 10,000 are 10,007 and 10,837.

   10,007 x 10,837 = 108,445,859

   So, 108,445,859 can be an encryption key.

**TIMING**

The time allocated to Step 3 will depend on the teacher's instructional decisions and differentiation routines.

15–30 min

PEARSON realize. PearsonRealize.com

Help | Practice Buddy | Tools | Games

## Technology Center    

Tools Games

### Math Tools and Math Games

A link to a specific math tools activity or math game to use with this lesson is provided at PearsonRealize.com.

## Leveled Assignment

 Items 1–6, 16–22, 26, 27  Items 7–12, 19–23, 25–27  Items 13–27

Name ____________________

### Homework & Practice 8-1

**Prime and Composite Numbers**

**Another Look!**

You can find the prime factorization of a composite number by breaking it down into prime factors or by using a factor tree. Find the prime factorization of 36.

$36 = \mathbf{2} \times 18$
$= 2 \times \mathbf{2} \times 9$
$= 2 \times 2 \times \mathbf{3} \times \mathbf{3}$

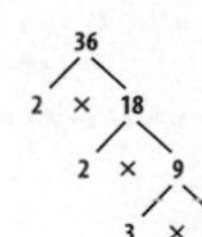


Remember, a prime number has exactly two factors, 1 and itself. A composite number has more than two factors.

The prime factorization of 36 is $2 \times 2 \times 3 \times 3$ or $2^2 \times 3^2$.

In **1–18**, find the prime factorization of each number. If it is prime, write *prime*.

1. 38
**$2 \times 19$**

2. 75
**$3 \times 5 \times 5$ or $3 \times 5^2$**

3. 20
**$2 \times 2 \times 5$ or $2^2 \times 5$**

4. 90
**$2 \times 3 \times 3 \times 5$ or $2 \times 3^2 \times 5$**

5. 66
**$2 \times 3 \times 11$**

6. 52
**$2 \times 2 \times 13$ or $2^2 \times 13$**

7. 86
**$2 \times 43$**

8. 27
**$3 \times 3 \times 3$ or $3^3$**

9. 99
**$3 \times 3 \times 11$ or $3^2 \times 11$**

10. 25
**$5 \times 5$ or $5^2$**

11. 49
**$7 \times 7$ or $7^2$**

12. 50
**$2 \times 5 \times 5$ or $2 \times 5^2$**

13. 68
**$2 \times 2 \times 17$ or $2^2 \times 17$**

14. 85
**$5 \times 17$**

15. 7
**Prime**

16. 97
**Prime**

17. 41
**Prime**

18. 100
**$2 \times 2 \times 5 \times 5$ or $2^2 \times 5^2$**



19. **MP.6 Be Precise** A sports car goes from 15 feet per second to 110 feet per second in 5 seconds. Use the formula $a = \frac{(f-s)}{t}$, where $a$ is the acceleration, $f$ is the final speed, $s$ is the starting speed, and $t$ is the time it takes to make the change. What is the acceleration (in feet per second squared) of the sports car?
**19 ft/s$^2$**

20. **Number Sense** Write the next three numbers in this pattern. Then describe the pattern.
7 3 11 7 15 11 19 15 23
**19, 27, 23; The pattern is subtract 4, add 8.**

21. **MP.2 Reasoning** Alisa's birthdate is a prime number in December. The date is between December 15 and December 20. What are Alisa's possible birthdates?
**December 17th or December 19th**

22. Evaluate the expression $(5^3 + 9) - 12 \div \frac{6}{2}$.
**130**

23. **MP.2 Reasoning** Mrs. James displayed the factor tree at the right on the board. Complete the factor tree to find the number that has a prime factorization of $2^4 \times 3$.

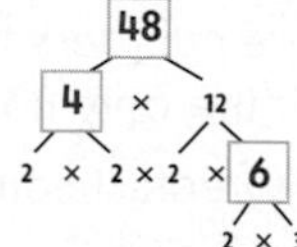


24. **MP.3 Construct Arguments** Tricia says that 2 is the only even prime number. Explain why Tricia is correct.
**Sample answer: Tricia is correct because 2 is the least prime number and is a factor of every other even number.**

25. **Higher Order Thinking** Martise says that the first 5 odd numbers greater than 2 are prime numbers. Provide a counterexample and explain why Martise is incorrect.
**Sample answer: 9, the fourth odd number greater than 2, is not a prime number. 9 is a composite number with a prime factorization of $3^2$.**

### Common Core Assessment

26. An average sixth grader takes 18 breaths per minute. What is the prime factorization of 18?
**$18 = 2 \times 3 \times 3$ or $2 \times 3^2$**

27. A jaguar at the local zoo weighs 100 kilograms. What is the prime factorization of 100?
**$100 = 2 \times 2 \times 5 \times 5$ or $2^2 \times 5^2$**

# LESSON 8-2

## FIND THE GREATEST COMMON FACTOR

### DIGITAL RESOURCES PearsonRealize.com

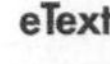
eText — Student and Teacher eTexts

PD — Listen and Look For Lesson Video

Think — Today's Challenge

Solve — Solve and Share

Learn — Visual Learning Animation Plus

Glossary — Animated Glossary

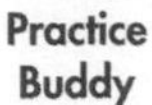
Practice Buddy — Online Personalized Practice

Tools — Math Tools

Assessment — Quick Check

Help — Another Look Homework Video

Games — Math Games

### LESSON OVERVIEW

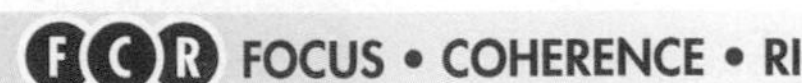
FOCUS • COHERENCE • RIGOR

#### FOCUS

**Domain 6.NS** The Number System

**Cluster 6.NS.B** Compute fluently with multi-digit numbers and find common factors and multiples.

**Content Standard 6.NS.B.4** Find the greatest common factor of two whole numbers less than or equal to 100 and the least common multiple of two whole numbers less than or equal to 12. Use the distributive property to express a sum of two whole numbers 1–100 with a common factor as a multiple of a sum of two whole numbers with no common factor. *For example, express $36 + 8$ as $4(9 + 2)$.*

**Mathematical Practices MP.1, MP.2, MP.4, MP.5, MP.8**

**Objective** Find the greatest common factor of two whole numbers.

**Essential Understanding** The greatest common factor (GCF) is the greatest factor that two or more numbers have in common. The GCF is 1 if the only common factor is 1.

**Vocabulary** Greatest common factor (GCF)

#### COHERENCE

In Grade 5, students used multiples and factors of whole numbers to generate equivalent fractions. In Lesson 8-1, they found the prime factorization of whole numbers. In this lesson, students extend their understanding of factors and prime factorization to identify the greatest common factor (GCF) of two whole numbers. Students then use the GCF and the distributive property to write equivalent expressions and solve problems. In algebra, they will use the GCF and the distributive property when factoring polynomials.

#### RIGOR

This lesson emphasizes **conceptual understanding** and **procedural skill**. Students extend their skill of identifying the prime factors of a number to find the greatest common factor of two whole numbers. They develop an understanding of what the GCF means and apply this understanding as they solve problems.

PD Watch the Listen and Look For Lesson Video.

### MATH ANYTIME

#### Daily Common Core Review

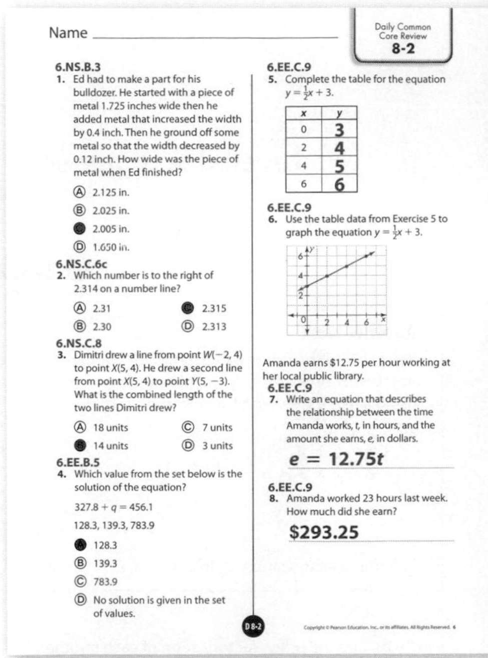
Name ______________

Daily Common Core Review 8-2

6.NS.B.3
1. Ed had to make a part for his bulldozer. He started with a piece of metal 1.725 inches wide then he added metal that increased the width by 0.4 inch. Then he ground off some metal so that the width decreased by 0.12 inch. How wide was the piece of metal when Ed finished?

Ⓐ 2.125 in.
Ⓑ 2.025 in.
● 2.005 in.
Ⓓ 1.650 in.

6.NS.C.6c
2. Which number is to the right of 2.314 on a number line?

Ⓐ 2.31 ● 2.315
Ⓑ 2.30 Ⓓ 2.313

6.NS.C.8
3. Dimitri drew a line from point $W(-2, 4)$ to point $X(5, 4)$. He drew a second line from point $X(5, 4)$ to point $Y(5, -3)$. What is the combined length of the two lines Dimitri drew?

Ⓐ 18 units Ⓒ 7 units
● 14 units Ⓓ 3 units

6.EE.B.5
4. Which value from the set below is the solution of the equation?

$327.8 + q = 456.1$

128.3, 139.3, 783.9

● 128.3
Ⓑ 139.3
Ⓒ 783.9
Ⓓ No solution is given in the set of values.

6.EE.C.9
5. Complete the table for the equation $y = \frac{1}{2}x + 3$.

| x | y |
|---|---|
| 0 | 3 |
| 2 | 4 |
| 4 | 5 |
| 6 | 6 |

6.EE.C.9
6. Use the table data from Exercise 5 to graph the equation $y = \frac{1}{2}x + 3$.

Amanda earns $12.75 per hour working at her local public library.

6.EE.C.9
7. Write an equation that describes the relationship between the time Amanda works, $t$, in hours, and the amount she earns, $e$, in dollars.

$e = 12.75t$

6.EE.C.9
8. Amanda worked 23 hours last week. How much did she earn?

$293.25

D 8-2



#### Today's Challenge

Think Use the Topic 8 problems any time during this topic.

### ENGLISH LANGUAGE LEARNERS

**Listening** Learn basic/academic vocabulary.

*Use with the Solve & Share on Student's Edition p. 397.*

Write *composite numbers* and *prime factorization*. Group students into pairs. Student A will listen to Student B define *composite numbers*, and Student B will listen to Student A define *prime factorization*. Read the Solve & Share as students listen. Instruct students to restate the problem to partners. *To solve the problem, find the greatest common factor (GCF) of 16 and 20.*

**Beginning** Write 16. *Use prime factorization to find the factors of 16.* Write 16 = ___ × ___ × ___ × ___. Instruct students to work with partners to find the prime factors of 16. Repeat the process with 20. *What is the GCF of 16 and 20?* Have students listen to partners respond using the sentence stem: ___ is the ____ ____ ___ of 16 and 20. [4, greatest common factor]

**Intermediate** Write 16 and 20. *Use prime factorization to find the factors of 16 and 20. What is the GCF of 16 and 20? How do you know?* Have students listen to partners respond using the sentence stem: ___ is the ____ ____ ___ of 16 and 20 because ____.

**Advanced** Instruct students to find the GCF of 16 and 20 using prime factorization and to listen to partners explain how prime factorization is used to find the GCF. *Could prime factorization be used to find the GCF if there were 17 sixth graders and 23 seventh graders? Explain your reasoning.*

**Summarize** How is prime factorization used to find the GCF of two numbers?

# DEVELOP: PROBLEM-BASED LEARNING

**COHERENCE: Engage learners by connecting prior knowledge to new ideas.**
Students extend what they know about identifying the factors of a number to find the greatest common factor (GCF) of two whole numbers less than or equal to 100.

10–15 min

Solve

## BEFORE

**1. Pose the Solve-and-Share Problem**
**MP.2 Reason Quantitatively** Listen and look for students who reason that the number of groups and the number of students in each group are the factor pairs of 16 and of 20.

**2. Build Understanding**
*How can you use the table to help you solve the problem?* [Sample answer: The table helps you organize the list of all possible group sizes. Then you can identify the greatest number of students who can be in each group.]

## DURING

**3. Ask Guiding Questions As Needed**
*How many sixth graders could there be in each group?* [1, 2, 4, 8, or 16] *How many seventh graders could there be in each group?* [1, 2, 4, 5, 10, or 20] *Which group sizes are common to both grades?* [1, 2, and 4] *What is the greatest group size common to both grades?* [4]

## AFTER

**4. Share and Discuss Solutions**
Solve Start with students' solutions. If needed, project Laura's work to discuss how to find the greatest common factor of 16 and 20 in order to solve the problem.

**5. Transition to the Visual Learning Bridge**
*You can use the greatest factor that is common to two numbers to solve some math problems.*

**6. Extension for Early Finishers**
*What is the greatest number of students who could be in each group if there were 18 sixth graders and 27 seventh graders?* [9]

---

Name ______________________ Solve

**Solve & Share**

There are 16 sixth graders and 20 seventh graders in the rocket club. Students will be arranged in equal groups to build models, but each group will have only sixth graders or only seventh graders. What is the greatest number of students who can be in each group? ***Solve this problem any way you choose.***

**Lesson 8-2**
**Find the Greatest Common Factor**

**I can ...**
find the greatest common factor of two numbers.

Content Standard 6.NS.B.4
Mathematical Practices MP.1, MP.2, MP.4, MP.5, MP.8

You can use **reasoning** to find a relationship between the number of equal groups of sixth graders and seventh graders.

| 16 Sixth Graders | | 20 Seventh Graders | |
|---|---|---|---|
| Number of Groups | Number of Sixth Graders in Each Group | Number of Groups | Number of Seventh Graders in Each Group |
| | | | |
| | | | |
| | | | |
| | | | |
| | | | |
| | | | |

**See margin for sample student work.**

**Look Back!** **MP.1 Make Sense and Persevere** Suppose that 4 more seventh graders join the rocket club. Now what is the greatest number of students who can be in each group?
**8**



---

## Analyze Student Work

**Laura's Work**

| 16 Sixth Graders | | 20 Seventh Graders | |
|---|---|---|---|
| Number of Groups | Number of Sixth Graders in Each Group | Number of Groups | Number of Seventh Graders in Each Group |
| 1 | 16 | 1 | 20 |
| 2 | 8 | 2 | 10 |
| (4) | (4) | 4 | 5 |
| 8 | 2 | (5) | (4) |
| 16 | 1 | 10 | 2 |
| | | 20 | 1 |

4 is the greatest number of students common to both grades.

Laura uses the table to organize the possible groups of sixth graders and seventh graders systematically. Then she finds the largest group size common to both grades.

**Lydia's Work**

16 Sixth Graders: (1), (2), (4), 8, 16
20 Seventh Graders: (1), (2), (4), 5, 10, 20
4 is the greatest number that is common in each group.

Lydia lists the factors of 16 and 20, finds the common factors, and identifies the greatest factor common to both.

# DEVELOP: VISUAL LEARNING

The *Visual Learning Bridge* connects students' thinking in Solve & Share to important math ideas in the lesson. Use the *Visual Learning Bridge* to make these ideas explicit. Also available as a *Visual Learning Animation Plus* at PearsonRealize.com

Visual Learning

PearsonRealize.com

Learn Glossary

**MP.1 Make Sense and Persevere**
*How many craft sticks are there?* [42] *How many glue bottles are there?* [12] *How do you know that the number of craft sticks and glue bottles will be different in each bag?* [You are starting with a different number of each.]

*Why are 1, 2, 3, 4, 6, and 12 factors of 12?* [Each number divides 12 with no remainder.] *How do you know that all of the factors for 42 are listed?* [Sample answer: I checked the whole numbers starting at 1 in numerical order. Once I got to 7, the pairs of factors started to repeat in reverse order (6 × 7 and 7 × 6), so I knew I was done.]

Visual Learning Bridge

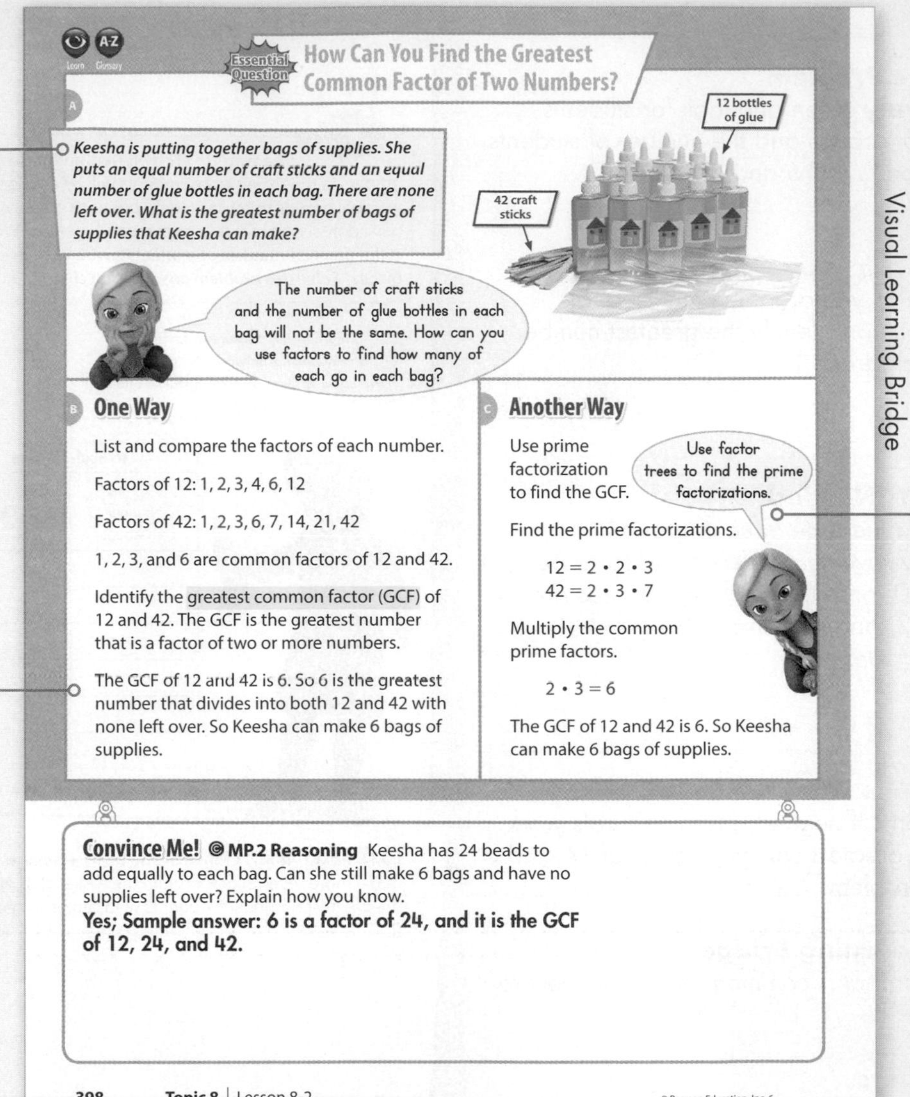

Essential Question How Can You Find the Greatest Common Factor of Two Numbers?
Keesha is putting together bags of supplies. She puts an equal number of craft sticks and an equal number of glue bottles in each bag. There are none left over. What is the greatest number of bags of supplies that Keesha can make?
12 bottles of glue
42 craft sticks
The number of craft sticks and the number of glue bottles in each bag will not be the same. How can you use factors to find how many of each go in each bag?
One Way
List and compare the factors of each number.
Factors of 12: 1, 2, 3, 4, 6, 12
Factors of 42: 1, 2, 3, 6, 7, 14, 21, 42
1, 2, 3, and 6 are common factors of 12 and 42.
Identify the greatest common factor (GCF) of 12 and 42. The GCF is the greatest number that is a factor of two or more numbers.
The GCF of 12 and 42 is 6. So 6 is the greatest number that divides into both 12 and 42 with none left over. So Keesha can make 6 bags of supplies.
Another Way
Use prime factorization to find the GCF.
Use factor trees to find the prime factorizations.
Find the prime factorizations.
12 = 2 • 2 • 3
42 = 2 • 3 • 7
Multiply the common prime factors.
2 • 3 = 6
The GCF of 12 and 42 is 6. So Keesha can make 6 bags of supplies.
Convince Me! MP.2 Reasoning Keesha has 24 beads to add equally to each bag. Can she still make 6 bags and have no supplies left over? Explain how you know.
Yes; Sample answer: 6 is a factor of 24, and it is the GCF of 12, 24, and 42.
398 Topic 8 | Lesson 8-2
© Pearson Education, Inc. 6


*What advantages are there to using prime factorization to find the GCF of two numbers?* [Sample answer: You can use a factor tree to find the prime factorization and then multiply the common factors. You don't have to worry about missing any of the factors.]

**Prevent Misconceptions** 
Students may multiply all occurrences of a common prime factor when finding the GCF. Remind students that they identify pairs of common prime factors and use each only once when multiplying.

**Convince Me! MP.2 Reason Quantitatively** *What is the prime factorization of 24?* [2 × 2 × 2 × 3] *Compare these prime factors to the common prime factors of 12 and 42. What do you notice?* [24 also has the factors 2 and 3.] *What can you conclude about the number 6?* [6 is the GCF of 12, 24, and 42.]

Revisit the Essential Question. The GCF can be found by listing the factors of each number and then identifying the greatest factor that is the same for the numbers. The GCF can also be found by determining the prime factorization of each number and then multiplying the common prime factors.

Practice Buddy | Tools | Assessment

20–30 min

## ✓ QUICK CHECK

Check mark indicates items for prescribing differentiation on the next page. Item 15 is worth 1 point. Items 21 and 22 are worth up to 2 points.

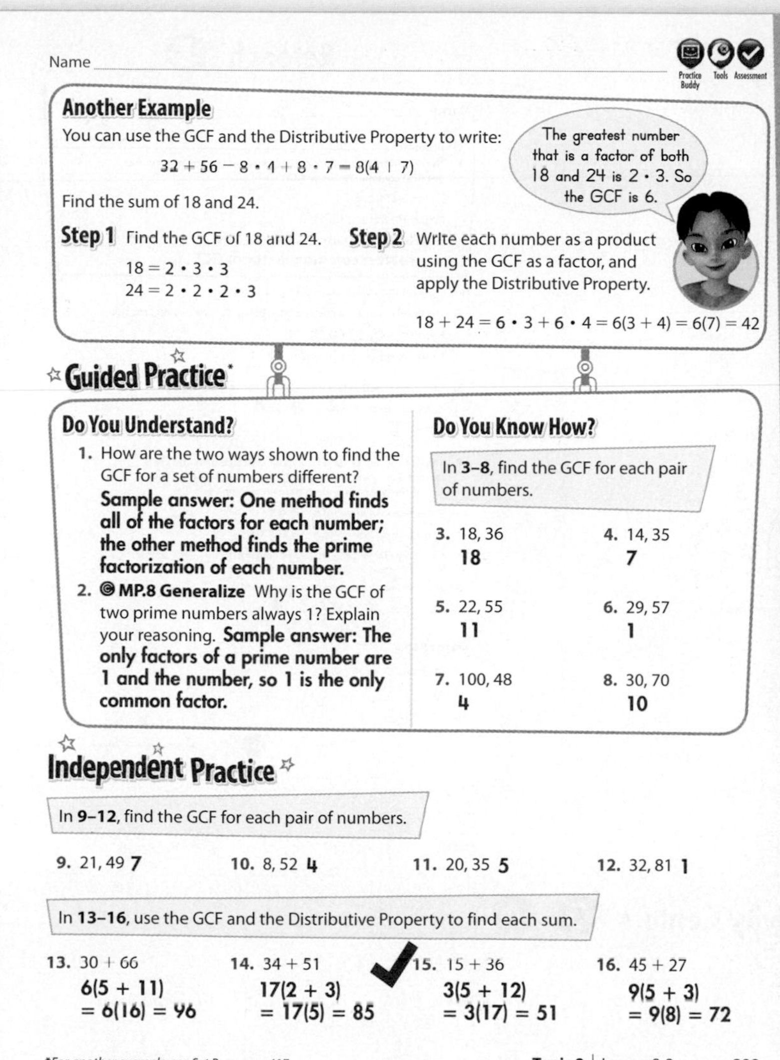

Name

### Another Example

You can use the GCF and the Distributive Property to write:

$32 + 56 = 8 \cdot 4 + 8 \cdot 7 = 8(4 + 7)$

Find the sum of 18 and 24.

**Step 1** Find the GCF of 18 and 24.

$18 = 2 \cdot 3 \cdot 3$
$24 = 2 \cdot 2 \cdot 2 \cdot 3$

**Step 2** Write each number as a product using the GCF as a factor, and apply the Distributive Property.

$18 + 24 = 6 \cdot 3 + 6 \cdot 4 = 6(3 + 4) = 6(7) = 42$

The greatest number that is a factor of both 18 and 24 is 2 • 3. So the GCF is 6.



### Guided Practice*

**Do You Understand?**

1. How are the two ways shown to find the GCF for a set of numbers different? **Sample answer: One method finds all of the factors for each number; the other method finds the prime factorization of each number.**
2. **MP.8 Generalize** Why is the GCF of two prime numbers always 1? Explain your reasoning. **Sample answer: The only factors of a prime number are 1 and the number, so 1 is the only common factor.**

**Do You Know How?**

In **3–8**, find the GCF for each pair of numbers.

3. 18, 36 **18**
4. 14, 35 **7**
5. 22, 55 **11**
6. 29, 57 **1**
7. 100, 48 **4**
8. 30, 70 **10**

### Independent Practice

In **9–12**, find the GCF for each pair of numbers.

9. 21, 49 **7**
10. 8, 52 **4**
11. 20, 35 **5**
12. 32, 81 **1**

In **13–16**, use the GCF and the Distributive Property to find each sum.

13. $30 + 66$ **$6(5 + 11) = 6(16) = 96$**
14. $34 + 51$ **$17(2 + 3) = 17(5) = 85$**
15. ✓ $15 + 36$ **$3(5 + 12) = 3(17) = 51$**
16. $45 + 27$ **$9(5 + 3) = 9(8) = 72$**

*For another example, see Set B on page 417.



### Math Practices and Problem Solving

17. **MP.4 Model with Math** The Venn diagram to the right shows the factors of 24 and 40.
   a. What is the meaning of each of the three shaded regions? **The left circle has the factors of 24; the right circle has the factors of 40; the shared region has the common factors.**
   b. Explain how you use the Venn diagram to find the GCF of 24 and 40. What is the GCF of 24 and 40? **Sample answer: The shared region shows all of the common factors, so to find the GCF, find the greatest number in the shared region. The GCF is 8.**

24: 3, 6, 12, 24 | Both: 1, 2, 4, 8 | 40: 5, 10, 20, 40

18. **MP.2 Reasoning** You have 50 blueberry scones and 75 cranberry scones. Make as many identical bags of scones as possible. Each bag should have an equal number of blueberry scones and an equal number of cranberry scones. What is the greatest number of bags you can fill? Explain how you know. **25 bags; The GCF of 50 and 75 is 25. Each bag can have 2 blueberry and 3 cranberry scones.**

19. **Algebra** The equation $3.2p = 16$ represents the total cost of $p$ pounds of fruit that Jamal bought at a farmer's market. Solve for $p$ to find the number of pounds of fruit Jamal bought. **$p = 5$ pounds**

20. **Math and Science** Periodical cicada species emerge in large numbers from their larval stage at intervals in years that are prime numbers, 13 or 17. What is the GCF of the years? **1**

21. ✓ **Higher Order Thinking** Gena has 28 trading cards, Sam has 91 trading cards, and Tiffany has 49 trading cards. Use the GCF and the Distributive Property to find the total number of trading cards Gena, Sam, and Tiffany have. **$28 + 91 + 49 = 7(4 + 13 + 7) = 7(24) = 168$**

### Common Core Assessment

22. ✓ Write the pairs of numbers in the correct box.

18, 72 57, 71
24, 60 12, 48
9, 51 17, 31

| GCF = 1 | GCF = 3 |
|---|---|
| **57, 71**<br>**17, 31** | **9, 51** |
| **GCF = 12** | **GCF = 18** |
| **24, 60**<br>**12, 48** | **18, 72** |





**Another Example** *Why would it be helpful to use the GCF and the Distributive Property to rewrite the sum of two numbers?* [Sample answer: It provides another way to find the sum and may be useful for finding the sum mentally.]

**Error Intervention: Item 7**

**If** students say that 2 is the GCF,

**then** guide them through one solution method. *What is the prime factorization of 100?* [$2 \times 2 \times 5 \times 5$] *What is the prime factorization of 48?* [$2 \times 2 \times 2 \times 2 \times 3$] Have students pair up common factors, one from each prime factorization. *How many pairs of 2's are common?* [2] *What is $2 \times 2$?* [4] *Are there any other pairs of common factors?* [No]

**Reteaching** Assign Reteaching Set B on p. 417.

**Items 13–16 Coherence** Students used the Distributive Property in Lesson 1-8 to write equivalent algebraic expressions. Here, they express a sum of two numbers with a common factor as a multiple of a sum of two numbers with no common factor. Application of the Distributive Property is a foundational concept for students' later work with factoring algebraic expressions and polynomials in Grade 7 and beyond.

**Item 17 MP.4 Model with Math** The meaning of each region should be described using correct mathematical language and include the terms *factors* and *common factors*.

**Item 18 MP.2 Reason Quantitatively** The following statement indicates that factors can be used: "Each bag should have an equal number of blueberry scones and an equal number of cranberry scones."

**Item 22** *Could any of the number pairs belong in more than one box? Explain.* [No; there is only one GCF of a number pair.]

**Multi-Step Problems** *Page 400 Items 18 and 21; Page 402 Items 15, 16, and 18*

# ASSESS AND DIFFERENTIATE

Use the **QUICK CHECK** on the previous page to prescribe differentiated instruction.

**I Intervention** 0–3 points on the Quick Check

**O On-Level** 4 points on the Quick Check

**A Advanced** 5 points on the Quick Check

## Intervention Activity 

### Find the Greatest Common Factor

- Organize students into four teams. Ask each team to use a factor tree to write the prime factorizations of 8, 12, 30, and 48 on the board.
- Then ask teams to use the prime factorizations to find the GCF of 8 and 12[4], 8 and 30[2], 8 and 48[8], and 12 and 30[6].
- Help students find the GCF by multiplying the common factors.

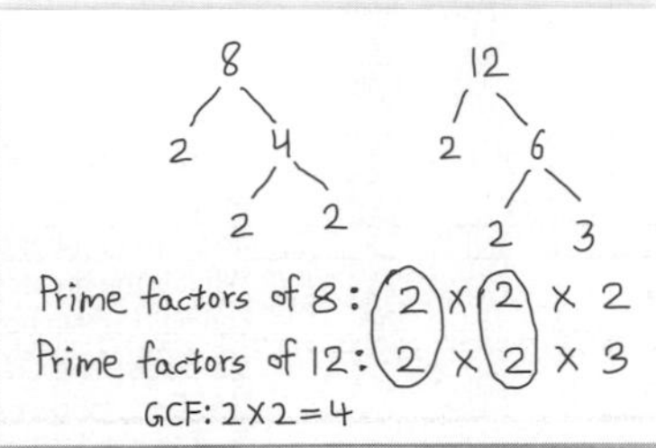


## Reteach I

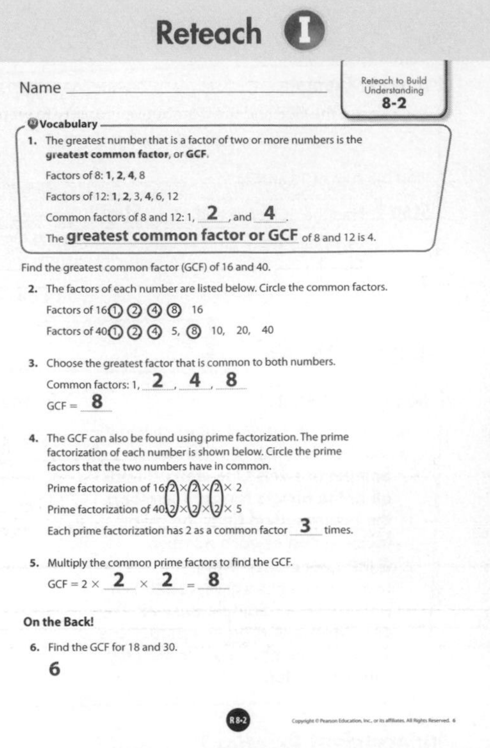

Name ____________________

Reteach to Build Understanding
**8-2**

**Vocabulary**

1. The greatest number that is a factor of two or more numbers is the **greatest common factor**, or **GCF**.

   Factors of 8: **1**, **2**, **4**, 8

   Factors of 12: **1**, **2**, 3, **4**, 6, 12

   Common factors of 8 and 12: 1, **2**, and **4**.

   The **greatest common factor or GCF** of 8 and 12 is 4.

Find the greatest common factor (GCF) of 16 and 40.

2. The factors of each number are listed below. Circle the common factors.

   Factors of 16: (1), (2), (4), (8), 16

   Factors of 40: (1), (2), (4), 5, (8), 10, 20, 40

3. Choose the greatest factor that is common to both numbers.

   Common factors: 1, **2**, **4**, **8**

   GCF = **8**

4. The GCF can also be found using prime factorization. The prime factorization of each number is shown below. Circle the prime factors that the two numbers have in common.

   Prime factorization of 16: 2 × 2 × 2 × 2

   Prime factorization of 40: 2 × 2 × 2 × 5

   Each prime factorization has 2 as a common factor **3** times.

5. Multiply the common prime factors to find the GCF.

   GCF = 2 × **2** × **2** = **8**

**On the Back!**

6. Find the GCF for 18 and 30.

   **6**

R 8•2



## On-Level and Advanced Activity Centers  

### Problem-Solving Reading Mat

Have students read the Problem-Solving Reading Mat for Topic 8 and then complete Problem-Solving Reading Activity 8-2.

See the Problem-Solving Reading Activity Guide for other suggestions on how to use this mat.

**TIMING**

The time allocated to Step 3 will depend on the teacher's instructional decisions and differentiation routines.

15–30 min

PEARSON realize.
PearsonRealize.com

Help

Practice Buddy

Tools

Games

## Technology Center   

 Tools  Games

### Math Tools and Math Games

A link to a specific math tools activity or math game to use with this lesson is provided at PearsonRealize.com.

## Leveled Assignment

 Items 1–6, 9–12, 15–17, 19  Items 1–4, 9–12, 15–19  Items 5–8, 12–19

Name ____________

Help Practice Buddy Tools Games

## Homework & Practice 8-2

### Find the Greatest Common Factor

**Another Look!**

Find the GCF of 12 and 40.

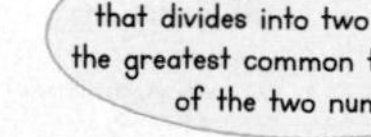

The greatest number that divides into two numbers is the greatest common factor (GCF) of the two numbers.

| List the Factors | Use Prime Factorization |
|---|---|
| **Step 1** List the factors of each number.<br>12: 1, 2, 3, 4, 6, 12<br>40: 1, 2, 4, 5, 8, 10, 20, 40 | **Step 1** Write the prime factorization of each number.<br>12: $2 \times 2 \times 3$<br>40: $2 \times 2 \times 2 \times 5$ |
| **Step 2** Circle the factors that are common to both numbers.<br>12: 1, (2), 3, (4), 6, 12<br>40: 1, (2), (4), 5, 8, 10, 20, 40 | **Step 2** Circle the prime factors that the numbers have in common.<br>12: (2) × (2) × 3<br>40: (2) × (2) × 2 × 5 |
| **Step 3** Choose the greatest factor that is common to both numbers. Both 2 and 4 are common factors, but 4 is greater. The GCF is 4. | **Step 3** Multiply the common factors.<br>$2 \times 2 = 4$ The GCF is 4. |

In **1–8**, find the GCF for each pair of numbers.

**1.** 45, 60
**15**

**2.** 24, 100
**4**

**3.** 19, 22
**1**

**4.** 14, 28
**14**

**5.** 12, 18
**6**

**6.** 60, 100
**20**

**7.** 55, 99
**11**

**8.** 83, 91
**1**

In **9–14**, use the GCF and the Distributive Property to find each sum.

**9.** 32 + 48
$16(2 + 3) = 16(5) = 80$

**10.** 15 + 57
$3(5 + 19) = 3(24) = 72$

**11.** 98 + 14
$14(7 + 1) = 14(8) = 112$

**12.** 55 + 88
$11(5 + 8) = 11(13) = 143$

**13.** 45 + 75
$15(3 + 5) = 15(8) = 120$

**14.** 81 + 99
$9(9 + 11) = 9(20) = 180$



**15. MP.5 Use Appropriate Tools** Complete the Venn diagram to show the common factors of 36 and 54. What is the GCF?
**The GCF is 18.**

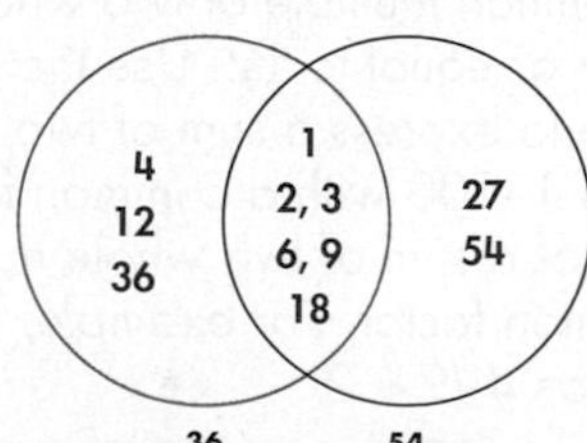


**16.** Al's garden is 18 feet long and 30 feet wide. He wants to put fence posts the same distance apart along all sides of the garden. What is the greatest distance apart that he can place the fence posts?
**6 feet**

**17. Vocabulary** How does finding the *prime factorizations* of two numbers help you find their GCF? Use an example to illustrate.
**Sample answer: You can easily identify the prime factors that they have in common and then multiply them to find the GCF. For example, $12 = 2 \times 2 \times 3$ and $16 = 2 \times 2 \times 2 \times 2$, so their GCF = $2 \times 2 = 4$.**

**18. Higher Order Thinking** The student council was preparing for the school bake sale. The members divided each type of the donated items equally onto plates. Each plate contained only one type of item and every plate had exactly the same number of items. There were no leftovers. What is the greatest number of items that could have been placed on each plate?
**12 items**

| Bake Sale Donations | |
|---|---|
| Muffins | 96 |
| Breadsticks | 48 |
| Rolls | 84 |

**Common Core Assessment**

**19.** Write the pairs of numbers in the correct box.

25, 30 51, 85
98, 84 10, 95
27, 45 42, 70

| GCF = 5 | GCF = 9 |
|---|---|
| **25, 30**<br>**10, 95** | **27, 45** |
| **GCF = 14** | **GCF = 17** |
| **42, 70**<br>**98, 84** | **51, 85** |

# LESSON 8-3

## LEAST COMMON MULTIPLE

### DIGITAL RESOURCES PearsonRealize.com

Student and Teacher eTexts
eText

Listen and Look For Lesson Video
PD

Today's Challenge
Think

Solve and Share
Solve

Visual Learning Animation Plus
Learn

Animated Glossary
Glossary

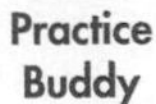
Online Personalized Practice
Practice Buddy

Math Tools
Tools

Quick Check
Assessment

Another Look Homework Video
Help

Math Games
Games

### LESSON OVERVIEW FCR FOCUS • COHERENCE • RIGOR

**FOCUS**

**Domain 6.NS** The Number System

**Cluster 6.NS.B** Compute fluently with multi-digit numbers and find common factors and multiples.

**Content Standard 6.NS.B.4** Find the greatest common factor of two whole numbers less than or equal to 100 and the least common multiple of two whole numbers less than or equal to 12. Use the distributive property to express a sum of two whole numbers 1–100 with a common factor as a multiple of a sum of two whole numbers with no common factor. *For example, express 36 + 8 as 4 (9 + 2).*

**Mathematical Practices MP.3, MP.7, MP.8**

**Objective** Find the least common multiple of two whole numbers.

**Essential Understanding** All non-zero whole numbers have multiples in common, including the smallest or least common multiple (LCM). Sometimes the LCM is one of the numbers.

**Vocabulary** Common multiple, Least common multiple (LCM)

**COHERENCE**

In Grade 4, students gained familiarity with multiples and determined whether a given whole number in the range 1–100 is a multiple of a given one-digit number. In this lesson, students will find the least common multiple (LCM) of two whole numbers less than or equal to 12. Students are expected to compute fluently with multi-digit numbers and find common factors and multiples by the end of Grade 6.

**RIGOR**

This lesson emphasizes **conceptual understanding** and **procedural skill**. Students deepen their understanding of multiples and learn procedures for finding the least common multiple including the method of prime factorization. They apply their understanding of least common multiple to solve problems.

PD Watch the Listen and Look For Lesson Video.

### MATH ANYTIME

**Daily Common Core Review**

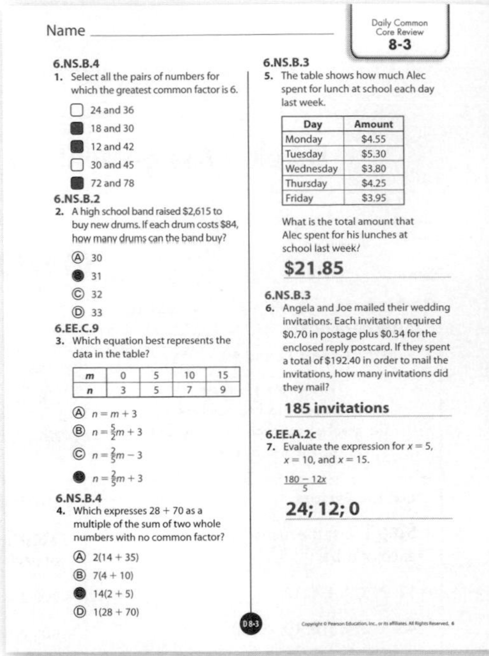

Name ____________

Daily Common Core Review 8-3

6.NS.B.4
1. Select all the pairs of numbers for which the greatest common factor is 6.
   - ☐ 24 and 36
   - ■ 18 and 30
   - ■ 12 and 42
   - ☐ 30 and 45
   - ■ 72 and 78

6.NS.B.2
2. A high school band raised $2,615 to buy new drums. If each drum costs $84, how many drums can the band buy?
   - Ⓐ 30
   - ● 31
   - Ⓒ 32
   - Ⓓ 33

6.EE.C.9
3. Which equation best represents the data in the table?

| *m* | 0 | 5 | 10 | 15 |
|---|---|---|---|---|
| *n* | 3 | 5 | 7 | 9 |

   - Ⓐ $n = m + 3$
   - Ⓑ $n = \frac{5}{2}m + 3$
   - Ⓒ $n = \frac{2}{5}m - 3$
   - ● $n = \frac{2}{5}m + 3$

6.NS.B.4
4. Which expresses 28 + 70 as a multiple of the sum of two whole numbers with no common factor?
   - Ⓐ 2(14 + 35)
   - Ⓑ 7(4 + 10)
   - ● 14(2 + 5)
   - Ⓓ 1(28 + 70)

6.NS.B.3
5. The table shows how much Alec spent for lunch at school each day last week.

| Day | Amount |
|---|---|
| Monday | $4.55 |
| Tuesday | $5.30 |
| Wednesday | $3.80 |
| Thursday | $4.25 |
| Friday | $3.95 |

What is the total amount that Alec spent for his lunches at school last week?

**$21.85**

6.NS.B.3
6. Angela and Joe mailed their wedding invitations. Each invitation required $0.70 in postage plus $0.34 for the enclosed reply postcard. If they spent a total of $192.40 in order to mail the invitations, how many invitations did they mail?

**185 invitations**

6.EE.A.2c
7. Evaluate the expression for $x = 5$, $x = 10$, and $x = 15$.

$\frac{180 - 12x}{5}$

**24; 12; 0**

D 8-3



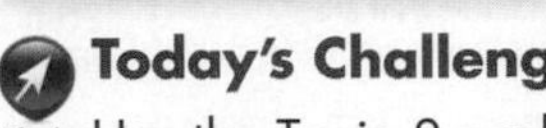

**Today's Challenge**

Think Use the Topic 8 problems any time during this topic.

### ENGLISH LANGUAGE LEARNERS 

**Reading** Expand comprehension by predicting.

*Use with the Visual Learning Bridge on Student's Edition p. 404.*

Ask students to explain the meaning of *multiples* to partners and predict the meaning of *common multiples*. Read Box A. Ask students to predict how the problem will be solved using common multiples of 6 and 8.

**Beginning** Read Box A to students. Write 6. *What are multiples of 6?* Write 6: ___, ___, ___, ___, ___. Ask students to provide the multiples of 6 to fill in the blanks. Repeat the process with 8. *What is a common multiple of 6 and 8?* Instruct students to circle a common multiple of 6 and 8.

**Intermediate** Read Box A with students. Ask students to predict what a common multiple of 6 and 8 might be and write it on an index card. *What are multiples of 6? Explain how they are determined.* Repeat the process with 8. *What is a common multiple of 6 and 8?* Instruct students to check to see if their predictions were correct.

**Advanced** Instruct students to read Box A with partners. Ask students to predict what a common multiple of 6 and 8 might be and write it on an index card. Have partners discuss their reasoning for their predictions. Instruct students to determine if their predictions were correct by working with partners to find the multiples of 6 and 8.

**Summarize** What are *common multiples*?

# DEVELOP: PROBLEM-BASED LEARNING

**COHERENCE: Engage learners by connecting prior knowledge to new ideas.**
Students extend what they know about multiples to find the least common multiple of two numbers.

10–15 min

Solve

## BEFORE

1. **Pose the Solve-and-Share Problem**
**MP.7 Look for Relationships** Listen and look for students who recognize patterns as they fill in the table and examine Mark's chore schedule.

2. **Build Understanding**
*How can you use the table to record Mark's chores?* [Label each row by the days of the week: 1, 2, 3, 4, and so on, and then list the chores that Mark will do on each of those days.]

## DURING

3. **Ask Guiding Questions As Needed**
*What chores will be listed for Day 1?* [None] *On what days will Mark set the dinner table?* [Days 2, 4, and 6] *On what days will he dry the dishes?* [Days 3 and 6] *On what day will Mark perform both chores?* [Day 6]

## AFTER

4. **Share and Discuss Solutions**
Solve Start with students' solutions. If needed, project Jake's work to discuss how to find the first day that Mark performs both chores, or the least common multiple of 2 and 3.

5. **Transition to the Visual Learning Bridge**
*You can list multiples or use prime factorization to find the least common multiple of two numbers in order to solve problems.*

6. **Extension for Early Finishers**
*If the pattern continues, on which day will Mark perform both chores again?* [Day 12]

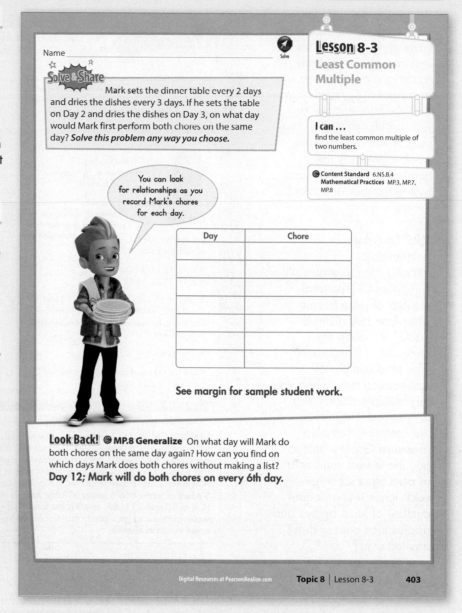

---

Name ______________________

**Solve & Share**

Mark sets the dinner table every 2 days and dries the dishes every 3 days. If he sets the table on Day 2 and dries the dishes on Day 3, on what day would Mark first perform both chores on the same day? ***Solve this problem any way you choose.***

**Lesson 8-3**
**Least Common Multiple**

**I can ...**
find the least common multiple of two numbers.

**Content Standard** 6.NS.B.4
**Mathematical Practices** MP.3, MP.7, MP.8

You can look for relationships as you record Mark's chores for each day.

| Day | Chore |
|---|---|
| | |
| | |
| | |
| | |
| | |
| | |
| | |

**See margin for sample student work.**

**Look Back!** **MP.8 Generalize** On what day will Mark do both chores on the same day again? How can you find on which days Mark does both chores without making a list?
**Day 12; Mark will do both chores on every 6th day.**



---

## Analyze Student Work

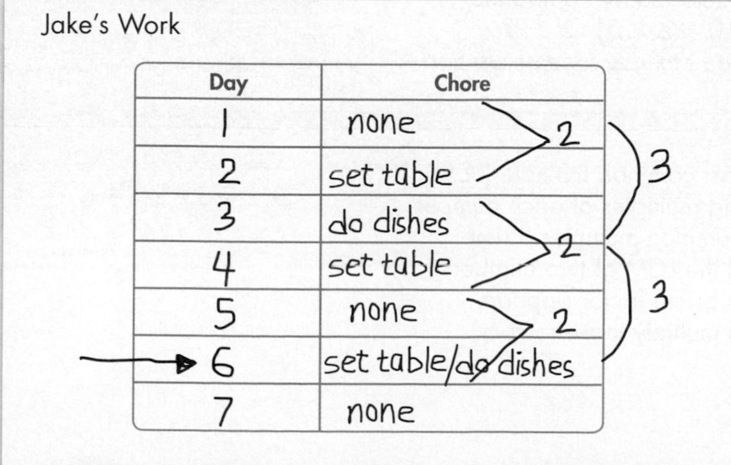

Jake's Work

| Day | Chore |
|---|---|
| 1 | none |
| 2 | set table |
| 3 | do dishes |
| 4 | set table |
| 5 | none |
| 6 | set table/do dishes |
| 7 | none |

Jake correctly completes the table with the list of chores. He also relates the problem to multiples of 2 and 3 to find that the least common multiple is 6.

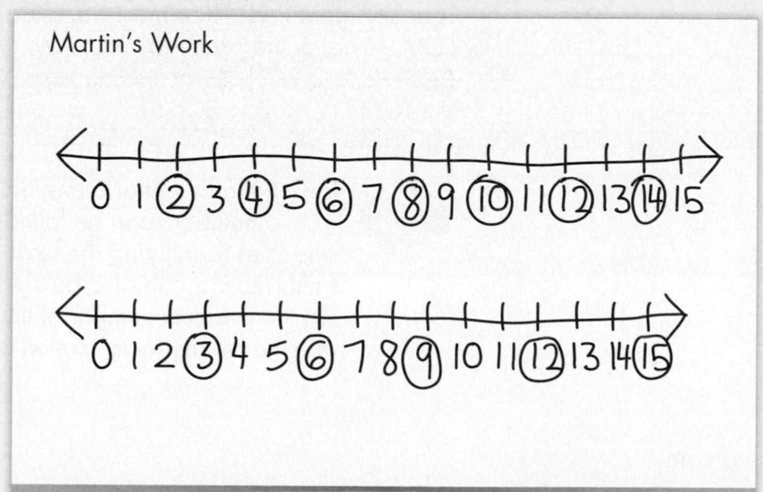


Martin drew number lines to represent the problem. On the top number line, he circled multiples of 2. On the bottom number line, he circled multiples of 3. He found that 6 was the first multiple in common.

# DEVELOP: VISUAL LEARNING

The *Visual Learning Bridge* connects students' thinking in Solve & Share to important math ideas in the lesson. Use the *Visual Learning Bridge* to make these ideas explicit. Also available as a *Visual Learning Animation Plus* at PearsonRealize.com

**MP.7 Look for Relationships** *How many juice bottles are in a pack?* [6] *How many applesauce cups are in a pack?* [8] *How do you find the total number of juice bottles or applesauce cups if you buy multiple packs?* [Multiply the number of bottles or cups by the number of packs.]

**MP.7 Look for Relationships** *What do the multiples of 6 represent?* [The total number of juice bottles when you buy multiple packs] *What do the multiples of 8 represent?* [The total number of applesauce cups when you buy multiple packs] *Why do you want to identify the common multiples?* [Because Grant wants to buy the fewest number of packages such that each lunch has an equal number of juice bottles and applesauce cups without any left over]

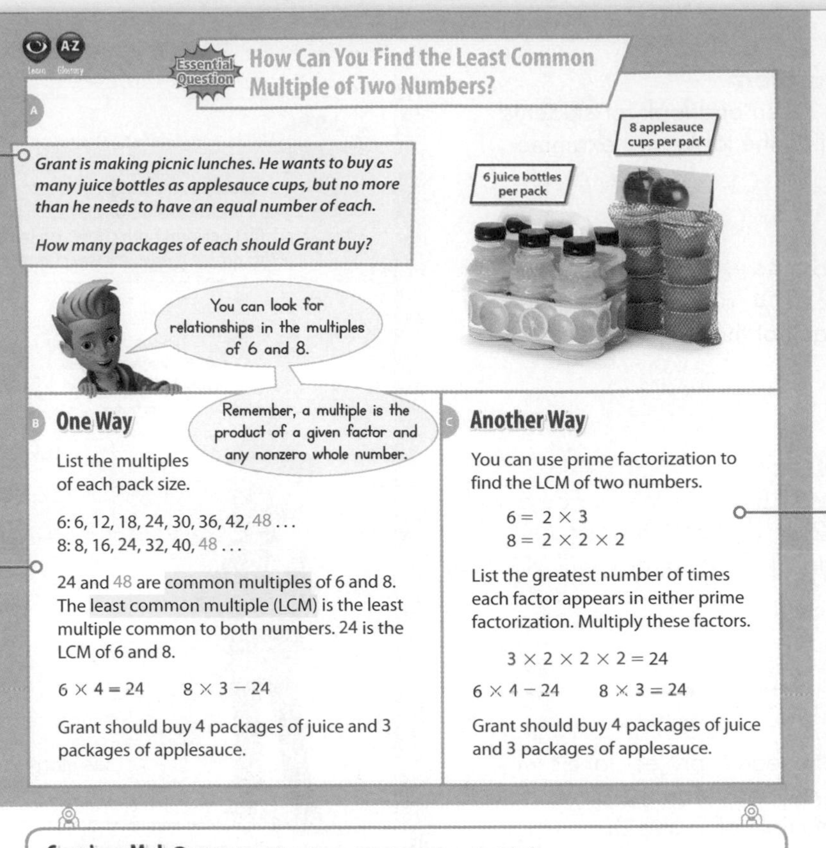

Essential Question **How Can You Find the Least Common Multiple of Two Numbers?**

A

*Grant is making picnic lunches. He wants to buy as many juice bottles as applesauce cups, but no more than he needs to have an equal number of each.*

*How many packages of each should Grant buy?*

8 applesauce cups per pack
6 juice bottles per pack
You can look for relationships in the multiples of 6 and 8.
Remember, a multiple is the product of a given factor and any nonzero whole number.



B **One Way**

List the multiples of each pack size.

6: 6, 12, 18, 24, 30, 36, 42, 48 . . .
8: 8, 16, 24, 32, 40, 48 . . .

24 and 48 are common multiples of 6 and 8. The least common multiple (LCM) is the least multiple common to both numbers. 24 is the LCM of 6 and 8.

$6 \times 4 = 24$ $8 \times 3 = 24$

Grant should buy 4 packages of juice and 3 packages of applesauce.

C **Another Way**

You can use prime factorization to find the LCM of two numbers.

$6 = 2 \times 3$
$8 = 2 \times 2 \times 2$

List the greatest number of times each factor appears in either prime factorization. Multiply these factors.

$3 \times 2 \times 2 \times 2 = 24$

$6 \times 4 = 24$ $8 \times 3 = 24$

Grant should buy 4 packages of juice and 3 packages of applesauce.

Visual Learning Bridge

**Convince Me!** **MP.7 Use Structure** Grant also buys bottled water and juice drinks for the picnic. There are 12 bottles of water in each case and 10 juice pouches in each box. He wants to buy the least amount but still have as many bottles of water as juice pouches. How many of each should Grant buy? Explain how you know.
**5 cases of water and 6 boxes of juice; Sample answer: The LCM of 10 and 12 is 60, so 60 is the least total number of water bottles and juice boxes that Grant can buy to have equal amounts of each.**

404 **Topic 8** | Lesson 8-3 

*How many times does the number 2 appear in the prime factorization of 6?* [1] *How many times does the number 2 appear in the prime factorization of 8?* [3] *Why do you include three factors of 2 to find the LCM?* [Sample answer: You use the greatest number of times a factor appears in either of the prime factorizations, not the total number of times.]

**Prevent Misconceptions**

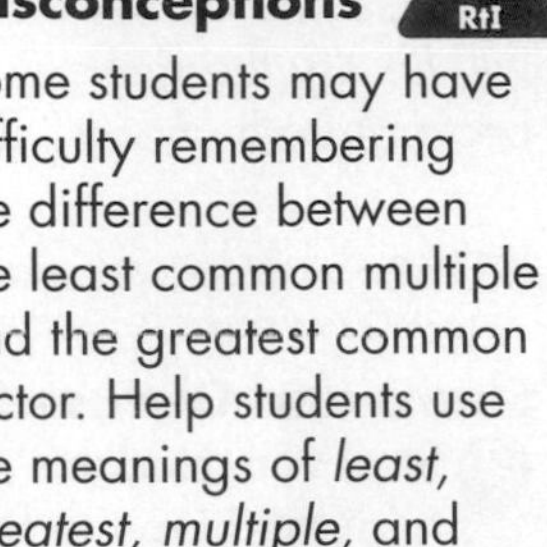


Some students may have difficulty remembering the difference between the least common multiple and the greatest common factor. Help students use the meanings of *least, greatest, multiple,* and *factor* to distinguish between the two. Encourage them to use this understanding to determine which procedure to use to find the LCM and GCF of two numbers.

**Convince Me!** **MP.7 Use Structure** Encourage students to list the multiples of each number in a structured and orderly way so that the LCM is easily identified. Then have them use prime factorization to find the LCM. *What is the prime factorization of 10?* [$10 = 2 \times 5$] *Of 12?* [$12 = 2 \times 2 \times 3$] *What prime factors would you multiply together to find the LCM?* [$2 \times 2 \times 3 \times 5$]

Revisit the Essential Question. The least common multiple (LCM) of two numbers can be found by listing multiples of each number and then identifying the least of the common multiples. Prime factorization can also be used to find the LCM of two numbers. List the greatest number of times each prime factor appears in either prime factorization and then multiply those factors.

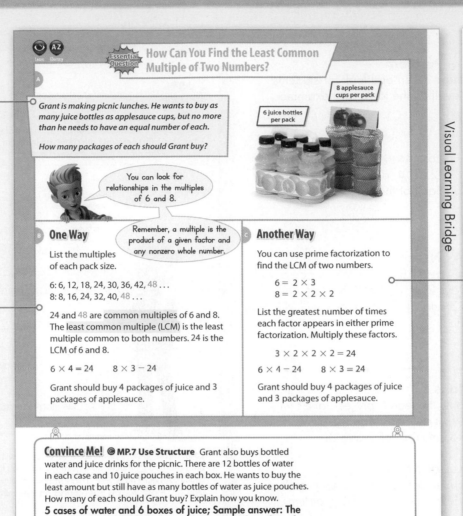

PEARSON realize.
PearsonRealize.com

## QUICK CHECK

Check mark indicates items for prescribing differentiation on the next page.
Items 9 and 23 are worth 1 point. Item 22 is worth up to 3 points.

20–30 min

Practice Buddy

Tools

Assessment

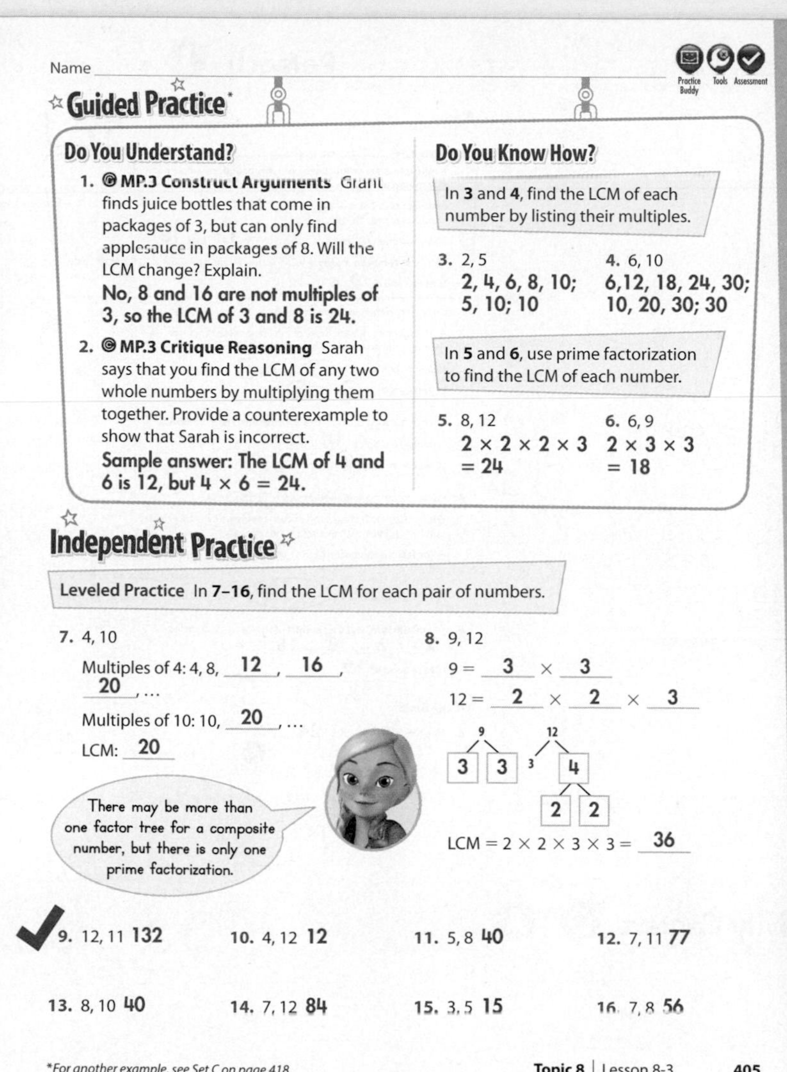

Name ____

## Guided Practice*

**Do You Understand?**

1. **MP.3 Construct Arguments** Grant finds juice bottles that come in packages of 3, but can only find applesauce in packages of 8. Will the LCM change? Explain.
**No, 8 and 16 are not multiples of 3, so the LCM of 3 and 8 is 24.**

2. **MP.3 Critique Reasoning** Sarah says that you find the LCM of any two whole numbers by multiplying them together. Provide a counterexample to show that Sarah is incorrect.
**Sample answer: The LCM of 4 and 6 is 12, but 4 × 6 = 24.**

**Do You Know How?**

In **3** and **4**, find the LCM of each number by listing their multiples.

3. 2, 5
**2, 4, 6, 8, 10; 5, 10; 10**

4. 6, 10
**6, 12, 18, 24, 30; 10, 20, 30; 30**

In **5** and **6**, use prime factorization to find the LCM of each number.

5. 8, 12
**2 × 2 × 2 × 3 = 24**

6. 6, 9
**2 × 3 × 3 = 18**

## Independent Practice*

Leveled Practice In **7–16**, find the LCM for each pair of numbers.

7. 4, 10
Multiples of 4: 4, 8, **12**, **16**, **20**, ...
Multiples of 10: 10, **20**, ...
LCM: **20**

8. 9, 12
9 = **3** × **3**
12 = **2** × **2** × **3**
9: **3** **3**; 12: 3, **4**; 4: **2** **2**
LCM = 2 × 2 × 3 × 3 = **36**

There may be more than one factor tree for a composite number, but there is only one prime factorization.

9. 12, 11 **132**
10. 4, 12 **12**
11. 5, 8 **40**
12. 7, 11 **77**
13. 8, 10 **40**
14. 7, 12 **84**
15. 3, 5 **15**
16. 7, 8 **56**

*For another example, see Set C on page 418.

Topic 8 | Lesson 8-3 405

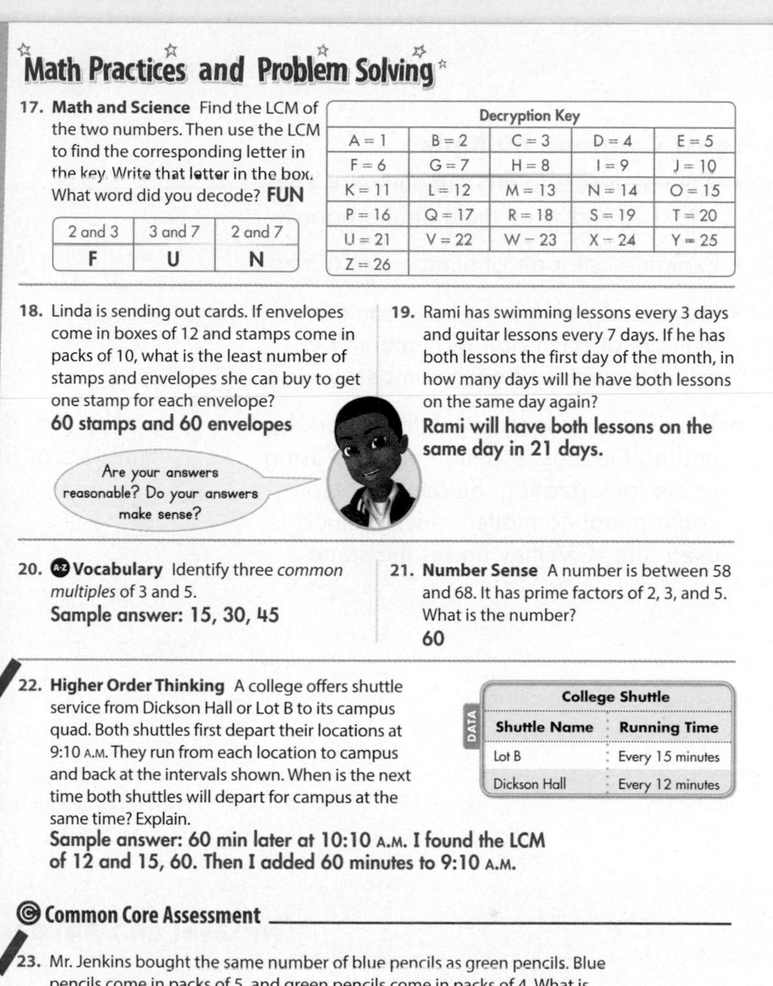

## Math Practices and Problem Solving*

17. **Math and Science** Find the LCM of the two numbers. Then use the LCM to find the corresponding letter in the key. Write that letter in the box. What word did you decode? **FUN**

| 2 and 3 | 3 and 7 | 2 and 7 |
|---|---|---|
| **F** | **U** | **N** |

| Decryption Key | | | | |
|---|---|---|---|---|
| A = 1 | B = 2 | C = 3 | D = 4 | E = 5 |
| F = 6 | G = 7 | H = 8 | I = 9 | J = 10 |
| K = 11 | L = 12 | M = 13 | N = 14 | O = 15 |
| P = 16 | Q = 17 | R = 18 | S = 19 | T = 20 |
| U = 21 | V = 22 | W = 23 | X = 24 | Y = 25 |
| Z = 26 | | | | |

18. Linda is sending out cards. If envelopes come in boxes of 12 and stamps come in packs of 10, what is the least number of stamps and envelopes she can buy to get one stamp for each envelope?
**60 stamps and 60 envelopes**

Are your answers reasonable? Do your answers make sense?

19. Rami has swimming lessons every 3 days and guitar lessons every 7 days. If he has both lessons the first day of the month, in how many days will he have both lessons on the same day again?
**Rami will have both lessons on the same day in 21 days.**

20. **Vocabulary** Identify three *common multiples* of 3 and 5.
**Sample answer: 15, 30, 45**

21. **Number Sense** A number is between 58 and 68. It has prime factors of 2, 3, and 5. What is the number?
**60**

22. **Higher Order Thinking** A college offers shuttle service from Dickson Hall or Lot B to its campus quad. Both shuttles first depart their locations at 9:10 A.M. They run from each location to campus and back at the intervals shown. When is the next time both shuttles will depart for campus at the same time? Explain.
**Sample answer: 60 min later at 10:10 A.M. I found the LCM of 12 and 15, 60. Then I added 60 minutes to 9:10 A.M.**

| College Shuttle | |
|---|---|
| **Shuttle Name** | **Running Time** |
| Lot B | Every 15 minutes |
| Dickson Hall | Every 12 minutes |

**Common Core Assessment**

23. Mr. Jenkins bought the same number of blue pencils as green pencils. Blue pencils come in packs of 5, and green pencils come in packs of 4. What is the least number of blue or green pencils Mr. Jenkins could have bought?
Ⓐ 10 pencils Ⓑ 15 pencils ● 20 pencils Ⓓ 40 pencils

406 Topic 8 | Lesson 8-3 © Pearson Education, Inc. 6

### Error Intervention: Items 5–6

**If** students have difficulty using prime factorization to find the LCM, **then** remind students to use each prime factor the greatest number of times it appears in either prime factorization.

**Item 9** Students should understand that the numbers 12 and 11 share no common factors since 11 is prime and it is not a factor of 12. Therefore, the least common multiple will be their product, 12 × 11 = 132.

**Reteaching** Assign Reteaching Set C on p. 418.

**Item 17 Math and Science** You may wish to challenge students to use the LCM of other pairs of numbers to write their own secret message that can be decoded using the decryption key shown.

**Item 18** Remind students that Linda doesn't want to have any envelopes or stamps left over. *How can you find the number of boxes of envelopes and packs of stamps that Linda should buy?* [Sample answer: Find the LCM of 10 and 12. Then divide the LCM by 12 and by 10 to find the number of boxes of envelopes and packs of stamps, respectively.]

**Item 21 Number Sense** Some students will reason that a number that has factors of 2, 3, and 5 must be even and end in 0, so it must be 60. Others may need to list the whole numbers between 58 and 68 and determine which numbers have factors of 2, 3, and 5. *Which numbers can you eliminate automatically? Explain.* [59, 61, and 67; they are prime numbers.] Encourage these students to use an organized and systematic approach to record their work.

**Multi-Step Problems** *Page 406 Items 17, 20, and 22; Page 408 Items 13 and 16*

# ASSESS AND DIFFERENTIATE

Use the **QUICK CHECK** on the previous page to prescribe differentiated instruction.

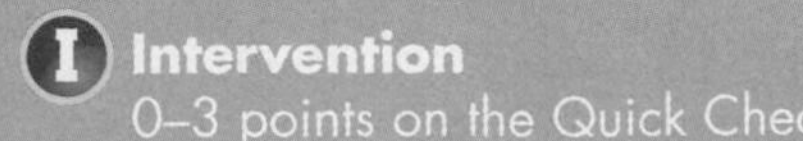

**Intervention**
0–3 points on the Quick Check

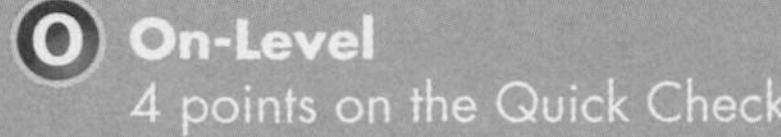

**On-Level**
4 points on the Quick Check

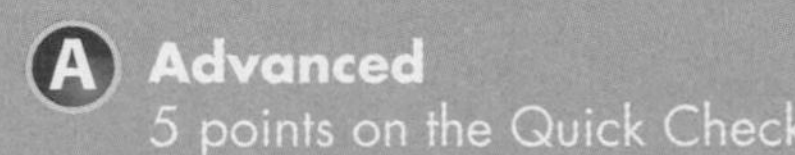

**Advanced**
5 points on the Quick Check

## Intervention Activity 

### Least Common Multiple

- Ask volunteers to call out numbers from 1 to 12, and write them on the board.
- Examine one pair of numbers at a time.
- Have students find the least common multiple of each pair of numbers by listing multiples of each number.
- Then have students check their work by finding the least common multiple using prime factorization. Students should confirm that no matter which method is used, the LCM they find is the same.

multiples of 4: 4, 8, 12, 16, (20), ...
multiples of 5: 5, 10, 15, (20), ...

4: 2 × 2
5: 1 × 5

LCM: 1 × 2 × 2 × 5 = 20

## Reteach

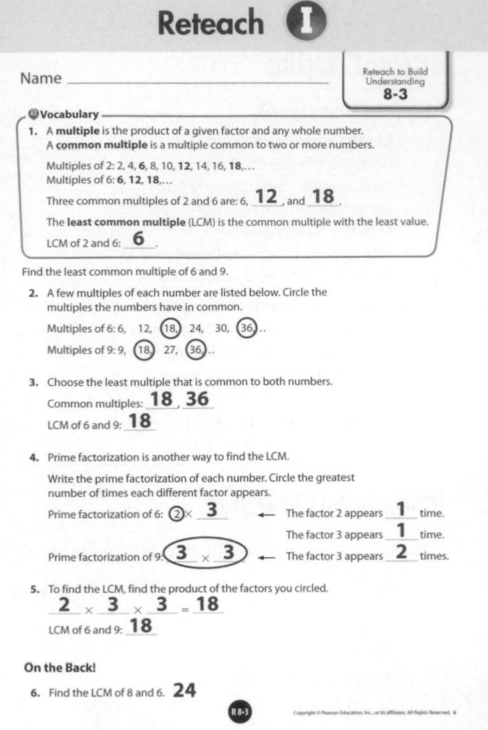

Name ______________________

Reteach to Build Understanding
8-3

**Vocabulary**

1. A **multiple** is the product of a given factor and any whole number.
A **common multiple** is a multiple common to two or more numbers.
Multiples of 2: 2, 4, **6**, 8, 10, **12**, 14, 16, **18**, ...
Multiples of 6: **6**, **12**, **18**, ...
Three common multiples of 2 and 6 are: 6, **12**, and **18**.
The **least common multiple** (LCM) is the common multiple with the least value.
LCM of 2 and 6: **6**.

Find the least common multiple of 6 and 9.

2. A few multiples of each number are listed below. Circle the multiples the numbers have in common.
Multiples of 6: 6, 12, (18), 24, 30, (36), ...
Multiples of 9: 9, (18), 27, (36), ...

3. Choose the least multiple that is common to both numbers.
Common multiples: **18**, **36**
LCM of 6 and 9: **18**

4. Prime factorization is another way to find the LCM.
Write the prime factorization of each number. Circle the greatest number of times each different factor appears.
Prime factorization of 6: (2) × **3** ← The factor 2 appears **1** time.
The factor 3 appears **1** time.
Prime factorization of 9: (**3** × **3**) ← The factor 3 appears **2** times.

5. To find the LCM, find the product of the factors you circled.
**2** × **3** × **3** = **18**
LCM of 6 and 9: **18**

**On the Back!**

6. Find the LCM of 8 and 6. **24**

R 8-3



## On-Level and Advanced Activity Centers  

### Problem-Solving Reading Mat

Have students read the Problem-Solving Reading Mat for Topic 8 and then complete Problem-Solving Reading Activity 8-3.

See the Problem-Solving Reading Activity Guide for other suggestions on how to use this mat.

**TIMING**

The time allocated to Step 3 will depend on the teacher's instructional decisions and differentiation routines.

15–30 min

**realize.** PearsonRealize.com

 Help  Practice Buddy  Tools Games

## Technology Center I O A

### Math Tools and Math Games

A link to a specific math tools activity or math game to use with this lesson is provided at PearsonRealize.com.

## Leveled Assignment

 Items 1–8, 13–15, 18  Items 5–15, 17, 18  Items 7–18

Name ____________

### Homework & Practice 8-3

**Least Common Multiple**

**Another Look!**

Find the LCM of 4 and 5.

You can find the least common multiple (LCM) in different ways.

**List Multiples**

**Step 1** List multiples of each number.

4: 4, 8, 12, 16, 20, 24, 28, 32, 36, 40, 44, 48...

5: 5, 10, 15, 20, 25, 30, 35, 40, 45, 50...

**Step 2** Circle the multiples the numbers have in common.

4: 4, 8, 12, 16, (20), 24, 28, 32, 36, (40), 44, 48...

5: 5, 10, 15, (20), 25, 30, 35, (40), 45, 50...

**Step 3** Determine which of the common multiples is the least.

20 and 40 are both common multiples, but 20 is the least.

The LCM of 4 and 5 is 20.

**Use Prime Factors**

**Step 1** List the prime factors of each number.

4: $2 \times 2$

5: 5

**Step 2** Circle the greatest number of times each different factor appears.

4: ($2 \times 2$)

5: (5)

**Step 3** Find the product of the factors you circled.

$2 \times 2 \times 5 = 20$

The LCM of 4 and 5 is 20.

In **1–12**, find the LCM of each pair of numbers.

**1.** 8, 12 **24** **2.** 6, 7 **42** **3.** 3, 4 **12** **4.** 4, 9 **36**

**5.** 3, 8 **24** **6.** 5, 11 **55** **7.** 4, 8 **8** **8.** 5, 6 **30**

**9.** 3, 6 **6** **10.** 2, 4 **4** **11.** 10, 11 **110** **12.** 3, 7 **21**



**13.** **MP.3 Critique Reasoning** Ron is trying to find the LCM of 4 and 6. His work is shown at the right. What is Ron's mistake? Explain how to find the correct LCM of 4 and 6. **Sample answer: Ron chose all factors of 4 and 6 instead of the greatest number of any one factor in each prime factorization. So he included an extra 2. The LCM of 4 and 6 is $2 \times 2 \times 3 = 12$.**

4: 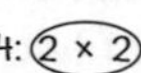 ($2 \times 2$)

6: 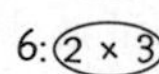 ($2 \times 3$)

$2 \times 2 \times 2 \times 3 = 24$, so the LCM of 4 and 6 is 24.

**14.** Peanuts are sold in 8-ounce and 12-ounce packages. What is the least number of ounces you can buy of each package to have equal amounts of each package size? **24**

**15.** **Algebra** A certain substance begins to melt at temperatures above 42°F. Write an inequality that represents the temperatures at which the substance will not melt. Show this on a number line. **Sample answer: Let $t$ = the temperatures, in °F, at which the substance will not melt. $t \leq 42$**

0 10 20 30 40 50

**16.** At what times between 10:00 A.M. and 5:00 P.M. do the chemistry presentation and the recycling presentation start at the same time? **10:30 A.M., 11:00 A.M., 11:30 A.M., 12:00 P.M., 12:30 P.M., 1:00 P.M., 1:30 P.M., 2:00 P.M., 2:30 P.M., 3:00 P.M., 3:30 P.M., 4:00 P.M., 4:30 P.M.**

Science Museum
– Show Schedule –
Chemistry – Every 10 minutes
Electricity – Every 20 minutes
Recycling – Every 6 minutes
Fossils – Every 45 minutes
The first showing for all shows is at 10:00 A.M.


**17.** **Higher Order Thinking** The museum performs shows in schools every Monday and shows in public libraries every fifth day (on both weekdays and weekends). If the museum did both a school show and a library show on Monday, how many days will it be until it does both shows on the same day again? **35 days**

### Common Core Assessment

**18.** The different kinds of beads Casey is using to make purses come in packages of 3 and 9. What is the least number of each kind of bead Casey can buy to have an equal number of each of the different kinds of beads?

Ⓐ 90 Ⓑ 27 ● 9 Ⓓ 6

# CRITIQUE REASONING

## DIGITAL RESOURCES PearsonRealize.com

eText — Student and Teacher eTexts

PD — Listen and Look For Lesson Video

Think — Today's Challenge

Solve — Solve and Share

Learn — Visual Learning Animation Plus

Glossary — Animated Glossary

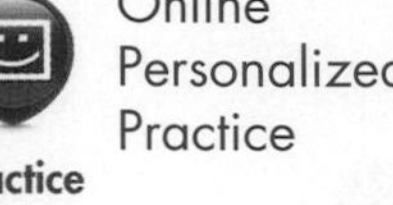
Practice Buddy — Online Personalized Practice

Tools — Math Tools

Assessment — Quick Check

Help — Another Look Homework Video

Games — Math Games

MP — Math Practices Animations

## LESSON OVERVIEW FCR FOCUS • COHERENCE • RIGOR

### FOCUS

**Mathematical Practices MP.3** Construct viable arguments and critique the reasoning of others. Also **MP.1, MP.6, MP.7**

**Domain 6.NS** The Number System

**Cluster 6.NS.B** Compute fluently with multi-digit numbers and find common factors and multiples.

**Content Standard 6.NS.B.4** Find the greatest common factor of two whole numbers less than or equal to 100 and the least common multiple of two whole numbers less than or equal to 12. Use the distributive property to express a sum of two whole numbers 1–100 with a common factor as a multiple of a sum of two whole numbers with no common factor. *For example, express 36 + 8 as 4 (9 + 2).*

**Objective** Critique the reasoning of others using what is known about factors and multiples.

**Essential Understanding** Good math thinkers use math to explain why they are right. They can talk about the math that others do, too.

**Vocabulary** Counterexample

### COHERENCE

Students have engaged MP.3 throughout this program. This lesson is an opportunity to stop and focus on the thinking habits that mathematically proficient students engage when they *critique the reasoning of others.* Although the content used in this lesson was developed in this topic, the instruction should focus on the use and management of MP.3.

### RIGOR

This lesson emphasizes **application**. Students apply their understanding of prime and composite numbers and how to find the greatest common factor or least common multiple of two numbers as they critique the reasoning of others. Students also learn that they can use a counterexample in their math arguments to expose a flaw in logic or to provide evidence of faulty reasoning.

PD Watch the Listen and Look For Lesson Video.

## MATH ANYTIME

### Daily Common Core Review

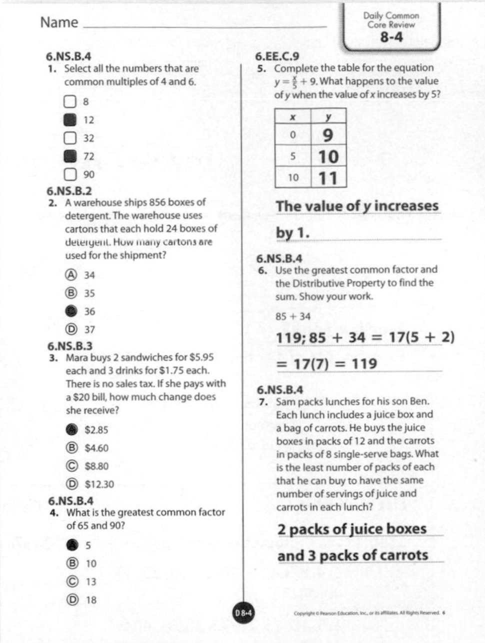
Name ____________

Daily Common Core Review 8-4

6.NS.B.4
1. Select all the numbers that are common multiples of 4 and 6.
- ☐ 8
- ■ 12
- ☐ 32
- ■ 72
- ☐ 90

6.NS.B.2
2. A warehouse ships 856 boxes of detergent. The warehouse uses cartons that each hold 24 boxes of detergent. How many cartons are used for the shipment?
- Ⓐ 34
- Ⓑ 35
- ● 36
- Ⓓ 37

6.NS.B.3
3. Mara buys 2 sandwiches for $5.95 each and 3 drinks for $1.75 each. There is no sales tax. If she pays with a $20 bill, how much change does she receive?
- ● $2.85
- Ⓑ $4.60
- Ⓒ $8.80
- Ⓓ $12.30

6.NS.B.4
4. What is the greatest common factor of 65 and 90?
- ● 5
- Ⓑ 10
- Ⓒ 13
- Ⓓ 18

6.EE.C.9
5. Complete the table for the equation $y = \frac{x}{5} + 9$. What happens to the value of $y$ when the value of $x$ increases by 5?

| $x$ | $y$ |
|---|---|
| 0 | 9 |
| 5 | 10 |
| 10 | 11 |

**The value of *y* increases by 1.**

6.NS.B.4
6. Use the greatest common factor and the Distributive Property to find the sum. Show your work.

85 + 34

**119; 85 + 34 = 17(5 + 2) = 17(7) = 119**

6.NS.B.4
7. Sam packs lunches for his son Ben. Each lunch includes a juice box and a bag of carrots. He buys the juice boxes in packs of 12 and the carrots in packs of 8 single-serve bags. What is the least number of packs of each that he can buy to have the same number of servings of juice and carrots in each lunch?

**2 packs of juice boxes and 3 packs of carrots**

D 8-4

### Today's Challenge

Think Use the Topic 8 problems any time during this topic.

## ENGLISH LANGUAGE LEARNERS ELL

**Learning Strategies** Use prior knowledge to understand meanings.

*Use with the Visual Learning Bridge on Student's Edition p. 410.*

*What is the meaning of factors, multiples, and greatest common factor? What strategies have you previously used to find the GCF of two numbers?* Read Box A. Ask students to identify the square numbers in Sara's list. *Sara says the GCF of any two square numbers is 1. Do you agree with Sara's reasoning?*

**Beginning** Point to the factors of 1 on Sara's list. *1 is a common factor. Do you see other square numbers with common factors?* Instruct students to respond by pointing to other common factors. [Examples: 2, 4] *Is 1 the GCF for each square number?* Instruct students to point to square numbers with a GCF greater than 1.

**Intermediate** Point to Sara's list. Ask students to identify a common factor for all of the square numbers. Instruct students to identify other square numbers with common factors. *Sara says 1 is the GCF for all square numbers. Do you agree with Sara?* Have students respond using the sentence stem: I _____ [do/do not] agree with Sara's reasoning because ______.

**Advanced** Instruct students to determine if Sara's reasoning is correct and to explain to partners their reasoning for agreeing or disagreeing with Sara's reasoning.

**Summarize** How did understanding the terms *factors, multiples,* and *GCF* help you determine that Sara's reasoning was incorrect?

# DEVELOP: PROBLEM-BASED LEARNING

**COHERENCE: Engage learners by connecting prior knowledge to new ideas.**
Students apply their understanding of prime and composite numbers to critique the reasoning of others.

10–15 min

Solve

## BEFORE

1. **Pose the Solve-and-Share Problem**
**MP.3 Critique Reasoning** Listen and look for students who use examples to test Sam's general statement. Words like "always" and "sometimes" are important as they can change the dynamic of a problem. Sam makes a claim using "always," but his reasoning is not sound since a counterexample can be found.

2. **Build Understanding**
*What are the first five consecutive odd prime numbers?* [3, 5, 7, 11, 13] *What are square numbers?* [Numbers that are found by multiplying a factor by itself.]

## DURING

3. **Ask Guiding Questions As Needed**
*Are the three sums shown enough examples to prove Sam's statement? How many sums should be checked?* [No; you should check sums until you find one that doesn't work or until you can find a pattern to write a general rule.] *What is the next sum of odd primes that you should test?* [1 + 3 + 5 + 7 = 16] *Is 16 a square number?* [Yes]

## AFTER

4. **Share and Discuss Solutions**
Start with students' solutions. If needed, project Carter's work to discuss how to critique Sam's reasoning.

5. **Transition to the Visual Learning Bridge**
*You can disprove a general statement by finding an example that doesn't fit the rule.*

6. **Extension for Early Finishers**
*How can Sam's statement be reworded so that it is true?* [By removing the word "prime"]

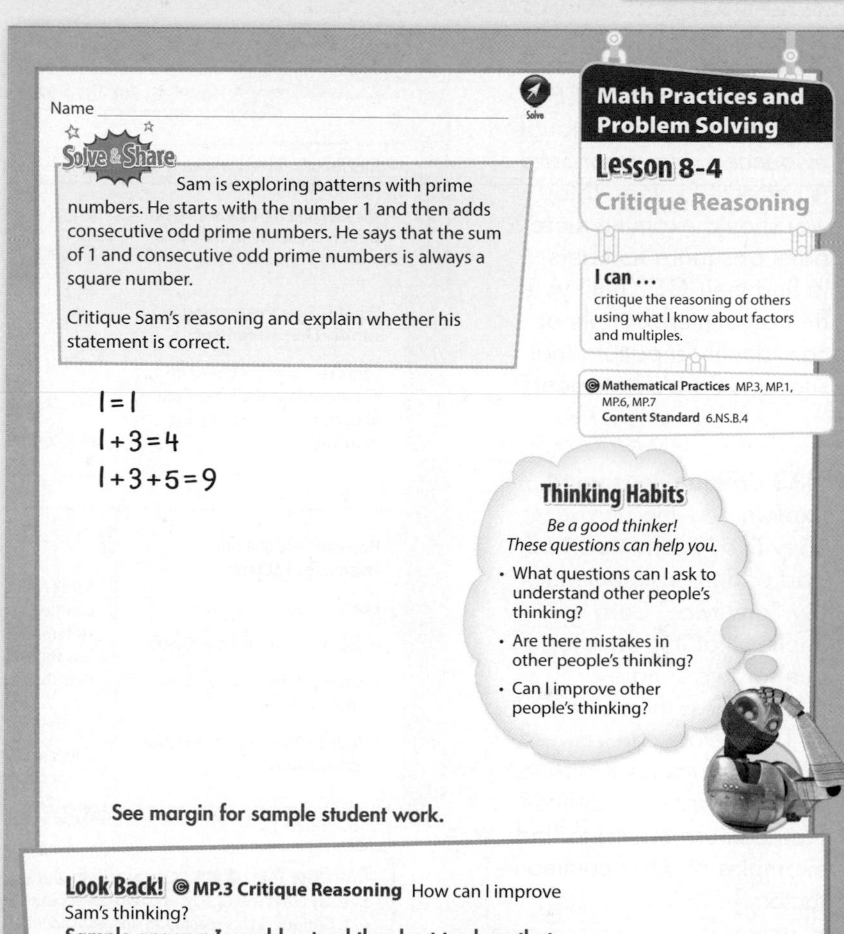

Name
Solve & Share
Sam is exploring patterns with prime numbers. He starts with the number 1 and then adds consecutive odd prime numbers. He says that the sum of 1 and consecutive odd prime numbers is always a square number.
Critique Sam's reasoning and explain whether his statement is correct.
1 = 1
1 + 3 = 4
1 + 3 + 5 = 9
Math Practices and Problem Solving
Lesson 8-4
Critique Reasoning
I can ...
critique the reasoning of others using what I know about factors and multiples.
Mathematical Practices MP.3, MP.1, MP.6, MP.7
Content Standard 6.NS.B.4
Thinking Habits
Be a good thinker! These questions can help you.
• What questions can I ask to understand other people's thinking?
• Are there mistakes in other people's thinking?
• Can I improve other people's thinking?
See margin for sample student work.
Look Back! MP.3 Critique Reasoning How can I improve Sam's thinking?
Sample answer: I would extend the chart to show that the sum of 1 and consecutive odd prime numbers is not always a square number.
Digital Resources at PearsonRealize.com
Topic 8 | Lesson 8-4
409


## Analyze Student Work

**Carter's Work**

$1 = 1^2$
$1 + 3 = 2^2$
$1 + 3 + 5 = 3^2$
$1 + 3 + 5 + 7 = 4^2$
$1 + 3 + 5 + 7 + 11 =$ 27 not a square
Sam is wrong.

Carter finds an example that shows that Sam's statement is not true.

**Jayme's Work**

1 = 1 ✓
1 + 3 = 4 ✓
1 + 3 + 5 = 9 ✓
1 + 3 + 5 + 7 = 16 ✓
Always true

Jayme tests only four examples and mistakenly thinks it is sufficient evidence that Sam's statement is always true.

# DEVELOP: VISUAL LEARNING

The *Visual Learning Bridge* connects students' thinking in Solve & Share to important math ideas in the lesson. Use the *Visual Learning Bridge* to make these ideas explicit. Also available as a *Visual Learning Animation Plus* at PearsonRealize.com

ELL Visual Learning

PEARSON realize. PearsonRealize.com

Learn Glossary

*What is the GCF of 1 and 4?* [1] *What is the GCF of 4 and 9?* [1] *Is this enough evidence to state that Sara is correct? Explain.* [No; you should examine more pairs of square numbers to find their GCF until you find a counterexample or can identify a pattern that supports Sara's statement.]

**MP.3 Critique Reasoning** *Explain why the phrase "any two" is an important part of Sara's statement.* [By "any two," Sara implies that it is always true for two square numbers less than or equal to 100.] *How can you use the list of factors to look for flaws in Sara's reasoning?* [You can use the list to find examples of other common factors.]

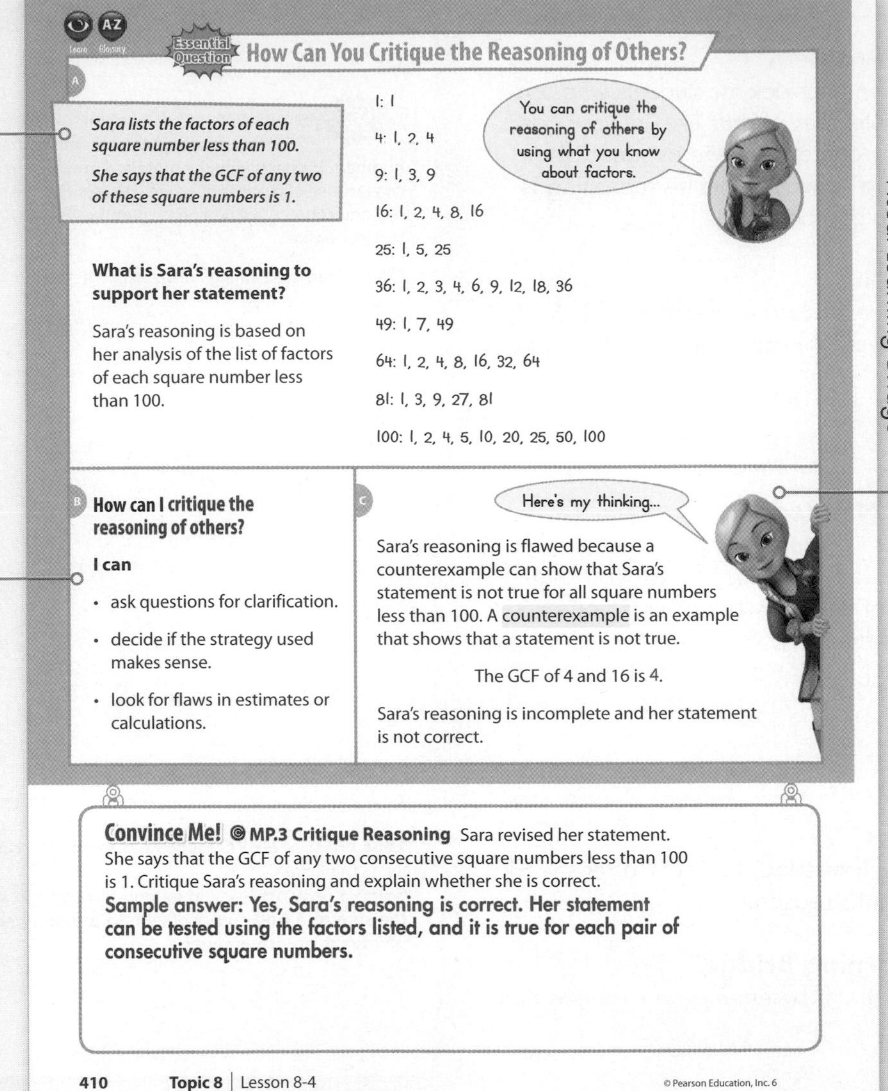

Essential Question **How Can You Critique the Reasoning of Others?**

A

*Sara lists the factors of each square number less than 100.*

*She says that the GCF of any two of these square numbers is 1.*

1: 1
4: 1, 2, 4
9: 1, 3, 9
16: 1, 2, 4, 8, 16
25: 1, 5, 25
36: 1, 2, 3, 4, 6, 9, 12, 18, 36
49: 1, 7, 49
64: 1, 2, 4, 8, 16, 32, 64
81: 1, 3, 9, 27, 81
100: 1, 2, 4, 5, 10, 20, 25, 50, 100

You can critique the reasoning of others by using what you know about factors.

**What is Sara's reasoning to support her statement?**

Sara's reasoning is based on her analysis of the list of factors of each square number less than 100.

B **How can I critique the reasoning of others?**

**I can**

- ask questions for clarification.
- decide if the strategy used makes sense.
- look for flaws in estimates or calculations.

C

Here's my thinking...

Sara's reasoning is flawed because a counterexample can show that Sara's statement is not true for all square numbers less than 100. A counterexample is an example that shows that a statement is not true.

The GCF of 4 and 16 is 4.

Sara's reasoning is incomplete and her statement is not correct.

**Convince Me!** **MP.3 Critique Reasoning** Sara revised her statement. She says that the GCF of any two consecutive square numbers less than 100 is 1. Critique Sara's reasoning and explain whether she is correct.
**Sample answer: Yes, Sara's reasoning is correct. Her statement can be tested using the factors listed, and it is true for each pair of consecutive square numbers.**

410 Topic 8 | Lesson 8-4 © Pearson Education, Inc. 6

Visual Learning Bridge

*Are there other counterexamples that could have been used to show that Sara's statement is not correct? Explain.* [Yes; Sample answer: The GCF of 25 and 100 is 25.]

**Convince Me! MP.3 Critique Reasoning** *How many sets of two consecutive square numbers should you check before you can say that Sara's revised statement is true?* [Sample answer: Enough to find a counterexample or all 8 possible sets of square numbers in this situation]

**Coherence** Students have developed procedural fluency with finding the greatest common factor and least common multiple of two whole numbers in Topic 8. This lesson provides the opportunity to use what they know to critique the reasoning of others and to use correct mathematical language, examples, and counterexamples to support and justify their claims.

Revisit the Essential Question. Students can critique the reasoning of others by asking questions for clarification, deciding if the strategy used makes sense, and looking for flaws in calculations.

**QUICK CHECK**

Check mark indicates items for prescribing differentiation on the next page. Items 4 and 5 are worth 1 point. Items 6–9 are worth up to 3 points.

20–30 min

Practice Buddy | Tools | Assessment

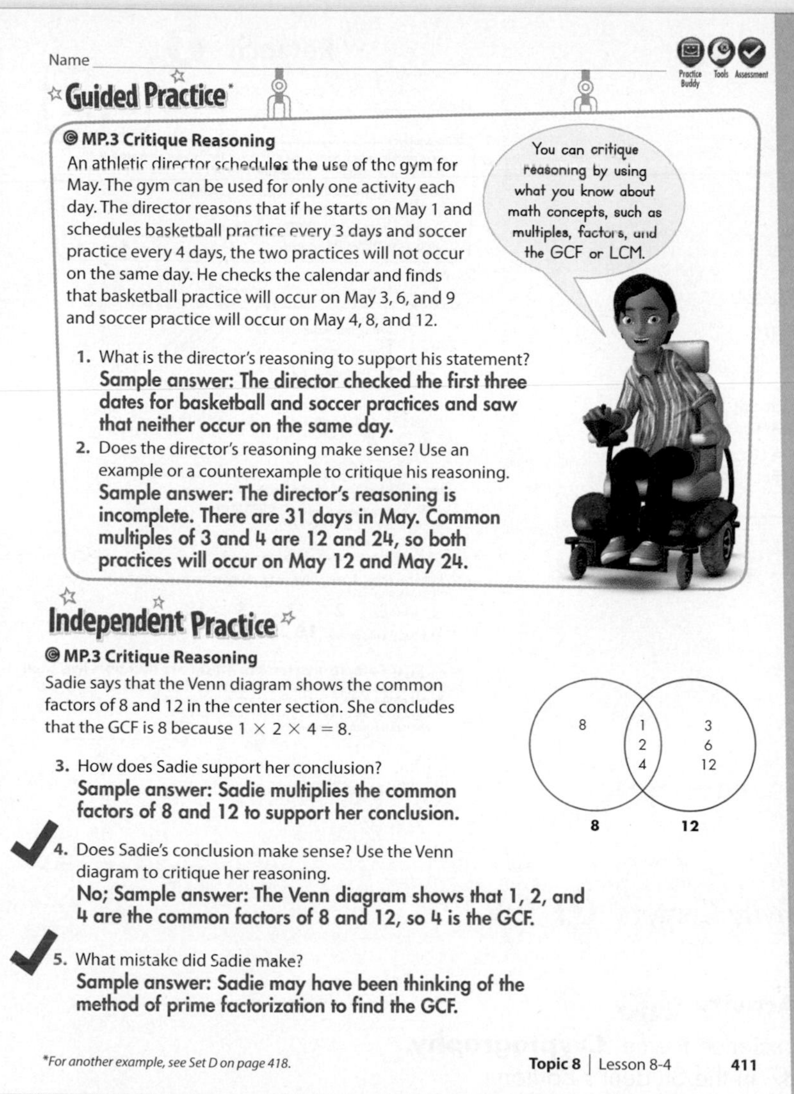

Name ______

## Guided Practice*

**MP.3 Critique Reasoning**

An athletic director schedules the use of the gym for May. The gym can be used for only one activity each day. The director reasons that if he starts on May 1 and schedules basketball practice every 3 days and soccer practice every 4 days, the two practices will not occur on the same day. He checks the calendar and finds that basketball practice will occur on May 3, 6, and 9 and soccer practice will occur on May 4, 8, and 12.

You can critique reasoning by using what you know about math concepts, such as multiples, factors, and the GCF or LCM.



1. What is the director's reasoning to support his statement?
   **Sample answer: The director checked the first three dates for basketball and soccer practices and saw that neither occur on the same day.**
2. Does the director's reasoning make sense? Use an example or a counterexample to critique his reasoning.
   **Sample answer: The director's reasoning is incomplete. There are 31 days in May. Common multiples of 3 and 4 are 12 and 24, so both practices will occur on May 12 and May 24.**

## Independent Practice

**MP.3 Critique Reasoning**

Sadie says that the Venn diagram shows the common factors of 8 and 12 in the center section. She concludes that the GCF is 8 because $1 \times 2 \times 4 = 8$.



3. How does Sadie support her conclusion?
   **Sample answer: Sadie multiplies the common factors of 8 and 12 to support her conclusion.**
4. ✓ Does Sadie's conclusion make sense? Use the Venn diagram to critique her reasoning.
   **No; Sample answer: The Venn diagram shows that 1, 2, and 4 are the common factors of 8 and 12, so 4 is the GCF.**
5. ✓ What mistake did Sadie make?
   **Sample answer: Sadie may have been thinking of the method of prime factorization to find the GCF.**

*For another example, see Set D on page 418.



## Math Practices and Problem Solving

**Common Core Performance Assessment**

✓ **Walk-a-Thon Snack Bags**

Juan is making snack bags for a walk-a-thon. He plans to put the same number of bottles of water and the same number of energy bars in each bag. He wants to make the greatest number of bags that he can with none of the supplies left over. Juan claims that the greatest number of bags he can make is 14, with 6 bottles of water and 4 energy bars in each bag.

| bottles of water | 84 |
|---|---|
| energy bars | 56 |

84+56=14(6+4)

14 snack bags: 6 bottles of water and 4 energy bars

6. **MP.7 Use Structure** How does Juan use the relationship between addition and multiplication to support his claim?
   **Sample answer: Juan has 84 bottles of water and 56 energy bars. He uses the Distributive Property and a factor of 14 to show that he can make 14 snack bags with 6 bottles of water and 4 energy bars in each bag.**
7. **MP.1 Make Sense and Persevere** How can you use Juan's math to check that his strategy makes sense?
   **Sample answer: I can examine his math to see whether there are any flaws in the calculations or whether it supports the claim that the greatest number of snack bags he can make is 14.**
8. **MP.3 Critique Reasoning** Does Juan's math support his claim that the greatest number of bags he can make is 14? Use an example or a counterexample to justify your answer.
   **No; Sample answer: Juan's equation is correct, but 14 is not the GCF of 84 and 56. Using prime factorization, the prime factors for 84 are 2, 2, 3, and 7. The prime factors for 56 are 2, 2, 2, and 7. The common prime factors are 2, 2 and 7. The GCF is $2 \times 2 \times 7 = 28$. So, the greatest number of bags Juan can make is 28.**
9. **MP.6 Be Precise** How many bottles of water and energy bars can Juan put in each bag? Justify your answer.
   **Sample answer: I can use the Distributive Property and the GCF to show the number of bottles of water and energy bars Juan can put in each bag. $84 + 56 = 28(3 + 2)$; Juan can put 3 bottles of water and 2 energy bars in each snack bag.**

When you critique reasoning, you can use math to explain why other people's work is correct or incorrect.





**MP.3 Critique Reasoning** Listen and look for these behaviors as evidence that students are exhibiting proficiency with MP.3.

- Asks questions to understand other people's thinking
- Identifies mistakes in other people's thinking
- Provides suggestions for improving other people's thinking

**Items 1–2 MP.3 Critique Reasoning** If students have difficulty determining whether the director's reasoning makes sense, make a calendar for May and fill in all the practices for the month.

**Items 3–5 MP.3 Critique Reasoning** Students must recall the procedures they learned to find the GCF to critique the method that Sadie used and to reason critically about whether Sadie's conclusion makes sense.

**Reteaching** Assign Reteaching Set D on p. 418.

**Item 6 MP.7 Use Structure** Juan uses the structure of the Distributive Property to write a sum of two whole numbers with a common factor as a multiple of a sum of two whole numbers that still have a common factor of 2.

**Item 7 MP.1 Make Sense and Persevere** Suggest to students that they check Juan's math work in the yellow box to make sure his calculations are correct. *Look at the numbers inside the parentheses. Do 6 and 4 have any common factors? Explain.* [Yes; 2 is a common factor of 6 and 4, so 14 is not the GCF of 84 and 56.]

**Item 8 MP.3 Critique Reasoning** *What is the difference between your answer and Juan's answer?* [It is twice as much.] *What is an error Juan might have made?* [He may have forgotten to multiply all the common factors in the prime factorization of 84 and 56.]

**Item 9 MP.6 Be Precise** Remind students to use correct math language and to provide examples or counterexamples to justify their answers.

# ASSESS AND DIFFERENTIATE

Use the **QUICK CHECK** on the previous page to prescribe differentiated instruction.

**I Intervention** 0–3 points on the Quick Check

**O On-Level** 4 points on the Quick Check

**A Advanced** 5 points on the Quick Check

## Intervention Activity 

### Math Practices and Problem Solving: Critique Reasoning

- Have students work in pairs.
- Have one student write a true or false statement related to GCFs or LCMs, and then show their statement to their partner.
- The partner decides whether the statement is true or false and justifies the choice with an explanation or a counterexample.
- Have students continue taking turns writing statements and critiquing their partner's statements.

STATEMENT:
The LCM of 12 and 60 is 120.

RESPONSE: The statement is false.

12 = 2 × 2 × 3

60 = 2 × 2 × 3 × 5

To find the LCM you find the greatest number of times each different factor appears

LCM = 2 × 2 × 3 × 5 = 60

So the LCM is 60, not 120.

## Reteach I

Name ____________

Reteach to Build Understanding 8-4

**Vocabulary**

1. A **counterexample** is an example that shows that a statement is not true. Write a counterexample for the statement below.

   Statement: All even numbers are composite numbers.
   Example: 4 is a composite number.

   Counterexample: 2 is a(n) **even** number that is not a(n) **composite** number.

Clara's Bagels ships bagels in boxes of 54 or 72. The bagels are put into plastic bags, then boxed. Clara wants to put the maximum number of bagels in each bag and claims that each bag should contain 6 bagels. Her work is shown below.

Prime factorization of 54: 2 × 3 × 3 × 3
Prime factorization of 72: 2 × 2 × 2 × 3 × 3
GCF of 54 and 72: 2 × 3 = 6

2. How does Clara support her claim?

   To find the GCF, Clara multiplied the common **prime** factors **2** and **3**.

3. Does Clara's math support her claim that the maximum number of bagels each bag should contain is 6? Explain.

   **No**. Clara overlooked a pair of **common** prime factors, so 6 is not the GCF of 54 and 72.

4. Use a counterexample to justify your answer.

   In the box above showing Clara's work, circle the common prime factors that Clara overlooked.

   GCF of 54 and 72: **2** × **3** × **3** = **18**

   Each bag should contain **18** bagels.

On the Back! **Sample answer: No; All square numbers less than 100 were tested and they have an odd number of factors.**

5. Peter says that every square number less than 100 has an odd number of factors. Is there a counterexample that proves his conjecture is not true? Explain.

R 8-4  6

## On-Level and Advanced Activity Centers  

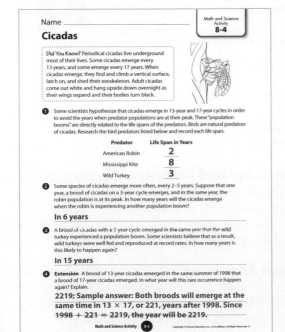

Name ____________

Math and Science Activity 8-4

### Cicadas

*Did You Know?* Periodical cicadas live underground most of their lives. Some cicadas emerge every 13 years, and some emerge every 17 years. When cicadas emerge, they find and climb a vertical surface, latch on, and shed their exoskeleton. Adult cicadas come out white and hang upside down overnight as their wings expand and their bodies turn black.

1. Some scientists hypothesize that cicadas emerge in 13-year and 17-year cycles in order to avoid the years when predator populations are at their peak. These "population booms" are directly related to the life spans of the predators. Birds are natural predators of cicadas. Research the bird predators listed below and record each life span.

| Predator | Life Span in Years |
|---|---|
| American Robin | **2** |
| Mississippi Kite | **8** |
| Wild Turkey | **3** |

2. Some species of cicadas emerge more often, every 2–5 years. Suppose that one year, a brood of cicadas on a 3-year cycle emerges, and in the same year, the robin population is at its peak. In how many years will the cicadas emerge when the robin is experiencing another population boom?

   **In 6 years**

3. A brood of cicadas with a 5-year cycle emerged in the same year that the wild turkey experienced a population boom. Some scientists believe that as a result, wild turkeys were well fed and reproduced at record rates. In how many years is this likely to happen again?

   **In 15 years**

4. **Extension** A brood of 13-year cicadas emerged in the same summer of 1998 that a brood of 17-year cicadas emerged. In what year will this rare occurrence happen again? Explain.

   **2219; Sample answer: Both broods will emerge at the same time in 13 × 17, or 221, years after 1998. Since 1998 + 221 = 2219, the year will be 2219.**

Math and Science Activity 8-4  6

### Math and Science Activity STEM

This activity revisits the science theme, **Cryptography,** introduced on page 387 in the Student's Edition.

### Sample Student Work

3. cicadas: 5, 10, 15, 20, 25...
   turkeys: 3, 6, 9, 12, 15, ...

The GCF is 15, so this will happen again in 15 years.

PEARSON realize. PearsonRealize.com

Help | Practice Buddy | Tools | Games

**TIMING**

The time allocated to Step 3 will depend on the teacher's instructional decisions and differentiation routines.

15–30 min

## Technology Center I O A

### Math Tools and Math Games

Tools Games

A link to a specific math tools activity or math game to use with this lesson is provided at PearsonRealize.com.

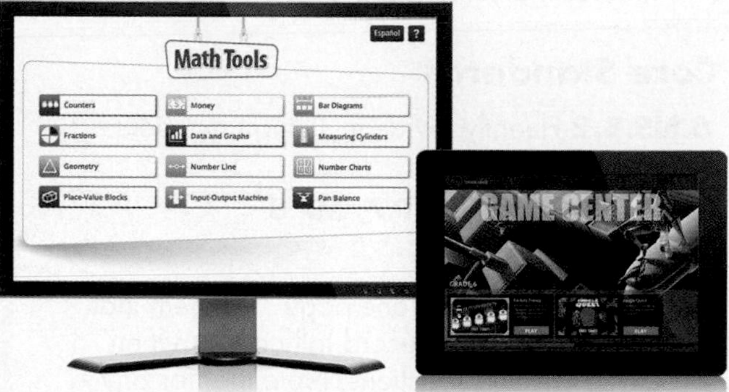


## Leveled Assignment I Items 1–5 O Items 1–5 A Items 1–5

Name ______________________

Help Practice Buddy Tools Games

**Homework & Practice 8-4**
**Critique Reasoning**

### Another Look!

Jim notices that 18 and 27 are multiples of 9 and that the sum of 18 and 27 is 45, which is also a multiple of 9. He reasons that for any two numbers that are multiples of 9, their sum will also be a multiple of 9. Explain whether Jim's reasoning makes sense.

You can critique reasoning by analyzing a person's thinking and then testing or questioning their approaches.

$9 \times 3 = 27$

$9 \times 2 = 18$

$18 + 27 = 45$ $\quad$ $45 = 9 \times 5$

Critique Jim's reasoning by testing more examples.

$9 \times 6 = 54$ $\quad$ $9 \times 1 = 9$
$9 \times 8 = 72$ $\quad$ $9 \times 4 = 36$

$54 + 72 = 126$ $\quad$ $9 + 36 = 45$

$126 = 9 \times 14$ $\quad$ $45 = 9 \times 5$

Use the Distributive Property to show why this works.

$9 \times 6 + 9 \times 8 = 9(6 + 8) = 9(14)$
$9 \times 1 + 9 \times 4 = 9(1 + 4) = 9(5)$

Writing the expressions using the Distributive Property shows that the sum of two numbers with a GCF of 9 will always be a multiple of 9.

Jim's reasoning makes sense.

**MP.3 Critique Reasoning**
Eva says the LCM of two odd numbers is the product of the two numbers.

Multiples of 3: 3, 6, 9, (15)
Multiples of 5: 5, 10, (15)

Multiples of 7: 7, 14, 21, 28, 35, 42, 49, 56, (63)
Multiples of 9: 9, 18, 27, 36, 45, 54, (63)

Remember, when you critique reasoning, just one counterexample proves the conjecture is incorrect.

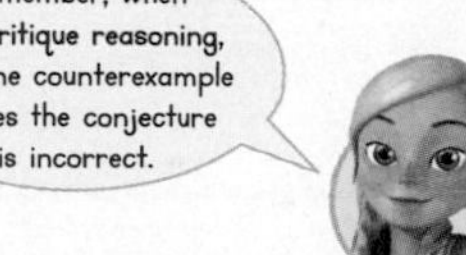

1. How does Eva support her conjecture?
**Sample answer: Eva supports her conjecture by showing that the LCM of 3 and 5 is 15 and the LCM of 7 and 9 is 63 and both are the products of the two numbers.**
2. Critique Eva's reasoning by testing more examples. Is there a counterexample that proves her conjecture is not true?
**Sample answer: The numbers 3 and 15 are odd numbers. Their LCM is 15, and their product is 45. The counterexample shows that Eva's conjecture is not true and her reasoning is incorrect.**



### Common Core Performance Assessment

**Balloons**
Jane is making balloon centerpieces for a school banquet. She wants to use $\frac{1}{3}$-pack of each balloon type per centerpiece. Jane states that the least number of centerpieces she can make with no balloons left over is 54.

6: 2 x 3
9: 3 x 3
LCM: 2 x 3 x 3 x 3 = 54

| Type of Balloon | Number of Balloons per Pack |
|---|---|
| Latex (6 pks.) | 9 |
| Mylar (6 pks.) | 6 |

3. **MP.1 Make Sense and Persevere** What is Jane's argument and how does she support it?
**Sample answer: Jane argues that the least number of balloon centerpieces she can make is 54. She supports her argument by finding the LCM of the two types of balloons that come in packs of 9 and 6.**

When you critique reasoning, you can look for flaws in calculations.

4. **MP.3 Critique Reasoning** How can you tell whether Jane's argument is correct?
**Sample answer: I can check her math for errors. If there are no errors, then her argument might be correct.**

5. **MP.3 Construct Arguments** Is Jane's math correct?
**No; Sample answer: Jane used prime factorization to find the LCM of 9 and 6. She used the correct prime factors, but used all of the factors in her calculation. To find the LCM, you only list the greatest number of times each factor is used. Then you multiply the factors. $2 \times 3 \times 3 = 18$, so the LCM of the numbers is 18.**

# TOPIC 8 FLUENCY PRACTICE ACTIVITY

PEARSON realize. PearsonRealize.com

Games Practice Buddy

## FLUENCY PRACTICE ACTIVITY

Students practice fluently dividing multi-digit numbers during a partner activity that reinforces mathematical practices.

### Common Core Standards

**Content Standard 6.NS.B.2** Fluently divide multi-digit numbers using the standard algorithm.

**Mathematical Practices MP.3, MP.6, MP.7, MP.8**

**Getting Started** Ask partners to share one page. Tell them that the other partner's page will be used to record tally marks when they repeat the activity. Go over the directions. Note that for any quotient, only one partner will get a tally mark.

When partners simultaneously point to two numbers, they may point to two numbers that they have already divided. In that case, students can point again to find two other numbers to divide.

**As Students Do the Activity** Remind students to compare and discuss their answers.

**Another Activity** Students can repeat the activity and record their tally marks on the other partner's page.

**Extra Challenge** *Take turns with a partner. Point to a quotient in one of the blue spaces. Ask your partner to get that quotient by dividing a number in the column at the left by a number in the column at the right.*

**Online Game** The Game Center at PearsonRealize.com provides opportunities for fluency practice.

**Steps to Fluency Success** To ensure all students achieve fluency, see pages 271K–271N for additional resources including practice/assessment masters and online practice/assessment on fluency subskills. You can also use the ExamView® CD-ROM to generate worksheets with multiple-choice or free-response items on fluency subskills.

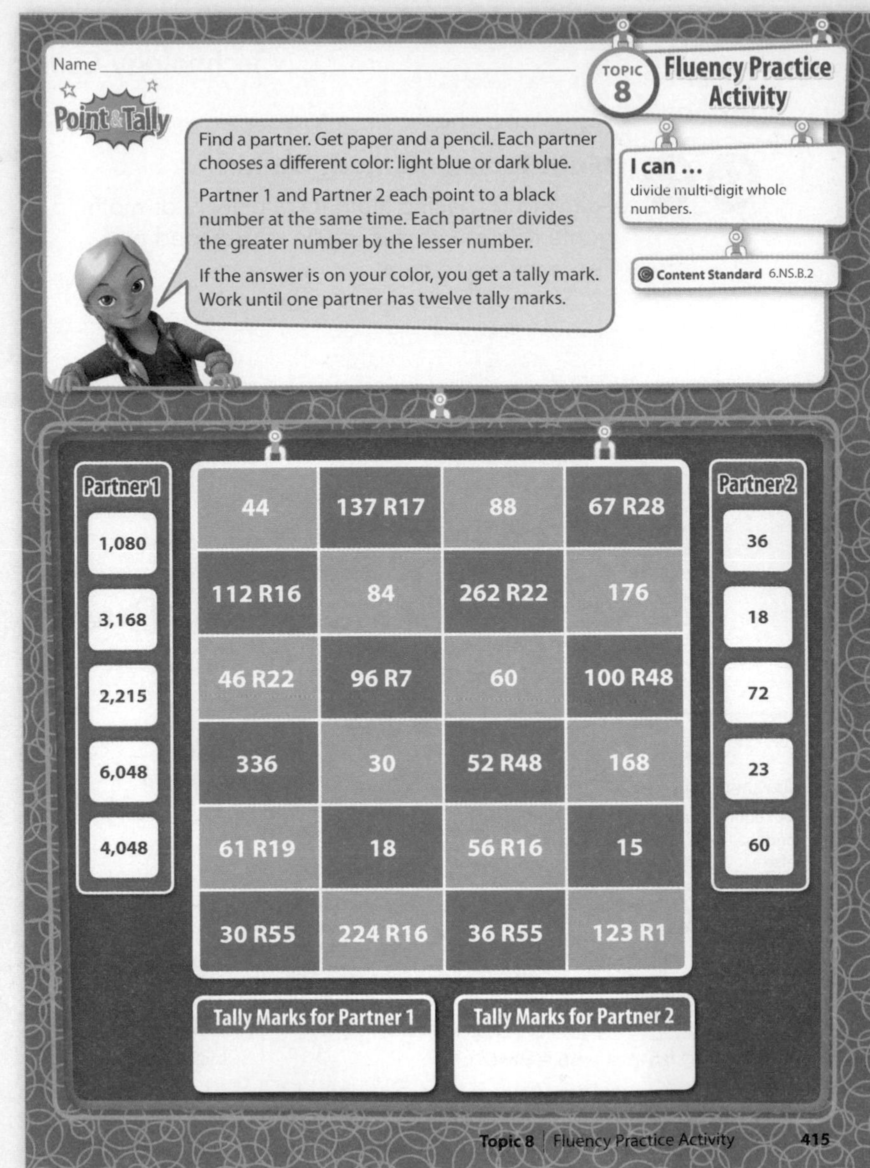

Name
Point & Tally
TOPIC 8
Fluency Practice Activity
Find a partner. Get paper and a pencil. Each partner chooses a different color: light blue or dark blue.
Partner 1 and Partner 2 each point to a black number at the same time. Each partner divides the greater number by the lesser number.
If the answer is on your color, you get a tally mark. Work until one partner has twelve tally marks.
I can ...
divide multi-digit whole numbers.
Content Standard 6.NS.B.2
Partner 1
1,080
3,168
2,215
6,048
4,048
44
137 R17
88
67 R28
112 R16
84
262 R22
176
46 R22
96 R7
60
100 R48
336
30
52 R48
168
61 R19
18
56 R16
15
30 R55
224 R16
36 R55
123 R1
Partner 2
36
18
72
23
60
Tally Marks for Partner 1
Tally Marks for Partner 2
Topic 8 | Fluency Practice Activity 415

PEARSON realize. PearsonRealize.com

Glossary

Games

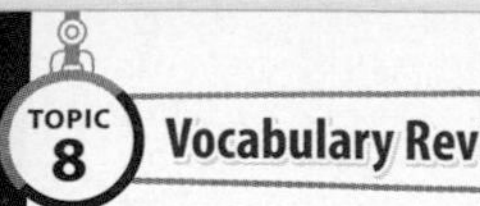

Word List
- common multiple
- composite number
- counterexample
- factor tree
- greatest common factor (GCF)
- least common multiple (LCM)
- prime factorization
- prime number

**Understand Vocabulary**

Choose the best term from the Word List. Write it on the blank.

1. Every composite number can be written as a product of prime factors called its **prime factorization**.
2. The number 5 is the **GCF** of 10 and 15.
3. A diagram that shows the prime factors of a composite number is a **factor tree**.
4. A number that has more than two factors is a **composite number**.
5. Write **P** next to each *prime number*. Write **C** next to each *composite number*.

2 **P** 9 **C** 65 **C** 73 **P**

6. Circle the *common multiples* of 8 and 12.

2 12 (24) (48) (72) 4 16 36 60

Draw a line from each pair of numbers in Column A to the *least common multiple* (*LCM*) of the numbers in Column B.

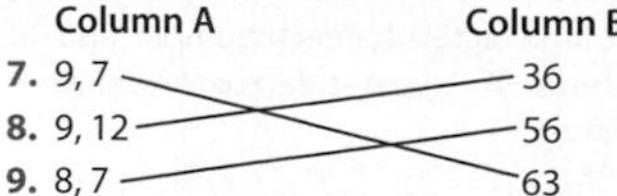

| Column A | Column B |
|---|---|
| 7. 9, 7 | 36 |
| 8. 9, 12 | 56 |
| 9. 8, 7 | 63 |

**Use Vocabulary in Writing**

10. Describe two ways to find the *prime factorization* of 16. Use at least 3 words from the Word List in your explanation.
**Sample answer: One way to write the *prime factorization* of 16 is to keep writing multiplication expressions that equal 16 until all of the factors are *prime numbers*. Start with the least prime factor 2 and write $2 \times 8 = 16$. 8 is a *composite number*, so write 8 as $2 \times 4$ to give $2 \times 2 \times 4 = 16$. 4 is a *composite number*, so write $2 \times 2 \times 2 \times 2 = 16$. All of the factors are prime factors, so $2 \times 2 \times 2 \times 2 = 16$ or $2^4$ is the *prime factorization* of 16. Another way is to draw a *factor tree*.**

416 Topic 8 | Vocabulary Review © Pearson Education, Inc. 6

## VOCABULARY REVIEW

Students review vocabulary words used in the topic.

**Oral Language** Before students complete the page, you might reinforce oral language through a class discussion involving one or more of the following activities.

- Have students say math sentences or ask math questions that use the words.
- Have students work with a partner. One student writes two different whole numbers for his or her partner. Then the partner determines the GCF, LCM, or a common factor or multiple of the two numbers. The student shows the partner the answer, and then asks the partner whether the answer is a GCF, LCM, or a common factor or multiple of the two numbers. Students take turns in the different roles.
- Play a "Right or Wrong?" game in which you or a student says a sentence that uses one of the words correctly or incorrectly. Then others say "right" or "wrong."

**Writing in Math** After students complete the page, you might further reinforce writing in math by doing one or more of the following activities.

- Have students write a letter to their partner explaining a particular word that their partner does not understand.
- Have students work with a partner. Each partner writes a math question that uses one of the words. Then students trade papers and give a written answer that uses the word. Be sure students check each other's spelling.

Games

**Online Game** The Game Center at PearsonRealize.com includes a vocabulary game that students can access any time.

# RETEACHING

## COMMON FACTORS AND MULTIPLES

### RtI Item Analysis for Diagnosis and Intervention

| Reteaching Sets | Standard | MDIS |
|---|---|---|
| Set A | 6.NS.B.4 | G61 |
| Set B | 6.NS.B.4 | G62 |
| Set C | 6.NS.B.4 | G63 |
| Set D | MP.3, MP.1, MP.6, MP.7 | G62 |

Name ________________

TOPIC 8

**Reteaching**

**Set A** pages 391–396

Find the prime factorization of 24.

Start with any two factors.
Keep finding factors until all factors are prime.

$24 = 4 \times 6$
$= 2 \times 2 \times 6$
$= 2 \times 2 \times 2 \times 3$

The prime factorization of 24 is $2 \times 2 \times 2 \times 3$ or $2^3 \times 3$.

You can also use a factor tree. Start with any two factors.

The factor tree shows that the prime factorization of 24 is $2 \times 2 \times 2 \times 3$ or $2^3 \times 3$.

24
2 × 12
2 × 6
2 × 3

**Remember** that a number is prime when its only factors are 1 and the number itself.

Write the prime factorization of each number. If the number is prime, write *prime*.

1. 39 **3 × 13**
2. 56 **$2 \times 2 \times 2 \times 7$ or $2^3 \times 7$**
3. 83 **prime**
4. 64 **$2 \times 2 \times 2 \times 2 \times 2 \times 2$ or $2^6$**
5. 42 **$2 \times 3 \times 7$**
6. 75 **$3 \times 5 \times 5$ or $3 \times 5^2$**
7. 29 **prime**

**Set B** pages 397–402

Find the greatest common factor, or GCF, of 24 and 66 by using prime factorization. Then use the GCF and the Distributive Property to find the sum of 24 and 66.

**Step 1** Find the prime factorization of each number.

$24 = 2 \times 2 \times 2 \times 3$ $\quad 66 = 2 \times 3 \times 11$

**Step 2** Multiply the common, prime factors. The GCF of 24 and 66 is $2 \times 3 = 6$.

**Step 3** Use the GCF and the Distributive Property to find the sum of 24 and 66.

$24 + 66 = 6 \times 4 + 6 \times 11 = 6(4 + 11)$
$= 6(15) = 90.$

**Remember** that to find the GCF, you can also list all of the factors for each number, and then choose the greatest factor they have in common.

Find the GCF for each pair of numbers. Then use the GCF and the Distributive Property to find the sum of each pair of numbers.

1. 30, 100 **10; 130**
2. 8, 52 **4; 60**
3. 28, 42 **14; 70**
4. 37, 67 **1; 104**
5. 75, 89 **1; 164**
6. 48, 72 **24; 120**

**Check students' work.**

**Set C** pages 403–408

Find the least common multiple (LCM) of 10 and 6.

List multiples of each number.

10: 10, 20, 30 . . .   6: 6, 12, 18, 24, 30 . . .

The LCM is 30.

You can also use prime factorization to find the least common multiple.

10: ②×⑤

6: ②×③

List the greatest number of times each factor appears in either prime factorization. Then multiply the factors.

$2 \times 5 \times 3 = 30$

**Remember** that you multiply a given number by any whole number to find a multiple.

Find the LCM for each pair of numbers.

1. 4, 9 **36**
2. 3, 6 **6**
3. 8, 10 **40**
4. 3, 5 **15**
5. 4, 12 **12**
6. 6, 11 **66**
7. 9, 12 **36**
8. 4, 10 **20**
9. 7, 8 **56**
10. 9, 7 **63**
11. 12, 11 **132**
12. 10, 2 **10**

**Set D** pages 409–414

Think about these questions to help you **critique the reasoning of others**.

**Thinking Habits**

- What questions can I ask to understand other people's thinking?
- Are there mistakes in other people's thinking?
- Can I improve other people's thinking?

**Remember** that you can critique reasoning by offering a counterexample.

Ms. Davis schedules after-school group activities for 18 girls and 24 boys. She wants to make equal groups with the same number of girls and the same number of boys in each group. Ms. Davis says that the greatest number of equal groups she can make is 3.

1. Is Ms. Davis correct? Use an example or counterexample to critique Ms. Davis's statement. **Sample answer: Another common factor of 18 and 24 is 6. It is greater than 3, and I know it is the greatest common factor. The factors of 18 are 1, 2, 3, 6, 9, and 18. The factors of 24 are 1, 2, 3, 4, 6, 8, 12, and 24. There's no other common factor greater than 6.**
2. What mistake did Ms. Davis make? **Sample answer: 3 is a common factor of 18 and 24, so Ms. Davis can make 3 equal groups, but 3 equal groups is not the greatest number of groups.**





## Response to Intervention

### Ongoing Intervention

- Lessons with guiding questions to assess understanding
- Support to prevent misconceptions and to reteach

### Strategic Intervention

- Targeted to small groups that need more support
- Easy to implement

### Intensive Intervention

- Instruction to accelerate progress
- Instruction focused on foundational skills

# TOPIC 8 TOPIC ASSESSMENT

## COMMON FACTORS AND MULTIPLES

Name ____________________

TOPIC 8

Assessment

**1.** Kristen buys sheets of elephant stickers and sheets of tiger stickers. There are 12 elephant stickers on each sheet and 10 tiger stickers on each sheet.

**Part A**

What is the least number of each type of sticker that Kristen can buy so that she has an equal number of each type of sticker? Show how you know. **1 point**

**60; Sample answer: I can list the multiples for each number to find the least common multiple: 12, 24, 36, 48, 60; 10, 20, 30, 40, 50, 60**

**Part B**

How many sheets of each type of sticker should she buy? Show how you know. **1 point**

**She should buy 5 pages of elephant stickers and 6 pages of tiger stickers; $12 \times 5 = 60$ and $10 \times 6 = 60$.**

**2.** For questions 2a–2d, choose Yes or No to tell whether 3 is the GCF of the pair of numbers. **1 point**

| | Yes | No |
|---|---|---|
| **2a.** 9, 15 | ● Yes | ○ No |
| **2b.** 12, 18 | ○ Yes | ● No |
| **2c.** 15, 27 | ● Yes | ○ No |
| **2d.** 30, 45 | ○ Yes | ● No |

**3.** Ziva notices a pattern when finding the LCM of two prime numbers. She reasons that because the only factors of each prime number are 1 and itself, the LCM of two prime numbers is always the product of the numbers.

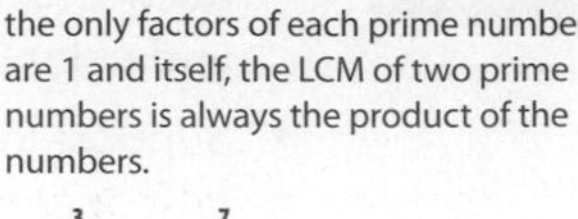


$3 = 1 \times 3$
$7 = 1 \times 7$
$LCM = 1 \times 3 \times 7 = 21$

Does Ziva's reasoning make sense? Explain how you know. **1 point**

**Sample explanation: Ziva's reasoning makes sense. The prime factorization of any prime number is the product of 1 and itself. The LCM can be found by listing the greatest number of times a factor is in each prime factorization. Because the only factors are 1 and itself, just 1 and both prime numbers will be the factors of the LCM.**

**4.** Which is the GCF of 36 and 54? **1 point**

Ⓐ 2
Ⓑ 6
Ⓒ 9
● 18



**5.** Jamie volunteers at the pet shelter every 3 days and at the food pantry every 6 days. This month he volunteers at the pet shelter on the 3rd day of the month and the food pantry on the 6th day of the month. Jamie says that the first time he will volunteer at both places will be the 18th day of the month because the LCM of 3 and 6 is 18.

Does Jamie's reasoning make sense? Use an example or a counterexample to explain your analysis. **2 points**

**No; Sample answer: Jamie's reasoning does not make sense. Jamie assumes that the LCM is the product of 3 and 6, but because 6 is a multiple of 3, the least common multiple is 6, not 18. So, the 6th will be the first time he works at both places.**

**6.** Use the GCF and the Distributive Property to find the sum of 49 + 56. Show your work. **1 point**

**105;** $49 + 56 = 7(7 + 8)$
$= 7(15)$
$= 105$

**7.** Jase wrote the prime factorization of 99. Which expression could he have written? Choose all that apply. **1 point**

■ $3^2 \times 11$
□ $9 \times 9$
□ $3 \times 3 \times 3 \times 11$
□ $3^4$
■ $3 \times 3 \times 11$

**8.** Draw lines to match each pair of numbers on the left to the LCM of the numbers on the right. **1 point**

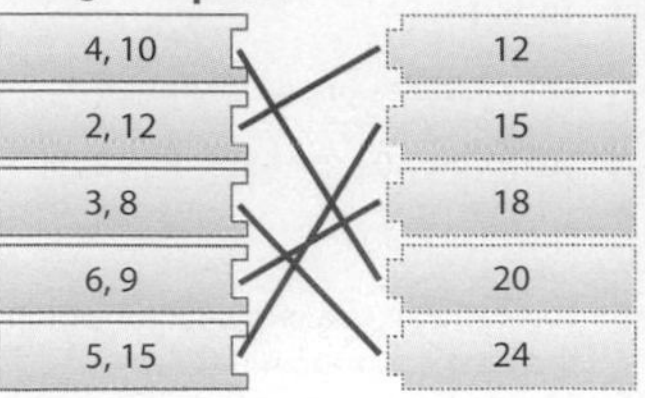


**9.** Elliot has 28 mystery books and 35 fantasy books that he wants to put on shelves. Each shelf will have the same number of books. Elliot wants to put only one type of book on each shelf.

**Part A**

What is the greatest number of books that he will put on each shelf? **1 point**

**He will put 7 books on each shelf.**

**Part B**

How many shelves will there be of mystery books? How many shelves will there be of fantasy books? **1 point**

**There will be 4 shelves of mystery books and 5 shelves of fantasy books.**

**10.** Find the GCF of 9 and 12. Explain your method. **1 point**

**3; Sample answer: Find the prime factorization of each number. Then multiply the common prime factors.**





## ANSWERING THE TOPIC ESSENTIAL QUESTION

**How can you find common factors and multiples of numbers?**

Restate the Topic Essential Question from the Topic Opener or project it from the Student's Edition eText.

Ask students to answer the Essential Question (verbally or in writing) and give examples that support their answers. The following are key elements of the answer to the Essential Question. Be sure these are made explicit when discussing students' answers.

- You can find common factors of two numbers by listing their factors and identifying the factors that are the same. You can determine the greatest common factor (GCF) by examining the lists of factors or by using prime factorization.

  **Example:** List and compare the factors of 18 and 42.

  Factors of 18: 1, 2, 3, 6, 9, 18
  Factors of 42: 1, 2, 3, 6, 7, 14, 21, 42

  1, 2, 3, and 6 are common factors, and the GCF is 6.

- You can find common multiples of two numbers by multiplying each number by consecutive whole-number factors and identifying the multiples that are the same. You can determine the least common multiple (LCM) by examining the lists of multiples or by using prime factorization.

  **Example:** Use the prime factorizations of 10 and 12 to find their LCM.

  $10 = 2 \times 5$

  $12 = 2 \times 2 \times 3$

  List each factor the greatest number of times it appears in either prime factorization. Multiply these factors.

  $2 \times 2 \times 3 \times 5 = 60$, so the LCM is 60.

## ONLINE TOPIC ASSESSMENT

An auto-scored Topic Assessment is provided at PearsonRealize.com.

## EXAMVIEW® TEST GENERATOR

ExamView can be used to create a blackline-master Topic Assessment with multiple-choice and free-response items.

## Topic Assessment Masters

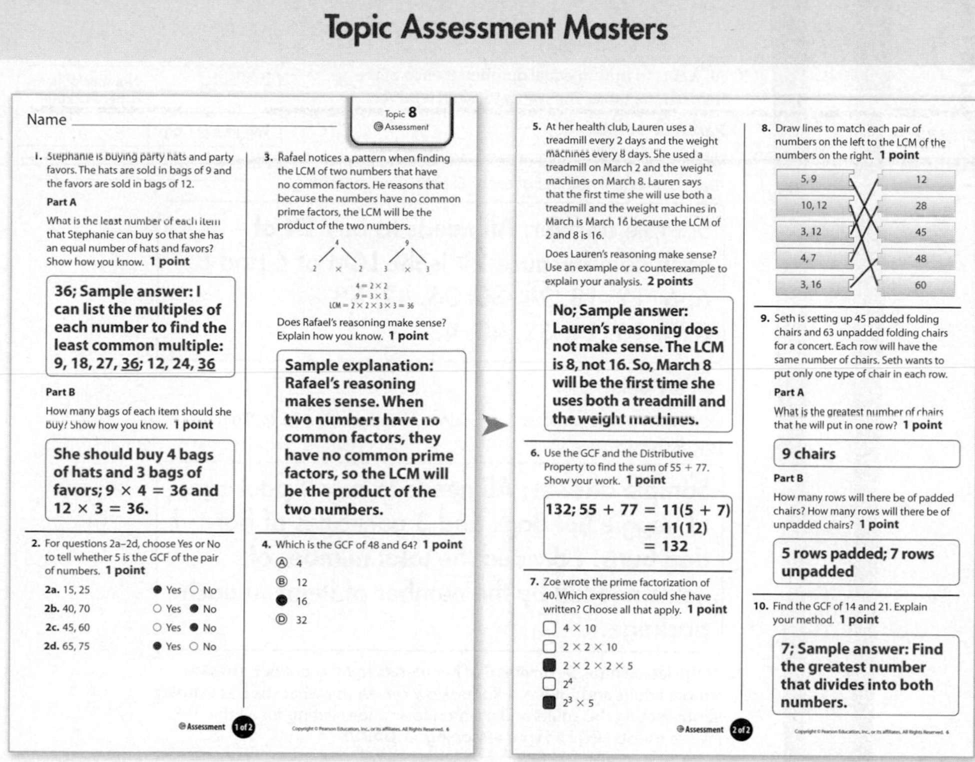

Name ______________________

Topic 8 Assessment

1. Stephanie is buying party hats and party favors. The hats are sold in bags of 9 and the favors are sold in bags of 12.

**Part A**

What is the least number of each item that Stephanie can buy so that she has an equal number of hats and favors? Show how you know. **1 point**

**36; Sample answer: I can list the multiples of each number to find the least common multiple: 9, 18, 27, 36; 12, 24, 36**

**Part B**

How many bags of each item should she buy? Show how you know. **1 point**

**She should buy 4 bags of hats and 3 bags of favors; $9 \times 4 = 36$ and $12 \times 3 = 36$.**

2. For questions 2a–2d, choose Yes or No to tell whether 5 is the GCF of the pair of numbers. **1 point**

**2a.** 15, 25 ● Yes ○ No

**2b.** 40, 70 ○ Yes ● No

**2c.** 45, 60 ○ Yes ● No

**2d.** 65, 75 ● Yes ○ No

3. Rafael notices a pattern when finding the LCM of two numbers that have no common factors. He reasons that because the numbers have no common prime factors, the LCM will be the product of the two numbers.

$4 = 2 \times 2$
$9 = 3 \times 3$
$LCM = 2 \times 2 \times 3 \times 3 = 36$

Does Rafael's reasoning make sense? Explain how you know. **1 point**

**Sample explanation: Rafael's reasoning makes sense. When two numbers have no common factors, they have no common prime factors, so the LCM will be the product of the two numbers.**

4. Which is the GCF of 48 and 64? **1 point**

Ⓐ 4
Ⓑ 12
● 16
Ⓓ 32

Assessment 1 of 2



5. At her health club, Lauren uses a treadmill every 2 days and the weight machines every 8 days. She used a treadmill on March 2 and the weight machines on March 8. Lauren says that the first time she will use both a treadmill and the weight machines in March is March 16 because the LCM of 2 and 8 is 16.

Does Lauren's reasoning make sense? Use an example or a counterexample to explain your analysis. **2 points**

**No; Sample answer: Lauren's reasoning does not make sense. The LCM is 8, not 16. So, March 8 will be the first time she uses both a treadmill and the weight machines.**

6. Use the GCF and the Distributive Property to find the sum of 55 + 77. Show your work. **1 point**

**$132;\ 55 + 77 = 11(5 + 7) = 11(12) = 132$**

7. Zoe wrote the prime factorization of 40. Which expression could she have written? Choose all that apply. **1 point**

☐ $4 \times 10$
☐ $2 \times 2 \times 10$
■ $2 \times 2 \times 2 \times 5$
☐ $2^4$
■ $2^3 \times 5$

8. Draw lines to match each pair of numbers on the left to the LCM of the numbers on the right. **1 point**

5, 9 | 10, 12 | 3, 12 | 4, 7 | 3, 16

12 | 28 | 45 | 48 | 60

9. Seth is setting up 45 padded folding chairs and 63 unpadded folding chairs for a concert. Each row will have the same number of chairs. Seth wants to put only one type of chair in each row.

**Part A**

What is the greatest number of chairs that he will put in one row? **1 point**

**9 chairs**

**Part B**

How many rows will there be of padded chairs? How many rows will there be of unpadded chairs? **1 point**

**5 rows padded; 7 rows unpadded**

10. Find the GCF of 14 and 21. Explain your method. **1 point**

**7; Sample answer: Find the greatest number that divides into both numbers.**

Assessment 2 of 2



## RtI Item Analysis for Diagnosis and Intervention

| Item | Standard | DOK | MDIS |
|---|---|---|---|
| 1A | 6.NS.B.4 | 2 | G63 |
| 1B | 6.NS.B.4 | 2 | F50 |
| 2 | 6.NS.B.4 | 1 | G62 |
| 3 | 6.NS.B.4 | 3 | G61, G63 |
| 4 | 6.NS.B.4 | 1 | G62 |
| 5 | 6.NS.B.4, MP.3 | 3 | G63 |
| 6 | 6.NS.B.4 | 2 | F42, G62 |
| 7 | 6.NS.B.4 | 1 | G61 |
| 8 | 6.NS.B.4 | 1 | G63 |
| 9A | 6.NS.B.4 | 2 | G62 |
| 9B | 6.NS.B.4 | 1 | F50 |
| 10 | 6.NS.B.4 | 2 | G62 |

The Topic Assessment Masters assess the same content item for item as the Topic Assessment in the Student's Edition.

## Scoring Guide

| Item | Points | Topic Assessment (Student's Edition and Masters) |
|---|---|---|
| 1A | 1 | Correct answer and explanation |
| 1B | 1 | Correct answer and explanation |
| 2 | 1 | All correct choices selected |
| 3 | 1 | Correct answer and accurate explanation |
| 4 | 1 | Correct choice selected |
| 5 | 2 | Correct answer and explanation |
| | 1 | Correct answer with incomplete or missing explanation |
| 6 | 1 | Correct answer and work shown |
| 7 | 1 | All correct choices selected |
| 8 | 1 | All matches correct |
| 9A | 1 | Correct answer |
| 9B | 1 | Correct answers |
| 10 | 1 | Correct answer and explanation |

# TOPIC 8 TOPIC PERFORMANCE ASSESSMENT

## COMMON FACTORS AND MULTIPLES

Name ____________________

TOPIC 8

**Performance Assessment**

**The Cookout**

Ali is planning a cookout for family and friends. There will be 24 people at her cookout.

1. Ali is renting tables for the cookout and wants to seat an equal number of people at each table. She needs to decide how many tables to get. How could she arrange the seating so that a reasonable and equal number of people sit at each table? Explain your reasoning. **2 points**

**Sample answer: I used prime factorization to help determine a reasonable seating for 24 people.**
**$24 = 4 \times 6 = 2 \times 2 \times 6 = 2 \times 2 \times 2 \times 3$**
**Ali could seat 4 people each at 6 tables, 6 people each at 4 tables, 8 people each at 3 tables, or 12 people each at 2 tables. It would not be reasonable to seat 1 person each at 24 tables or 24 people at 1 table. She could seat 3 people each at 8 tables, but 3 is an odd number of people per table and 8 tables for 24 people seems like too many.**

2. Ali has invited 18 adults and 6 children. Mo, Ali's best friend, suggests that Ali seat an equal number of adults and an equal number of children at each table. What is the greatest number of tables Ali would need? How many adults and children would be seated at each table? Explain how you found your answer. **2 points**

**Sample answer: Ali would need 6 tables. There would be 3 adults and 1 child seated at each table. I used the GCF to find the number of tables: 18: 1, 2, 3, (6), 9, 18; 6: 1, 2, 3, (6)**
**Then I used the GCF and the Distributive property to find the number of adults and children at each table: $18 + 6 = 6(3 + 1)$.**



3. Ali wants to buy an equal number of each of the items in the table. She wants to avoid leftovers.

| Item | Number of Items per Package |
|---|---|
| Veggie Hot Dogs | 6 |
| Hot Dog Buns | 8 |

**Part A** **2 points**

What is the least number of items Ali needs to buy so there is an equal number of each? Explain your reasoning.

**Sample answer: Ali needs to buy 24 of each item because 24 is the LCM of 6 and 8.**
**6: 6, 12, 18, (24), 30, 36, 42, 48**
**8: 8, 16, (24), 32, 40, 48**

**Part B** **1 point**

How many packages of each item does Ali need to buy? Explain how you decided.

**Sample answer: Ali needs to buy 4 packages of veggie hot dogs and 3 packages of hot dog buns. I divided the total number of items needed by the number of items in each package.**

4. At the last minute, Mo invites 6 of her friends to Ali's cookout. There are 4 more adults and 2 more children. How can Ali use what she has learned about seating the adults and children to arrange seating for all the invited guests? Explain your reasoning. **3 points**

**Sample answer: There are now 30 people to seat; 22 adults and 8 children. The GCF of 22 and 8 is 2, so Ali could seat 11 adults and 4 children at each of 2 tables to seat an equal number of adults and an equal number of children at each, but this is not reasonable. Ali can seat either 6 people at 5 tables or 5 people at 6 tables.**




## Scoring Guide

| Item | Points | Topic Performance Assessment in the Student's Edition |
|---|---|---|
| 1 | 2 | Reasonable answer and explanation |
| | 1 | Reasonable answer with incomplete or missing explanation |
| 2 | 2 | Correct answers and explanation |
| | 1 | Correct answers with incomplete or missing explanation |
| 3A | 2 | Correct answer and explanation |
| | 1 | Correct answer or explanation |
| 3B | 1 | Correct answer and explanation |
| 4 | 3 | Correct answer and explanation |
| | 2 | Correct answer and incomplete explanation |
| | 1 | Partially correct answer or explanation |

## Item Analysis for Diagnosis and Intervention

| Item | Standard | DOK | MDIS |
|---|---|---|---|
| 1 | 6.NS.B.4, MP.1, MP.2 | 2 | G61 |
| 2 | 6.NS.B.4, MP.2, MP.3 | 2 | G62 |
| 3A | 6.NS.B.4, MP.2, MP.4 | 2 | G63 |
| 3B | 6.NS.B.4, MP.1, MP.3 | 2 | F50 |
| 4 | 6.NS.B.4, MP.3 | 3 | G62 |

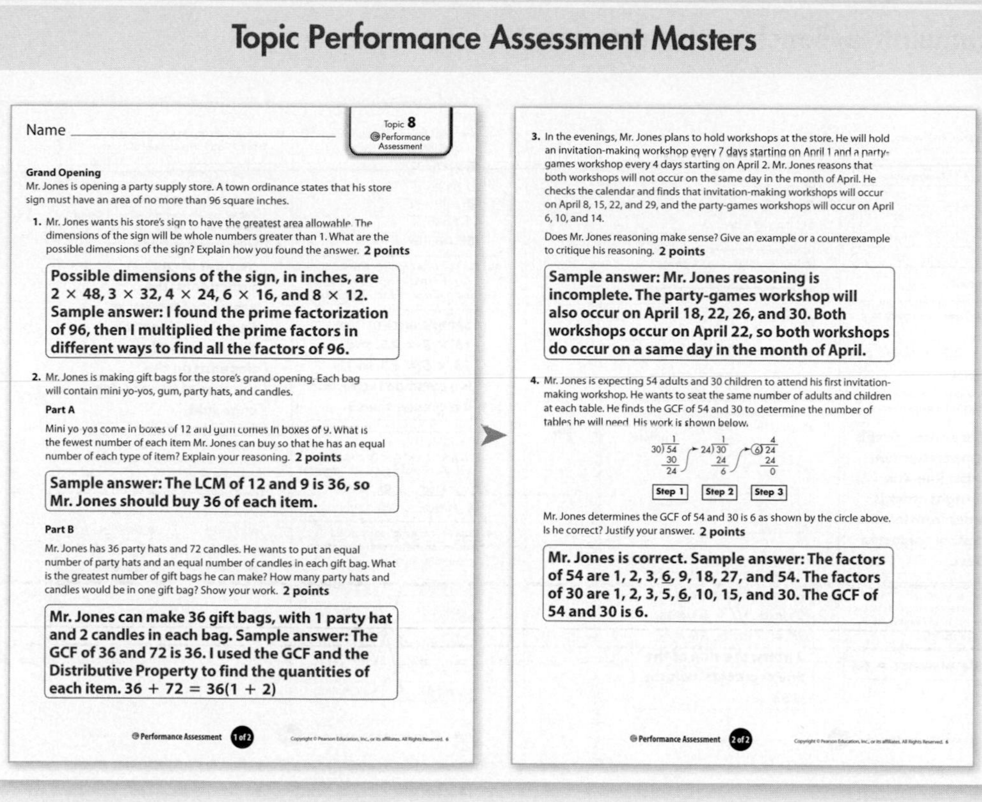

## Topic Performance Assessment Masters

Name ______________________ Topic 8 Performance Assessment

**Grand Opening**

Mr. Jones is opening a party supply store. A town ordinance states that his store sign must have an area of no more than 96 square inches.

1. Mr. Jones wants his store's sign to have the greatest area allowable. The dimensions of the sign will be whole numbers greater than 1. What are the possible dimensions of the sign? Explain how you found the answer. **2 points**

**Possible dimensions of the sign, in inches, are 2 × 48, 3 × 32, 4 × 24, 6 × 16, and 8 × 12. Sample answer: I found the prime factorization of 96, then I multiplied the prime factors in different ways to find all the factors of 96.**

2. Mr. Jones is making gift bags for the store's grand opening. Each bag will contain mini yo-yos, gum, party hats, and candles.

**Part A**

Mini yo-yos come in boxes of 12 and gum comes in boxes of 9. What is the fewest number of each item Mr. Jones can buy so that he has an equal number of each type of item? Explain your reasoning. **2 points**

**Sample answer: The LCM of 12 and 9 is 36, so Mr. Jones should buy 36 of each item.**

**Part B**

Mr. Jones has 36 party hats and 72 candles. He wants to put an equal number of party hats and an equal number of candles in each gift bag. What is the greatest number of gift bags he can make? How many party hats and candles would be in one gift bag? Show your work. **2 points**

**Mr. Jones can make 36 gift bags, with 1 party hat and 2 candles in each bag. Sample answer: The GCF of 36 and 72 is 36. I used the GCF and the Distributive Property to find the quantities of each item. 36 + 72 = 36(1 + 2)**

Performance Assessment 1 of 2

3. In the evenings, Mr. Jones plans to hold workshops at the store. He will hold an invitation-making workshop every 7 days starting on April 1 and a party-games workshop every 4 days starting on April 2. Mr. Jones reasons that both workshops will not occur on the same day in the month of April. He checks the calendar and finds that invitation-making workshops will occur on April 8, 15, 22, and 29, and the party-games workshops will occur on April 6, 10, and 14.

Does Mr. Jones reasoning make sense? Give an example or a counterexample to critique his reasoning. **2 points**

**Sample answer: Mr. Jones reasoning is incomplete. The party-games workshop will also occur on April 18, 22, 26, and 30. Both workshops occur on April 22, so both workshops do occur on a same day in the month of April.**

4. Mr. Jones is expecting 54 adults and 30 children to attend his first invitation-making workshop. He wants to seat the same number of adults and children at each table. He finds the GCF of 54 and 30 to determine the number of tables he will need. His work is shown below.

Step 1: 54 ÷ 30 = 1 R 24; Step 2: 30 ÷ 24 = 1 R 6; Step 3: 24 ÷ 6 = 4 R 0

Mr. Jones determines the GCF of 54 and 30 is 6 as shown by the circle above. Is he correct? Justify your answer. **2 points**

**Mr. Jones is correct. Sample answer: The factors of 54 are 1, 2, 3, 6, 9, 18, 27, and 54. The factors of 30 are 1, 2, 3, 5, 6, 10, 15, and 30. The GCF of 54 and 30 is 6.**

Performance Assessment 2 of 2

## RtI Item Analysis for Diagnosis and Intervention

| Item | Standard | DOK | MDIS |
|---|---|---|---|
| 1 | 6.NS.B.4, MP.1, MP.6 | 3 | G61 |
| 2A | 6.NS.B.4, MP.2 | 2 | G63 |
| 2B | 6.NS.B.4, MP.2 | 2 | G62 |
| 3 | 6.NS.B.4, MP.2, MP.3 | 3 | G63 |
| 4 | 6.NS.B.4, MP.2, MP.3 | 2 | G62 |

## Scoring Guide

| Item | Points | Topic Performance Assessment Masters |
|---|---|---|
| 1 | 2 | Correct answer and explanation |
| | 1 | Correct answer with incomplete or missing explanation |
| 2A | 2 | Correct answer and explanation |
| | 1 | Correct answer with incomplete or missing explanation |
| 2B | 2 | Correct answers and work shown |
| | 1 | Correct answers or work shown |
| 3 | 2 | Correct answer and counterexample |
| | 1 | Correct answer with incomplete or missing counterexample |
| 4 | 2 | Correct answer and justification |
| | 1 | Correct answer with incomplete or missing justification |

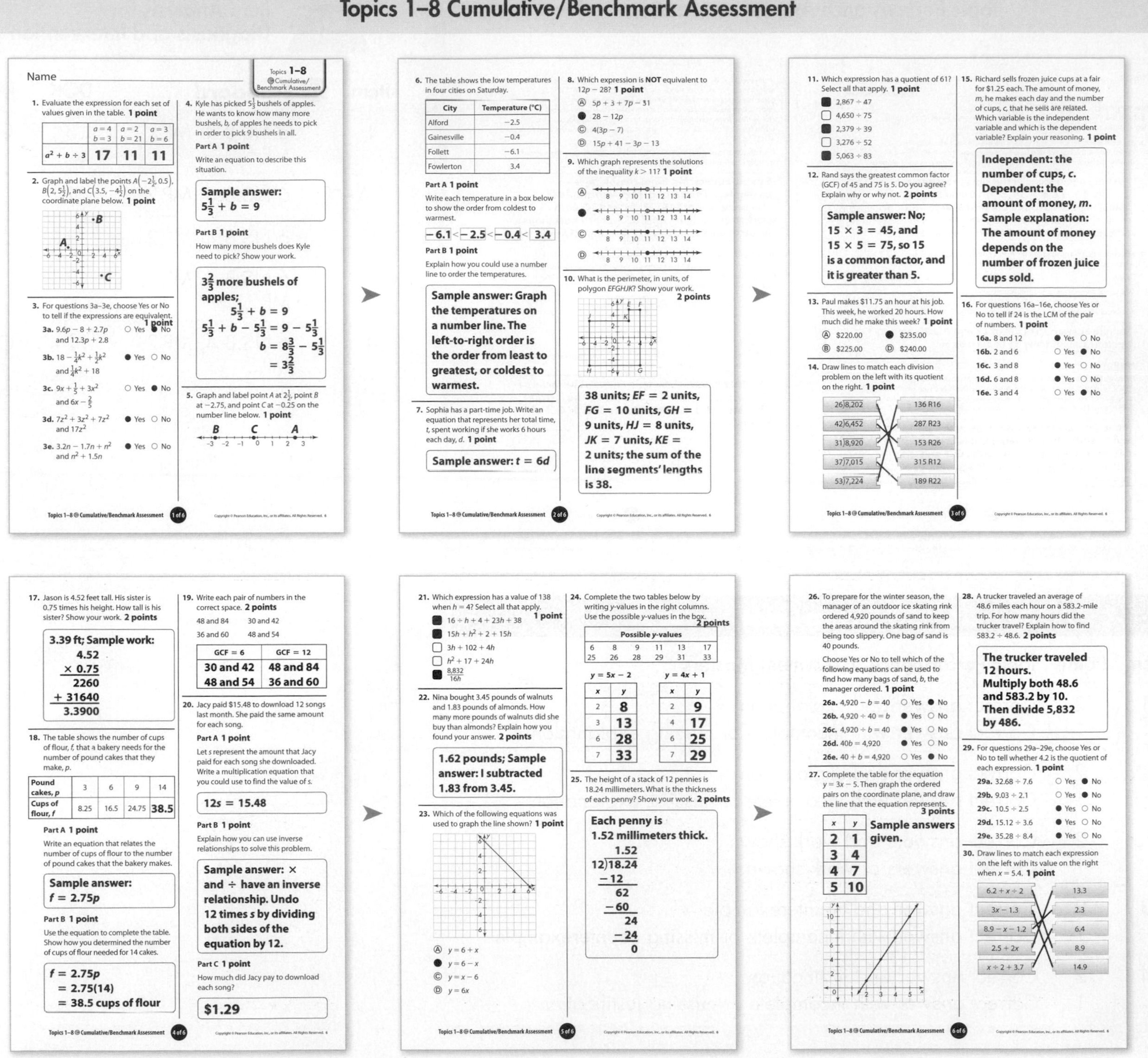

## Topics 1–8 Cumulative/Benchmark Assessment

Name ____________________ Topics **1–8** Cumulative/Benchmark Assessment

**1.** Evaluate the expression for each set of values given in the table. **1 point**

| | $a = 4$, $b = 3$ | $a = 2$, $b = 21$ | $a = 3$, $b = 6$ |
|---|---|---|---|
| $a^2 + b \div 3$ | **17** | **11** | **11** |

**2.** Graph and label the points $A\left(-2\frac{1}{2}, 0.5\right)$, $B\left(2, 5\frac{1}{2}\right)$, and $C\left(3.5, -4\frac{1}{2}\right)$ on the coordinate plane below. **1 point**

**3.** For questions 3a–3e, choose Yes or No to tell if the expressions are equivalent. **1 point**

- **3a.** $9.6p - 8 + 2.7p$ and $12.3p + 2.8$ ○ Yes ● No
- **3b.** $18 - \frac{1}{4}k^2 + \frac{1}{2}k^2$ and $\frac{1}{4}k^2 + 18$ ● Yes ○ No
- **3c.** $9x + \frac{1}{5} + 3x^2$ and $6x - \frac{2}{5}$ ○ Yes ● No
- **3d.** $7z^2 + 3z^2 + 7z^2$ and $17z^2$ ● Yes ○ No
- **3e.** $3.2n - 1.7n + n^2$ and $n^2 + 1.5n$ ● Yes ○ No

**4.** Kyle has picked $5\frac{1}{3}$ bushels of apples. He wants to know how many more bushels, *b*, of apples he needs to pick in order to pick 9 bushels in all.

**Part A 1 point**

Write an equation to describe this situation.

**Sample answer: $5\frac{1}{3} + b = 9$**

**Part B 1 point**

How many more bushels does Kyle need to pick? Show your work.

**$3\frac{2}{3}$ more bushels of apples;**

$$5\frac{1}{3} + b = 9$$
$$5\frac{1}{3} + b - 5\frac{1}{3} = 9 - 5\frac{1}{3}$$
$$b = 8\frac{3}{3} - 5\frac{1}{3}$$
$$= 3\frac{2}{3}$$

**5.** Graph and label point *A* at $2\frac{1}{2}$, point *B* at −2.75, and point *C* at −0.25 on the number line below. **1 point**

Topics 1–8 Cumulative/Benchmark Assessment 1 of 6 — Copyright © Pearson Education, Inc., or its affiliates. All Rights Reserved. 6

**6.** The table shows the low temperatures in four cities on Saturday.

| City | Temperature (°C) |
|---|---|
| Alford | −2.5 |
| Gainesville | −0.4 |
| Follett | −6.1 |
| Fowlerton | 3.4 |

**Part A 1 point**

Write each temperature in a box below to show the order from coldest to warmest.

**−6.1** < **−2.5** < **−0.4** < **3.4**

**Part B 1 point**

Explain how you could use a number line to order the temperatures.

**Sample answer: Graph the temperatures on a number line. The left-to-right order is the order from least to greatest, or coldest to warmest.**

**7.** Sophia has a part-time job. Write an equation that represents her total time, *t*, spent working if she works 6 hours each day, *d*. **1 point**

**Sample answer: $t = 6d$**

**8.** Which expression is **NOT** equivalent to $12p - 28$? **1 point**

- Ⓐ $5p + 3 + 7p - 31$
- ● $28 - 12p$
- Ⓒ $4(3p - 7)$
- Ⓓ $15p + 41 - 3p - 13$

**9.** Which graph represents the solutions of the inequality $k > 11$? **1 point**

**10.** What is the perimeter, in units, of polygon *EFGHJK*? Show your work. **2 points**

**38 units; $EF = 2$ units, $FG = 10$ units, $GH = 9$ units, $HJ = 8$ units, $JK = 7$ units, $KE = 2$ units; the sum of the line segments' lengths is 38.**

Topics 1–8 Cumulative/Benchmark Assessment 2 of 6 — Copyright © Pearson Education, Inc., or its affiliates. All Rights Reserved. 6

**11.** Which expression has a quotient of 61? Select all that apply. **1 point**

- ■ 2,867 ÷ 47
- □ 4,650 ÷ 75
- ■ 2,379 ÷ 39
- □ 3,276 ÷ 52
- ■ 5,063 ÷ 83

**12.** Rand says the greatest common factor (GCF) of 45 and 75 is 5. Do you agree? Explain why or why not. **2 points**

**Sample answer: No; $15 \times 3 = 45$, and $15 \times 5 = 75$, so 15 is a common factor, and it is greater than 5.**

**13.** Paul makes $11.75 an hour at his job. This week, he worked 20 hours. How much did he make this week? **1 point**

- Ⓐ $220.00
- Ⓑ $225.00
- ● $235.00
- Ⓓ $240.00

**14.** Draw lines to match each division problem on the left with its quotient on the right. **1 point**

| | |
|---|---|
| 26)8,202 | 136 R16 |
| 42)6,452 | 287 R23 |
| 31)8,920 | 153 R26 |
| 37)7,015 | 315 R12 |
| 53)7,224 | 189 R22 |

**15.** Richard sells frozen juice cups at a fair for $1.25 each. The amount of money, *m*, he makes each day and the number of cups, *c*, that he sells are related. Which variable is the independent variable and which is the dependent variable? Explain your reasoning. **1 point**

**Independent: the number of cups, *c*. Dependent: the amount of money, *m*. Sample explanation: The amount of money depends on the number of frozen juice cups sold.**

**16.** For questions 16a–16e, choose Yes or No to tell if 24 is the LCM of the pair of numbers. **1 point**

- **16a.** 8 and 12 ● Yes ○ No
- **16b.** 2 and 6 ○ Yes ● No
- **16c.** 3 and 8 ● Yes ○ No
- **16d.** 6 and 8 ● Yes ○ No
- **16e.** 3 and 4 ○ Yes ● No

Topics 1–8 Cumulative/Benchmark Assessment 3 of 6 — Copyright © Pearson Education, Inc., or its affiliates. All Rights Reserved. 6

**17.** Jason is 4.52 feet tall. His sister is 0.75 times his height. How tall is his sister? Show your work. **2 points**

**3.39 ft; Sample work:**

```
   4.52
 × 0.75
   2260
+ 31640
 3.3900
```

**18.** The table shows the number of cups of flour, *f*, that a bakery needs for the number of pound cakes that they make, *p*.

| Pound cakes, *p* | 3 | 6 | 9 | 14 |
|---|---|---|---|---|
| Cups of flour, *f* | 8.25 | 16.5 | 24.75 | **38.5** |

**Part A 1 point**

Write an equation that relates the number of cups of flour to the number of pound cakes that the bakery makes.

**Sample answer: $f = 2.75p$**

**Part B 1 point**

Use the equation to complete the table. Show how you determined the number of cups of flour needed for 14 cakes.

**$f = 2.75p$**
**$= 2.75(14)$**
**$= 38.5$ cups of flour**

**19.** Write each pair of numbers in the correct space. **2 points**

48 and 84  30 and 42
36 and 60  48 and 54

| GCF = 6 | GCF = 12 |
|---|---|
| **30 and 42** | **48 and 84** |
| **48 and 54** | **36 and 60** |

**20.** Jacy paid $15.48 to download 12 songs last month. She paid the same amount for each song.

**Part A 1 point**

Let *s* represent the amount that Jacy paid for each song she downloaded. Write a multiplication equation that you could use to find the value of *s*.

**$12s = 15.48$**

**Part B 1 point**

Explain how you can use inverse relationships to solve this problem.

**Sample answer: × and ÷ have an inverse relationship. Undo 12 times *s* by dividing both sides of the equation by 12.**

**Part C 1 point**

How much did Jacy pay to download each song?

**$1.29**

Topics 1–8 Cumulative/Benchmark Assessment 4 of 6 — Copyright © Pearson Education, Inc., or its affiliates. All Rights Reserved. 6

**21.** Which expression has a value of 138 when $h = 4$? Select all that apply. **1 point**

- ■ $16 \div h + 4 + 23h + 38$
- ■ $15h + h^2 + 2 + 15h$
- □ $3h + 102 + 4h$
- □ $h^2 + 17 + 24h$
- ■ $\frac{8,832}{16h}$

**22.** Nina bought 3.45 pounds of walnuts and 1.83 pounds of almonds. How many more pounds of walnuts did she buy than almonds? Explain how you found your answer. **2 points**

**1.62 pounds; Sample answer: I subtracted 1.83 from 3.45.**

**23.** Which of the following equations was used to graph the line shown? **1 point**

- Ⓐ $y = 6 + x$
- ● $y = 6 - x$
- Ⓒ $y = x - 6$
- Ⓓ $y = 6x$

**24.** Complete the two tables below by writing *y*-values in the right columns. Use the possible *y*-values in the box. **2 points**

| Possible *y*-values | | | | | |
|---|---|---|---|---|---|
| 6 | 8 | 9 | 11 | 13 | 17 |
| 25 | 26 | 28 | 29 | 31 | 33 |

$y = 5x - 2$

| *x* | *y* |
|---|---|
| 2 | **8** |
| 3 | **13** |
| 6 | **28** |
| 7 | **33** |

$y = 4x + 1$

| *x* | *y* |
|---|---|
| 2 | **9** |
| 4 | **17** |
| 6 | **25** |
| 7 | **29** |

**25.** The height of a stack of 12 pennies is 18.24 millimeters. What is the thickness of each penny? Show your work. **2 points**

**Each penny is 1.52 millimeters thick.**

```
    1.52
12)18.24
  −12
    62
   −60
    24
   −24
     0
```

Topics 1–8 Cumulative/Benchmark Assessment 5 of 6 — Copyright © Pearson Education, Inc., or its affiliates. All Rights Reserved. 6

**26.** To prepare for the winter season, the manager of an outdoor ice skating rink ordered 4,920 pounds of sand to keep the areas around the skating rink from being too slippery. One bag of sand is 40 pounds.

Choose Yes or No to tell which of the following equations can be used to find how many bags of sand, *b*, the manager ordered. **1 point**

- **26a.** $4,920 - b = 40$ ○ Yes ● No
- **26b.** $4,920 \div 40 = b$ ● Yes ○ No
- **26c.** $4,920 \div b = 40$ ● Yes ○ No
- **26d.** $40b = 4,920$ ● Yes ○ No
- **26e.** $40 + b = 4,920$ ○ Yes ● No

**27.** Complete the table for the equation $y = 3x - 5$. Then graph the ordered pairs on the coordinate plane, and draw the line that the equation represents. **3 points**

| *x* | *y* |
|---|---|
| **2** | **1** |
| **3** | **4** |
| **4** | **7** |
| **5** | **10** |

**Sample answers given.**

**28.** A trucker traveled an average of 48.6 miles each hour on a 583.2-mile trip. For how many hours did the trucker travel? Explain how to find 583.2 ÷ 48.6. **2 points**

**The trucker traveled 12 hours. Multiply both 48.6 and 583.2 by 10. Then divide 5,832 by 486.**

**29.** For questions 29a–29e, choose Yes or No to tell whether 4.2 is the quotient of each expression. **1 point**

- **29a.** 32.68 ÷ 7.6 ○ Yes ● No
- **29b.** 9.03 ÷ 2.1 ○ Yes ● No
- **29c.** 10.5 ÷ 2.5 ● Yes ○ No
- **29d.** 15.12 ÷ 3.6 ● Yes ○ No
- **29e.** 35.28 ÷ 8.4 ● Yes ○ No

**30.** Draw lines to match each expression on the left with its value on the right when $x = 5.4$. **1 point**

| | |
|---|---|
| $6.2 + x \div 2$ | 13.3 |
| $3x - 1.3$ | 2.3 |
| $8.9 - x - 1.2$ | 6.4 |
| $2.5 + 2x$ | 8.9 |
| $x \div 2 + 3.7$ | 14.9 |

Topics 1–8 Cumulative/Benchmark Assessment 6 of 6 — Copyright © Pearson Education, Inc., or its affiliates. All Rights Reserved. 6

Items 1–10 assess content taught in Topics 1–4. Items 11–30 assess content taught in Topics 5–8.

**ONLINE CUMULATIVE/BENCHMARK ASSESSMENT**

An auto-scored Cumulative/Benchmark Assessment is provided at PearsonRealize.com.

## RtI Item Analysis for Diagnosis and Intervention

| Item | Standard | DOK | MDIS |
|---|---|---|---|
| 1 | 6.EE.A.2c | 1 | F45 |
| 2 | 6.NS.C.6c, MP.7 | 1 | F35 |
| 3 | 6.EE.A.4 | 1 | F59 |
| 4A | 6.EE.B.7 | 1 | F53 |
| 4B | 6.EE.B.7 | 1 | F55 |
| 5 | 6.NS.C.6c | 1 | F20 |
| 6A | 6.NS.C.7b, MP.2 | 2 | F19 |
| 6B | 6.NS.C.7a, MP.4 | 3 | F19 |
| 7 | 6.EE.B.7 | 1 | F54 |
| 8 | 6.EE.A.4 | 1 | F59, F60 |
| 9 | 6.EE.B.8 | 1 | F62 |
| 10 | 6.NS.C.8, 6.G.A.3 | 2 | I41, F33 |
| 11 | 6.NS.B.2 | 1 | G75 |
| 12 | 6.NS.B.4, MP.3 | 2 | G62 |
| 13 | 6.NS.B.3 | 1 | H60 |
| 14 | 6.NS.B.2 | 1 | G75 |
| 15 | 6.EE.C.9 | 2 | F63 |
| 16 | 6.NS.B.4 | 1 | G63 |
| 17 | 6.NS.B.3, MP.6 | 1 | H64 |
| 18A | 6.EE.C.9, MP.4 | 2 | F31 |
| 18B | 6.EE.C.9 | 1 | F29 |
| 19 | 6.NS.B.4 | 1 | G62 |
| 20A | 6.EE.B.7 | 1 | F54 |
| 20B | 6.EE.B.7 | 3 | F50 |
| 20C | 6.NS.B.3, MP.1 | 2 | F50 |
| 21 | 6.EE.A.2c, 6.NS.B.2 | 1 | F44, G75 |
| 22 | 6.NS.B.3 | 2 | H57 |
| 23 | 6.EE.C.9 | 1 | F34 |
| 24 | 6.EE.C.9 | 2 | F31 |
| 25 | 6.NS.B.3 | 1 | H67 |
| 26 | 6.EE.B.7, MP.4 | 2 | F54 |
| 27 | 6.EE.C.9 | 2 | F34 |
| 28 | 6.NS.B.3 | 2 | H69 |
| 29 | 6.NS.B.3 | 1 | H69 |
| 30 | 6.EE.A.2c | 1 | F45, H54, H64, H69 |

For items worth 1 point, responses should be completely correct to get a score of 1 point. For other items, use the Scoring Guide below.

## Scoring Guide

| Item | Points | Topics 1–8 Cumulative/Benchmark Assessment |
|---|---|---|
| 10 | 2 | Correct answer with work shown |
| | 1 | Correct answer without work shown |
| 12 | 2 | Correct answer and explanation |
| | 1 | Correct answer with incomplete or missing explanation |
| 17 | 2 | Correct answer with work shown |
| | 1 | Correct answer without work shown |
| 19 | 2 | Correct chart |
| | 1 | Partially correct or partially completed chart |
| 22 | 2 | Correct answer and explanation |
| | 1 | Correct answer with incomplete or missing explanation |
| 24 | 2 | Correct tables |
| | 1 | Partially correct or partially completed tables |
| 25 | 2 | Correct answer with work shown |
| | 1 | Correct answer without work shown |
| 27 | 3 | Correct table and graph |
| | 2 | Correct table and graph with missing labels or line |
| | 1 | Partially correct table and corresponding graph |
| 28 | 2 | Correct answer and explanation |
| | 1 | Correct answer with incomplete or missing explanation |